# nature

## The Living Record of Science
## 《自然》百年科学经典

英汉对照版　套装共十卷

# 第二卷
1931-1933

总顾问：李政道（Tsung-Dao Lee）
英方主编：Sir John Maddox
Sir Philip Campbell
中方主编：路甬祥

外语教学与研究出版社 · 麦克米伦教育 · 自然科研
FOREIGN LANGUAGE TEACHING AND RESEARCH PRESS · MACMILLAN EDUCATION · NATURE RESEARCH
北京 BEIJING

**图书在版编目（CIP）数据**

《自然》百年科学经典 ：套装共十卷. 第二卷 ：英汉对照 /（英）约翰·马多克斯（John Maddox），（英）菲利普·坎贝尔（Philip Campbell），路甬祥主编. -- 北京 ：外语教学与研究出版社，2020.9

ISBN 978-7-5213-2021-3

Ⅰ. ①自… Ⅱ. ①约… ②菲… ③路… Ⅲ. ①自然科学－文集－英、汉 Ⅳ. ①N53

中国版本图书馆 CIP 数据核字（2020）第 155152 号

地图审图号：GS（2020）5244 号

出 版 人 徐建忠
项目统筹 章思英
项目负责 刘晓楠 黄小斌
责任编辑 王丽霞
责任校对 黄小斌
封面设计 高 蕾
版式设计 孙莉明
插图设计 麦克米伦提供原图扫描版
出版发行 外语教学与研究出版社
社　　址 北京市西三环北路 19 号（100089）
网　　址 http://www.fltrp.com
印　　刷 北京华联印刷有限公司
开　　本 787×1092 1/16
印　　张 54.5
版　　次 2021 年 1 月第 1 版 2021 年 1 月第 1 次印刷
书　　号 ISBN 978-7-5213-2021-3
定　　价 8000.00 元

购书咨询：（010）88819926 电子邮箱：club@fltrp.com
外研书店：https://waiyants.tmall.com
凡印刷、装订质量问题，请联系我社印制部
联系电话：（010）61207896 电子邮箱：zhijian@fltrp.com
凡侵权、盗版书籍线索，请联系我社法律事务部
举报电话：（010）88817519 电子邮箱：banquan@fltrp.com
物料号：320210001

记载人类文明
沟通世界文化
www.fltrp.com

# 《自然》百年科学经典（英汉对照版）

## 编译委员会

### 本卷翻译工作组稿人（以姓氏笔画为序）

王耀杨　　刘　明　　刘晓楠　　关秀清　　李　琦　　何　铭　　沈乃澂
张　健　　郭红锋　　黄小斌　　蔡　迪

### 本卷翻译人员（以姓氏笔画为序）

王　峰　　王　静　　王耀杨　　毛晨晖　　史春晖　　伍　岳　　刘振明
刘浩芳　　刘　霞　　齐红艳　　李　飞　　李世媛　　吴　彦　　汪　浩
沈乃澂　　林元章　　金世超　　周志华　　周　杰　　姜　薇　　高如丽
曹惠来　　韩玲俐　　曾红芳　　管　冰　　魏　韧

### 本卷校对人员（以姓氏笔画为序）

王丽霞　　甘秋玲　　丛　岚　　乔萌萌　　刘　明　　刘东亮　　刘晓楠
齐文静　　李　琦　　李世媛　　何　铭　　陈思原　　顾海成　　徐秋燕
崔天明　　黄小斌　　韩玲俐　　曾红芳　　游　丹　　蔡　迪　　管　冰

# Contents
# 目录

# Volume II

# (1931-1933)

# Evidence for a Stellar Origin of the Cosmic Ultra-penetrating Radiation

V. F. Hess

## Editor's Note

**Physicists were still pondering the nature of cosmic rays. Earlier studies failed to find any evidence that the Sun emitted such rays, but here Victor Hess reports new experiments showing that it does. As he notes, recent experiments at high altitude in the Swiss Alps found the average intensity of radiation to be higher during the day and lower at night. Further experiments with lead shielding showed that the Sun's light included a component of highly penetrating rays, with intensity equal to about 0.5 percent of the total observed cosmic ray intensity. Hess argues that cosmic rays most probably have a stellar origin, as all other stars probably emit them much as the Sun. The precise nature of these particles remained unknown.**

WHILE in former years all observers were agreed that the sun does not contribute any noticeable amount to the total intensity of the cosmic ultra-radiation, the increase in the sensitivity of the apparatus used within recent years, and the increase in the number of observations made at different stations and under different experimental conditions, makes it possible to investigate once more whether the influence of the sun is altogether negligible.

Very accurate and trustworthy registrations of the cosmic radiation have been carried out with Prof. G. Hoffmann's high-pressure ionisation chamber at Muottas Muraigl (2,456 m. above sea-level) in the Engadine. These measurements show, beyond any doubt, that the average intensity of the radiation is somewhat greater in daytime than during the night. G. Hoffmann and F. Lindholm[1] give the average difference between day and night intensities as 0.12 mA., ~0.0125 ions per c.c. per sec. while the apparatus was unscreened from above, and 0.04 mA., ~0.0042 *I* with a lead-screening of 6 cm. and 9 cm. thickness. (The letter "*I*" always denotes "ions per c.c. and sec.".) F. Lindholm,[2] with the same apparatus, found from longer series of observations (8 months) the values in the accompanying table (see Table 6 of his paper).

In Hoffmann and Lindholm's apparatus a compensation current of one milliampere corresponds to an ionisation of 0.104 *I*. Therefore the total intensity of the ultra-radiation with the apparatus unscreened from above was about 2.50 *I* at Muottas Muraigl.

The difference between day and night intensity can be taken, provisionally at least, as the actual intensity of the solar penetrating radiation. One can see at once that at Muottas

# 宇宙超穿透性辐射起源于恒星的证据

维克托·赫斯

编者按

物理学家们仍在思考宇宙射线的性质。以前的研究未能找到任何证据证明太阳发射了这类射线，如今维克托·赫斯报告了他用新的实验结果说明确实如此。正如他所指出的，在瑞士阿尔卑斯山上的高海拔区进行的一项最新实验发现，辐射的平均强度白天比晚上高。采用铅屏蔽板以后再做的实验表明，太阳光中包含一个穿透力很强的射线成分，其强度约为宇宙射线总观测强度的0.5%。赫斯认为宇宙射线很可能起源于恒星，因为除太阳以外所有其他恒星发射的宇宙射线很可能与太阳发射的一样多。这些粒子的确切性质现在还不清楚。

在过去，所有的观测者一致认为，在宇宙超级辐射的总强度中，太阳没有任何值得注意的贡献。近年来，随着观测仪器灵敏度的不断增强，以及在不同国家、不同实验环境下进行的观测次数不断增多，于是有可能再一次研究由太阳造成的影响是不是可以完全忽略不计。

有人把霍夫曼教授的高压电离室放在瑞士恩加丁地区的穆拉古尔山(海拔 2,456 m)上，由此得到了一些非常准确而且可靠的有关宇宙辐射的数据。这些测量结果毫无疑问地说明白天的平均辐射强度要略高于夜晚。霍夫曼和林霍尔姆[1]给出了昼夜间强度差异的平均值：当仪器上方没有屏蔽时，平均值为 0.12mA，或 ~0.0125 个离子每立方厘米每秒；当使用 6 cm 和 9 cm 厚的铅板屏蔽时，平均值是 0.04 mA，~0.0042 $I$（符号“$I$”通常表示“每立方厘米每秒的离子数”）。林霍尔姆[2]使用同样的仪器进行了更长期的观测（8 个月），所得数据列于附表中（参见他文章中的表 6）。

在霍夫曼和林霍尔姆使用的仪器中，一个 1 mA 的补偿电流相当于 0.104 $I$ 的电离值。由此得出，在穆拉古尔山上由顶部没有铅板屏蔽的仪器测得的超级辐射的总强度大约为 2.50 $I$。

我们至少可以暂时把昼夜间的强度差视为太阳贯穿辐射的实际强度。于是马上就可以看到在海拔 2,456 m 的穆拉古尔山上，大约有一半这类太阳辐射成分能够穿

Muraigl, 2,456 m. above sea-level, about one-half of this solar radiation component is able to penetrate through 10 cm. of lead. This component is therefore far more penetrating than the gamma rays from radioactive substances. If we assume that all of the above-mentioned 0.011 $I$ is of solar origin, we can compute the absorption coefficient in lead $\mu_{Pb}$ (it will suffice to take the case of perpendicular incidence) from the equation $I = I_0 e^{-\mu_{Pb} d}$ taking $I_0 = 0.011$, $I = 0.0058$, and $d = 10$ cm.; thus we obtain $\mu_{Pb} = 0.064$ cm.$^{-1}$ and the mass absorption coefficient $\left(\frac{\mu}{\rho}\right)_{Pb} = 5.7\times10^{-3}$ cm.$^2$/gm.

This value is almost exactly equal to the mass absorption coefficient value of the total cosmic radiation at the same altitude ($(\mu/\rho)_{Pb} = 6.3\times10^{-3}$ cm.$^2$/sec. as found by Büttner on the Eiger glacier 2.3 km. above sea-level).[3] If we assume that part of the (0.011 $I$) difference between day and night values with unscreened apparatus is due to an increase in the average content of radium emanation and its products in the air during daytime, then we should get an even more pronounced hardness of the solar penetrating rays, that is, a smaller value for their mass absorption coefficient. Therefore we are justified in concluding that *the sun emits penetrating rays of at least the same penetrating power as the well-known cosmic ultra-radiation. The total amount of the solar penetrating rays (at 2,456 m. above sea-level) is about one-half percent of the total intensity of the cosmic radiation, as it is seen from the accompanying table*. Of course, one might think it possible to explain the increase in the total radiation during daytime as due to an indirect influence of the sun (that is, an increase in the scattering of the ultra-rays by the heating of the atmosphere during the day). In this case, however, one would expect that this scattered radiation, represented by the difference between the day and night values, would be much softer than the general cosmic radiation; but this is in contradiction to the experimental results analysed above.

Recent observations of R. Steinmaurer[4] on the summit of the Sonnblick (3,100 m. above sea-level) in the summer of 1929, made with three different instruments (two of the Kolhörster double loop-electrometer type and one of the Wulf–Kolhörster type), also show clearly that the total ultra-radiation in daytime is slightly higher than at night; the difference amounts to about 0.7 percent (0.06 $I$, average difference for the three forms of apparatus mentioned above, the total intensity on the Sonnblick being about 8.7 $I$ with the screening open on the top). The increase of radiation was also observed with apparatus screened with 7 cm. iron all around, but the number of these observations on the Sonnblick is not sufficient for quantitative calculations. It may be mentioned that even in the old observations on the summit of the Obir (2,000 m. above sea-level), made by V. F. Hess and M. Kofler,[5] the solar influence is noticeable (the total intensity of the ultra-radiation plus earth-radiation during the day being 11.11, during the night 11.09 $I$, in the average for 13 months), although at that time the apparatus were not screened from the earth radiation. The difference of 0.02 $I$ was—at that time—considered as practically amounting to zero.

Observations with apparatus of the Wulf– or Kolhörster type for shorter periods (like those of Kolhörster–v. Salis on the Jungfraujoch, on the Mönch, and of Büttner at other places

过 10 cm 厚的铅板。因此这部分辐射的穿透性大大高于放射性物质发出的 $\gamma$ 射线。如果我们假设所有上述的 0.011 $I$ 全部起源于太阳，我们就可以根据方程 $I = I_0 e^{-\mu_{Pb} d}$ 计算出铅的吸收系数 $\mu_{Pb}$(只考虑垂直入射的情况已经足够)，代入 $I_0 = 0.011$，$I = 0.0058$ 和 $d = 10$ cm，我们得到 $\mu_{Pb} = 0.064\ \text{cm}^{-1}$ 和质量吸收系数 $\left(\frac{\mu}{\rho}\right)_{Pb} = 5.7 \times 10^{-3}\ \text{cm}^2/\text{g}$。

这个数值几乎精确地等于所有宇宙辐射在这个高度上的质量吸收系数（比特纳在海拔 2.3 km 的艾格尔冰川上的测量值为$(\mu/\rho)_{Pb} = 6.3 \times 10^{-3}\ \text{cm}^2/\text{sec}$）。[3] 如果我们假设在没有屏蔽层的仪器上测量到的昼夜间差异（0.011 $I$）中，有一部分是由于白天空气中镭射气和其产物的平均含量上升引起的，那么我们观察到的太阳贯穿射线会更硬，即它们的质量吸收系数会更小。因此我们认为以下结论是合理的：**太阳发出的贯穿射线的穿透能力至少与著名的宇宙超穿透辐射相当。太阳贯穿射线的总量（在海拔 2,456 m 处）大约占宇宙辐射总强度的** 0.5%，**如附表所示**。当然，有人可能将白天辐射总量的升高解释为受太阳间接影响所致（即白天被加热的大气增加了对超穿透射线的散射）。然而在这种情况下，因散射造成的辐射——由昼夜间辐射量的差异表示，会比一般的宇宙辐射更软；而这与上面分析的实验结果是矛盾的。

1929 年夏天，斯坦莫勒[4]在松布利克山峰顶(海拔约 3,100 m)用三种不同仪器(两台柯尔霍斯特型双环静电计和一台伍尔夫–柯尔霍斯特型）的最新观测也明确显示出测量的超级辐射总量白天的数值略高于夜晚；差值大约为 0.7%（用上面提到的三种仪器测量的差值取平均后得到 0.06 $I$，顶部没有屏蔽的仪器在松布利克山测量的总强度约为 8.7 $I$。）当仪器四周用 7 cm 厚的铁板屏蔽时仍然可以观测到辐射量的增加，但是在松布利克山上的观测次数太少不足以作出定量计算。人们也许会提到即使从之前赫斯和科夫勒[5]在奥柏（海拔 2,000 m）山顶的观测数据中也可以看出太阳带来的影响（超级辐射加上地球辐射的总强度在 13 个月中的平均值：白天为 11.11 $I$，晚上为 11.09 $I$），尽管那时的仪器没有屏蔽掉地球辐射的影响。0.02 $I$ 的差别在当时几乎可以被看作是零。

至于使用伍尔夫型或柯尔霍斯特型仪器进行的短周期观测（比如冯萨利斯在少女峰和修士峰以及比特纳在阿尔卑斯山其他地方用柯尔霍斯特型仪器所做的观测），

in the Alps) naturally do not show the influence of the solar component of the ultra-rays, on account of the lesser degree of accuracy of the means; therefore Corlin,[6] using the observations on the Mönch and the Zugspitze, came to negative conclusions as to the solar influence. From the data given below it is quite safe to conclude, according to the most accurate and most numerous observations at present available, that *the sun contributes an amount of about 0.5 percent to the total intensity of the cosmic ultra-radiation at 2.5 km. above sea-level. The penetrating power of the solar ultra-rays is at least as great as that of the total cosmic radiation.* There is no doubt that this solar component of the ultra-radiation is also present at lower levels; on account of its very small absolute intensity it will, of course, be far more difficult to prove its existence in these levels. An analysis of the very accurate registrations of the total radiation by Hoffmann and Steinke in Königsberg and in Halle in this direction might be successful.

| Period | Number of Days | Armour open above | | |
|---|---|---|---|---|
| | | Mean Values | | Difference (Day–Night) |
| | | Day | Night | |
| 1928 January–March | (32) | 24.46 mA. | 24.34 mA. | 0.12 mA. = 0.0125 *I* |
| 1928 June, July, October | (39) | 23.98 mA. | 23.88 mA. | 0.10 mA. = 0.0104 *I* |
| 1929 January–February | (11) | 24.68 mA. | 24.59 mA. | 0.09 mA. = 0.0094 *I* |
| Weighted average difference | | | 0.011 *I* | |

| Period | Number of Days | Armour closed (10 cm. lead screening all around) | | |
|---|---|---|---|---|
| | | Mean Values | | Difference (Day–Night) |
| | | Day | Night | |
| 1928 March | (2) | 19.54 mA. | 19.50 mA. | 0.04 mA. = 0.0042 *I* |
| 1928 July | (8) | 19.21 mA. | 19.17 mA. | 0.04 mA. = 0.0042 *I* |
| 1929 February | (6) | 19.46 mA. | 19.38 mA. | 0.08 mA. = 0.0084 *I* |
| Weighted average difference behind 10 cm. lead | | | 0.0058 *I* (ions/c.c./sec.) | |

If the sun, as the fixed star nearest to our planet, emits rays of about the same qualities as the total cosmic penetrating radiation, one cannot but assume that all fixed stars are sources of a radiation of similar qualities. The sun being a relatively old star of the yellow dwarf type may, of course, be expected to yield far less total quantity of the ultra-penetrating radiation than, for example, the younger giant stars. Naturally, the ultra-penetrating rays which we observe can only come from the outermost layers of the stars, since they are not able to penetrate material layers of more than a few hundred metres water equivalent.

It is not possible, at present, to say more about the nature of these stellar ultra-rays: whether they are electrons or protons accelerated in cosmic electric fields, or indeed photons (quanta) created by atomic mass shrinking or annihilation processes. This hypothesis of a partly stellar origin of the ultra-penetrating cosmic radiation does not necessarily exclude the possibility that another part of this radiation is created in interstellar space by the formation of certain elements out of hydrogen, according to

由于仪器精度不够高，自然也测不出太阳的超级射线成分的影响；因此科兰[6]使用在修士峰和楚格峰上的观测结果得出太阳对辐射量无影响的结论。从下表的数据中完全可以得到以下结论，根据目前能得到的所有最精确的观测结果，我们认为**在海拔 2.5 km 处，太阳辐射占宇宙超级辐射总强度的 0.5%。太阳超能射线的穿透能力至少与宇宙辐射的总体穿透能力相当**。毫无疑问，目前太阳的这一超穿透辐射成分的贡献仍然处于较低的水平。由于这一成分的绝对强度值很小，要想证实其存在非常困难，霍夫曼和施坦因克在柯尼斯堡和哈雷对总辐射量的非常精确的数据进行了分析，他们在这方面的努力也许会取得成功。

| 周期 | 天数 | 上方防护外壳打开 | | |
|---|---|---|---|---|
| | | 平均值 | | 差值（日—夜） |
| | | 日 | 夜 | |
| 1928 年 1~3 月 | (32) | 24.46 mA | 24.34 mA | 0.12 mA = 0.0125 $I$ |
| 1928 年 6、7、10 月 | (39) | 23.98 mA | 23.88 mA | 0.10 mA = 0.0104 $I$ |
| 1929 年 1~2 月 | (11) | 24.68 mA | 24.59 mA | 0.09 mA = 0.0094 $I$ |
| 加权平均差值：0.011 $I$ | | | | |

| 周期 | 天数 | 防护外壳关闭（四周用 10 cm 厚铅板屏蔽） | | |
|---|---|---|---|---|
| | | 平均值 | | 差值（日—夜） |
| | | 日 | 夜 | |
| 1928 年 3 月 | (2) | 19.54 mA | 19.50 mA | 0.04 mA = 0.0042 $I$ |
| 1928 年 7 月 | (8) | 19.21 mA | 19.17 mA | 0.04 mA = 0.0042 $I$ |
| 1929 年 2 月 | (6) | 19.46 mA | 19.38 mA | 0.08 mA = 0.0084 $I$ |
| 用 10 cm 铅板屏蔽后的加权平均差值：0.0058 $I$（离子数 /c.c./ 秒） | | | | |

作为离地球最近的恒星，如果太阳发出的射线具有与总的宇宙穿透性辐射大致相同的性质，则我们不得不假定所有恒星都是发出类似射线的辐射源。太阳是一颗年代比较久远的黄矮星，它释放出的超级穿透性射线在总量上自然会远远少于那些年轻一些的巨星。当然，我们观察到的超级穿透性射线只能来自恒星的最外层，因为它们不可能穿过厚度超过几百米水当量的物质层。

我们现在还不能对恒星超级射线的性质作更多的说明：不能判断它们到底是被宇宙电场加速的电子或质子，还是在原子质量减小或湮灭过程中放出的光子（量子）。按照爱丁顿和密立根的想法，虽然最小值原理假说更倾向于引导我们尝试用以太阳超穿透性辐射为实验证据的恒星起源假说来解释全部观察到的现象，但是一部分超穿透性宇宙辐射源自恒星的假说未必非要排除另一部分宇宙辐射来自星际空间的可

Eddington's and Millikan's ideas, although the principle of minimum hypothesis would rather induce us to try whether the stellar origin hypothesis, based on the experimental evidence of the solar ultra-penetrating rays, would suffice to explain the observed facts.

The conclusions put forward in this note certainly support the original ideas of Prof. Nernst first mentioned in 1921.[7] A few years ago, when the first results of observations on the daily period according to sidereal time were published, he wished that it were possible to increase the sensitivity of our apparatus until we could detect the ultra-rays from a single stellar nebula or a single star. I think the results put forward here indicate that a modest beginning has been made in this direction. At least it has been possible now to detect the influence and the penetrating power of the ultra-rays from the sun. It may be added that the evidence here brought forward for a stellar origin of the cosmic ultra-rays is completely independent of the existence of a daily period according to sidereal time, a subject which is still under discussion.

(**127**, 10-11; 1931)

Victor F. Hess: Institute of Experimental Physics, University of Graz, Austria, Nov. 4.

References:

1 *Gerlands Beitr. z. Geophysik*, **20**, 52 (1928).

2 *Gerlands Beitr. z. Geoph.*, **26**, 416-439 (1930).

3 *Zeitschr. f. Geophys.*, **3**, 179 (1927).

4 *Sitz. Ber. Akad. d. Wiss. Wien*, II. a. **139**, 281-318 (1930).

5 *Phys. Zeitschr.*, **18**, 585 (1917).

6 *Zeitschr. f. Physik*, **50**, 808-848 (1928).

7 *Das Weltgebäude im Lichte der neueren Forschung* (Verlag Springer, Berlin).

能性，星际空间中的宇宙辐射是在氢元素合成某些较重元素的过程中产生的。

这篇短文中的结论理所当然地支持了能斯特教授在 1921 年时就已经率先提出的想法[7]。几年前，当基于恒星时的日周期的首次观测结果发表出来时，他就希望能够提高仪器的灵敏度，直到我们能够分辨出来自单个恒星或单一恒星星云的超级射线。我认为本文提供的结果可以表明朝这方面的努力已经开始。至少现在检测出太阳超级射线的影响力和穿透力已经成为可能。需要补充说明的是，这里提出的有关宇宙超级射线起源于恒星的证据完全独立于基于恒星时的日周期的存在，后者是一个仍在讨论之中的课题。

（史春晖 翻译；马宇蒨 审稿）

# Stellar Structure and the Origin of Stellar Energy*

E. A. Milne

## Editor's Note

**Here the astronomer Edward Milne offers an extensive review of new thinking on stellar structure. Astronomers then knew of two distinct classes of stars, one having densities roughly comparable to matter on Earth, and another, known as white dwarfs, with densities roughly 100,000 times greater than water. Physicist Ralph Fowler had recently shown that white dwarfs are prevented from further gravitational collapse by an effective pressure produced by the prohibition in quantum theory of electrons to occupy the same quantum state. Without the benefit of an understanding of nuclear fusion, attempts to link the process of energy generation within a star, involving the conversion of mass to radiation, to the natural evolution of stars, were at that stage severely hampered.**

PERHAPS the most striking general characteristic of the stars is that they can be divided into two groups of widely differing densities. In the first group, which comprises the majority of the known stars, the densities are of "terrestrial" order of magnitude; that is to say, their mean densities are of the order of the known densities of gases, liquids, and solids. They range from one-millionth of that of water to ten or, in rare cases, perhaps fifty times that of water. In the second group the densities are of the order of 100,000 times that of water. Of the second group, the "white dwarfs", only a few examples are known, but they are all near-by stars, and it is generally agreed that they must be of very frequent occurrence in Nature, though difficult of discovery owing to their faintness. Whether stars exist of intermediate density remains for future observation. The possibility of the existence of matter in this dense state offers no difficulty. As pointed out by Eddington, we simply have to suppose the atoms ionised down to free electrons and bare nuclei. At these high densities the matter will form a degenerate gas, as first pointed out by R. H. Fowler. But this leaves entirely unsolved the question of why, under stellar conditions, matter sometimes takes up the "normal" density and sometimes the high density. Owing to the probable great frequency of occurrence of dense stars, it might reasonably be asked of any theory of stellar constitution hat it should account for dense stars in an unforced way.

There are two main theories of stellar structure at the present moment. That of Sir James Jeans accounts for the existence of giants, dwarfs, and white dwarfs, but only at the cost of *ad hoc* hypotheses quite outside physics. It assumes stars to contain atoms of atomic weight higher than that observed on earth, and it assumes them to be relentlessly disappearing in the form of radiation; it appeals to discontinuous changes of state consequent on successive ionisations, for which there is little warrant. I think it is true to say that the majority of astronomers do not accept this theory.

---

* Substance of lectures delivered at the Royal Institution on Dec. 2 and Dec. 9, 1930.

# 恒星的构造和恒星能量的起源*

爱德华·米耳恩

## 编者按

在本文中，天文学家爱德华·米耳恩全面回顾了关于恒星构造的新理论。当时的天文学家已经知道有两种完全不同的恒星，其中一种的密度与地球上物质的密度相当，而另一种就是被称为白矮星的恒星，其密度约为水的100,000倍。物理学家拉尔夫·福勒最近表明：由于量子理论中禁止电子占据同一量子态而产生的有效压力使白矮星无法进一步发生引力坍缩。当时在不了解核聚变反应的情况下，试图把恒星内部质量向辐射转化的能量产生过程与恒星的自然演变过程联系起来是相当困难的。

也许恒星最为显著的特点就是它们可以分为密度差异很大的两类。第一类恒星，包括我们已知的大多数恒星，其密度所在的量级与地球上的物质相当，也就是说，其平均密度与大家都知道的气体、液体和固体的密度相近。这些恒星的密度从水密度的100万分之一到水密度的10倍，在某些极特殊的情况下可能达到水密度的50倍。对于第二类恒星，其密度的量级相当于水密度的100,000倍。第二类恒星中有“白矮星”，现在只知道几个这样的例子，但它们距离地球都很近，大家普遍认为这类恒星必定会频繁地出现在宇宙中，只是由于其亮度微弱难以发现。至于是否存在密度介于以上两类之间的恒星，仍然有待进一步观测。致密物质的存在在解释上不存在困难。正如爱丁顿曾经指出的那样，我们只需假设原子离解为自由电子和裸露的原子核，就可以解释密度问题。福勒最早指出，在这样高的密度下，物质将形成简并气体。但这完全没有解答为什么在恒星中物质的密度有时是“正常的”，而有时又非常高。因为致密恒星很可能是大量存在的，所以任何关于恒星构造的理论应该能够合理地解释出致密恒星是自然形成的。

目前，关于恒星构造的理论主要有两种。詹姆斯·金斯爵士的理论解释了巨星、矮星和白矮星的存在，但需要引入一些与物理学毫不相干的特殊假设。该理论假设恒星中包含的原子所具有的原子量大于在地球上的观测值，而且这些原子在以辐射形式不断地被消耗；持续电离会引起状态的非连续变化，而这一点是缺乏根据的。我认为事实上大多数天文学家并不接受这一理论。

---

* 本文取自作者于1930年12月2日和12月9日在英国皇家研究院发表的演讲。

The theory of Sir Arthur Eddington does not claim to account for the observed division of stars into dense stars and stars of ordinary density; nor does it establish the division of ordinary stars into giants and dwarfs. On the other hand, it claims to establish what is known as the mass-luminosity law from considerations of equilibrium only, that is, without introducing anything connected with the physics of the generation of energy. It claims to show that the observed fact that the brighter stars are the more massive can be deduced from the conditions expressing that the star is in a steady state, mechanically and thermally. It does this by making the hypothesis that the stars (giants and ordinary dwarfs) consist of perfect gas. Closer consideration of the actual formulae used by the theory shows that it scarcely bears out the claims made for it by its originator. The "formula for the luminosity" of a star makes the luminosity very nearly proportional to its effective temperature, and so the so-called proof of the mass-luminosity law involves a semi-empirical element, namely, an appeal to the observed effective temperatures of the stars, for the observed values of which the theory fails to account. Another difficulty encountered by the theory is that it makes the interiors of the more luminous (giant) stars cooler than those of the fainter stars, and it makes the interiors of both too cool for the temperature to have any appreciable influence on the rate of generation of energy, by stimulating, for example, the production of radioactive elements or the conversion of matter to radiation.

The claim to establish the mass-luminosity law from mere equilibrium considerations cannot, however, be sustained for a moment. We may regard a star in a steady state as a system provided with an internal heating apparatus (the source of energy). It adjusts itself—state of aggregation, density distribution, temperature distribution—until the surface emission equals the internal generation of energy $L$. But provided the luminosity $L$ is not too large (in order that the mass shall not burst under radiation pressure), it is clear that a given mass $M$ can adjust itself to suit any arbitrary value of $L$. If, starting with one steady state, we then alter $L$ (upwards or downwards) by altering the rate of supply of energy, the star will simply heat up or cool down until the surface emission is equal to the new volume of $L$—precisely like an electric fire. $L$ and $M$ are thus independent variables so far as steady-state considerations are concerned. The fact that $L$ and $M$ show a degree of correlation in Nature must be connected with facts of an altogether different order, namely, with the physics of energy-generation. It is essential to recognise the difference between the formal independence of $L$ and $M$ as regards steady-state considerations and the observed correlation of $L$ with $M$ in Nature. The observed mass-luminosity law must depend on the circumstance that in some way the more massive star contrives to provide itself with a stronger set of sources. The claim to establish the mass-luminosity law from equilibrium considerations only appears to me a philosophical blunder. Further, it is unphilosophical to *assume* the interior of a gas to be a perfect gas; either knowledge of the interior is for ever unattainable or we should be able to infer it from the observable outer layers.

When we dispense with the perfect gas hypothesis and at the same time recognise the independence of $L$ and $M$ as regards steady-state considerations, it is found that a rational

阿瑟·爱丁顿爵士并没有声称他的理论可以解释观察到的恒星可分为致密恒星和普通密度恒星，也没有确认普通恒星能够分为巨星和矮星。另一方面，这一理论认为，不考虑任何与能量生成相关的物理过程，仅从平衡出发，就可以推出“质量—光度”定律。他提出，恒星越亮其质量越大这一观测事实，可以从满足恒星处于力学、热学稳定状态的条件中推导出来。该理论是通过假设恒星（巨星和普通矮星）由理想气体构成而得到以上结论的。进一步考虑该理论中使用的实际公式发现，这一理论根本没有证实创立人为它所作的假设。恒星的“光度公式”说明恒星的光度非常接近于与它的有效温度成正比；而质量—光度定律的所谓证据事实上包含了半经验的因素，即需要求助于实测的恒星有效温度，因为观测值与理论值不符合。该理论遇到的另一个困难是，它使更亮恒星（巨星）的内部温度低于那些更暗淡的恒星；而且两者的内部温度都不足以使能量生成速率受到可观的影响，以激发像生成放射性元素或者使物质转化为辐射这样的过程。

无论如何，仅仅根据平衡过程就确立质量—光度定律是站不住脚的。我们可以将一颗处于稳态的恒星看作是一个具有内在加热装置（能量源）的系统。该系统可以调整自己的聚集状态、密度分布以及温度分布，直至表面辐射等于内部产生的能量 $L$。如果光度 $L$ 不是非常高（这样，物质就不会在辐射压作用下爆发），一个质量为 $M$ 的系统显然可以通过调整自身以适应任意的光度值 $L$。对于处于稳态的恒星系统，我们可以通过改变能量供给速率来改变 $L$ 值（增大或减小），这颗恒星的温度将随之升高或降低，直至表面辐射等于新的 $L$ 值，其原理与电暖炉十分相似。因此，对于稳态系统而言，光度 $L$ 与质量 $M$ 是两个独立的变量。自然界中光度 $L$ 与质量 $M$ 具有一定关联性的事实，一定与一个完全不同的原因有关，也就是说与能量生成的物理过程有关。有必要意识到 $L$ 和 $M$ 在稳态系统中的独立性与 $L$ 和 $M$ 在自然界中的关联性之间存在的矛盾。观测到的质量—光度定律必须依赖于以下条件，即质量较大的恒星可以通过某种方式为自己提供更多的能源。在我看来，仅通过平衡过程就确立质量—光度定律的看法是科学上的大谬。此外，无论我们对恒星内部的认识是永远无法达到的，还是应该能从观测到的外层推出内层的情况，**假设**气体内部为理想气体都不具有科学性。

如果我们摒弃理想气体假说，并承认 $L$ 和 $M$ 在稳态情况下相互独立，那么就会发现对恒星结构的合理分析自然而然地解释了致密恒星的存在，而无须引入特殊的

analysis of stellar structure automatically accounts for the existence of dense stars without special hypothesis. Further, it shows, as common sense would lead us to expect, that the more luminous stars must have the hotter interiors. Here the temperatures are found to range up to $10^{10}$ degrees or higher, depending on luminosity—a temperature sufficient to stimulate the conversion of matter into radiation. In addition, it shows that the central regions of stars must be very dense, ranging up to $10^7$ grams cm.$^{-3}$ or higher. Thus the difficulties met by earlier theories fall away as soon as the ground is cleared philosophically.

The foregoing ideas suggest the following as the fundamental problems of stellar structure: (1) What are the configurations of equilibrium of a prescribed mass $M$ as its luminosity $L$ ranges from 0 upwards, $M$ remaining constant? (2) What is the effective temperature $T_e$ associated with a given pair $(M, L)$ in a steady state? (3) What is the value of $L$ which will actually occur for the physical conditions disclosed by the answer to problem (1)?

We observe that the outer parts of a star are gaseous. Consequently we can solve the problem of the state of any actual star by integrating the equations of equilibrium *from the boundary inwards*; we are entitled to assume the gas laws to go on holding until we find that the conditions are incompatible with them. We then change to a new equation of state, and carry on as before. We change our equation of state as often as may be necessary until we arrive at the centre.

The answer to the first of the problems formulated above has been worked out, for certain types of source-distribution and opacity, by the method of inward integration. The results are sufficiently alike to be taken as affording insight into the nature of stellar structure in general, and are as follows. For a given mass $M$, of prescribed opacity, there exist two critical luminosities $L_1$ and $L_0$ $(L_1>L_0)$ such that for $L>L_1$ no configurations of equilibrium exist; for $L_1>L>L_0$ the density and temperature increase very rapidly as the center is approached $\left(T \propto r^{-1}\left(\log\frac{\text{const.}}{r}\right)^{-\frac{1}{2}}\right)$, so that in the centre there is a region of very high temperatures and densities where the gas laws are violated; for $L=L_0$ a diffuse perfect gas configuration is possible; for $L_0>L>0$ the only perfect gas configuration is a hollow shell provided with an internal, rigid supporting surface of spherical shape. Since in Nature no internal supporting surface is provided, to find the actual configuration when $L_0>L>0$ we construct the artificially supported hollow configuration and then remove the supporting surface. The mass must collapse, and collapse will proceed until a steady-state is attained in which, except for a gaseous outer fringe, the gas laws are violated. Such configurations may be termed "collapsed". Configurations for which $L_1>L>L_0$ may be termed "centrally-condensed". The physical origin of the different types of configuration is simply the varying effect of light-pressure. For $L=L_0$ the light-pressure due to $L$ is just sufficient to distend the star against its self-gravity and maintain it in the form of a perfect gas. For $L_1>L>L_0$ light-pressure is so high that for equilibrium to be maintained gravity at any given distance from the centre must be assisted by concentrating as much matter as possible inside the sphere in question; when this process is carried out for all spheres, we get a central condensation. For $L_0>L>0$, light-pressure due to $L$ is so low that the mass

假说。另外，常识也告诉我们，明亮的恒星一定具有较高的内部温度。人们发现其温度大约为 $10^{10}$ 度或更高，由光度大小决定——应达到足以使物质转化为辐射能的温度。此外，这表明恒星的中心区域会非常致密，密度达到 $10^7$ g/cm$^3$ 或更高。因此，只要科学地摒弃一些基础假设，早期理论遇到的困难就可以得到很好的解决。

上述观点提出了以下关于恒星结构的基本问题：(1) 质量 $M$ 值一定，在光度 $L$ 从 0 开始逐渐增加的过程中平衡结构是怎样的？(2) 处于稳定状态时与特定 $M$、$L$ 相关的有效温度 $T_e$ 是多少？(3) 在满足问题 (1) 答案的物理条件下，实际的光度值 $L$ 是多少？

我们注意到恒星的外部是气态的，因此通过对平衡方程**从边界向内积分**，我们可以解出任意恒星所处的状态；我们有理由认为可以一直应用气体定律，直到我们发现条件与它不再相容。然后我们再转换到一个新的状态方程，仍用以前的方式处理。我们按照需要不断改变状态方程直至积分到中心。

这样上述第一个问题的答案就可以解决，对于某些类型的源分布和不透明度，可以采用向内积分的方法。由此得到的结果具有足够的相似性，从而可以理解恒星构造的总体特性，具体结果如下。对于给定的质量 $M$ 和不透明度，存在两个临界光度值 $L_1$ 和 $L_0$ ($L_1>L_0$)：当 $L>L_1$ 时，不存在平衡结构；当 $L_1>L>L_0$ 时，在不断接近中心的过程中，密度和温度急剧增加 $\left(T \propto r^{-1}\left(\log\frac{\text{常数}}{r}\right)^{-\frac{1}{2}}\right)$，所以中心处是高温高密度区域，气体定律不再适用；对于 $L=L_0$ 的情况，可能存在扩散的理想气体结构；当 $L_0>L>0$ 时，理想气体结构只能是一个内部具有刚性球形支撑面的空壳。在自然界中不存在这样的内部支撑表面，为了复原 $L_0>L>0$ 时的实际结构，我们人为地构造了一个中空的支撑结构，然后把支撑面去除。那么质量一定会发生塌陷，塌陷会一直持续直至达到新的稳定状态；在此状态下，除了气态的外部边界以外，其他区域均不符合气体定律。这样的结构可以被称为“塌陷”。而 $L_1>L>L_0$ 时的结构可以被称为“中心凝聚”。不同结构类型的物理根源仅在于光压的变化。对于 $L=L_0$ 的情况，由 $L$ 产生的光压刚好可以对抗恒星自身的引力，从而保持理想气体的状态。对于 $L_1>L>L_0$ 的情况，由于光压非常高，为了维持平衡态，在距离中心任意远处，引力肯定会因聚集了球面内尽可能多的物质而增加；当该过程在所有球面内同时发生的时候，就会导致中心凝聚。对于 $L_0>L>0$ 的情况，由 $L$ 产生的光压非常低，以致于理想状态下的物质无法支撑自身的重量，从而发生塌陷直到气体定律不再适用。由于 $L$ 的微小变动，$L= L_0$ 时对应的扩散结构是不稳定的。

cannot support itself against its own weight in the form of perfect gas, and collapse sets in until the gas-laws are disobeyed. The diffuse configurations $L=L_0$ are unstable with respect to small changes of $L$.

For collapsed or centrally-condensed configurations the center will be occupied by a gas in a degenerate state. When the mean densities or effective temperatures of collapsed configurations are calculated, using the Fermi-Dirac statistics for the degenerate gas, they are found to agree with the observed order of magnitude for white dwarfs. Thus, collapsed configurations may be identified with white dwarfs. A white dwarf is thus a dense star simply because its luminosity is too low, and its light-pressure accordingly too low, for it to support its own mass against its own gravity. From another point of view the calculation affords an observational verification of the numerical value of the "degenerate gas constant" the coefficient $K$ in the degenerate gas law $p = K\rho^{\frac{5}{3}}$, and so a check on the Fermi-Dirac statistics.

If collapsed configurations may be identified with white dwarfs, centrally-condensed configurations may be provisionally identified with ordinary giants and dwarfs, though the full determination of the properties of centrally-condensed configurations awaits the construction of certain tables. Centrally-condensed configurations appear to have the properties that as $L$ decreases from $L_1$ to $L_0$ the effective temperature rises to a maximum and then decreases again. This would correspond to the observed division into giants and dwarfs. I give this deduction with some caution, as it is not yet demonstrated rigorously in the absence of the tables above mentioned.

A point not yet settled is the question of the continuity of the series of centrally-condensed configurations with the collapsed configurations (Figs. 1 and 2). There are indications that as $L$ passes through $L_0$ from above to below, the external radius of the configuration may decrease discontinuously, the gaseous envelope collapsing on to the dense core. If this is confirmed, it would follow that a star, when its steady-state luminosity $L$ falls through a certain critical value (depending on its mass), exhibits the phenomena of a nova or temporary star. For it would have to disengage a large amount of gravitational potential energy in a short time, so that the actual emission would undergo a temporary increase, falling again to a value just below its previous value. It would be highly interesting to have observational data as to the densities of a nova before and after the outburst. The early-type spectrum of the later stage of a nova may indeed be taken to indicate a high effective temperature, and so a small radius and high density, in accordance with our prediction.

塌陷或中心凝聚结构的中心将充满处于简并态的电子气。根据简并气体的费米－狄拉克统计，我们可以计算出塌陷结构的平均密度和有效温度，该结果与白矮星的实测数量级相符合。因此，白矮星很可能具有塌陷结构。白矮星之所以属于致密恒星只是因为它的光度过低，相应的光压也很小，以至于其重量无法对抗自身引力的缘故。从另一个角度看，上面的计算也可以验证简并气体常数的数值，即简并气体定律 $p = K\rho^{\frac{5}{3}}$ 中的系数 $K$，并同时检验了费米－狄拉克统计。

如果认为白矮星具有塌陷结构，则可以暂时假设普通巨星和矮星具有中心凝聚结构，虽然为了完全确定中心凝聚结构的属性，尚需要构建特定的资料表。中心凝聚结构看起来具有以下特点，随着 $L$ 从 $L_1$ 减小到 $L_0$，有效温度先升到一个最大值然后再下降。这与观测到的巨星和矮星一致。我以审慎的态度提出这个结论，因为在缺乏上面提到的资料表的情况下，尚不能得到严格的证明。

现在，尚未解决的问题是带有塌陷结构的中心凝聚结构的连续性（如图 1 和图 2 所示）。一些迹象表明，当光度 $L$ 从高往低经过 $L_0$ 的时候，该结构的外半径可能会不连续地下降，气体外壳塌陷到致密的内核上。如果这一点得到确认，那么当一颗恒星的稳态光度 $L$ 下降到某一个临界值（取决于星体质量）时，该星体就会发生新星或暂星现象。由于它要在很短的时间内释放大量的引力势能，因此实际的辐射会出现暂时的增加，而后再降低到比先前略小的值。人们在新星爆发前后观察到的密度值变化很有趣。一个新星晚期的早型光谱确实可以说明其具有较高的有效温度、较小的半径和较高的密度，这与我们的预测相符。

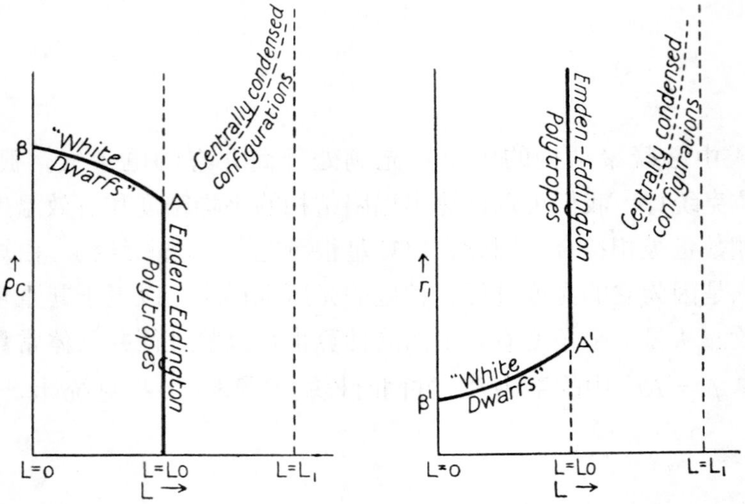


Figs. 1. and 2. The linear series of steady-state configurations of a mass $M$, of prescribed opacity, as its luminosity $L$ varies. (The "white dwarfs" are the "collapsed" configurations of the general theory. The "Emden-Eddington polytropes" are the gaseous diffuse configurations of the general theory; they are unstable, in general, with regard to deviations of $L$ on either side of the value $L_0$. The "centrally-condensed" series has not been fully worked out—it awaits the construction of certain tables—but it may be provisionally identified with stars in the state of giants and ordinary dwarfs. The diagram is to be understood as classificatory, not evolutionary.) ($\rho_c$=central density, $r_1$=external radius.)

The important point about all the foregoing analysis is that it involves at no stage any special properties of matter or special assumptions. The observed features of the stars are thus found to depend only on the most general properties of matter in association with light-pressure.

A question logically distinct from these is the origin of stellar energy. Here we require to know something of the physics of energy-generation. The following suggestions are frankly of a speculative character. Let us assume, in accordance with a hypothesis first made by Jeans (not his later hypothesis of super-radioactive atoms), that protons and electrons can unite to form radiation. Then thermodynamic considerations show that the process must be reversible—photons can generate matter. We know that matter at ordinary temperatures is stable. Hence we may postulate the existence of a critical temperature above which the process can go on in either direction. Suppose this critical temperature has been passed at $10^{11}$ degrees. Calculation then shows that at $10^{11}$ degrees almost the whole of the *mass* in an *enclosure* would be in the form of radiation; and further, that lowering of the temperature of the enclosure would result in more of the surviving matter present disappearing in the form of radiation. The process is in fact the thermodynamic opposite of evaporation: steam condenses to water with emission of energy, and the process is accordingly encouraged by cooling; matter "evaporates" (to radiation) with emission of energy, and the process is encouraged by cooling. Now, the centre of a star is a sort of thermodynamic enclosure with a slight leak. It follows that if (as the steady-state theory indicates) the central region of a fairly luminous star is at a temperature of $10^{11}$

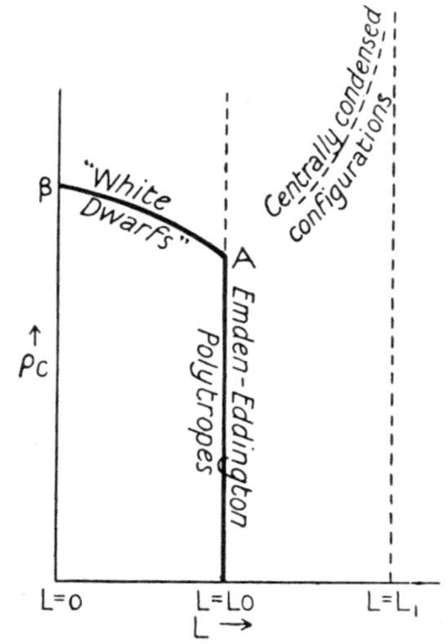


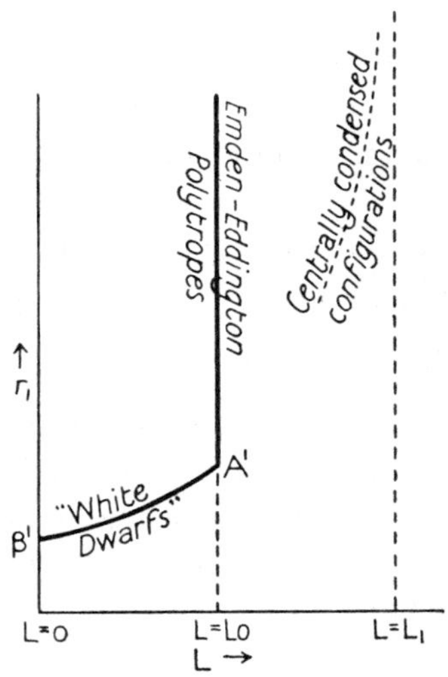


图 1 与图 2. 给定质量 $M$ 与不透明度，稳态结构的中心密度、外部半径与光度 $L$ 的关系。（一般认为，"白矮星"具有"塌陷"结构；"埃姆登 – 爱丁顿多层球"具有气态扩散结构，通常在 $L_0$ 的两侧，与 $L$ 值的任何偏离都会造成不稳定。由于需要建立特定的资料表，所以"中心凝聚"结构尚未完全解出，但是暂时可以认为该系列与巨星和普通矮星所处的状态一样。以上两图只是为了分类，并不表示演化。）（$\rho_c$= 中心密度，$r_1$= 外部半径）

在上述分析中，非常重要的一点是，我们没有引入物质的任何特殊属性或者某些特别的假设。因而观测到的恒星特征仅仅依赖于与光压相关的、最一般的物质属性。

当然，恒星能量的起源问题有别于上述问题。现在我们需要知道一些有关能量生成的物理规则，坦白地说，下面的分析仍具有推测的性质。让我们根据由金斯先生首先提出的假说（不是指他后来提出的超放射性原子假说）假设质子和电子在结合时能产生辐射。而热力学要求这一过程必须是可逆的，即光子也可以生成物质。我们知道，物质在常温下是稳定的。因此我们可以假定一个临界温度的存在，高于这个温度，则转化过程向两个方向都可以进行。假设这个临界温度已经达到了 $10^{11}$ 度。计算表明，当温度达到 $10^{11}$ 度的时候，一个星体**内部**的所有**质量**都将转化为辐射能；当恒星内部温度降低时，将导致有更多的剩余物质以辐射能的形式消耗掉。事实上在热力学中，这一过程与蒸发过程是相反的：蒸汽凝聚为水时要放出能量，所以该过程是由冷却驱动的；而物质"蒸发"（指的是辐射过程）时也要释放能量，这一过程也是受冷却驱动的。这样，恒星的中心就会成为一种稍微有一点泄漏的热力学封闭系统。于是假设（见稳态理论中的说明）在一颗相当明亮的恒星的中心区域，温度达到了 $10^{11}$ 度且有很高的密度，那么事实上中心区域就会成为一个拥有极高辐射

degrees and a high density, then this central region is effectively a reservoir of very dense radiant energy, with a mere sprinkling of ordinary matter present. Natural cooling of this reservoir provides the star's emission to space, and the reservoir is itself maintained by the conversion of matter into radiation inside it and on its confines.

Calculations based on this idea are consistent with the usually accepted evolutionary time scale, and predict a rate of "generation" of energy $\varepsilon$ per gram of the right order, namely, $\varepsilon = -\frac{4c^2}{T}\frac{dT}{dt}$ throughout the mass of the core, where $-dT/dt$ is the rate of cooling. The rate of loss of mass is given by the usual formula $\frac{dM}{dt} = -\frac{L}{c^2}$. By combination of these formulae it is found possible in principle to establish a relation linking $M$ with $T_c$ (the central temperature); this is the additional relation which, by expression of $T_c$ in terms of $L$ and $M$ by means of the steady-state theory, must lead in due course to a mass-luminosity correlation. Whether it agrees with the observed mass luminosity law remains for future investigation, but it is a final satisfaction that, after first considering $L$ and $M$ as independent variables, we are able to use the equilibrium configurations thus disclosed to arrive in outline at a solution of the problem of the actual correlation of mass and luminosity in Nature. It is to be noted that the star's generation of energy is naturally non-explosive, for it is simply a consequence of the natural tendency of the star to cool. The star behaves, in fact, simply like a freely cooling body containing a central region of very high specific heat—namely, a pool of intense radiant energy, which is gradually drained away though partially reinforced by the conversion of matter. From this point of view, it is not that a star descends an evolutionary path because its rate of generation of energy slackens; it is rather that the act of evolving and the act of radiating energy are identical.

These suggestions as to the origin of stellar energy and the mode of stellar evolution are not to be pressed. They are to be sharply distinguished from the steady-state theory, which by the rational process of proceeding from the known stellar exterior step by step into the unknown interior indicates an inevitable series of configurations which correspond to the observed bifurcation of celestial objects into "ordinary" stars and "dense" stars.

NOTE.—The fundamental result of the rational method of analysis of stellar structure described in the foregoing article is the division of configurations into two types, the "collapsed" and the "centrally-condensed". The existence of these two types can be demonstrated without complicated mathematics by the following argument. Let $r_1$ be the radius of a configuration, arbitrarily assigned beforehand. Let us endeavour to construct a gaseous configuration with this radius. If such a configuration be capable of being constructed, let us in imagination take a journey inwards to the centre, starting from the boundary. Let $M$ be the total mass, $M(r)$ the "surviving" mass left inside the sphere of radius $r$ when we have reached the distance $r$ from the centre. Then $M–M(r)$ is the mass already traversed. Consider now the influence of light-pressure. If $L$ is large, light-pressure will be large and will balance an appreciable fraction of gravity, and accordingly the density-gradient will be small. But if $L$ is small, light-pressure will be small, and the density-gradient will be large. Thus, when $L$ is large, we shall have traversed a smaller mass

能的存储器，其中只存在非常少量的普通物质。该存储器的自然冷却过程使恒星能够向外界空间辐射能量,而存储器本身则可以通过内部和边缘物质转化为辐射能来维持。

根据以上分析进行的计算与通常认可的演化时间尺度相符，计算结果预测了核心区域中每克质量的能量“生成”速率 $\varepsilon$ 的正确量级，即 $\varepsilon=-\frac{4c^2}{T}\frac{dT}{dt}$，其中 $-dT/dt$ 代表冷却速率。质量损失速率由通用公式 $\frac{dM}{dt}=-\frac{L}{c^2}$ 给出。将以上公式联合考虑，可以发现原则上在 $M$ 与 $T_c$（中心温度）之间可以建立某种相关性；这是另外的一个关系式——利用稳态理论将 $T_c$ 表达为带有 $L$ 与 $M$ 的式子，通过这一关系必然可以推导出质量—光度之间的关联性。至于是否与观测到的质量—光度定律一致，尚需进一步研究；但这是具有决定意义的结果，首先将 $L$ 与 $M$ 视为独立变量，然后我们就能够利用由此得到的平衡结构，勾画出自然界中实际存在的质量—光度关联性的大致轮廓。需要注意的是，恒星能量的生成是自然地非爆炸的，因为这只不过是恒星逐渐自然冷却的结果。事实上，恒星就像是一个自然冷却的天体，中心区域含有高热源，即聚集着大量的辐射能；尽管由于物质的转化可以补充一部分能量，但整体上是在渐渐枯竭。根据以上观点可以认为，与其说恒星向下延伸一个演化程是由于能量生成速率的放缓，不如说演化行为与能量辐射行为是同一的。

以上关于恒星能量起源和恒星演化模式的观点并非生搬硬套。这些想法与稳态理论极为不同，它通过理性分析从已知的恒星外部一步步推导到未知的内部，从而说明必然存在一系列结构，这与人们观察到的“普通”恒星和“致密”恒星之间的差别相符。

注意：上述文章描述了如何用理性的方法分析恒星结构，该方法得到的基本观点是，恒星按照结构的不同可分为“塌陷”和“中心凝聚”两种类型。通过以下的推导可以证明这两种类型的存在且不需要复杂的数学计算。令 $r_1$ 表示一个结构的半径,这个结构是预先任意给定的。现在让我们用这个半径尽力去构造一个气态的结构。如果这样一个结构可以建成，我们不妨想象自己从边界开始向中心作一次旅行。令 $M$ 表示总质量，$M(r)$ 表示当我们到达与中心的距离为 $r$ 的地方时，“未走过的”半径为 $r$ 的球体的质量。那么 $M-M(r)$ 就表示已走过的区域的质量。下面考虑光压的作用。如果 $L$ 很大，则光压也会很大，并将抵消相当一部分引力，因而密度梯度会很小。但是如果 $L$ 很小，光压也很小，而密度梯度将会很大。因此，当 $L$ 较大时，我们从外层半径 $r_1$ 到 $r$ 之间所走过的区域的质量 $M-M(r)$ 将小于 $L$ 较小的情况。相应地，当

$M$–$M(r)$ in the shell between $r_1$ and $r$ than when $L$ is small. Consequently, when $L$ is large, $M(r)$ will be larger than when $L$ is small. In other words, as we journey inwards, when $L$ is small we "consume our mass" faster than when $L$ is large. If $L$ is sufficiently small, we may have consumed our whole mass $M$ before we arrive at the centre; in that case the only configuration of radius $r_1$ and mass $M$ is a hollow shell internally supported by a rigid spherical surface. If $L$ is sufficiently large, we shall, however, tend to have an appreciable mass $M(r)$ surviving unconsumed however near we approach the centre, and this surviving mass $M(r)$ can only be packed inside $r$ at the cost of high density with violation of the gas laws. Thus these configurations for large $L$ must be centrally condensed. For small $L$, on the other hand, no configurations of radius $r_1$ and mass $M$, unsupported, can exist, and the actual configurations must be "collapsed" ones. "Collapsed" configurations prove to be much more nearly homogeneous than "centrally-condensed" ones.

(**127**, 16-18 & 27; 1931)

$L$ 较大时，$M(r)$ 也将大于 $L$ 较小的情况。换言之，当我们向内走的时候，如果 $L$ 较小，则我们“走过的质量”要比 $L$ 较大时多。如果 $L$ 特别小，我们可能在到达中心之前就走完了全部质量 $M$；在这种情况下，半径 $r_1$ 和质量 $M$ 组成的结构只能是一个内部由刚性球面支撑的中空壳体。反之，如果 $L$ 足够大，则无论我们多么靠近中心，未走过的剩余质量 $M(r)$ 仍会很大；这些质量只能聚集在半径为 $r$ 的区域之内，具有非常高的密度，气体定律也不再适用。因此具有较大 $L$ 值的结构一定是中心凝聚的；另一方面，对于较小的 $L$，半径为 $r_1$ 质量为 $M$ 的非支撑结构是不可能存在的，实际结构只能是“塌陷”结构。已证明，“塌陷”结构比“中心凝聚结构”要均匀得多。

（金世超 翻译；蒋世仰 审稿）

# Embryology and Evolution

E. W. MacBride

## Editor's Note

**The pages of *Nature* were alive with a debate about whether Mendelian genetics could account for the complexities of embryonic development and inheritance. With genetics still in its infancy, there remained many uncertainties and several scientists felt more comfortable with the Lamarckian view of inheritance: the idea that characteristics acquired by an organism during its lifetime can be passed on to its offspring. In his frequent contributions to *Nature*, Ernest William MacBride was particularly outspoken in his critique of Mendelian genetics, a stance that drew an aggressive response from those working in this expanding field. Here MacBride responds to the latest views of genetics advocate J. B. S. Haldane.**

I should like to comment on two letters by Mr. Haldane: one on "Natural Selection Intensity as a Function of Mortality Rate", in *Nature* of Dec. 6, and the other on "Embryology and Evolution", in the issue of Dec. 20. In the first, Mr. Haldane criticises as "fallacious" Prof. Salisbury's argument that mortality amongst plants is mainly confined to the seedling stage and that at this period natural selection mainly works. He goes on to consider a case where two races vary as to a single character! Now, this is a travesty of what occurs in Nature. Two allied races do not differ from one another in a single character: they differ in a multitude of minute points, and it is quite impossible to say whether one or another of these points determines their survival. The "characters", in fact, are mere abstractions. The organism is a whole, and the characters are the expression of its constitution; in a word, of the vigour of its reaction to its surroundings. The whole point of Prof. Salisbury's argument was that natural selection chooses the most vigorous, not that which possesses some special character, and this argument I believe to be perfectly sound.

In his second letter Mr. Haldane objects to four of the statements in my reply to Prof. Gates. I shall deal with these seriatim.

(1) Mr. Haldane claims that some microscopists have seen "genes". What they have seen are segregations of material in the stained and fixed chromosomes which they have identified as genes—a purely hypothetical conclusion. He further says that the presence or absence of a "trabant", that is, not a gene but a small chromosome, makes a difference in the constitution of the plant *Matthiola*. This is quite possible, and I shall be glad to have it demonstrated. Prof. Gates was, I think, the first to show that an extra chromosome made a difference to the appearance of the mutant.

# 胚胎学与进化

欧内斯特·威廉·麦克布赖德

## 编者按

大家正在《自然》杂志的专栏中激烈地讨论孟德尔遗传学是否能解释胚胎发育和遗传的复杂性。由于遗传学刚刚兴起，还存在着许多不确定的因素，所以一些科学家还是更愿意接受拉马克的遗传理论，即认为有机体后天获得的特征可以传给后代。欧内斯特·威廉·麦克布赖德经常在《自然》杂志上投稿，毫不避讳地公开批评孟德尔的遗传学说，因而他的立场引起了这一迅速发展领域中的研究人员的反击。在本文中，麦克布赖德回应了孟德尔遗传学支持者霍尔丹最近提出的意见。

我想对霍尔丹先生的两篇快报发表一下自己的看法：一篇是在 12 月 6 日的《自然》杂志上刊登的《与死亡率有关的自然选择强度》，另一篇是 12 月 20 日刊登的《胚胎学与进化》。在第一篇快报里，霍尔丹先生批评索尔兹伯里教授的观点是“错误的”，索尔兹伯里教授认为植物的死亡主要发生在苗期，并且自然选择主要在此阶段发生作用。霍尔丹先生竟然继而举证两个物种区分于某一单一性状的例子！这是对大自然中发生的事实的歪曲。两个近缘种在单一性状上不能区分彼此：它们在许多微小的方面都有所不同，不可能说出这些方面中的哪一个方面能够决定它们的生存。事实上，“性状”只是抽象的概念。生物体是一个整体，性状是对其构成的表达；简言之，性状是生物体对周围环境的反应活力的表达。索尔兹伯里教授的中心论点是自然选择选出的是最有活力的生物，而非拥有某些特别性状的生物，我认为这一观点是相当合理的。

在第二篇快报中，霍尔丹先生对我在回应盖茨教授时所作的四点说明进行了反驳。下面我将逐一回复。

（1）霍尔丹先生声称有些显微镜学家已经看到了“基因”。其实，他们看到的被认定为基因的物质只不过是经染色固定的染色体上的分离物——这是一个纯粹假想性的结论。他还说“随体”的存在或缺失会对紫罗兰属植物的构造产生影响，其中，随体并不是基因，而是一小染色体。这是完全可能的，我很高兴这一点已经得到了实证。我认为盖茨教授是第一个表明额外染色体能影响突变体外观的人。

(2) Mr. Haldane asserts that scores of cases are known where in interspecific crosses characters behave in a Mendelian manner, that is, are due to genes. All I know on this subject is that my friends who are systematists, and have devoted their lives to the study of species and races, deny that such is the case. Of course, a mutant such as the domesticated race almost always "mendelises" when crossed with the wild type; that is just what distinguishes a mutant from a racial character, and the case quoted by Mr. Haldane is such a cross.

(3) Mr. Haldane states that autocatalytic reactions are common in physical chemistry. By this is meant reactions in aqueous solutions which are accelerated by the products of the reaction. I put this question to three first-class chemists, all of them fellows of the Royal Society and one of them a bio-chemist, and as they were all unaware of any such case, I prefer to accept their testimony.

(4) Mr. Haldane objects to my posing the alternative of the organs being preformed in miniature in the embryo or being due to an "unknown cause". He says that bone is formed by an enzyme "phosphatase". This is a mere quibble. Enzymes are *means* employed by the embryo to develop its powers, and their orderly appearance is just as much a mystery as the appearance of the organs themselves.

Mr. Haldane's remarks about my refusing to take cognisance of the recent advances of science and his invitation to acquaint myself with the "facts" of genetics and chemistry I prefer to disregard. I have quoted the authorities on whom I rely in chemical matters. As to genetics, I have served for seventeen years on the Council of the Institution to which Mr. Haldane is attached as statistician, and I have watched all the work going on there, and the more I see of it the more I am convinced that Mendelism has nothing to do with evolution.

(**127**, 55-56; 1931)

E. W. MacBride: 43 Elm Park Gardens, Chelsea, S.W.10, Dec. 23, 1930.

（2）霍尔丹先生断言有大量为人们所知的例子表明：在种间杂交中，性状以孟德尔式遗传，也就是说是由于基因。对于这一问题，我所知道的是，我的那些一生都致力于物种和种族研究的分类学家朋友们都否认情况是这样的。当然，当一个突变体，如家养种，与野生型杂交时，几乎总是按“孟德尔式”遗传的；这恰恰是区分突变性状和种族性状的要点，霍尔丹先生引用的例子就是这样一种杂交类型。

（3）霍尔丹先生认为自催化反应在物理化学界很普遍。这指的是发生在水溶液中的反应，其生成的产物可以加速该反应。我向三位一流的化学家咨询了这一问题。他们都是英国皇家学会的会员，有一位还是生化学家。由于他们都不知道有任何此类的例子，所以我更倾向于接受他们的证词。

（4）霍尔丹先生反对我提出的以下这个二者择一的说法：器官或者是在胚胎中以缩影形式预先存在或者是由于“不明原因”而发生。他说骨骼是通过一种被称为“磷酸酶”的酶形成的，这纯粹是诡辩。酶是胚胎用于发育的**工具**，酶的有序出现与器官本身的出现一样神秘。

霍尔丹先生评论说我拒绝认知最新的科学进展，并且要请我去了解一下遗传学和化学中的“事实”，对于这个提议，我宁愿漠视不理。在化学方面，我已经指出了一些我可以依靠的权威人士。至于遗传学，我已经在理事会机构工作了 17 年，而霍尔丹先生只是该机构的一名统计员。我则监视那里进行的所有工作，并且我看到的越多，就越相信孟德尔遗传学说与进化毫无关系。

（刘皓芳 翻译；陈平富 审稿）

# Embryology and Evolution

C. O. Bartrum

## Editor's Note

**Following a long-running tit-for-tat correspondence in the pages of *Nature* between supporters and opponents of a synthesis of Darwinian natural selection and Mendelian genetics, C. O. Bartrum attempts to bring some philosophical clarity to the dispute. In an earlier issue, botanist Ruggles Gates and neo-Lamarckian zoologist Ernest William MacBride had gone head to head. Here Bartrum backs Gates and gently scolds MacBride for straying onto philosophical territory. Scientists should restrict themselves to discovering facts and marshalling them into testable hypotheses, he says.**

THE discussion between Prof. R. Ruggles Gates and Prof. E. W. MacBride, in *Nature* of Dec. 6, bears in an important way upon the philosophy of science. May one without authority in biology offer what he hopes may be a useful contribution from the philosophical point of view?

It is the function of the scientific man to discover facts, to endeavour to co-ordinate them, and by generalisation to build up a useful scheme of hypotheses. Such a scheme must be a deterministic scheme or it cannot be useful, that is, it cannot be used to forecast further facts. When Prof. MacBride writes of mechanical hypotheses, he refers, presumably, to such a deterministic scheme. Whether the resulting scheme represents the truth is not the business of the scientific man as such, but of the philosopher.

As a philosopher Prof. Gates may believe himself to be a "mere mechanism" or a Drieschian entelechian organism. For science this is beside the question. A scientific man must continue to have faith in "so-called mechanical hypotheses", or, as Prof. Gates says, "there would be no further incentive to experimental embryology", and his function would cease. As a philosopher he may doubt whether such deterministic schemes will ultimately prevail, but as a scientific man he must carry on.

(**127**, 56; 1931)

C. O. Bartrum: 32 Willoughby Road, Hampstead, London, Dec. 10.

# 胚胎学与进化

巴特拉姆

编者按

对于综合达尔文自然选择学说和孟德尔遗传学的新理论，支持者和反对者一直在《自然》杂志的专栏中针锋相对地互相抨击，巴特拉姆想用哲学观点来解决争端。植物学家拉各尔斯·盖茨和新拉马克主义者动物学家欧内斯特·威廉·麦克布赖德曾在《自然》杂志上激烈地争辩过。巴特拉姆支持盖茨的观点，他温和地指责麦克布赖德偏离到了哲学领域。他说：科学家的本职工作应该是发现事实并基于这些事实形成可以被检验的假说。

拉各尔斯·盖茨教授和麦克布赖德教授之间的讨论与科学哲学有很重要的关联，讨论的内容发表于《自然》杂志 12 月 6 日版。尽管我并非生物学的权威，但我是否可以从哲学观点出发提供一份我所期望的可能对此讨论有用的帮助呢？

科学工作者的职责是发现事实、努力整合事实、并归纳建立一套有用的假说体系。这样的体系必须是具有决定性的，否则它们丝毫用处也没有，也就是说，不能用它们来预测更多的事实。当麦克布赖德教授在文中提到机械假说时，他理当指的就是这样一种具有决定性的体系。产生的假说体系是否代表了事实就不是科学工作者本身的事情，而是哲学家的事情了。

盖茨教授作为一位哲学家，可以认为自己是一台“纯粹的机械”，或者是一种德里施（译者注：德国生物学家与哲学家）式的蕴含生机本源的生物。对于科学而言，这与本文要讨论的问题无关。科学工作者必须继续怀着对“所谓的机械假说”的信仰，否则就如盖茨教授所说的“将不会有进一步研究实验胚胎学的动力了”，那时科学工作者的作用也就停止了。作为一位哲学家，他可以怀疑这样的决定性体系能否最终得到普及；而作为一位科学工作者，他却必须继续进行下去。

（刘皓芳 翻译；陈平富 审稿）

# Stellar Structure

## Editor's Note

**In a recent review in *Nature* of new theories of stellar structure, Edward Milne dismissed the views of James Jeans as requiring *ad hoc* hypotheses outside known physics. Here Jeans writes in response. He did not, he claims, simply hypothesise the existence in stars of atomic mass greater than anything on Earth, but drew this possibility from the best possible fit to the latest observed relationship between the luminosity of known stars and their temperature. Jeans also comments on Milne's mathematical treatment of stellar structure, concluding that he has been led to his views by unnecessary presuppositions, and that anything novel in his theory will vanish as soon as these are relaxed.**

IN *Nature* of Jan. 3, Prof. Milne writes that my theory of stellar structure accounts for the existence of giant, dwarf, and white dwarf stars, "only at the cost of *ad hoc* hypotheses quite outside physics. It assumes stars to contain atoms of atomic weight higher than that observed on earth, and it assumes them to be relentlessly disappearing in the form of radiation; it appeals to discontinuous changes of state consequent on successive ionisations, for which there is little warrant."

This seems to me a mass of highly concentrated inaccuracy. My actual hypotheses are that the stars we observe in the sky must be stable and need not be gaseous; it seems odd to describe these as "*ad hoc* hypotheses quite outside physics". What Milne describes as "assumptions" are inferences after the main results have been obtained. After the Russell diagram has been obtained, an atomic number of 95 seems to give the *best* fit with observation, but I could have "assumed" a far lower number and obtained quite a *good* fit. Incidentally, no other theory gives any fit at all—or even anything to fit. The appeal "to discontinuous changes of state" appears to be a highly coloured description of the fact that I find that bands of stability and instability alternate.

I find it hard to believe that other astronomers understand my theory as little as does Prof. Milne. If they do, he is no doubt right in saying that the majority do not accept it.

I am not writing to challenge Milne's inaccuracies, so much as to ask whether his new theory must not ultimately prove identical with my own theory, which "the majority of astronomers do not accept". We start out on the same road, by not seeing eye-to-eye with Sir Arthur Eddington. Milne's recent discoveries—that mass and luminosity are independent, that the mass-luminosity relation is a happy (or unhappy) accident, etc.—are merely old familiar landmarks on a road which I travelled and described fully in *Nature* and *Mon. Not. R.A.S.* more than ten years ago.

# 恒星的构造

编者按

在最近《自然》杂志关于恒星构造新理论的回顾文章中，爱德华·米耳恩否定了詹姆斯·金斯的理论，因为他的理论需要用到一些物理学领域之外的特殊假设。而在这篇文章中，金斯反驳了这一观点。他声称自己并没有无端地假设恒星内存在的原子的质量高于地球上的所有物质，而是从最近观测到的已知恒星光度和温度之间关系的最佳拟合中推出来的。金斯还评价了米耳恩对恒星结构的数学处理，认为他的结论是从几个没有必要的假设中推出来的，一旦没有了这些假设，米耳恩理论中的新奇之处也就荡然无存了。

在1月3日出版的《自然》杂志中，米耳恩教授提到了我用来解释巨星、矮星和白矮星的存在的理论，他是这么说的“但这一理论需要引入一些与物理学毫不相干的特殊假设。该理论假设恒星中包含的原子所具有的原子量大于在地球上的观测值，而且这些原子在以辐射形式不断地被消耗；持续电离会引起状态的非连续变化，而这一点是缺乏根据的。”

在我看来，以上理解是非常不准确的。实际上我的观点是，我们在天空中观测到的恒星必须是稳定的，但未必一定是气态的；把我的观点说成是“与物理学毫不相干的特殊假设”令人感到很奇怪。米耳恩所称的“假设”其实是一些基于主要结果的推论。在有了罗素图之后，我发现当原子序数为95时，可以对观测结果做出**最佳**的拟合；但是我其实可以“假设”一个低得多的原子序数，同样可以得到**很好**的拟合。需要顺便提及的是，没有任何其他理论可以对上述结果进行拟合，甚至连可以用来拟合的根据都没有。米耳恩在文中还提到，我的理论要求“状态的非连续变化”，这显然是对我发现稳定带和非稳定带交替出现这一事实的歪曲。

我很难相信其他天文学家对我理论的理解也会像米耳恩教授那样浅薄。如果真是这样，那么他所说的多数人都不会接受这一理论无疑将是正确的。

我写这篇文章的目的并不是为了挑战米耳恩教授的错误，更不是为了质疑他的新理论是否有必要一定不同于我的所谓“大多数天文学家并不接受”的理论。我们的起点相同，即我们都不完全同意阿瑟·爱丁顿爵士的观点。米耳恩最近的发现——质量和光度是相互独立的，而质量—光度之间的关联是一个令人愉快（或不愉快）的偶然等等，都只不过是我以前有过的阶段性想法，十余年前，我在《自然》杂志和《皇家天文学会月刊》上已对此进行过全面的阐述。

Milne and I part company on the question of stellar boundary conditions. The classical Emden solution starts with a finite density at the star's centre and integrates outwards. Eddington, and then I, followed Emden in thinking that *Nature* was bound to look after the boundary conditions somehow or other. Then I noticed ("Astronomy and Cosmogony", §§ 80, 81) that what appears to be a single solution in a star's interior, spreads out into a whole tassel near the photosphere; it proves to be merely an asymptote to a whole family of solutions which correspond to different boundary conditions. This shows that any boundary condition can be satisfied, so that "the influence of the special conditions which prevail at the surface soon disappears as we pass inwards into the star" (l.c. § 80).

This fundamental point can be illustrated by a simple model suggested by Milne (*M. N.*, **90**, p. 53). Represent a star by a sphere of copper $s$ with a heating coil at its centre, and its photospheric layers by $s'$, a thin coat of asbestos, paint, or other substance. Varying the substance of $s'$ represents varying the photospheric conditions of a star; we want to find how interior conditions depend on $s'$. Milne solves the problem wrongly, as I think, and concludes that the sphere coated with asbestos will be "much hotter inside" than one wholly of copper, "for it is jacketed by a bad conductor". As every plumber knows, this is not so; only a thick layer of asbestos will make things much hotter inside. It is, I think, the same with the stars. Whatever the photospheric conditions, the photospheric layers are not thick enough to make any real difference.

Thus Milne's involved procedure of integrating inwards, getting infinite or zero density, and then letting masses of unsupported gas crash to finite densities, seems to me all unnecessary; he could have assumed a finite central density to begin with and integrated outwards, and as this is the exact procedure followed in my theory I cannot see how our final results can be different—unless one of us makes a mistake in analysis or arithmetic.

It is, of course, also the procedure followed by Eddington in his classic papers. Where I differ from Eddington is not on general questions of procedure; it is that he thinks a star's centre must be gaseous, whereas I do not. Also, we differ as to whether his very restricted model with $\kappa\eta$ constant is a very good or a very bad model. Milne appears to have followed Eddington so far in tying himself down to this particular restriction. Unless I am greatly mistaken, all that is essentially novel in his theory (as shown in Figs. 1 and 2 in his *Nature* article) will vanish to nothing as soon as he frees himself from this impossible and misleading restriction.

J. H. Jeans

(**127**, 89; 1931)

* * *

米耳恩和我在恒星边界条件的问题上存在分歧。埃姆登的经典解法是从恒星中心的有限密度处开始向外积分。爱丁顿，以及后来的我，都继承了埃姆登的思路，认为物质世界必然会以某种方式寻找边界条件。然后我注意到（《天文学与宇宙演化论》，§§ 80，81）：看似是恒星内部的单一解，可以向外扩展到光球层附近的所有流苏结构；事实上可以证明该解只不过是与不同边界条件对应的一组解的渐进表达。这说明任何边界条件都可以被满足，所以“当我们向恒星内部积分的时候，在表面处占优势的特殊条件很快就会失去影响”（上述引文 § 80）。

这一点可以用米耳恩提出的简单模型来进行解释（《皇家天文学会月刊》，第 90 卷，第 53 页）。不妨让一个铜球 $s$ 代表恒星，在其中心用线圈加热，并在该铜球表面覆上薄的石棉层、涂料或其他物质以代表光球层 $s'$。改变组成 $s'$ 的物质就意味着改变恒星光球层的条件；我们希望知道 $s'$ 是如何影响内部条件的。我认为，米耳恩解决该问题的方法是错误的，他认为覆盖着石棉的铜球会比只有铜球本身时“内部热很多”，“因为前者覆有热的不良导体”。每个水管工都清楚，事实并非如此；只有很厚的石棉层才会使内部更热。我认为这和恒星的情况是一样的。无论光球层条件如何，光球层的厚度都不足以造成任何真正意义上的区别。

因此，米耳恩采取向内积分的方法，由此得到无限的密度或零密度，并令没有支撑的气体物质塌陷为有限的密度，这些在我看来都是没有必要的。他本可以假定一个有限的中心密度，然后由中心开始向外积分，这就是我的理论所采用的方法。我不认为我们得到的最终结果会有所不同——除非我们俩之中的一个在分析或计算上出现错误。

当然，爱丁顿在他的经典论文中也采用了这一方法。我与爱丁顿的不同之处并非源于方法上的差异，而在于他认为一个恒星的中心必须是气态的，我却不这么认为。同时我们在常数为 $\kappa\eta$ 的爱丁顿受限模型究竟是一个好模型还是一个差模型的问题上也有分歧。米耳恩看起来同意爱丁顿的观点，因此也采用了这一特殊限制。除非是我犯了很大的错误，否则一旦米耳恩放弃这个根本不成立且令人误入歧途的限制，他理论中的那些新颖之处也会自然消失（参见米耳恩在《自然》杂志上发表的文章中的图 1 和图 2）。

金斯

* * *

Referring to Sir James Jeans's letter in *Nature* of Jan. 17, p. 89, I may say that I fully acknowledged in my paper of November 1929 (*Mon. Not. Roy. Ast. Soc.*, **90**, p. 20) that Sir James was the first to recognise the principle that the mass $M$ and luminosity $L$ of a star are independent variables as regards steady state considerations. On p. 53 of that same paper (a page of which Jeans himself quotes in another connexion) I made a general reference of obligation to his work. In my last paper (*Mon. Not. Roy. Ast. Soc.*, **91**) I build on Jeans's permanent contributions to science in three places, mentioning him by name (pp. 4, 9, 51). I could not, however, adduce any of the specific results of his theory of stellar equilibrium in support of my conclusions, for they are totally different; and I could not contrast his results with mine without venturing to discuss his mathematics.

I cannot assent to Jeans's mathematics, because his theory of stellar equilibrium is in formal contradiction with his own ($L$, $M$) independence principle. It is an immediate consequence of this principle that for a given mass $M$ in equilibrium the ratio $\lambda$ of gas pressure to radiation pressure may have any value whatever between zero and infinity, depending on the arbitrarily assigned $L$. This is fundamental in my analysis. According to Jeans ("Astronomy and Cosmogony", pp. 88, 89) $\lambda$ is small for large masses and large for small masses, and is calculable in terms of $M$ (p. 97). Jeans may claim the principle, but his theory is not consistent with it.

The point of my analysis is the construction of configurations which satisfy the ($L$, $M$) independence principle, even for models for which $\kappa\eta$ is constant. The special properties attributed to these models by both Jeans and Eddington then disappear, and the new general properties which emerge (explaining as they do why some stars are very dense and others not) are shared by other models, since they depend only upon the occurrence of the central singularity $r$=0 in a certain system of differential equations. Jeans uses throughout Emden's solutions, which possess no singularities.

As regards the branching-out of solutions near the boundary of a star, Jeans is considering a variety of models. *For any one model*, the solution is unique up to the boundary. The work of Mr. Fowler, Mr. Fairclough, and myself published in *Mon. Not. Roy. Ast. Soc.*, **91** (November 1930), discusses the family of such solutions arising from Emden's equation; with any definite configuration, of arbitrarily assigned mass, luminosity, and opacity, there is associated *one* member of the family of solutions, selected by a boundary condition which ensures that the boundary layers, of the prescribed opacity, enclose $M$ and radiate $L$.

E. A. Milne

(**127**, 269; 1931)

J. H. Jeans: Cleveland Lodge, Dorking, Jan. 5.
E. A. Milne: Wadham College, Oxford, Feb. 5.

看罢詹姆斯·金斯爵士在 1 月 17 日《自然》杂志第 89 页发表的快报，我要说的是，我在 1929 年 11 月的一篇论文（《英国皇家天文学会月刊》第 90 卷，第 20 页）中就已经完全承认了詹姆斯爵士是第一个认识到稳态下恒星的质量 $M$ 与光度 $L$ 是两个独立变量的人。在同一篇文章的第 53 页（金斯本人曾在其他地方引用过这一页的内容），我对他的工作进行了全面的介绍。在我最近的一篇论文（《英国皇家天文学会月刊》第 91 卷）中，我三度（第 4、9、51 页）提到了金斯的名字，赞扬了他对自然科学的永恒贡献。但我不能通过引用由他的恒星平衡理论推出的特殊结果来支持我的论点，因为它们是完全不同的两回事；在没有仔细分析他的数学推导过程之前，我无法把他的结论与我的进行比较。

我不能认同金斯的数学推导，因为他的恒星平衡理论与他所说的（$L$、$M$）相互独立原则存在形式上的矛盾。根据这一原则可以直接推出，对于平衡态中的一个给定质量 $M$，气体压强与辐射压强的比值 $\lambda$ 可以取从 0 到无穷大中的任意值，具体大小由任意给定的 $L$ 值决定。这在我的分析中是最基本的。按照金斯（《天文学与宇宙演化论》第 88、89 页）的说法，质量较大时 $\lambda$ 值较小，质量较小时 $\lambda$ 值较大，且 $\lambda$ 值可以用 $M$ 的关系式计算出来（第 97 页）。金斯可以提出这个原则，不过他的理论与这个原则并不一致。

我在分析中的关键点是构造满足（$L$、$M$）相互独立原则的关系式，也包括 $\kappa\eta$ 是常量的模型。如此一来，金斯和爱丁顿所创建的模型中的一些特殊性质就会消失，新出现的一般属性（它们能解释为什么有些恒星非常致密，另一些则不是）可以和其他模型共享，因为它们只取决于在一个确定的微分方程系统中是否出现中心奇点 $r = 0$。金斯完全照搬了没有奇点的埃姆登解法。

至于方程解在恒星边界附近的拓展性，金斯正在考虑各种模型的适用性。**对于任意一个模型而言**，其解一直到边界处都是唯一的。福勒先生、费尔克拉夫先生和我在共同发表于《英国皇家天文学会月刊》第 91 卷（1930 年 11 月）的论文中讨论了由埃姆登方程得到的一组解；对于任意一个给定质量、光度和不透明度的确定体系，这组解中都存在**一个**与之相关且满足边界条件的解，使得具有指定不透明度的边界层能够封入质量 $M$ 和光度 $L$。

米耳恩

（王锋 翻译；蒋世仰 审稿）

# Vitamin B

## Editor's Note

**There are eight separate chemical compounds in the family of B vitamins, but all were once thought to be a single substance, deemed essential for the growth of organisms. This anonymous report describes how that former picture began to change. Following work that suggested vitamin B had two forms that relieve pain and a concatenation of ailments called pellagra, it seemed by this stage that there were at least four B vitamins. Vitamin $B_1$ (thiamine), the focus here, was the best characterised, its chemical composition and properties being already sketchily known. Vitamin chemistry became an important strand of biochemistry in the prewar era, although it was some time before their molecular structures and physiological roles were understood.**

### Assay and Vitamin $B_1$

THE separation of vitamin B into two factors, antineuritic and antipellagrous, a few years ago, led to considerable attention being devoted to the properties of this vitamin, with the result that it is now possible to distinguish at least four B factors, quite apart from any grouped under the name "Bios", which may be necessary for the growth of lower organisms. The factors are distinguished by differences in their chemical properties and physiological effects: their differentiation has necessitated a revision of the methods of assay, since it is possible that a failure to respond to an addition to the diet is an indication of the absence of a factor other than that for which the test was designed. In this type of research a preventive test is less delicate than a curative, whilst the growth test may be considered still cruder: a single factor should cure the specific symptoms due to its absence, preventive tests may test for more than one, whilst it is clear that a positive growth response can only be obtained when every factor is adequately supplied; and our knowledge of all the factors required for growth is still incomplete, as the recent work on vitamin B has shown.

H. W. Kinnersley, R. A. Peters, and V. Reader[1] have analysed the pigeon curative test for vitamin $B_1$, or the antineuritic factor. By adherence to certain principles, the test can be made reasonably accurate and has been successfully used in following the vitamin in its concentration from a yeast extract. The birds should be in the laboratory for a month on a mixed grain diet before being placed on the diet of polished rice, and only those developing symptoms within 30 days should be used. As soon as signs of head retraction appear, the bird should be transferred to a warm room for 2 hours and given 50 mgm. glucose in water by stomach tube: this procedure eliminates birds showing false cures. The dose of extract must be given within 6–12 hours of the onset of symptoms and, provided the cure lasts more than 1 and less than 10 days, the amount of active principle

# 维生素 B

## 编者按

在 B 族维生素中共有 8 种不同的化合物，但是，以前人们曾把它们看作是单一的物质，有机体的成长离不开这些物质。这份匿名报告告诉我们：以前的观念正在发生变化。研究表明：有两种形式的维生素 B 可以减轻人类的痛苦并能缓解一系列被称为糙皮病的病症，这使维生素 B 家族中的成员数达到至少 4 个。本文详细介绍了维生素 $B_1$（硫胺素）的特征，当时人们对它的化学组成和性质已经有所了解。虽然维生素的分子结构和生理作用是在一段时间以后才为人们所熟知的，但维生素化学在战前时代就已经成为了生物化学领域的重要分支。

### 检验与维生素$B_1$

不久之前，维生素 B 被分离为两个因子：抗神经炎因子和抗糙皮病因子，因此，人们开始对这种维生素的性质给予充分的重视，结果发现它可能至少可以被分为四种截然不同的因子，与基于“生长素”名称的分类结果相去甚远，这种“生长素”对于低等生物的生长可能是必需的。这些因子可以由化学性质和生理学活性的差异加以区别：而这种差异性要求我们对检测方法进行修订，因为当一种检测方法不能检测出食品中的相应添加物质时，人们有可能会认为此种因子并不存在，而并非实验设计有问题。在此类研究中，预防性检测不如治疗性检测那么灵敏；同时，生长检测被认为更加粗糙：一种单独的因子应该可以治愈由于其缺乏而引起的特定病症；预防性检测可以检测多种因子的存在，但同时非常清楚的是，只有当每一种因子都充分给予的时候，才能够获得阳性生长的结果；而我们对于生长所需的所有因子的了解还不全面，最近在维生素 B 方面的研究工作中也体现出了这一点。

金纳斯利、彼得斯和里德[1]分析研究了维生素 $B_1$ 或抗神经炎因子对鸽子的治疗效果。遵照一定的原则，这个实验可以得到相当精确的结果，而且已经被成功地应用于随后从酵母提取液中得到的维生素浓缩液实验中。这些禽类首先需要在实验室中用混合谷物饲料喂养一个月，然后用精制大米喂养，只有那些在 30 天时间内产生相应病症的个体被用于随后的实验。一旦头部萎缩现象出现，就应把这些鸟禽转移到温室中搁置 2 小时，同时通过胃管给予 50 mg 的葡萄糖水溶液。这个处理过程消除了鸟禽表现出假阳性治愈的可能性。酵母提取物必须在病理症状出现后的 6 ~ 12 小时之内喂食，如果治疗时间超过 1 天，少于 10 天，则可以认为出现的有效

present can be considered as directly proportional to the length of the cure. After the test is over, the bird is given marmite and kept warm for a few days. It is then placed on the stock diet again for about a month, when it is ready for another period of polished rice feeding. Individual birds show a remarkable constancy in the time symptoms appear after commencement of the experimental diet, but there is no correlation between this interval and the duration of the subsequent cure, or between it and the colour or weight of the bird.

H. Chick and M. H. Roscoe[2] have used the growth of young rats as a criterion for the presence of vitamin $B_1$. It is difficult to carry out a curative test with this animal, since there is only a very short interval between the onset of acute symptoms and death: Reader has, however, been successful and has found that the adult rat requires about one pigeon day dose each day (quoted by Peters, the Harben Lectures, 1929). Chick and Roscoe used synthetic diets free from vitamin $B_1$: vitamin $B_2$ was supplied as autoclaved yeast or as fresh egg-white. After 2–3 weeks the animals began to lose weight: growth was resumed if Peters' antineuritic concentrate was then administered. The egg-white diet, however, did not maintain growth to maturity. B. C. Guha and J. C. Drummond[3] have used both the pigeon curative and the rat growth tests: in the latter, vitamin $B_2$ was supplied as marmite autoclaved at an alkaline reaction.

Chick and Roscoe[4] have used a similar method for the assay of vitamin $B_2$, young rats being placed on a diet complete except for this vitamin, and the $B_1$ factor being supplied as Peters' concentrate. It was found that the caseinogen used contained traces of vitamin $B_2$ unless it was reprecipitated with acetic acid and thoroughly extracted with alcohol before being heated at 120°. Animals on this diet fail to grow but respond to a supplement containing vitamin $B_2$. If the supplement is not given, after about six weeks a generalised dermatitis appears, which can be cured by administration of the vitamin.

B. C. P. Jansen and W. F. Donath[5] obtained highly active preparations of vitamin $B_1$ from rice polishings by a process involving extraction with acid water, adsorption on fuller's earth, eleution with baryta, and fractionation of the extract with silver sulphate and baryta. The activity was precipitated with phosphotungstic acid, the precipitate decomposed with baryta, and after removal of barium the concentrated solution was treated with platinic chloride, which precipitated the vitamin. Further purification was effected by acetone precipitation from alcoholic solution and by treatment with picrolonic acid or gold chloride. 0.012 mgm. of the final fraction a day was sufficient to maintain pigeons in health over six weeks: C. Eykman[6] confirmed the activity with both pigeons and cocks. The final product was obtained in crystalline form, as a hydrochloride, a picrolonate, or a double salt with gold chloride.

Kinnersley and Peters[7] have continued their work on antineuritic yeast concentrates[8]. It is not yet certain whether the curative substance is the same as that obtained from rice polishings by Jansen and Donath: the activity of the final product does not appear to be quite so great and its properties are not quite the same. In all work on the concentration

成分的数量与治疗时间的长度成正比。当实验结束的时候，再给这些鸟禽喂食含酵母的食物，并在几天内保持温房喂养环境。然后再用普通食物喂养大概一个月的时间，以便准备开始下一个阶段的精制大米喂养。当开始使用实验用食物喂养后，个别鸟禽表现出了显著的周期性发病，但周期的长短与随后的治愈时间、或者与鸟禽的颜色以及体重都没有关系。

奇克和罗斯科[2]用幼年大鼠的生长作为判断维生素 $B_1$ 存在的标准。用这种动物很难进行治愈性实验研究，原因在于这种动物从急症发作到死亡只间隔很短的时间；然而，里德获得了成功，他发现成年个体老鼠每天需要差不多一只鸽子一天的使用量（引自彼得斯，哈本演讲稿，1929 年）。奇克和罗斯科采用不含维生素 $B_1$ 的合成饲料进行喂养，并以喂食高压灭菌酵母或新鲜蛋清的方式补充维生素 $B_2$。经过两到三周之后，这些动物的体重开始减轻；如果在食物中添加彼得斯抗神经炎浓缩物质，身体会再次开始生长。然而，添加蛋清的食物并不能维持生长到成熟阶段。古哈和德拉蒙德[3]同时进行了鸽子治愈实验和老鼠生长实验；在后一个实验中，补充维生素 $B_2$ 的方式是用碱性反应条件下的高压灭菌酵母。

奇克和罗斯科[4]采用了一种类似的方法来检验维生素 $B_2$，他们用完全缺失这种维生素的食物来喂养幼鼠，通过彼得斯抗神经炎浓缩物质提供维生素 $B_1$ 因子。结果发现所使用的酪蛋白原含有微量的维生素 $B_2$；除非它在被加热到 120℃之前曾用乙酸沉淀并用乙醇进行彻底的萃取。采用这种类型食物喂养的动物不能生长，但在补充维生素 $B_2$ 后会有效果。如果没有补充维生素 $B_2$，大概六个星期之后就会出现普遍性的皮炎，这种病症可以通过补充维生素而得到治愈。

詹森和多纳特[5]通过以下处理过程从米糠中获得了高活性的维生素 $B_1$ 制备物。这个过程包括酸水萃取、漂白土吸附、氧化钡洗脱，以及用硫酸银和氧化钡对提取物的分馏。得到的活性物质采用磷钨酸进行沉淀，沉淀物采用氧化钡进行分解；去除钡元素之后，浓缩溶液采用能使维生素沉淀的氯化铂处理。进一步的纯化过程还包括采用丙酮从醇溶液中沉淀，以及采用苦酮酸或者氯化金进行处理。每天喂食 0.012 mg 的这种最终提取物就足以保证鸽子在六个星期的时间内处于健康状态。艾克曼[6]利用鸽子和公鸡进一步确定了这种生物学活性。最终产物可以以盐酸盐、苦酮酸盐或者氯化金复盐的晶体形式获得。

金纳斯利和彼得斯[7]继续了他们在抗神经炎酵母浓缩物方面的研究[8]。然而还无法确认这种治疗性物质是否与詹森和多纳特从米糠中得到的物质完全一样，因为最终产物的活性并不是表现得非常明显，它的性质也不是十分一致。在所有有关维

of vitamin $B_1$, it has been found that the properties of the active fractions vary according to the nature of the accompanying impurities, so that methods developed for use with an extract of rice polishings may not be applicable without modification to an extract of yeast. The extract from the charcoal adsorption, after removal of metals, can be fractionated by successive additions of alcohol, the vitamin passing into the portion soluble in 99 percent ethyl alcohol. The authors failed to get consistently successful results with a silver fractionation, but were more successful with the use of phosphotungstic acid and platinic chloride. The most active preparations contained a day dose in 0.027 mgm., but more lately some have been obtained with a curative activity of 0.01 mgm. a day dose.

Guha and Drummond (*loc. cit.*) prepared active concentrates from wheat embryo. After extraction by means of acid alcohol, two different methods of concentration were employed: in the first, impurities were precipitated by lead acetate, and the activity adsorbed on norite charcoal at *p*H 4.5 and eleuted with acid alcohol: it was then precipitated by phosphotungstic acid, adsorbed on silver oxide, and the product fractionated with alcohol. Picrolonic acid then precipitated impurities from the material, which was soluble in alcohol. The first product had a pigeon day dose of 0.043 mgm. In the second method, Jansen and Donath's process was followed, namely, adsorption on fuller's earth at *p*H 4.5 and elution with baryta, and fractionation with silver nitrate and baryta followed by precipitation with phosphotungstic acid. The product was then submitted to precipitation with platinic chloride, followed by gold chloride; at the last stage most of the activity passed into the precipitate, but it was observed that smaller doses of both precipitate and filtrate together restored growth in the rat or cured the pigeon than of either when given separately, suggesting that vitamin $B_1$ may itself be composed of more than one factor. The smallest pigeon day dose was 0.0025 mgm., and 0.015 mgm. promoted good growth in rats. These figures indicate that the preparations were more active than the crystals obtained by Jansen and Donath.

Although formulae have been assigned to vitamin $B_1$ preparations, it does not appear that a pure substance has yet been isolated. A certain amount is, however, known about its properties. It appears to be a tertiary base: it is soluble in water and alcohol, but is unstable in the latter solvent when highly purified: it is insoluble in the other common organic solvents. It is destroyed by alkali, but is stable to oxidising and reducing reagents and to nitrous acid. Cruder preparations give a definite Pauly reaction, but as purification proceeds the reaction becomes very weak. Sulphur is absent, and the purer preparations do not give the xanthoproteic, purine, or Millon's reactions. In extracts from rice polishings, after treatment with lead acetate and concentration of the filtrate, vitamin $B_1$ is destroyed by fermentation and by heating to 95°, and is removed by filtration through a Berkefeld filter[9], although it will dialyse through cellophane.

The isolation from concentrates of supposedly pure substances and the fact that false positives may be given by the pigeon test have led to claims that different pure compounds are the vitamin. J. M. Gulland and Peters[10] have examined the claims that certain

生素 $B_1$ 浓缩物的研究中，人们发现活性组分的性质与所含的杂质有关，因此，以使用米糠萃取物为基础的方法也许不能原样照搬到酵母提取物上。从木炭吸附得到的提取物，经过去除金属离子的操作后，可以通过连续注入乙醇的方法进行分馏处理，维生素会转移进入 99% 纯度的乙醇溶液中。研究者采用银分馏法未能得到可重复的成功结果，但是在采用磷钨酸和氯化铂时取得了更好的效果。活性最高的制备物能使一天的剂量为 0.027 mg；但是最近的一些研究已经取得了一天给药剂量只需要 0.01 mg，就可以达到治疗活性的效果。

古哈和德拉蒙德（在上述引文中）从麦芽中制备得到了活性提取物。通过酸性乙醇溶液萃取处理后，采用了两种不同的浓缩方法。在第一种方法中，杂质采用乙酸铅进行沉淀处理，活性物质在 pH 值为 4.5 的条件下吸附到苏长岩木炭上，然后用酸性乙醇溶液洗脱。接着用磷钨酸进行沉淀，用氧化银吸附；再用乙醇分馏产物。随后，采用苦酮酸将杂质从可溶于乙醇的物质中沉淀出来。第一种方法制得的产物要求鸽子每天的摄取量为 0.043 mg。第二种方法采用的是詹森和多纳特的处理过程，即首先在 pH 值为 4.5 时，采用漂白土进行吸附处理，然后用氧化钡进行洗脱；接着选用硝酸银和氧化钡进行分馏，再用磷钨酸进行沉淀处理。产物通过氯化铂转入到沉淀中，然后用氯化金进行处理。在最后阶段，绝大多数的活性物质都转移到了沉淀中；但发现同时使用沉淀和上清物质时，在恢复大鼠生长或鸽子治疗实验上的有效使用剂量都要比它们单独使用时的剂量要小，这说明维生素 $B_1$ 可能含有不止一种因子。鸽子每天所需的最小有效剂量为 0.0025 mg，而促进大鼠健康成长的有效剂量为 0.015 mg。这些结果表明制备物的活性要高于詹森和多纳特得到的晶体。

尽管分子式被写成维生素 $B_1$ 制备产物，但看上去依然没有分离到一种纯的物质。然而，现在对于它的性质已经有了一定的了解。它看上去应该是一种叔碱：它可以溶解在水和乙醇中，但纯度高时在乙醇中不稳定；它不能在其他的常用有机溶剂中溶解。它可以被碱破坏，但是对氧化和还原试剂以及硝酸都是稳定的。粗提物可以发生明显的波利反应，但是随着纯化过程的进行，这个反应会变得很弱。在没有硫黄存在的情况下，较纯的制备物质不能发生黄蛋白、嘌呤或者米隆反应。从米糠得到的萃取物质，在经过乙酸铅的处理和过滤浓缩后，维生素 $B_1$ 在发酵和加热到 95℃的过程中被破坏，可以采用贝克菲尔德滤器进行过滤去除 [9]，尽管它可以通过玻璃纸的透析。

从浓缩物中分离得到假定的纯物质以及基于鸽子实验可能给出假阳性结果的事实，使我们有理由相信这些不同的纯化合物就是维生素。格兰德和彼得斯 [10] 经仔细

quinoline and glyoxaline derivatives have curative properties. Without exception all those examined, including 4 (or 5) glyoxaline methylethyl carbinol hydrochloride and 2:6-dihydroxyquinoline, were quite inactive when tested on pigeons by Peters' technique.

(**127**, 95-96; 1931)

---

References:

1 Kinnersley, H. W., Peters, R. A., and Reader, V., *Biochem. Jour.*, **22**, 276 (1928).

2 Chick, H., and Roscoe, M. H., *Biochem. Jour.*, **23**, 498 (1929).

3 Guha, B. C., and Drummond, J. C., *Biochem. Jour.*, **23**, 880 (1929).

4 Chick, H., and Roscoe, M. H., *Biochem. Jour.*, **22**, 790 (1928).

5 Jansen, B. C. P., and Donath, W. F., *Mededeelingen van den Dienst der Vdksgezondheid in Ned.-Indië*, Part 1 (Anno 1927).

6 Eykman, C., *Kon. Akad. van Wetensch. Amsterdam*, **30**, 376 (1927).

7 Kinnersley, H. W., and Peters, R. A., *Biochem. Jour.*, **22**, 419 (1928).

8 Kinnersley, H.W., and Peters, R. A., *Nature*, **121**, 516 (1928.)

9 Rosedale, J. L., and Oliveiro, C. J., *Biochem. Jour.*, **22**, 1362 (1928).

10 Gulland, J. M., and Peters, R. A., *Biochem. Jour.*, **23**, 1122 (1929).

研究发现：某些喹啉和咪唑的衍生物具备治疗的性质。毫无例外的是，在采用彼得斯的方法对鸽子进行实验时，所有这些被研究的物质，包括4（或者5）咪唑甲基乙基甲醇盐酸盐和2,6 –二羟基喹啉，都根本没有活性。

（刘振明 翻译；刘京国 审稿）

# Vitamin B

## Editor's Note

**Following on from an earlier article on the B vitamins, this paper examines what was known about vitamins $B_2$ and $B_3$, mostly from extracts of yeast. That these extracts were rich in such nutrients contributed to the popularity in the UK of the "marmite" mentioned here—a dietary supplement whose attractions have met a mixed reception elsewhere in the world. The article serves as a testament to the difficulties of making progress in biochemistry while extraction, purification and identification techniques were still rather rudimentary.**

### Vitamins $B_2$ and $B_3$: Bios

THE possibility of obtaining vitamin $B_1$ in a relatively pure condition has facilitated the differentiation of the other factors which, with $B_1$, make up the vitamin B complex. Chick and Roscoe used Peters' concentrate to demonstrate that the rat required two factors, the second being known as $B_2$ or the antipellagrous vitamin. More recently, they have published papers dealing with the chemical properties of this factor[1].

Yeast extracts contain vitamin $B_2$, but the final antineuritic concentrate none: examination of the by-products of the concentration showed that about half the $B_2$ was precipitated by lead acetate, in the treatment of the extract with this reagent (at *p*H 4.5) and another third in the treatment with baryta and sulphuric acid, the remainder being precipitated during the treatment with acid mercuric sulphate and the subsequent passage of hydrogen sulphide through the filtrate. The lead acetate precipitate was the most convenient source for obtaining a concentrated preparation: examination of this stage in detail showed that all the vitamin was carried down when the precipitation was carried out at a neutral reaction, but less than half at *p*H 2.6. The vitamin was recovered by decomposing the precipitate with hydrogen sulphide: to ensure precipitation of the lead sulphide at an acid reaction, at which the vitamin is not adsorbed on the precipitate, it was necessary first to hydrolyse the yeast gum in the extract with hydrochloric acid. Unfortunately, the lead precipitate also carries down some vitamin $B_1$, and it was not found possible to obtain a preparation of $B_2$ free from $B_1$ by dialysis, by making use of their different solubilities in alcohol or their different rates of destruction by ultra-violet light. The concentrate was active in a dose of 0.03 gm., equivalent to 0.5 gm. dried yeast daily. It is possible that yeast extract is an unsuitable medium for effecting a separation. Rosedale[2] precipitated from rice polishings extract (by means of lead acetate) a factor which was not $B_1$, although enabling pigeons to grow and maintain health on a diet of polished rice. It cannot yet be said with certainty, however, that this factor is vitamin $B_2$.

# 维生素 B

## 编者按

与前面那篇介绍维生素 B 的文章不同，这篇文章分析了来自酵母提取物中的维生素 $B_2$ 和 $B_3$ 的已知性质。这些提取物中含有大量的维生素 $B_2$ 和 $B_3$，这也是“酸制酵母”在英国如此流行的原因之一——这种膳食补充剂也已经被其他国家的人所接受。文中也谈到了生物化学领域在发展中遇到的困难，因为在当时，抽取、提纯和鉴定技术都十分不完善。

### 维生素$B_2$和$B_3$：生长素

在人们有可能得到较高纯度的维生素 $B_1$ 以后就开始区分与 $B_1$ 一起构成 B 族维生素复合体系的其他因子了。奇克和罗斯科采用彼得斯浓缩法证实大鼠需要两种因子，第二种因子被称为维生素 $B_2$，或者抗糙皮病的维生素。就在最近，他们又发表了一些与这种因子的化学性质相关的文章[1]。

酵母提取物包含维生素 $B_2$，但是在最终的抗神经炎浓缩物中却不含这种物质。对这种浓缩物产生过程中的副产物的检验结果显示，在用乙酸铅处理这种提取物的过程中（在 pH 值为 4.5 的条件下），大概一半的维生素 $B_2$ 都被沉淀掉了；另外三分之一在用氧化钡和硫酸处理时被沉淀，剩下的在用酸性硫酸汞处理以及随后使用硫化氢过滤的过程中被沉淀了。乙酸铅沉淀法是最便于获得维生素 $B_2$ 浓缩制备产物的方法；对这个过程的仔细研究发现，在中性反应条件下，所有的维生素都会沉淀下来；但当 pH 值为 2.6 时，沉淀的维生素量不到上述情况时的一半。使用硫化氢分解这些沉淀时，又可重新回收维生素：为了保证在酸性条件下产生硫化铅的沉淀，且维生素不会被沉淀吸附，就需要首先用盐酸对提取液中的酵母胶进行水解。不幸的是，铅沉淀中还是吸附了一些维生素 $B_1$；目前人们仍无法获得不含维生素 $B_1$ 的维生素 $B_2$ 制备物，无论是采取透析，利用它们在乙醇中的不同溶解性，还是根据它们在紫外光下被破坏的程度不同等都无法实现。这种浓缩物在剂量为 0.03 g 时就有活性，相当于每天给予 0.5 g 的干酵母。也许酵母提取物并不是最合适的分离媒介。罗斯黛尔[2]从米糠的提取物中沉淀（采用乙酸铅的方法）出一种因子，这种因子不是维生素 $B_1$；尽管它可以使得采用精制米喂养的鸽子继续生长和保持健康，但不能完全确定这种因子就是维生素 $B_2$。

B. T. Narayanan and J. C. Drummond have also carried out experiments on the concentration of vitamin $B_2$[3]. Yeast was extracted with dilute alcohol and the extract concentrated; lead acetate was then added, sometimes following a preliminary hydrolysis of the extract with baryta. The lead precipitate was decomposed with sulphuric acid, vitamin $B_2$ passing into the filtrate. It could be adsorbed on fuller's earth in strongly acid solution, but no satisfactory method of eleuting it again was found. Norite charcoal was not efficient as an adsorbing agent, and its use led to disappearance of the activity.

A certain amount is known about the properties of vitamin $B_2$: it is soluble in dilute, but insoluble in strong ethyl alcohol, and exposure to the latter results in its destruction. It is stable to hydrogen peroxide and nitrous acid and, to a certain extent, to heat, provided the reaction is acid. Autoclaving or even boiling at an alkaline reaction brings about rapid destruction. It is more easily destroyed by exposure to ultra-violet light than vitamin $B_1$.

Narayanan and Drummond examined a number of chemical compounds, including nucleic acid, purines, nicotinic acid, betaine and inositol, for vitamin $B_2$ activity, but all were, without exception, inactive.

V. Reader has adduced evidence that a third factor, tentatively called vitamin $B_3$, is necessary for the nutrition of the rat[4]. Animals kept on an apparently complete synthetic diet, in which Peters' concentrate supplied vitamin $B_1$ and alkaline autoclaved yeast $B_2$, failed to grow after some weeks; substitution of yeast extract for the two supplements led to an immediate resumption of growth. The failure did not appear to be due to lack of either vitamin $B_1$ or $B_2$, since increasing the amounts given did not improve growth. More convincing evidence of the existence of the third factor rests in the fact that it was found to be precipitated by the mercuric sulphate used in the preparation of the $B_1$ concentrate, and was recoverable, to the extent of 75 percent of that present in the original extract, from the precipitate. Vitamin $B_3$ is even more easily destroyed by heat than $B_1$; under certain conditions it is soluble in ether. Rats fed on an ordinary diet carry a larger store of vitamin $B_3$ than of $B_2$; it is, therefore, possible that in short-time growth experiments, such as were used by Chick and Roscoe in the assay of $B_1$ or $B_2$, lack of $B_3$ does not play a part; again, it is also possible that antineuritic concentrates, unless highly purified, or autoclaved yeast, may be contaminated with traces of the third factor.

Chick and Roscoe found that vitamin $B_2$ was alone present in egg-white, but that rats on a synthetic diet with this material as source of the vitamin instead of autoclaved yeast, showed subnormal growth after a few weeks. They suggest that yeast contains a third B factor, which is, however, thermostable in contradistinction to Reader's $B_3$. M. A. Boas, some years ago, found that a diet containing dried egg-white produced skin lesions and nervous symptoms in rats, whereas fresh egg-white had no such effect[5]. A number of foodstuffs contained a factor which counteracted the ill-effects of the ingestion of dried egg-white; it could not be identified with either vitamin $B_1$ or $B_2$.

纳拉亚南和德拉蒙德也进行了浓缩维生素 $B_2$ 的相关实验[3]。先用稀释的醇对酵母进行提取，再对提取液进行浓缩处理；然后加入乙酸铅；有时候，还需要采用氧化钡对提取物进行水解预处理。铅沉淀物采用硫酸进行分解处理，维生素 $B_2$ 转移到滤液中。在强酸溶液中它可以被漂白土吸附，但是还没有发现一种令人满意的方法可以将它从漂白土上洗脱下来。苏长岩木炭不是一种有效的吸附试剂，使用它会导致维生素丧失活性。

我们对于维生素 $B_2$ 的性质已经有所了解；它溶解于稀醇溶液，但在高浓度乙醇中却无法溶解，接触后者会导致它被破坏。它与过氧化氢和亚硝酸不发生反应，当反应条件为酸性时，它在某种程度上对受热也是稳定的。在碱性反应条件下，使用高压蒸煮甚至只是沸腾状态就会导致它的迅速破坏。当暴露在紫外光下面时，它比维生素 $B_1$ 更容易被破坏。

纳拉亚南和德拉蒙德检查了很多种化合物，包括核酸、嘌呤、尼克酸、甜菜碱和肌醇，希望能够找到具有维生素 $B_2$ 的生物活性的物质；但是毫无例外，上述化合物都没有这种活性。

里德提出证据证明有第三种因子存在，暂时可以称作维生素 $B_3$，它是大鼠生长不可缺少的营养物[4]。完全用合成饲料喂养的动物在几个星期后就会停止生长，其中彼得斯浓缩物提供维生素 $B_1$，碱性条件下高温高压处理后的酵母粉提供维生素 $B_2$。采用酵母提取物替代上述两种物质在食物中进行补充，动物很快就恢复了生长。由上述情况看来，停止生长不是由于缺少维生素 $B_1$ 或者维生素 $B_2$，因为增加给予的量并不会改善动物的生长状况。能够证明第三种因子存在的更为令人信服的证据是它可以被维生素 $B_1$ 制备过程中所使用的硫酸汞沉淀出来，通过处理沉淀物可重新获得；含量可达最初提取物中的 75%。维生素 $B_3$ 比维生素 $B_1$ 更容易因受热而被破坏；在特定条件下，它可以溶解在乙醚中。采用普通食物喂养的大鼠，相对于维生素 $B_2$ 而言，可以吸收更多的维生素 $B_3$。因此，在短时间的生长实验中，例如奇克和罗斯科用于检测维生素 $B_1$ 或者维生素 $B_2$ 的实验，缺乏维生素 $B_3$ 并没有造成影响。另一方面，还有可能是因为抗神经炎浓缩物没有经过高度纯化，或是在高压灭活的酵母粉中混有痕量的第三种因子。

奇克和罗斯科研究发现，蛋清中只存在维生素 $B_2$；但是对于用合成食物喂养的大鼠，如果只采用这种物质作为维生素的来源而没有食用高压灭菌的酵母粉，那么经过数周之后大鼠就会表现出生长缓慢的迹象。他们认为酵母中含有第三种因子，然而，它却比里德的维生素 $B_3$ 更为耐热稳定。博厄斯在几年前发现，食用含有干蛋清的食物会导致大鼠的皮肤受损及引发神经系统病症，而选用新鲜的蛋清却不会出现这种情况[5]。很多食物中都含有一种可以清除因摄取干蛋清而造成的不良影响的因子；它既不是维生素 $B_1$，也不是维生素 $B_2$。

The above account by no means exhausts the work which has been done on the chemistry of vitamin B. That three or four factors are included under this term appears certain, but it is not easy to relate the work of different investigators, especially when the claim for a new factor is based on the supplementary effects of different foodstuffs. Peters, in his Harben Lectures, reviews some of these investigations. Williams and Waterman found that pigeons maintained their weight on a polished rice diet when supplemented with marmite; transference to wheat, however, produced growth. Hence there is a factor in wheat which is absent from marmite and cannot be $B_3$. Hunt found that the residue of autolysed yeast, after thorough extraction with water, contained a factor which supplemented two obtainable from the extract; again this third factor does not appear to be $B_3$, which is soluble in water. Peters has also found that pigeons require for growth, in addition to $B_1$ and the factor of Williams and Waterman, a thermolabile factor which is present in yeast extract, and may be considered provisionally as identical with $B_3$: pigeons apparently do not require $B_2$. It appears, therefore, that the rat requires $B_1$, $B_2$, and $B_3$ with possibly Hunt's factor, whilst the pigeon requires $B_1$, $B_3$, and the factor of Williams and Waterman.

It may be of value to refer also to some recent work upon a substance which has been related by many observers to vitamin B, the yeast-growth stimulant or "Bios". Confusion was caused by the fact that it was not realised that different yeasts behave differently on various media, that their requirements for bios vary, and that the requirements of other micro-organisms need not necessarily be the same as those of yeast. Peters and his colleagues have investigated the growth factors required by *Streptothrix corallinus*[6]. When the organism was grown on a synthetic medium, a growth-stimulating factor was found in tryptic beef broth, yeast, rabbit muscle, serum, and wheat embryo; it is organic, soluble in water but not in ether, dialysable, and not precipitated by lead acetate. It accompanies vitamin $B_1$ in the preparation of the antineuritic concentrate but is stable to alkali in this concentrate (although unstable when crude) and is not, therefore, the same factor as the vitamin. It is synthesised by the meningococcus. It is not vitamin $B_2$. By parallel tests on the organism and on pigeons, it was shown that the factor and vitamin $B_1$ fractionate quantitatively together through all stages into the final concentrate.

The pitfalls encountered in such work are disclosed by certain anomalous results obtained with this organism, impure preparations of the factor sometimes appearing to contain relatively more growth-promoting activity when used in high concentrations than when used in lesser amounts. Reader has found that this effect can also be produced by adding mannitol to the purer extracts[7]. Mannose itself and related alcohols cannot replace mannitol; it appears that the organism uses the alcohol as a specific source of food supply.

Working on the relation of bios to yeast, A. M. Copping[8] has found that the necessity for bios depends on the yeast and the medium used. Those which grow in a synthetic medium without the addition of a factor such as is supplied by an autoclaved extract of yeast, produce a stimulant for other yeasts. Bios is required by yeasts which only ferment and do not respire in its absence; added bios then stimulates both respiration and fermentation.

上面的论述并没有把人们在维生素 B 化学性质方面的研究工作全部列举出来。这个专业术语下面必然包含着三到四种因子，但要在不同研究工作之间建立联系并非易事，特别是当采用不同食物喂养产生的附加效应来证实一种新的因子的存在时。彼得斯在哈本演讲中回顾了一些研究进展。威廉斯和沃特曼发现，鸽子在使用精制米作为食物喂养时，辅助加入酵母可以保持它们的体重；转而使用小麦时，会促进其生长。因此，小麦中有一种因子是酵母中所没有的，并且不可能是维生素 $B_3$。亨特发现在用水对自溶酵母进行彻底提取之后，剩余残渣中含有一种因子，与提取物中的另外两种因子同时存在；这种因子也不是维生素 $B_3$，因为后者可以溶解在水中。彼得斯还发现，为了满足鸽子的生长需要，除了维生素 $B_1$ 和威廉斯和沃特曼发现的因子之外，还需要一种在酵母提取液中存在的、不耐热的因子，这种因子可以暂时被认为是维生素 $B_3$；鸽子显然不需要维生素 $B_2$。由此看来，大鼠需要的是维生素 $B_1$、维生素 $B_2$、维生素 $B_3$，还有可能需要亨特因子；鸽子需要的是维生素 $B_1$、维生素 $B_3$，以及威廉斯和沃特曼发现的因子。

许多研究者认为，酵母生长刺激因子或称“生长素”与维生素 B 有关，也许有必要谈及最近的一些基于该物质的研究工作。混乱的来源事实是，我们没有意识到不同种类的酵母在不同的介质中行为各异，它们对于生长素的需求也是变化各异的；其他微生物的需求也不一定和酵母完全一样。彼得斯和他的同事研究了珊瑚红诺卡氏菌所需的生长因子[6]。当微生物体在合成培养基上生长时，人们发现有一种生长刺激因子存在于胰蛋白酶消化的牛肉膏、酵母、野兔肌肉、血清以及小麦胚芽中；这是一种有机物，可以溶解在水中但不溶解于醚，可以通过透析装置，不会被乙酸铅沉淀。它与维生素 $B_1$ 一起共存于抗神经炎浓缩物的制备液中，但在浓缩物中，它对碱性环境是稳定的（尽管在粗提物状态下是不稳定的）；因此，它和维生素不属于同一个因子。它由脑膜炎球菌合成，它并不是维生素 $B_2$。通过在微生物体和鸽子上的平行试验，结果显示这种因子可以和维生素 $B_1$ 一起在整个阶段都定量地分馏到最终的浓缩物中。

在这种微生物体上所获得的某些反常结果暴露出此类研究工作存在不少缺陷。当选用高浓度浓缩物时，该因子的不纯制备物有时可以显现出相对更高的生长促进活性。里德发现这种效应也可以通过在更纯净的提取物中加甘露糖醇获得[7]。甘露糖本身以及相关的醇不能够代替甘露糖醇；似乎这种生物体将醇作为了一种特殊的食物来源。

在研究生长素与酵母之间的关系时，科平[8]发现是否需要生长素取决于酵母以及选用的培养介质。在不添加任何因子（例如高压灭菌后的酵母提取液）的情况下，生长在合成培养基中的酵母可以为其他酵母制造一种生长刺激因子。对于那些当生长素缺失时只发酵而不呼吸的酵母而言，生长素才是必需的；当加入生长素后可以同时促进呼吸和发酵过程。

Narayanan has separated a yeast bios from vitamin $B_2$ in yeast extract, since the former is not precipitated by lead acetate in the hydrolysed extract[9]. The bios is not adsorbed on norite charcoal, but is soluble in strong alcohol; it is precipitated by phosphotungstic acid but not by silver or platinic chloride. By a series of fractionations a highly active concentrate was obtained. The material contained nitrogen but no phosphorus: most tests for nitrogenous compounds were negative, but a positive Pauly reaction was obtained. It is stable to nitrous acid but destroyed by hydrogen peroxide. Narayanan also tested a large number of pure substances, such as nucleic acid, purines, nicotinic acid, betaine, lipoids, and various bases and amino acids for bios activity, but all were found to be inactive.

(**127**, 131-133; 1931)

---

References:

1 Chick, H., and Roscoe, M. H., *Biochem. Jour.*, **23**, 504 and 514 (1929): **24**, 105 (1930).

2 Rosedale, J. L., *Biochem. Jour.*, **21**, 1266 (1927).

3 Narayanan, B. T., and Drummond, J. C., *Biochem. Jour.*, **24**, 19 (1930).

4 Reader, V., *Biochem. Jour.*, **23**, 689 (1929): **24**, 77 (1930).

5 Boas, M. A., *Biochem. Jour.*, **21**, 712 (1927).

6 Reader, V., *Biochem. Jour.*, **22**, 434 (1928); Orr-Ewing, J., *Biochem. Jour.*, **22**, 440 and 443 (1928); Peters, R. A., and Kinnersley, H. W., *Biochem. Jour.*, **22**, 445 (1928).

7 Reader, V., *Biochem. Jour.*, **23**, 61 (1929).

8 Copping, A. M., *Biochem. Jour.*, **23**, 1050 (1929).

9 Narayanan, B. T., *Biochem. Jour.*, **24**, 6 (1930).

纳拉亚南已经从酵母提取得到的维生素 $B_2$ 中分离出了一种酵母生长素，因为这种生长素在水解提取液中不被乙酸铅沉淀[9]。这种生长素不能被苏长岩木炭所吸附，但是可以溶解在高浓度的醇溶液中；它可以被磷钨酸沉淀，但不能被氯化银或者氯化铂沉淀。在经过一系列的分馏之后可以得到一种高活性的浓缩物。这种物质含氮不含磷：针对含氮化合物的绝大多数检测结果都是阴性的，但是波利反应的结果是阳性的。该物质对于亚硝酸是稳定的，但是可以被过氧化氢破坏。纳拉亚南还检测了大量的纯净物质，例如核苷酸、嘌呤类、尼克酸、甜菜碱、类脂以及各种各样的碱和氨基酸，希望能发现生长素的活性，但研究结果表明所有这些物质都不具备这种活性。

（刘振明 翻译；刘京国 审稿）

# Vitamin B

## Editor's Note

**The third in a series of articles on the current understanding of B vitamins, this paper looks at what was known about the distribution and roles of these substances in the body. Animals such as pigeons and rodents deficient in "vitamin B" show a range of dysfunctions, from dermatitis to weight loss and paralysis. It was a challenge to explain this breadth of effects, but the studies point to the emerging appreciation of how complex dietary factors can be in health.**

### Distribution and Physiology

THE general distribution of vitamin B is now fairly well defined, but the adequacy of different food substances in this respect for different species and the distribution of the various factors in the B complex are still subjects for investigation. R. H. A. Plimmer, with W. H. Raymond, J. Lowndes, and J. L. Rosedale, has examined the comparative vitamin B value of cereals, pulses, and nuts[1]. The preventive method was employed, using pigeons, and the criterion was maintenance for at least 26 weeks. All the vitamins required by the pigeon were therefore included in the estimation; symptoms of deficiency were paralysis and loss of weight. The diets used contained 5 percent fish meal, white flour or white rice, and the substance under test in varying proportions. Dried yeast contained most vitamin: of the other foodstuffs, wheat germ was about half as good as the yeast, whole wheat, bran, and middlings contained about a tenth of the amount present in yeast, and other cereals about a twentieth. The majority of the pulses and nuts examined contained between a fifth and a tenth of the quantity present in yeast. More vitamin B is required for hatching and rearing young than for maintenance. Chickens require half as much again as pigeons, rats only about half; the requirements of human beings may be intermediate between those of the pigeon and the rat.

A. L. Bacharach and E. Allchorne[2] found that the vitamin B content of malted flour was the same as that of the original unmalted flour, but that the malt extract appeared to contain more: the experiments were carried out on rats and the effect is attributed to the improvement in appetite brought about by the extract.

The content of vitamin B in seeds has been shown to be markedly influenced by the manure applied to the plant, by M. J. Rowlands and B. Wilkinson[3]. Two similar plots of grass and clover were manured with an artificial manure and pigs' dung respectively: the pigs were fed on barley meal, middlings, and a small amount of a mixture of meat meal, rye and wheat embryo, bone meal, and cod liver oil. The manured patch produced a heavier crop, containing more clover, but the growth on the dunged patch was bigger. By preventive and curative growth tests on rats, it was shown that the vitamin B content

# 维生素 B

## 编者按

这是有关B族维生素的系列文章中的第三篇，作者在文中考查了B族维生素在人体中的分布以及对人体的作用。有些动物，如鸽子和啮齿类动物因为缺乏“维生素B”而表现出一定程度的功能失调，从皮炎到体重减轻甚至瘫痪。要解释维生素B这么多的作用对我们来说是一种挑战，但是这些研究使人们认识到饮食因素对于健康的影响是多么复杂。

### 分布与生理学

对于维生素 B 的一般性分布规律，现在已经了解得非常清楚了；但是不同物种对各种食物的需求量到底为多少才合适以及不同因子在 B 族维生素中的分布仍然是我们研究的课题。普利玛与雷蒙德、朗兹以及罗斯黛尔一道研究和比较了谷物、豆类以及坚果中维生素 B 的相对含量 [1]。研究采用了预防性的方法，以鸽子作为实验对象，所使用的标准至少在 26 周内保持不变。鸽子所需的所有维生素都被事先计算在内；缺乏这些物质的症状是神经麻痹以及体重减轻。所选用的食物包含 5% 的鱼肉、白面或白米以及不同比例的测试用物质。干酵母中含有最多的维生素：在其他食物中，麦芽中维生素的含量只有酵母的一半，全麦、麸糠和小麦粗粉包含的维生素大概是酵母中含量的 1/10，其他谷物中的含量大概是酵母的 1/20。绝大多数用于测试的豆类和坚果中所含有的维生素量介于酵母中含量的 1/5~1/10 之间。孵化过程以及幼体的喂养过程需要更多的维生素 B。小鸡对于维生素 B 的需求量比鸽子多一半，大鼠只需要鸽子需求量的一半；人体对维生素 B 的需求量也许介于鸽子和大鼠之间。

巴卡拉克和奥科恩 [2] 发现，发芽的麦粒中维生素 B 的含量与最初没有发芽的麦粒含量相同；但是，麦芽提取物中似乎含量更高一些；实验是在大鼠上进行的，产生效果的原因是提取物改善了大鼠的食欲。

罗兰兹和威尔金森 [3] 发现，种子中的维生素 B 含量明显受到对植物所施的肥料的影响。两块相似的苜蓿地分别选用人工肥料和猪粪进行施肥：这些猪采用大麦粉、麦麸以及少量的肉粉、黑麦、麦芽、骨粉以及鱼肝油混合物来喂养。在施人工肥料的地里，植株生长得更茂盛，苜蓿的产量也更高；但是在选用猪粪进行施肥的地里，苜蓿植株生长得更大。对大鼠进行预防性试验和治愈性生长试验的结果显示：维生

of the seeds from the manured patch was much less than that of those from the dunged patch. In further experiments vitamin B was extracted from pigs' dung by means of alcohol.

There is evidence that lower organisms can synthesise vitamin B or similar growth factors, and that this synthesis may occur also in the intestinal tract in higher animals. Thus, Reader has found that the meningococcus can synthesise a growth factor for a streptothrix, all the vitamin $B_1$ being previously removed from the medium; and G. L. Peskett[4] has shown that yeast can synthesise vitamin $B_1$. Intraintestinal synthesis may be the explanation of "refection" which has been described by L. S. Fridericia and H. Chick and M. H. Roscoe[5]. In this condition rats maintained on a vitamin B free diet containing uncooked rice starch passed bulky white faeces, and at the same time were cured of their symptoms and put on weight. The faeces contained abundant vitamin. The condition appeared to depend on the presence of uncooked starch in the diet and a virus in the intestine.

W. R. Aykroyd and M. H. Roscoe[6] have investigated the distribution of vitamin $B_2$. Wheat and maize were poor sources: the germ and bran of wheat contained more than the endosperm, but maize germ contained less than wheat germ: dried peas also contained little. Dried yeast and ox liver and fresh milk were excellent sources, and egg-yolk and dried meat good. It was possible to cure rats suffering from the dermatitis of vitamin $B_2$ deficiency, as well as to stimulate their growth.

The physiological functions of the vitamin B complex are incompletely understood: in its absence the metabolic processes of the tissues are imperfectly performed, and investigations have thrown some light upon the details of the defects. Thus the vitamin is related to both protein and carbohydrate metabolism. G. A. Hartwell has found that young rats die, with engorgement of the kidneys, when the synthetic diet contains 20 percent edestin and 5 percent yeast extract, although older animals thrived on the diet even with a lower allowance of yeast[7]. Increasing the amount of yeast extract permitted normal growth: the factor responsible was found to be thermostable. Caseinogen and egg-albumin required less yeast extract than edestin for normal metabolism.

H. W. Kinnersley and R. A. Peters have investigated the relation between the lactic acid content of the brain and the symptoms of head retraction in pigeons fed on a diet of polished rice[8]. Using a special technique, it could be demonstrated that birds showing opisthotonos had more lactic acid in their brains than normal birds, and that this increase was most marked in the parts below the mid-brain and occurred here first at a time when symptoms were threatening. The increase was not observed after cure by a dose of vitamin $B_1$ concentrate. The symptoms appear to be due to this accumulation of lactic acid, and the fact that it is localised indicates that vitamin $B_1$ is intimately concerned in the intermediary metabolism of carbohydrates, apparently with the oxidative removal of lactic acid. In this connexion it might be remarked that H. Yaoi found that muscle from polyneuritic pigeons reduced methylene blue more feebly than normal muscle, but

素 B 在人工肥料施肥地块的种子中的含量，远远少于在猪粪施肥地块的种子中的含量。在进一步的试验中，采用醇萃取法从猪粪中得到了维生素 B。

有证据证明低等生物可以合成维生素 B 或者类似的生长因子，这种合成过程或许也会发生在高等动物的肠道内。因此，里德发现脑膜炎球菌可以合成一种链丝菌生长所需的生长因子，而培养介质中的维生素 $B_1$ 已经被提前移除了；佩斯凯特 [4] 的研究结果表明，酵母可以合成维生素 $B_1$。肠内的合成过程可以解释为弗里德里西和奇克以及罗斯科描述的“点心” [5]。在这种环境下，长期用不含维生素 B 的食物（其中包含有未煮过的大米淀粉）喂养的大鼠会排出大量的白色粪便，病症得到了治愈，体重增加，并且粪便中含有丰富的维生素。这种情况似乎与食物中未烹饪过的淀粉以及肠道中的细菌有关。

艾克罗伊德和罗斯科 [6] 研究了维生素 $B_2$ 的分布情况。小麦和玉米中的含量都很低：麦芽和麦麸中维生素 $B_2$ 的含量要高于小麦胚乳中的含量；但是玉米胚芽中的含量要低于麦芽中的含量：干豆中含量也很少。干酵母、牛肝以及鲜牛奶是维生素 $B_2$ 的最佳来源，蛋黄和干肉也是不错的来源。也许能治愈由于维生素 $B_2$ 缺乏而患皮炎的大鼠，还能促进它们的生长。

我们对 B 族维生素的生理学功能了解得还不够透彻：当它们缺失时，组织的代谢过程不能很好地完成；目前的研究已经揭示出了在维生素缺失时的一些具体表现。因此维生素与蛋白质和碳水化合物的代谢都有关系。哈特韦尔发现，当选用包含 20% 麻仁球蛋白和 5% 酵母提取物的人工合成食物进行喂养时，幼年大鼠就会因为肾充血而死亡；而成年鼠即使在酵母添加量更低的情况下也能健壮生长 [7]。当增加酵母提取物的含量时，幼年大鼠恢复正常生长：与之相关的因子被认为具有耐热性。对于正常的代谢过程，酪蛋白原和鸡蛋清蛋白代谢所需的酵母提取物要少于麻仁球蛋白。

金纳斯利和彼得斯研究了当采用精制大米作为食物喂养时，鸽子产生脑萎缩症状和脑中乳酸含量之间的关系 [8]。利用一种特殊的技术，可以证明出现角弓反张症状的鸟类的脑中所含的乳酸要高于正常鸟类，在中脑偏下部分的含量增加是最为明显的，当症状产生时，最先表现出来的也是这一位置。当用一定量的维生素 $B_1$ 浓缩物进行治疗后,乳酸浓度增加的现象就消失了。这种症状的产生似乎与乳酸的积聚相关，而且它局部发作的事实也说明维生素 $B_1$ 与碳水化合物的中间代谢过程是密切相关的，显然是因为维生素 $B_1$ 的氧化消耗了乳酸。在谈到这方面的联系时，我们有必要谈及矢追的研究工作，他发现患有多神经炎的鸽子的肌肉代谢亚甲基蓝的能力小于正常

that there was no difference in the glutathione contents[9]. Peters in his Harben Lectures has adduced some evidence that vitamin $B_3$ may be concerned with the mobilisation of water, and that in its absence together with that of vitamin $B_1$ oedema accompanies the polyneuritis in its terminal stages.

C. W. Carter and A. N. Drury have examined the nature of the slowing of the heart beat in rice-fed pigeons[10]: it appears to be due to an overaction of the vagal centres producing a heart block. The condition is cured by whole wheat, so that the factor responsible may be that described by Williams and Waterman.

G. F. Marrian, L. C. Baker, J. C. Drummond, and H. Woollard[11] noticed changes in the adrenal glands of pigeons starved or fed on rice only, and Marrian has investigated these alterations in more detail[12]. Hypertrophy was found in inanition, even though vitamin $B_1$ was given, and in vitamin B deficiency, whether accompanied or not by inanition: oedema accounted for half the hypertrophy in inanition. The adrenaline content was increased in the latter condition, but was relatively low in vitamin B deficiency. It appeared that the hypertrophy in inanition affected chiefly the medulla, and in vitamin B deficiency, the cortex of the gland.

It is now well known that vitamin B deficiency is associated with loss of appetite. B. Sure has made a detailed study of the anorexia in the rat and found that it is promptly cured by the administration of a vitamin B concentrate[13]. The loss of appetite may be associated with the failure of the gut to empty itself, and a decrease in the digestive secretions. J. L. Rosedale and C. J. Oliveiro[14] found that in pigeons suffering from beri-beri the pancreas failed to form the enzymes required to digest protein and fat.

It might be expected that animals suffering from vitamin B deficiency would show derangements of the sexual function. H. M. Evans, however, found that in male rats, provided vitamin E was supplied, fertility was unaffected and sex interest was decreased only a few days before death[15]. In the female rat the oestrous cycle stopped abruptly after about four weeks on the deficient diet; loss of weight followed immediately[16]. Injections of oestrin produced the signs of oestrus during the anoestrus, but without stimulating the ovaries, which had become much atrophied.

W. Nakahara and E. Sanekawa have found that chicken sarcoma and rat sarcoma and carcinoma do not apparently require vitamin $B_1$, and contain little of it[17]. In the first set of experiments, chickens were fed on polished rice and a salt mixture; the livers from healthy birds, and those carrying growths of the Rous sarcoma, were found to contain equal amounts of vitamin B by test on rats, indicating that the tumour did not deplete the birds' store of vitamin. In the second set, the rat tumours were fed to pigeons and rats maintained on vitamin B free diets: only minimal amounts of the vitamin were found to be present.

(**127**, 204-205; 1931)

个体；但是两者的谷胱甘肽含量并没有明显的差别[9]。彼得斯在他的哈本演讲中已经举出一些证据证明维生素 $B_3$ 可能和水的代谢有关；当它和维生素 $B_1$ 同时缺失时，在多神经炎发生的末期，会伴有水肿症状的出现。

卡特和德鲁里研究了采用稻米喂养的鸽子心跳会放缓的本质[10]。它似乎与迷走中枢神经的过度反应导致了心传导阻滞相关。喂食全麦可以治愈这种病，因此发挥作用的因子可能就是威廉斯和沃特曼曾经描述过的那种物质。

马里安、贝克、德拉蒙德以及伍拉德[11]注意到了饥饿的、或者只喂养稻谷的鸽子在肾上腺器官上的一些变化，马里安对这种改变在更深的层面上进行了研究[12]。研究发现在饥饿的情况下鸽子的肾上腺变得肥大，即使补充了维生素 $B_1$ 仍然如此；而当维生素 B 缺乏时，无论是否伴随有饥饿，都会出现肾上腺肥大的症状：在饥饿时，水肿是造成肾上腺肥大的部分原因。在后一种情况下，肾上腺素的含量会增加；但在维生素 B 缺乏时，其含量会相对较低。研究结果显示，似乎在饥饿的时候，肾上腺肥大主要影响的是肾的髓质；而当维生素 B 缺乏时，肾上腺肥大主要影响的是肾的皮质。

现在大家都知道，维生素 B 的缺乏会导致食欲的减退。休尔仔细研究了大鼠食欲减退的情况，他发现服用维生素 B 浓缩物能很快治愈食欲减退[13]。食欲的减退也许与肠道无法有效排空和消化液分泌减少有关。罗斯黛尔和奥利维罗[14]发现，对于患有脚气病的鸽子，其胰腺无法产生消化蛋白和脂肪所需的酶。

我们可以认为，患有维生素 B 缺乏症的动物会出现性功能的紊乱。然而，埃文斯发现，对于雄性大鼠，在给予维生素 E 的前提下，其生育能力不会受到影响，其性欲只有在临死的前几天才会发生减退[15]。对于雌性大鼠，用缺乏维生素 B 的食物喂养大概四周之后，其发情周期会突然停止；接着很快出现体重下降[16]。注射雌激素可以诱发处于不动情期的雌性大鼠发情，但不会刺激已经发生了严重萎缩的卵巢。

中原麻衣和实川发现，小鸡肉瘤和大鼠肉瘤以及癌症的发生与维生素 $B_1$ 的存在与否没有明显的关联，肿瘤中只含有极少量的维生素 $B_1$[17]。在第一组实验中，采用精制大米和盐的混合物喂养小鸡；在对大鼠的实验中发现：健康小鸡的肝脏和长有鲁斯肉瘤的肝脏含有相同量的维生素 B，从而说明肉瘤的存在不会耗尽小鸡体内贮存的维生素。在第二组实验中，用大鼠肉瘤来喂养鸽子，该大鼠持续摄取不含维生素 B 的食物；结果发现只有很少量的维生素出现在喂给鸽子的食物中。

（刘振明 翻译；刘京国 审稿）

References:


1 Plimmer, R. H. A., Raymond, W. H., Lowndes, J., and Rosedale, J. L., *Biochem. Jour.*, **21**, 1141 (1927): **23**, 545 (1929).

2 Bacharach, A. L., and Allchorne, E., *Biochem. Jour.*, **22**, 313 (1928).

3 Rowlands, M. J., and Wilkinson, B., *Biochem. Jour.*, **24**, 199 (1930).

4 Peskett, G. L., *Biochem. Jour.*, **21**, 1102 (1927).

5 Fridericia, L. S., Chick, H., and Roscoe, M. H., *Lancet*, **1**, 37 (1928).

6 Aykroyd, W. R., and Roscoe, M. H., *Biochem. Jour.*, **23**, 483 (1929).

7 Hartwell, G. A., *Biochem. Jour.*, **22**, 1212 (1928).

8 Kinnersley, H. W., and Peters, R. A., *Biochem. Jour.*, **23**, 1126 (1929): **24**, 711 (1930).

9 Yaoi, H., *Proc. Imp. Acad. Tokyo*, **4**, 233 (1928).

10 Carter, C. W., and Drury, A. N., *Jour. Physiol.*, **68**, *Proc.*, p. i. (1929).

11 Marrian, G. F., Baker, L. C., Drummond, J. C., and Woollard, H., *Biochem. Jour.*, **21**, 1336 (1927).

12 Marrian, G. F., *Biochem. Jour.*, **22**, 836 (1928).

13 Sure, B., *Jour. Nutrition*, **1**, 49 (1928).

14 Rosedale, J. L., and Oliveiro, C. J., *Biochem. Jour.*, **22**, 1362 (1928).

15 Evans, H. M., *Jour. Nutrition*, **1**, 1 (1928).

16 Parkes, A. S., *Quart. Jour. Exp. Physiol.*, **18**, 397 (1928).

17 Nakahara, W., and Sanekawa, E., *Proc. Imp. Acad. Tokyo*, **5**, 55 (1929): **6**, 116 (1930): *Scient. Pap. Instit. Physic. and Chem. Res.*, **10**, 211 (1929).

# Stellar Structure

## Editor's Note

**Edward Milne's theory of the structure of stars provoked strong disagreement among British astronomers, which was the subject of a discussion organised by the Royal Astronomical Society on 9 January 1931. The discussion itself, reported here, was inconclusive, although events later showed that Milne's approach correctly predicted the very high densities and temperatures at the centre of stars like the Sun.**

THE investigation of the structure of the stars, which has for long been a subject of disagreement between Sir James Jeans and Sir Arthur Eddington, has now entered on a new phase through the work of Prof. E. A. Milne. A long paper on this matter by Prof. Milne, which appears in the November number of the *Monthly Notices of the Royal Astronomical Society* together with related papers by Messrs. R. H. Fowler, N. Fairclough, and T. G. Cowling, was introduced to the Society in November last, but no time was available for discussion. The whole of the meeting of the Royal Astronomical Society on Friday, Jan. 9, was accordingly devoted to a debate on the subject, which was briefly opened by Prof. Milne, and in which many astronomers and mathematicians took part.

Prof. Milne's views were outlined in *Nature* of Jan. 3, p. 16. In opening the discussion, he stated that the pioneer work in the subject had been done by Sir Arthur Eddington, and what he himself had done was to rationalise Eddington's theory by clearing it of *ad hoc* hypotheses. He could not accept Sir James Jeans's theory, because it depended on unlikely extrapolations of the laws of physics. He considered that the mass-luminosity law which Eddington claimed to have established was not a possible deduction from the fundamental formulae. It could follow only from the addition of a missing equation expressing the unknown dependence on physical conditions of the rate of generation of energy in stars. He had, therefore, begun his investigations with observed quantities, representing conditions at the surface of the star, and had worked inwards, without making any assumptions unwarranted by observation.

Sir Arthur Eddington, who followed, pointed out that disagreements in physical discussions could be of two kinds: first, those which depended on the adoption of different assumptions or hypotheses in the absence of definite knowledge; and secondly, disagreements on the logical or mathematical deductions from given premises. He thought that the disagreement between Sir James Jeans and himself was entirely of the first kind; but between Prof. Milne and himself there appeared to be a mathematical disagreement, which was very unfortunate. He did not approach Prof. Milne's latest work in a spirit of opposition. He regarded it as quite a permissible attempt to improve the existing theory in points where room for improvement undoubtedly existed. The main feature of Milne's

# 恒星的构造

## 编者按

*爱德华·米耳恩关于恒星构造的理论在英国天文学界引起了极大的争议，这即是1931年1月9日皇家天文学会举办的讨论会的主要论题。尽管后来人们发现米耳恩的理论正确地预测到了太阳等恒星中心的极高温度和极高密度，但在这次讨论会上并没有形成定论。*

恒星构造问题是詹姆斯·金斯爵士和阿瑟·爱丁顿爵士长期争执不下的论题，现在由于米耳恩教授的工作而有了新的转机。米耳恩教授发表在《英国皇家天文学会月刊》1930年11月号上关于这一主题的长篇论文，以及福勒、费尔克拉夫和考林等人的有关论文已经在去年11月被提交给了该学会，但尚没有时间就这一主题进行讨论。因此在今年1月9日（星期五）举行的皇家天文学会大会上专门就这一主题进行了讨论。米耳恩教授用简短的发言拉开了大会的序幕，许多天文学家和数学家都出席了本次会议。

米耳恩教授的观点已发表在1月3日的《自然》杂志上（第16页）。米耳恩在讨论会开始时谈到阿瑟·爱丁顿爵士对这一问题已做了先驱性的工作，而他所做的事情不过是澄清了一些特殊的假设，从而使爱丁顿的理论更加合理化。他不能接受詹姆斯·金斯爵士的理论，因为该理论依赖于物理定律的推论，而这一推论并不可靠。他认为爱丁顿宣称已建立的质量–光度定律并非是从某些基本公式推导出来的，而只能是来自一个附加的缺失方程，这个方程与影响恒星产能率的物理条件之间的依赖关系是未知的。因此，他的研究是从代表恒星表面物理条件的可观测量开始的，然后向恒星内部延伸，并没有作出任何不能被观测所证实的假定。

接着阿瑟·爱丁顿爵士指出，物理学中讨论的分歧可以分为两种：一种是由于在缺乏确定知识的情况下采用了不同的假定，另一种则是由于从给定前提出发的逻辑或数学推导不同。他认为自己与詹姆斯·金斯爵士之间的分歧完全属于第一种；而自己与米耳恩教授的分歧似乎是数学上的分歧，这是很不幸的。他并没有用反对的态度去看待米耳恩教授的最新研究。他认为米耳恩的工作是改进现有理论的一种可行的尝试，这个理论显然存在改进的余地。米耳恩的恒星模型的主要特征是：大部分物质集中在具有很高密度的炽热核心区，并由稀薄的外层包围着。爱丁顿自己

picture of the stars was that the mass was largely concentrated in a dense hot core with a surrounding rarefied envelope. His own theory gave a much more gradual and uniform increase of density from the centre outwards. For the sun it gave a central density of 70, whereas Milne's theory gave a value of about 700,000. The matter there was therefore, according to Milne, not in the condition of a perfect gas, and hence the mass-luminosity relation could not be deduced. There were certainly loopholes in that relation—it did not apply to a star composed mainly of hydrogen, for example—but he did not believe that Milne's theory had sealed up those loopholes. Milne himself had confessedly not been able to satisfy himself that the equations for his stars possessed solutions, and Sir Arthur thought that it was *a priori* unlikely that they did. If such solutions existed, however, it still remained to decide between the two widely different central densities. This might be done by considering the intrinsic opacity in the interior, or its average if it was variable. An appeal on this ground, however, would show that both theories were wrong—that was the long-outstanding discrepancy between the physical and astronomical opacities of matter. Both theories required a larger opacity than would follow from current physical theory, but he had found that the discrepancy on Milne's theory was far greater than that on his own. A great deal depended on how large a mass was concentrated at the centre. If it was merely a point-source of extremely high temperature and density, with the rest of the star following a distribution of density almost identical with that of his own theory, he might be willing to accept the modification as a useful addition to that theory: it would provide a source of stellar energy. The large amount of mass, however, which Milne placed around the centre, inevitably made worse the existing discrepancy with regard to the opacity. Prof. Milne had objected to his theory being called a hypothesis, regarding it rather as an inevitable conclusion. It was inevitable only if the premises were granted, and Sir Arthur had been denying them for fourteen years.

Sir James Jeans found himself in almost complete agreement with what Sir Arthur Eddington had said, because Sir Arthur had not touched on the points on which they differed. If Sir Arthur, Prof. Milne, and himself all suddenly became infallible and omnipotent as mathematicians, he and Sir Arthur would still differ on the same points as before, but Prof. Milne would agree with one or the other accordingly as he considered the stars to be gaseous inside or otherwise. There was nothing new in Milne's theory; all that was accurate in it had been done previously by Eddington or himself. He had shown long ago that if you integrated outwards from the centre of a star you got definite results right up to the boundary, but that there an infinite number of solutions were possible, and Nature itself decided which was the actual one. When, therefore, Milne reversed the process by integrating from the boundary inwards, it did not matter with which of those solutions his initial data corresponded; he would necessarily arrive at the same conditions in the interior. The work, however, would be much more cumbersome. He agreed with Eddington about the opacity discrepancy, but considered that the case had not been put strongly enough. The factor 10 in the luminosity, by which Eddington's own theory deviated from observation, was much greater than was permissible. Expressed in terms of volume, it meant that the sun should be as big as Antares. Since Milne's theory made matters worse still, he considered that that theory was ruled out of court entirely.

的理论则给出恒星密度由中心向外逐渐均匀增大的模型。对于太阳，爱丁顿理论给出的中心密度是 70，而米耳恩理论给出的太阳中心密度约为 700,000。因此，米耳恩认为，太阳中心区的气态物质已不是理想气体，所以不能推导出质量－光度关系。这个关系肯定存在漏洞，例如不适用于主要由氢组成的恒星，但他也不相信米耳恩的理论已填补了这些漏洞。米耳恩自己承认他不能证实他的恒星方程组存在解，而阿瑟爵士也认为不太可能有解。不过如果这些解存在，仍然需要在两个差别很大的恒星中心密度之间作出选择。这或许可以根据恒星内部固有的不透明度，或者当不透明度变化时，用平均不透明度来进行判断。不过这种诉求会表明两种理论都是错误的——这是因为长期以来人们对于物质的物理不透明度和天文不透明度一直存在分歧。两种理论均要求有更大的不透明度，并且都超出了现有物理理论的最大值，但是爱丁顿发现米耳恩理论与现有物理理论的差异远远大于他自己的理论。这在很大程度上取决于有多少物质被集中到恒星的中心区。如果只有恒星的中心点具有极高的温度和密度，而恒星其余部分的密度分布几乎与他自己的理论相同，那他或许愿意把这种修正看作是对自己理论的有益补充：这个核将提供一种恒星能源。然而米耳恩把大量的物质安置到恒星中心区，就必定会使已有的关于不透明度的分歧进一步扩大。米耳恩教授反对人们把他的理论称为假说，他认为这样的结果是必然的。这样的结果只有在承认相应前提的条件下才会是必然的，而阿瑟爵士对这些前提持否定态度已有 14 年之久了。

詹姆斯 · 金斯爵士觉得自己几乎完全同意阿瑟 · 爱丁顿爵士的说法，因为阿瑟爵士并未谈到他们之间的分歧。如果阿瑟爵士、米耳恩教授和他自己突然变得像数学家那样确实可靠并且无所不能，那么他同阿瑟爵士之间还会像以前那样保持同样的分歧，而米耳恩教授将会与上述二人中的一位相一致，到底与谁一致取决于米耳恩认为恒星内部是否为气态。米耳恩的理论并不是新东西，其中所有正确的部分都来自于爱丁顿或他本人以前的研究成果。他在很早之前就曾指出，如果从恒星中心向外作积分，那么你得到的解一直到边界处都是确定的，但可能存在不定数目的解，而大自然将会决定哪一个解是符合实际的。所以当米耳恩反过来从恒星边界向恒星内部积分时，他的初始数据对应的到底是哪一个解就变得无关紧要了；他必然在恒星内部得到同样的条件。不过这样工作就变得非常繁琐。他同意爱丁顿关于不透明度存在分歧的意见，但认为这一点尚未引起足够的重视。爱丁顿从自己理论中得到的光度与观测值相差 10 倍，远超过误差允许的范围。若用体积表示，则意味着太阳将有心宿二（译者注：天蝎星座 $\alpha$ 星，也称大火，是一颗红巨星）那样大。鉴于米耳恩的理论把问题变得更糟，他认为这个理论根本不值得考虑。

Dr. W. M. Smart directed attention to the fact that the problem was an idealised one, since we knew nothing at all about the interior of a star from observation. Assumptions had to be made, and it should not be forgotten that they were assumptions. He considered the stars themselves were the final umpires in the matter. Sir Arthur Eddington had suggested the opacity as the criterion by which the umpires gave their decision; he would suggest one of several other criteria. Sir James Jeans's theory had been very successful in explaining the formation of spectroscopic binaries by fission, but he did not think that Prof. Milne's centrally condensed stars would provide a satisfactory explanation.

Prof. F. A. Lindemann hoped that Prof. Milne would maintain his theory, because it was the only one which gave really high temperatures in the stars. The temperatures required by Sir Arthur Eddington were, on thermodynamical grounds, incapable of permitting the conversion of matter into radiation. It was all very well to say that Milne's conclusions were inevitable only if you presupposed something. Something had to be presupposed, and Eddington's *ad hoc* assumptions did not meet the facts of the generation of energy. He considered that the discrepancy of a million-fold in the densities of stars according to Eddington's theory was sufficiently large to make the increase to several million-fold in Milne's theory of no significance in deciding between the theories.

Sir Oliver Lodge remarked that what struck him most in the discussion was the remarkable agreement between the three protagonists. They were agreed on knowledge of fundamental importance which was not available twenty years ago, and, in comparison with that, the differences were unimportant. His idea of dealing with the problem would be to start with what we know—the surface temperature of the sun, its rate of generation of energy, the fact that energy comes from the disintegration of atoms. Prof. Lindemann had assured us that the last-named process required a very high temperature. Let that temperature at the centre be assumed. Then we knew the relation between radiation pressure and gravitational pressure, and with regard to the opacity the Compton effect would give us some information. From all these data a mathematician might work out some definite result. He was fascinated by Milne's theory of a nova resulting from the collapse of a star. Such a possibility had not occurred to him, but it seemed to work out.

Several other speakers contributed to the discussion, which concluded with brief comments by Prof. Milne. He did not agree that his work covered the same ground as Sir James Jeans's. He had started from the surface and worked inwards because it was only the surface that we could observe, and he had avoided assumptions which were necessary if you started in an unknown region.

Although it could not be said that the discussion led to a greater measure of agreement between the various speakers, it undoubtedly helped, by bringing together different methods of dealing with the question, to focus the nature of the problem more clearly in the minds of those present.

(**127**, 130-131; 1931)

斯马特博士注意到这是一个理想化的问题，因为我们看不到恒星内部的任何东西。因此，人们必须采用一些假定，但是不要忘记它们仅仅是假定。他认为最终的裁判依然是恒星本身。阿瑟 · 爱丁顿爵士曾指出，裁判作出判决的判据是不透明度，而他宁愿从另外几个判据中选择一个。詹姆斯 · 金斯爵士的理论非常成功地用分裂解释了分光双星的形成，但他不认为米耳恩教授的中心高密度恒星能够提供满意的解释。

林德曼教授希望米耳恩教授坚持自己的理论，因为这是唯一一个认为恒星内部温度确实很高的理论。根据热力学原理，阿瑟 · 爱丁顿爵士所需的温度不能使物质热到辐射出能量。可以合理地认为米耳恩的结论只有在某种前提下才是成立的。某种假定是必需的，但爱丁顿的特殊假定与恒星能量的产生事实不相吻合。他认为既然根据爱丁顿理论得到的恒星密度有一百万倍的差异，那么在米耳恩的理论中把这个差异扩大到几百万倍也就无关紧要了，这不足以作为判定这两种理论优劣的依据。

奥利弗 · 洛奇爵士表示这次讨论会中令他印象最深刻的是三位主角之间的不寻常的一致性。他们均同意这些 20 年前还不知晓的知识的重要性，而与此相比，分歧是次要的。对于这个问题的处理，他的想法是应该从我们知道的事实出发，即太阳表面的温度、它的产能率以及能量来自原子衰变的事实。林德曼教授使我们确信原子衰变需要非常高的温度。假定这一温度即为恒星的中心温度，于是我们就可以知道辐射压力与重力之间的关系。至于不透明度，康普顿效应会向我们提供一些信息。从这些资料出发，数学家也许会得到某种确定的结果。他对米耳恩关于新星起源于恒星塌陷的理论非常感兴趣，他没有想到会有这样的可能性，但结果似乎就是如此。

还有其他一些参加者在讨论会上发了言，最后由米耳恩教授作简要的评论。他不认为自己的研究与詹姆斯 · 金斯爵士的研究是建立在同一个基础上的。他的研究是从恒星表面出发向恒星内部延伸，因为我们只能观测到恒星的表面，他避免作出假定，而如果从未知的区域开始研究，这些假定就是必需的了。

尽管不能说各位发言者在这次讨论会上已经达成了更广泛的共识，不过借这个机会将处理问题的不同方法放到一起进行交流，的确有助于把与会者的思想明确地统一到问题的本质上去。

（林元章 翻译；蒋世仰 审稿）

# Present Status of Theory and Experiment as to Atomic Disintegration and Atomic Synthesis*

R. A. Millikan

## Editor's Note

**In the mid-1920s, Robert Millikan coined the term "cosmic rays" for the high-energy radiation recently detected in the upper atmosphere. While some physicists suggested that the rays might come from atmospheric electricity, Millikan favoured an extraterrestrial origin. Here he describes recent evidence supporting this view. The discovery of unstable radioactive elements showed that some process must have created these atoms in the relatively recent past by building heavier elements up out of lighter ones. Perhaps cosmic-ray collisions are the cause, Millikan suggests. He proposes a broader process of heavy-element formation in space, but today's well-founded theory locates it in thermonuclear reactions within stars and supernovae, or during processes in the very early universe.**

MY task is to attempt to trace the history of the development of scientific evidence bearing on the question of the origin and destiny of the physical elements. I shall list ten discoveries or developments, all made within the past hundred years, which touch in one way or another upon this problem and constitute indications or sign-posts on the road toward an answer.

Prior to the middle of the nineteenth century, little experimental evidence of any sort had appeared, so that the problem was wholly in the hands of the philosopher and the theologian. Then came, first, the discovery of the equivalence of heat and work, and the consequent formulation of the principle of the conservation of energy, probably the most far-reaching physical principle ever developed.

Following this, and directly dependent upon it, came, second, the discovery, or formulation, of the second law of thermodynamics, which was first interpreted, and is still interpreted by some, as necessitating the ultimate "heat-death" of the universe and the final extinction of activity of all sorts; for all hot bodies are observed to be radiating away their heat, and this heat after having been so radiated away into space apparently cannot be reclaimed by man. This is classically and simply stated in the humpty-dumpty rhyme. As a natural if not necessary corollary to this was put forward by some, in entire accord with the demands of medieval theology, a *Deus ex machina* initially to wind up or start off this running-down universe.

* Retiring presidential address to the American Association for the Advancement of Science, delivered at Cleveland on Dec. 29.

# 原子衰变与原子合成的理论和实验现状*

罗伯特·密立根

## 编者按

20 世纪 20 年代中期，罗伯特·密立根将最新在高层大气中发现的高能辐射命名为“宇宙射线”。虽然有些物理学家认为这种射线可能来自大气电，而密立根则赞成其起源于地球之外。他在这篇文章中介绍了近期得到的一些证据以支持这一观点。不稳定放射性元素的发现说明：在不久以前，一定有某种轻元素合成重元素的过程产生了这些原子。密立根认为宇宙射线的碰撞可能就是起因。他还提出了较为广泛地在宇宙空间中形成重元素的过程，但当今确立的理论则认为重元素的生成过程起源于恒星和超新星内部的热核反应，或者形成于早期宇宙的某些反应之中。

我的任务是试图追溯关于物质元素起源和命运问题的科学证据的发展历史。我将列出 10 个最近 100 年内的发现或进展，它们会以这种或那种方式与此问题相关联，并且充当着通向答案之路上的指示灯或者路标。

在 19 世纪中叶以前，人们几乎得不到任何实验上的证据，所以这个问题的解答完全由哲学家和神学家说了算。然后出现了第一个发现，即热和功的等价性，由此导致了能量守恒定律，后者或许能称得上是迄今为止影响最为深远的物理定律。

在这之后，并与此直接相关，热力学第二定律作为第二个发现或构想出现了，该定律最初被解释为（某些人至今仍作此解释）宇宙必然要走向最终的“热寂”，各种活动最终都将停止；因为人们发现所有热的物体都在向外辐射自己的热量，以这种方式散发到宇宙中去的热量显然无法被人类收回。这和经典而简单的《汉普蒂·邓普蒂》歌谣中描述的情况相符（译者注：humpty-dumpty 在歌谣中被比作“一经损坏就无法修复的东西”）。有些人提出这即使不是必然结果也是一种很自然的结果，完全适合了中世纪神学的要求，即最初是由**救世主**灭世或创世这个不断被耗尽的宇宙的。

* 卸任美国科学促进会会长的演说辞，12月29日发表于克利夫兰市。

Then came, third, the discovery, through studies both in geology and biology, of the facts of evolution—facts which showed that, so far as the biological field is concerned, the process of creation, or upbringing from lower to higher forms, has been continuously going on for millions upon millions of years and is presumably going on now. This tended to direct attention away from the *Deus ex machina*, to identify the Creator with his universe, to strengthen the theological doctrine of immanence, which represents substantially the philosophic position of Leonardo da Vinci, Galileo, Newton, Francis Bacon, and most of the great minds of history down to Einstein.

Neither evolution nor evolutionists have in general been atheistic—Darwin least of all—but their influence has undoubtedly been to raise doubts about the legitimacy of the dogma of the *Deus ex machina* and of the correlative one of the heat-death. This last dogma rests squarely on the assumption that we, infinitesimal mites on a speck of a world, know all about how the universe behaves in all its parts, or more specifically, that the radiation laws which seem to us to hold here cannot possibly have any exceptions anywhere, even though that is precisely the sort of sweeping generalisation that has led us physicists into error half a dozen times during the past thirty years, and also though we know quite well that conditions prevail outside our planet which we cannot here duplicate or even approach. Therefore the heat-death dogma has always been treated with reserve by the most thoughtful of scientific workers. No more crisp or more cogent statement of what seems to me to be the correct position of science in this regard has come to my attention than is found in the following recent utterance of Gilbert N. Lewis, namely, "Thermodynamics gives no support to the assumption that the universe is running down". "*Gain of entropy always means loss of information and nothing more.*"

The fourth discovery bearing on our theme was the discovery that the dogma of the immutable elements was definitely wrong. By the year 1900 the element radium had been isolated and the mean lifetime of its atoms found to be about two thousand years. This meant definitely that the radium atoms that are here now have been formed within about that time; and a year or two later the element helium was definitely observed to be growing out of radium here and now. This raised insistently the question as to whether the creation, or at least the formation, of all the elements out of something else may not be a continuous process—stupendous change in viewpoint the discovery of radioactivity brought about, and a wholesome lesson of modesty it taught to the physicist. But a couple of years later, uranium and thorium, the heaviest known elements, were definitely caught in the act of begetting radium, and all the allied chain of disintegration products. Since, however, the lifetime of the parent atom, uranium, has now been found to be a billion years or so, we have apparently ceased to inquire whence it comes. We are disposed to assume, however, that it is not now being formed on earth. Indeed, we have good reason to believe that the whole radioactive process is confined to a very few, very heavy elements which are now giving up the energy which was once stored up in them—we know not how—so that radioactivity, though it seemed at first to be pointing away from the heat-death, has not at all, in the end, done so. Indeed, it seems to be merely one mechanism by which stored-up energy is being frittered away into apparently unreclaimable radiant heat—another case of humpty-dumpty.

然后出现了第三个发现，地质学和生物学对进化现象的研究结果表明：就生物学领域而言，创造生命的过程或从低级形式向高级形式发展的过程，已经持续了亿万年而且据推测现在还在继续。这似乎使人们的视线从**救世主**中转移开来，认为造物主与他的天地万物是等同的，从而强化了上帝无所不在的神学理论，这一理论充分反映了历史上大多数伟大的思想家，从列奥纳多·达·芬奇、伽利略、牛顿、弗朗西斯·培根，一直到爱因斯坦的哲学立场。

一般而言，进化论和进化论者都不倾向于无神论——达尔文尤其如此——但是由于他们的影响，人们的确已开始怀疑**救世主**理论以及与之相联系的热寂说的合理性。这个最后的学说直接需要假设，我们人类，这些宇宙中某一点上的无限小微粒，已经了解了宇宙中所有组成部分的行为，或者更明确地说，我们现在认定的辐射定律不可能在任何地方出现例外情况，尽管它就是那个曾让我们这些物理学家在过去的 30 年里犯过 6 次错误的并非普适的定律，也尽管我们很清楚地知道我们所在行星之外的环境是我们无法复制甚至是无法介入的。因此，大多数有思想的科学工作者都对热寂说采取保留的态度。在我所注意到的关于该问题的正确科学观点方面，没有谁的观点比吉尔伯特·刘易斯在最近讲话中的下述论断更简明、更有说服力，即“热力学并不支持宇宙在退化的假设”。**“熵的增加通常只意味着信息的减少，仅此而已”**。

第四个与我们这个主题相关的发现是，元素不可改变的观点是完全错误的。到 1900 年，元素镭已经被分离出来，并得出镭原子的平均寿命大约为 2000 年。这显然说明现在的镭原子大约是在那个时间范围内形成的；一两年以后，人们可以观测到从镭中生成的氦元素。这使人们急切地想知道，所有这些由其他元素生成新元素的创造过程，或至少可以说是形成过程，是否不会连续进行——放射性的发现带来了观念上的巨大变化，也有益地告诫了物理学家们要谦虚。然而几年之后，目前已知的两种最重的元素——铀和钍，已被确认都能在生成镭以及一系列相关的衰变产物的过程中得到。既然现在发现作为母原子铀的寿命在 10 亿年左右，显然我们不用再去追问它是从哪儿来的了。然而，我们倾向于假定它不是现在在地球上形成的。实际上，我们有足够的理由相信所有的放射性过程只局限于极少数很重的元素，它们目前正在释放曾经储存在其内部的能量——我们不知道这种储存是怎样实现的——所以虽然放射现象起初似乎远离了热寂说，可到了最后却不是完全如此。放射现象看起来其实仅仅是储存能慢慢转化为明显不可逆转的辐射热的一种机制——“汉普蒂·邓普蒂”的另一个实例。

The fifth significant discovery was the enormous lifetime of the earth—partly through radioactivity itself, which assigns at least a billion and a half years—and the still greater lifetime of the sun and stars—thousands of times longer than the periods through which they could possibly exist as suns if they were simply hot bodies cooling off. This meant that new and heretofore unknown sources of heat energy had to be found to keep the stars pouring out such enormous quantities of radiation for such ages upon ages.

The sixth discovery, and in many ways the most important of all, was the development of evidence for the interconvertibility of mass and energy. This came about in three ways. In 1901 Kaufman showed experimentally that the mass of an electron could be increased by increasing sufficiently its velocity: that is, energy could be definitely converted into mass. About the same time the pressure of radiation was experimentally established by Nichols and Hull at Dartmouth College, New Hampshire, and Lebedew at Moscow. This meant that radiation possesses the only distinguishing property of mass, the property by which we define it, namely, inertia. The fundamental distinction between radiation and matter thus disappeared. These were direct, experimental discoveries. Next, in 1905, Einstein developed the interconvertibility of mass and energy as a necessary consequence of the special theory of relativity. If, then, the mass of the sun could in any way be converted into radiant heat, there would be an abundant source of energy to keep the sun going so long as necessary, and all our difficulties about the lifetimes of the sun and stars would have disappeared. But what could be the mechanism of this transformation?

Then came the seventh discovery, which constituted a very clear finger-post, pointing to the possibility of the existence of an integrating or building-up process among the physical elements, as well as in biological forms, in the discovery that the elements are all definitely built up out of hydrogen; for they—the ninety-two different atoms—were all found, beginning about 1913 by the new method of so-called positive ray analysis, to be exact multiples of the weight of hydrogen within very small limits of uncertainty. This fact alone raises very insistently the query as to whether they are not being built up somewhere out of hydrogen now. They certainly were once so put together, and some of them, the radioactive ones, are now actually caught in the act of splitting up. Is it not highly probable, so would say any observer, that the inverse process is going on somewhere, especially since the process would involve no violation either of the energy principle or of the second law of thermodynamics; for hydrogen, the element out of which they all must be built, has not a weight exactly one in terms of the other ninety-two, but about 1 percent more than one, so that since mass or weight had been found in the sixth discovery to be expressible in terms of energy, the union of any number of hydrogen atoms into any heavier element, meant that 1 percent of the total available potential energy had disappeared and was therefore available for appearance as heat.

When, about 1914–15, this fact was fitted by MacMillan, Harkins, and others into the demand made above in the fifth discovery for a new source of energy to keep the sun pouring out heat so copiously for such great lengths of time, is seemed to the whole

第五个重大发现是发现地球已经存在了很长时间——部分是根据元素放射性确定的，地球年龄至少为 15 亿年，而太阳和其他恒星的年龄则更长——这个年龄要比假设恒星作为一个炽热的天体仅是单纯地不断冷却所耗的时间长几千倍。这意味着我们不得不去寻找能使恒星在漫长岁月里不断释放出大量辐射的热能的新来源，这种能源迄今为止尚不可知。

第六个发现是找到了质量和能量相互转化的证据，从许多方面来看，这个发现是所有发现中最重要的。这可以从三方面说明。1901 年考夫曼用实验证明，通过充分提高电子的速度可以增加电子的质量：也就是说，能量确实可以转化为质量。几乎是同时，新罕布什尔州达特茅斯学院的尼科尔斯、赫尔和莫斯科的列别捷夫用实验验证了辐射压的存在。这说明辐射具有质量的唯一与众不同的特征，即惯性。这样辐射和物质之间的根本区别就消失了。这些都是直接由实验发现的。紧接着在 1905 年，爱因斯坦利用狭义相对论推导出质量和能量之间的相互转化这一必然结果。假如太阳的质量可以通过某种方式转化为辐射热，那么就有了充足的能量来源以保持太阳在如此长的时间里放出热，而我们对太阳及其他恒星年龄的疑问也就不复存在了。但是这种转变机制又是什么呢?

于是就有了第七个发现，这个发现非常明确地指出：组成物质的元素之间有可能出现积聚或合成的过程，在生物形态中也是如此，人们发现元素无疑都是由氢元素构成的；因为自 1913 年以来用所谓的阳射线分析法发现：92 种不同原子的重量均为氢元素重量的精确倍数且误差极小。仅仅是这一事实就使人们迫切想知道它们是不是现在正在某个地方由氢合成。它们肯定曾被这样合成过，而且现在它们之中的那些放射性元素会在裂变的过程中被发现。任何观测者都会说，很有可能在某处正进行着裂变的逆过程，特别是当这个过程并不违反能量原理和热力学第二定律的时候。氢作为构建其他元素的必要成分，相对于其他 92 个元素来说，其重量并不正好是 1，而是比 1 大 1%。所以既然在第六个发现中质量或重量可以表现为能量的形式,则任意数目的氢原子合并成任何较重元素时意味着全部可利用势能的1%消失了，并转化成了可以释放的热能。

大约在 1914 至 1915 年，这个事实被麦克米伦、哈金斯等人用作解释第五个发现中所需的一种新能源，以保持太阳长期散发出巨大的热量。对整个物理学界来说，由氢构成更重元素的过程实际上已被证明在太阳和恒星内部环境下确实在发生。这

world of physics that the building up of the heavier elements out of hydrogen under the conditions existing within the sun and stars had been practically definitely proved to be taking place. This would not provide an escape from the heat-death, but it would enormously postpone it, that is, until all the hydrogen in the universe had been converted into the heavier elements.

By this process, however, the suns could stoke at most but 1 percent of their total mass, assuming they were wholly hydrogen to begin with, into their furnaces, and 99 percent of the mass of the universe would remain as cold, dead ash when the fires were all gone out and the heat-death had come. But about 1917 the astronomer began to chafe under the time-limitation thus imposed upon him, and this introduced the eighth consideration bearing upon our theme. He could get a hundred times more time—from now on, much more than that, because only a small fraction of the matter in the universe is presumably now hydrogen—by assuming that, in the interior of heavy atoms, occasionally a negative electron gets tired of life at the pace it has to be lived in the electron world, and decides to end it all and commit suicide; but, being paired by Nature in electron-fate with a positive, he has to arrange a suicide pact with his mate, and so the two jump into each other's arms in the nucleus, and the two complementary electron lives are snuffed out at once; but not without the letting loose of a terrific death-yell, for the total mass of the two must be transformed into a powerful ether pulse which, by being absorbed in the surrounding matter, is supposed to keep up the mad, hot pace in the interiors of the suns. This discovery, or suggestion, to account for the huge estimated stellar lifetimes, of the complete annihilation of positive and negative electrons within the nucleus, makes it unnecessary to assume, at least for stellar lifetime purposes, the building up of the heavier elements out of hydrogen. Indeed, it seems rather unlikely that both kinds of processes, atom-building and atom-annihilating, are going on together in the same spot under the same conditions, so we must turn to further experimental facts to get more light.

The ninth sign-post came into sight in 1927, when Aston made a most precise series of measurements on the relative masses of the atoms, which made it possible to subject to a new test the Einstein formula for the relation between mass and energy, namely, $E = Mc^2$. This Aston curve is one of the most illuminating finger-pointings we now have. It shows that:

1. Einstein's equation actually stands the quantitative test for radioactive or disintegrating processes right well, and therefore receives new experimental credentials.

2. The radioactive or disintegrating process with the emission of an alpha ray must be confined to a very few heavy elements, since these are the only ones so situated on the curve that mass can disappear, and hence heat energy appear, through such disintegration.

3. All the most common elements, except hydrogen, are already in their most stable condition, that is, their condition of minimum mass, so that if we disintegrate them we shall have to do work upon them, rather than get energy out of them.

并不能使宇宙摆脱热寂的结局，但可以极大地推迟它的到来，也就是说，可以推迟到宇宙中所有的氢都被转化成了较重的元素时才发生。

然而，假设这些像太阳一样的恒星全部由氢元素构成，并将它们投入其自身的熔炉之中，这一过程最多只能消耗掉其总质量的 1%，宇宙中 99% 的质量在燃料烧尽热寂来临时将变为冰冷的死灰。但在 1917 年前后，天文学家开始对这个强加给他的时间限制感到烦扰，并由此引出了与我们这个主题相关的第八个设想。他从现在起可以获得比那个时间限制长几百倍甚至更长的时间，因为据推测现在宇宙中的物质只有一小部分是氢——假设在重原子内部，偶尔一个负电子对自己不得不生活在电子世界中感到厌倦而决定通过自杀结束这一切；但自然界注定电子要和正电子配成对，它必须筹划与自己的搭档一起自杀，这样在原子核中它们两个分别跳到了对方的怀抱中，这两个正负互补的电子的生命同时结束；但在死亡时并非没有发出临死前那可怕的叫喊，因为它们两个的总质量必然转化成一个强大的以太脉冲，并被周围物质吸收，该过程被认为是保持恒星内部剧烈热反应的原因。这个发现或提议，即利用原子核内部正负电子的彻底湮灭来解决预测的恒星年龄大得不可思议的难题，使人们至少在恒星年龄问题上不需要假设由氢合成重元素的过程。的确，原子合成和原子湮灭这两类过程在同一地点同一条件下同时进行看起来不太可能，所以我们必须通过更多的实验得到更清楚的解释。

1927 年，当阿斯顿对原子的相对质量进行了一系列非常精确的测定，使爱因斯坦在质量和能量之间建立的公式，即 $E = Mc^2$ 得到了新的验证之后，第九个里程碑也就出现在了人们的视野中。阿斯顿曲线是我们目前拥有的最具启发性的指证之一。它说明了以下几点：

1. 爱因斯坦方程实际上可用作放射性或衰变过程的有效的定量检验，因而增加了实验的可信度。

2. 放出一个 $\alpha$ 射线的放射性或衰变过程肯定只局限于很少几个重元素之中，因为它们在曲线中处于质量可能减少的位置上，因而可以通过这样的衰变过程释放出热能。

3. 所有除氢以外的最常见的元素都处于最稳定的状态之中，也就是说，它们处于质量最小的状态，所以如果我们想让它们发生衰变必须对它们做功，而不是从中获取能量。

4. Therefore, man's only possible source of energy other than the sun is the upbuilding of the common elements out of hydrogen or helium, or else the entire annihilation of positive and negative electrons; and there is no likelihood that either of these processes is a possibility on earth.

5. If the foregoing upbuilding process is going on anywhere, the least penetrating and the most abundant radiation produced by it, that corresponding to the formation of helium out of hydrogen, ought to be about ten times as energetic as the hardest gamma rays, that is, it ought to correspond to about twenty-six million electron-volts in place of two and a half million.

6. Other radiations corresponding to the only other abundant elements, namely, oxygen (oxygen, nitrogen, carbon), silicon (magnesium, aluminium, silicon), and iron (iron group), should be found about four times, seven times, and fourteen times as energetic as the "helium rays".

7. The radiation corresponding to the smallest annihilation process that can take place—the suicide of a positive and negative electron—is three hundred and fifty times as energetic as the hardest gamma ray, or thirty-five times as energetic as the "helium ray".

This brings us to the tenth discovery, that of the cosmic rays. These reveal:*

1. A radiation, the chief component of which, according to our direct comparison, is five times as penetrating as the hardest gamma ray, which, with the best theoretical formula we have relating energy and penetrating power (Klein–Nishina), means a ray ten times as energetic as the hardest gamma ray, *precisely according to prediction.*

2. Special bands of cosmic radiation that are roughly where they should be to be due to the formation of the foregoing abundant elements out of hydrogen, though (for reasons to be given presently) no precise quantitative check is to expected except in the case of helium.

3. No radiation of significant amount anywhere near where it is to be expected from the annihilation hypothesis, thus indicating that at least 95 percent of the observed cosmic rays are due to some other less energetic processes.

4. A radiation that is completely independent of the sun, the great hot mass just off our bows, and not appreciably dependent on the Milky Way or the nearest spiral nebula, Andromeda, one that comes in to us practically uniformly from all portions of the celestial dome, and is so invariable with both time and latitude at a given elevation that the observed small fluctuations at a given station reflect with much fidelity merely the changes

* See articles by Millikan and by Millikan and Cameron, *Phys. Rev.*, Dec. 1, 1930, and in press.

4. 因此，除了太阳以外，人类可能获得能量的方式只有通过用氢或氦合成普通元素，或正负电子全部湮灭的过程；这两个过程都不可能在地球上发生。

5. 假如上述合成过程可以在任意地点进行，由此产生的穿透力最弱、强度最高的辐射，按照由氢合成氦的过程推算，应该能够达到最硬的 $\gamma$ 射线能量的 10 倍左右，也就是说，大致相当于 26 百万电子伏特而不是 2.5 百万电子伏特。

6. 与其他含量丰富的元素，即氧（氧、氮、碳），硅（镁、铝、硅）和铁（铁族元素）相关联的辐射过程所对应的能量应当分别约为“氦射线”的 4 倍、7 倍和 14 倍。

7. 由可能发生的最小的湮灭过程——正负电子的自杀过程发出的辐射是最硬的 $\gamma$ 射线能量的 350 倍，是“氦射线”能量的 35 倍。

这把我们引入了与宇宙射线相关的第十个发现。观测表明 * ：

1. 我们根据直接对比发现：一个主体部分是穿透力为最硬的 $\gamma$ 射线 5 倍的辐射，用能量与穿透力之间最好的理论公式——克莱因 – 仁科公式计算，该射线的能量为最硬的 $\gamma$ 射线的 10 倍，**这是根据预测推算的精确结果**。

2. 宇宙辐射的特殊频带，大致位于由氢合成上述含量丰富元素时产生的辐射应在的位置，尽管（由于马上要提到的原因）除了氦元素以外，我们都不能进行精确的定量计算。

3. 在正负电子湮灭假设对应的位置附近没有观测到数量显著的辐射，这说明观测到的宇宙射线至少有 95% 是由其他一些能量较低的过程造成的。

4. 这种辐射与就在我们凸窗外面的那个巨大的发热体，即太阳完全不相干，而且与银河系或离我们最近的旋涡星云——仙女座星云也没有关系，它几乎均匀地从天穹的各个位置向我们而来，在某一特定的高度，其观测值不随时间和纬度而变，个别观测站观测值的微小涨落仅仅是由于射线在到达观测器之前必须要穿过的大气

* 见密立根以及密立根和卡梅伦发表在《物理学评论》上的文章，1930年12月1日，即将出版。

in the thickness of the absorbing air blanket through which the rays have had to pass to get to the observer.

This last property is the most amazing and the most significant property exhibited by the cosmic rays, and before drawing the final conclusions its significance will be discussed. For it means that at the time these rays enter the earth's atmosphere, they are practically pure ether waves or photons. If they were high-speed electrons or even had been appreciably transformed by Compton encounters in passing through matter into such high-speed electrons or beta rays, these electrons would of necessity spiral about the lines of force of the earth's magnetic field and thus enter the earth more abundantly near the earth's magnetic poles than in lower latitudes. This is precisely what the experiments made during the last summer at Churchill, Manitoba (lat. 59° N.), within 730 miles of the north magnetic pole, showed to be *not true*, the mean intensity of the rays there being not measurably different from that at Pasadena in lat. 34° N.

Nor is the conclusion that the cosmic rays enter the earth's atmosphere as a practically pure photon beam dependent upon these measurements of last summer alone. It follows also from the high altitude sounding-balloon experiments of Millikan and Bowen in April 1922, taken in connexion with the lower balloon flights of Hess and Kolhörster in 1911-14. For in going to an altitude of 15.5 km. we got but one-fourth the total discharge of our electroscope which we computed we should have obtained from the extrapolation of our predecessors' curves. This shows that somewhere in the atmosphere below a height of 15.5 km. the intensity of the ionisation within a closed vessel exposed to the rays goes through a maximum, and then decreases, quite rapidly, too, in going to greater heights. We have just taken very accurate observations up to the elevation of the top of Pike's Peak (4.3 km.), and found that within this range the rate of increase with altitude is quite as large as that found in the Hess and Kolhörster balloon flights, so that there can be no uncertainty at all about the existence of this maximum. Such a maximum, however, means that the rays, before entering the atmosphere, have not passed through enough matter to begin to get into equilibrium with their secondaries—beta rays and photons of reduced frequency—in other words, *that they have not come through an appreciable amount of matter in getting from their place of origin to the earth.*

This checks with the lack of effect of the earth's magnetic field on the intensity of the rays; and the two phenomena, of quite unrelated kinds and brought to light years apart, when taken together, prove most conclusively, I think, that the cosmic rays cannot originate even in the outer atmospheres of the stars, though these are full of hydrogen and helium in a high temperature state, but that they must originate rather in those portions of the universe from which they can come to the earth without traversing matter in quantity that is appreciable even as compared with the thickness of the earth's atmosphere—in other words, that *they must originate in the intensely cold regions in the depths of interstellar space.*

Further, the more penetrating the beta rays produced by Compton encounters, the greater the thickness of matter that must be traversed before the beam of pure photons

吸收层的厚度变化造成的，这种涨落是吸收层厚度变化的真实反映。

最后一个特性是宇宙射线最令人惊异也是最重要的特性，在下最终定论之前将对这个问题的重要性进行讨论。因为这意味着宇宙射线在进入地球大气层时基本上是由纯以太波或光子组成的。如果它们是高速运动的电子，或曾经在穿透物质的过程中因发生康普顿碰撞而转化成了高速电子或 $\beta$ 射线，那么这些电子必然是以围绕地球磁力线的螺旋形轨迹前进的，因此进入地球两磁极的射线应该比低纬度地区的多。但去年夏天在距离北磁极 730 英里的马尼托巴省丘吉尔市（北纬 59°）进行的实验说明**事实并非如此**，在那里测量的射线平均强度值与在北纬 34° 的帕萨迪纳得到的测量值没有什么区别。

进入地球大气层的宇宙射线几乎全部由光子组成这一结论并不仅仅是根据去年夏季的测量结果，它也能从 1922 年 4 月密立根和鲍恩利用探空气球在高空处进行的实验和与之相关联的赫斯和柯尔霍斯特 1911 年 ~1914 年低空区的气球实验中找到根据。因为在到达 15.5 千米的高度时，验电器的放电量并没有达到我们根据前人实验曲线外推得到的计算值，而仅为它的四分之一。这说明在大气中某个低于 15.5 千米的地方，密闭容器内宇宙射线导致的电离程度先是达到了一个最大值，但当升至更高的高度后又开始急剧下降。我们刚刚对派克峰（4.3 千米）峰顶以下各个高度处的射线强度进行了精确的测量，发现在这个范围内，射线强度随高度上升的增加率与赫斯和柯尔霍斯特在气球飞行实验中得到的结果一致，所以存在一个最大值是毋庸置疑的。但这个最大值说明宇宙射线在到达地球大气层之前并没有穿过足够厚的物体以能与它们的次级粒子——$\beta$ 射线和频率降低的光子达到平衡。也就是说，**这些射线在从它们的发源地到地球之间未曾穿过数量可观的物质。**

这证实了地球磁场对宇宙射线强度没有影响；这两个现象完全不相干，并且相距若干光年，当把它们联系在一起的时候，我认为可以下结论说：宇宙射线不可能发源于恒星，哪怕是在它的大气外层，尽管那里有大量处于高温中的氢和氦。不过它们肯定是来自宇宙中那些能让它们甚至不必穿透和地球大气层一般厚的物质就可以到达地球的地方——换句话说，**宇宙射线必定起源于星际空间深处的超低温区域。**

此外，由康普顿碰撞产生的 $\beta$ 射线的穿透力越强，进入大气层的纯光子束在与它的次级粒子达到平衡之前需要穿透的物质厚度就越大；且当达到此种平衡时，测

which enters the atmosphere gets into equilibrium with its secondaries; and until such equilibrium is reached, the apparent absorption coefficient must be less than the coefficient computed with the aid of the Klein–Nishina formula from the energy released in the process from which the radiation arises. Now the Bothe–Kolhörster experiments of about a year ago show that when the energies of the incident photons are sufficiently high, the beta rays released by Compton encounters do indeed become abnormally penetrating: so that it is to be expected that, for the cosmic rays produced by the formation of the heavier of the common elements like silicon and iron out of hydrogen, the observed absorption coefficients will be somewhat smaller than those computed from the energy available for their formation. This is precisely the behaviour which our cosmic ray depth-ionisation curve actually reveals. At the highest altitudes at which we have recently observed (14,000 ft.), the helium rays have reached equilibrium with their secondaries, and the observed and computed coefficients agree as they should. For the oxygen rays the observed coefficent is a little lower than the computed value—about 17 percent lower; for the silicon rays still lower—about 30 percent; and for the iron rays considerably lower still—about 60 percent: all in beautiful qualitative agreement with the theoretical demands as outlined.

The foregoing results seem to point with much definiteness to the following conclusions:

1. The cosmic rays have their origin not in the stars but rather in interstellar space.

2. They are due to the building up in the depths of space of the commoner heavy elements out of hydrogen, which the spectroscopy of the heavens shows to be widely distributed through space. That helium and the common elements oxygen, nitrogen, carbon, and even sulphur, are also found between the stars is proved by Bowen's beautiful recent discovery that the "nebulium lines" arise from these very elements.

3. These atom-building processes cannot take place under the conditions of temperature and pressure existing in the sun and stars, the heats of these bodies having to be maintained presumably by the atom-annihilating process postulated by Jeans and Eddington as taking place there.

4. All this says nothing at all about the second law of thermodynamics or the *Wärme-Tod*, but it does contain a bare suggestion that if atom formation out of hydrogen is taking place all through space, as it seems to be doing, it may be that the hydrogen is somehow being replenished there, too, from the only form of energy that we know to be all the time leaking out from the stars to interstellar space, namely, radiant energy. This has been speculatively suggested many times before, in order to allow the Creator to be continually on his job. Here is, perhaps, a little bit of *experimental* finger-pointing in that direction. But it is not at all proved or even perhaps necessarily suggested. If Sir James Jeans prefers to hold one view and I another on this question, no one can say us nay. The one thing of which we may all be quite sure is that neither of us *knows* about it. But for the continuous building up of the common elements out of hydrogen in the depths of interstellar

得的表观吸收系数肯定小于根据辐射产生过程中释放的能量通过克莱因－仁科公式计算得到的系数。因为一年前的博思－柯尔霍斯特实验证明，当入射光子的能量足够高的时候，由康普顿碰撞产生的 $\beta$ 射线确实表现出格外强的穿透力；所以可以预测，如果宇宙射线是在由氢合成像硅和铁这样较重的常见元素时产生的，则所观察到的吸收系数将比根据合成过程可获得的能量计算得到的系数低一些。这正是我们的宇宙射线深度–电离曲线揭示出来的特性。在我们最近测量的最大高度处（14,000 英尺），氦射线已经和它们的次级粒子达到了平衡，因而系数测量值和计算值达到了应有的一致。对于氧射线，系数测量值略低于计算值——约低 17%；硅射线更低一些——约 30%；而铁射线则低得更多——约 60%；但它们都与所述的理论要求定性地一致。

根据上述结果显然可以得到以下结论：

1. 宇宙射线的发源地不是恒星，而是在星际空间。

2. 宇宙射线起源于太空深处的氢合成较为常见的重元素的过程，太空的光谱表明这些重元素广泛地分布于宇宙中。鲍恩的最新发现证明氦和常见元素氧、氮、碳甚至硫都存在于恒星间的太空中，这个出色的发现即“氰线”就是由这些元素引起的。

3. 这样的原子合成过程不可能在太阳或其他恒星内的高温高压环境下进行，根据金斯和爱丁顿的设想，这些天体的热量也许只能靠发生在那里的原子湮灭过程来维持。

4. 所有这些都没有提及热力学第二定律或**热寂**，但它确实包含了这样一个假设：假如由氢合成其他原子的过程在宇宙空间中普遍存在，就像我们现在看到的这样，那么氢元素有可能也在同一地点以某种方式得到补充，即通过我们已知的从恒星向星际空间不断释放能量的唯一方式——辐射能。为了使造物主的工作得以延续下去，这一点以前已经被设想过多次了。在这方面也许有一点点**实验上的**迹象。但它根本就得不到验证，甚至可能连提出的必要都没有。如果在这个问题上詹姆斯·金斯爵士支持一个论点而我倾向于另一个，没有人能说我们不对。也许只有一件事情我们能完全确定，那就是我们俩对此都**一无所知**。不过宇宙射线就可以很好地为在广漠星际空间中存在由氢不断合成常见元素的过程提供实验上的证据。我不是不知道

space the cosmic rays furnish excellent experimental evidence. I am not unaware of the difficulties of finding an altogether satisfactory kinetic picture of how these events take place, but acceptable and demonstrable facts do not, in this twentieth century, seem to be disposed to wait on suitable mechanical pictures. Indeed, has not modern physics thrown the purely mechanistic view of the universe root and branch out of its house?

(**127**, 167-170; 1931)

Robert A. Millikan: California Institute of Technology, Pasadena, California.

要找到一个完全令人满意的动力学解释来说明这些现象的来龙去脉是困难的，但是在20世纪，可接受的明显事实似乎无意于长期等候合适的机械性理论解释的出现。事实上，当代物理学不是已经彻底把纯粹机械的宇宙观赶出门外了吗？

（王锋 翻译；朱永生 审稿）

# Stellar Structure

F. A. Lindemann

## Editor's Note

**The British physicist Frederick Lindemann had earlier suggested that particles within stellar interiors would need kinetic energies comparable to their relativistic rest energy if the annihilation of matter were to be the source of stellar energy. Here he writes to change his view. Equilibrium thermodynamics, he notes, does not control the processes generating energy. Rather, the rate of energy release follows from the concentration of particles, and from the details of the rare circumstances required to initiate key reactions. These details would not necessarily demand high velocities for the particles. Lindemann's new analysis meant that nuclear reactions could indeed fuel stellar processes at temperatures well below 1.1 × 10$^{13}$ K, as his earlier arguments had suggested.**

IT has frequently been stated, by myself amongst others, that it is necessary to assume in the inside of stars a temperature of the order of $mc^2/k$ in order to explain the generation of energy by the annihilation of matter, $m$ being the mass destroyed in each process, $c$ the velocity of light, and $k$ Boltzmann's constant. This letter is written in order to make clear that this assumption is not necessary. It is perfectly true that the equilibrium constant of a process, subject to the laws of thermodynamics, is of the order $e^{-\varepsilon/kT}$, $\varepsilon$ the energy of the process in this case, of course, being equal to $mc^2$. The equilibrium constant does not, however, determine the generation of energy. What one is concerned with in the case of a star is the rate at which energy is produced; in other words, if one presupposes the simplest process of annihilation, the rate at which protons and electrons disappear in the form of radiation. This is analogous to the rate of chemical reaction, not to the equilibrium constant of a reversible reaction.

In most chemical processes the rate of reaction is governed by the number of molecules activated per second, which again depends upon the number of particles the energy of which exceeds a certain value, say, $\varepsilon_1$. This number is proportional to $e^{-\varepsilon_1/kT}$, and one therefore finds, roughly speaking, that the rates of reaction are negligible unless the temperature is such that the mean energy of the molecule is comparable with the energy of excitation. Since this activation energy is usually of the same order as the energy of the reaction, the conclusion is often extended without great inaccuracy to the total energy of the process.

In the case under consideration, the annihilation of protons and electrons, it seems difficult to imagine any form of excitation, and the rate at which it proceeds can therefore scarcely depend upon a function of this type. Presumably, in such collisions as are effective, certain circumstances, which occur but rarely, have to be fulfilled. When these are fulfilled, and they may not be such as require any high velocities, matter is converted into radiation; in

# 恒星的构造

弗雷德里克·林德曼

## 编者按

英国物理学家弗雷德里克·林德曼早先曾经指出：如果恒星的能量来源于物质的湮灭过程，那么恒星内部粒子所需的动能就应该与相对论中的静止能量差不多。不过他在本文中改变了这种看法。他认为平衡态热力学不能决定能量的生成过程。更确切地说，能量释放速率是由粒子的浓度，以及引发关键反应所需的特有环境中的具体要素决定的。这些具体要素并不要求粒子具有很高的速度。林德曼的新观点是，核反应在低于 $1.1\times10^{13}$ K 的温度下的确可以在恒星内部发生，他在早期的理论中也曾暗示过这一点。

我和其他人都常常提起：为了解释由物质湮灭所引发的能量的产生，有必要假设恒星内部的温度达到 $mc^2/k$ 数量级，其中 $m$ 为在每一个过程中损失的质量，$c$ 为光速，$k$ 是玻耳兹曼常数。我写这个快报是为了说明这个假设并非必需。根据热力学定律，一个过程的平衡常数约为 $e^{-\varepsilon/kT}$，在这种情况下 $\varepsilon$ 是该过程的能量，等于 $mc^2$。但是平衡常数不能决定能量的产生过程。人们关心的是一个恒星中的能量生成速率；换言之，对最简单的湮灭过程而言，就是质子和电子以辐射形式消失的速率。这类似于化学反应的速率，而不是可逆反应的平衡常数。

在大多数化学作用中，反应速率是由每秒内被激活的分子数目决定的，而这个数目又与能量超过某一特定值（如 $\varepsilon_1$）的粒子数多少相关。因为该值正比于 $e^{-\varepsilon_1/kT}$，所以我们可以粗略地认为，如果温度没有升高到使分子的平均能量接近于激发能，反应速率就可以忽略不计。因为这种激活能通常和反应能具有相同的数量级，所以我们把激活能看作是反应过程总能量的惯用作法就不会产生太大的偏差。

对于质子和电子的湮灭，很难想象有任何形式的激发存在，因此湮灭速率不太会由这类作用所决定。引发湮灭的有效碰撞可能必须满足某种很少发生但具有决定意义的条件。当这些条件得到满足的时候，也许并不需要太高的速度，物质就能被

the vast majority of cases, a collision has no such result. If this view is correct, the rate of annihilation, and therefore the rate of generation of energy, will depend in the first instance on the number of collisions per second, which of course varies with the density and with something like the square root of the temperature; and in the second instance, upon the special circumstances which render a collision effective, and which may, or may not, depend upon the temperature. In either event the simple exponential expression is not applicable, and the conclusion that matter can only be annihilated and energy produced in stars where interiors are at temperatures of the order $mc^2/k$, that is, $1.1 \times 10^{13}$ degrees, is valid.

It would be true if the matter-radiation equilibrium has been attained and any further production required a change in the equilibrium constant. It is incorrect if the system has not reached equilibrium, for in this case thermodynamical reasoning is insufficient to determine the rate at which equilibrium will be approached.

(**127**, 269; 1931)

F. A. Lindemann: Clarendon Laboratory, Oxford, Feb. 5.

转化成辐射；在绝大多数情况下，一次碰撞不会引发湮灭。如果这个观点是正确的，那么湮灭速率，也就是能量产生的速率，首先将取决于每秒内的碰撞次数，碰撞次数必然随密度和温度的平方根而变化；其次取决于引发有效碰撞的特殊条件，这个条件可能与温度有关，也可能与温度无关。简单的指数型表达式对两者均不适用，但以下结论是有效的：只有当恒星内部温度达到 $mc^2/k$ 数量级，也就是 $1.1\times10^{13}$ 度时，才可能发生通过湮灭而产生能量的过程。

如果物质–辐射已经达到了平衡，要想再发生任何反应都需要平衡常数的改变，这是毋庸置疑的。但是，如果系统没有达到平衡，上述表述就是错误的，因为在平衡未达到之前，热力学条件不足以影响将达到平衡的速率。

（王锋 翻译；蒋世仰 审稿）

# New Aspects of Radioactivity*

C. D. Ellis

## Editor's Note

**With the quantum theory of atomic structure in place, physicists began to ponder the structure of the nucleus. Observations of high-energy electromagnetic radiation called gamma rays emitted by radioactive nuclei seemed to offer information on internal nuclear states. Here Charles D. Ellis discusses several of the most promising techniques for investigating these gamma rays. The most useful involved measuring the energies of secondary electrons ejected from an atom by the photoelectric effect, involving fine wires coated with an atomically thin layer of radioactive material. Although the gamma ray energies could only be measured to an accuracy of one part in 500, Ellis is hopeful that such data will clarify nuclear structure in the near future.**

### $\gamma$-Ray and Nuclear Structure

UNTIL a few years ago, the fundamental problems of physics were those concerned with the structure of the atom. The nucleus was necessarily often referred to, but only in relation to its effect on the behaviour of the electrons in the atom. It was found that for most purposes the net charge, $Ze$, was a sufficient description of the nucleus. Within, however, the last three years, the whole attitude of physicists to this problem has changed; on one hand, our knowledge of those phenomena which depend on the intimate structure of the nucleus has been greatly increased; on the other hand, wave mechanics has proved to be eminently suitable for a theoretical attack on this problem, and has already provided a solution of some of the outstanding problems.

Of the many lines of investigation which have been developed, not the least interesting is that of the characteristic electromagnetic radiation that can be emitted by radioactive nuclei. These radiations are termed the $\gamma$-rays and are in general of considerably shorter wave-length than the X-rays. They bear the same relation to the structure of the nucleus as do the ordinary optical and X-ray spectra to the structure of the electronic system of the atom, but there is this one point of difference. The optical and X-ray spectra can conveniently be studied for a series of elements because the process of excitation is under control, but it is only in a few isolated cases that it has yet been possible to excite a nucleus by external agencies to emit characteristic radiation. Some of the radioactive bodies, however, emit these radiations spontaneously, since the process of disintegration leaves the newly formed nucleus in an excited state and able to emit its characteristic radiation. The nuclear spectra have therefore only been examined in detail for those radioactive bodies which happen to emit them, and it has been impossible as yet to find any general laws

* Substance of two lectures delivered at the Royal Institution on Nov. 4 and 11.

# 放射性研究的新面貌 *

查尔斯·埃利斯

## 编者按

考虑到原子结构在量子理论中的重要地位，物理学家们开始研究原子核的结构。通过观察从放射性原子核发射出的高能电磁辐射——$\gamma$ 射线，人们也许可以得到关于原子核内部状态的信息。查尔斯·埃利斯在文中讨论了几种用以研究这种 $\gamma$ 射线的最有前景的技术。其中最有价值的是测量次级电子能量的技术，在细金属丝表面涂上一层原子那么薄的放射性材料，发生光电效应的原子就会释放出这些次级电子。虽然这种测量 $\gamma$ 射线能量的方法只能达到 1/500 的精确度，但埃利斯对用这种方法得到的数据能在不远的未来破解原子核的结构充满信心。

## $\gamma$ 射线和核结构

直至几年前，物理学的基本问题还是关于原子的结构。通常核是必然要涉及的，但仅涉及其对原子中电子行为的影响。人们发现，在大多数场合净电荷 $Ze$ 足以描述原子核。然而在近三年内，物理学家们对此问题的总体看法已发生了变化，原因如下：一方面，我们对那些依赖于核的本质结构的有关现象的认识已大大增加；另一方面，波动力学已被证明非常适合从理论上攻破这个问题，并且已经为某些重要问题提供了一个解决方式。

在已经开展的许多研究中，比较令人感兴趣的是对放射性核发射的特征电磁辐射的研究。这些辐射被命名为 $\gamma$ 射线，它们通常具有比 X 射线短得多的波长。$\gamma$ 射线和核结构的关系就如同普通光及 X 射线光谱与原子中电子系统结构的关系一样，但是有一点不同：因为激发过程处于控制之下，一系列元素的普通光和 X 射线光谱很方便进行研究；然而，到目前为止，仅在个别情况下有可能用外部因素激发一个原子核来发射特征辐射。不过，某些放射体可以自发发射这些辐射，因为衰变过程使新形成的核处于激发态，并能发射其特征辐射。因此，只有那些碰巧发射辐射的放射体的核谱得到了详细的研究，迄今为止尚不太可能通过观察接连的一系列不同原子核核谱的相似性来找出支配这些核谱分布的任何普遍规律。

---

* 本文中的内容来自作者11月4日和11日发表于英国皇家研究院的两个报告。

governing the arrangement of these spectra by noting the similarities in the spectra from a succession of different nuclei.

The result of this was that, until a few years ago, while there was a great deal of information about the nuclear spectra of several radioactive bodies, it was still impossible to associate this with any definite feature of the structure. Recently the position has changed greatly, and it now seems possible to view in the nuclear level systems which can be deduced from the $\gamma$-ray measurements the characteristic stationary states of $\alpha$-particles or protons in the nucleus, and to associate such level systems directly with the ground states deducible from other evidence.

## Methods of Investigating the $\gamma$-Rays

A simple method that was of great importance in the early days of radioactivity was to investigate the absorption of the radiation emitted by a particular body by placing a radioactive source at some distance from an electroscope and observing how the ionisation decreased when successive sheets of some material such as aluminium or lead were interposed. It was frequently possible to analyse the resulting absorption curve into a series of simple exponential curves, and thus to obtain a general idea of the different components of the complex radiation. Methods such as this could never yield very precise information, and they have now been superseded by more accurate methods.

The crystal method, in the forms used for X-rays, has been applied with considerable success to $\gamma$-rays[1]. In one respect the technique is simpler, since in place of the X-ray tube with all the apparatus necessary to run it, it is only necessary to use a fine tube containing the radioactive material, but in other respects the experiments are far more difficult. Owing to the very short wave-length, of the order of 40 X.U. to 4 X.U., the glancing angles are extremely small, and not only is the adjustment of the apparatus considerably more difficult but it is also impossible to measure the wave-length with much accuracy. Further, in comparison with an X-ray tube, the normal amount of radioactive material constitutes an extremely weak source of radiation. As a result it has not yet been possible to push this method when using photographic registration beyond 16 X.U. Recently Steadman[2] has devised an arrangement, using an electrical counter in place of a photographic plate, which may overcome some of these difficulties.

The method which has given us most of our information is based on the photoelectric effect. The general principle is very simple and is as follows[3]. A tube containing the radioactive body, the $\gamma$-rays of which are under investigation, is placed inside a small tube of some material of high atomic weight, such as platinum. In their passage through the platinum, the $\gamma$-rays eject groups of photoelectrons the energies of which are connected with the frequency of the $\gamma$-rays by the Einstein law. Thus the $\gamma$-ray of frequency $v$ will lead to the ejection of a series of groups of electrons of energies $hv\text{-}K_{Pt}$, $hv\text{-}L_{Pt}$, etc., according to whether the conversion occurs in the $K$, $L$, etc., state of the platinum atoms. This electronic emission can be separated out into a corpuscular spectrum by

直至几年前，尽管有了关于某些放射体核谱的大量信息，但是仍然不可能将其与原子结构的任何确定特性联系在一起。最近，情况发生了很大的变化，现在似乎可以把核中 $\alpha$ 粒子或质子的特征定态看作是由 $\gamma$ 射线测量推导出的核能级系统中的一部分，并将此能级系统直接与由其他证据推断出的基态相联系。

## 研究 $\gamma$ 射线的方法

在放射性研究早期，一个极为重要的简单方法是研究特殊物体所发射的辐射的吸收，具体做法是将放射源置于与验电器有一定距离的地方，然后观测在接连插入诸如铝或铅这些材料的薄片时，电离如何减小。通常可以将生成的吸收曲线分解成一系列简单的指数曲线，进而大致了解复合辐射中不同组分的情况。利用这类方法不可能得到很精确的信息，因而它们现在已被更精确的方法所代替。

在 X 射线研究中所用的晶体方法已经非常成功地应用到了 $\gamma$ 射线的研究中[1]。从一方面来看技术上会变得更为简单，因为不再需要 X 射线管以及运行它所需的所有装置，只需要使用含有放射性材料的细管;但从其他方面来看，实验却要困难得多：由于 $\gamma$ 射线的波长很短，数量级从 40 X.U. 到 4 X.U.，因此掠射角极小，这不仅使装置的调整更加困难，而且不可能很准确地测量波长。此外，与 X 射线管比较起来，正常量的放射性材料只是极弱的辐射源。因此，当使用的波长范围超出 16 X.U. 时，还不能使用这种方法。最近，斯特德曼[2]已设计了一台装置，用电子计数器来代替照相底片，这也许能克服某些困难。

基于光电效应的方法已经给我们带来了大部分信息。一般原理非常简单，叙述如下[3]：将一个装有能放出所要研究的 $\gamma$ 射线的放射体的管，放入由某些高原子量材料，例如铂，制成的小管内。在它们通过铂时，$\gamma$ 射线发射成组的光电子，它们的能量与 $\gamma$ 射线频率的关系符合爱因斯坦定律。因此，频率为 $v$ 的 $\gamma$ 射线将按照转换是否发生在铂原子的 $K$、$L$ 等能量态，发射一系列能量为 $hv\text{-}K_{\mathrm{Pt}}$、$hv\text{-}L_{\mathrm{Pt}}$ 等的光电子群。用一般的半圆磁聚焦方法，可以将这类电子发射分离为微粒谱，通常用照相法记录微粒谱。因为在大多数情况下，只有从 $K$ 能级来的电子群才会有足够的强度产

the usual method of semicircular magnetic focusing. It is usual to register these spectra photographically, and there is not a great deal of difficulty in analysing them and deducing the corresponding $\gamma$-rays, since in most cases it is only the electronic group from the $K$ level which is sufficiently intense to give a detectable effect. The general application of the method is greatly limited by the fact that the photographic impression of the groups of electrons always shows as a broad, rather diffuse band. The reason is that, although the photoelectrons are ejected from the platinum atoms with sharply defined energies, only those from the surface of the tube actually emerge with their full velocity. Those from the lower layers are retarded in their passage out, and cause the diffuse character of the band.

Fortunately, the radioactive atoms themselves provide us with much more favourable opportunities for observing this photoelectric conversion, by what is termed internal conversion. This is by itself an extremely interesting phenomenon, and will be referred to in detail later. For the present purpose it is convenient to describe it as follows. When a radioactive nucleus emits a quantum $h\nu$ of radiation, this does not always escape as such from the atom but may be absorbed by the electronic structure of the atom in its passage out. This internal conversion follows the usual photoelectric laws, and thus a radioactive body which emits $\gamma$-rays will also emit a corpuscular spectrum similar in every respect to that coming from the platinum tube already mentioned, except that the energies are now $h\nu$-$K_{\mathrm{rad}}$, $h\nu$-$L_{\mathrm{rad}}$, ... The result is in principle in no way different from the previous case where the $\gamma$-rays were converted in the platinum, but the importance of this phenomenon for determining the wave-length of the $\gamma$-rays depends on the following facts. If a normal amount of radioactive material is deposited on the surface of a fine wire, the actual number of atoms is so small that the layer is in general less than one atom deep. The electrons liberated by this internal photoelectric effect therefore all escape with their full energy and give extremely sharp lines on a photographic plate, in striking contrast to the broad bands obtained by the normal external photoelectric effect. There is the further advantage that the probability of this internal conversion is so great that measurable lines can be obtained with far shorter exposures than by the other method, and the effects of $\gamma$-rays are detectable which are so weak as to be quite unattackable by the other method.

The $\gamma$-rays of many radioactive bodies have been analysed by this method, and the main features of the characteristic nuclear spectra are known. The accuracy with which the frequencies can be determined is, however, considerably lower than that realised with X-ray spectra. Even in the case of the bodies radium B and radium C, which have been extensively investigated, the relative frequencies are probably not known to much better than one part in five hundred, and the absolute error may be greater. The chief cause for this lies in the difficulty of obtaining a homogeneous magnetic field over a large area.

## Intensities of the $\gamma$-Rays

An important method[4] of investigating the intensities has been developed by Skobeltzyn, based on the Compton effect of the $\gamma$-rays. A narrow pencil of $\gamma$-rays is allowed to pass

生可检测到的光电效应，所以分析这些谱线以及导出相应的 $\gamma$ 射线并没有多大的困难。这个方法的普遍推广大大受限于以下事实：电子群的照相印记经常呈现为一个宽而弥散的条带。因为，尽管光电子是以确定的能量从铂原子上发射出来的，但实际上只有管表面的光电子才能全速发射。较底层的电子在发射穿透出金属表面的路径上受到阻滞减速，从而引起条带的弥散性。

所幸的是，放射性原子自身为我们观测这种被称作内转换的光电转换提供了更多有利的机会。这本身就是一个极有趣的现象，后面将详细提及。就目前的目的而言，可方便地将其描述如下：当放射性核发射一个辐射量子 $h\nu$ 时，这个量子并不总会从原子中逃逸，而是可能在逃逸路上被原子的电子结构所吸收。这种内转换遵从通常的光电定律，因此发射 $\gamma$ 射线的放射体将也会发射微粒谱，各方面都类似于前面提到的来自铂管的微粒谱，只不过现在的能量是 $h\nu\text{-}K_{\text{rad}}$、$h\nu\text{-}L_{\text{rad}}$……这个结果基本上与以前 $\gamma$ 射线在铂中转换的情况并无不同，但这类现象对于测定 $\gamma$ 射线波长的重要性取决于以下事实：将放射性物质的正常量放在细金属丝的表面，那么原子的实际数目会很少，以至于该层通常不到一个原子的深度。因此，这种内部光电效应释放的电子都能以全部能量逃逸，并在照相底片上产生极其清晰的谱线，它与从正常的外部光电效应中得到的宽而弥散的谱线形成鲜明的对比。这种方法还有另一个好处，即这种内转换的几率如此之大，以至于在比其他方法短得多的曝光时间下就可以获得可测量的谱线。在这种情况下 $\gamma$ 射线的效应是可以检测得到的，而用其他方法很难检测到这种非常微弱的效应。

人们已用这种方法对许多放射体的 $\gamma$ 射线作了分析，从而了解了特征核谱的主要特性。然而，用此方法测定 $\gamma$ 射线频率的准确度比用 X 射线谱法测得的要低很多。即使在已经进行过大量研究的镭 B 和镭 C 中，也没有发现相对频率会大大高于 1/500，绝对误差可能更大。其主要原因是，在一个较大的范围内，要获得均匀磁场是有困难的。

## $\gamma$ 射线的强度

斯科别利兹根据 $\gamma$ 射线的康普顿效应已建立了一种研究 $\gamma$ 射线强度的重要方法[4]。让一束 $\gamma$ 射线的窄光锥通过膨胀室，并以常规方式观测由 $\gamma$ 射线的康普顿效

through an expansion chamber and the recoil electrons liberated by the Compton effect of the $\gamma$-rays are observed in the usual manner. In addition, a magnetic field parallel to the axis of the chamber is applied at the moment of expansion, so that the tracks of the recoil electrons are curved by an amount depending on their velocity. By observing both the curvature and the direction of emission of the recoil electrons, it is possible to associate each electron with a $\gamma$-rays of definite frequency. A statistical study is made of the relative number of the recoil electron tracks, and from a knowledge of the general laws of scattering it is possible to deduce the relative intensities of the $\gamma$-rays.

Owing to a variety of experimental causes, the resolution of the method is not very high, and the effect of two neighbouring $\gamma$-rays cannot always be clearly separated. This disadvantage, however, is far outweighed by the definiteness of the results about the intensity distribution throughout the spectrum, and by the fact that the method detects weak $\gamma$-rays equally efficiently as strong $\gamma$-rays. The interpretation involves a knowledge of the laws of scattering, but there is both a reasonable theoretical foundation and internal evidence from these experiments which combine to render the uncertainties due to this cause of little importance at present.

The photoelectric method has been applied to determine the intensities of the $\gamma$-rays by Ellis and Aston[5]. The corpuscular spectra liberated from the radioactive atoms themselves by the internal conversion are clearly of no use in this connexion, since the relative intensities of the groups depend upon the unknown laws of internal conversion. If, however, the corpuscular spectrum ejected from platinum is observed, we are concerned only with the normal photoelectric effect. Supposing that the X-ray absorption results could be extrapolated to the $\gamma$-ray region, it would then be possible to deduce the intensities of the $\gamma$-rays from the intensities of the corresponding electronic groups. It is, however, precisely this point which is doubtful, and the accuracy of this method is at present limited by the accuracy of the empirical formula which it was necessary to assume for the photoelectric method. The method, however, has one extremely important advantage, which is, that if a $\gamma$-ray is sufficiently intense to give a measurable corpuscular group, then the intensity of this group can be determined independently of neighbouring weak $\gamma$-rays. It will be seen that these two methods are really complementary, one supplying the deficiencies of the other. The $\gamma$-rays of radium B and radium C are the only ones that have yet been intensively investigated, but the results seem consistent, and we know not only the general distribution throughout the spectrum but also the individual intensities of all the strong $\gamma$-rays.

The results that have just been mentioned referred to the relative intensities of the $\gamma$-rays, and in the analogous case of X-rays or optical spectra this would be all that could be stated. However, in the case of the radioactive bodies it is possible to define and to deduce the absolute intensities. This depends upon the fact that the process of excitation is due to the disintegration of the atom. When a nucleus disintegrates, the departure of the disintegration particle, $\alpha$ or $\beta$, may leave the nucleus in an excited state, and its subsequent return to its normal state is the cause of the emission of the $\gamma$-rays. The $\gamma$-rays

应释放的反冲电子。此外，在膨胀瞬间，施加一个方向平行于膨胀室轴线的磁场，于是反冲电子轨迹的弯曲度取决于其速度。通过观测反冲电子发射轨迹的曲率和方向，可以将每个电子与确定频率的 $\gamma$ 射线联系起来。通过对反冲电子轨迹的相对数进行统计研究，并根据散射的基本定律，可以推导出 $\gamma$ 射线的相对强度。

由于各种实验原因，这种方法的分辨率不是很高，并且也不是总能将两个相邻 $\gamma$ 射线的效应清楚地分开。然而，以下两个优点的价值在很大程度上掩盖了这个缺点：其一是能得到整个谱线结果中 $\gamma$ 射线强度的确定分布，其二是这种方法检测弱 $\gamma$ 射线与检测强 $\gamma$ 射线一样有效。数据的解释需要用到散射定律的知识，但是有合理的理论基础和来自这些实验本身的证据，这两者的结合使得目前散射知识带来的不确定性变得无关紧要了。

埃利斯和阿斯顿[5]已将光电方法应用于测定 $\gamma$ 射线的强度。放射性原子本身通过内转换释放的微粒谱显然不能用于与此相关联的问题，因为成组光电子的相对强度与尚不为人所知的内转换定律有关。然而，如果观测从铂中发射的微粒谱，我们可以只关心正常的光电效应。假定 X 射线的吸收结果可以外推到 $\gamma$ 射线区，那么从相应的电子群强度推导 $\gamma$ 射线的强度就将成为可能。然而，不可靠的恰恰是这一点，目前这种方法的准确度受限于在光电方法中必须假设的经验公式的准确度。然而，这种方法具有一个极其重要的优点，即如果 $\gamma$ 射线的强度强到足以获得可测的微粒电子群，那么这组电子强度的测定可与邻近的弱 $\gamma$ 射线无关。由此可见，这两种方法实际上是互补的，一种方法弥补了另一种方法的缺陷。虽然镭 B 和镭 C 的 $\gamma$ 射线是迄今为止唯一得到深入研究的 $\gamma$ 射线，但结果似乎是一致的，我们不仅知道了 $\gamma$ 射线整个光谱的大致分布，而且知道了所有强 $\gamma$ 射线各自的强度。

上面所提到的结果指的是 $\gamma$ 射线的相对强度。如果是在与 X 射线或光学光谱类似的情况下，相对强度将是所能说明的全部情况。不过，在放射体的情况下，要确定和推导出绝对强度是可能的。这是因为激发过程是由于原子的衰变造成的。当原子核衰变时，会释放出衰变粒子（$\alpha$ 粒子或者 $\beta$ 粒子），从而有可能使核处于激发态，随后它又回到正常态，并发射 $\gamma$ 射线。因此，$\gamma$ 射线仅在这类衰变之后发射，可以

are, therefore, emitted only after this disintegration, and it is possible to define the absolute intensity of a $\gamma$-ray as the average number of quanta emitted per disintegration. It follows that the absolute intensity of any $\gamma$-ray cannot be greater than unity. The simplest way of deducing these absolute intensities is to make use of the measurements of the total amount of energy emitted in the form of $\gamma$-rays. Knowing both the frequencies and the relative intensities of the $\gamma$-rays, it is easy to calculate the average number of quanta of each frequency emitted per disintegration. This further step has already been carried out for the $\gamma$-rays of radium B and radium C.

If we now review the information that we possess about the $\gamma$-rays of radium B and C and anticipate that which we shall no doubt in time possess about the rays of other bodies, it will be seen that on the whole it compares very favourably with that available about X-ray spectra. The accuracy of the wave-length determinations is certainly much lower, but we have this important information about the absolute intensities. For example, a prominent $\gamma$-ray of radium C has a wave-length of 20.2 X.U., which may be in error by one part in five hundred to even one part in three hundred, but on the other hand, we can say that a quantum of this radiation is emitted by the nucleus on the average twice in every three disintegrations.

## Applications to the Structure of the Nucleus

The preceding account will have shown the extent to which the spectroscopy of the $\gamma$-rays has advanced. Its application to the problem of nuclear structure is only at the beginning, but it is already possible to indicate the possible lines of advance.

It has been realised for some time that there were many examples of combination differences between the frequencies of the $\gamma$-rays from any one body, and that this indicated, what was otherwise probable, that the $\gamma$-rays could be associated with a nuclear level system. Little progress, however, was made with this idea for several years, due to the realisation of the difficulty of associating such a level system with any specific part of the nucleus. In the nucleus there are $\alpha$-particles, protons, and electrons, and in general any of these particles might be the emitters of the $\gamma$-rays. This question is still open, but there is now sufficient evidence to make it reasonable to try the hypothesis that the $\gamma$-rays are emitted by transitions of $\alpha$-particles between stationary states in the nucleus.

The theories of Gamow and of Gurney and Condon[6] have shown that we may regard the process of emissions of an $\alpha$-particle as due to the gradual leak of the wave function through a potential barrier. An extremely important result of this view is that the energy of the $\alpha$-particle outside the atom, which can of course be measured, is the same as the energy of the $\alpha$-particle in the stationary state in the nucleus which it occupied before the disintegration. For example, the $\alpha$-particle from radium C is found to be emitted with an energy of 7.68 million volts. We therefore deduce that in the radium C nucleus there is an $\alpha$-particle level with a positive energy of this amount. Such a level gives a natural basis on which to build the level system deducible from the $\gamma$-rays. We imagine that as a result of

将 $\gamma$ 射线的绝对强度定义为每次衰变发射的平均量子数。由此可以断定，任何 $\gamma$ 射线的绝对强度都不能大于 1 个单位。导出这些绝对强度的最简单的方法是利用对以 $\gamma$ 射线形式发射的总能量的测量结果。知道了 $\gamma$ 射线的频率和相对强度，就很容易计算出每次衰变时发射的对应于每个频率的平均量子数。人们已经对镭 B 和镭 C 的 $\gamma$ 射线应用了这种深层次的研究方法。

如果现在回顾一下我们所拥有的关于镭 B 和镭 C 的 $\gamma$ 射线的信息，并预期我们无疑将及时获得其他放射体 $\gamma$ 射线的信息，就会发现，与从 X 射线光谱得到的可用信息相比，$\gamma$ 射线的信息在总体上是非常令人满意的。测定波长的准确度确实会降低很多，但我们有了绝对强度的重要信息。例如，镭 C 的一种主要 $\gamma$ 射线的波长为 20.2 X.U.，其误差可能为 1/500，甚至可以达到 1/300，但另一方面，我们也可以说，原子核在每三次衰变中平均辐射两次这样的量子。

## 在核结构研究中的应用

前面的叙述显示出 $\gamma$ 射线光谱学已经发展到了怎样的程度。虽然将其应用于解决核结构问题仅仅是刚刚起步，但我们已经可以看到可能的发展方向。

之前人们就已经认识到，有许多例子显示来自任何一个放射体的 $\gamma$ 射线在频率上存在多组差异，这表明 $\gamma$ 射线可能与核能级系统相关，尽管别的解释也有可能。然而，多年以来，由于很难将这样一个核能级系统与核的任何特定部分联系起来，因而人们在这一构想上没有取得什么进展。在核中，存在 $\alpha$ 粒子、质子和电子，一般来说这些粒子中的任何一个都有可能发射 $\gamma$ 射线，这个问题仍然是一个尚未解决的问题。但是现在有足够的证据说明这样去假设是合理的，即认为 $\gamma$ 射线是因核内 $\alpha$ 粒子在定态之间的跃迁而发射的。

伽莫夫以及格尼和康登的理论[6]指出，我们可以认为 $\alpha$ 粒子的发射过程是由于波函数通过势垒的逐渐泄漏。由这个观点可以得到一个极为重要的结果，即原子外面 $\alpha$ 粒子的能量（当然可以测量）与核衰变前在核中处于定态的 $\alpha$ 粒子的能量相等。例如，我们发现镭 C 发射的 $\alpha$ 粒子能量是 7.68 百万电子伏特。于是可以推出，在镭 C 的核内，存在一个具有 7.68 百万电子伏特正能量的 $\alpha$ 粒子能级。这一能级给出了建立根据 $\gamma$ 射线推导的能级系统的自然基础。我们可以设想，某些内核排列激发 $\alpha$ 粒子，使其到达某一个更高的激发态，然后通过发射频率相当于能量差的 $\gamma$ 射线又

some internal nuclear arrangement an $\alpha$-particle is excited to one of certain higher states, and that from these states it arrives at the ground state by emitting $\gamma$-rays of frequencies corresponding to the energy differences. It now follows, however, that if an $\alpha$-particle can leak out through the potential barrier from the ground level, it can do so still more easily from the excited levels. We should therefore expect to find a certain number of high-speed $\alpha$-particles corresponding to these modes of disintegration.

The existence of such long-range $\alpha$-particles has of course been known for a long time, and in fact many tentative suggestions have been put forward associating the energy differences of the groups of $\alpha$-particles with the frequencies of the $\gamma$-rays. The present-day point of view, however, goes much further than this, since it predicts definite relations between the intensities of the $\gamma$-rays and the number of long-range particles. That such a relation must exist can be easily seen in the following way. Suppose that on the average out of every thousand disintegrations there are $n$ cases where an $\alpha$-particle is excited to a certain state, the rate of leak through the potential barrier is given to a fair approximation by theory, and the probability of the nuclear transition can at least be estimated. We are therefore able in terms involving only the unknown quantity $n$ to write down the number of long-range $\alpha$-particles we should expect and the number of quanta of radiation. Both these quantities can also be measured, perhaps not with a very high accuracy, but yet sufficient to see whether there is an agreement with theory or not.

This is really a stringent test for the theory, because although the theories of the probabilities of nuclear transitions are necessarily tentative, any adjustment which proved necessary for one $\gamma$-ray must also apply to all the others. By arguments of this type Fowler[7] has been led to associate one excited $\alpha$-particle level of the radium C nucleus with the corresponding nuclear transition formed from the $\beta$-ray spectrum. It seems likely that this line of investigation will lead to definite and valuable results. It is of course quite probable that several nuclear transitions will not be able to be associated with long-range $\alpha$-particles, but it would then be possible to draw the important conclusion that these transitions were due to protons or $\alpha$-particles of small positive or of negative energy.

## Internal Conversion

Reference was made above to internal conversion and it was pointed out that groups of electrons are ejected from the *K*, *L*, *M* states of radioactive atoms with just those energies that they would have if radiation were emitted from the nucleus but was absorbed photoelectrically before it escaped. It has been frequently pointed out that there was no need and, in fact, no justification to assume that in this case the radiation was ever actually emitted at all[8]. All that could be truly inferred from the experimental results was that an excited nucleus could either emit its excess energy as radiation or had some means of transferring this energy to the electronic structure of the atom.

On the old quantum mechanics, it was difficult to imagine any method other than that of radiation transfer, but the wave mechanics suggests that there is a far more intimate

从激发态回到基态。然而，如果一个 $\alpha$ 粒子在从基态能级穿过势垒时会泄漏，那么它就更容易从激发态能级泄漏。因此我可以预期将发现有一定数量的高速 $\alpha$ 粒子与这些衰变模式相对应。

诚然，很久以前我们就知道这类长程 $\alpha$ 粒子是存在的，事实上我们已提出过很多将 $\alpha$ 粒子群的能量差与 $\gamma$ 射线的频率联系起来的初步建议。然而，目前的观点比这已更进了一步，因为它预测了 $\gamma$ 射线强度与长程 $\alpha$ 粒子数量之间的确定关系。通过以下方式很容易看出这种确定关系是必然存在的：假定平均每千次衰变有 $n$ 个 $\alpha$ 粒子被激发到某个激发态上，根据理论可以非常好地近似得到穿出势垒的泄漏率，因而至少可以估计出核跃迁的几率。因此我们能够用只包含未知数 $n$ 的项写出我们所预期的长程 $\alpha$ 粒子的数量及 $\gamma$ 辐射的量子数。这两个量都可以通过测量得到，也许准确度不是很高，但已足以了解它与理论是否一致。

这实际上是对理论的严格检验，因为虽然核跃迁几率理论目前还不够完备，但是，被一种 $\gamma$ 射线证明是必要的调整也应适用于所有其他的 $\gamma$ 射线。这种观点引导福勒[7]将镭 C 核 $\alpha$ 粒子的一个激发态能级与 $\beta$ 射线谱形成的相应核跃迁联系起来。看起来这类研究路线有可能会导致确定和有价值的结果。当然完全有可能，一些核跃迁与长程 $\alpha$ 粒子不相联系，但由此可能得出如下重要结论：这些核跃迁是由具有微正能量或负能量的质子或 $\alpha$ 粒子产生的。

## 内转换

上面已经提到了内转换，并已指出从放射性原子的 $K$，$L$，$M$ 态发射出来的电子群所具有的能量刚好等于如果这些从核中发出的辐射量子在逃逸前被光电吸收的能量。已屡次指出，假定在内转换情况下 $\gamma$ 光子会完全发射出来是没有必要的，也是不正确的[8]。根据实验结果能够真正推出来的是，一个激发核或者会以辐射形式发射其过剩的能量，或者会以一些方式将这类能量传递给原子的电子结构。

按照旧的量子论，很难想象除了辐射转换之外还有其他方法，但波动力学提出，在核粒子与电子结构之间存在着更为密切的联系。核内粒子的波函数将在一定程度

connexion between the nuclear particles and the electronic structure. The wave functions of the particles in the nucleus will extend out to a certain extent into the electronic region of the atom, and conversely the electronic wave functions will exist throughout the nucleus. As a model, we may think that every electron in the atom occasionally passes right through the nucleus, and that a nuclear particle might sometimes for a very short time be found to be actually outside the nucleus.

We have thus no difficulty in seeing, in a general way, how the nuclear energy might be transferred to the electronic system by a direct collision process. Which process, radiation or collision, is predominant can only be settled by experiment, and the answer given by experiment in this case is fortunately unambiguous. The measurements of Ellis and Aston[5] of the extent of this internal conversion and of the way in which it depends on the frequency of the associated radiation show clearly that the behaviour is incompatible with the radiation hypothesis, and we are thus led to conclude that the collision process is the most important. It will be seen that this process is really a collision of the second kind, between an electron and an excited nucleus.

The peculiar interest of this phenomenon lies in the fact that it represents an easily measurable example of direct interaction between the nucleus and the electronic system. There are several other cases where the interaction between the nucleus and the electronic system must be taken into account, but only in order to give the finer details. The importance of the phenomenon of internal conversion is that the entire phenomenon, even to its first approximation, depends upon interaction, and that no approach can be made to it with a simple point nucleus.

However, quite apart from the intrinsic interest of this interaction, the phenomenon of internal conversion seems likely to provide valuable information about the stationary states in the nucleus. The quantity that can actually be measured, the internal conversion coefficient, is the ratio of the probabilities of occurrence of this collision of the second kind and of the nuclear radiation transition. The latter is determined mainly by the energy difference of the initial and final states, whilst the absolute energies are involved in the former. In a general way it can be seen that the internal conversion should lead to a classification of the levels responsible for the $\gamma$-rays, or, in other words, should enable the $\gamma$-rays to be associated with a definite part of the nucleus.

While but little has yet been accomplished along these various lines of investigation of the nuclear levels, it is certainly true that the most difficult step has already been made. The problem can now be clearly envisaged, and definite lines of work proposed which seem likely to lead to results. The way appears open to an experimental investigation of certain radioactive nuclei, and to an interpretation of the experimental results in terms of nuclear phenomena.

(**127**, 275-278; 1931)

上延伸到原子的电子区域，反过来，电子的波函数也将存在于整个核内。作为模型，我们可以认为，原子中的每一个电子都偶尔会穿过核，核粒子实际上有时也可能在核外出现很短的时间。

因此我们不难看到，在一般情况下，核能量可通过直接碰撞过程转移到电子系统。辐射还是碰撞，这两种过程哪一个更占优势只能通过实验来确定。幸运的是，在这种情况下由实验给出的回答是明确的。埃利斯和阿斯顿[5]对内转换的程度以及它对相关辐射频率的依赖方式进行了测量，结果明确显示出与辐射假说的不相容。因此，我们得出的结论是碰撞过程才是最重要的。我们将会看到这个过程实际上是电子与激发核的第二类碰撞。

这种现象之所以具有特殊意义是因为它代表了核与电子系统之间发生直接相互作用的一个易于测量的例子。还有其他几种情况必须考虑核与电子系统之间的相互作用，但只是为了给出更精细的细节。内转换现象的重要性是整个现象（即使在一级近似下）依赖于核与电子的相互作用，哪种方法都不可能仅仅把原子核看成点粒子。

然而，除了对这类相互作用本身的意义之外，内转换现象似乎还能提供关于核内定态的重要信息。实际上能被测量的量是内转换系数，它是第二类碰撞与核辐射跃迁出现几率的比值。后者主要由初态和终态的能量差决定，而前者涉及绝对能量。就通常意义而论，内转换将导致引起 $\gamma$ 射线发射的能级分类，换言之，它能将 $\gamma$ 射线与核的某个确定部分联系起来。

尽管人们以各种方式对核能级的研究尚未取得明显的进展，不过，可以肯定的是我们已迈出了最困难的一步。现在可以清晰地设想问题，并且可以提出有可能得到结果的明确工作路线。这种方式为用实验研究某些放射性核以及根据核现象解释实验结果提供了可能。

（沈乃澂 翻译；尚仁成 审稿）

References:

1 Rutherford and Andrade, *Phil. Mag.*, **27**, 854; **28**, 262 (1924). Thibaud, Thèse, Paris (1925). Frilly, Thèse, Paris (1928). Meitner, *Zeit. f. Physik*, **52**, 645 (1928).

2 Steadman, *Phys. Rev.*, **36**, 460 (1930).

3 Ellis, *Proc. Roy. Soc.*, A, **101**, 1 (1922). Thibaud, Thèse, Paris (1925).

4 Skobeltzyn, *Zeit. f. Physik.*, **43**, 354 (1927): **58**, 595 (1929).

5 Ellis and Aston, *Proc. Roy. Soc.*, A, **129**, 180 (1930).

6 Gamow, *Zeit. f. Physik*, **51**, 204 (1928). Gurney and Condon, *Nature*, **122**, 439 (1928).

7 Fowler, *Proc. Roy. Soc.*, A, **129**, 1 (1930).

8 Smekal, *Zeit. f. Physik.*, **10**, 275 (1922). *Ann. d. Phys.*, **81**, 399 (1926). Rosseland, *Zeit. f. Physik*, **14**, 173 (1923).

# Protein Structure and Denaturation

C. Rimington

## Editor's Note

**It was known since the nineteenth century that heat, acidity or chemical reagents could make soluble proteins coagulate, a phenomenon called denaturation. But no one knew what caused this change. Here industrial chemist Claude Rimington ponders the question in the light of two recent findings: the changes in structure of keratin, the main component of wool, when stretched, and the observation that the denaturing of haemoglobin can be reversed. Previously, denaturation was thought to be one-way, as it is for boiled egg white (albumin). Rimington offers the first intimations that denaturation is a crucial aspect of the issue of protein folding, the process in which a peptide chain reversibly collapses into its enzymatically active form with a specific three-dimensional shape.**

ASTBURY and Woods' fundamental work upon the micellar structure of the protein of wool fibres,[1] and the hypothesis they put forward as an explanation of the changes observed in the X-ray pattern when such fibres are stretched, would seem to be full of significance for protein chemistry in general.

Within the last ten years, different lines of evidence have been converging upon the view that some regularity, as regards pattern and molecular size, underlies the disordered confusion of data we possess relating to the proteins of the animal and vegetable kingdoms. The two most striking demonstrations in recent years of such uniformity are afforded by Svedberg's brilliant application of the ultracentrifuge to determine the particle mass of soluble proteins,[2] classes of "molecular weight" 1, 2, 3, and 6 times the common factor 34,500 being distinguished, and Gorter and Grendel's demonstration[3] that under appropriate conditions soluble proteins exhibit the phenomenon of surface spreading on liquids, and that all occupy the same surface area irrespective of particle mass (1, 2, 3, or 6 times 34,500). Using Svedberg's common factor 34,500 for the basis of their calculations, the Dutch workers obtain a value for the radius of the unit particle (22.5 A.) identical with that determined by Svedberg experimentally.

The most significant feature of Gorter and Grendel's work, however, is that their results imply a loosening, brought about by the surface forces, of the cohesive attraction holding the units of the aggregated proteins together. Astbury and Woods' investigations reveal a somewhat similar, although internal, deformation of the keratin structure of the wool fibre, brought about by purely physical means. Our conceptions of the chemical reactivity of protein structures clearly need revision in an attitude of greater attention to modern valence conceptions.

# 蛋白质的结构与变性

克劳德·里明顿

编者按

从19世纪开始人们就已经认识到热、酸或某些化学试剂可以导致可溶性蛋白质凝固，这种现象被称为蛋白质的变性。但没有人知道为什么会发生这种变化。工业化学家克劳德·里明顿根据最近的两个发现思索这个问题的答案：一个发现是羊毛的主要成分——角蛋白在被拉伸时会发生结构变化；另一个发现是血红蛋白的变性可以逆转。以前人们认为变性过程是单向的，就像煮熟的蛋白（白蛋白）无法再回到煮之前的状态。里明顿第一个指出变性是蛋白质折叠问题的重要方面，在蛋白质折叠过程中，肽链可逆地折叠成具有特定三维形状并可行使酶功能的活性形式。

在我看来，阿斯特伯里和伍兹在羊毛纤维蛋白胶束结构上的基础性工作[1]，以及他们为解释在羊毛纤维被拉伸时从X射线图谱中观察到的结构变化而提出的假说，对于蛋白质化学的总体发展具有非常重大的意义。

在过去的10年里，来自各方面的证据都表明这样一个观点：在我们研究动植物蛋白时得到的扑朔迷离的数据背后，显示出衍射图谱与蛋白质分子大小之间存在着某种规律性的联系。近年来，有两个最显著的成果证明了这种一致性。一个是斯韦德贝里用超速离心机成功地测定了可溶性蛋白粒子的质量[2]，在他的研究中“分子量”是按照公因子34,500的1、2、3、6倍进行分级的；另一个是戈特和格伦德尔发现[3]可溶性蛋白在适宜条件下可在液面铺展的现象，而且它们占据相同的表面积，不受粒子质量（34,500的1、2、3或6倍）大小的影响。荷兰的研究人员以斯韦德贝里的公因子34,500为基础计算出了单位粒子的半径值（22.5 Å），这一结果与斯韦德贝里用实验测得的结果相同。

然而，在戈特和格伦德尔的研究成果中最重要的意义是：他们的结论暗示促使蛋白颗粒单元聚集在一起的内聚力会因表面力的作用而减弱。阿斯特伯里和伍兹在应用纯物理学方法研究羊毛纤维角蛋白结构时也发现了一些发生在蛋白质内部的类似结构变化。显然，随着人们对现代价态理论关注度的提高，我们需要对蛋白质结构的化学反应性的概念进行修正。

One more point cannot be too clearly emphasised which is common to the essential findings of Svedberg, Astbury and Woods, and Gorter and Grendel: the changes observed by these workers are strictly *reversible*.

In conclusion, I should like to touch upon the problem of protein denaturation, and to inquire whether it is not in the direction of such work as that of Astbury and Woods that we have to look for a solution of this problem? Denaturation of proteins, which can be brought about by mechanical as well as by chemical forces, is characterised by a loss of solubility at the isoelectric point. It was always thought to be an irreversible change, but Anson and Mirsky[4] have recently demonstrated its reversible nature in the case of globin. Some internal alteration takes place during denaturation, as evidenced by the change in reactivity of the sulphur groups,[5] but neither acid or base binding capacity[6] nor osmotic pressure[7] are affected—that is to say, there is no scission. Clearly, loss of isoelectric solubility must be due to change in some internal tautomeric configuration.

It is difficult to avoid the suggestion that a change, similar to that postulated by Astbury and Woods in explanation of the behaviour of the stretched and unstretched wool fibre, may in reality be the essential happening attending denaturation. The –CO–NH– group possesses strong polarity, but, by the rearrangement of peptide linkages into what are virtually closed ring systems, affinity for water would be enormously diminished. At present there exists no satisfactory hypothesis offering an explanation of denaturation. Such a scheme as the above may reasonably be entertained until further evidence can be brought forward of a chemical or physico-chemical nature which will throw more light upon the problem. Considering the remarkable and wholly unexpected results, mentioned above, of Gorter and Grendel, working upon protein surface films, it would seem that quantitative data bearing upon denaturation is likely to be obtained most readily by studies having a similar approach. The forces at play within the liquid and at the interface possess no mean magnitude. They are, however, susceptible of more precise control and exact manipulation than those involved in, let us say, heat coagulation or the application of vigorous chemical reagents. From a study of the surface phenomena exhibited by proteins under varying conditions, coupled possibly with an application of the X-ray method to films of such proteins as can be made to give readily detectable diffraction photographs,[8] a solution not only of the denaturation process but also of the structure of native proteins may, in the future, be obtained.

(**127**, 440-441; 1931)

C. Rimington: Biochemical Department, Wool Industries Research Association, Leeds, Feb. 13.

References:

1 Astbury and Woods, *Nature*, **126**, 913 (1930).

2 Svedberg, *Koll. Zeit.*, **51**, 10 (1930).

3 Gorter and Grendel, *Proc. Acad. Sci. Amsterdam*, **32**, 770 (1929).

还有一个无论如何强调都不为过的观点，也是斯韦德贝里、阿斯特伯里和伍兹以及戈特和格伦德尔这三个研究小组各自重要发现的共同点：他们观察到的蛋白质结构的变化，严格说来都是**可逆**的。

最后，我想谈一谈蛋白质变性这个问题，探讨一下此问题是否与阿斯特伯里和伍兹的研究方向不一致，因而我们必须为解决这个问题另找一个答案？机械力或化学力可能会引起蛋白质变性，变性的标志是蛋白质在等电点处丧失水溶性。人们以前一直认为蛋白质变性是不可逆的，但安森和米尔斯基[4]最近在研究球蛋白时发现蛋白质的变性是可逆的。在变性过程中蛋白质分子内部会发生一些改变，例如含硫基团反应活性的变化[5]，但其酸碱结合能力[6]和渗透压[7]都不会改变，也就是说，蛋白质分子中的肽键没有发生断裂。很明显，蛋白质在等电点处水溶性的丧失必定与其内部互变异构体构型的改变有关。

一个不容忽视的观点是，变化，类似于阿斯特伯里和伍兹在解释拉伸状态和非拉伸状态的羊毛纤维时所提到的变化，实际上可能是伴随蛋白质变性的基本事件。蛋白质的肽键，即 –CO–NH– 基团具有很强的极性，但是在经过肽链的重排，形成几乎封闭的环状结构后，其亲水性会大大降低。目前还没有一个能够圆满解释变性现象的假说。我们有理由暂且接受上述说法，直到能提供更多证据揭示蛋白质的化学或物理化学特性，才能更好地阐明这一问题。前面提到戈特和格伦德尔在研究蛋白表面膜时得出的一些值得关注并且完全出乎意料的结果，表明通过类似的研究方法将可能很容易地获得有关蛋白质变性的定量数据。尽管在液体内部和界面处的蛋白质间的相互作用力是不弱的。然而，这种相互作用力比热凝聚力或强化学试剂的作用力更易被严格控制和准确操纵。通过研究一些蛋白质在不同条件下的表面特性，结合应用 X 射线法获得这些蛋白膜的衍射图像[8]，我们就可能在不久的将来揭示出蛋白质的变性过程，或许还能破解天然蛋白的结构。

（韩玲俐 翻译；周筠梅 审稿）

4 Anson and Mirsky, *J. Gen., Physiol.*, **13**, 469 (1930).
5 Harris, *Proc. Roy. Soc.*, B, **94**, 426 (1923).
6 Booth, *Biochem. J.*, **24**, 158 (1930).
7 Huang and Wu, *Chinese J. Physiol.*, **4**, 221 (1930).
8 Ott, *Kolloidchem. Beih.*, **23** , 108 (1926).

# The End of the World: from the Standpoint of Mathematical Physics*

A. S. Eddington

## Editor's Note

**This supplement contains a somewhat light-hearted address on "the end of the world" that Arthur Eddington delivered at the Mathematical Association. One must first ask "which end?", he says. Space itself may have no end: current cosmology suggested a universe shaped like the surface of a sphere, finite but without edges. As for time, the second law of thermodynamics suggests that the entire universe will eventually reach a state of thermodynamic equilibrium marked by complete disorganisation. However, if time is infinite then every conceivable fluctuation in the universe's particles will happen, temporarily disturbing this equilibrium. Eddington ends by predicting how the world will really end: as a ball of radiation growing ever larger, roughly doubling its size every 1,500 million years.**

THE world—or space-time—is a four-dimensional continuum, and consequently offers a choice of a great many directions in which we might start off to look for an end; and it is by no means easy to describe "from the standpoint of mathematical physics" the direction in which I intend to go. I have therefore to examine at some length the preliminary question, Which end?

### Spherical Space

We no longer look for an end to the world in its space dimensions. We have reason to believe that so far as its space dimensions are concerned the world is of spherical type. If we proceed in any direction in space we do not come to an end of space, nor do we continue on to infinity; but, after travelling a certain distance (not inconceivably great), we find ourselves back at our starting-point, having "gone round the world". A continuum with this property is said to be finite but unbounded. The surface of a sphere is an example of a finite but unbounded two-dimensional continuum; our actual three-dimensional space is believed to have the same kind of connectivity, but naturally the extra dimension makes it more difficult to picture. If we attempt to picture spherical space, we have to keep in mind that it is the *surface* of the sphere that is the analogue of our three-dimensional space; the inside and the outside of the sphere are fictitious elements in the picture which have no analogue in the actual world.

We have recently learnt, mainly through the work of Prof. Lemaître, that this spherical space is expanding rather rapidly. In fact, if we wish to travel round the world and get

* Presidential address to the Mathematical Association, delivered on Jan. 5.

# 以数学物理的视角看宇宙的终点*

阿瑟·爱丁顿

## 编者按

本文的内容是阿瑟·爱丁顿在数学协会上发表的一篇关于“宇宙的终点”的非正式讲话。他说，人们肯定首先要问“宇宙的终点是时间方向上的终点还是空间方向上的终点？”空间本身也许不存在终点：现代宇宙学认为宇宙类似于一个球体的表面，有限但无界。至于时间，热力学第二定律预言整个宇宙最终将达到一个以完全无序为标志的热平衡状态。然而，如果时间是无限的，那么宇宙粒子的每一次可能的涨落都会短暂地打破这种平衡。爱丁顿在结束语中预言了宇宙终结的实际方式：宇宙作为一个充满辐射的球不断地变大，每 15 亿年其大小约膨胀一倍。

宇宙或者说时空是一个四维连续区，因此我们可以从很多不同的角度来讨论它的终点。毫无疑问“以数学物理的视角”来描述以下我试图展开讨论的内容绝非易事。所以我必须相当仔细地考虑这个最初的问题：宇宙的终点是时间方向上的终点还是空间方向上的终点？

### 球面空间

我们不再寻找宇宙在空间方向上的终点。因为我们有理由相信，宇宙的空间部分具有球面结构。如果朝着空间中的任何一个方向一直走下去，我们不会到达空间的终点，也不会走到无穷远处；但是，当我们走了一段距离（并不是无法想象的远）以后，我们发现自己又回到了原来的出发点，相当于“绕了宇宙一圈”。我们把具有这种特性的连续区说成是有限但无界。球的表面即为有限无界二维连续区的一个例子；我们生活的三维空间被认为具有同样的连通性，但是由于比二维空间多出了一个空间维度，这使得我们很难用图形把这样的三维连续体表示出来。如果我们试图画出一个三维球面空间的话，我们必须要记住，只是这个三维球**面**对应于我们的三维空间；而这个球面的里面和外面都是我们虚构出来的，因而并不与现实的宇宙相对应。

最近，主要通过勒迈特教授的工作，我们已经获知，我们生活的这个三维球面空间正在快速地膨胀着。事实上，如果我们想环绕宇宙空间一周而回到出发点的话，

---

* 这篇文章来自爱丁顿于1月5日在数学协会上发表的讲话。

back to our starting-point, we shall have to move faster than light; because, whilst we are loitering on the way, the track ahead of us is lengthening. It is like trying to run a race in which the finishing-tape is moving ahead faster than the runners. We can picture the stars and galaxies as embedded in the surface of a rubber balloon which is being steadily inflated; so that, apart from their individual motions and the effects of their ordinary gravitational attraction on one another, celestial objects are becoming farther and farther apart simply by the inflation. It is probable that the spiral nebulae are so distant that they are very little affected by mutual gravitation and exhibit the inflation effect in its pure form. It has been known for some years that they are scattering apart rather rapidly, and we accept their measured rate of recession as a determination of the rate of expansion of the world.

From the astronomical data it appears that the original radius of space was 1,200 million light years. Remembering that distances of celestial objects up to several million light years have actually been measured, that does not seem overwhelmingly great. At that radius the mutual attraction of the matter in the world was just sufficient to hold it together and check the tendency to expand. But this equilibrium was unstable. An expansion began, slow at first; but the more widely the matter was scattered the less able was the mutual gravitation to check the expansion. We do not know the radius of space today, but I should estimate that it is not less than ten times the original radius.

At present our numerical results depend on astronomical observations of the speed of scattering apart of the spiral nebulae. But I believe that theory is well on the way to obtaining the same results independently of astronomical observation. Out of the recession of the spiral nebulae we can determine not only the original radius of the universe but also the total mass of the universe, and hence the total number of protons in the world. I find this number to be either $7\times10^{78}$ or $14\times10^{78}$.* I believe that this number is very closely connected with the ratio of the electrostatic and the gravitational units of force, and, apart from a numerical coefficient, is equal to the square of the ratio. If $F$ is the ratio of the electrical attraction between a proton and electron to their gravitational attraction, we find $F^2 = 5.3\times10^{78}$. There are theoretical reasons for believing that the total number of particles in the world is $\alpha F^2$, where $\alpha$ is a simple geometrical factor (perhaps involving $\pi$). It ought to be possible before long to find a theoretical value of $\alpha$, and so make a complete connexion between the observed rate of expansion of the universe and the ratio of electrical and gravitational forces.

## Signposts for Time

I must not dally over space any longer but must turn to time. The world is closed in its space dimensions but is open in both directions in its time dimension. Proceeding from "here" in any direction in space we ultimately come back to "here"; but proceeding from

* This ambiguity is inseparable from the operation of counting the number of particles in finite but unbounded space. It is impossible to tell whether the protons have been counted once or twice over.

我们的行进速度必须要比光速还快；这是因为我们在路上行进的同时，我们前面的路途也在变长。就好像参加了一场终点线向前移动得比运动员跑步速度还快的赛跑一样。想象一下恒星和星系都镶嵌在一个橡胶气球的表面，而这个气球正在持续不断地膨胀着；这样，如果不考虑恒星和星系各自的运动以及它们之间的万有引力，这些天体之间的距离将由于宇宙空间的膨胀而变得越来越大。由于旋涡星云彼此相距很远，以至于它们几乎不会受到相互作用的引力影响，因而它们的形状很可能就体现了宇宙膨胀的效果。几年前我们就已经知道它们正在迅速地相互分散远离，我们可以通过测量它们之间的退行速度来推算宇宙的膨胀速度。

天文学数据表明宇宙空间最初的半径大约为 12 亿光年。要知道，远至几百万光年的天体实际上已经被我们观测到了，所以 12 亿光年也并非是不可想象的距离。在那种尺度下，宇宙中物质间相互作用的引力刚好可以把物质聚合在一起与宇宙空间的膨胀趋势相平衡。但是这种平衡并不稳定。于是宇宙开始膨胀，最初膨胀得比较慢；但随着物质之间的距离越来越远，它们之间的引力也越来越小，以至于越来越没有办法抑制宇宙的膨胀。我们不知道宇宙现在的半径，但我估计当今宇宙的半径应该至少是最初半径的 10 倍。

现在，我们的计算结果依赖于旋涡星云间分离速度的天文观测数据。但是我相信，我们也能从理论上顺利地得出不依赖天文观测数据的相同计算结果。从旋涡星云的退行速度我们不但可以推算出宇宙最初的尺度，还可以估算出宇宙总的质量，进而得到宇宙中总的质子数。我得出的宇宙中的总质子数为 $7 \times 10^{78}$ 或 $14 \times 10^{78}$。* 我相信这个数值与静电力和引力的比值有密切的关系，并且只与这个比值的平方相差一个常数因子。如果 $F$ 是质子和电子之间的静电力与万有引力的比值，我们得到 $F^2 = 5.3 \times 10^{78}$。理论上我们有理由相信宇宙中的粒子总数是 $\alpha F^2$，其中 $\alpha$ 是一个简单的几何因子（也许和 $\pi$ 有关）。可能不久我们就能得到 $\alpha$ 的理论值，从而给出宇宙膨胀速度的观测值同静电力与引力的比值之间的完整关系。

## 时间的指示牌

我不能继续讨论跟空间有关的问题，而必须开始讨论与时间有关的内容了。宇宙在空间上是闭合的，但是在时间尺度的两个方向上却都是开放的。从“这里”朝着空间中的任意方向出发，最后我们都会回到“这里”；但是从“现在”出发，无论

* 这个结果的不确定性与在有限无界的空间中计算粒子数有不可分割的联系。因为我们无法分辨这些质子到底被计算过一次还是两次。

"now" towards the future or the past we shall never come across "now" again. There is no bending round of time to bring us back to the moment we started from. In mathematics this difference is provided for by the symbol $\sqrt{-1}$, just as the same symbol crops up in distinguishing a closed ellipse and an open hyperbola.

If, then, we are looking for an end of the world—or, instead of an end, an indefinite continuation for ever and ever—we must start off in one of the two time directions. How shall we decide which of these two directions to take? It is an important question. Imagine yourself in some unfamiliar part of space-time so as not to be biased by conventional landmarks or traditional standards of reference. There ought to be a signpost with one arm marked "To the future" and the other arm marked "To the past". My first business is to find this signpost, for if I make a mistake and go the wrong way I shall lead you to what is no doubt an "end of the world", but it will be that end which is more usually described as the *beginning*.

In ordinary life the signpost is provided by consciousness. Or perhaps it would be truer to say that consciousness does not bother about signposts; but wherever it finds itself it goes off on urgent business in a particular direction, and the physicist meekly accepts its lead and labels the course it takes "To the future". It is an important question whether consciousness in selecting its direction is guided by anything in the physical world. If it is guided, we ought to be able to find directly what it is in the physical world which makes it a one-way street for conscious beings. The view is sometimes held that the "going on of time" does not exist in the physical world at all and is a purely subjective impression. According to that view, the difference between past and future in the material universe has no more significance than the difference between right and left. The fact that experience presents space-time as a cinematograph film which is always unrolled in a particular direction is not a property or peculiarity of the film (that is, the physical world) but of the way it is inserted into the cinematograph (that is, consciousness). In fact, the one-way traffic in time arises from the way our material bodies are geared on to our consciousness:

> "Nature has made our gears in such a way
> That we can never get into reverse".

If this view is right, "the going on of time" should be dropped out of our picture of the physical universe. Just as we have dropped the old geocentric outlook and other idiosyncrasies of our circumstances as observers, so we must drop the dynamic presentation of events which is no part of the universe itself but is introduced in our peculiar mode of apprehending it. In particular, we must be careful not to treat a past-to-future presentation of events as truer or more significant than a future-to-past presentation. We must, of course, drop the theory of evolution, or at least set alongside it a theory of anti-evolution as equally significant.

是向着未来还是向着过去前进，我们将永远不可能再回到“现在”。在这里并没有弯曲的时间回路能把我们带回到原来出发的时刻。从数学上说这种差别是由记号 $\sqrt{-1}$ 造成的，正如闭合椭圆和开放双曲线之间的区别也是由这个记号造成的一样。

于是，如果我们要找寻宇宙的终点——其实并不是终点，而是一种永无休止的持续，那么我们就必须从时间的两个方向中选一个作为开始的方向。但是我们如何决定应该选取哪一个时间方向呢？这是个很重要的问题。想象一下你处在时空中的某个陌生的部分，在那里你不会受到常规标志或传统参考标准的影响。但是那里应该有一个时间的指示牌，一边写着“通向未来”，而另一边写着“通向过去”。我要做的第一件事情就是要先找出这个指示牌，否则一旦我弄错了方向，那么无疑，我还是会把你们带到“宇宙的终点”，不过这个“终点”更通常地是被描述为宇宙的**起点**。

在日常生活中，我们的意识充当了时间的指示牌。或者更准确地说，我们的意识根本不关心所谓的时间指示牌；但是无论什么地方，在紧急情况下意识总是朝着某一个特定的方向行进思考，而物理学家也温和地接受了意识的引导并把它的行进方向标记为“通向未来”的方向。这里有一个重要的问题，意识在选择它的行进方向时是否也受到物理世界中的某种事物的影响？如果确实如此，那么我们应该能够直接找出究竟是物理世界中的什么因素使得有意识的人类认为时间是沿单向车道行进的。有观点认为“时间的流逝”只是一种主观的想法而不是物理世界中真实存在的现象。按照这个观点，物质世界中过去和未来的区别只不过相当于左和右之间的区别而已。事实上我们的经验显示时空就像一组电影胶片，它总是按照某种特定的方向放映，但这并不是由胶片（物理时空）本身的性质或特点所决定的，而是与胶片插入放映机的方式（意识）有关。这种观点认为，把事物储存到我们意识中的方式使我们认为时间具有单向性：

> “大自然给我们配备了这样的意识思维方式
> 使得我们永远不能倒退”。

如果以上的观点是对的，那么在我们关于物理世界的图像中就应该抛弃“时间的流逝”这种观点。就像我们放弃旧的时空观以及其他对周围事物观察得到的个人看法一样，我们必须抛弃事物是动态呈现的这种观念，因为这并不是世界本身的性质而只是我们人类在认识物理世界时引入的一种人类特有的理解方式。我们要特别注意的是，如果真是这样，那么我们就不能先入为主地认为“过去到未来”的呈现比“未来到过去”的呈现更正确或更重要。当然，我们也必须放弃进化论，或者至少要同时建立一种具有同样重要性的反进化论。

If anyone holds this view, I have no argument to bring against him. I can only say to him, "You are a teacher whose duty it is to inculcate in youthful minds a true and balanced outlook. But you teach (or without protest allow your colleagues to teach) the utterly one-sided doctrine of evolution. You teach it not as a colourless schedule of facts but as though there were something significant, perhaps even morally inspiring, in the progress from formless chaos to perfected adaptation. This is dishonest; you should also treat it from the equally significant point of view of anti-evolution and discourse on the progress from future to past. Show how from the diverse forms of life existing today Nature anti-evolved forms which were more and more unfitted to survive, until she reached the sublime crudity of the palaeozoic forms. Show how from the solar system Nature anti-evolved a chaotic nebula. Show how, in the course of progress from future to past, Nature took a universe which, with all its faults, is not such a bad effort of architecture and—in short, made a hash of it."

## Entropy and Disorganisation

Leaving aside the guidance of consciousness, we have found it possible to discover a kind of signpost for time in the physical world. The signpost is of rather a curious character, and I would scarcely venture to say that the discovery of the signpost amounts to the same thing as the discovery of an objective "going on of time" in the universe. But at any rate it serves to discriminate past and future, whereas there is no corresponding objective distinction of left and right. The distinction is provided by a certain measurable quantity called entropy. Take an isolated system and measure its entropy $S$ at two instants $t_1$ and $t_2$. We want to know whether $t_1$ is earlier or later than $t_2$ without employing the intuition of consciousness, which is too disreputable a witness to trust in mathematical physics. The rule is that the instant which corresponds to the greater entropy is the later. In mathematical form

$dS/dt$ is always positive.

This is the famous second law of thermodynamics.

Entropy is a very peculiar conception, quite unlike the conceptions ordinarily employed in the classical scheme of physics. We may most conveniently describe it as the measure of disorganisation of a system. Accordingly, our signpost for time resolves itself into the law that disorganisation increases from past to future. It is one of the most curious features of the development of physics that the entropy outlook grew up quietly alongside the ordinary analytical outlook for a great many years. Until recently it always "played second fiddle"; it was convenient for getting practical results, but it did not pretend to convey the most penetrating insight. But now it is making a bid for supremacy, and I think there is little doubt that it will ultimately drive out its rival.

There are some important points to emphasise. First, there is no other independent signpost for time; so that if we discredit or "explain away" this property of entropy, the distinction of past and future in the physical world will disappear altogether. Secondly,

如果有谁坚持时间的行进具有单向性这种观点，我没有任何办法说他是错的。我只能对他说："你是一个致力于把一个真实均衡的世界观灌输给年青学生的老师。但是你所教授的（或没有阻止你的同事去教授的）是完全片面的进化论学说。你并没有告诉学生进化论只是单纯事实的罗列，而是让他们认为似乎从混乱无形到完美有序的过程才是重要的，才真正会是鼓舞人心的。你这样做其实是不诚实的；你应该把反进化论也放在同样重要的位置并讲述从未来到过去的演化过程。你应该向他们展示：现今自然界存在的丰富多彩的生命形态是如何反进化到越来越不适合生存，直到古生代最原始的形态的；自然界是如何从太阳系反进化成混沌的星云；以及，随着从未来到过去的时间进程，自然界是如何选择了一个充满问题的宇宙，而这些问题并不是宇宙本身的构造不好，总而言之，最初的宇宙是一团糨糊。"

## 熵和无序度

撇开意识的引导性不谈，我们已经发现在物理世界里有可能找到一种时间的指示牌。这个指示牌具有非常奇特的性质，当然，我还不敢说这个指示牌的发现与当年在宇宙中发现客观的"时间流逝"有一样的重要性。但是不管怎样，这个指示牌可以用来区别过去和未来，而空间上的左和右却没有相应的客观区分。我们可以用某种称为熵的可测量量来标志这种时间方向上的差别。假设有一个孤立的系统，我们在两个不同的时刻 $t_1$ 和 $t_2$ 分别测量它的熵 $S$。因为意识这个概念在数学物理领域里并不是可靠的证据，所以我们想在不靠意识直觉的情况下知道 $t_1$ 究竟比 $t_2$ 早还是晚。这里用到的规则是：熵越大，时间越晚。在数学形式中为：

$$dS/dt \text{ 总是大于零。}$$

这就是著名的热力学第二定律。

熵是个很特殊的概念，与经典物理学常用的概念很不一样。我们可以把熵简单地描述为：熵是衡量系统无序性的物理量。于是，根据熵这个时间的指示牌，我们得到了这样的规律：从过去到未来，无序性是增加的。物理学发展的最奇妙的特点之一就是：多年来，与其他常规的分析方法一样，我们对于熵的认知一直都在悄悄地发展着。直到最近，熵在科学研究中仍只是"居于次要位置"。由熵可以很方便地得到实用的结果，但并不能由此表明人们对熵有了深刻的洞察力。不过现在熵正在谋求更大的发展，并且我认为，毫无疑问，它最终会超过它的对手。

这里还需要强调几个重要的地方。首先，世界上没有其他独立的时间指示牌；所以如果我们不信任或者"通过辩解来消除"熵作为时间指示牌的这个性质，那么物理学关于过去和未来的差别也会随之消失。第二，检验熵的实验结果应该都是一

the test works consistently; isolated systems in different parts of the universe agree in giving the same direction of time. Thirdly, in applying the test we must make certain that our system is strictly isolated. Evolution teaches us that more and more highly organised systems develop as time goes on; but this does not contradict the conclusion that on the whole there is a loss of organisation. It is partly a question of definition of organisation; from the evolutionary point of view it is quality rather than quantity of organisation that is noticed. But, in any case, the high organisation of these systems is obtained by draining organisation from other systems with which they come in contact. A human being as he grows from past to future becomes more and more highly organised—at least, he fondly imagines so. But if we make an isolated system of him, that is to say, if we cut off his supply of food and drink and air, he speedily attains a state which everyone would recognise as "a state of disorganisation".

It is possible for the disorganisation of a system to become complete. The state then reached is called thermodynamic equilibrium. The entropy can increase no further, and, since the second law of thermodynamics forbids a decrease, it remains constant. Our signpost for time disappears; and so far as that system is concerned, time ceases to go on. That does not mean that time ceases to exist; it exists and extends just as space exists and extends, but there is no longer any one-way property. It is like a one-way street on which there is never any traffic.

Let us return to our signpost. Ahead there is ever-increasing disorganisation. Although the sum total of organisation is diminishing, certain parts of the universe are exhibiting a more and more highly specialised organisation; that is the phenomenon of evolution. But ultimately this must be swallowed up in the advancing tide of chance and chaos, and the whole universe will reach a state of complete disorganisation—a uniform featureless mass in thermodynamic equilibrium. This is the end of the world. Time will *extend* on and on, presumably to infinity. But there will be no definable sense in which it can be said to *go* on. Consciousness will obviously have disappeared from the physical world before thermodynamical equilibrium is reached, and $dS/dt$ having vanished, there will remain nothing to point out a direction in time.

## The Beginning of Time

It is more interesting to look in the opposite direction—towards the past. Following time backwards, we find more and more organisation in the world. If we are not stopped earlier, we must come to a time when the matter and energy of the world had the maximum possible organisation. To go back further is impossible. We have come to an abrupt end of space-time—only we generally call it the "beginning".

I have no "philosophical axe to grind" in this discussion. Philosophically, the notion of a beginning of the present order of Nature is repugnant to me. I am simply stating the

致的；宇宙中任何地方的孤立系统都应该给出相同的时间方向。第三，在进行这类实验时，我们必须保证我们的系统是严格孤立的系统。进化论告诉我们，随着时间的推移，越来越高的有序系统产生了；但是这与整体上有序性的减少并不矛盾。这在一定程度上是有序性的定义问题；从进化的角度看，需要注意的是有序性的质而非量。但无论如何，有序性很高的系统是通过吸取其他与之接触的系统的有序性来实现的。一个人从过去到未来总是变得越来越有序，至少他自己愿意这么认为。但是如果我们使他成为一个孤立的系统，即切断他的饮食和空气供应，那么他很快就会达到一种大家都认同的“无序状态”。

系统可能达到完全的无序状态，我们称之为热力学平衡态。此时，熵不能再继续增加了，而热力学第二定律又不允许它减少，于是熵就只能保持为一个常数。这时，我们的时间指示牌也消失了，因而对于这样的一个系统，时间变得固定不动了。但这并不表示时间不存在；时间仍然像空间一样存在并延续着，但是它已经不再具有任何单向性了。或者说，单行道仍然存在，但不再有汽车在上面行驶了。

让我们回到时间指示牌的讨论上来。通过前面的讨论我们已经知道，无序性是不断增加的。虽然总的有序性正在减少，但是宇宙中的某些部分却展示出越来越高的特殊有序性；这就是进化现象。但是这些有序的系统最终会被不断增加的机遇与混沌所吞没，然后整个宇宙会达到一种完全无序的状态，即变成热力学平衡态下的一堆毫无特征的均匀物质。这就是宇宙的终点。时间仍然会永远地**延续**下去，可能没有尽头。但是时间的这种**延续**没有了明确的意义。很明显，在热力学平衡态即将到来之前，物理世界中已经不存在意识了，$dS/dt$ 也成为零，再也没有一种指示牌能告诉我们，哪个时间方向通向未来，而哪个又是通向过去的。

## 时间的起点

如果我们朝着“时间流逝”相反的方向，即朝着过去的方向看，我们将会发现更加有趣的现象。当我们沿着“时间流逝”的方向往回走时，会发现宇宙的有序性越来越大。如果我们一直不停地走下去，就会到达一个物质和能量的有序度都为允许的最高限的时刻。这时，再想进一步走下去已经不可能了。我们已经来到了时空戛然而止的终点——只不过我们通常称之为“起点”。

在这里的讨论中我没有“涉足哲学”的意思。我并不认同哲学中那些与现在自然界秩序的起点有关的概念。我只是想说明物理规律中现有的基本概念使我们陷入

dilemma to which our present fundamental conception of physical law leads us. I see no way round it; but whether future developments of science will find an escape I cannot predict. The dilemma is this:—Surveying our surroundings, we find them to be far from a "fortuitous concourse of atoms". The picture of the world, as drawn in existing physical theories, shows arrangement of the individual elements for which the odds are multillions to 1 against an origin by chance. Some people would like to call this non-random feature of the world purpose or design; but I will call it non-committally anti-chance. We are unwilling to admit in physics that anti-chance plays any part in the reactions between the systems of billions of atoms and quanta that we study; and indeed all our experimental evidence goes to show that these are governed by the laws of chance. Accordingly, we sweep anti-chance out of the laws of physics—out of the differential equations. Naturally, therefore, it reappears in the boundary conditions, for it must be got into the scheme somewhere. By sweeping it far enough away from the sphere of our current physical problems, we fancy we have got rid of it. It is only when some of us are so misguided as to try to get back billions of years into the past that we find the sweepings all piled up like a high wall and forming a boundary—a beginning of time—which we cannot climb over.

A way out of the dilemma has been proposed which seems to have found favour with a number of scientific workers. I oppose it because I think it is untenable, not because of any desire to retain the present dilemma. I should like to find a genuine loophole. But that does not alter my conviction that the loophole that is at present being advocated is a blind alley. I must first deal with a minor criticism.

I have sometimes been taken to task for not sufficiently emphasising in my discussion of these problems that the results about entropy are a matter of probability, not of certainty. I said above that if we observe a system at two instants, the instant corresponding to the greater entropy will be the later. Strictly speaking, I ought to have said that for a smallish system the chances are, say, $10^{20}$ to 1, that it is the later. Some critics seem to have been shocked at my lax morality in making such a statement, when I was well aware of the 1 in $10^{20}$ chance of its being wrong. Let me make a confession. I have in the past twenty-five years written a good many papers and books, broadcasting a large number of statements about the physical world. I fear that for not many of these statements is the risk of error so small as 1 in $10^{20}$. Except in the domain of pure mathematics, the trustworthiness of my conclusions is usually to be rated at nearer 10 to 1 than $10^{20}$ to 1; even that may be unduly boastful. I do not think it would be for the benefit of the world that no statement should be allowed to be made if there were a 1 in $10^{20}$ chance of its being untrue; conversation would languish somewhat. The only persons entitled to open their mouths would presumably be the pure mathematicians.

## Fluctuations

The loophole to which I referred depends on the occurrence of chance fluctuations. If we have a number of particles moving about at random, they will in the course of time go through every possible configuration, so that even the most orderly, the most non-

了困境。我没有办法解决这个矛盾；也不能预料未来科学的发展能否避开这个矛盾。这个矛盾是这样的：考虑我们周围的物质，我们发现它们远不是“原子的偶然集合”。现有的物理理论所描述的物理世界图像表明，这些单个元素的分布情况是偶然出现的几率仅仅是 10 的 10 次方的 10 次方分之一。有人喜欢把这种现象称之为宇宙意图或设计的非随机特性；但是，我要把它称为不受约束的反几率性。在物理学领域内，我们不愿意承认反几率性在我们所研究的包含数以十亿的原子和量子系统的相互作用中发挥了作用；而且实际上我们所有的实验结果也证实了所有这些现象都是由随机定律决定的。于是，我们就可以把反几率性从物理定律（微分方程）中剔除了。因为它总要出现在物理框架中的某个地方，所以它会很自然地在方程的边界条件里再次现身。通过把它置于我们现有的物理问题的范围之外，我们幻想着我们已经摆脱了这个困难。只有当我们中的某些人被误导着试图穿越几十亿年的时间回到过去时，我们才会发现被我们剔除的所有反几率性现象都堆在那里像一堵高墙一样形成了一个不可逾越的边界，这即是时间的起点。

目前已经有人提出了一种可以解决以上矛盾的方法，这个方法似乎还得到了一些科学工作者的支持。然而，我不同意那种解释，因为我觉得它是站不住脚的，并不是因为我想让这个矛盾继续存在下去。我更愿意去找一个确切的着眼点，但是我确信现在鼓吹的着眼点其实是个死胡同。我必须首先回应对我的一些小的批评意见。

有时，我会因为没有在我所讨论的内容中充分强调熵是概率性而非确定性的物理量而受到批评。如前所述，如果我们在不同的时刻观察同一个系统，那么熵较大的时刻将是较晚的时刻。严格来讲，我应该如此表述：对于一个较小的系统，上述结论正确的可能性为 $10^{20}$ : 1。虽然我清楚地知道这个结论出错的几率是 $1/10^{20}$，但是，由于我在陈述上述结论时不够严谨，有些批评者仍会为此感到震惊。坦白地说：在过去的 25 年里，我撰写了很多文章和书籍，对物理现象做了大量的解释，恐怕我所做的各种解释中没有多少结论的出错几率会小于 $1/10^{20}$。在纯数学领域之外，我的结论的正误比估计更接近 10 : 1，而不是 $10^{20}$ : 1；尽管如此，还是自负不已。我认为出错率为 $1/10^{20}$ 的结论对我们认识世界并不会有什么坏处；而我们应该稍微搁置关于出错几率的讨论。如果按照反对者的说法，这个世界上唯一能发表言论的就只可能是纯粹的数学家了。

## 涨落

我前面所说的着眼点依赖于几率的涨落。我们考虑一群随机运动的粒子，随着时间的推移它们会经历任何可能的状态，所以只要我们等待足够长的时间，即使是

chance configuration, will occur by chance if only we wait long enough. When the world has reached complete disorganisation (thermodynamic equilibrium) there is still infinite time ahead of it, and its elements will thus have opportunity to take up every possible configuration again and again. If we wait long enough, a number of atoms will, just by chance, arrange themselves in systems as they are at present arranged in this room; and, just by chance, the same sound-waves will come from one of these systems of atoms as are at present emerging from my lips; they will strike the ears of other systems of atoms, arranged just by chance to resemble you, and in the same stages of attention or somnolence. This mock Mathematical Association meeting must be repeated many times over—an infinite number of times, in fact—before $t$ reaches $+\infty$. Do not ask me whether I expect you to believe that this will really happen.*

"Logic is logic. That's all I say."

So, after the world has reached thermodynamical equilibrium the entropy remains steady at its maximum value, except that "once in a blue moon" the absurdly small chance comes off and the entropy drops appreciably below its maximum value. When this fluctuation has died out, there will again be a very long wait for another coincidence giving another fluctuation. It will take multillions of years, but we have all infinity of time before us. There is no limit to the amount of the fluctuation, and if we wait long enough we shall come across a big fluctuation which will take the world as far from thermodynamical equilibrium as it is at the present moment. If we wait for an enormously longer time, during which this huge fluctuation is repeated untold numbers of times, there will occur a still larger fluctuation which will take the world as far from thermodynamical equilibrium as it was one second ago.

The suggestion is that we are now on the downward slope of one of these fluctuations. It has quite a pleasant subtlety. Is it chance that we happen to be running down the slope and not toiling up the slope? Not at all. So far as the physical universe is concerned, we have *defined* the direction of time as the direction from greater to less organisation, so that, on whichever side of the mountain we stand, our signpost will point downhill. In fact, on this theory, the going on of time is not a property of time in general, but is a property of the slope of the fluctuation on which we are standing. Again, although the theory postulates a universe involving an extremely improbable coincidence, it provides an infinite time during which the most improbable coincidence might occur. Nevertheless, I feel sure that the argument is fallacious.

If we put a kettle of water on the fire there is a chance that the water will freeze. If mankind goes on putting kettles on the fire until $t = \infty$, the chance will one day come off and the individual concerned will be somewhat surprised to find a lump of ice in his kettle. But it will not happen to *me*. Even if tomorrow the phenomenon occurs before my eyes, I shall not explain it this way. I would much sooner believe in interference by a demon than

* I am hopeful that the doctrine of the "expanding universe" will intervene to prevent its happening.

最有秩序的、几率上最不可能的状态也会偶然出现。当宇宙达到完全的无序状态（热力学平衡态）后，时间仍然会无限地存在，宇宙中的元素将有机会反复经历各种可能的状态。如果我们观察足够长的时间，我们会发现，系统中一些原子所处的状态结构可能会偶然地与我们现在这个空间中的原子一样；同样偶然地，原子所组成的系统中的某一个系统出现的声波将可能与我口中现在发出的声波一样；而不管你是处于清醒还是昏昏欲睡的状态，这些声波都将去冲击由其他原子所组成的偶然与你的耳朵类似的系统。这个模拟的数学协会报告会将会在时间 $t$ 达到无穷大之前重复很多次，实际上是无穷多次。别问我是否期望你们相信这些真的会发生。*

“逻辑就是逻辑，这就是我所说的全部。”

因此，当宇宙到达热力学平衡时，熵就会稳定地处在它的最大值上，除非出现一个千载难逢的极小的几率，使得熵从最大值回落到明显比最大值小的值。这个涨落消失之后，要等很长时间才会碰巧发生下一次涨落。尽管也许要等 10 的 10 次方的 10 次方年的时间，但是不用担心，我们拥有无限延续的时间。这种涨落的大小并没有什么限制，如果我们等待足够久，也许我们可以碰上一次大的涨落，使宇宙远离热力学平衡态，变成和我们现在这个宇宙一样的状态。如果我们等候更长的时间，其间会有数不清的类似的大涨落发生，也许还会有一次较大的涨落使宇宙远离热力学平衡态，变回到一秒钟以前的状态。

有人提出，我们现在正处在某个涨落的下坡过程中。这种提法存在令人兴奋的微妙之处。我们的宇宙刚好处在涨落的下坡过程而非往上的爬坡过程，这是一种巧合吗？完全不是。就物理世界而言，我们已经**定义**了时间的方向为有序度减少的方向，因此，无论我们站在山坡的哪一边，我们的指示牌都是指向下坡的。事实上，在这个理论里，总的来说时间的流逝并不是时间本身的性质，而是我们所处的那个涨落的山坡的性质。尽管这个理论假设宇宙包含了一个极不可能发生的概率事件，但同时该理论却提供了无限长的时间使得最不可能发生的概率事件最终总能发生。无论怎样，我个人觉得以上的说法是不合理的。

如果我们把一壶水放到火上，这壶水有可能结冰吗？如果一个人把一壶水放到火上无限长的时间，某一天这个人可能会惊讶地发现，他壶里的水居然结冰了。但这类事情不可能发生在**我**身上。即使将来有一天这种事情真的在我眼前发生了，我也不会用上面那样的方式去解释它。我宁愿相信这是一个魔鬼干的，而不是小概率

* 我希望“宇宙膨胀”说会阻止它的发生。

in a coincidence of that kind coming off; and in doing so I shall be acting as a rational scientist. The reason why I do not at present believe that devils interfere with my cooking arrangements and other business, is because I have become convinced by experience that Nature obeys certain uniformities which we call laws. I am convinced because these laws have been tested over and over again. But it is possible that every single observation from the beginning of science which has been used as a test, has just happened to fit in with the law by a chance coincidence. It would be an improbable coincidence, but I think not quite so improbable as the coincidence involved in my kettle of water freezing. So if the event happens and I can think of no other explanation, I shall have to choose between two highly improbable coincidences: (*a*) that there are no laws of Nature and that the apparent uniformities so far observed are merely coincidences; (*b*) that the event is entirely in accordance with the accepted laws of Nature, but that an improbable coincidence has happened. I choose the former because mathematical calculation indicates that it is the less improbable. I reckon a sufficiently improbable coincidence as something much more disastrous than a violation of the laws of Nature; because my whole reason for accepting the laws of Nature rests on the assumption that improbable coincidences do not happen—at least, that they do not happen in my experience.*

Similarly, if logic predicts that a mock meeting of the Mathematical Association will occur just by a fortuitous arrangement of atoms before $t = \infty$, I reply that I cannot possibly accept that as being the explanation of a meeting of the Mathematical Association in $t = 1931$. We must be a little careful over this, because there is a trap for the unwary. The year 1931 is not an absolutely random date between $t = -\infty$ and $t = +\infty$. We must not argue that because for only $1/x$th of time between $t = -\infty$ and $t = \infty$ a fluctuation as great as the present one is in operation, therefore the chances are $x$ to 1 against such a fluctuation occurring in the year 1931. For the purposes of the present discussion, the important characteristic of the year 1931 is that it belongs to a period during which there exist in the universe beings capable of speculating about the universe and its fluctuations. Now I think it is clear that such creatures could not exist in a universe in thermodynamical equilibrium. A considerable degree of deviation is required to permit of living beings. Therefore it is perfectly fair for supporters of this suggestion to wipe out of account all those multillions of years during which the fluctuations are less than the minimum required to permit of the development and existence of mathematical physicists. That greatly diminishes $x$, but the odds are still overpowering. The *crude* assertion would be that (unless we admit something which is not chance in the architecture of the universe) it is practically certain that at any assigned date the universe will be almost in the state of maximum disorganisation. The *amended* assertion is that (unless we admit something which is not chance in the architecture of the universe) it is practically certain that a universe containing mathematical physicists will at any assigned date be in the state of maximum disorganisation which is not inconsistent with the existence of such creatures. I think it is quite clear that neither the original nor the amended version applies. We are thus driven

* No doubt "extremely improbable" coincidences occur to all of us, but the improbability is of an utterly different order of magnitude from that concerned in the present discussion.

事件发生了；而这样做的时候，我总该更像是一个理性的科学家吧。我现在之所以不相信魔鬼会干预我的烹调事务或者其他事情，是因为日常经验使我相信自然界会遵循一定的统一性，即物理定律。我相信这些定律是因为它们已经被反复验证过。当然，也有可能所有这些用来验证物理定律的实验一开始就恰好满足这些定律只是一种巧合。这或许是个难以置信的巧合，但是我相信这种巧合不会像我壶里的水发生结冰的巧合那样难以置信。一旦这种事件发生了，而我又找不到其他合适的解释，那么我只能在以下两种极为难以置信的巧合之间做出选择：(*a*) 这个世界上并不存在物理定律，迄今为止观察到的一致性仅仅是巧合。(*b*) 这个事件是符合物理定律的，只不过难以置信的巧合事件发生了。我更愿意接受前一种解释，因为数学计算的结果表明它的可能性更高一点。相比于违反物理定律而言，我把难以置信的巧合事件的发生看成是更加糟糕的事情；因为我之所以接受存在于自然界中的物理定律只是因为我相信难以置信的巧合事件不会发生——至少在我有生之年不会发生。*

同样，如果逻辑上预言在 $t=\infty$ 之前仅仅是由于原子的随机排列而出现了一个模拟的数学协会的报告会，那我要说的是，我不能接受这就是今天 $t=1931$ 年的这个数学协会报告会发生的理由。我们必须小心这一点，因为这里有个不小心就容易陷入的圈套。在 $t=-\infty$ 到 $t=+\infty$ 之间，1931 年并不是一个完全随机的时间。我们不能因为在 $t=-\infty$ 到 $t=+\infty$ 之间只是在第 $1/x$ 个时间里有一个与今天的数学报告会一样的涨落发生了，就说在 1931 年里发生这种涨落的几率是 $1/x$。从我们现在的讨论情况来看，1931 年的重要性就在于在这段时间里宇宙中出现了能够思考宇宙以及它的涨落的人类。现在我认为有一点是很清楚的，就是人类不可能在处于热力学平衡态下的宇宙中生存。要让生物能够生存下去，宇宙就必须在很大程度上偏离平衡态。因此，对于涨落论的支持者来说，不对在 10 的 10 次方的 10 次方年这段时间中发生涨落的几率比数学物理学家成长和存在的最小几率还小的情况进行说明是完全合理的。这就大大缩小了 $x$ 的值，但是问题仍然存在。**最初**的假设应该是这样的（除非我们承认某些状态在宇宙的结构中不可能发生）：几乎可以肯定地说宇宙在给定的任一时间都将近似处于最无序的状态。**改进**后的说法是（除非我们承认某些状态在宇宙的结构中不可能发生）：几乎可以肯定地说有数学物理学家存在的宇宙在给定的任一时间都将处于最无序的状态，而这个状态也适合人类的生存。我想，我们已经很清楚地看出以上两种说法都是站不住脚的。于是我们被迫接受反几率论；而对待它的最好办法显然是，正如之前所说过的，把所有反几率性现象整理在一起并堆

* 毫无疑问，"极不可能"发生的巧合会在我们面前发生，只是这种巧合事件的发生几率与我们在此讨论的巧合事件有完全不同的数量级。

to admit anti-chance; and apparently the best thing we can do with it is to sweep it up into a heap at the beginning of time, as I have already described.

The connexion between our entropy signpost and that dynamic quality of time which we describe as "going on" or "becoming" leads to very difficult questions which I cannot discuss here. The puzzle is that the signpost seems so utterly different from the thing of which it is supposed to be the sign. The one thing on which I have to insist is that, apart from consciousness, the increase of entropy is the only trace that we can find of a one-way direction of time. I was once asked a ribald question: How does an electron (which has not the resource of consciousness) remember which way time is going? Why should it not inadvertently turn round and, so to speak, face time the other way? Does it have to calculate which way entropy is increasing in order to keep itself straight? I am inclined to think that an electron does do something of that sort. For an electric charge to face the opposite way in time is the same thing as to change the sign of the charge. So if an electron mistook the way time was going it would turn into a positive charge. Now, it has been one of the troubles of Dr. P. A. M. Dirac that in the mathematical calculations based on his wave equation the electrons do sometimes forget themselves in this way. As he puts it, there is a finite chance of the charge changing sign after an encounter. You must understand that they only do this in the mathematical problems, not in real life. It seems to me there is good reason for this. A mathematical problem deals with, say, four electric charges at the most; that is about as many as a calculator would care to take on. Accordingly, the unfortunate electron in the problem has to make out the direction of past to future by watching the organisation of three other charges. Naturally, it is deceived sometimes by chance coincidences which may easily happen when there are only three particles concerned; and so it has a good chance of facing the wrong way and becoming a positive charge. But in any real experiment we work with apparatus containing billions of particles—ample to give the electron its bearings with certainty. Dirac's theory predicts things which never happen, simply because it is applied to problems which never occur in Nature. When it is applied to four particles alone in the universe, the analysis very properly brings out the fact that in such a system there could be no steady one-way direction of time, and vagaries would occur which are guarded against in our actual universe consisting of about $10^{79}$ particles.

## Heisenberg's Principle

A discussion of the properties of time would be incomplete without a reference to the principle of indeterminacy, which was formulated by Heisenberg in 1927 and has been generally accepted. It had already been realised that theoretical physics was drifting away from a deterministic basis; Heisenberg's principle delivered the knock-out blow, for it actually postulated a certain measure of indeterminacy or unpredictability of the future as a fundamental law of the universe. This change of view seems to make the progress of time a much more genuine thing than it used to be in classical physics. Each passing moment brings into the world something new—something which is not merely a mathematical extrapolation of what was already there.

积在时间的起点上。

熵这个指示牌和被称作“流逝”或“发展”的时间动态特征之间的关系导致了一些非常困难的问题，在这里我不可能做详细的讨论。其中的困难之处在于熵这个指示牌似乎和我们预期的时间标记非常不同。我需要强调的是，除了意识以外，熵的增加是我们发现时间具有单向性的唯一线索。曾经有人向我提出一个粗鄙的问题：一个电子（它没有意识）是如何记住时间的流向的？为什么它不会无意中改变方向，即，朝向时间的另一个方向？它需要事先计算好朝哪个方向熵会增加，然后再决定往哪个方向前进吗？我倾向于认为电子确实会作这样的判断。对一个电荷来说，朝相反的时间方向意味着它的电荷符号要发生变化。所以，如果一个电子错误地选择了时间方向，那么它就会变成一个正电荷。这跟狄拉克博士在以电子波动方程为基础进行数学计算时碰到的一个麻烦是一样的，在他的计算里电子真的会走错方向。就像狄拉克所发现的，在一次碰撞之后，电子有一定的几率可以改变电荷的符号。你必须要明白的是，这仅仅是数学的计算结果，并未在现实生活中发现。之所以是这样，我认为似乎有很合理的理由可以解释。假设我们考虑一个最多涉及四个电荷的数学问题，这个问题是任何一个计算器都能够处理的。于是，其中一个倒霉的电子不得不通过观察其他三个电荷的有序性来判断时间从过去到将来的流向。很自然，当我们只考虑三个电子的情况时，很容易发生偶然的巧合使得电子弄错方向；所以电子有很好的机会可以因为弄错了时间的方向而变成一个正电荷。但是在现实实验中，我们所用的仪器会包含几十亿个粒子——多到足够让电子准确地确定出时间的方向。狄拉克理论预言的情况从来就没有发生过，因为与之相适的问题从来没有出现在现实世界中。如果将狄拉克理论应用于只有四个电子的宇宙中，那么经过分析很可能会给出这样的结论：在这个系统中不会存在一个稳定的单向的时间方向，奇特的事情会不断地发生，而这些在我们这个包含了约 $10^{79}$ 个粒子的真实宇宙中是完全不可能发生的。

## 海森堡原理

如果我们不考虑不确定性原理的话，那么我们对时间的讨论将是不完整的。这个原理是海森堡在 1927 年用公式表达出来并已得到一致认可的。人们已经意识到理论物理学正慢慢地偏离确定性这个基础；海森堡不确定性原理对人们的思维产生了巨大的冲击，因为这个原理作为物理世界的基本定律实际上认为未来理应具有一定程度上的不确定性或不可预测性。相比于经典物理学，这种观念上的转变使得时间的进展具有了更加真实的意义。每一个瞬间过后，世界都可能增添一些新事物——这些事物不可能单纯使用数学方法从过去已经发生的事件中推测出来。

The deterministic view which held sway for at least two centuries was that if we had complete data as to the state of the whole universe during, say, the first minute of the year 1600, it would be merely a mathematical exercise to deduce everything that has happened or will happen at any date in the future or past. The future would be determined by the present as the solution of a differential equation is determined by the boundary conditions. To understand the new view, it is necessary to realise that there is a risk of begging the question when we use the phrase "complete data". All our knowledge of the physical world is inferential. I have no direct acquaintance with my pen as an object in the physical world; I infer its existence and properties from the light waves which fall on my eyes, the pressure waves which travel up my muscles, and so on.

Precisely the same scheme of inference leads us to infer the existence of things in the past. Just as I infer a physical object, namely, my pen, as the cause of certain visual sensations now, so I may infer an infection some days ago as the cause of an attack of measles. If we follow out this principle completely we shall infer causes in the year 1600 for all the events which we know to have happened in 1930. At first sight it would seem that these inferred causes have just as much status in the physical world as my fountain pen, which is likewise an inferred cause. So the determinist thinks he has me in a cleft stick. If the scientific worker poking about in the universe in 1600 comes across these causes, then he has all the data for making a correct prediction for 1930; if he does not, then he clearly has not complete knowledge of the universe in 1600, for these causes have as much right to the status of physical entities as any of our other inferences.

I need scarcely stop to show how this begs the question by arbitrarily prescribing what we should deem to be complete knowledge of the universe in 1600, irrespective of whether there is any conceivable way in which this knowledge could be obtained at the time. What Heisenberg discovered was that (at least in a wide range of phenomena embracing the whole of atomic physics and electron theory) there is a provision of Nature that just half of the data demanded by our determinist friend might with sufficient diligence be collected by the investigators in 1600, and that complete knowledge of this half would automatically exclude all knowledge of the other half. It is an odd arrangement, because you can take your choice which half you will find out; you can know either half but not both halves. Or you can make a compromise and know both halves imperfectly, that is, with some margin of uncertainty. But the rule is definite. The data are linked in pairs and the more accurately you measure one member of the pair the less accurately you can measure the other member.

Both halves are necessary for a complete prediction of the future, although, of course, by judiciously choosing the type of event we predict we can often make safe prophecies. For example, the principle of indeterminacy will obviously not interfere with my prediction that during the coming year zero will turn up approximately $\frac{1}{37}$ of the total number of times the roulette ball is spun at Monte Carlo. All our successful predictions in physics and astronomy are on examination found to depend on this device of eliminating the inherent uncertainty of the future by averaging.

确定性的观点占主导地位至少有两个世纪了，确定论认为如果我们知道了某个时刻宇宙状态的完整数据，比如说 1600 年第一分钟的完整数据，那么单纯的数学推算就可以告诉我们这个世界以前是什么样子以及未来将会是什么样子。未来是由现在所决定的，因为一个微分方程的解由边界条件决定。要理解这个全新的观点，我们必须意识到我们一开始提出的“完整数据”这个概念是存在回避问题实质的风险的。而我们对物理世界的所有认识都是推论性的。我的钢笔并不是作为一个在物理世界中存在的物体使我直接认识到的；我是通过从笔上反射进我眼睛里的光以及握笔时在我肌肉中传播的压力波等感知它的存在和性质的。

我们对过去事物的感知也遵循着完全一样的模式。就像现在我可以通过我的视觉感受去推断一个客观的物体，即我的钢笔一样，我也可以从患上麻疹这个情况推断出几天前应该受到了感染。如果我们完全依照这个规律，就可以就 1930 年已经发生的全部事件去推断在 1600 年使它们发生的原因。乍一看似乎这些推断出来的原因与钢笔（也是一种推断出来的原因）的存在状态一样对我们认识物理世界具有同样重要的作用。于是确定论者们认为这令我陷入了进退两难的境地。如果某个科学工作者在 1600 年的世界中四处探寻并且恰好找到了这些事情的起因，那么他就有完整的数据来准确地预测 1930 年发生的事情；如果他做不到，那么他肯定没有完全认识 1600 年的宇宙，因为这些起因跟我们在其他推论过程中得出的起因一样都是些物理实体。

我还需要继续说明他们是如何为了回避问题的实质而武断地规定哪些内容应该被视为是 1600 年的世界的完整数据，而不考虑那时是否存在可以想象的方式去获取这些数据。海森堡发现（至少在包括整个原子物理学和电子理论的广泛物理现象中），按照自然界的规律，在我们支持确定论的朋友们所需的数据中，只有一半有可能被 1600 年的研究者通过不懈的努力收集到，而对这一半数据的完整认识将使我们自动失去了得到另一半数据的机会。这是个很奇怪的约定，因为你可以选择要了解哪一半数据；你可以知道任何一半的数据，但就是不能同时知道全部的数据。或者你也可以做出妥协而选择不完全地知道这两个一半的全部数据，即有不确定的部分。这个物理规律是确定的：数据是成对出现的，你对一对数据中的一个测量得越精确，则对另一个的测量结果就会越不精确。

当然，想要预测未来，全部数据的两个部分都是必要的，但是如果我们谨慎地选择预测的对象，我们还是可以做出一些可靠的预言的。例如，不确定性原理不会对我预测未来一年蒙特卡洛轮盘赌上的数字零出现的次数造成影响，这个次数大概是小球总的旋转次数的$\frac{1}{37}$。实践证明，所有物理学和天文学上的成功预测都是通过这种取平均的办法来消除未来的内在不确定性的。

As an illustration, let us consider the simplest type of prediction. Suppose we have a particle, say an electron, moving undisturbed with uniform velocity. If we know its position now and its velocity, it is a simple matter to predict its position at some particular future instant. Heisenberg's principle asserts that the position and velocity are paired data; that is to say, although there is no limit to the accuracy with which we might get to know the position and no limit to the accuracy with which we might get to know the velocity, we cannot get to know both. So our attempt at an accurate prediction of the future position of the particle is frustrated. We can, if we like, observe the position now and the position at the future instant with the utmost accuracy (since these are not paired data) and then calculate what has been the velocity in the meantime. Suppose that we use this velocity together with the original position to compute the second position. Our result will be quite correct, and we shall be true prophets—after the event.

This principle is so fully incorporated into modern physics that in wave mechanics the electron is actually pictured in a way which exhibits this "interference" of position and velocity. To attribute to it exact position and velocity simultaneously would be inconsistent with the picture. Thus, according to our present outlook, the absence of one half of the data of prediction is not to be counted as ignorance; the data are lacking because they do not come into the world until it is too late to make the prediction. They come into existence when the event is accomplished.

I suppose that to justify my title I ought to conclude with a prophecy as to what the end of the world will be like. I confess I am not very keen on the task. I half thought of taking refuge in the excuse that, having just explained that the future is unpredictable, I ought not to be expected to predict it. But I am afraid that someone would point out that the excuse is a thin one, because all that is required is a computation of averages and that type of prediction is not forbidden by the principle of indeterminacy. It used to be thought that in the end all the matter of the universe would collect into one rather dense ball at uniform temperature; but the doctrine of spherical space, and more especially the recent results as to the expansion of the universe, have changed that. There are one or two unsettled points which prevent a definite conclusion, so I will content myself with stating one of several possibilities. It is widely thought that matter slowly changes into radiation. If so, it would seem that the universe will ultimately become a ball of radiation growing ever larger, the radiation becoming thinner and passing into longer and longer wavelengths. About every 1,500 million years it will double its radius, and its size will go on expanding in this way in geometrical progression for ever.

(**127**, 447-453; 1931)

作为一个例证，让我们来考虑一个最简单的预测。假设我们有一个粒子，例如电子，没有受到任何扰动而做匀速直线运动。如果我们知道它现在的位置和速度，那么预测它未来某个时刻的位置是一件很简单的事情。海森堡不确定性原理告诉我们，位置和速度是结成对的数据；也就是说，我们可以无限精确地知道它的位置，也可以无限精确地知道它的速度，但是我们就是不能同时精确地知道这两个量。所以我们在试图准确预测这个粒子未来某个时刻对应的位置时遇到了困难。如果我们愿意的话，我们可以观察这个粒子现在时刻和未来时刻的精确位置（因为它们不是结成对的数据），然后计算出这段时间的平均速度。假如当我们由这个平均速度和最初时刻的位置来计算未来时刻的位置时，我们发现结果完全正确，于是我们成了真正的预言家——其实只是事后诸葛亮。

这个不确定性原理已经完全融入了现代物理学，在波动力学中的确可以认为在电子的位置和速度之间就表现出了那种“相干关系”。由于这种相干关系，同时精确地知道电子的位置和速度是与以上的物理图像相矛盾的。因此，按照我们现在的观点，缺少预测未来所需数据中的一半算不上是信息不灵通；数据不完整是因为在我们做出预测之前它们并不存在。它们是在我们的测量行为发生之时才出现的。

我认为为了充分说明我的主题，我应当用一个预言来作为对宇宙终点可能会是什么样子这个问题的总结。我承认我并不十分情愿回答这个问题。我甚至想，既然我刚才已经解释了未来是不可预测的，我就可以以此为借口拒绝回答这个问题。但恐怕有人会说，你这个借口太勉强，你所需要做的只是计算一下平均值，而那种类型的预言并不违背不确定性原理。过去我们认为宇宙中的所有物质最终会聚集到一起变成一个温度均匀、密度极大的圆球；但是球面空间的学说，尤其是由此得到的宇宙膨胀的最新结论改变了以前的看法。现在还存在一两个未得到解决的问题，这使得我不能得出明确的结论，所以我在这里只是给出其中的一种可能性。大家普遍认为物质会慢慢地转变成辐射。如果是那样的话，整个宇宙就会变成一个不断膨胀的充满辐射的球，辐射会变得越来越弱，相应的波长也变得越来越长。大概每过 15 亿年，宇宙的半径就会增加一倍，宇宙的大小将会以这种几何级数的增长方式永远地膨胀下去。

（沈乃澂 翻译；张元仲 审稿）

# Chemistry of Vitamin $B_2$

B. C. Guha

## Editor's Note

**_Nature_ was much concerned with the chemistry of B vitamins this year, and this paper from Bires Chandra Guha at Cambridge—an important figure in the development of biochemistry in India—reports some progress in decoding the chemical nature of vitamin $B_2$. Guha reports a suite of tests which suggest that this substance, now known as riboflavin, is a neutral compound, and neither an acid nor a base. Perhaps more usefully, Guha suggests that vitamin $B_2$ in liver extract is not the same as the "factor" known to alleviate pernicious anaemia. The latter later proved to be vitamin $B_{12}$, which played a pivotal role in chemical synthesis and crystallography.**

A chemical study of vitamin $B_2$ in a cold aqueous extract of commercial liver extract (Eli Lilly, No. 343) has been made. This solution is very rich in vitamin $B_2$, being effective in producing good growth in young rats on a $B_2$ deficient diet, in a daily dose representing 40–60 mgm. of the original liver extract.

Picric acid and benzoyl chloride do not precipitate the vitamin, nor is it precipitated or destroyed by nitrous acid. It is not precipitated by flavianic acid. Neutral lead acetate partially precipitates the active material both at *p*H 4.6 and 7, while litharge does not precipitate it at all. Silver nitrate precipitates the bulk of the vitamin. Baryta does not precipitate it either in an aqueous solution or in a medium of 50 percent alcohol. "Norite" charcoal adsorbs the factor at the natural *p*H of the aqueous liver extract (*p*H 4.6), which, however, could not be eluted by acid, alkaline or neutral water-alcohol mixtures, or by a dilute solution of saponin. Three extractions with 30 percent propyl alcohol appeared to extract it partially with a considerable loss of activity. Treatment with phosphotungstic acid gives an inactive precipitate and a filtrate with a small degree of activity. A combination of the two is equally unsatisfactory. Esterification with ethyl alcohol leaves the bulk of the activity in the non-esterified portion, the ester itself being almost wholly devoid of activity. Trypsin has no effect on the vitamin.

On the basis of the present evidence it appears that, if the vitamin is a single chemical entity, it is probably not a base, an acid, or a peptide, but a neutral substance. Preliminary experiments on the electrodialysis of vitamin $B_2$, carried out with Mr. T. W. Birch, also appear to support this conclusion. These fractionation experiments have given the general impression that vitamin $B_2$ is fairly readily adsorbed by neutral precipitates. Thus, the partial precipitation by lead acetate and also by silver nitrate is probably merely due to the adsorption of the vitamin on to the precipitates formed.

# 维生素 $B_2$ 的化学性质

拜尔斯·钱德拉·古哈

## 编者按

在这一年中，《自然》杂志对 B 族维生素的化学性质给予了更多的关注，这篇由印度生物化学领域的重要代表人物——拜尔斯·钱德拉·古哈在剑桥大学完成的论文记述了他在剖析维生素 $B_2$ 化学性质方面取得的进展。古哈通过一系列实验说明：这种物质——现在被称为核黄素——其实是一种中性化合物，既不是酸也不是碱。古哈指出肝提取物中的维生素 $B_2$ 与现在认为可以缓解恶性贫血的"因子"不同，这一点对人们来说也许价值更大。后来证明能有效抑制贫血的成分是维生素 $B_{12}$，维生素 $B_{12}$ 在化学合成和晶体学方面发挥了关键的作用。

我们研究了来自商业肝浸膏（礼来药厂，第343号）冷水提取液的维生素$B_2$的化学性质。这种溶液富含维生素$B_2$，在饮食中缺乏维生素$B_2$的条件下，每天40 ~ 60毫克剂量的肝浸膏原液可以有效促进幼鼠的生长。

苦味酸和苯甲酰氯都不能使这种维生素沉淀，亚硝酸也不能使它沉淀或者破坏。同样，黄胺酸也不能使它沉淀。中性醋酸铅可以在 pH 为 4.6 或 7 的时候使这种活性物质部分沉淀，而密陀僧根本不能使其沉淀。硝酸银能使这种维生素大量沉淀，而氧化钡无论是在水溶液中，还是在含 50% 酒精的介质中都不能使其沉淀。"苏长岩"活性炭可以在肝浸膏水溶液的自然 pH 值（pH 4.6）下吸附这种物质，然而酸性、碱性以及中性的水—酒精混合物或是皂苷稀溶液都不能将其洗脱下来。用 30% 的丙醇溶液进行三次萃取，似乎可以将其部分提取出来，但会使它的活性大大降低。用磷钨酸处理会产生非活性沉淀物，以及带有轻微活性的滤液。将二者混合，结果同样不令人满意。乙醇的酯化作用使绝大部分活性物质都留在了非酯化部分，而酯本身几乎完全没有活性。另外，胰蛋白酶对这种维生素没有任何影响。

基于现有证据，可以看出，如果这种维生素是一种简单的化学实体，它很可能不是碱，不是酸，也不是肽，而是一种中性物质。我和伯奇先生所做的关于维生素 $B_2$ 电渗析的初步实验似乎也印证了这一结论。我们从这些分离实验中大致了解到：维生素 $B_2$ 非常容易吸附在中性沉淀物上。因此，醋酸铅和硝酸银的部分沉淀作用很可能仅仅是由于维生素吸附到了所形成的沉淀物上。

Though the liver extract is potent in both vitamin $B_2$ and the factor specific for pernicious anaemia, they appear to be different from evidence of the methods of their fractionation and also on other grounds.

The stability of vitamin $B_2$ to heating under pressure in an alkaline medium shows curious discrepancies. Commercial liver concentrate and commercial yeast extract ("marmite") are both fairly stable to autoclaving at *p*H 9 at 124°C., while aqueous extracts made from brewer's yeast, fresh ox liver, and ox muscle are markedly unstable under the same conditions. The stability appears to be connected with the presence of certain protective materials in a given fraction.

The vitamin is stable to sulphur dioxide, hydrogen peroxide, and ozone.

(**127**, 594-595; 1931)

B. C. Guha: Biochemical Laboratory, Cambridge.

虽然肝浸膏既具有维生素 $B_2$ 的功效，又具有专门针对恶性贫血症的因子的功效，但上述两种物质从分离方法以及其他方面的证据看，似乎并不相同。

在碱性环境中、高压条件下加热维生素 $B_2$，其稳定性会表现出奇怪的差异。商业肝浓缩剂和商业酵母提取物（“酸制酵母”）在 pH 为 9、温度为 124℃的高压下都很稳定，而在相同条件下从啤酒酵母、新鲜牛肝和牛的肌肉中得到的水提出物却非常不稳定。其稳定性似乎与一定含量的某种保护性物质的存在有关。

这种维生素在二氧化硫、过氧化氢和臭氧条件下都很稳定。

（李世媛 翻译；刘京国 审稿）

# Stellar Structure

H. N. Russell and R. d'E. Atkinson

## Editor's Note

**Henry Norris Russell and Robert d'Escourt Atkinson were both distinguished astronomers, who here give one of the first accounts of the properties of the stars known as white dwarves. In particular, they were concerned to reconcile the very high temperatures of the surface of these stars with the fact that their output of radiation is usually small compared with the Sun. Their conclusion was that white dwarves were indeed much smaller than the Sun. They also introduced the idea that the matter of which these stars consist might, with time, become degenerate, the atoms splitting into electrons and nuclei which separately form very compact atomic structures. Degenerate stars of this kind are now most clearly typified by neutron stars, discovered only in the 1960s.**

ZANSTRA'S recent determination of the temperatures of the *O*-stars in planetary nebulae[1] makes it appear extremely likely that these stars are all generically in the "white dwarf" class, with mean densities far above anything known on the earth. He has found temperatures between 30,000° and 100,000° for about twenty of these objects, and yet their luminosities are comparatively small. For a fairly typical nebular nucleus we may assume a photographic magnitude of 12.5 with a parallax of 0.002″, making the absolute magnitude +4, or about eight magnitudes fainter than typical galactic *O*-stars. It is, of course, true that the luminous *efficiency* falls off with rising temperature in this range, but an increase in temperature at constant radius must always involve an increase in brightness, proportional, even in the farthest part of the Rayleigh–Jeans region, to at least the first power of the temperature. Thus these stars must be of very small radius.

Zanstra obtains his figures from the difference between the measured brightness of the star and that of the nebula, which latter is assumed to be excited by the main (Schumann region) radiation of the star, and to convert all of it to long wave-lengths. The nebula thus performs the correction from visual to bolometric magnitude for us, as it were; if it does not do so completely, the star must be still hotter than is calculated. The correction is found to vary between 2 and 7 or 7.5 magnitudes; in an average case it would be about 5 magnitudes, and the temperature would be rather more than 55,000°. Such a star would then be about 5.9 magnitudes brighter than the sun bolometrically, with ten times its surface temperature; this means a radius 1/43 of the sun's, so that even with the sun's mass its density would be more than 100,000 gm./c.c.

The masses are, however, certainly greater. In a typical planetary, the line-of-sight rotational velocity can be taken as 5 km./sec. at 6″ from the nucleus, and with a parallax of 0.002″ this gives a mass 80 times the sun's.[2] If the gas is partly supported by radiation

# 恒星的构造

亨利·罗素，罗伯特·阿特金森

编者按

亨利·诺里什·罗素和罗伯特·阿特金森是两位著名的天文学家，他们在本文中讨论了白矮星的性质，这篇文章也是最早报告这方面研究的文章之一。特别是他们致力于解决白矮星表面温度高而辐射却比太阳低的矛盾，他们的结论是白矮星实际上比太阳小得多。他们还提出这些恒星中的物质也许会随着时间推移而变成简并状态的思想，即原子中的电子和原子核分离开来，并且各自形成了非常致密的结构。20 世纪 60 年代发现的中子星就是这类简并星中最典型的代表。

赞斯特拉最近对行星状星云中的 *O* 型星的温度进行了测定[1]，结果表明，这些恒星极有可能全部属于“白矮星”类型，其平均密度比地球上已知的任何物质都大。他对大约 20 颗这类恒星进行观测，测得的温度在 30,000℃到 100,000℃之间，而它们的光度却相对较低。对于一个典型的行星状星云核，我们可以假设照相星等为 12.5 等时的视差为 0.002 角秒，这使得这类恒星的绝对星等为 +4，大约比典型的银河系内 *O* 型星暗 8 个星等。诚然，在这个范围里，随着温度的升高发光效率会降低，但是在半径恒定时，温度升高一定伴随着亮度成比例地增大，而即使在瑞利–金斯黑体辐射区域的最远端，亮度的增大也至少与温度的一次方成正比。因此这些恒星的半径一定非常小。

赞斯特拉根据测定的恒星亮度与星云亮度之间的差别得到了这些数值，而现在人们认为星云的发光是由恒星辐射（舒曼区激发）产生的，并且全部被转化成长波辐射。因此星云给我们提供了由目视星等到热星等的改正方法。如果不是完全转化，那么恒星温度要比计算得到的温度高。改正值介于 2 个星等到 7 或 7.5 个星等之间，平均情况在 5 个星等左右，因此温度应当大于 55,000℃。这样，恒星的热星等应当比太阳亮大约 5.9 个星等，而表面温度是太阳的 10 倍。这就意味着其半径为太阳的 1/43，因而即使它的质量等于太阳的质量，其密度也要大于 100,000 g/cm$^3$。

然而，这些恒星的质量当然会更大。就一个典型的行星状星云而言，在距离核心 6 个角秒处，其自转速度沿视线方向的速度分量可取为 5 km/s，而视差为 0.002

pressure, or if the axis is inclined to the line of sight, the figure comes out even greater. This may be set off against the allowance for the mass of the nebular envelope. The data indicate, therefore, a mean density of $10^6$ or $10^7$ gm./c.c., which is greater than has even been suggested for any other bodies, and points conclusively to a degenerate state of matter.

These bodies appear to be at the upper end of a sequence of "white" dwarfs, as may be seen from the following summary:

| | *Mv* | Spectrum. |
|---|---|---|
| Planetary nuclei | +4 | *O* |
| *o* Ceti *B* | 6 | *B8e* |
| $o^2$ Eridani *B* | 11 | *A0* |
| Sirius *B* | 10 | *A5* |
| van Maanen's star | 14.5 | *F* |
| Wolf 489 | 13 | *G* |

It looks as if this sequence were roughly parallel to the main sequence, probably separated from it by a sparsely populated band, and with considerable scattering within it; at least, the general trend is evident, and the reason why no red stars of the "collapsed" type have been discovered is of course obvious.

There are grave difficulties in the assumption that the source of energy within these white dwarfs is of the same nature as that within giants and main sequence stars, so that it seems worth while to point out that they have no very obvious need for a subatomic source at all. Just before degeneracy sets in, the internal temperatures must be of the order of at least 50 times those of a main sequence star built on the "diffuse" model, or fully $10^9$ degrees; Milne's calculation for the companion of Sirius[3] indicates a central temperature not exceeding (but apparently approaching) $3\times10^9$ degrees. The rate of radiation of such a star is only about 1/100 of that of the sun, or say one calorie per gram in 60 years; taking the specific heat as 3 (when the gas is still on the edge of degeneracy) we see that there is an internal store of heat sufficient for radiation at the white dwarf rate for something of the order of $10^{11}$ years. Of course, the very fact that the star is about to become degenerate means that not nearly all the kinetic energy of the nuclei and electrons will actually be available for radiation; much of it must remain as zero-point energy permanently in the star. But against this we must set the further energy to be obtained from such contraction as is still possible; at these small radii this energy is large. On the whole, then, the life of a white dwarf comes out, without any subatomic sources, entirely comparable with that of any star that derives its energy from the transmutation of hydrogen into heavier elements.

If the available subatomic energy of a main sequence star is exhaustible, the period spent in the main sequence will be followed by one of gravitational contraction; in the early stages this will be rapid, because the radius is large, and because at least half the energy gained will go into heating the interior of the star; in the late stages, the internal temperature will actually be falling, gravitational contraction will be very effective (if

角秒，由此推出其质量是太阳的 80 倍 [2]。如果气体部分地由辐射压力支撑，或其自转轴与视线方向倾斜，其质量数值将更大。这就可以作为补充从而平衡星云外包层的质量。这个数值还表明，其平均密度为 $10^6$ 或 $10^7$ g/cm$^3$ 之间，因此远远大于任何其他物体的密度，可以认为这里的物质处在简并态。

这些天体出现在“白”矮星星序的上端，参见如下的汇总结果：

| | 目视星等 | 光谱型 |
|---|---|---|
| 星云核 | +4 | *O* |
| 鲸鱼座 *o* 星 | 6 | *B8e* |
| 波江座 $o^2$ 星 | 11 | *A0* |
| 天狼星伴星 | 10 | *A5* |
| 范玛宁星 | 14.5 | *F* |
| 豺狼座489号星 | 13 | *G* |

粗看起来这个星序与主星序大致平行，似乎通过一个稀少族带和主星序分开，并且内部有明显的弥散。至少这个总趋势是显而易见的，同时为何没有发现“塌陷”的红矮星的原因也是明显的。

很难假设这些白矮星的能源与巨星和主序星的能源是一样的，因此，值得指出的是它们并没有非常明确地表现出对亚原子能源的需要。在进入简并态以前其内部温度的数量级至少是按“扩散”模型计算的主序星温度的 50 倍，可达 $10^9$ 度。米耳恩对天狼星伴星 [3] 的计算表明，其中心温度没有超过（但明显接近）$3\times10^9$ 度。其辐射率仅是太阳的 1/100，或者说在 60 年中每克仅产生 1 卡路里热能。假设比热是 3（当气体仍处在简并态的边缘）我们可以看到如果以天狼星伴星的辐射率计算，其内部的储能足以辐射约 $10^{11}$ 年。当然，白矮星即将变为简并态表明，并非原子核和电子的所有动能都将可以用来辐射，大部分动能会以零点能量的形式永久地保留在白矮星内。与此相反，我们也必须假定仍有可能从这类收缩过程中获取更多的能量，因为收缩到如此小的体积时这种能量也是很大的。总之在没有亚原子提供能量的情况下，白矮星的寿命完全可以与任何从氢转变成重元素的过程中获得能量的恒星的寿命相当。

如果主序星恒星可被利用的亚原子能被耗尽，那么在主星序阶段之后将会出现一个引力收缩阶段。在最初阶段这个过程进行得很快，因为其半径很大，而且至少有一半的能量被用来加热中心部分。到晚期恒星内部温度将下降，此时引力收缩效应将非常明显（如果简并还不太显著），而辐射率将变小，因此演化晚期要比早期缓

degeneracy is not too marked), and the rate of radiation will have become small. The fairly late stages will therefore be passed through very much more slowly than the early ones, and there will be a marked statistical concentration of the stars at radii perhaps two or three times the minimum figures calculated by Milne for a fully degenerate star. The minimum values are roughly $M^{-1/3}/80$ times the sun's radius, for a star of mass $M$ times that of the sun, and where the masses are known the radii are all of about the anticipated size. Particularly high densities are clearly to be expected for the *O*-stars. In van Maanen's star, with a radius of 0.007 times the sun, it is tempting to suppose we have a massive star in a very late stage indeed; if Milne's formula is applicable, the mass must be at least 8 times the sun, which would mean an Einstein shift corresponding to at least 700 km./sec. This could easily be tested by observation.

It is worth remarking that in a century or less the true radial velocity of a star of such large proper motion and parallax as this could be found from the second order term in the proper motion; the relativity effect, even if much smaller than 700 km./sec., could then be fairly definitely determined.

However that may be, we have now fairly good evidence that stars of all masses can "die"; this does not prove that transmutation rather than annihilation of matter is the source of stellar energy, but it clearly favours it. For Milne's theory leads to the conclusion that a mainly or nearly degenerate star will have a central temperature that may be much less than, but cannot be greater than $3.9\times10^{9}M^{5/6}$, and this seems inadequate to stimulate a source of energy that was not active in the main sequence, especially if all stars have dense hot cores, as Milne believes. Thus the very latest stages of degeneracy, where the specific heat is small and contraction difficult, must be run through rapidly, and the total duration of the white dwarf stage probably is not much greater than we have already calculated. The probable relative abundance of white dwarfs is then somewhat difficult to reconcile with a time-scale of $10^{13}$ or $10^{14}$ years, but fits well with the transmutation theory time-scale.

The view that the nuclei of planetary nebulae are "white dwarfs" has, we now find, already been propounded by Jeans in "The Universe Around Us", pp. 309–311. That we had both failed to notice this can be excused, if at all, only by the great popularity of the publication in which the theory was announced, but we sincerely regret the oversight. In the application of this result we differ from Jeans, since he tentatively placed these stars at the beginning of stellar evolution, while we place them, with the other white dwarfs, at the end.

(**127**, 661-662; 1931)

H. N. Russell: Princeton University, Mar. 31.
R. d'E. Atkinson: Rutgers University, Mar. 31.

References:

1 *Zeit. f. Astrophysik*, 2, 1 (1931).

2 Cf. Russell, Dugan, and Stewart, *Astronomy*, 835.

3 *Mon. Not. R.A.S.*, 91, 39 (1930).

慢得多。当恒星半径达到米耳恩计算的简并最小半径的2~3倍时，将出现明显的统计富集现象。对于质量为太阳质量的$M$倍的恒星，其半径最小值约为太阳的$M^{-1/3}/80$倍。只要已知质量，半径大小就可以预测出来。显然我们可以预期$O$型星具有特别高的密度。对半径为太阳0.007倍的范玛宁星，我们倾向于把它看作是演化到很晚阶段的大质量恒星。假定可以使用米耳恩公式，其质量至少应是太阳的8倍，这说明对应的爱因斯坦红移大约是700 km/s，这很容易用观测来检验。

值得一提的是，在近一个世纪的时间里，一个如此大自行和视差的恒星，其视向速度可以由自行的二次项而求得。即使是远小于700 km/s的相对论效应也能很确切地测定出来。

无论如何，我们已有很好的证据证明所有质量的恒星都会“死亡”，虽然这并不能证明恒星能源是由物质转换产生的而不是由湮灭产生的，但却明显地对此有利。由米耳恩的理论可以推出：接近简并态的恒星的中心温度可能会远远小于，但不可能大于$3.9\times10^{9}\,M^{5/6}$，因此不足以激活在主星序没有被激活的产能机制，尤其是在如米耳恩认为的所有恒星均具有致密而热的核心的情况下。因此在比热很小而收缩困难的简并最后阶段，演化进行得非常快，处于白矮星阶段的总时间很可能不会大大高于我们已经计算出来的数值。因此白矮星的相对丰度很难用$10^{13}$或$10^{14}$年的时间尺度来估算，但却与转换理论的时间尺度相符。

我们现在发现，行星状星云核是“白矮星”的观点已经被金斯在《我们周围的宇宙》一书的第309页~311页中提出。我们俩以前没有提及这一点也许可以得到大家的原谅，因为发布这个理论的文章很多，但我们也为自己的疏忽而感到遗憾。不过在运用这个理论时，我们与金斯的观点不一致，因为他试探性地认为这类恒星是处在恒星演化的初始阶段，而我们认为这些恒星以及其他白矮星都处在演化的最后阶段。

（曹惠来 翻译；蒋世仰 审稿）

# The Molecular Weights of Proteins

W. T. Astbury and H. J. Woods

## Editor's Note

**Although the importance of proteins in living things was widely recognised in the 1930s, there were only rudimentary ideas of how these molecules were constructed. William Astbury at the University of Leeds had made a special study of natural proteins, such as the keratin of which hair is made, using X-ray diffraction. As he explains here, his attention had been captivated by the work of The Svedberg in Uppsala in Sweden, who had developed an ultra-centrifuge for measuring the molecular weights of complex molecules. Astbury and Henry John Woods, his colleague, used this as a starting point for an entirely speculative (and mistaken) account of how protein molecules in general might be constructed.**

ONE of the most satisfactory features of recent advances in the X-ray analysis of compounds of high molecular weight has been the degree of co-ordination between the efforts of the structure analyst and those of the chemist. Especially is this true in the case of investigations of the structure of cellulose and its derivatives. The question of protein structure, however, appears to bring in its train problems of quite another order of complexity, and it does not seem to be at all clear what is connoted by the phrase "molecular weights of proteins". Such X-ray photographs of fibrous proteins as have been obtained point to the periodic repetition of comparatively simple units with imperfect or variable side-linkages. In the quest for chemical data to correlate with these results, the crystallographer is at once brought up against the remarkable observations of Svedberg, that there are groups of soluble proteins of "molecular weights" which are simple multiples of 34,500. The present situation is most simply described by quotations from two recent letters[1,2] to *Nature*: —

1. "The two most striking demonstrations in recent years of such uniformity are afforded by Svedberg's brilliant application of the ultracentrifuge to determine the particle mass of soluble proteins, classes of "molecular weight" 1, 2, 3, and 6 times the common factor 34,500 being distinguished, and Gorter and Grendel's demonstration that under appropriate conditions soluble proteins exhibit the phenomenon of surface spreading on liquids, and that all occupy the same surface area irrespective of particle mass (1, 2, 3, or 6 times 34,500). Using Svedberg's common factor 34,500 for the basis of their calculations, the Dutch workers obtain a value for the radius of the unit particle (22.5 A.) identical with that determined by Svedberg experimentally."

2. "Three determinations of the sedimentation equilibrium of insulin at a *p*H of 6.7–6.8 gave as a mean value for the molecular weight 35,100, which within the limits of experimental error is the same as that for egg albumin, 34,500, and for Bence Jones

# 蛋白质的分子量

威廉·阿斯特伯里，亨利·约翰·伍兹

## 编者按

尽管在20世纪30年代蛋白质在生物体中的重要作用就得到了广泛的认可，但当时人们对于蛋白质分子是如何组成的还只有一些初步的概念。利兹大学的威廉·阿斯特伯里应用X射线衍射法对包括构成头发的角蛋白等多种天然蛋白进行了专门的研究。阿斯特伯里在这篇文章中指出，瑞典乌普萨拉的斯韦德贝里发明了一种能够测量复杂分子分子量的超速离心机，这一工作引起了他的注意。阿斯特伯里和他的同事亨利·约翰·伍兹正是以此为出发点推测了（尽管是错误地）总体上蛋白质分子的可能构建方式。

在利用X射线衍射方法分析高分子化合物方面的最新进展中，其中一个最令人满意的方面是结构分析学家和化学家之间的高度合作，尤其是对纤维素及其衍生物结构的分析。然而，在对蛋白质结构问题的研究中似乎还会遇到一系列另一种层面上的难题，并且我们也根本不清楚“蛋白质分子量”一词的确切内涵。已经得到的纤维蛋白的X射线照片显示，蛋白质是由一些相对比较简单的单元通过周期性重复构成的，这些单元带有一些可变的侧链基团。在寻找与这些结果相对应的化学数据时，晶体学家要想办法解释斯韦德贝里的怪异实验结果：许多可溶性蛋白质的“分子量”都是34,500的整数倍。对目前研究情况的最简单的描述可以从《自然》杂志的两篇快报文章[1, 2]中得知：

1．“近年来关于这种一致性的两项最激动人心的成果分别来自于斯韦德贝里与戈特和格伦德尔。斯韦德贝里巧妙地用超速离心机测定了可溶性蛋白质的分子量，并按“分子量”是公因子34,500的1、2、3、6倍而对它们进行了分级。戈特和格伦德尔的研究则表明，可溶性蛋白质在合适的条件下会铺展于液体表面，此时不管蛋白质的分子量有多大（公因子34,500的1、2、3、6倍），它们都占据相同的表面积。此外，荷兰的研究者以斯韦德贝里得到的公因子34,500为计算的基础，测算出了单元粒子的半径值（22.5 Å），这一数值与斯韦德贝里通过实验测定的结果完全一致。”

2．“在pH值为6.7 ~ 6.8的条件下，采用沉降平衡法对胰岛素的分子量进行测定，三次测定结果的平均值表明该蛋白的分子量为35,100，考虑到实验误差范围，可以认为这一数值和其他一些蛋白质的分子量是相同的，比如，卵清蛋白的分子量为34,500，

protein, 35,000....The sedimentation equilibrium determinations show that crystalline insulin is homogeneous with regard to molecular weight, that is, the molecules in the sample studied were all of the same weight."

If now we consider this problem from the purely crystallographic point of view—and it has been demonstrated that proteins under certain conditions can give rise to X-ray crystal photographs—the numbers 1, 2, 3, and 6 immediately invite attention as being possible numbers of "molecules" which can go to form a unit of pattern. The suggestion thus arises that, provided we can explain the occurrence of the weight 34,500, the rest may be merely another aspect of that grouping of molecules which is called crystalline. But if this is so, we have to account for the non-occurrence of the number 4, and the explanation of this gap must be given in terms of some outstanding characteristic of proteins in general.

In order to explain the sequence of numbers observed, it does not seem necessary to invoke anything more unfamiliar than the ordinary peptide chain, –CO–NH–CHR–CO–NH–CHR–, which is built up of a succession of triads of which the –CO– and –NH– groups are unsaturated; for if we postulate that the –CO– and –NH– groups of neighbouring chains can be linked together by secondary valences, the following simple crystallographic combinations[3] are at once available (Figs. 1 *a*, 1 *b*, 1 *c*, 1 *d*).

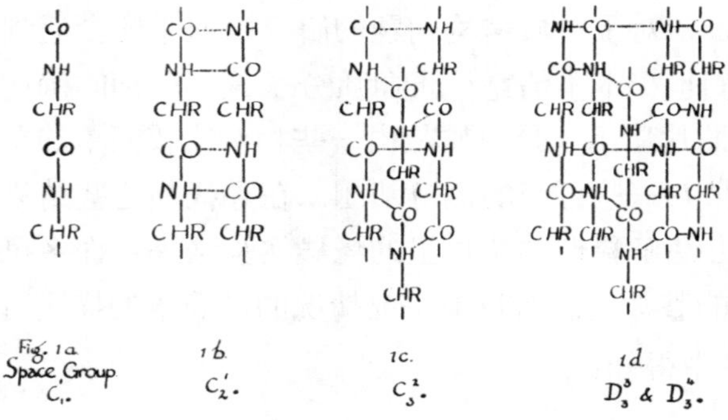


Fig. 1.

In Fig. 1 *b*, corresponding to the crystallographic space-group $C_2^1$, the unit of pattern is a pair of chains pointing in opposite directions, while the basis of Fig. 1 *c*, space-group $C_3^2$, is a self-contained threefold screw of chains all pointing in the same direction. In Fig. 1 *d* one of the chains has been omitted to avoid confusion, but it will be seen that it is a grouping which is a combination of (*b*) and (*c*) based on the space-groups $D_3^3$ and $D_3^4$, and is also a self-contained threefold screw, but this time not of single chains, but of pairs of chains such as are shown in Fig. 1 *b*. All these molecular associations are well-defined crystallographic types—the arrangement shown in Fig. 1 *d*, for example, corresponds to the structure of such a common crystal as quartz—which might be expected to undergo reversible dissociation into their constituent units, or sub-groups. That such a process actually does take place is best illustrated by the words[4] of Svedberg himself: —"The protein molecules containing more than one group of weight 34,500 are, as a rule,

本周蛋白的分子量为 35,000 等。沉降平衡的测定结果表明从分子量的角度上说结晶胰岛素是均一的，也就是说，被测样品中的所有分子都具有相同的分子量。”

如果现在我们完全从晶体学角度来思考这个问题，或者说我们已经证实蛋白质在某些条件下可以产生 X 射线晶体衍射图，那么我们会立刻联想到上述数字 1、2、3、6 可能就是能够产生某种衍射图样单元的“分子”的个数。如果这种猜想成立，而且若是我们能够解释分子量为 34,500 的结构单元的存在，那么剩下的可能就只是晶体分子中单元结构如何分组的问题了。但是，即使这样，我们还是必须说明数字 4 为何没有出现，对这个缺口的解释必须考虑蛋白质总体上的一些突出特点。

为了解释观测到的数字序列，我们没有必要引入任何比普通肽链更不熟悉的东西。我们知道，肽链 –CO–NH–CHR–CO–NH–CHR– 是由一系列三联体组成的，其中的 –CO– 和 –NH– 是不饱和基团。如果我们假设相邻肽链中的 –CO– 和 –NH– 可以通过副价键连接起来，那么就可以立刻得到以下这些简单的晶体组合样式[3]（图 1*a*、1*b*、1*c*、1*d*）。

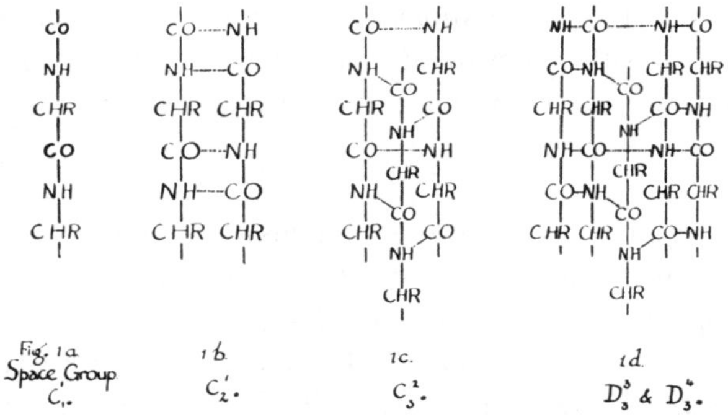


图 1

在图 1*b* 中，样式单元是方向相反的一对肽链，这对应于晶体学上的空间群 $C_2^1$，而图 1*c* 中的样式单元是由三条方向一致的肽链组合成的独立的三螺旋，这对应于晶体学上的空间群 $C_3^2$。在图 1*d* 中，为避免过于混乱我们省略了其中的一条肽链，但可以看出这是在空间群 $D_3^3$ 和 $D_3^4$ 的基础上形成的一种晶体组合样式，它结合了图 *b* 和图 *c* 的特点，其样式单元也是独立的三螺旋，不过每股螺旋并不是单条肽链，而是如图 1*b* 中所示的三对肽链。所有这些分子缔合都有明确的晶型。比如，图 1*d* 所示的结构排列就是一种非常常见的晶型结构——石英，也许可以认为这种晶型结构能够可逆地解离成其组成单元，或者叫亚基。斯韦德贝里本人的一段话[4]很好地描述了实际发生的这种过程：“一般来说，当溶液 pH 升高到超过某一特定值时，由多个分子

dissociated into molecules of lower numbers of groups of 34,500 when the *p*H of the solution is raised over a certain value. Thus the proteins of weight (6×34,500) split up into molecules of 1/2, 1/3, and 1/6 of the original molecule, but never into molecules of 1/4 or 1/5 of the original. This is in line with the fact that proteins possessing these latter weights at or near their isoelectric point have not been met with. At sufficiently high alkalinity all proteins have the same molecular weight, viz., 34,500."

The problem embodied in the last sentence still remains for discussion, and we should like to suggest as the interpretation of this, the most fundamental difficulty of all, that the observed constancy of unit molecular weight is simply a case of the vibrational instability of peptide chains when their length exceeds a certain value. If we accept the X-ray indications that the fibrous proteins, such as hair[5] and silk,[6] are based on the periodic repetition of comparatively simple units, then the probability of disruptive resonance occuring among the constituents of the peptide chain will continually increase with the length, so that excessively long chains would be liable to spontaneous decomposition into shorter chains. We may imagine some such process taking place in the laboratory of the living cell as the amino-acids are laid down in long chains at a surface and consolidated by crystallographic groupings in the manner suggested above, or by intra-molecular folding such as has been demonstrated in the case of wool and hair.[5] From this point of view, it does not seem likely that the unit molecular weight of proteins is strictly constant—this, too, is in agreement with experiment—but there is a strong probability that, given the appropriate conditions, many proteins will be based on a roughly constant weight of peptide chain.*

A phenomenon which appears to involve analogous reasoning is the decay of tension at constant length which takes place in stretched hair containing moisture, and which has been investigated by Speakman.[7] A large part of this loss of tension is quite permanent,[8] in spite of the fact that the stretched hair still retains its power of recovering at least its original length in water. The rate of decay of tension varies with the type of wool or hair and with the nature of the wetting agent, and increases with rise of temperature. It is extremely rapid in steam, a short treatment with which permanently alters the load/extension curve, and so loosens the internal structure of the fibre that it may be caused to contract to two-thirds of its original length.[5]

It is clear, of course, that the wetting agent plays an important part in this permanent destruction of internal tension, but it seems not at all unlikely that vibrational instability

---

* If we assume the essential correctness of the structure proposed,[5] we may make an estimate of the length of peptide chain in animal hairs. The average molecular weight of the chief amino-acids in wool (which are present in roughly equal molecular proportions) is about 121, and three amino-acids occupy a length of 5.15 A. along the fibre axis. The length, corresponding to 34,500, is thus about 500 A. It is a striking fact that this is approximately the length which is the minimum possible to give the observed X-ray diffraction effects[9], That it is also near the actual length is indicated by the fuzziness which appears in X-ray photographs of hairs which have developed pronounced permanent decay of tension.

量为 34,500 的基团组成的蛋白质分子会降解为由较少分子量为 34,500 的基团组成的小分子。这样，分子量为 6 × 34,500 的蛋白分子就会分解为分子量只有原分子的 1/2、1/3 或 1/6 的小分子，但绝不可能产生分子量为原分子的 1/4 或 1/5 的小分子。这和实验事实是相吻合的，即在相应的等电点处及其附近并没有发现具有后两种分子量的蛋白质。在碱性足够强的条件下，所有蛋白质都具有相同的分子量，即 34,500。”

前段最后一句话涉及了一个仍有待讨论的问题，这是个最基本也最难的问题，我们倾向于这样来解释，实验中发现的单元分子量的恒定性，仅仅是由于当肽链长度超过某一值时产生的振动不稳定性造成的。如果我们认可从 X 射线衍射结果得到的推论，即认为组成头发 [5] 和蚕丝 [6] 等的纤维蛋白都是由相对简单的单元结构周期性重复构成的，那么，随着肽链长度的增加，组成肽链的各部分之间的共振造成肽链断裂的可能性也会增加，这样，过长的肽链肯定会自发地分解为短一些的肽链。我们可以设想发生在活细胞“加工厂”中的某些类似的过程，在合成蛋白质的细胞器的膜表面，氨基酸被添加到长的肽链上，然后按照前面所述的晶体组合样式，或者通过像羊毛和头发中那样的分子内折叠 [5] 组合在一起。从这种观点来看，蛋白质结构单元的分子量应该不会是严格恒定的，这和实验结果也是吻合的。但很有可能的是，在给定的适宜条件下，许多蛋白质将是由分子量大致恒定的肽链组成的。*

另一个可能由类似原因导致的现象是关于毛发张力消退的。斯皮克曼发现，被拉直的湿发在保持长度不变的同时张力会逐渐消退 [7]。尽管这些被拉直的头发至少在水中仍能恢复到它原来的长度，但大部分张力的损失是永久性的 [8]。张力消退的速度随着羊毛或头发的类型及浸润溶剂的性质的变化而变化，随着温度的升高而加快。在蒸汽中张力消退的速度非常快。一个短暂的蒸汽处理就可以永久性地改变毛发的载荷 – 伸展曲线，使纤维的内部结构变松弛，以至于可能使毛发的长度收缩到原长的 2/3[5]。

当然，现在已经很清楚，在内部张力被永久性破坏的过程中浸润溶剂起着重要的作用，但是，肽链振动的不稳定性可能也是这一过程中的一个必需因素。对拉直

---

* 如果我们假设前面提出的结构基本上是正确的[5]，那么我们就可以估计动物毛发中肽链的长度了。羊毛中主要氨基酸（这些氨基酸在羊毛中的分子比例基本相等）的平均分子量大约为121，另外知道3个氨基酸沿纤维轴方向的长度为5.15 Å，那么分子量34,500对应的长度大约为500 Å。令人吃惊的是，这大致等于能够观测到X射线衍射效应的最小长度[9]，同时也与由发生张力永久性显著消退的毛发的X射线衍射照片中的模糊衍射斑推测得到的毛发中蛋白质的实际长度相接近。

also is an essential factor in the process. After treatment of stretched hair with steam, the longitudinal swelling of the fibre in water is considerably increased, a fact which, taken in conjunction with the observation that X-ray photographs of hair which has been held stretched in water for several weeks show a definite fuzziness of the reflections associated with the length of the peptide chains, suggests that the average length of the chains is decreased by sustained tension in the presence of water.

We have recently commenced an investigation of the influence of radiations, such as ultra-violet light and X-rays, on the elastic and other properties of animal hairs, so that in this connexion it is convenient to mention here some remarkable observations which we have made on *unstretched* wool exposed for some sixty hours to the full beam of a Shearer X-ray tube (copper anticathode). After this treatment the fibres show many of the properties which are characteristic of wool which has been exposed *in the stretched state* to the action of steam. For example, they have the property of contracting in steam by as much as 37 percent below their unstretched length, and their longitudinal swelling in water after steaming is found to be increased from the 1 percent of normal wool to as much as 10 percent. This seems to be a clear case of the disruptive action of high-energy quanta on the length and cohesion of peptide chains, and must be closely related to the influence of various radiations on biological activity.

These experiments are being continued and will be reported in detail in due course.

(**127**, 663-665; 1931)

W. T. Astbury, H. J. Woods: Textile Physics Laboratory, University, Leeds, Mar. 27.

---

References:

1 Rimington, C., *Nature*, **127**, 440 (1931).

2 Svedberg, T., *Nature*, **127**, 438 (1931).

3 Astbury, W. T., and Yardley, K., *Phil. Trans. Roy. Soc.*, A, **224**, 221 (1924). (See Plate 5 (1), (7), Plate 16 (144), Plate 18 (157 and 158).).

4 Svedberg, T., *Trans. Faraday Soc.*, *General Discussion on Colloid Science applied to Biology*, 741 (1930).

5 Astbury, W. T., *J. Soc. Chem. Ind.*, **49**, 441 (1930): *J. Textile Science*, **4**, 1 (1931). Astbury, W. T., and Woods, H. J., *Nature*, **126**, 913 (1930). Astbury, W. T., and Street, A., *Phil. Trans. Roy. Soc.*, A, **230**, 75 (1931).

6 Brill, R., *Ann. Chem.*, **434**, 204 (1923). Meyer, K. H., and Mark, H., *Ber.*, **61** (1932; 1928). Kratky, O., *Z. phys. Chem.*, **B5**, 297 (1929).

7 Speakman, J. B., *Proc. Roy. Soc.*, B, **103**, 377 (1928).

8 Speakman, J. B., *Trans. Farad. Soc.*, **25**, 169 (1929).

9 Hengstenberg, J., and Mark, H., *Zeit. f. Krist.*, **69**, 271 (1928).

的头发进行蒸汽处理后，该纤维在水中的纵向延伸显著增加。另外，在水中被拉伸了几个星期的头发的 X 射线衍射照片显示，存在一个与肽链长度有关的边界明确的模糊图案。以上这些事实提示我们在水中毛发肽链平均长度的减少可能是由于持续的张力引起的。

我们最近开始了一项关于紫外线、X 射线等辐射对动物毛发弹性和其他特性的影响的研究，这里我们要提及一些相关的值得注意的实验结果。我们对在希勒 X 射线管（铜对阴极）的最大强度束下照射约 60 个小时的**未被拉伸**的羊毛进行了观察。结果发现，经过这样处理后的羊毛纤维表现出了很多与**拉伸状态下**接受蒸汽处理的羊毛一样的特征。例如，它们在蒸汽中都具有长度可以收缩到比未被拉伸时短 37% 的特性，另外，蒸汽处理后它们在水中纵向的延伸都会增加，增加幅度从普通羊毛的 1% 到 10% 不等。这也许就是高能量子对肽链长度和内聚性具有破坏作用的实例，各种辐射对生命活动的影响一定与此密切相关。

这些实验正在进行之中，详细的实验结果将在适当的时候公布出来。

（李飞 翻译；周筠梅 审稿）

# Cytological Theory in Relation to Heredity*

C. D. Darlington

## Editor's Note

**Cyril Dean Darlington was trained as a botanist but converted himself into a cytologist after it had been recognised that chromosomes, located in the cell nuclei of plants and animals, carry genes that to determine the organisation of living things. This article is an attempt to explain the distinction between the two forms of cell division that occur in living things: the division of body cells into two essentially identical cells, called mitosis, which is the basis for the growth of tissues in plants and animals, and the process of meiosis, which gives rise to cells containing half as many chromosomes as the original and which is the means by which germ cells are produced (in animals as well as plants). At this early stage in the development of genetics there were no known means of identifying of even locating the genes carried on the chromosomes.**

THE chromosome theory of heredity, by relating chromosome behaviour with the phenomena of inheritance, has obviously made it possible to apply the cytological method to the study of inheritance. With this profitable field before them, geneticists and cytologists have not hesitated to draw conclusions in the one field from observations made in the other, but in order to do so they have had to apply certain rules of interpretation. Their method has naturally been to assume, so far as possible, a direct relationship between cytological and genetical observations. The geneticist has therefore not only assumed that the material of every part of the chromosome has a specific genetic effect, which is a widely verified assumption; but also that the capacity of the chromosome for variation is equally specific, so that it is possible to refer to hereditary differences and to particles of chromosome alike as "genes". This second assumption is also widely verified; but it is subject to serious exceptions in that two different kinds of change have been shown to befall the same particle, namely, internal change and external change such as loss or re-arrangement. This constitutes no primary objection to the theory of the gene but rather indicates a necessary enlargement of its scope.

Cytologists, on the other hand, in translating their observations into genetical terms, have sought to apply the chromosome theory to the interpretation of meiosis. With the help of the simple rule that the pairing of chromosomes is a criterion of their relationship, they have set to work to examine meiosis in hybrids and in ring-forming plants (such as various species of *Oenothera*). The results of these studies have been confusing because investigators have not first examined the principles they were applying to see if they were indeed principles or merely empirical rules of special derivation and therefore of limited application. We now have evidence by which to test them.

---

* Substance of three lectures given at the Royal Institution on Mar. 10, 17, and 24.

# 遗传的细胞学理论 *

西里尔·迪安·达林顿

## 编者按

西里尔·迪安·达林顿原本是要被培养成为一名植物学家的，然而当人们认识到位于植物和动物细胞核中的染色体是携带基因的载体，基因决定生物的组织结构之后，他便转向这一领域，成为了一名细胞学家。本文试图阐释生物体内两种细胞分裂形式之间的差别：即有丝分裂和减数分裂。前者是指体细胞分裂成两个含有相同遗传信息的细胞，是动植物组织生长的基础；而后者分裂得到的细胞所含的染色体数目只有原来的一半，是动植物产生生殖细胞的方式。那个时候还处在遗传学发展的早期阶段，尚未出现可以鉴别基因的方法，甚至连染色体上基因的定位都无从下手。

遗传的染色体理论将染色体行为与遗传现象联系起来，这使得将细胞学方法应用于遗传研究成为可能。在这一回报丰厚的领域里，遗传学家和细胞学家们可以根据一个领域内的观察结果毫不迟疑地推出另一个领域中的结论，但为了能够顺利地进行这一工作，就必须建立某些解释规则。他们的方法自然是尽可能地设想出细胞学和遗传学观察二者之间存在的直接关联。因此遗传学家不仅假设染色体的每部分都具有特定的遗传作用（该假设已被广泛证实），而且还假设染色体具有特定的变异能力，因此就可以将遗传差异和诸如染色体颗粒之类称为“基因”。第二个假设也已被广泛证实，但存在严重异常的情况，即缺失或重排等内部变化和外部变化发生在同一颗粒上时。但是这些例外不足以构成反对基因学说的条件，相反表明该学说的作用范围需要进一步拓展。

另一方面，当细胞学家用遗传学词汇描述他们的观察结果时，他们已经是在尝试用染色体学说来解释减数分裂了。在这一以染色体配对为关系准则的简单规则的指导下，细胞学家们开始研究杂交体及成环植物（例如月见草属的各种植物）的减数分裂情况。这些研究的结果是令人怀疑的，因为研究者们并没有首先验证他们所参照的原则，以证实这些原则确实是真正的法则，还是仅仅是根据特定情况推导出来的适用范围有限的经验法则。现在，我们有了可以检验它们的证据。

---

* 本文是作者分别于 3 月 10 日、17 日和 24 日在英国皇家科学院所发表的演讲的主要内容。

Meiosis consists in the occurrence of two successive divisions of a nucleus in the course of which the chromosomes divide once instead of twice as they would in two ordinary mitoses. Where the distribution of the chromosomes is regular, the four daughter nuclei therefore have half the number of chromosomes of the parent nucleus (Fig. 1).

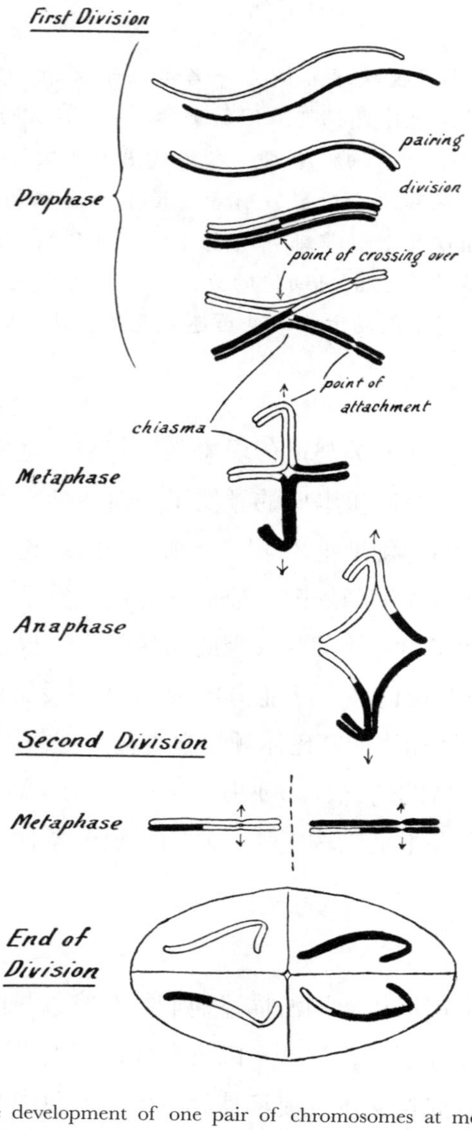


Fig. 1. Diagram to show the development of one pair of chromosomes at meiosis, and their relationship on the assumption that crossing over is the cause of chiasma formation. The four stages of prophase shown are : (1) leptotene, (2) pachytene before division, (3) pachytene after division, (4) diplotene to diakinesis.

At the first division, the chromosomes come together in pairs, and a whole chromosome of each pair passes to one pole to divide at the second division of the nucleus. To express this comparatively with regard to mitosis, we may say that while two half-chromosomes (or "chromatids") are associated in pairs at a mitosis, four are associated at the first metaphase

在减数分裂过程中，细胞核连续分裂两次而染色体只分裂一次，这与有丝分裂不同，在两次正常的有丝分裂过程中，细胞核分裂两次染色体也分裂两次。因而当染色体正常分配时，减数分裂产生的四个子细胞核具有母细胞核染色体数的一半（图 1）。

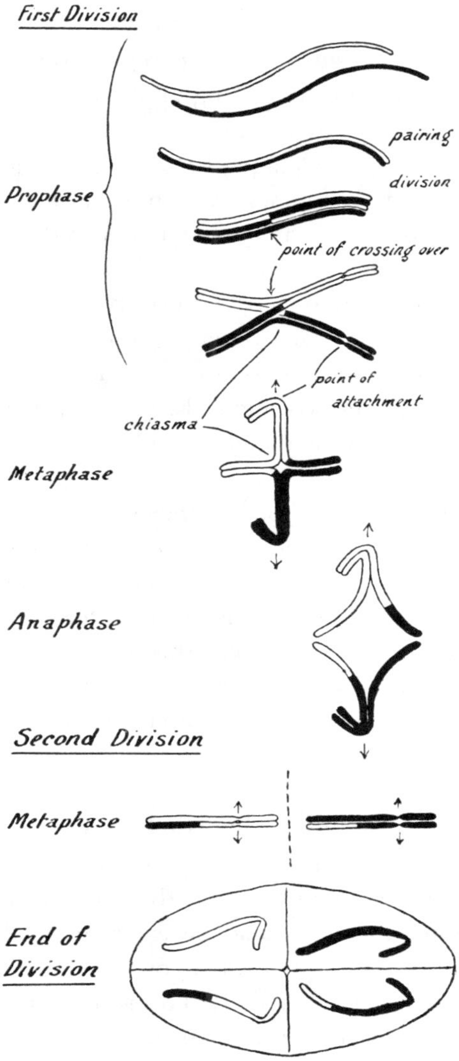


图 1. 一对染色体发生减数分裂的过程及这对染色体的关系示意图（假定形成交叉的原因是基因交换）。前期包括的四个阶段是：(1) 细线期，(2) 分裂前的粗线期，(3) 分裂后的粗线期，(4) 双线期至终变期。

第一次减数分裂时，染色体成对地聚集在一起，每对中都有一整条染色体移向细胞的一极，在细胞核第二次分裂时，该条染色体将发生分离。如果要以与有丝分裂进行对比的方式来表达，我们可以说：在有丝分裂过程中是两条“半染色体”（或

of meiosis. A numerical reduction in the chromosomes must be attributed directly to the lack of any splitting of the chromosomes in the interval between the two divisions of the nucleus such as ordinarily occurs. But this is readily related to the fact that each chromosome is already split into the two chromatids which have passed together to one pole. This in turn is related to the pairing of the chromosomes.

It has therefore seemed natural (since 1890) to regard the essential difference between meiosis and mitosis as consisting in the pairing of the chromosomes. Since different pairs of chromosomes pass at random to the two poles (so that $A_1$–$A_2$ and $B_1$–$B_2$ may give daughter nuclei $A_1B_1$ and $A_2B_2$ or, equally, $A_1B_2$ and $A_2B_1$), and since the chromosomes are qualitatively differentiated, it follows that those which pair and pass to opposite poles must be similar if meiosis is to yield similar reduced nuclei (Boveri). Clearly, likeness is a condition of pairing. But since the chromosomes that pair can be seen to be morphologically alike and therefore to be corresponding structures derived (so far as observation then showed) from opposite parents (Montgomery), it seemed enough to say that this pairing was due to the likeness of the chromosomes. An "incipient" association is often to be seen at mitosis in the somatic cells. Perhaps, therefore, meiosis was the final step in the sexual process in which the maternal and paternal elements at last united.

Such is, in a general way, the "explanation" of meiosis that is current today. To be sure, we now know that the association cannot be attributed to an attraction between chromosomes derived from opposite gametes, since pairing has been found in meiosis in parthenogenetic organisms,[1,2] and very often between chromosomes derived from the same gamete in polyploid plants. It may also be objected that this is merely to explain *ignotum per ignotius*. But it is still taken to be a satisfactory basis for cytological, genetical, and evolutionary deduction. Incompatible observations are freely ascribed to "mechanical" or "physiological" conditions.

There are many recent observations of this kind. There are tetraploid plants (such as *Primula sinensis*[3]), the nuclei of which contain four identical chromosomes of each of the twelve types that are represented twice in the diploid. These chromosomes usually associate in fours at meiosis, as they would be expected to do if likeness were the sole condition of pairing. But nearly always one, two, or three of these groups fail to be formed and their chromosomes appear merely paired. This is not explicable on the affinity theory. The chromosomes should be either *all* in fours or *all* in pairs.

Other observations of the same type are : (1) The occurrence of unpaired chromosomes in triploids, instead of all three identical chromosomes of each type being associated (*Zea*,[4] *Tulipa*,[5] *Lilium*[6]). (2) The occurrence of unpaired fragment chromosomes, although these have identical mates with which they can pair (*Secale*,[7] *Matthiola*,[8] *Tradescantia*[9]).

称“染色单体”）连接在一起成对存在；而在第一次减数分裂中期是四条染色单体聚集在一起。染色体数目减少的直接原因是在细胞核两次分裂的间期，染色体通常会少分裂一次。但这显然与每条染色体已经分裂成了两条染色单体，这两条染色单体共同移向细胞的一极有关，反过来后者又与染色体配对相关。

因此大家很自然地（从 1890 年开始）认为减数分裂和有丝分裂的本质区别就存在于染色体配对的过程中。因为不同对染色体是随机地移向两极的（因此 $A_1$–$A_2$ 和 $B_1$–$B_2$ 可以产生子细胞核 $A_1B_1$ 和 $A_2B_2$，也同样可以产生 $A_1B_2$ 和 $A_2B_1$），并且由于染色体是定性分化的，如果减数分裂产生的是相似的但染色体数目减少的细胞核，那么进行配对并移向相反两极的染色体也一定是相似的（博韦里）。这显然说明，相似性是染色体得以配对的一个条件。由于配对的染色体在形态学上是相似的，所以可以将它们看作是来自于（就继后进行的观察而言）异性双亲的对应结构（蒙哥马利），这似乎足以说明配对的原因是染色体的相似性。在体细胞有丝分裂时就经常可以看到“萌芽状态”的联会现象，因此，减数分裂很可能是有性生殖过程的最后一步，母本元素和父本元素在有性生殖过程中得以最终结合。

这是目前普遍接受的对减数分裂的“解释”。诚然，我们现在知道联会的发生并不是由于来自异性配子的染色体间存在某种吸引力，因为已经发现孤雌生殖的生物也存在减数分裂配对现象 [1,2]，而且在多倍体植物中，配对总是发生在来自相同配子的染色体间。也可能有人提出反对意见，认为这种释义解释得比原来需要解释的事物更难懂，但人们仍然把它当作是细胞学、遗传学和进化演绎的合理依据。而把与之矛盾的现象随意归咎于“机械条件”或“生理状态”的影响。

最近有许多这样的研究，例如四倍体植物（如藏报春 [3]）的细胞核含有四套相同的染色体组，每组含有 12 条不同类型的染色体，即二倍体的两倍。这些染色体在减数分裂时通常是以四条为一组进行联会，如果相似性是配对的唯一条件，则这和预期的结果是一致的。但是这些染色体中几乎总会有一组、两组或三组不能联会成功，而只是以成对形式出现。这种情况用亲近度理论是解释不通的，因为根据该理论，这些染色体应该**全部**是四条一组，或者**全部**是两条一组。

同类的研究还有：(1) 三倍体中存在着不发生配对的染色体，而不是三套染色体组中每种类型的染色体都进行联会（例如玉蜀黍属 [4]、郁金香属 [5]、百合属 [6]）。(2) 存在未配对的零散染色体，尽管在这些染色体上存在着完全相同的可以配对的对象，（如黑麦属 [7]、紫罗兰属 [8]、紫露草属 [9]）。

The only difference between these fragments and the other chromosomes which pair regularly appears to be their smaller size. If the triploids are examined, it is similarly found that the chromosomes which fail to associate regularly in threes are the small ones (*Hyacinthus*[10]). Therefore, not only *likeness* but also *size* bears some relation to the pairing of chromosomes.

If now we turn to consider the structures of the paired chromosomes at meiosis we find a variety of form that shows, at first sight, neither a rule in itself nor any clear relationship with ordinary mitosis. The two processes must be studied in their development in order to be seen in relationship.

The prophase of mitosis is characterised by a linear contraction of two threads, associated side by side, to become the two cylindrical rods which constitute the metaphase chromosome. At meiosis we find at the earliest stage a difference. The threads observed are single. They soon come together in pairs side by side and reproduce the conditions observed at the prophase of mitosis very closely indeed. But on account of their pairing they are present at this pachytene stage in half the number found at the prophase of a mitosis in the same organism. Evidently, therefore, the single threads at the earlier stage were chromosomes still undivided although in the earliest visible stage in mitosis they have already divided.

After an interval, splits appear in the pachytene thread, separating it into two threads, each of which is now seen to be double. But instead of these splits passing right along the paired chromosomes and separating them entirely, it is found, when they meet, that the double threads that separate in one part are not the same pair of threads that separate in another. The separated pairs of threads therefore change partners, and the points at which they change partners (there are often several distributed along the paired chromosome) are called "chiasmata". This stage is diplotene (Fig. 1).

Between diplotene and metaphase there is further linear contraction, and the structure of the paired chromosomes may remain the same in regard to the relationships of the four threads of which they are composed: that is, the chiasmata may remain stationary. But they may undergo a change which consists in the opening out of the loop that includes the spindle-attachment, at the expense of the adjoining loops, as though the spindle-attachments of the chromosomes were repelling one another. In other words, the chiasmata appear to move along the chromosome towards the ends: finally, the chromatids are associated in pairs with changes of partners only at the ends. Such changes of partners are called "terminal chiasmata", and the frequency of the end-to-end unions at metaphase corresponds with the frequency of the chiasmata seen earlier, when they were still interstitial, in small chromosomes (fragments) which only have one chiasma at most.[11] Further, in organisms with large chromosomes it is still possible to see the change of partner: at the end the association is double; it is between the ends of two pairs of chromatids, not merely between the ends of one pair of chromosomes.

这些不配对的染色体片段和其他进行正常配对的染色体的唯一区别就是它们会比较短小。对三倍体的联会研究同样可以发现，那些未能正常形成三倍体的染色体往往长度较短（如风信子属[10]）。因此，除了**相似性**之外，染色体的**长短**也与其能否发生配对有一定的关联。

如果我们转而考虑减数分裂中配对染色体的结构，我们会发现染色体配对的类型存在着多种方式，乍看起来，这些方式本身并无规律可循，且与普通有丝分裂的关系也不十分明确。要想了解有丝分裂和减数分裂的关系，就必须深入研究它们的详细过程。

有丝分裂前期的特点是，两条紧密相连的染色质丝发生线性收缩，从而形成了分裂中期的圆棒状染色体。我们发现减数分裂的起始期与此完全不同，它的染色质丝是单条的。不久之后，它们会聚集到一起，两两成对紧密排列，随后的过程的确与有丝分裂前期特别相似。但是在同一生物体内，染色体配对使得在减数分裂粗线期所观察到的染色体数目仅为有丝分裂前期的一半。由此可见，减数分裂初期的单条线状结构其实是尚未分开的染色体。而在有丝分裂中，染色体在可见阶段的最初就已经分开了。

减数分裂进行一段时间之后，粗线期的染色质丝开始出现分离，每条染色质丝分成两条，从而可以观察到双线状的结构。研究发现这些分裂并没有将配对的染色体完全分离，两个双线状结构分开的部位发生在染色体的不同区域。因而分离产生的一对双线状结构是染色体片段变换过的重新组合，它们发生交换的位点（一般认为配对染色体上分布着数个这样的位点）叫做“交叉”。这一时期被称为双线期（图 1）。

在双线期和中期之间，染色体会发生进一步的线性收缩，这时配对染色体四条线的结构关系还是相同的。也就是说，交叉可能尚处于静止状态。但似乎因为染色体上纺锤丝的附着部位相互排斥，导致相邻的环状结构被打开，并且分开的区域逐步扩大，预示着此时的染色体可能正经历着某种变化。换言之，交叉是沿着染色体向其末端移动的，最后染色单体成对连接在一起，仅在末端发生了交换，这种变化被称为“末端交叉”。研究表明，小染色体（片段）至多只发生一次交叉，它们在中期的末端结合频率与其交叉频率是一致的[11]。此外，在大染色体生物中，也可能会观察到交换发生在配对的染色体之间，这时染色体末端存在着两处连接，即不只是一对染色体的末端之间发生了交换，而是两对染色单体的末端都发生了交换。

These observations point to the chiasmata being the immediate cause of pairing between chromosomes. How can such a hypothesis be tested? It is found that given pairs of chromosomes have a constant range in the number of chiasmata formed. For example, in the *M* chromosome of *Vicia Faba*[12,11] from 3 to 13 chiasmata are found at the metaphase, with a mean of 8.1. The *M* chromosome, which is much shorter has a range of 1 to 6, with a mean of 3.0. If we suppose that small chromosomes arising by fragmentation have a chiasma frequency proportionate to their length as compared with their larger neighbours, then we can predict from observations of their size and of the observed frequency of chiasmata in the large chromosomes what their frequency of pairing will be, on this hypothesis. Thus, in the variety "Yellow" of *Fritillaria imperialis* it was found that the chiasma-frequency was 2.58 in the large chromosomes. The fragments were about one-ninth of the length of the large chromosomes. They should therefore have chiasmata in a frequency of 2.58/9 per pair, or 0.29. This means that they should pair in 0.29 cases (neglecting the frequency of one pair forming two chiasmata, which should be slight). They were observed to pair in 0.22 of cases.[11] Here is an example of the type of observation which is susceptible of statistical analysis and supports this hypothesis.

Now, if we admit chiasmata as the condition of chromosome pairing, a considerable simplification is possible in stating the relationship of mitosis and meiosis. Throughout the prophase of mitosis, the threads are held together by an attraction in pairs. The same rule applies to meiosis, for the evidences of failure of pairing of fragments, of odd chromosomes in triploids, and of the four chromosomes of a type in tetraploids all point to the chromosomes having no present attraction at metaphase. They are merely held together by the chiasmata—that is, by the attraction between the pairs of half chromosomes and the exchanges of partners amongst them; and this attraction exists equally at mitosis.

This being so, we must look to the earliest stage of prophase to find the essential difference between the two types of nuclear division. It evidently lies in the time at which the chromosomes split into their two halves. At mitosis, it is probable that this has already happened before the chromosomes appear at prophase. At meiosis, it does not happen until pachytene (possibly at the moment at which the diplotene loops appear). The prophase of meiosis therefore starts too soon, relative to the splitting of the chromosomes. If we consider that there is a universal attraction of threads in pairs at the prophase of any nuclear division, as we see it at mitosis, it follows that this condition is fulfilled by the pairing of chromosome threads when they are still single, and their separation at diplotene when they have at last come to divide. The decisive difference would therefore appear to be in the singleness of the early prophase threads in meiosis. This singleness may be attributed to one or both of two causes: (i) a delayed division of the chromosomes, (ii) a precocious onset of prophase. The second of these seems the more likely explanation, on account of the short duration of the pre-meiotic prophase in some animals. Either assumption would account for the most characteristic of all secondary features of meiosis, namely, the exaggerated linear contraction of the chromosomes, paired or unpaired, if the time relationship of metaphase to the division of the chromosomes remains the same.

上述观察表明交叉才是染色体配对的直接原因。那么怎样才能验证这一假说？研究发现给定染色体对中形成的交叉数都有一个恒定的范围。例如蚕豆的*M*染色体[12,11]在中期可以形成3到13个交叉，平均值为8.1。*M*染色体要短很多，可以形成1到6个，平均值为3.0。如果我们假设，断裂产生的小染色体的交叉频率和它们的长度所成的比例与邻近的长染色体一致，那么依据这一假说，我们就可以根据由观测得到的染色体片段长度以及长染色体发生交叉的频率来预测它们的配对频率。因此，我们发现冠花贝母的“黄花”品种中长染色体的交叉频率为2.58，染色体片段的长度约为长染色体的1/9，所以每对染色体片段的交叉频率应为2.58/9，即0.29。这意味着这些染色体片段之间发生配对的比例为0.29（每对染色体形成两个交叉的可能性很小，因而可以忽略不计）。实际观察到的配对比例为0.22[11]。上述这类观察结果就是一个易受统计分析影响并能印证本假说的例子。

在接受交叉是染色体配对条件的前提下，再来描述有丝分裂和减数分裂的关系就相当简单了。在有丝分裂前期，线状结构通过某种引力而结合在一起。同样的规则也适用于减数分裂，对于不能配对的染色体片段、三倍体中不能配对的剩余染色体以及四倍体中不能配对的同一类型的四条染色体，它们的存在都说明在减数分裂中期，这些染色体间缺乏这样的吸引力。它们仅仅由交叉维系在一起，即它们是由半染色体对之间的吸引力和交换维系在一起的，这种吸引力同样存在于有丝分裂中。

在这种情况下，要想找到这两种核分裂类型的本质区别，就必须从前期的最初阶段入手。很明显，区别就在于染色体是何时解离成两条染色单体的。在有丝分裂中，染色体很可能在前期之前就已经完成了这一解离；而在减数分裂中，染色体直到粗线期才发生解离（也可能是在双线期的交叉环出现的时候）。因此，相对于染色体的分离而言，减数分裂前期开始得太早了。假如我们认为在任何核分裂的前期，成对的染色质丝之间都普遍存在吸引力，正如在有丝分裂中看到的那样，则当减数分裂单体状态的染色质丝配对的时候，以及它们在双线期最终分离的时候就满足这一条件。因此决定性差异应该是在减数分裂前期的早期染色体为单体结构。造成单体结构的原因可能是下述两个中的一个或者兼而有之：(1）染色体的延迟分裂，(2）前期的早发性。用第二个理由来解释似乎更易被接受，因为在有些动物中，减数分裂前期之前的阶段持续时间比较短。如果中期和染色体分裂的时间关系也是一样的，那么在减数分裂的所有次要特征中最为特殊的一个特征就可以用这两个假设之中的任意一个来说明，即配对或未配对染色体的超常线性收缩。早熟论[13]可以通过观察减

This hypothesis of precocity[13] may be tested by the observation of a correlation between irregularities in meiosis and (*a*) abnormality in the timing of meiosis, and (*b*) diminished contraction of the chromosomes at metaphase.

The first of these tests is applicable to many organisms with occasional suppression of reduction; the aberrant nuclei enter on the prophase of meiosis either earlier or later than the normal nuclei.[14,15,16,17] When they are too early, it may be supposed that a premature division of the chromosomes has precipitated the prophase; when too late, it may be supposed that the prophase has been delayed. In either case, the chromosomes would no longer be single at early prophase and the condition of their pairing would be lost.

Such a cause of failure of pachytene pairing may be expected to be distinguishable by its effect on the contraction (the second kind of test). For when failure of metaphase pairing is not due to an upset in the timing of prophase but merely to failure of chiasma formation, we might expect normal meiotic contraction; this is the case in maize.[18] Where the prophase has been delayed, we might expect an approach to mitotic conditions; this is the case in *Matthiola*.[19,20] Other critical evidence in favour of the hypothesis has already been quoted in these columns.[21]

By trying to define in this way the relationship of meiosis to mitosis, we find out what is essential and therefore universal in meiosis, and what is unessential and secondary. Only when the direct interpretation of events in the nucleus is clear (as it now seems to be) can we attempt their genetical interpretation on a satisfactory basis.

Two examples of the genetical interpretation of chromosome behaviour at meiosis are of immediate importance. It has been shown in every organism that has been adequately tested that crossing-over can occur between corresponding parts of the paired chromosomes at meiosis, actually between the chromatids, so that crossing-over in the region between *C* and *D* in a pair of chromosomes *ABCDE* and *abcde* will give four kinds of chromatid: *ABCDE*, *ABCde*, *abcDE*, and *abcde* (Fig. 1). We may suppose that this crossing-over has no relation with anything observable cytologically; that it takes place when the chromosomes are intimately associated at pachytene and has no connexion with later behaviour. This view can only be taken when other possibilities are eliminated. We may also assume that crossing-over has some relationship with chiasmata, either as a cause ("chiasmatypy")[22,23], or as a consequence, through breakage and reunion of new threads.[10,9] The last possibility has been eliminated by the statistical demonstration that terminal unions correspond in frequency with interstitial chiasmata,[11] and that the number of terminal chiasmata increases *pari passu* with the reduction of interstitial chiasmata.[3,4,20] The first possibility, that the chromosomes fall apart as they come together, and that the exchanges of partners at chiasmata are therefore due to exchanges in linear continuity or crossing-over between the chromatids, has been demonstrated in two ways.

数分裂中染色体出现的异常行为与以下两者之一的相关性来检验：(*a*) 减数分裂在时间上的异常，(*b*) 减数分裂中期染色体凝聚强度减弱。

上述两种检验中，前者适于出现在选择压力降低状况下的许多生物，这时异常核会比正常核或早或晚进入减数分裂前期 [14,15,16,17]。当细胞核过早进入前期时，可以假设染色体的过早分裂会使前期加速；而过晚时，可以假设前期就会延迟。无论过早还是过晚，在分裂前期的早期染色体都不再是单体状态，因而失去了配对的条件。

导致粗线期配对失败的原因可以通过其对染色体凝聚状态的影响加以辨别（上述两种检验方法中的第二种）。因为当中期配对失败不是由于前期的时间出现紊乱，而仅仅是由于不能形成交叉所致时，我们可以推测减数分裂的凝聚状态仍是正常的，玉米就属于这种情况 [18]。当前期延迟时，我们猜测可能有一种途径可以令其转而进行有丝分裂，紫罗兰属便是如此 [19,20]。支持该假说的其他关键性证据已经在专栏文章中被引用过 [21]。

在试图通过这种方式确定减数分裂和有丝分裂的关系时，我们发现了何为减数分裂必要而普遍的特征，何为减数分裂非必要且次要的特征。只有当细胞核中发生的所有事件都获得明确解释时（起码现在需要如此），我们才能在一个良好的基础上去尝试对这些细胞学观察做出遗传学解释。

有两个对减数分裂中染色体行为进行遗传学解释的例子具有非常重要的现实指导意义。已有研究显示，在被认真检验过的每一种生物中，减数分裂过程中的交换都会发生在配对染色体的对应部位，实际上是发生在染色单体之间，因此 *ABCDE* 和 *abcde* 这对染色体如果在 *C* 和 *D* 之间的区域发生交换，那么就可以产生四种染色单体：*ABCDE*，*ABCde*，*abcDE* 和 *abcde*（图 1）。我们可以假设这一交换与任何可观察到的细胞学现象都没有关系，它在粗线期染色体紧密联会时发生，并与染色体后来的行为毫无关联。这一观点只有在排除了其他可能性之后才能被接受。我们也可以假定交换通过断裂及重接成新的线状结构而与交叉存在某种关系，或者是其原因（染色体交叉）[22,23]，或者是其结果 [10,9]。统计论证表明末端结合与中间交叉的频率是一致的 [11]，而末端交叉增加的数目与中间交叉减少的数目是成相同比例的 [3,4,20]，这就排除了上面提到的后一种可能性。第一种可能性认为当染色体聚集到一起时，原来的染色体就不复存在了。所以染色体在交叉处发生交换或者是由于沿着染色体全长发生线性连续性的交换，或者是由于染色单体之间发生了交换。这一可能性已经从两方面得到了证实。

In tetraploid *Hyacinthus* and *Primula* associations occur with such a spatial relationship that they can only be interpreted as the result of crossing-over.[3,25] In ring-forming *Oenothera*[28], chiasmata occur interstitially between a pair of chromosomes associated terminally with two others to give a "figure-of-eight". Such an arrangement also can arise only on the assumption of crossing-over. These demonstrations confirm Belling's interpretation of the *Hyacinthus* trivalents, which was not in itself indisputable.[5] Whether the observations are of universal application (the simplest assumption) or not, can only be shown by cytological tests of organisms which have been studied genetically.

A second problem is that of ring formation. Since, on the present hypotheses, the pairing of chromosomes at metaphase is conditioned by the formation of chiasmata at prophase between *parts* of chromosomes of identical structure, it follows that ring formation (where one chromosome pairs in different parts with parts of two others) must always be due to different arrangement of parts, that is, different structure, in the chromosomes contributed by opposite parents.[26,27,9] Thus the relationship of the chromosomes of two organisms can always be specified from the observation of the pairing behaviour of the chromosomes at meiosis in the hybrid. It is therefore possible to study differences of such a magnitude as will sterilise a hybrid and are therefore not susceptible of genetical analysis. This method is now being widely applied.

(**127**, 709-712; 1931)

---

References:

1 Seiler, J., *Zeits. f. indukt. Abstamm. u. Vererb Lehre*, **31**, 1-99 (1923).

2 Belar, K., *Biol. Zentrabl.*, **43**, 513-518 (1923).

3 Darlington, C. D., *Jour. Genet.*, **24**, 65-96 (1931).

4 McClintock, B., *Genetics*, **14**, 180-222 (1929).

5 Newton, W. C. F., and Darlington, C.D., *Jour. Genet.*, **21**, 1-16 (1929).

6 Takenaka, Y., and Nagamatsu., S., *Bot. Mag. Tokyo*, **44**, 386-391 (1930).

7 Gotoh, J., *Bot. Mag. Tokyo*, **38**, 135-152 (1924).

8 Lesley, M. M., and Frost, H. B., *Amer. Nat.*, **62**, 21-33 (1928).

9 Darlington, C. D., *Jour. Genet.*, **21**, 207-286 (1929).

10 Darlington, C. D., *Jour. Genet.*, **21**, 17-56 (1929).

11 Darlington, C. D., *Cytologia*, **2**, 37-55 (1930).

12 Maeda, T., *Mem., Coll. Sci. Kyoto*, B, **5**, 125-137 (1930).

13 Darlington, C. D., *Biol. Rev.*, **6** (in the press) (1931).

14 Rosenberg, O., *Hereditas*, **8**, 305-338 (1927).

15 Rybin, V. A., *Bull., Appl. Bot.* (Leningrad), **17**, 191-240 (1927).

16 Darlington, C. D., *Jour. Genet.*, **22**, 65-93 (1930).

17 Chiarugi, A., and Francini, E., *Nuo. Gio. Bot. Ital.* n.s., **37**, 1-250 (1930).

18 Burnham, C. R., *Proc. Nat. Acad. Sci.*, **16**, 269-277 (1930).

19 Lesley, M. M., and Frost, H. B., *Genetics*, **12**, 449-460 (1927).

20 Philp, J., and Huskins, C. L., *Jour. Genet.* (in the press).

21 Darlington, C. D., *Nature*, **124**, 62-64, 98-100 (1929).

22 Janssens, F. A., *La Cellule*, **34**, 135-359 (1924).

在四倍体植物风信子属和报春花属中，联会是伴随着一定的空间关系发生的，因此只能将其理解为交换的结果[3,25]。在成环植物月见草属中[28]，联会的一对染色体中有两条发生了中间交叉，另两条则发生了末端交叉，从而呈现出了“数字8的形状”，只有在交换时才可能出现这种排列。这些事例证实了贝林对风信子三价染色体的解释是无可置疑的[5]。这些观察是否具有普遍适用性（最简单的假设），只能通过对已用遗传学方法研究过的生物进行细胞学试验来检验。

第二个问题是关于成环作用的。因为，根据现在的假说，减数分裂中期染色体配对是以前期染色体在相同**部位**形成交叉为条件的，所以成环作用（一条染色体与另外两条染色体在不同部位配对）肯定是由于来自异性双亲染色体配对部位的排列不同，即结构不同造成的[26,27,9]。因此，通常可以通过观察杂合体在减数分裂过程中染色体的配对行为来具体说明两个生物体的染色体关系。因此有可能在杂合体不育的层面上来研究差异，这样就不易受遗传分析的影响了，目前这一方法正在被广泛地应用。

（刘皓芳 翻译；程祝宽 审稿）

23 Belling, J., *Univ. Calif. Pub. Bot.*, **14** (18), 379-88 (1929).

24 Erlanson, E. W., *Cytologia* (in the press) (1931).

25 Darlington, C. D., *Proc. Roy. Soc.*, **107**, 50-59 (1930).

26 Belling, J., *Jour. Genet.*, **18**, 177-205 (1927).

27 Darlington, C. D., *Jour. Genet.*, **20**, 345-363 (1929).

28 Darlington, C. D., *Jour. Genet* (in the press).

# Obituary

## Editor's Note

**In the nineteenth century, the propagation of light raised considerable difficulty in the minds of scientists. As Maxwell had demonstrated, light consists of electromagnetic waves, but people found it difficult to visualise the occurrence of wave motion in an entirely empty space. So there became established the idea that light travels through an insubstantial (that is, massless) medium called the lumeniferous ether. Albert Michelson and his chemist colleague Edward Morley carried out an experiment using a specially constructed interferometer designed by Michelson to compare the velocity of light in two directions perpendicular to each other. The outcome of the experiment suggested that the behaviour of light in the two perpendicular arms of the equipment was identical, thus throwing doubt on the whole concept of the lumeniferous ether—a point from which Einstein's Special Theory of Relativity was founded in 1905.**

### Prof. A. A. Michelson, For Mem. R. S.

WE much regret to announce the death, which occurred on May 9, of Prof. A. A. Michelson, the distinguished physicist of the University of Chicago. Prof. Michelson was probably best known for his wonderful experimental work to detect any effect of the earth's rotation on the velocity of light. At the end of 1929, he resigned his position at the University of Chicago and went to Pasadena, where he proposed to carry out further work on this subject, and it is reported that preliminary measurements have already been made. Prof. Michelson had worked previously at Mount Wilson Observatory, Pasadena, and a brief account of repetitions of the famous Michelson-Morley experiment, as it is generally called, with a diagram of the apparatus, was contributed to *Nature* of Jan. 19, 1929, by him and his collaborators. The results then obtained showed no displacement of the interferometer fringes so great as one-fifteenth of that to be expected on the supposition of an effect due to a motion of the solar system of three hundred kilometres per second through the ether. Since then, Prof. Michelson has been awarded the Duddell Medal for 1929 of the Physical Society of London for his work on interferometry.

In *Nature* of Jan. 2, 1926, we were fortunate in being able to publish, as one of our series of "Scientific Worthies", an appreciation of Prof. Michelson and his work by Sir Oliver Lodge. We print below extracts from that article.

"Albert Abraham Michelson was born in Strelno, Poland, on Dec. 19, 1852. In 1854 his parents migrated to the United States. After emerging from High School in San Francisco, young Michelson was appointed to the Naval Academy, from which he graduated in 1873, and two years later became instructor in physics and chemistry under Admiral

# 讣 告

## 编者按

在 19 世纪，科学家们对光的传播的理解仍面临着很大的困难。麦克斯韦指出，光是由电磁波构成的，但人们觉得很难想象波会在真空中传播。所以有人提出光在质量为零的以太中传播。阿尔伯特·迈克尔逊与他的化学家同事爱德华·莫雷用迈克尔逊本人设计的干涉仪测量并比较了互相垂直的两束光在传播速度上的差异。实验结果说明，光在干涉仪两个相互垂直的臂上的行为是相同的，这使人们对传光以太的概念产生了怀疑——而基于这一点爱因斯坦在 1905 年提出了狭义相对论。

### 英国皇家学会为纪念迈克尔逊教授所写的悼词

我们非常遗憾地告诉大家：芝加哥大学杰出的物理学家迈克尔逊教授在 5 月 9 日与世长辞了。迈克尔逊教授最著名的工作大概要算他检测地球旋转对光速影响的完美实验。1929 年末，他放弃了在芝加哥大学的职位，赴帕萨迪纳继续开展这方面的研究，据报道他已经完成了前期的测量工作。迈克尔逊教授先前曾在帕萨迪纳的威尔逊山天文台工作过，他和他的合作者们在 1929 年 1 月 19 日的《自然》杂志上发表了有关迈克尔逊－莫雷实验的文章，他们用装置图简单再现了这个为大家所公认的著名实验。后来得到的结果表明，假设太阳系以每秒 300 公里的速度在以太中运动，干涉条纹的位移不会超过预期值的 1/15。1929 年，迈克尔逊教授因在干涉测量法方面的贡献而被伦敦物理学会授予达德尔奖章。

我们很荣幸能在 1926 年 1 月 2 日《自然》杂志的“杰出科学家”系列介绍中发表奥利弗·洛奇爵士对迈克尔逊教授及其研究工作的评论。以下内容是我们从那篇文章中摘录出来的。

“阿尔伯特·亚伯拉罕·迈克尔逊于 1852 年 12 月 19 日出生于波兰的斯特列罗。1854 年，他随父母移居美国。年轻的迈克尔逊在旧金山读完高中后被指派到海军学院学习一直到 1873 年毕业，两年后他成为桑普森上将手下的一名物理和化学教员，

Sampson, continuing this work until 1879. After a year in the Nautical Almanac Office at Washington, Michelson, now an ensign, went abroad for further study at the Universities of Berlin and Heidelberg, and at the Collège de France and the École Polytechnique in Paris. Upon his return to the United States in 1883 he became professor of physics in the Case School of Applied Science, Cleveland, Ohio; whence, after six years, he was called to Clark University, where he remained as professor until 1892, when the University of Chicago opened its doors. Prof. Michelson went to this new institution as professor of physics and head of the department. In June 1925 he was honoured by being appointed to the first of the Distinguished Service Professorships made possible by the new development programme of the University.

"It was while he was at Cleveland that Prof. Michelson collaborated with Prof. Morley in their joint experiment; and it may have been for the purpose of that experiment that he invented his particular form of interferometer, with the to-and-fro beams at right angles. Later, he applied it in Paris to the determination of the metre, with an estimated accuracy of about one part in two million.

"During the War, Prof. Michelson re-entered the Naval Service with the rank of Lieutenant-Commander, giving his entire time to seeking new devices for naval use, especially a range-finder, which became part of the U.S. Navy Equipment.

"A Nobel Prize was awarded to Prof. Michelson in 1907, the first American to get one for science; and the Copley Medal, the most distinguished honour of the Royal Society of London, was awarded him in the same year.

"The gold medal of the Royal Astronomical Society was presented to Prof. Michelson on Feb. 9, 1923; and the compact exposition of the reasons for that award, by the president, Prof. Eddington, on that occasion will be found in *Nature*, vol. 111, p. 240.

"Michelson touched on many departments of physics, but in optics, the highest optics, he excelled. In this subject he can be regarded as the most fertile and brilliant disciple of the late Lord Rayleigh, for his inventions are based on a thorough assimilation of the principles of diffraction, interference, and resolving power; and his great practical achievements are the outcome of this knowledge. Michelson seemed to have a special instinct for all phenomena connected with the interference of light, with a taste for exact measurement surpassed by none in this particular region. The interferometer with which he began became in his hands much more than an interferometer. He applied it to the determination of the standard metre in terms of the wave-length of light, with exact results which will enable remote posterity millions of years hence to reconstruct, if they want to, the standard measures in vogue at this day. He applied it also to analyse the complex structure of spectrum lines, and with remarkable completeness to determine the shape and size of invisible objects, such as to ordinary vision, however much aided by telescopic power, will probably remain mere points of light.

并在此一直工作到 1879 年。后来他又为华盛顿的航海天文历编制局工作了一年，此时已是海军少尉的迈克尔逊走出了国门，先后到柏林大学、海德堡大学、法兰西学院和巴黎理工学校深造。他在 1883 年回到美国，随即成为位于俄亥俄州克利夫兰的凯斯应用科学学院的物理教授；6 年后，克拉克大学邀请他担任该校的教授，他在那里一直工作到 1892 年芝加哥大学成立。迈克尔逊教授在这个新建的大学中担任物理学教授和物理系系主任。1925 年 6 月，由于该大学新发展规划的需要，他荣幸地被提名为首位对社会有杰出贡献的教授。

“正是在克利夫兰工作的时候，迈克尔逊教授与莫雷教授合作进行了他们的实验；为完成这个实验，迈克尔逊教授发明了可以在相互垂直方向上使光线来回反射的干涉仪。后来他在巴黎用这个仪器测量了标准米，估计精度在 1/2,000,000 上下。

“在第一次世界大战期间，迈克尔逊教授重返海军服役，军衔为少校，他把自己全部的时间都用于研制适用于海军需要的新仪器，尤其是已经成为美国海军装备组成部分的测距仪。

“迈克尔逊教授获得了 1907 年的诺贝尔奖，他是第一位获此殊荣的美国科学家；在同一年，他还荣获了代表伦敦皇家学会最高荣誉的科普利奖章。

“1923 年 2 月 9 日，迈克尔逊教授被授予皇家天文学会金奖；《自然》杂志在第 111 卷的第 240 页上刊登了皇家天文学会主席爱丁顿教授在颁奖仪式上对其获奖原因的简短说明。

“迈克尔逊曾经涉足过物理学的许多领域，但他在光学领域，最前沿的光学领域所取得的成就最为突出。在这个领域中，他可以被认为是已故瑞利勋爵的所有弟子中成果最丰硕和最优秀的一位，因为他的发明是建立在透彻理解衍射、干涉原理以及分辨率的基础上的；而他在实践上的伟大成就就是能够充分运用这些知识的结果。迈克尔逊似乎对所有与光干涉相关的现象都有一种特别的直觉，在这个特定领域中他对精确测量的判断力是无人能及的。在他眼中，自己早先发明的干涉仪远远不只是一部干涉仪。他利用干涉仪根据光的波长测定了标准米，得到的结果非常精确，可以让几百万年以后的子孙重新构建当今流行的计量标准，只要他们愿意。他还利用干涉仪分析了谱线的复杂结构，并且完美地测定了不可见物体的形状和大小，这些不可见物体对于视力正常的人来说，即使借助大倍率望远镜也只能看到几个光点。

"In a magnificent paper in the *Phil. Mag.* of July 1890, Michelson suggested the application of interference methods to astronomy. He knew well that the resolving power of a telescope depended on the diameter of its aperture, and that the formation of an image was essentially an interference phenomenon; the minuteness of a point image, and therefore the clearness of definition, depending on the size of the object-glass. But he pointed out that if the aperture was limited to slits at opposite edges—so that no actual image anything like the object would be formed, but only the interference bands which the beams from the two slits could produce—a study of those bands would enable us to infer about the source of light very much more than we could get by looking at its image. For example, suppose it was a close double star, and suppose the slits over the object-glass were movable, so that they could be approached nearer together, or separated the whole distance of the aperture apart. A gradual separation of the slits would now cause the fringes to go through periods of visibility and invisibility; and the first disappearance of the fringes would tell us that the distance apart of the two components of the star (multiplied by the distance between the slits and divided by the distance of the star) would equal half a wave-length of light. The two components might be far too near together ever to be seen separately, and yet we could infer that the star was a double one; and by further attention to the visibility curve we could infer the relative brightness of the two components and their position relative to our line of sight.

"Furthermore, if, instead of looking at a star, we turned the slit-provided telescope on a planet with a disc too small for ordinary measurement, the size of that disc could be estimated from the behaviour of the interference fringes produced by its light in a suitable interferometer, or by the telescope converted into one.

"In view of the great interest aroused by the application of this method by Michelson himself, with the aid of collaborators at Mount Wilson Observatory, Pasadena, California, and with the hundred-inch telescope established there, it may be interesting to quote here part of the conclusion of his paper of date 1890:

" '(1) Interference phenomena produced under appropriate conditions from light emanating from a source of finite magnitude become indistinct as the size increases, finally vanishing when the angle subtended by the source is equal to the smallest angle which an equivalent telescope can resolve, multiplied by a constant factor depending on the shape and distribution of light in the source and on the order of the disappearance.

" '(2) The vanishing of the fringes can ordinarily be determined with such accuracy that single readings give results from fifty to one hundred times as accurate as can be obtained with a telescope of equal aperture.'

" 'If among the nearer fixed stars there is any as large as our sun, it would subtend an angle of about one hundredth of a second of arc; and the corresponding distance required to observe this small angle is ten metres, a distance which, while utterly out of question as

“1890年7月，迈克尔逊在一篇发表于《哲学杂志》上的优秀论文中提到了干涉法在天文学中的应用。他非常清楚望远镜的分辨力取决于其孔径的大小，而从本质上看，像的形成是一种干涉现象；点像的精确性以及与此相关的轮廓清晰度取决于物镜的尺寸。但他指出，如果孔径受到对面边缘狭缝的限制，则不能形成与物体类似的实像，而来自两个狭缝的光束只能形成干涉带，通过研究这些干涉带推出的有关光源的信息要比我们从观察图像本身得到的信息多很多。例如，假设有一对相离很近的双星，并假设物镜上的狭缝是可移动的，它们可以靠得更近，也可以相距整个孔径那么大的距离。使两个狭缝逐渐远离就能实现条纹从可见到不可见的周期变化；条纹的首次消失将告诉我们，恒星两组分之间的距离（乘以狭缝间的距离，除以双星到地球的距离）等于光的半波长。也许双星之间的距离过于接近，以至于我们从未观测到它们是分开的两颗星，但我们已经可以推测出该恒星是一对双星；通过对可见度曲线的进一步研究，我们还可以推断出双星的相对亮度以及它们相对于我们视线的位置。

“此外，除了观察恒星以外，我们还可以将装有狭缝的望远镜对准一颗星盘很小、用普通测量方法难以观测到的行星，来自星盘的光在适当的干涉仪中或由望远镜改装成的干涉仪中形成干涉条纹，根据这些条纹的变化情况可以估算出星盘的尺寸。

“迈克尔逊本人把自己的方法应用于天文学领域激起了人们极大的兴趣，他得到了加州帕萨迪纳威尔逊山天文台的工作人员的帮助，并使用了安装在那里的孔径可达百英寸的望远镜，考虑到这一点，在此引述他在1890年论文中的部分结论也许是一件有意思的事情：

“‘(1) 在适当条件下，如果干涉现象的产生源于有限强度光源发出的光，那么随着光源尺寸的增加，干涉现象就会逐渐变模糊，当光源所张的角度等于等效孔径望远镜所能分辨的最小角度乘上一个常数因子时，干涉现象将最终消失，这个常数因子取决于光源中光的状态和频率分布以及干涉现象消失的量级。

“‘(2) 通常用于测量条纹相消的方法有很高的精确度，其单次测量所得结果的精度是等孔径望远镜的50至100倍。’

“‘如果在比较靠近我们的恒星中存在着一个与太阳大小差不多的恒星，那么它所张的角度将大约是1/100角秒；而观测这么小的角度需要10米的距离，望远镜物镜的直径完全可以达到这么长的距离，这个距离对于折光仪来说也毫无问题。然而，

regards the diameter of a telescope-objective, is still perfectly feasible with a refractometer. There is, however, no inherent improbability of stars presenting a much larger angle than this; and the possibility of gaining some positive knowledge of the real size of these distant luminaries would more than repay the time, care, and patience which it would be necessary to bestow on such a work.'

"There seemed little hope at that time, and certainly no reasoned expectation, that any stars, except perhaps some of the very nearest, could have discs big enough for perception and measurement even by this virtual telescope of thirty feet aperture. The possibility of giant stars came, however, above our mental horizon; and Eddington made the notable prediction that a star like Betelgeuse must be in a highly rarefied state at a tremendously high temperature, and that it would be swollen out by the pressure of light to a size almost comparable with the dimensions of a solar system, although it could not contain very much more matter than, say, two or five times our sun. His argument, in brief, is that the spectrum of a young red star like Betelgeuse shows that it cannot be radiating furiously. Why then is it so conspicuous an object to our vision? It can only be because it is of enormous size, its density perhaps a thousand times less than atmospheric air. By utilisation of the data available in the light of his theory of stellar constitution, Eddington made an estimate of the diameter of the star.

"So with great skill Michelson and his collaborators got the interferometer to work. After many preliminary adjustments, on Dec. 13, 1920, Dr. F. G. Pease at Mount Wilson, with Michelson's apparatus, measured the diameter of a star for the first time, using Betelgeuse for the purpose. The interference-fringes formed by the star were observed, the object mirrors were gradually separated, and it must have been a joyful moment when, as they grew farther and farther and farther apart, the fringes at the eye end became less distinct and ultimately disappeared. The distance apart of the mirrors now, multiplied by the proper fraction, gave the angular dimensions of the star—a thing which had never before been observed in the history of the world. An estimate of the star's distance gave its actual diameter, and confirmed Eddington's prediction!

"Other stars have since been measured, and the giant stars well deserve their name. Moreover, an instrument has been put in the hands of posterity to the power of which we can scarcely set a limit in investigating utterly invisible details, both about the heavenly bodies and about atoms, by the new and powerful method of analysing the radiation which they emit.

"The form of instrument adapted to the heavens is, however, not applicable to the atoms. The spectrum of atomic radiation is formed by a grating; and Rayleigh showed that the power of a prism spectroscope is expressed approximately by the number of centimetres of available thickness of glass, which is one form of saying that, to get high definition or separating power, we must use interference depending on a great number of wavelengths retardation. Michelson perceived that the retardation principle might be employed so as to make a grating which combined with its own effect the resolving power of a prism.

恒星所张角度大大高于 1/100 角秒的情况未必不可能出现；获得这些遥远发光体实际尺寸的有用信息是有可能的，而且值得人们投入时间、精力和耐心，而完成该项工作也需要这样的投入。'

“在当时几乎无法希望，当然也没有理由期望，恒星的星盘能够大到足以感知和测量的地步，即便是采用孔径为 30 英尺的虚拟望远镜，不过一些最接近我们的恒星也许可以除外。然而，可能存在巨星的想法进入了我们的视野；爱丁顿提出了那个著名的猜想，即像参宿四这样的恒星必然会处在极高温度下的高度稀薄状态，它在光压的作用下将膨胀到几乎与整个太阳系相近的尺寸，尽管它含有的物质不可能比太阳上的物质多多少，也就多 2 倍或 5 倍。简言之，他的结论是，从一颗类似于参宿四的年轻红巨星的光谱判断，它不可能在强烈地辐射能量。然而为什么我们很容易看到这样的天体呢？原因只能是它具有特别大的尺寸，而它的密度可能仅为空气密度的 1/1000。爱丁顿利用根据自己提出的恒星构造理论得到的数据估算出了这个恒星的直径。

“于是迈克尔逊和他的合作者们开始熟练地操作干涉仪进行研究。1920 年 12 月 13 日，在经过了多次调试之后，皮斯博士在威尔逊山上用迈克尔逊的装置首次测出了一颗恒星的直径，测量的恒星正是参宿四。可以观测到由恒星形成的干涉条纹，令物镜逐渐分离，当物镜之间的距离越来越远时，肯定会出现那个令人欣喜的时刻，目端的干涉条纹逐渐变模糊直至最终消失。这时用物镜之间的距离乘以一定的比例就得到了这颗恒星的角度大小——这在世界历史上还从未被人观测到过。根据对恒星距离的估计可以算出它的实际直径，从而验证了爱丁顿的预言！

“后来又测量了其他的恒星，发现那些巨星果然具有很大的体积。再者，这种已经传到后人手中的仪器功能非常了得，在用这种功能十分强大的新方法分析天体和原子发出的辐射时，我们简直不知道它是否有做不到的事情。

“然而，适用于观察天体的仪器规格并不适用于原子。原子辐射光谱是由光栅得到的；瑞利发现棱镜分光镜的分辨率可近似表示为玻璃可用厚度的厘米数，也就是说，为了达到更高的清晰度或分辨率，我们必须用到与大量波长延迟有关的干涉现象。迈克尔逊意识到也许可以利用延迟原理制成一个光栅，这个光栅既具有自己的特殊功用又具有棱镜的分辨能力。也许可以用一片厚度为 1 厘米或更厚的玻璃实现所需的几千个波长的相位滞后，由此获得以前无法想象的清晰度和分辨率。于是迈

A slab of glass, a centimetre or more thick, might be used to give the necessary lag in phase of many thousand wavelengths, and thereby secure a definition and resolving power unthought of before. So Michelson designed the Echelon spectroscope, consisting of thick slabs of glass, each protruding a millimetre or so beyond the other—a staircase spectroscope—which is now a regular instrument in the examination of the minute structure of spectrum lines.

"What, however, is popularly the best-known work of Michelson is the application of his interferometer to determine if possible the motion of the earth through the ether. The speed expected was of the order one-ten-thousandth of the velocity of light; but since the journey of the light in the instrument is a to-and-fro journey—one half-beam going as nearly as possible with and against the hypothetical stream of ether, while the other half-beam goes at right angles to that direction—the amount to be measured was not one-ten-thousandth but the square of that quantity; that is to say, the observer had to measure one part in a hundred million—no easy matter. The interferometer was mounted on a stone slab floating in mercury, and the whole observation conducted with great care. The result was zero; and that zero was used afterwards as the corner-stone of the great and beautiful edifice of relativity."

(**127**, 751-753; 1931)

克尔逊设计出了由厚玻璃片组成的阶梯光栅分光仪，每一个玻璃片都比另一个约长出 1 毫米，这种阶梯状的分光镜现在已经成为检测谱线精细结构的常规仪器。

“然而，大家普遍认为迈克尔逊最著名的成就是利用干涉仪来测定地球在以太中的运动，如果这种运动是存在的。人们预期其速度的数量级大概为光速的 1/10,000；但由于光在仪器中所走的路线是连续往返的，有一半的光束可以尽可能地与假想的以太流方向一致或相反，而另一半光束的行进方向与此垂直，测量出来的结果不该是 1/10,000，而应是 1/10,000 的平方；换言之，观测者要测量的是这个量的 1/100,000,000——这绝非易事。干涉仪被放在浮于水银表面的石板上，在整个观测过程中的操作都非常小心。最后得到的结果是零；后来这个零成为壮观美丽的相对论大厦的基石。”

（沈乃澂 翻译；张泽渤 审稿）

# The Peking Skull*

G. E. Smith

## Editor's Note

**After the discovery of the first skull of Sinanthropus in 1928, responsibility for extracting the fragments of bone from the travertine rock in which the bone was embedded fell to Davidson Black, who was trained as an anatomist in Toronto, Canada, and who found his first job as an anatomy teacher at the Peking Union Medical College. (Black had raised funds for the excavation at Chou Kou Tien from the Rockefeller Foundation in New York, which continued to support the work after a skull had been found.) Black was a firm sinophile; born in 1884, he died at the early age of 59 in 1943.**

WITH characteristic promptitude, Prof. Davidson Black has now provided us with a full report upon the features of the Peking skull, giving a detailed description of its external form, illustrated by 16 photographic plates (each photograph provided with a transparent explanatory drawing) and 37 text-figures. The drawings represent exact orthogonal projections not only of the type skull but also of the second skull of *Sinanthropus*, the finding of which was discussed in *Nature* of Aug. 9, 1930 (p. 210), and of a series of other fossil human skulls. The purpose of this comparision is to define the distinctive characters of *Sinanthropus* and to emphasise the contrasts in size and proportions that differentiate it from *Pithecanthropus* and the series of Neanderthal skulls. An elaborate series of measurements is provided, together with a statistical analysis of the significance of the figures, in comparison with those of other fossil human types, as well as of representatives of modern races of men. Hence complete data are now available to enable the anthropologist to realise the distinctive features of the Peking skull and the reasons which induced Prof. Davidson Black to differentiate it from all other known human types and assign it a distinctive generic rank.

The history of the finding of the skull by Mr. W. C. Pei on Dec. 2, 1929, has already been told in *Nature* (Mar. 22, 1930, p. 448). It was not until four months later that Dr. Black completed the process of removing from the surface of the skull the hard mass of travertine in which it was embedded. He then began to make casts and photographs of the specimen and to prepare the preliminary reports. After this was accomplished, he set to work to expose the interior of the skull, and in this he was inspired by the motive of preserving if possible the natural endocranial cast. Fortunately, this was possible because the braincase was fractured, enabling the bones to be removed piecemeal. Moreover, the

* Davidson Black, "On an Adolescent Skull of *Sinanthropus Pekinensis* in Comparison with an Adult Skull of the same Species and with other Hominid Skulls, Recent and Fossil", *Palaeontologia Sinica*, Series D, vol. 7, Fascicle 2. (Peiping: Geological Survey of China, Peiping, April 28, 1931.)

# 北京人的头骨*

埃利奥特·史密斯

## 编者按

自从 1928 年发现了北京人的第一具头骨之后，从埋藏该头骨的石灰华中取出骨头破片的责任就落到了步达生身上。他曾在加拿大的多伦多学习解剖学，并在北京协和医学院找到了他的第一份工作——担任解剖学教师。（步达生已从纽约的洛克菲勒基金会筹集到了用于周口店挖掘工作的资金，在发现了一具头骨之后，该基金会便继续资助此项挖掘工作。）步达生是一名坚定的亲华人士；他出生于 1884 年，卒于 1943 年，终年仅 59 岁。

步达生教授特别及时地为我们提供了一份完整的关于北京人头骨特征的报告。在这份报告中，他用 16 张照相图版（每张照片都附有清晰的说明图）和 37 张插图详细描述了该头骨的外部形态。这些图片不仅精确展示了这具正型标本头骨的正交投影图，也呈现了第二具北京人头骨（该头骨的发现曾在《自然》杂志 1930 年 8 月 9 日版的第 210 页讨论过）和一系列其他人类头骨化石的正交投影图。这一比较旨在确定北京人的区别性特征，并强调北京人与爪哇猿人及尼安德特人头骨系列在大小和比例方面的差别。在报告中，步达生教授提供了北京人与其他类型的人类化石以及与现代人的各个种族代表相比所得到的一系列精确的测量值以及这些数值的统计学分析结果。现在，这些完整的数据有助于人类学家搞清北京人头骨的区别性特征，以及步达生教授为什么要将北京人与其他已知的人类类型区别开来，并将其定为一种特别的属。

裴文中先生于 1929 年 12 月 2 日发现了第一具北京人头骨，其发现的历史早已在《自然》杂志上（1930 年 3 月 22 日，第 448 页）介绍过。可是直到 4 个月后，步达生博士才将覆盖在该头骨表面的石灰华硬块清除干净。接着他便开始制作这个标本的模型，为它照相，并准备对其进行初步报道。完成这些工作之后，他便开始着手暴露头骨的内部。在这一过程中，他一直把尽可能保全这具头骨的天然颅内模作为目标激励自己。很幸运，由于这具头骨的脑腔是断裂的，因而骨头可以被一片

* 步达生，“比较青年北京人头骨和成年北京人头骨以及其他原始人类的头骨，根据全新世的化石”，《中国古生物志》，丁种，第 7 卷，第 2 分卷（北平：中国地质调查所，北平，1931 年 4 月 28 日）

skull is that of a young adolescent, whose age, in Dr. Black's opinion, corresponds to that of a modern child between the time of eruption of the second permanent molar teeth and the attainment of adolescence, say 15±2 years. Thus it was possible easily to disarticulate the constituent bones. This work lasted until well into the summer of 1930, when Dr. Black succeeded in removing the cranial bones from the surface of the endocranial cast and then reconstituted each individual bone, and eventually rearticulated the skull with more precision than it had at the time when it was found. Before doing so, however, he made photographs and models of each separate bone, and took X-ray photographs to display the sinuses and other details in the texture of the bones, such, for example, as the labyrinth in the temporal bone. Then the skull was rearticulated and an artificial cast made of the cranial cavity.

The present monograph describes the external surface of the skull and each individual bone. The description of the endocranial cavity and cast which Prof. Davidson Black has obtained of it will be discussed in a second monograph that is now in course of preparation.

In July 1930 a large part of a second braincase was obtained from certain blocks of limestone which had been brought into the laboratory in October 1930. In his monograph Dr. Black gives full details of the comparison of the two skulls and the evidence upon which he relied to interpret the sexual characters and ages of the two individuals. The skull obtained in December 1929 he now regards (for reasons set forth in full in this report) as that of a youth in a stage of development between puberty and adolescence, and the second skull that of a woman. Partial obliteration of the left side of the coronal suture suggests that the latter was an adult, possibly more than ten years older than her companion. In the accompanying diagram (Fig. 1) Prof. Davidson Black's drawings of median longitudinal projections of the young skull (shaded) and of the adult (female) skull have been superimposed. The female skull is slightly thinner than that of the youth and is also larger, being somewhat higher and longer than the male skull (Fig. 1) and presenting other differences which are probably expressions of the difference in sex.

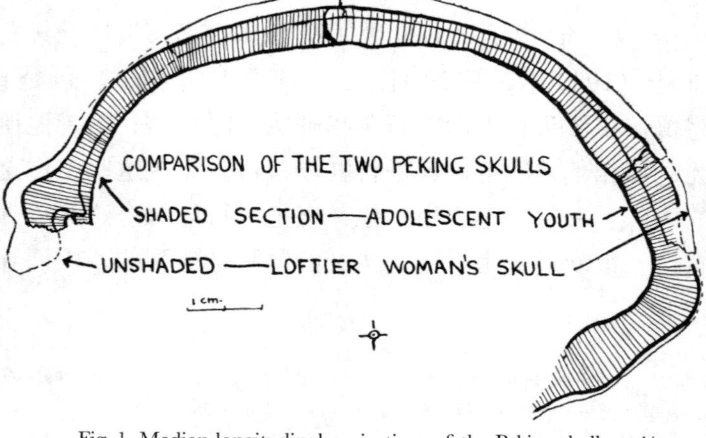


Fig. 1. Median longitudinal projections of the Peking skulls. × ½

一片地取下来，这使得保全这具头骨的天然颅内模成为可能。此外，该头骨是一位青少年的，步达生认为其年龄相当于一个现代孩子长出第二恒臼齿与青春期后期之间的时期，大约 15±2 岁。因此组成头骨的各块骨头很容易拆解开。这项工作一直持续到 1930 年的夏末，当时步达生博士已成功地将颅骨从颅内模的表面剥离，然后将每一块骨头重新拼接，最终将该头骨以比发现时更高的精度重新连接了起来。不过，在做这些工作以前，他对每一块分离下来的骨头都进行了拍照和模型制作，并且拍了 X 光片以看清骨窦及骨组织中的其他细节，例如，颞骨中的迷路。然后，他重新拼接了头骨，并且制作了颅腔的人工模型。

现在这篇专题报告描述了北京人头骨的外表面及每一块骨头。步达生教授在正在准备之中的第二本专著里将对他已得到的该头骨的颅内腔和颅内模进行描述。

1930 年 7 月，从石灰岩块中得到了第二具北京人头骨的大部分，并已于 1930 年 10 月被带回了实验室。在步达生博士的专著中，他对两具头骨进行了详细的比较，并给出了他用于判断两个个体的性征和年龄的证据。现在他认为：在 1929 年 12 月得到的头骨是处于青春期发育阶段的青年人（本报告完整地陈述了作出此判断的原因）的头骨，第二具头骨是一个女人的头骨。左侧冠状缝的部分消失意味着后者是一位成年人，可能比前者大十多岁。在附图（图 1）中，步达生教授将青年人的头骨（阴影部分）与成年女性的头骨的正中纵向投影图进行了重叠效果的展示。图 1 显示这位女性的头骨比青年人的稍微薄一些、大一些，比男性的头骨高一点、长一点，还有一些差异可能是性别差异的表现。

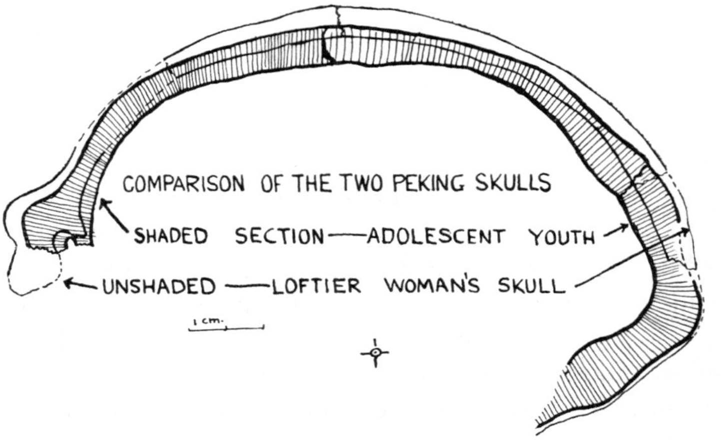


图 1. 北京头盖骨的正中纵向投影图。×½

In view of the claims put forward by certain writers that the Peking skull should be included in the genus *Pithecanthropus* or, alternately, in the species *H. neanderthalensis*, Prof. Black has devoted a large amount of attention to the comparison of the projections of the skulls of *Pithecanthropus* and the various representatives of the Neanderthal species. By means of statistical comparisons he has made out a conclusive case in justification of the necessity of making a new genus and species for the reception of the Peking skulls.

While it is evident that the crania of *Sinanthropus* and *Pithecanthropus* resemble one another (Fig. 2) much more closely than they do any other human type, it is no less certain that they differ from one another in point of size, proportions, and detail to a degree amply sufficient to proclaim their generic distinction. It is a remarkable fact, Prof. Black adds, that in all its cranial parts *Pithecanthropus* shows "evidence of an archaic specialisation in marked contrast to the evidences of archaic generalisation so abundantly preserved in the crania and teeth of *Sinanthropus*". In other words, the apparent primitiveness of the Java fossil is in part probably due to degenerative changes responsible for the uncouth shape of the skull, which presents so striking a contrast to the elegant and undistorted braincase of the Peking man. Apart from its massive supraorbital torus and reduced third molar tooth, the Peking skull presents no highly specialised features. On the contrary, its general proportions, the morphology of the teeth, and the features of the tympanic and other individual elements of the skull, all provide evidence that *Sinanthropus* was a generalised and progressive type.

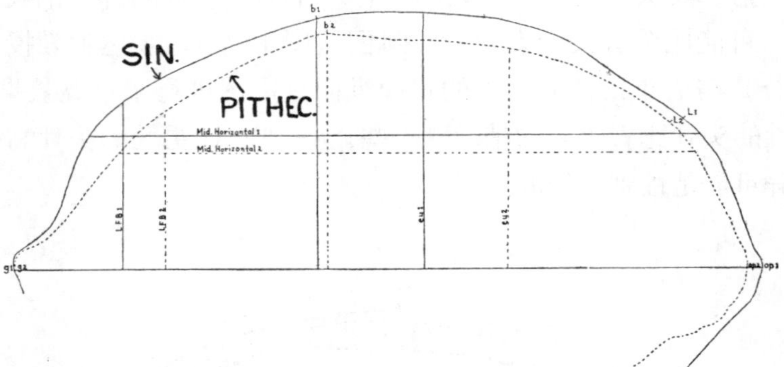


Fig. 2. Mid-sagittal skull contours of *Sinanthropus* and *Pithecanthropus*; left norma lateralis view. ×½

Prof. Black does not devote much attention to the comparison with the Piltdown skull. The purpose of the present work is to provide anthropologists with a detailed description of his specimen and an exact comparison with other specimens of unquestioned and generally recognised authenticity. For this reason, as well as to avoid partiality, he uses the data collected by Dr. H. Weinert in the case of *Pithecanthropus*, based upon the study of the actual fossil, with information provided by Prof. Dubois in amplification. Similarly, for the

鉴于某些作者主张应该将北京人头骨归到爪哇猿人属或者尼安德特人种中，步达生教授倾注了大量精力比较北京人头骨与爪哇猿人头骨和尼安德特种的不同代表的头骨投影图。通过具有统计意义的比较，他提出了确凿的证据，证实有必要建立一个新的属和种来接纳北京人头骨。

尽管很明显，北京人与爪哇猿人的头盖骨的接近程度（图 2）远远高于它们与其他任何人类类型的头盖骨的接近程度，但是同样明显的是，它们彼此在大小、比例和细节上都有所不同，不同的程度足以表明它们在属一级上是有区别的。步达生教授补充道，一个值得注意的事实是爪哇猿人头盖骨的各部分都显示了“古老的特化迹象，这与北京人的头盖骨和牙齿中充分保留下来的古老的一般化证据形成了鲜明的对比”。换句话说，爪哇化石的明显原始性在某种程度上可能是由于发生过导致头骨形状怪异的退行性变化，其头骨形状与北京人头骨的精美无畸变形成了强烈对比。除了眶上圆枕较大以及第三臼齿有所缩小以外，北京人头骨没有表现出高度特化的特征。相反，该头骨的一般比例、牙齿的形态、鼓部和头骨其他个别成分的特征都证明北京人是一个一般化的、进步的类型。

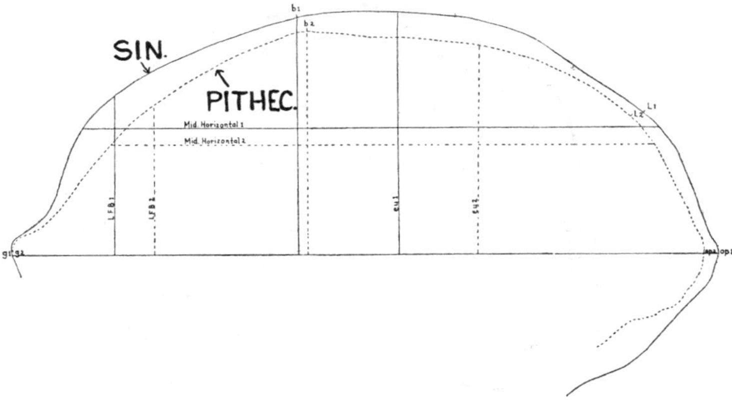


图2. 北京人和爪哇猿人头骨矢状面轮廓；左侧面观视图。× ½

步达生教授没有花费太多精力来比较北京人头骨和皮尔当头骨。目前工作的目的是为人类学家提供一份关于北京人头骨标本的详细描述，并将其与其他公认为真实可靠的头骨标本进行精确的比较。因为这个原因并为了避免偏见，步达生教授引用了韦纳特博士在研究爪哇猿人时根据对真实化石标本的研究搜集到的资料，以及杜波依斯教授在详细描述爪哇猿人时提供的信息。与此相似，步达生教授引用了莫

Neanderthal skulls Dr. Black relies on the data and figures provided by Dr. G. M. Morant. As, unfortunately, there is still considerable doubt in the minds of many anthropologists concerning the Piltdown skull and the mode of its reconstruction, Dr. Black does not make much use of it for comparison. He does, however, emphasise the fact that the peculiarly developed postero-inferior parietal boss in the Peking skull resembles in certain important features the similar, if less obtrusive, development of the Piltdown parietal. He also directs attention to the similar thickness of the skull in the genera *Sinanthropus* and *Eoanthropus*, but points out that the range of unevenness in thickness of the Peking skull presents a marked contrast to the more uniform Piltdown fragments.

Although Dr. Black himself has refrained from instituting detailed comparisons with the Piltdown skull, it is interesting to compare (Fig. 3) the transverse section he provides of the skull of *Sinanthropus* (the thick lines) with a section made in the corresponding plane (auditory meatus) of the reconstruction of the Piltdown skull (the larger shaded area) made by the late Prof. John Hunter. This section, like the view of the two skulls from the posterior aspect, brings out the essential identity of their architectural plan in a most striking way, and reveals a similarity of form and proportions which is unexpectedly close. Apart from the difference in thickness, the adult skull of *Sinanthropus* approaches even nearer to the Piltdown skull in some respects. Thus (see Fig. 1) it is loftier than the type skull and its height is identical with that of *Eoanthropus*, but the latter is considerably wider and correspondingly more capacious.

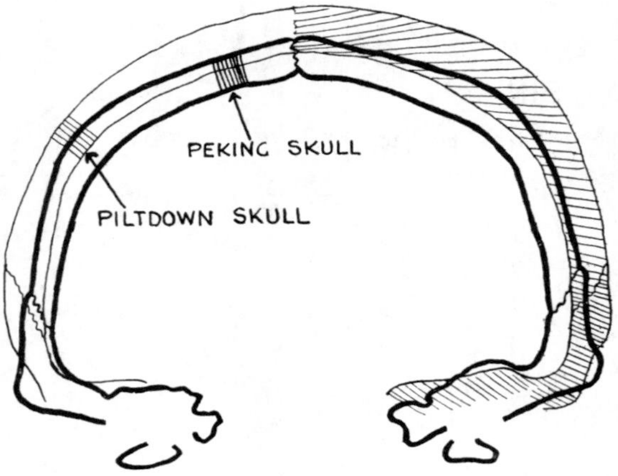


Fig. 3. Transverse sections of Peking and Piltdown skulls. ×½

The general form and proportions of the Peking skull, as well as the details of many of its constituent parts, are surprisingly modern in character. The man of China was clearly a very primitive and generalised member of the human family close to the main line of descent of *Homo sapiens*.

Prof. Black devotes particular attention to the unique character of the temporal bone, which presents a marked contrast to that of all other known men and apes. Of special

兰特博士提供的关于尼安德特头骨的资料和插图。遗憾的是，因为仍然有很多人类学家对皮尔当头骨及其复原头骨颇为疑惑，所以步达生博士没有充分利用它与北京人头骨进行比较。但是他强调北京人头骨中特殊发育的后下顶骨突起与皮尔当顶骨的发育在某些重要特征上有几分相像，只是前者不如后者凸出。他也注意到北京人和曙人头骨（即皮尔当头骨）厚度相似，但他指出北京人头骨的厚度不均匀程度与皮尔当头骨碎片厚度的相对均一形成了鲜明的对照。

尽管步达生博士自己已尽量避免对北京人头骨与皮尔当头骨进行详细的比较，但是将他提供的北京人头骨的横切面（图中用粗线表示）与已故的约翰·亨特教授复原的皮尔当头骨（图中较大的阴影区域）相应的（经过外面耳道的）截面进行比较（图 3），还是很有趣的。这一截面就像这两具头骨的后面观一样，以一种非常引人注目的方式反映了二者结构比例的本质上的一致性，并且揭示了二者在形状和比例上的惊人相似性。除了厚度上的差异，成年北京人的头骨在某些方面与皮尔当头骨甚至更加接近。因此（见图 1）成年北京人的头骨比正型标本的头骨更高，与曙人头骨的高度一致，但是曙人头骨要宽很多，相应地容积也更大。

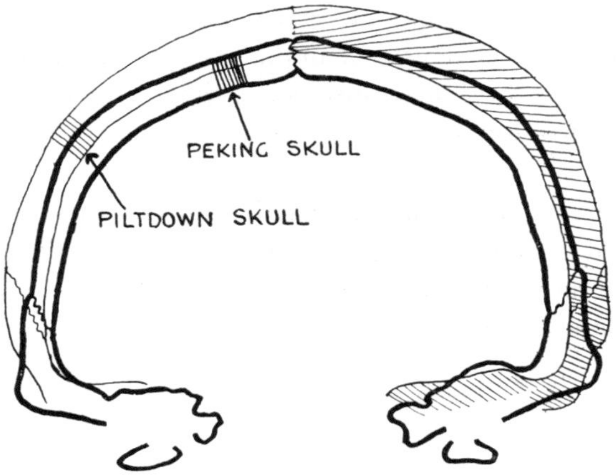


图3. 北京人和皮尔当头骨的横切面。× ½

北京人头骨的一般形状和比例以及其众多组成部分的细节在特征上都惊人地与现代人相近。很明显中国人是人科中一个非常原始的、一般化的成员，与智人后代的主干很接近。

步达生教授对北京人头骨颞骨的独特特征给予了特别关注，因为该颞骨与所有其他已知人类和猿类的颞骨都形成了鲜明对照。他尤为感兴趣的是鼓部和乳突部的

interest are the distinctive features of the tympanic and mastoid portions, showing, not only in the case of the mastoid but also in the form of the auditory meatus and middle ear, characters which in modern man occur only in new-born infants and very young children—a widely open meatus terminating at an ear drum the inclination of which closely approaches the horizontal. This state of affairs is lost in *Homo sapiens* long before the age of puberty is attained. As Dr. Black remarks, the features of the tympanic region of *Sinanthropus* are admirably suited to serve as a starting-point for phylogenetic speculation. "With this generalised type before us it is not difficult to imagine developmental stages through which such an element in a stem-form may well have passed, leading to the modifications such as are characteristic of the Piltdown, Neanderthal, and modern men". On the other hand, since all the essentials of the tympanic morphology of the great anthropoid apes may be recognised in these elements of *Sinanthropus*, a comparison of the latter may serve to indicate in some measure the degree of their divergence from a common type. In spite of this provocative comment, Prof. Davidson Black refrains from discussing the intriguing problems he mentions. He does not depart from the admirable restraint that characterises all he has written upon this subject, which makes his monograph a reliable guide to those who want the data and prefer to form their own opinions as to their meaning.

The great importance of the discoveries in China lies in the fact, not only that the material is more abundant than the remains found at Trinil and Piltdown, and their geological age is unquestionable, but also that, while *Sinanthropus* is differentiated from the genera *Pithecanthropus* and *Eoanthropus*, it is much more generalised than either, yet definitely linked to both. While it is the most primitive type of human being so far discovered, its structural affinities with both the Javanese and the British genera link together all the known types of Pleistocene men and give cohesion to our knowledge.

It is fortunate that the information concerning this unique material has been so fully and so promptly supplied to anthropologists in a monograph which is distinguished by admirable clearness and impartiality. Once more Prof. Davidson Black deserves our congratulations on a great achievement.

(**127**, 819-821; 1931)

区别性特征，不仅在乳突部，而且在外耳道形状和中耳方面，都显示出在现代人中只见于新生儿和很小的儿童中的特征——终止于鼓膜的外耳道开口广阔，鼓膜位置接近于水平。而这种情况早在智人的青春期到来之前就会消失。正如步达生博士所说，北京人鼓室区域的特征非常适合作为推测系统发育的出发点。“因为有了这一一般化的类型，我们就不难想象出鼓室可能经过的发育阶段，这些发育阶段导致了那些使皮尔当、尼安德特和现代人具有不同特征的改变”。另一方面，因为大型类人猿鼓室形态的所有特点都可以在北京人的相应部位找到，所以对鼓室特征进行的比较可能揭示他们从一个共同的祖先趋异进化的程度。尽管这一说法很具煽动性，步达生教授还是忍住不去讨论他所提到的这些引人入胜的问题。他在对这一主题的所有叙述中一直保持着令人钦佩的严谨，这使得他的专著给那些想要得到资料并且更喜欢对这些资料的意义形成自己的观点的人提供了可靠的指导。

在中国发现北京人头骨的巨大价值不仅在于这里的材料比特里尼尔和皮尔当的遗存骸更丰富，它们的地质年代也是确定无疑的，而且，还在于尽管北京人不同于爪哇猿人属和曙人属，它比后两者都更一般化得多，但肯定与后两者都存在联系。尽管北京人是迄今发现的最原始类型的人类，其与在爪哇和在英国发现的化石人属在结构上的亲缘关系将所有已知的更新世人类都联系在了一起，也使我们的知识融会在了一起。

很幸运，步达生教授将与北京人头骨这一独特材料有关的信息如此充分而且迅速地以一部条理清晰、论述公正的专著提供给了人类学家。步达生教授的伟大成就值得我们再一次祝贺。

（刘皓芳 翻译；林圣龙 审稿）

# Recent Advances in the Chemistry of the Vitamins

## Editor's Note

**Despite the complaint of neglect that opens this piece by English biochemist Frederick Gowland Hopkins, president of the Royal Society, vitamin chemistry was being pursued with much energy in the 1930s. Hopkins had himself won a Nobel Prize two years earlier for his work in this field. Yet the molecular structures of none of the vitamins discussed here—A, B and D, the latter two being in fact several substances—was then known in detail, nor were their precise modes of biochemical action. Indeed, the rather technical and laborious chemical procedures detailed here are an indication of how painstakingly those answers had to be sought.**

AT the meeting of the Royal Society held on June 18, the President, Sir Frederick Gowland Hopkins, opened a discussion on the chemistry of the vitamins. He said that although many discoveries had been communicated in the past to the Society, there had been very few papers dealing with the vitamins. He felt great satisfaction that this discussion should occur during the first year of his presidency, especially as the subject was still growing in interest. The Society were to be congratulated on the presence of a number of foreign workers, so that the discussion would have an international character. As the subject was so vast, he proposed to limit it to the chemistry of the vitamins, and suggested that vitamins D, A, and the B complex be taken in that order.

### Vitamin D

Prof. A. Windaus said that up to the present, investigations had had to be carried out on impure substances and chiefly by means of physical experiments. No stable equilibrium was formed between ergosterol and the products of irradiation. By further irradiation two crystalline substances could be obtained, neither of which could be converted into the other; it appeared therefore that two series of products were formed on irradiation. Reerink and van Wijk had found that no matter whether 10 or 50 percent of the ergosterol was changed by long wave irradiation, the absorption spectrum of the product was always the same. He suggested that this was due to several substances being formed in constant proportion, and that the absorption spectrum was that of the mixture. None of the products of irradiation are precipitated by digitonin. Failure of precipitation, however, does not imply that a change has taken place in the hydroxyl group. On treatment with phenyl isocyanate the antirachitic activity of the irradiated ergosterol is destroyed. Treatment with warm caustic potash results in the reconversion of the phenyl urethane to vitamin D.

# 维生素在化学方面的新进展

## 编者按

*尽管皇家学会主席，英国生物化学家弗雷德里克·高兰·霍普金斯在开篇时抱怨维生素化学领域没有得到足够的重视，但在20世纪30年代人们还是对此付出了很大的努力。两年前霍普金斯本人因在这个领域中的成就而赢得了诺贝尔奖。不过，这里讨论的几种维生素（维生素A、B、D，后两者实际上是由多种物质组成的）的分子结构和准确的生化反应模式在当时并不清楚。的确，文中所描述的非常专业和繁复的化学过程足以说明探索答案的过程是多么艰辛。*

在6月18日召开的皇家学会会议上，学会主席弗雷德里克·高兰·霍普金斯爵士在有关维生素化学的讨论中首先发言。他表示：尽管学会以往对许多新发现都进行过交流，但在维生素方面的文章却是少之又少。能在自己的第一年任期内举行这样的讨论，他感到非常满意，尤其是因为这一主题正在引起越来越广泛的关注。学会为有许多国外的研究者参会而感到庆幸，因此这将是一次国际性的盛会。鉴于这一主题非常宽泛，他提议将其限定在维生素的化学特性方面，并建议按照维生素D、维生素A和维生素B复合物的顺序进行讨论。

### 维生素D

温道斯教授说，迄今为止人们不得不对混合物进行研究，而且研究主要依靠的是物理实验。在麦角甾醇和其照射产物之间没有形成稳定的平衡，通过更长时间的照射可以得到两种结晶体，而这两种结晶体是不能相互转化的。因此可以得出结论：麦角甾醇在照射过程中生成了两个系列的产物。雷林克和范维克发现在经过长波照射后，无论发生变化的麦角甾醇是10%还是50%，其产物的吸收光谱通常都是相同的。温道斯教授认为这是由于形成的几种物质具有恒定的比例，而得到的吸收光谱正是这个混合物的吸收光谱。没有一种照射产物能用毛地黄皂苷沉淀出来。然而不能沉淀出来并不意味着羟基发生了变化。在用异氰酸苯酯处理照射过的麦角甾醇后，其抗佝偻病的活性被破坏。而用温和的氢氧化钾进行处理，则会使苯氨基甲酸乙酯重新转化为维生素D。

Prof. Windaus had found that the vitamin had the same molecular weight and formula as ergosterol and also contained three double bonds. The dihydro derivative obtained from irradiated ergosterol by treatment with sodium in alcoholic solution was inactive, but it is not certain that it is a derivative of vitamin D itself. The vitamin is more sensitive to a temperature of 180° than ergosterol; after heating, the absorption spectrum shows a band at 2820–2920 A.

Crude vitamin D is stable in oil, although the absorption spectrum and specific rotation rapidly change. The toxicity of the crude product varies with the potency, but it is still possible that the two properties may be due to different substances. The problem has not yet been solved. He had noticed that in vacuum tubes, in which crude vitamin D had been sealed, crystals appeared, but he had not been able to obtain them in a pure state by recrystallisation from cold acetone or by fractional precipitation. He had found, however, that when irradiated ergosterol was treated with maleic or citraconic anhydride in ethereal solution at room temperature for one to three days, a reaction occurred between certain of the substances present and the anhydride. When these inactive products were removed by solution in dilute caustic potash, crystals could be obtained from the ethereal layer on evaporation of the solvent. The yield was 50 percent of the crude product, or 60–70 percent of the material which failed to react with maleic anhydride.

Vitamin D crystallises in long needles of melting point 122°; $[a]_{D}^{18} = +136°$ in acetone, and $[a]_{Hg}^{18} = +168°$ in acetone.

The crystals show a band in the absorption spectrum at 2650–2700 A. Their potency was found to be 2–2½ times that of the M.R.C. standard.

He considered that the product obtained by Reerink and van Wijk was different from his, since it had a lower specific rotation and an absorption spectrum of a different shape, but that Bourdillon's crystals were probably the same. He agreed with the suggestion of the latter that there might be several compounds showing vitamin D activity, but considered that his crystals were responsible at any rate for the chief part of it. Vitamin D is an isomer of ergosterol in which there has been a structural rearrangement with an increase in the spatial size of the molecule.

Prof. B. C. P. Jansen said that Reerink and van Wijk had now obtained crystals of a melting point 140°. Their former product with a lower melting point had contained ether of crystallisation.

Dr. R. B. Bourdillon said that the discovery of the method of obtaining crystals of vitamin D by means of maleic anhydride was of outstanding importance and likely to lead to a solution of the problem of its constitution. He and his co-workers had obtained very similar crystals by distillation of irradiated ergosterol in a high vacuum. Their melting

温道斯教授发现维生素 D 具有与麦角甾醇相同的分子量和分子式，并同样具有三个双键。由照射过的麦角甾醇在乙醇溶液中用钠处理后得到的二氢衍生物是没有活性的，但不能确定该物质就是维生素 D 本身的一个衍生物。在 180℃下，维生素 D 比麦角甾醇更加敏感；加热后，在吸收光谱的 2820 Å ~ 2920 Å 处会出现一条谱带。

天然的维生素 D 在油中是稳定存在的，尽管其吸收光谱和比旋光度会迅速地发生变化，此外其毒性也会随着效价而改变。但这两种特性仍有可能是基于不同的化学物质而产生的，这个问题一直没有得到解决。温道斯教授还发现将天然的维生素 D 封在真空管中会出现结晶，但是他尝试在冷的丙酮中进行重结晶或者采用分级沉淀的方法都未能获得纯的维生素 D 结晶。然而，他发现照射过的麦角甾醇在室温下用马来酸酐或者柠康酸酐的醚溶液处理 1 ~ 3 天后，其中的某些物质与酸酐发生了化学反应。当用稀释的氢氧化钾溶液除去这些无活性的产物后，蒸发溶剂，就可从醚层中得到结晶，其产率按照粗品计算为 50%，按照没有与马来酸酐发生反应的物质计算则为 60% ~ 70%。

维生素 D 结晶为长针状，熔点是 122℃ ； $[a]_D^{18}$ = +136°（丙酮），$[a]_{Hg}^{18}$ = +168°（丙酮）。

此结晶体的吸收光谱在 2650 Å ~ 2700 Å 处有一条谱带。其效价为英国医学研究理事会（M.R.C.）规定标准的 2 ~ 2.5 倍。

他认为雷林克和范维克得到的产物与他得到的不同，因为他们的产物比旋光度值较低，而且吸收光谱的形状也不一样，不过鲍迪伦获得的结晶体也许与他的是相同的。他同意鲍迪伦的看法，认为可能有好几种化合物都能表现出维生素 D 活性，但又把自己所获得的结晶体看作是起主要作用的部分。维生素 D 是麦角甾醇的一个异构体，是通过结构重排而得到的空间尺寸更大的分子。

詹森教授说，雷林克和范维克现在已经得到了一个熔点为 140℃的结晶体。他们先前制得的熔点较低的产物含有醚的结晶。

鲍迪伦博士认为发现用马来酸酐获得维生素 D 结晶的方法具有重大意义，很有可能帮助我们解决维生素 D 的构成问题。他和他的同事们通过在高真空下蒸馏照射过的麦角甾醇得到了极其类似的结晶体，其熔点为 123℃ ~ 125℃，在醇溶液中对汞

point was 123–125°. The specific rotation to the mercury line in alcoholic solution was +250 to +260°. The maximum absorption occurred at 2700 A. and was greater than that of ergosterol. The potency was 18–22,000 M.R.C. U./mgm., that is approximately the same or slightly less than that shown by Prof. Windaus' crystals. They had been able to prepare an oxalate and acetate and reconvert these back to the original crystals. They had found the rotation and potency to remain constant for some weeks in dry air or in vacuo. Neither by distillation at a temperature of 160° nor by further irradiation with loss of two-thirds of the potency had they been able to separate their crystals into two separate compounds. Moreover, on irradiation the loss of antirachitic activity and the changes in the absorption coefficient and specific rotation were absolutely parallel. They therefore considered that their crystals were a definite chemical compound and had ventured to call it "Calciferol". However, the unity of the compound was not absolutely certain, owing to variations in the specific rotation of different preparations. They had recently obtained some crystals with a rotation of + 290°. He suggested that there were at least two vitamins, isomorphic and with the same absorption spectra, the laevo form being very unstable, while the dextro form was stable. This suggestion would explain the discrepancies in his own work and that of other observers.

Dr. O. Rosenheim said he considered the work now reported was the most important since the original researches on vitamin D. He thought that Windaus' and Bourdillon's crystals were identical, although it was possible that there might be an impurity present as in Reerink and van Wijk's preparation. Spectroscopic methods had not led to much advance, but success had come from biological and organic chemical research, and especially from Bourdillon's method of fractional condensation. He pointed out that if ergosterol was irradiated until 20 percent had been changed and the 80 percent of inactive material removed, the activity of the residue was only the same as that of the original irradiated material. On distillation of the residue, 20 percent was obtained as crystals, but the activity was only twice that of the crude product.

## Vitamin A

Prof. H. von Euler said that it was early noticed that fat soluble growth-promoting material was frequently associated with a red or yellow coloration but that the converse was not true. Working with Karrer, he had found that of all red or yellow substances examined, only carotene had vitamin A activity. Carotene was usually supposed to be optically inactive, but he, as well as Rosenheim and Kuhn working independently, had found that it could be fractionated into two forms, one melting at 170° and optically active, and the other melting at 183° and optically inactive. Both forms had growth-promoting power. The latter gave an earlier growth response, but after three weeks the differences between the two disappeared. A dose of 0.003 mg. daily would produce a daily increase in weight of one gram in the rat. Complete hydrogenation of carotene inactivated it, but reduction with aluminium amalgam at first increased the activity. Hydrocarotene containing eight double bonds is much more active than carotene, the daily dose required being only 0.0005 mg. It also gives a higher blue value with the Carr and Price colour test. The absorption

线的比旋光度值为 +250°～ +260°。它最大的光谱吸收出现在 2700 Å，这比麦角甾醇的还要大。这个结晶体的效价为 18～22,000 M.R.C. U/mg，这与温道斯教授得到的结晶体的效价大致相同或者略微偏低。他们已经能够用这种结晶体制备草酸盐和醋酸盐，并能将它们重新转化为原来的结晶体。他们发现在干燥的空气中或者真空下结晶体的旋光度和效价会持续几个星期保持不变。既不用在 160℃下进行蒸馏，也不需要更长时间的光照射（这样会损失 2/3 的效价），他们就能将得到的结晶体分离为两个单独的化合物。而且在光的照射下，这两种化合物的抗佝偻病活性损失与吸收系数和比旋光度的变化完全一致。因此，他们认为自己得到的结晶体是一种明确的化合物，并大胆地把它称为“钙化醇”。然而，由于在不同的制备方法中这个化合物的比旋光度会发生变化，所以不能完全确定该化合物的性质是统一的。最近他们获得了一些旋光度为 +290° 的结晶体。鲍迪伦博士认为这些结晶体中至少存在着两种结构和吸收光谱相同的维生素，其中左旋形式的维生素非常不稳定，而右旋形式的维生素是稳定的。这样的观点也许能够解释他的研究与其他观测者的研究之间的差异。

罗森海姆博士认为现在报道的研究工作是自人们开展对维生素 D 的研究以来最为重要的工作。他认为温道斯和鲍迪伦的结晶体是相同的，尽管有可能会像雷林克和范维克的制备物一样存在一定的杂质。在光谱学方法的研究上并没有取得什么进展，但在生物学和有机化学方面却取得了成功，尤其是鲍迪伦的分级凝缩方法。他指出如果光照射麦角甾醇直到 20% 的物质发生了变化，然后将 80% 的无活性物质除去，那么残留物的活性才跟最初被照射的物质相同。将残留物进行蒸馏，可以得到占残留物 20% 的结晶，但其活性仅是天然产品的两倍。

## 维生素 A

冯欧勒教授说，人们很早就注意到脂溶性的促生长物质常常与红色或黄色相关联，但不能倒推。他与卡勒一起研究发现，在所有检测过的红色或黄色物质中，只有胡萝卜素具有维生素 A 活性。人们通常认为胡萝卜素是不具备光学活性的，但与罗森海姆和库恩的独立研究结果一样，冯欧勒教授也发现胡萝卜素可以分成两种：一种熔点为 170℃，具有光学活性；另一种熔点为 183℃，不具有光学活性。这两种胡萝卜素都有促进生长的作用。后者的促生长作用出现得比较早，但 3 周以后两者之间就没有什么差别了。每天以 0.003 mg 的剂量给大鼠喂食胡萝卜素，可以使它的体重每天增加 1 g。完全氢化胡萝卜素会消除它的促生长作用，但如果先用铝汞合金进行还原却会使它的活性增加。含有 8 个双键的氢化胡萝卜素比胡萝卜素的活性要高很多，所以要使大鼠体重增加 1 g，每天只需 0.0005 mg 的剂量。而且它在卡尔和普赖斯颜色试验（卡 – 普二氏试验）中表现出更高的蓝色值。这种氢化胡萝卜素的

spectrum is very similar to that attributed to vitamin A in cod liver oil.

Moore considers that carotene is converted to vitamin A in the body of the rat. Prof. von Euler had tried to effect this conversion in vitro, but only with the serum of the hen had he found that carotene could be converted into a substance very similar to vitamin A although not spectroscopically identical. He considered it probable that the transformation occurs in the blood, and that vitamin A may act as a catalyser in oxidation. He had also examined the anti-infective action of carotene and had found that it did not affect haemolysis in vitro nor react with amboceptor, but that when it was given in excess to rabbits, the amboceptor in their blood was increased.

Dr. Rosenheim said that carotene is a mixture which has not yet been completely separated, and that it is dangerous to attribute activity to any particular isomer. The optical activities obtained by different observers vary considerably. It is possible that the transformation of carotene into vitamin A in the body may be only the accumulation of vitamin A present as a contaminant in the carotene. The band in the absorption spectrum of cod liver oil at 3280 A. may not be due to vitamin A but to a substance accompanying it.

Dr. R. A. Morton said that if the band at 3280 A. is to be attributed to vitamin A, then the latter cannot be present in carotene as an impurity. Dihydrocarotene is not vitamin A, since the band in its absorption spectrum is at 3170 A., the blue colour given with antimony trichloride is not the same as that given by the vitamin, and the ratio of blue colour to intensity of absorption is different.

## Vitamin B

Prof. B. C. P. Jansen said that when 100 kgm. of rice polishings were extracted with dilute acid alcohol, 30 kgm. went into solution. By treatment with acid clay it was possible to adsorb nearly all the vitamin $B_1$, but only 100 grams of contaminating solid material. The vitamin $B_1$ present accounted for only 1 percent of the adsorbed material. By fractional precipitation with silver nitrate and baryta it was possible to remove impurities at a strongly acid reaction and to precipitate two-thirds of the vitamin at *p*H 4–7: above this *p*H impurities were precipitated as well.

Further purification could be effected by precipitation with phosphotungstic acid, and decomposition of the precipitate with baryta, and precipitation with platinum chloride from alcoholic solution. When the platinum was removed with powdered silver, 1.4 gram was obtained, of which 0.4 gram was pure vitamin. By numerous fractionations with acetone from solution in absolute alcohol, 30 mgm. of pure vitamin were obtained. The formula by analysis was $C_6H_{10}ON_2HCl$. The process he had devised was therefore very wasteful. It could be improved by the use of Peters' method of fractional precipitation with phosphotungstic acid. Prof. Jansen had found that silicotungstic acid was as suitable. When the original 100 grams obtained by adsorption on acid clay were treated with this

吸收光谱非常类似于鱼肝油中维生素 A 的吸收光谱。

穆尔认为胡萝卜素是在大鼠体内转化成维生素 A 的。冯欧勒教授曾试图在体外完成这样的转化。但他发现只有用母鸡的血清才能使胡萝卜素转化为一种与维生素 A 非常类似的物质，尽管二者的光谱并不一致。于是，他认为这种转化很可能是在血液中发生的，而维生素 A 可能是氧化过程中的一个催化剂。他还对胡萝卜素的抗感染作用进行了研究，结果发现它既不影响体外的溶血，也不与溶血素发生反应，但当给兔子的剂量过多时，兔子血液中的溶血素会增多。

罗森海姆博士认为胡萝卜素是一种混合物，这种混合物到现在也没有被完全分离开，把它的活性归因于任何一种异构体都是有风险的。因为，首先，不同的研究者得到的光学活性存在着很大的差异。其次，胡萝卜素在体内转化成维生素 A 的过程可能仅仅是维生素 A 作为胡萝卜素中的一种杂质积聚在了一起。再次，在鱼肝油的吸收光谱中位于 3280 Å 的谱带也许并不是由维生素 A 引起的，而是由于一种与之相伴的物质。

莫顿博士认为如果在 3280 Å 的谱带是由维生素 A 引起的，那么维生素 A 就不可能是胡萝卜素中的杂质。二氢胡萝卜素不是维生素 A，因为它的光谱吸收带在 3170 Å，并且由三氯化锑试验（译者注：就是上面提到的卡－普二氏试验）给出的蓝色值与维生素 A 的不同，此外蓝色值与吸收强度的比值也不一样。

## 维生素 B

詹森教授指出在用稀释的酸醇溶液萃取 100 kg 的米糠时，会有 30 kg 的米糠进入溶液中。再用酸性黏土进行处理，可能会吸附几乎所有的维生素 $B_1$，不过只得到 100 g 含杂质的固体物质。把全部的维生素 $B_1$ 加起来也只占被吸附物质的 1%。通过硝酸银和氧化钡的分级沉淀，可能会在强烈的酸性反应中除去杂质，并在 pH 值 4～7 的条件下析出三分之二的维生素，pH 值高于 7 时，杂质也会一起析出。

进一步的纯化可以通过以下过程进行：用磷钨酸进行沉淀，然后用氧化钡分解此沉淀物，再用氯化铂从醇溶液进行沉淀。在用银粉除去铂之后，得到了 1.4 g 的产物，其中含有 0.4 g 纯的维生素。再将此产物溶于无水乙醇中，用丙酮进行多次分馏，最终可以得到 30 mg 纯的维生素。通过分析得知其分子式为 $C_6H_{10}ON_2HCl$。可以说，詹森教授所设计的这个制备方法是非常不经济的。也许可以用彼得斯的磷钨酸分级沉淀法对其加以改进。詹森教授已经发现硅钨酸也同样适用。在用硅钨酸处理从酸性黏土中吸收得到的 100 g 粗品时，有 2/3 的维生素会沉淀出来，不过析出的质量只

reagent, two-thirds of the vitamin were precipitated, but only 20 percent of the total solid. A further improvement had been effected by Seidell's benzoylation process, which removes impurities. By this method von Ween had obtained 140 mgm. of pure vitamin $B_1$ from 75 kgm. rice polishings.

Prof. A. Seidell said that Prof. Jansen had had success with a method that had failed in his hands. He had felt that precipitating agents ought to be avoided, and so was led to the method of benzoylation in chloroform solution, which removes a considerable amount of nitrogenous material. He had not succeeded in obtaining crystals, although his purest preparation was nearly as active on rats, but when tested on pigeons by Peters' method the activity was found to be only 1/5 to 1/10 that of the crystals.

Prof. R. A. Peters said that he had hoped to be able to use the animal as a test object only and not concern himself with the physiological side of the problem, but he had found that it was only possible to reach a final conclusion on the chemistry when the physiology was also taken into account. He had been able to confirm Prof. Jansen's process up to the platinum chloride stage. Working with yeast he had obtained purification by removal of inactive material with lead acetate and baryta followed by adsorption of the vitamin by charcoal. By fractional precipitation with phosphotungstic acid at *p*H 5–7, vitamin $B_1$ was obtained. Its activity was 0.012 mgm. per dose, while that of Prof. Jansen's crystals in his hands was 0.008 mgm. Both preparations gave the Pauly reaction with the same intensity. Miss Reader had shown that 25–50 percent of Prof Jansen's crystals had vitamin $B_4$ activity. She had now been able to isolate vitamin $B_1$ from $B_4$ by fractional adsorption on to charcoal in the earlier stages of the purification, but the separation of $B_4$ from $B_1$ was less complete.

Dr. B. C. Guha said that he had been able to separate $B_1$ from $B_2$ by electrodialysis. Vitamin $B_1$ appeared to be a strong base, while $B_2$ was a neutral substance.

The President, in summing up the discussion, said that the progress of the last few years should make them optimistic. He expected that we should soon know the constitution of vitamin D. The chemical problems involved were *a priori* difficult, but workers were finding that the compounds were amenable to the methods of organic chemistry. He thanked the visitors from overseas for taking part in the discussion.

(**128**, 39-40; 1931)

有总固体量的 20%。塞德尔用苯甲酰化方法去除杂质，使得纯化进行得更加彻底。通过这个方法，冯维恩从 75 kg 米糠中得到了 140 mg 纯的维生素 $B_1$。

塞德尔教授说，詹森教授用一个在他手上失败了的方法获得了成功。他曾认为应当避免使用沉淀剂，而正是如此才产生了在氯仿溶液中进行苯甲酰化的方法，这种方法能够除去大量的含氮物质。他还没有成功地获得结晶体，尽管他所制备的最纯物质在大鼠身上与维生素 $B_1$ 结晶体有近似的活性，但在用彼得斯的方法对鸽子进行试验的时候，发现其活性只有维生素 $B_1$ 结晶体的 1/5 ~ 1/10。

彼得斯教授说，他曾希望能够只把动物作为测试对象而不考虑其生理学方面的问题，但是他发现只有在同时考虑生理学问题的时候，才有可能在化学方面得出最终的结论。他能够确定詹森教授的制备过程直到用氯化铂溶液进行沉淀的阶段。他从对酵母的研究中得到了这样的纯化方法：用醋酸铅和氧化钡除去无活性物质，接着用活性炭吸附维生素。在 pH 值为 5 ~ 7 下用磷钨酸进行分级沉淀就得到了维生素 $B_1$，其活性为每次剂量 0.012 mg，而詹森教授的结晶体活性为 0.008 mg。在这两种制备方法中都发生了剧烈程度相同的波利反应。里德小姐曾表示詹森教授的结晶体中有 25% ~ 50% 具有维生素 $B_4$ 的活性。现在她已经能够在纯化阶段前期用活性炭分级吸附的方法从维生素 $B_4$ 中分离出维生素 $B_1$，但是从维生素 $B_1$ 中却不能完全分离出维生素 $B_4$。

古哈博士说他已经能够用电渗析的方法从维生素 $B_2$ 中分离出维生素 $B_1$。维生素 $B_1$ 似乎是一种强碱，而维生素 $B_2$ 是一种中性物质。

学会主席在总结这次讨论时说，最近几年的研究发展使他们感到很乐观。他预计我们应该很快就能确定维生素 D 的构成。其中所涉及的化学问题是推理上的难点，但是研究人员发现这些化合物可以用有机化学方法进行检验。他对参加这次讨论的海外人士表示感谢。

（刘振明 翻译；刘京国 审稿）

# The Annihilation of Matter*

J. Jeans

## Editor's Note

**James Jeans notes here that one of the sacred principles of science was giving way. It had been a bedrock belief of physicists for centuries that matter can be neither created nor destroyed. Yet now, he points out, it looked increasingly certain that the process by which stars generate energy could only be explained through the annihilation of matter. Evidence showed that the average star has already emitted many times its own mass in radiation. The life history of a star seemed to be a continual annihilation of its substance, as massive particles give up their energy to produce radiation. The explanation for this is now seen to come from nuclear fusion, in which mass and energy are interconverted via Einstein's $E = mc^2$.**

THROUGHOUT the greater part of the history of science, matter was believed to be permanent, incapable either of annihilation or of creation. Yet a large amount of astronomical evidence now seems to point to the annihilation of matter as the only possible source of the energy radiated by the stars. A position has thus been reached in which the majority of astronomers think it probable that annihilation of matter constitutes one of the fundamental processes of the universe, while many, and perhaps most, physicists look on the possibility with caution and even distrust. I have thought it might be of interest to attempt a survey of the present situation in respect to this question.

### The Astronomical Evidence

The astronomical argument for the annihilation of matter is based, not on the intensity of stellar radiation, but on its duration. No transformation of a less drastic nature than complete annihilation is found capable of providing continuous radiation for the immense periods of time throughout which the stars have, to all appearances, lived. For, with one conspicuous exception, to be discussed later, all available methods of estimating stellar ages are found to indicate that the stars, as a whole, have already lived through periods of millions of millions of years.

Some of these methods depend on the rate of gravitational interaction between adjacent stars; for example, the velocities with which the stars move through space show an approximation to equipartition of energy, such as must have required millions of millions of years for its establishment. The individual members of the groups of stars known as moving star clusters appear to have had their courses changed by the gravitational pull of passing stars to an extent which again indicates action extending over millions of millions

*The substance of lectures delivered before the Universities of Princeton, Yale, and Harvard on May 23, 26, and 27 respectively, under the auspices of the Franklin Institute of Pennsylvania.

# 物质的湮灭*

詹姆斯·金斯

## 编者按

詹姆斯·金斯在文中指出：科学发展最神圣的原则之一是新旧理论的更迭。几百年来，物理学家们一直对物质既不能产生也不能灭亡这一原则深信不疑。可是现在，他指出，人们越来越相信恒星只有通过物质的湮灭过程才能获取能量。有证据表明：一般的恒星早已在过去的岁月里辐射掉了现有质量的好多倍。恒星存在的过程似乎就是其物质不断湮灭的过程，因为有质量的粒子会将其能量用于产生辐射。现在人们利用核聚变原理来解释这一现象，质量和能量的相互转化关系可以由爱因斯坦方程 $E = mc^2$ 表示。

在贯穿整个科学史的大部分时间里，物质都被看作是守恒的，它们既不会凭空产生，也不会凭空消失。但是现在大量天文学的证据似乎表明，物质的湮灭是恒星辐射能量的唯一来源。从而出现了这样一种局面：大多数天文学家认为物质湮灭可能是宇宙中的一个基本过程，而同时，许多也可能是大部分的物理学家对这种可能性持谨慎态度，甚至干脆不相信。我一直认为试着评述与这个问题相关的现状会是一件有意义的事情。

### 天文学的证据

天文学上关于物质湮灭的论证，不是以恒星辐射的强度为依据，而是基于恒星存在的时间。尚未发现一种不如完全湮灭那么剧烈的能量转化，能够在恒星显然存在的漫长岁月里，始终为其提供持续辐射所需要的能量。所有可以用来估算恒星寿命的方法都表明，整体看来，恒星已经存在了万亿年，只有一个方法明显例外，我将在后面讨论它。

有些方法取决于临近恒星的引力作用速度；例如，恒星穿越空间的速度表明它的能量是近似均分的，而要实现这样的均分必须经过数以万亿年的时间。被称为运动星团的星群中的个体成员，由于在其旁边经过的恒星的一定程度上的引力作用，它们的路径已经出现了改变，这再次表明活动过程已延续了数万亿年。目视双星的轨道也是如此。在这三个例子中，我们所使用的时钟的单位时间类似于在气体理论

* 这个由美国宾夕法尼亚州富兰克林科学馆赞助的演讲分别于 5 月 23 日、26 日和 27 日发表于普林斯顿大学、耶鲁大学和哈佛大学。

of years. The same is true of the orbits of visual binary stars. In each of these three cases, the clock we use has for its unit a time analogous to what is called the "time of relaxation" in the theory of gases; in this comparison the single stars correspond to monatomic molecules, and binary stars to diatomic molecules, while the disintegration of a moving star cluster provides the counterpart of the process of gaseous diffusion.

These estimates of stellar ages are, of course, valid only if we assume that the changes in stellar motions and arrangements are produced solely by the gravitational pulls of other stars. Other causes are conceivable, and must indeed contribute something—pressure of radiation, bombardment by stray matter in space, or by the atoms of cosmic clouds diffused through space. But calculation shows that the contributions from these sources are quite negligible. Indeed, when we take them into account, the discussion of stellar movements is no longer a problem of astronomy, but of physics; we have to treat the stars as Brownian "particles" in a physical medium. When they are so treated, we find that the starry medium has a temperature—in the sense in which we speak of the temperature of moving Brownian particles—of the order of $10^{62}$ degrees. Both individual and binary stars exhibit the equipartition of energy which corresponds to a temperature of this order, whence it is obvious that physical agencies such as pressure of radiation and atomic pressures, which are in equilibrium with far lower temperatures of the order only of $10^4$ degrees, cannot have made any appreciable contributions to the establishment of this equipartition; they act as mere drags on the stellar motions, tending on the average to check their speed.

In a second class of binary stars, the spectroscopic binaries, the two components are so close together that the gravitational pull from passing stars is approximately the same on each, and so cannot exert the differential action which would change the relative orbits of the constituent masses. Clearly there can be no question of any approximation to equipartition of energy in the internal motions of these systems. Nevertheless, it is possible to trace a steady sequence of configurations, beginning with almost circular orbits in which the two constituents are practically in contact—this being probably the condition of a system which has just formed by fission—and proceeding to orbits which are far from circular in shape, in which the components are at a substantial distance apart. It seems likely, although not certain, that this sequence is one of advancing age; when the parent star first breaks up to form a binary, the newly formed system starts at the first-mentioned end and moves gradually along the sequence. Now observation shows, beyond all doubt, that the stars at the far end of this sequence are substantially less massive than those at the beginning. We know the rate at which the various types of stars are radiating their mass away in the form of radiation, and from this we can calculate the time needed to produce the difference of mass which is observed to exist between the two ends of the sequence; again it proves to be a matter of millions of millions of years. Here the clock we use is the rate of outflow of radiation from a star, or its equivalent, the rate of loss of mass.

Against these various estimates must be set one piece of evidence which, if interpreted in the most obvious way, seems to point in exactly the opposite direction. This is, that the

中所称的“弛豫时间”；在这个类比中，单个恒星被当作单原子分子处理，双星被当作双原子分子，而运动星团的瓦解对应于气体的扩散过程。

当然，只有当我们假定其他恒星的引力作用是引起恒星运动和排列改变的唯一原因时，这些对恒星年龄的估计才成立。可以想象其他原因也是存在的，并且必然在某些方面有一定的贡献——辐射压力，由宇宙空间中的游离物质或弥散在空间中的宇宙云原子造成的轰击。但是计算表明源于这些过程的贡献是相当微不足道的。实际上，当我们把这些因素考虑进去时，对恒星运动的讨论就不再是一个天文学问题，而变为一个物理问题；我们必须把恒星当作是在物理介质中作布朗运动的“粒子”。做这样的处理之后，我们发现这个布满恒星的介质，以我们谈及运动着的布朗粒子的温度的方式而论，它的温度可达 $10^{62}$ 度数量级。单个恒星和双星都表现出与此数量级温度相对应的能量均分，显而易见，物理中介作用，比如辐射压力和原子压力等建立平衡的温度要低得多，只有 $10^4$ 度的量级，不可能对建立均分的过程有任何可观的贡献；它们不过是作为恒星运动的阻力罢了，平均而言往往是在减慢它们的速度。

在第二类双星系统，即光谱双星中，两颗子星是如此之近，以至于从它们附近经过的恒星对它们两个的吸引效果几乎相同，因此就不能以不同的作用效果改变双星系统组成物的相对轨道。显然对于这种系统的内部运动，毫无疑问可以采取任意近似方式以达到其能量均分的状态。尽管如此，仍然可以描绘出双星系统结构所固有的演变过程，从仍相互接触的两组分所处的近似圆轨道开始，这很可能就是一个系统刚刚分裂形成的状态；然后继续发展到形状远不是圆的轨道，此时这两个组分产生了实质上的分离。尽管还不能确定，但似乎可以认为这种演变过程就是一种老化的过程。当母星刚刚分裂形成双星系统时，新形成的系统从刚提到的结构变化的末端，逐渐沿着一系列变化过程演化。现在观测表明，毫无疑问，处于该演化过程末端的恒星所具有的质量大大低于初始阶段的质量。我们知道不同类型恒星以辐射形式损失质量的速率，由此可以计算出为产生存在于演化过程两端的质量差而需要的时间。结果再一次证明这个过程需要数万亿年。在这里我们所用的度量标准是恒星辐射的流失率，或与之相对应的，物质损失率。

反对这几种估算方法的人一定会提到这样一个证据，如果用最一目了然的方式解释的话，它似乎会得出完全相反的结论。即遥远的河外星云的谱线都发生了红移，

remote extra-galactic nebulae all show a shift of their spectral lines to the red, the amount of shift being approximately, although not exactly, proportional to the distance of the nebula. If this is interpreted in the most direct way, as a Doppler effect, the nebulae must all be scattering away from us and from one another in space, at so great a speed that the whole universe doubles its size about once in every 1,400 million years. Such a rate of increase seems quite inconsistent with the estimate which assigns ages of millions of millions of years to the stars. Calculation suggests that the original radius of the universe must have been of the order of 1,200 million light-years (Eddington), while the present radius of the universe appears to be only of the order of 2,000 million light-years (de Sitter). If these estimates could be treated as exact, we could fix the age of the universe definitely at just more than 1,000 million years, which is substantially less even than the age of the earth as indicated by its radioactive rocks. No one would claim any great degree of exactness for either of these estimates, especially the second, yet the general situation seems to forbid that the universe can have been doubling in size every 1,400 million years throughout a period of millions of millions of years.

Although alternative interpretations are tenable, none of them seems entirely convincing, and the present situation is extremely puzzling. While there is obviously room for much difference of opinion, many astronomers consider it likely that some other explanation of the apparent recessions of the nebulae will be found in time, in which event the road will be clear for the acceptance of ages of millions of millions of years for the stars, as suggested by the main bulk of astronomical evidence.

If such ages are provisionally accepted, calculation shows that the average star has already emitted many times its total mass in radiation; in other words, the average star must have started life with many times its present mass. Indeed, the sequence of spectroscopic binaries gives us a sort of picture of the life-history of a typical star. It starts with anything from ten to a hundred times the mass of the sun, and ends with a mass comparable to, or even less than, that of the sun. It is difficult to see where the enormous weight of the newly-born star can have been stored if not in the form of material atoms, or at any rate of material electrons and protons. Thus we are led to suppose that the life-history of the star is one of continual annihilation of its substance, the electrons and protons annihilating one another, and providing the energy for the star's radiation in so doing. Such, at least, is the conjecture suggested to us by astronomy; the testing of the conjecture rests with physics.

## Highly Penetrating Radiation

If any direct evidence of this process of annihilation is to be obtained, it seems most likely that it will be found in the highly penetrating radiation which McLennan, Rutherford, and others discovered in the earth's atmosphere at the beginning of the present century. The reason, as we shall see later, is that here, and here alone in the whole of physics, we are dealing with photons of radiation whose mass is comparable with that to be expected in

红移量与星云的距离近似成正比，但不精确。如果这个现象被解释成最直接的原因，即多普勒效应，则这些星云必须全部从我们身边分散开去，并且在空间中互相远离。远离的速度是如此之大以至于大约每过 14 亿年宇宙的尺度就要增加一倍。这样的膨胀率似乎完全无法与之前对恒星存在了万亿年的估计相符。计算表明宇宙的初始半径必须在 12 亿光年量级（爱丁顿），而现在的宇宙半径似乎只有 20 亿光年量级（德西特）。如果可以把以上的这些估计看作是准确的，那么我们就可以确定宇宙的年龄只比 10 亿年多一些，甚至比由地球上岩石的放射性推得的地球年龄小很多。没有人对这两种估计的精确性提出太高的要求，尤其是对第二种，但总的情况似乎不允许宇宙在这万亿年间每 14 亿年就膨胀一倍。

尽管还有其他站得住脚的解释可供选择，但它们中没有一个可以让人完全信服，因而目前的局面令人十分困惑。尽管现在还有很多意见分歧，许多天文学家认为，其他一些关于星云存在明显退行的解释将很可能被适时发现。到那时，由大量天文学证据所支持的恒星已存在万亿年的观点就可以毫无阻碍地得到人们的认可了。

如果暂时接受这样的恒星年龄，那么通过计算可以得到，普通恒星已经辐射出相当于自身质量很多倍的能量了。换言之，普通恒星在诞生之初的质量必定是现在的很多倍。确实，光谱双星的演化过程为我们描画了一颗典型恒星的生命历程。它最初的质量是太阳质量的 10 到 100 倍，而终结时，它的质量与太阳的质量不相上下，甚至比太阳的质量还要小。很难想象，若不是以实物原子或者至少以实物电子和质子的形式，这些新生恒星的巨大能量能存储在哪里。因此我们就得到了这样的结论，恒星的生命历程就是其自身物质不断湮灭的过程，电子和质子相互湮灭，并以这种方式为恒星辐射提供能量。至少，从天文学上我们可以得到这样的推测，而检验这些推测则要有赖于物理学了。

## 高穿透性辐射

如果要找出湮灭过程的直接证据，那么该证据最有可能从本世纪初麦克伦南、卢瑟福和其他科学家在地球大气中发现的穿透力很强的辐射中获得。这是因为在整个物理学中只有这里涉及的辐射光子的质量与期望中由电子和质子湮灭产生的光子质量相当，这些我们在后面还会谈到。最近几年，赫斯、密立根和雷格纳等人十分

photons resulting from the annihilation of electrons and protons. In the last few years, this radiation has been studied in great detail by Hess, Millikan, Regener, and many others. Their investigations scarcely leave room for doubt that the radiation enters the earth's atmosphere from outer space; for which reason it is often described as "cosmic radiation".

It was at first taken for granted that this radiation must be of the nature of $\gamma$-radiation, since its penetrating power was greater than seemed possible for any kind of corpuscular radiation. This reason is now known to be inadequate, theoretical investigations having shown that corpuscular radiation, consisting of either $\alpha$- or $\beta$-particles, might conceivably possess as high a penetrating power as the observed radiation.

Other arguments have, however, stepped into the breach, and show very convincingly that the radiation cannot be of the nature of either $\alpha$ or $\beta$ radiation. The central fact is, in brief, that radiation which consisted of charged particles would be influenced by a magnetic field, whereas cosmic radiation is not. An electron or other charged particle in motion acquires magnetic properties in virtue of its motion; the faster it moves, the greater the force which a magnetic field exerts upon it. Now the penetrating power of the radiation under consideration is so great that it could only be attained by charged particles, if these were moving with very high speeds indeed. If a swarm of such particles became entangled in the earth's magnetic field, their high speed of motion would cause them to describe spiral paths coiled quite closely around the earth's lines of magnetic force, with the result that they would fall far more abundantly near the earth's magnetic poles than elsewhere. Epstein[1] estimates that for a shower of electrons to have the penetrating power of cosmic radiation, they would have to move with the energy produced by a fall through about 1,000 million volts, and has calculated that the incidence of electrons moving with this energy would be limited entirely to comparatively small circles surrounding the two magnetic poles. Actually the observed radiation falls so evenly on the different parts of the earth's surface that no variations have ever been detected. Members of the B.A.N.Z. Antarctic Expedition[2] found the same intensity of radiation within 250 miles of the south magnetic pole as they had previously measured in South Australia, and as others had found in the United States, Canada, and the North Atlantic. This seems to leave little room for doubt that the radiation is of the nature of very hard $\gamma$ radiation.[3]

At first, some experiments by Bothe and Kohlhörster seemed to throw doubt on this conclusion. They had placed two Geiger counters, one vertically above the other, and found that the number of coincident discharges in the two counters was just about that which would be expected from purely geometrical considerations, if the radiation was corpuscular. Of course, the radiation which produced these ionisations was not necessarily the primary radiation which fell on the earth from outer space. Any primary radiation, as it traverses the atmosphere, is bound to produce secondary radiation of a variety of kinds, and any one of these might have been the immediate cause of the ionisation observed by Bothe and Kohlhörster. The primary radiation which first enters the earth's atmosphere might quite conceivably be electromagnetic, while the ionisation might be produced by a secondary corpuscular radiation.

细致地研究了这种辐射。他们的研究几乎不容置疑地表明这些辐射是从外太空进入到地球大气的；这就是这些辐射通常被称为“宇宙射线”的原因。

一开始人们理所当然地认为这种辐射本质上肯定是$\gamma$辐射，因为它的穿透力比被认为有可能的任何种类的粒子辐射都强。现在看来这个理由并不充分，理论研究已经证明粒子辐射，包括 $\alpha$ 粒子和 $\beta$ 粒子的辐射，可能拥有和观测到的辐射一样强的穿透力。

然而其他的论证已经十分令人信服地表明这种辐射不可能是 $\alpha$ 或 $\beta$ 辐射。简言之，其中心论点是，由带电粒子构成的辐射会受到磁场的影响，而宇宙辐射则不会。运动着的电子或其他带电粒子会受到磁场的作用，这是由于它在运动；它运动得越快，磁场对它施加的力也就越大。这种辐射的穿透力非常强，只有以很高速度运动的带电粒子才能达到这么强的穿透力。如果一大群这样的粒子进入地球磁场，高速运动会使它们绕着非常接近地球磁力线的轨道做螺旋运动，结果在地球磁极附近落下的粒子要远远多于其他地方的粒子。爱泼斯坦[1]估计对于一大批电子，若要具有宇宙辐射那样的穿透力，它们必须以大约穿过 10 亿伏特才能获得的能量运动，他还计算出以这个能量运动的入射电子将被完全限制在两磁极附近的相对较小的圆里。而实际上，观测到的辐射非常平均地落在地球表面的各个区域，并没有发现明显的差异。B.A.N.Z. 南极探险队[2]的成员发现，在南磁极周围 250 英里区域内的辐射强度，与他们之前在南澳大利亚测得的，以及其他人在美国、加拿大和北大西洋得到的结果相同。此辐射具有极硬 $\gamma$ 辐射的性质这一点似乎是无可置疑的[3]。

最初，博特和科尔霍斯特的一些实验结果似乎不支持这个推论。他们设置了两个盖革计数器，将其中一个垂直置于另一个的上面，并且发现如果这个辐射是粒子辐射，两个计数器记录的同时放电的粒子数几乎与用纯几何方式预计的结果相同。当然，产生这些电离的辐射不一定是从外太空进入地球的初级辐射。当任何初级辐射穿过大气层时，都必然会产生各种类型的次级辐射，其中任一种次级辐射都可能会直接导致博特和科尔霍斯特在实验中观察到的电离作用。首先进入地球大气的初级辐射非常可能是电磁辐射，而造成电离的辐射则是次级粒子辐射。

To examine this possibility, Bothe and Kohlhörster placed a block of gold between their two counters. This naturally caused a reduction in the number of coincidences, and from the amount of the reduction it was possible to calculate the penetrating power of the radiation which actually effected the ionisations. It was found to be approximately the same as that of the primary radiation. So far, then, everything could be explained by supposing that it was the primary radiation itself which produced the ionisations in the counters, and that this was corpuscular in its nature.

Recently this explanation has been tested by Moss-Smith[4] and found wanting. He extended the apparatus used by Bothe and Kohlhörster, by mounting yet a third counter vertically below the original two, and first verified that the number of coincident ionisations in all three counters was that which their geometrical arrangement would lead us to expect. Now if the radiation which produced these ionisations were corpuscular, it ought to be deflected by a magnetic field. For example, if a sufficiently strong magnetic field were inserted between the second and third counters, the third counter ought to be entirely shielded from the radiation which had passed through the first two counters, so that the number of coincident ionisations in the first two counters would remain as before, while the number in the third counter would fall to zero. Moss-Smith found that this did not happen. Although his magnetic field had many times the strength needed to shield the third counter completely, its insertion had no effect on the number of coincident ionisations. This showed that the ionising radiation was not corpuscular, and as Bothe and Kohlhörster had already shown that the ionising radiation was probably identical with the primary radiation, it confirmed the theoretical arguments of Millikan and Epstein, which proved the primary radiation to be of the nature of $\gamma$ radiation.

## The Mode of Production of the Radiation

If the primary radiation is of the nature of $\gamma$ radiation, as these arguments and experiments seem to show, its origin ought to be disclosed by its penetrating power. Such radiation consists of photons, which may be compared to bullets, all moving with the same speed—the velocity of light. Their penetrating power accordingly depends solely on their mass, and a theoretical investigation enables us to deduce the one from the other. Every photon is, however, produced originally by an atomic upheaval, and its mass is exactly equal to the decrease of mass which the parent atom experienced as the result of this upheaval. For example, if the atom was one of hydrogen and the upheaval consisted of annihilation, the photon resulting from this annihilation must have a mass exactly equal to the original mass of the hydrogen atom, namely, $1.66\times10^{-24}$ gm. Or again, if a proton and an electron mutually annihilate one another in any atom whatever, thus reducing its atomic weight by unity, the mass of the resulting photon must be equal to the combined masses of the proton and electron in situ in the atom, which again, except for a small "packing-fraction" mass, is equal to the mass of a hydrogen atom.

The most effective means of investigating the penetrating power of cosmic radiation is to sink suitable apparatus to varying depths below the surface of a lake, and observe the

为了检验这种可能性，博特和科尔霍斯特在两个计数器之间放置了一块金板。这自然就会造成同时发生放电的粒子数目减少，并且通过减少的数量就可以计算出真正引起电离的辐射的穿透力。结果发现它的穿透力和初级辐射的穿透力近似相同。假若是初级辐射本身造成了计数器中的电离作用，并且它本质上是粒子辐射，那么到目前为止的所有现象都可以得到解释。

最近莫斯–史密斯[4]对这个解释进行了验证并发现了不足之处。他改进了博特和科尔霍斯特使用的设备，在原有的两个计数器下面加入了垂直于它们的第三个计数器。他首先证实在三个计数器中同时发生的电离个数正是我们通过它们的几何排列得到的预期值。现在，如果引发这些电离的是粒子辐射，那么它应该在磁场中发生偏转。例如，如果一个足够强的磁场加到第二和第三个计数器之间，第三个计数器应该被完全屏蔽而免受从前两个计数器穿过的辐射，因此前两个计数器的计数将保持不变而第三个将减少为零。但是莫斯–史密斯发现这种情况并没有发生。尽管他的磁场强度已经是完全屏蔽第三个计数器所需强度的很多倍，但这个磁场的加入并没有对同时电离的计数情况产生任何影响。这表明电离辐射不是粒子性的，而博特和科尔霍斯特也已经指出电离辐射很可能就是初级辐射，这样就证实了密立根和爱泼斯坦的理论依据，从而得到初级辐射具有$\gamma$辐射的性质。

## 产生辐射的模式

如果就像前面的讨论和实验所表明的那样，初级辐射具有 $\gamma$ 辐射的性质，那么它的起源就应该能够通过其穿透力揭示出来。这样的辐射由光子构成，可以把它们比作许多发以相同速度——光速运动着的子弹。因而它们的穿透能力也仅由其质量决定，并且我们可以通过理论研究从一个光子推导出另一个光子。然而每个光子都起源于原子激变，并且光子的质量精确地等于母原子在这个激变过程中减少的质量。例如，如果这里的原子是氢原子且激变由湮灭过程组成，那么湮灭产生的光子的质量必须精确等于氢原子的原始质量，即 $1.66 \times 10^{-24}$ g。再比如，无论什么原子中的一个质子和一个电子相互之间发生了湮灭，这在整体上减少了原子量，那么产生的光子的质量必定等于原子中原来位置上的电子和质子质量之和。除去少量的“结合部分”的质量外，它也与氢原子的质量相等。

研究宇宙辐射穿透力最有效的方式，是把合适的仪器沉入到湖面以下不同深度，并观测入射的宇宙射线在不同深度被水吸收后引起的电离作用。密立根、雷格纳和

ionisation produced by the incidence of the cosmic rays after absorption by varying depths of water. Observations of this type have been performed with great care and skill by Millikan, Regener, and others.

Their results are none too easy of interpretation. L. H. Gray has shown[5] that there is a sort of softening effect continually in progress by which the absorption of a quantum of energy produces a recoil electron, which in turn produces radiation of energy comparable to, although somewhat lower than, the energy of the original quantum. After the radiation has travelled through a certain thickness of absorbing material, the observed ionisation no longer gives a true measure of the intensity of the primary radiation which has escaped absorption, but of this primary radiation in equilibrium with all its softer secondary components.

When this complication has been allowed for, the ionisation curve gives the intensity of the true primary radiation which remains after passing through varying thicknesses of absorbing matter. If this primary radiation consists of a mixture of constituents of different and clearly defined wavelengths, so that it has a line spectrum in the language of ordinary optics, these different constituents will have different coefficients of absorption. In such a case, it ought to be possible to analyse the observed curve into the superposition of a number of simple exponential curves, one for each constituent of the radiation.

Actually, it is found that this can be done. Different experimenters do not obtain results which are altogether accordant, but all agree in finding that there is a long stretch, near the end of the range of the radiation, over which its intensity decreases according to a simple exponential law. This can only mean that one particular constituent of the radiation is so much harder than the others that it persists in appreciable amount after traversing a thickness of matter which has completely absorbed all the softer constituents. Regener, who has studied the problem in great detail, finds that the hardest radiation of all has an absorption coefficient of 0.020 per metre of water. Other experimenters have found values which agree with this to within about 10 percent.

The mass of the photon can be deduced from the observed absorption coefficient $\mu$ of the radiation, by the use of a theoretical formula given by Klein and Nishina.[6] This can be written in the form

$$\mu = \frac{2\pi N e^4}{m^2 c^4} f\left(\frac{M}{m}\right),$$

where $M$ is the mass of the photon, $m$ of an electron, $e$, $c$ have their usual meanings, and $f$ represents a fairly complicated function of $M/m$. In all the applications of the formula to cosmic radiation, $M/m$ is quite large, and for such values of $M/m$, $f$ assumes the form

$$f\left(\frac{M}{m}\right) = \frac{1}{4}\left(\frac{M}{m} + 2\log\frac{2M}{m}\right).$$

其他一些人非常细心巧妙地完成了这样的实验观测。

他们的结果很难解释。格雷指出[5]有一种软化效应持续在起作用。由于这种效应持续在起作用，当一个能量量子被吸收时，就会产生一个反冲电子，这个电子反过来又引起了能量辐射。辐射的能量与原始量子的能量相比，尽管略低一些，但也大致相当。当辐射在吸收介质中传播一段距离之后，观察到的电离就不再能反映未被吸收的初级辐射的真实强度，而是对应于与所有较软的次级辐射部分保持平衡的初级辐射的值。

考虑到这个复杂的情况以后，就可以从电离曲线中得到穿过不同厚度吸收介质之后依然存在的真实的初级辐射强度。如果初级辐射包含波长不同的成分，那么它就会有像普通光学那样的线状谱，这些不同成分的吸收系数是不同的。在这种情况下，应该可以把观测到的曲线看作是多条简单指数曲线的叠加，每一个辐射成分都对应着一条指数曲线。

实际上人们发现这是可以做到的。不同的实验者并没有得到完全一致的结果，但是他们都一致认为在辐射区域的末端附近有一段很长的延伸范围，在这个范围内辐射强度呈简单的指数率衰减。这只能说明辐射中存在着一个特殊的成分，它比其他成分硬很多，以至于在经过一定厚度的介质后，所有较软的成分都已经被完全吸收，而这个成分的辐射仍然保持着相当的强度。雷格纳在对上述现象进行了仔细的研究之后发现，全部辐射中最硬的那个成分在被水吸收时的吸收系数为每米 0.020。其他实验者得到的数值与此一致，偏差不超过 10%。

利用克莱因 – 仁科给出的理论公式，我们可以从观测到的辐射吸收系数 $\mu$ 中推导出光子的质量[6]。这个公式可以由下面的形式给出：

$$\mu = \frac{2\pi N e^4}{m^2 c^4} f\left(\frac{M}{m}\right),$$

其中：$M$ 为光子质量，$m$ 为电子质量，$e$、$c$ 为它们的通常定义，$f$ 表示以 $M/m$ 为变量的一个相当复杂的函数。对于所有的宇宙辐射，该公式中的 $M/m$ 都非常大，而当 $M/m$ 取这些值时，可以假设 $f$ 有如下形式：

$$f\left(\frac{M}{m}\right) = \frac{1}{4}\left(\frac{M}{m} + 2\log\frac{2M}{m}\right)$$

These formulae are calculated on the supposition that the absorption is caused by $N$ electrons per unit volume, and that these are entirely free. This last condition can never be fully realised in Nature, since every electron is bound, more or less closely, to other electric charges. If an electron is bound to a system of mass $m'$, we can allow for this binding by increasing $m$ in the formula by a fraction of $m'$, the fraction being large or small according as the coupling is tight or loose. Thus a loosely coupled electron behaves almost like a free electron, but an electron coupled tightly to a massive system, such, for example, as a proton or an atomic nucleus, behaves like an electron of very great mass, and the formula shows that this has no appreciable absorbing power.

The Klein–Nishina formula has been tested by comparing it with observation for $\gamma$-rays. In the case of the lighter elements, it gives values which agree well with the observed absorption, provided all the extra-nuclear electrons are treated as free, while the nuclear electrons are disregarded entirely. It is natural to disregard these, because the coupling of nuclear electrons in the lighter elements is known to be so close that even the hardest $\gamma$-rays make but little impression on them. This is true for the lighter elements only; in the case of lead, Chao[7] has found an additional scattering of the hardest $\gamma$-rays, which he believes to be of nuclear origin. In other words, he finds that some at least of the nuclear electrons in lead are not so closely coupled as to resist the onslaught of the hardest $\gamma$-radiation. Still less, then, can they be so closely coupled as to resist the incidence of the far more massive photons of cosmic radiation. From theoretical considerations of a very general nature[8] it appears probable that in dealing with cosmic radiation, the $N$ in the Klein–Nishina formula should refer to all electrons, nuclear as well as extra-nuclear, and not merely to the latter. A further term ought also to be added to represent scattering by nuclear protons, but calculation shows that this is entirely insignificant in amount. The result of taking the nuclear electrons into account is to replace atomic number by atomic weight, so that the absorption by a given thickness of matter becomes strictly proportional to the mass of the matter, and absolutely independent of its nature, except possibly in so far as a further small absorption, caused by photoelectric action, may depend on the latter. The effect of this is to double, or more than double, the capacity of all atoms except hydrogen for absorbing cosmic radiation; it increases the absorbing power of water to 80 percent above the value usually calculated.

The following table shows the absorption coefficients (per metre of water) which I have calculated for the radiation produced by the synthesis of iron and by the annihilation of 1 and 4 protons respectively, with their accompanying electrons. The calculation is based on the Klein–Nishina formula, all electrons, including the nuclear electrons, being treated as absolutely free:

| Process | $\frac{M}{m}$ | Calculated $\mu$ (per metre, water) | Observed $\mu$ (Regener) |
|---|---|---|---|
| 56H → Fe | 876 | 0.136 | .. |
| +, − → 0 | 1845 | 0.071 | 0.073 |
| 4+, 4− → 0 | 7380 | 0.020 | 0.020 |

这些公式的计算基于这样的假设：吸收是由单位体积内 $N$ 个完全自由的电子所引起的。电子是完全自由的这个条件在自然界中永远不可能完全满足，因为每个电子都会被其他电荷束缚着，不论束缚是强是弱。如果一个电子被一个质量为 $m'$ 的系统所束缚，那么对于这种情况我们可以考虑把 $m'$ 的一部分增加到公式中的质量 $m$ 上，增加部分的大小取决于耦合的强弱。因此弱耦合电子的表现几乎与自由电子一样，但是对于一个与质子或原子核等大质量系统紧紧耦合的电子，它会表现得如同质量非常大的电子，公式表明在这种情况下它不具有明显的吸收能力。

通过与观测到的$\gamma$射线进行比较，人们已经检验了克莱因－仁科公式。对于较轻的元素，它给出的值与观测到的吸收曲线符合得相当好，条件是这里所有的核外电子都被当作自由电子处理，同时完全忽略核内电子。这样的忽略是自然的，因为我们知道较轻元素的核内电子耦合很强，即使是最硬的$\gamma$射线也只会对它们造成很小的影响。但是，这仅对较轻元素成立；就铅而言，赵[7]发现在最硬的$\gamma$射线下存在一个附加散射，他认为这来源于原子核。换句话说，他发现至少铅的某些核内电子的耦合强度还抵御不了最硬 $\gamma$ 辐射的冲击。更不用说以它们的耦合强度去抵御数量巨大的宇宙辐射光子的冲击。从理论角度作非常一般性的考虑[8]，在处理宇宙辐射时，很可能克莱因－仁科公式中的 $N$ 指的是包括核内和核外的所有电子，而不应该仅仅是后者。此外还应该增加一项，用来表示原子核内质子的散射，然而计算表明质子散射的作用量很小，完全可以忽略不计。把核内电子计算在内的结果就是要用原子量取代原子序数，因此对于给定厚度的介质，它的吸收就严格正比于射线所经过区域的介质质量，而与它的性质毫无关系，除非是由光电效应造成的更少量的吸收有可能与后者相关。这样就使除氢以外的所有原子在吸收宇宙辐射的能力上加倍，甚至大于原来的两倍。经过这样的处理，水的吸收能力比通常的计算值高出了 80%。

对于由铁的合成以及由 1 个质子和 4 个质子分别与它们的伴随电子发生湮灭而产生的辐射，我分别进行了计算，并在下表中给出了吸收系数（水中，每米）。结果是根据克莱因－仁科公式计算出来的，计算过程中把所有的电子，包括核内电子，都视为自由电子：

| 过程 | $\frac{M}{m}$ | 计算值 $\mu$<br>（水中，每米） | 观测值 $\mu$<br>（雷格纳） |
|---|---|---|---|
| 56H → Fe | 876 | 0.136 | .. |
| +,– → 0 | 1845 | 0.071 | 0.073 |
| 4+,4– → 0 | 7380 | 0.020 | 0.020 |

The last column gives the absorption coefficients of the two most penetrating constituents of cosmic radiation, as analysed by Regener. Their agreement with the figures in the preceding column is probably well within errors of observation and analysis, and is rather too good to be attributed with much plausibility to mere accident; the odds against a double agreement, within 5 percent in one case and 2.7 percent in another, being about 3000 to 1. This seems to me to suggest quite strongly that the most penetrating constituent so far observed in cosmic radiation may originate in the annihilation of an $\alpha$-particle and its two neutralising electrons (the components of a helium atom), while the next softer constituent may originate in the annihilation of a proton and its one neutralising electron (the components of a hydrogen atom).

An alternative possibility, which was first suggested by Millikan and has been championed mainly by him, is that the cosmic radiation may result from the building of electrons and protons into atoms. Yet the hardest constituents of the cosmic radiation appear to be far too hard to be produced by the synthesis of iron, while Millikan himself considers that the synthesis of heavier elements is probably ruled out by their rarity in the universe. If, as I have suggested, the annihilation of matter is the true origin of the two hardest constituents of the cosmic radiation, then it becomes possible to suppose, with Millikan, that the softer constituents are produced by the synthesis of simple atoms into complex. Many will, however, hesitate to accept such a mixed origin for the radiation. It certainly seems simpler to suppose that the two hardest constituents, and these alone, form the fundamental radiation, while all other constituents represent mere softened or degraded forms of these. Yet this supposition brings its own difficulties, since if we measure the intensity of the radiation by its ionising power, the supposed secondary radiation is found to have many times the ionising intensity of the primary. But whatever the origin of the softer constituents may be, the two hardest constituents, with their photons equal in mass to the atoms of hydrogen and helium respectively, appear to provide weighty evidence that matter can be, and is, annihilated somewhere out in the depths of space. If we can assume that this process occurs on a sufficiently large scale, this supposition brings order and intelligibility into a vast series of problems of astronomy and cosmogony in a way in which no other suppositions can.

## The Place of Production of the Cosmic Radiation

Various suggestions have been made as to the place of origin of this highly penetrating radiation. Many of them are put out of court by the fact, which must now, I think, be regarded as well established, that the radiation is nearly constant in intensity at all times of day and night,[9] any variation being, at most, of the order of one part in 200. There seems to be a real variation of this amount, but in the main it appears to follow the variation of the barometer. Millikan considers that it is adequately explained by fluctuations in the absorbing power of the air blanket formed by the earth's atmosphere. It was at one time suggested that the radiation might consist of electrons ejected from thunder-clouds high up in the earth's atmosphere, or of electrons moving with enormous speeds acquired by drifting through electrostatic fields in space, the potential gradients in these fields being

最后一列给出的是宇宙辐射中两种穿透力最强的成分的吸收系数，这是雷格纳通过分析得到的。观测值与前一列中的计算值也许相符得还不错，其偏差在观测和分析所引起的误差范围内。很难把这么好的符合度仅仅归因于巧合。两次吻合，一次误差在 5% 以内，另一次在 2.7% 以内，出现错误的几率为 1/3,000。在我看来这个结果强烈地显示出：在迄今为止观测到的宇宙辐射中，穿透力最强的成分有可能起源于一个 $\alpha$ 粒子和它的两个使其变为电中性的电子（组成氦原子的成分）的湮灭，而另一个较软的成分可能来源于一个质子和一个使其变为电中性的电子（组成氢原子的成分）的湮灭。

由密立根首先提出并且主要由他倡导的另一种可能性是，宇宙辐射起源于电子和质子形成原子的过程。然而宇宙辐射中最硬的成分似乎比铁合成过程中产生的辐射硬很多，而密立根自己也认为更重元素的合成可以被排除掉，因为它们在宇宙中是很稀少的。如果按照我提出的，物质的湮灭是宇宙辐射中最硬的两个成分的真正来源，那么我和密立根设想，很可能较软的成分是在简单原子组成复合原子的过程中产生的。但是很多人会对宇宙辐射有多种起源表示怀疑。显然比较简单的假设是认为只有两种最硬的成分构成了基本辐射，而所有其他成分仅仅是这部分辐射的软化或降阶形式。但是这种假设给自己带来了一些难题，因为如果我们用电离能力去衡量宇宙辐射的强度，那么这个假设的次级辐射的电离强度会是初级辐射的很多倍。但是无论较软成分的来源是什么，这两个最硬成分中的光子所具有的质量分别与氢原子和氦原子的质量相同，这似乎为物质可以在遥远的空间中湮灭提供了有力的证据。如果我们假定这个过程发生在一个足够大的尺度内，那么这个假设就会使大量的天文学和宇宙学问题变得有条理并且易于理解，这是其他假设无法做到的。

## 宇宙辐射产生的位置

对于这种高穿透性辐射起源于何处人们有不同的看法。其中的很多观点都被以下这个在我看来现在已被牢固确立的事实排除掉了，即无论是白天还是黑夜，宇宙辐射的强度在任何时候几乎都是一个常数 [9]，它的变化幅度至多为 1/200 量级。这个量似乎确实会发生一定的变化，但主要是随着气压而变化。密立根认为这些变化用地球大气层吸收能力的涨落就足以解释。曾经有人认为这些辐射可能包含那些由地球大气中的高空雷雨云发射出来的电子，或者包含因在空间静电场中漂移而获得极高速度的运动电子。这个静电场的电势梯度虽然微不足道，但是由于电场范围极为宽广，因而电势差非常大。即便仍然认为宇宙辐射由粒子辐射产生，也很难将这

slight, but the potential differences immense simply on account of the vast extent of the fields. Even if the radiation could still be treated as corpuscular, it would be very difficult to reconcile either of these suggested origins with the steadiness and uniformity with which the radiation falls on the earth's surface.

The fact that the intensity of the radiation is very approximately independent of both solar and sidereal time seems to show that no appreciable part of the radiation comes from the sun or stars. Counting the sun as a star, we receive more than 100,000,000 times as much starlight at midday as at midnight, yet apart from the purely local "barometer" effect just mentioned, we receive the same intensity of the radiation at both times. The fact that the intensity is approximately independent of the position of the Milky Way seems to show that the bulk at least of the radiation must come even from beyond the confines of the galactic system, thus justifying the name "cosmic radiation".

Where, then, does the radiation originate? For reasons which will be clear at the end of our quest, it is simpler to conduct our search in time rather than in space. The average density of matter in space is probably of the order of $10^{-30}$ gm. per c.c., and in each second of its existence, a beam of cosmic radiation passes through a layer of space $3\times10^{10}$ cm. thick. Thus every second it passes on the average through $3\times10^{-20}$ gm. per sq. cm. of its cross-section. We have, however, seen that the hardest constituent must pass through 50 gm. per sq. cm. before it is reduced in intensity by one percent, and this requires an average time of $16\times10^{20}$ seconds, or about $5\times10^{13}$ years—a period which, on any reckoning, is greater than the age of the stars; its intensity is reduced to $1/e$ times its original value after $5\times10^{15}$ years, which is greater, so far as we know, than the age of the universe.

Thus, to an approximation, we may think of the hardest constituent of the cosmic radiation as indestructible, since the universe has not yet existed long enough for any appreciable amount of it to be absorbed. To a slightly less good approximation, the same is true of the softer constituents. This leads us to regard space as being permeated with all, or nearly all, of the cosmic radiation which has ever been generated since the world began. The rays come to us as messengers, not only from the farthest depths of space, but also from the remotest eras of time. And, since we cannot produce cosmic rays on earth, their message appears to be that the physics which prevails out in these far depths of space and time is something different from our terrestrial physics: different processes result in different products. So far as we can read the riddle of the rays, one at least of these processes appears to be the annihilation of matter, although whether this annihilation is taking place now, or occurred only in the remote past, or even only at the beginning of the world's history, we have no means of knowing; all that the rays show is that somewhere and sometime in the history of the universe, matter has been annihilated.

Similar remarks may be made with respect to the softer constituents. Millikan believes that these originate in the synthesis of complex atoms out of lighter ones, and so argues

些假定起源中的任何一个与落向地球表面的辐射所具有的稳定性和均匀性统一起来。

辐射强度与太阳时和恒星时近似无关这一事实似乎表明，可测到的辐射不会来源于太阳或者恒星。如果将太阳当作普通恒星处理，那么我们在正午接收到的星光比在午夜接收到的星光强 100,000,000 倍。然而排除刚才提到的纯粹由局部“气压”不同引起的作用之后，我们在这两个时刻得到的辐射强度仍然相同。而辐射强度与银河系的位置几乎无关这一事实也说明，宇宙辐射中至少有一大部分会来自于银河系范围以外，这也印证了“宇宙辐射”这个名字是恰如其分的。

那么这些辐射是从哪里来的？为了能够最终找到原因，从时间入手比从空间入手更简单。宇宙中的平均物质密度约为 $10^{-30}$ $g/cm^3$，并且在宇宙存在的每一秒钟，一束宇宙射线会穿越 $3\times10^{10}$ cm 厚的宇宙空间层。因此每秒钟它穿越的辐射截面是 $3\times10^{-20}$ $g/cm^2$。然而我们已经发现，这个最硬成分的强度要减少 1%，就必须穿过 50 $g/cm^2$，这个过程所需的平均时间为 $16\times10^{20}$ 秒，或者约 $5\times10^{13}$ 年——以任何方式计算，这个时间都要比恒星的寿命长；辐射强度减小到初始值的 $1/e$ 需要 $5\times10^{15}$ 年，比我们现在认为的宇宙的年龄都要长。

因此，我们可以近似认为宇宙辐射中最硬的成分是不会衰减的，因为宇宙存在的时间长度还不足以使它被吸收的部分达到任何可观的量。也可作一个稍差一点的近似，认为较软的成分也是不会被吸收的。这使我们可以把宇宙空间看成是充满了自宇宙诞生以来到现在曾经产生的所有或几乎所有的宇宙辐射。我们接收到的这些射线不仅带来了太空最深处的信息，还带来了时间最久远的年代的信息。并且，因为我们不能在地球上制造出宇宙射线，所以它们所携带的信息显示出这些普遍适用于遥远空间和时间的物理定律有别于我们地球上的物理定律：不同的过程导致不同的结果。就我们现在对宇宙射线之谜的解读情况来看，其中至少有一个过程应该是物质的湮灭，尽管我们没有办法知道这种湮灭是发生在现在，还是发生在遥远的过去，或者甚至仅是在宇宙诞生之初；这些射线的存在已经能够充分说明，在宇宙演化史中的某个地点和某个时刻，物质发生了湮灭。

类似的说明也适用于较软的成分。密立根确信它们产生于较轻原子合成复杂原子的过程之中，并因此认为这种合成还在进行。但是由于这些较软的成分同样具有

that the act of creation is still in progress. But these softer constituents also have such high penetrating powers as to be virtually indestructible. Even if Millikan's interpretation of the origin of these rays were established, it would only prove that synthesis of matter had occurred somewhere and sometime during the long past history of the universe; it would not prove that any such synthesis was still in progress.

Indeed, the fact that the radiation does not vary in intensity with the position of the Milky Way may be thought to suggest that it is merely a relic of past eras in the history of the universe. It may be argued that if the radiation were still being generated, the huge mass of the Milky Way, comparatively close to our doors, would surely make its influence felt. It is, however, possible (and, I think, likely) that the radiation is still being generated in extra-galactic nebulae of earlier type than the galactic system; it may be that they only emit this radiation before they condense into stars; and that the atoms which can produce such radiation in the galactic system are all shut up inside the stars, so that the radiation is transformed into starlight before it reaches us.

Millikan has estimated that the total amount of cosmic radiation received on earth has about a tenth of the energy of starlight, sunlight not being counted in. Near the earth, the energy of radiation from the stars is intense enough to raise space to a temperature of about 3.5 degrees absolute, whereas the energy of cosmic radiation will raise this space only to about 2 degrees absolute. Out in the inter-galactic darkness the position is reversed. Here the feeble starlight and star-heat from distant galaxies can at most raise space to a fraction of a degree above absolute zero, but the intensity of cosmic radiation is probably the same as nearer home, corresponding to about 2 degrees absolute. Space as a whole appears likely to contain far more of cosmic radiation than of light and heat, although in assessing this fact, we must remember that cosmic radiation is virtually endowed with immortality, whereas ordinary radiation, in the form of light and heat, is not. The total annihilation of all the matter in the universe would raise space to about 10 degrees absolute, so that the cosmic radiation we observe could be produced by the annihilation of quite a small fraction of the universe.

This is not surprising, since the cosmic radiation which pervades space is necessarily quite distinct from the similar radiation which astronomers regard as the source of stellar light and heat. The annihilation of matter in stellar interiors would produce radiation of exactly the same high frequency as the observed cosmic radiation, but as this radiation fought its way outwards to lower temperatures, and finally to outer space, it would be continually softened, by a long succession of Compton encounters, until it finally emerged in the familiar form of starlight—ordinary temperature radiation at anything from 1650° abs. to about 60,000° abs.; none of it could reach the earth in its original form.

The mere fact of its not having been completely absorbed shows that the cosmic radiation we receive on earth cannot have passed through more than a few kilometres of stellar matter at most; its penetrating power, high though it is, will not carry it through a greater thickness of matter than this. Consequently, it can scarcely have been generated at a

很强的穿透力，因此实际上也是不会衰减的。即便密立根对这些射线起源的解释可以成立，也只能证明在宇宙漫长的发展史中，物质的合成过程曾经在某个地点和某个时刻发生过，而不能证明这样的合成仍在进行。

实际上，辐射强度与银河系的位置无关这一事实也许可以这样来理解：宇宙辐射仅仅是宇宙发展史中的一个遗迹。如果这个辐射过程还在继续，而银河系的主体又离我们那么近，显然我们应该察觉到它所造成的影响。然而还有可能（我认为非常可能）这个辐射仍然在不断地从比银河系存在时间更长的河外星云中产生出来，也许它们只在凝聚成恒星之前发出这样的辐射，而银河系中能产生这种辐射的原子都被密闭在了恒星的内部，所以辐射在到达我们这里之前已经被转变为星光了。

密立根曾经估算过，在不把太阳光计算在内的情况下，地球上接收到的宇宙辐射的总能量大约为星光能量的 1/10。在地球附近，恒星发出的辐射能量足以使空间的绝对温度上升大约 3.5 度,而宇宙辐射的能量则只能使此空间的绝对温度升高 2 度。在星系间的黑暗区域，情况则截然相反。在那里，来自于遥远星系的微弱星光和恒星热量最多只能使空间温度稍稍升高到绝对零度以上不到 1 度，而宇宙辐射的强度则可能和地球附近的强度相同，对应的绝对温度大约为 2 度。总体来说，宇宙空间包含的宇宙辐射很可能会远远多于光和热，虽然在确定这一点的时候我们也必须记得，事实上宇宙辐射是永远不会消失的，而以光和热为呈现方式的普通辐射则会。宇宙中所有物质的完全湮灭将使空间的绝对温度上升 10 度左右，因此，产生我们观测到的宇宙辐射只需要湮灭掉极小部分的宇宙物质。

遍及空间的宇宙辐射和那些被天文学家们认作是恒星光和热来源的相似的辐射必然是明显不同的，这并不奇怪。恒星内部物质的湮灭会产生频率和观测到的宇宙辐射完全相同的高频辐射，但是当这种辐射向恒星外部温度较低的地方传播并最终到达外层空间时，它会因长期发生连续的康普顿散射而被不断软化，直到最终显现为我们所熟悉的星光形式——从绝对温度 1,650 度到绝对温度约 60,000 度之间的普通温度辐射，这种辐射不可能以原始形式到达地球。

宇宙辐射没有被完全吸收的事实足以说明：我们在地球上接收到的宇宙辐射，不可能曾穿透过超过几公里的恒星物质；尽管它的穿透能力很强，但也不能穿过比这更厚的物质。因此，在温度高于 100,000 度的地方几乎不可能产生这种辐射。我

place where the temperature was more than about 100,000 degrees. We must suppose that it originated fairly near to the surfaces of astronomical bodies, or, more probably still, in unattached atoms or molecules in free space. In contrast to this, the radiation which provides the energy poured out by the stars was probably generated in their central regions. Thus it must have been generated in matter at very high temperatures, while the similar radiation we receive on earth must have been generated at comparatively low temperatures.

## Physical Principles

According to classical theories of electro-magnetism, any acceleration of a moving electron is accompanied by an emission of radiation, of amount given by the well-known formula of Larmor. Thus an electron, describing an orbit in an atom of, say, hydrogen, must continually radiate energy away, so that the orbit will continually shrink.

The quantum theory replaces this continuous emission of energy by a succession of discontinuous emissions; at each moment there is a definite calculable chance that the orbit will shrink in size by a finite amount, and emit a photon in the process. The orbit of lowest energy is anomalous; when an electron is describing this orbit, no further shrinkage in orbit or emission of radiation is possible.

The concept of annihilation of matter removes this anomaly by providing a state of still lower energy, in which proton and electron have both disappeared in radiation. The energy emitted in the process of annihilation corresponds, of course, to that which would be emitted continuously on the classical electro-dynamics while the orbit was shrinking to zero radius.

Although neither the new quantum theory nor the theory of wave mechanics in any way predicts that this process must actually happen, they are in no way definitely antagonistic to its occurrence. Certain forms of both, on the whole, seem rather to favour the possibility, but theoretical calculation based on these does not at present agree with numerical estimates derived from astronomical evidence. Dirac[10] has recently calculated the probability of annihilation given by the new quantum theory, and obtained a value which is substantially too large; according to his calculations, the universe ought to have dissolved into radiation long ago. Or, to put the same thing in another way, the stars ought to radiate energy far more furiously than they do.

The general principles of the quantum theory show that annihilation of matter might either occur spontaneously, after the manner of radioactive disintegration, or might be incited by a sufficiently high temperature, like the atomic changes which produce ordinary temperature radiation. The second process will only occur when the matter is traversed by photons with energy equal to that set free by annihilation of matter; the requisite temperature is found to be of the order of a million million degrees. Now it is quite impossible that the cosmic radiation we receive on earth can have originated in

们必须假设它产生于非常接近天体的表面的地方，或者，更有可能的是，产生于自由空间中的独立原子或分子。与此相反，能使恒星发出能量的辐射则可能来源于恒星的中心区域。因此它必定是在温度非常高的物质中产生的，而我们在地球上接收到的相似的辐射应该产生于相对较低的温度。

## 物理原理

根据经典电磁理论，任何作加速运动的电子都会产生辐射，其辐射量可由著名的拉莫尔公式给定。因此，某一个原子，比如说氢原子，其中沿一定轨道运动的电子必须持续地辐射出能量，因而其运动轨道将不断收缩。

量子理论用一系列不连续的辐射取代了这种连续的能量辐射，在每一个时刻都可以确切地计算出轨道收缩一个固定值并放出光子的概率。能量最低的轨道是反常的，当一个电子处于这个轨道时，它既不可能再降低轨道，也不可能再发出辐射。

物质湮灭的概念提出了一个能量更低的状态，消除了这个反常情况。在这种状态下，质子和电子同时消失并转化为辐射。当然，湮灭过程中放射的能量，应该与经典电动力学中轨道半径收缩为零时持续放射的能量相当。

尽管新的量子理论和波动力学理论都没有以任何方式预言这个过程真的一定会发生，但是它们也没有以任何确定的方式来否定它的出现。两种理论的特定形式总体上看来都颇为支持这种可能性，但是基于这两种理论的计算结果目前尚不能与通过天文学观测证据估算的数值相符。最近，狄拉克[10]根据新的量子理论计算了湮灭概率，但是得到的数值明显太大了。根据他的计算结果，宇宙早就应该变为辐射消失了。或者换个说法，恒星放出能量的方式应该比现在猛烈得多。

量子理论的普遍原理指出，物质的湮灭既可能是在放射性衰变之后自发发生的，也可能是被足够高的温度所激发，就像发出普通辐射的原子变化一样。第二种情况只能在当穿过物质的光子所具有的能量与物质湮灭释放的能量相等时才会发生，其需要的温度要达到万亿度的量级。而目前我们在地球上观测到的宇宙辐射根本不可能是从温度能达到这么高的区域中产生的。实际上我们发现它的温度很难超过

regions where the temperature approaches this; indeed, we have seen that it can scarcely have been more than 100,000° or so. Thus this radiation can only have originated from spontaneous annihilation. Cosmic radiation can, and very possibly does, provide evidence of the spontaneous annihilation of matter at low temperatures, but it cannot, from the nature of the case, give any evidence of annihilation being produced by high temperatures, since any radiation so produced could never get out to empty space.

There seem to me to be two strong reasons for supposing that this latter process is not operative in the stars, and that any radiation which is produced by annihilation inside the stars must be produced spontaneously, like the cosmic radiation which is produced outside.

In the first place, if the generation is not spontaneous, the temperature at the star's centre must be of the order of a million million degrees. An immensely steep temperature gradient would be needed to connect this temperature with that of a few thousand degrees at the surface of the star, and so steep a gradient can only be reconciled with the observed flow of heat out of the star by postulating a very high opacity for the stellar material. It has so far proved impossible to reconcile such a high value for the opacity with the theoretical value given by Kramers.

The second reason is as follows. If the generation of energy results from high temperature, the rate of generation will involve a factor of the usual type $e^{-Mc^2/RT}$, where $M$ is the mass annihilated. As the temperature increases from zero up, this factor first becomes appreciable when $RT$ begins to be appreciable in comparison with $Mc^2$. This happens at the temperature of about a million million degrees already mentioned. When this temperature is first approached, the exponential term is increasing very rapidly in comparison with the temperature $T$. But a dynamical investigation shows that when this happens, the star must be very unstable. In brief, the emission of appreciable radiation would be accompanied by instability in the star, so that the very stable structures we describe as stars cannot radiate by means of this mechanism. The dynamical result has, it is true, been rigorously proved only for a simple, and very idealised, model of stellar structure; but general thermodynamical principles show that any structure in which a small change of physical conditions results in a very great liberation of heat, is likely to be unstable—in brief, it is in an explosive state.

On the other side, there is one strong argument against supposing that stellar radiation is produced by spontaneous annihilation of matter; it is that if the sun's heat were produced by the spontaneous annihilation of its atoms, we might, expect that the earth's atoms would be subject to spontaneous annihilation at an equal or similar rate. Yet calculation shows that annihilation at even a ten-thousandth part of this rate would make the earth too hot for human habitation. Clearly, then, no appreciable annihilation of matter can occur inside the earth. This must be formed of atoms of a kind which do not undergo spontaneous annihilation, and if the sun derives its heat from the spontaneous annihilation of atoms, these must be of a different kind from the atoms of which our earth is formed.

100,000 度左右。因此这个辐射只能来源于自发的湮灭。宇宙辐射能够，并且很可能已经，为物质在低温下的自发湮灭提供了证据，但是从这种情况的本质上说，它不能提供任何高温导致湮灭的证据，因为没有任何这样产生的辐射能逃逸到太空中。

在我看来，似乎有两个强有力的理由可以让我们认为后一种过程不会在恒星中发生，并且任何由恒星内部的湮灭过程所产生的辐射必定是自发发生的，就像恒星外产生的宇宙辐射一样。

首先，如果恒星中的湮灭不是自发的，那么恒星中心的温度就必须达到万亿度的量级。这就需要一个变化极大的温度梯度，以便将这个温度与恒星表面几千度的温度联系起来，只有在恒星物质不透明度非常高的条件下，这么大的梯度才可能与观测到的恒星外热流相一致。现在已经证明如此高的不透明度不可能与克拉默斯给出的理论计算值相符。

下面给出第二条理由。如果能量的产生是由高温引起的，那么产能率就会引入一个通常形式为 $e^{-Mc^2/RT}$ 的因子，其中 $M$ 是湮灭的质量。随着温度由零度开始不断升高，当 $RT$ 升至和 $Mc^2$ 接近的量值时，这个因子的影响开始变得明显。当温度大约达到前面已经提到的万亿度时，这种情况就会发生。第一次达到这个温度时，这个指数项与温度 $T$ 相比，增长得非常迅速。但动力学研究表明，当这种情况发生时恒星肯定是极不稳定的。简言之，明显的能量释放总会与恒星的不稳定性相伴，因此被我们认定为结构非常稳定的恒星是不会以这种机制发生辐射的。确实，只有在一个理想化程度非常高的简单恒星结构模型下，动力学结果才能得到严格的证明；但是普遍的热力学原理表明，若在一种结构中，物理状态很小的一个改变就会释放大量的热，那么任何这样的结构都很可能是不稳定的——简言之，它处在一个一触即发的状态。

另一方面，对于恒星辐射是由物质自发湮灭产生的猜想，存在一个有力论据可以反驳它，即如果是在太阳自身原子的自发湮灭中产生了太阳的热量，那么我们是否可以认为地球上的原子也会以相同或者相近的速率自发湮灭。然而计算表明，哪怕湮灭速率仅是这个速率的万分之一，也会使地球非常热，以至于人类无法居住。那么显然，地球内部不可能有明显的物质湮灭。地球必须由不会发生自发湮灭的原子所构成，而如果太阳的热量来自于原子的自发湮灭，那么这些原子与构成我们地球的原子一定不属于同样的类型。这并不是没有理由的，从地球的形成模式可知，

This is not in itself unreasonable; from the mode of the earth's formation, its atoms can be a sample only of those in the sun's outer layers. If we conjecture that those kinds of atoms which undergo spontaneous annihilation are of very great atomic weight, and so sink to the interiors of the stars, this difficulty disappears, and with it the problem of why no cosmic radiation is received directly from the Milky Way.

(**128**, 103-110; 1931)

References:

1 *Proceedings: National Academy of Sciences* (Oct. 1930).
2 *Nature*, **127**, 924 (June 20, 1931).
3 Millikan, Dec. 29, 1930, Lecture at Pasadena, reprinted in *Nature*, **127**, 167 (Jan. 31, 1931).
4 *Physical Review* (April 15, 1931).
5 *Proc. Roy. Soc.*, **122**, 647.
6 *Nature*, **122**, 398 (Sept. 15, 1928).
7 *Physical Review* (Nov. 15, 1930).
8 *Nature*, **127**, 594 (April 18, 1931).
9 Hess, V. F., *Nature*, **127**, 10 (Jan. 3, 1931).
10 *Proceedings of Cambridge Philosophical Society* (July 1930).

地球上的原子可能只与太阳外层的物质相同。如果我们推测，这种发生自发湮灭的原子具有很大的原子量，因而会陷入到恒星的内部，那么不但以上的问题不存在了，而且还能解释为什么没有接收到直接从银河系发出的宇宙辐射。

（周杰 翻译；尚仁成 审稿）

# Oxidation by Living Cells*

J. B. S Haldane

## Editor's Note

**Since 1921, J. B. S. Haldane had been a reader in biochemistry at the University of Cambridge, where he concentrated on studies of enzyme kinetics. Here, after almost a decade of research into the action of enzymes and following a series of lectures delivered at the Royal Institution, Haldane summaries what is known about oxidation taking place in a cell. What is particularly surprising is just how much detail was still wanting, especially as it was only a matter of years before Hans Krebs worked out the biochemical steps behind the citric acid cycle. Krebs is known to have read and been influenced by Haldane's 1930 book *Enzymes*.**

UNTIL recently our knowledge of the chemistry of respiration stopped abruptly at the boundary of the cell. We knew how the oxygen was carried to it in vertebrate blood, and the carbon dioxide carried away. We also knew that the rate of oxygen consumption by the body as a whole, and by certain organs, was a function of numerous variables, such as temperature, hydrogen ion concentration, nervous stimulation, and so on. A certain number of partially oxidised metabolites, such as $\beta$-hydroxybutyric acid, had been isolated. But such quantitative knowledge as existed with regard to the details of oxidation was mainly confined to reactions in which coloured molecules were involved: for example, the reduction of methylene blue to a colourless substance, or the oxidation of *p*-phenylene-diamine to a coloured one.

The modern period began with the work of Batelli and Stern, and of Bach and Chodat, in Geneva, and since the War the most important centres of research have been the laboratories of Thunberg in Sweden, of Warburg and Wieland in Germany, and of Hopkins in England. This work has led to the recognition of a number of distinct catalysts, each responsible for a different part in the process of respiration. Inorganic catalysts of oxidation may activate the oxidant, the reducer, or both. Thus, Langmuir concluded that when a hot platinum surface catalyses the union of hydrogen and oxygen, a layer of adsorbed $O_2$ molecules is so activated as to unite with $H_2$ striking them; but adsorbed $H_2$ does not unite with bombarding $O_2$. On the other hand, when the same reaction is catalysed by porcelain, both molecular species must be adsorbed side by side before they react.

We need not, therefore, be surprised to find in the cell catalysts which activate $O_2$, alongside of activators of reducers such as the lactate ion, and shall be prepared to steer a course between the unitary theories of Warburg[1] and Wieland[2], who respectively regard

---

* Substance of lectures delivered at the Royal Institution on Feb. 5, 12, and 19.

# 活细胞氧化*

约翰·波顿·桑德森·霍尔丹

## 编者按

从 1921 年起，霍尔丹一直在剑桥大学作生物化学专业的高级讲师，他在那里潜心研究酶动力学。在花了近十年的时间研究酶反应以及随后在英国皇家研究院作了一系列的报告之后，霍尔丹对细胞中发生的氧化反应进行了总结。令人格外惊讶的是：仅仅在几年之后，汉斯·克雷布斯就提出了柠檬酸循环背后的生物化学原理，而与这个发现有关的很多细节在这篇文章中都没有涉及。大家都知道克雷布斯曾经研读过霍尔丹 1930 年的著作《酶》并深受它的影响。

最近，人们对呼吸化学的认识在细胞周边区域突然止步不前。我们已经知道氧气是如何被运送至脊椎动物血液中的细胞里的，也知道二氧化碳是如何释放的。我们还知道机体整体和特定器官的氧气消耗率会受到很多因素的影响，如温度、氢离子浓度以及神经刺激等等。虽然人们已经分离得到了一些不完全氧化的代谢产物如 $\beta$-羟基丁酸，但是目前涉及氧化过程的定量研究还只局限于有色分子参与的反应，如亚甲基蓝从蓝色还原成无色产物的反应，或者对苯二胺被氧化成有色产物的反应。

新的发展阶段始于巴泰利和斯特恩以及巴赫和肖达在日内瓦的研究工作；而第一次世界大战以来，瑞典的通贝里实验室、德国的沃伯格和维兰德实验室以及英国的霍普金斯实验室成为世界上最重要的几个研究中心。他们的研究工作使人们可以识别很多种催化剂，每一种在呼吸过程中都起着不同的作用。无机的氧化反应催化剂可以活化氧化剂或者还原剂，或者既活化氧化剂又活化还原剂。据此，朗缪尔得出结论，当用高温的铂表面催化氢与氧的化合时，吸附态的氧分子层被高度活化，受到氢攻击后极易与其化合；但是反过来，吸附态的氢却很难与攻击态的氧发生化合反应。另一方面，当相同的化学反应被瓷器催化时，那么两种分子必须被吸附到彼此靠近的位置才能发生反应。

因此，我们无需惊讶于这样的发现，即细胞催化剂不仅能激活氧气，还可以作为乳酸离子等还原剂的激活剂；鉴于沃伯格 [1] 和维兰德 [2] 分别主张氧气和还原剂的激活

* 这是霍尔丹于 2 月 5 日、12 日和 19 日在英国皇家研究院发表的演讲。

the activation of oxygen and of reducers as the fundamental feature of respiration.

When an enzyme catalyses the reaction between two molecular types, one very restricted, the other very general, we describe it as specific for the former. Thus Dixon[3] and Coombs[4] found that xanthine dehydrogenase catalyses the reaction $AH_2+B=A+BH_2$, where A must be one of a small number of purine bases (it is possible that the same enzyme also activates aldehydes; if so, they are oxidised at about one percent of the rate of the purines). But B may be oxygen, iodine, nitrate, permanganate, or any of a large number of dyes, such as methylene blue. These latter are perhaps all held on the enzyme surface near the former, but it is difficult to imagine that there is a single molecular grouping responsible for activating all of them. For reaction it is not sufficient that a molecule should be united with the enzyme; it must be activated as well. Thus, uric acid unites with xanthine dehydrogenase at the same spot as xanthine, thus inhibiting its oxidation, but is not oxidised, though another enzyme can accomplish this process.

A large number of dehydrogenases are known which act in a similar manner, each causing the activation of one or more organic substrates. Thus, lactic dehydrogenase, which can be obtained in solution from a number of sources, activates several $\alpha$-hydroxyacids; succinic dehydrogenase, another enzyme easily obtained in solution, activates succinic and methyl-succinic acids; and so on. The activity of these enzymes is generally measured by the rate at which they catalyse the reduction of methylene blue by their substrates. They usually have a wide range of optimal *p*H from about 7 to 10, instead of a small range like hydrolytic enzymes, and a fairly constant $Q_{10}$ in the neighbourhood of 2, that is, a critical increment of about 12,000 calories. They are not inhibited by small concentrations of cyanide or sulphide, but are so by the usual enzyme poisons, such as heavy metals and nitrites, and oxidising agents. The formic dehydrogenase of *Bacillus coli* appears to be a copper compound, but there is no evidence that most dehydrogenases contain metals. Quastel[5] and his colleagues have made a very thorough study of the dehydrogenases on the surface of *Bacillus coli*. There are probably at least seven different ones, and possibly many more. In this case they can readily be shown to be concerned in oxygen uptakes. In certain conditions malonic acid inhibits methylene blue reduction by succinic acid, both uniting with the enzyme at the same point; and in high concentrations of both, the rate of reduction of methylene blue depends on the ratio of the two. Cook[6] found that oxygen is reduced at nearly the same rate as methylene blue, and malonic acid inhibits its reduction to about the same extent.

When a dehydrogenase and its specific substrate act directly on $O_2$ it is reduced to $H_2O_2$. Some anaerobic bacteria act in this way. Bertho and Glück[7] found that at least 90 percent of the $O_2$ consumed by *Bacillus acidophilus* is converted into $H_2O_2$, which damages the bacteria. But some dehydrogenases when separated will not reduce $O_2$, and a separate activator is required. We know rather less about the activation of $O_2$ than of $H_2O_2$. This latter can be activated by two different enzymes, catalase and peroxidase, and by heat-stable peroxidase-like substances such as cytochrome and haematins.

作用是呼吸的基本特征，我们将会在这两种理论之间找到一条前进的道路。

参与酶促反应的两类分子中，一种的范围非常有限，而另一种则具有很广泛的适用性，我们将前者称为专一性。狄克逊[3]和库姆斯[4]发现，在黄嘌呤脱氢酶催化的反应 $AH_2+B=A+BH_2$ 中，A 必须是少数嘌呤碱中的一种（这种酶也许还可以活化醛基，但是其氧化醛基的效率大约只有嘌呤的百分之一），而 B 可以是氧气、碘、硝酸盐、高锰酸盐，或者是为数众多的染料中的一种，如亚甲基蓝。虽然这些 B 类分子可能都会紧挨着 A 吸附在酶分子的表面，但很难想象只用一种分子就能把它们全部激活。分子与酶的结合不足以使反应发生，它们还必须要被激活。因此，尿酸能以与嘌呤相同的位点紧密结合在黄嘌呤脱氢酶上，以此抑制嘌呤氧化；但尿酸自身不被氧化，尽管另一种酶可以完成其氧化过程。

已知有大量的脱氢酶都以与上述相似的方式发生作用，它们都能激活一个或多个有机底物。例如，可以从多种原料的溶液中获取的乳酸脱氢酶能够活化好几种的 $\alpha$–羟基酸；另一种很容易从溶液中获取的琥珀酸脱氢酶能够活化琥珀酸和甲基琥珀酸等等。这些酶的活力通常以它们用催化底物还原亚甲基蓝的效率来衡量。脱氢酶常常拥有广泛的最适 pH 范围，可以从 7 一直到 10，这一点不同于最适 pH 范围很窄的水解酶；脱氢酶还具有相当稳定的 $Q_{10}$，大约为 2，即临界增量约为 12,000 卡路里。它们不会被低浓度的氰化物或硫化物所抑制，但是会被各种常规的酶失活剂，如重金属、亚硝酸盐，以及氧化剂抑制。虽然大肠杆菌的甲酸脱氢酶似乎是一种含铜的化合物，但是并没有证据说明大多数的脱氢酶都含有金属离子。夸斯特尔[5]及其同事对大肠杆菌表面的脱氢酶进行了彻底的研究。这些脱氢酶可能至少有七种或更多，在研究中很容易发现它们都参与了氧气摄入过程。在特定条件下，丙二酸能够抑制琥珀酸对亚甲基蓝的还原作用，因为二者都结合在酶的相同位点上；当两者浓度都很高时，亚甲基蓝被还原的速率取决于两者之比。库克[6]发现，氧气被还原的速率与亚甲基蓝几乎相同，而丙二酸对这个还原反应的抑制程度也大致等于对亚甲基蓝的抑制程度。

当脱氢酶及其特异性底物与 $O_2$ 直接发生反应时，$O_2$ 被还原成了 $H_2O_2$。一些厌氧细菌就是以这种方式发生反应的。贝尔托和格吕克[7]发现，嗜酸杆菌所消耗的 $O_2$ 至少有 90% 转化成了对细菌有害的 $H_2O_2$。不过，有一些脱氢酶一旦被分离就失去了还原氧气的能力，必须有激活剂的协助才能完成还原反应。我们对 $O_2$ 活化过程的了解比 $H_2O_2$ 更少，后者不仅能够被两种不同的酶所活化，即过氧化氢酶和过氧化物酶，还可以被耐高温的过氧化物酶类似物所活化，如细胞色素和羟高铁血红素。

Catalase catalyses the reaction $2H_2O_2=2H_2O+O_2$. Zeile and Hellström[8] have shown that it is a derivative of haematin with a definite spectrum, and convertible into a haemochromogen, or into protophyrin. It unites with HCN to give an inactive compound. Under suitable conditions a catalase molecule can destroy more than $10^5$ $H_2O_2$ molecules per second. Peroxidase catalyses the reactions $H_2O_2+X=H_2O+XO$, or $nH_2O_2+nX=nH_2O+nXO$, where X may be a large variety of molecules, generally aromatic, but including nitrite and HI. It can be very highly concentrated, and appears to be a coloured iron compound. Its extreme sensitivity to cyanide suggests that it is of a similar nature to catalase.

The oxygen activators (oxygenases or *Atmungsferment*) have been specially studied by Warburg.[1] They unite not only with $O_2$ but also with CO, for which they have a rather smaller affinity. Like CO-haemoglobins, the CO-oxygenases are generally sensitive to light. Thus the oxygen uptake of yeast in presence of glucose or alcohol is reduced to about 50 percent, in a mixture containing ten parts of CO to one of $O_2$, in the dark. In strong light it returns to almost normal values. By studying the relative efficiencies of different monochromatic lights, Warburg and Negelein[9] found that its spectrum is very similar to that of alkaline haematin, and still closer to that of iron-phaeophorbide-*b*.

Cook, Haldane, and Mapson[10] worked with *B. coli* in toluene-saturated buffer solutions. Under these conditions, succinic, lactic, and formic acids each lose two hydrogen atoms and no more. It is thus possible to study reactions much simpler than the complete oxidation of a substance such as glucose. They found that CO and HCN, which in moderate amounts do not prevent oxidations by methylene blue, inhibit oxygen reduction. In both cases the oxidation of lactate is more sensitive than that of formate, while that of succinate is intermediate. Hence there appear to be three oxygenases with specific relative affinities for CO and $O_2$, like those of the haemoglobins, and also with different affinities for HCN. Each dehydrogenase is associated with a particular set of oxygenase molecules, for oxygen uptakes in presence of formate and lactate are strictly additive, even when oxygenase activity has been reduced by HCN. If the various dehydrogenases could draw on the same common stock of oxygenase molecules for activated oxygen, this would not be so. This rather rigid organisation is probably exceptional, for oxidations by *B. coli* are largely carried out on its surface, instead of internally, and it does not contain all the three cytochromes. In the absence of toluene, similar but not quite so clear-cut results are obtained.

Cytochrome is the name for a group of metal-porphyrin compounds, the metal being probably iron, which are found in almost all cells, and have been studied by Keilin[11]. When the cell runs short of oxygen, through asphyxia, intense metabolism, or cyanide poisoning, a strong spectrum of cytochrome, resembling that of a mixture of haemochromogens, appears. If the supply of oxygen becomes adequate, the characteristic bands disappear, being replaced by a fainter spectrum of the alkaline haematin type. Cytochrome is not oxygenase, as it does not combine readily with CO or HCN. One of the three components of cytochrome, cytochrome *c*, has been obtained in fairly strong solution. It

过氧化氢酶催化的反应是 $2H_2O_2 = 2H_2O + O_2$。蔡勒和赫尔斯特伦[8]指出，在这个反应过程中羟高铁血红素产生了具有特定光谱的衍生物，并且转换为血色原或者原卟啉。与 HCN 的结合能够使该酶失去活性。在合适的条件下，一个过氧化氢酶分子每秒可以分解超过 $10^5$ 个 $H_2O_2$ 分子。过氧化物酶催化的反应是 $H_2O_2+X=H_2O+XO$，或 $nH_2O_2+nX=nH_2O+nXO$。在该反应中，X 可以是一大类分子，一般是芳香类分子，也包含亚硝酸盐和 HI。该酶可以高度浓缩，是一种有色的含铁化合物，对氰化物的高度敏感性表明它与过氧化氢酶具有相似的特性。.

沃伯格[1]专门研究了氧活化剂（加氧酶或者呼吸酶）。氧活化剂不仅与 $O_2$ 结合，还可以与 CO 相结合，只是它们之间的亲和力稍弱。与 CO– 血红蛋白相似，CO– 加氧酶一般也会对光敏感。因此，将 CO 与 $O_2$ 以 10∶1 的比例混合，如果有葡萄糖或乙醇存在，酵母在黑暗条件下对混合物中氧气的摄入量会减少到 50%，而在强光下会恢复到接近于正常水平。通过研究不同单色光的相对效率，沃伯格和内格莱茵[9]发现此复合物的光谱与碱性羟高铁血红素很相似，而与铁–脱镁叶绿酸 –*b* 的光谱更为相近。

库克、霍尔丹和马普森[10]三人将大肠杆菌置于甲苯饱和的缓冲溶液中进行研究，在这种条件下琥珀酸、乳酸以及甲酸都只脱去了两个氢原子。这就使得对反应的研究比研究像葡萄糖那样的完全氧化要简单得多。他们发现适量的 CO 和 HCN 不会抑制亚甲基蓝的氧化活力，但是会抑制氧气的还原力。在这两种分子存在的条件下，乳酸比甲酸更容易被氧化，而琥珀酸氧化则位于两者之间，这表明可能有三种加氧酶存在，它们像血红蛋白一样对 CO 和 $O_2$ 的相对亲和力各不相同，对 HCN 的亲和力也不相同。每一种脱氢酶都与一个特定系列的加氧酶相关联，因为在甲酸和乳酸存在的条件下，即使加氧酶的活力被 HCN 抑制，氧气的摄入量也是严格遵守相加性法则的。如果不同的脱氢酶能帮助相同的加氧酶携带等量的活化态氧，那么结果就不会如此。这种严格的组织很可能具有例外，因为大肠杆菌的氧化作用主要发生在其表面而不是内部，另外，大肠杆菌也不含有全部的三种细胞色素。在去除甲苯后，研究人员获得了虽然相似但不很确定的实验结果。

细胞色素指的是金属与卟啉之间形成的一类复合物，与卟啉结合的金属通常是铁，在几乎所有的细胞中都存在，而且基林[11]也对此进行了研究。当细胞缺氧并导致窒息、剧烈代谢或氰化物中毒时，会产生很强的细胞色素光谱，与血色原混合物的光谱类似。而当氧气的供应变得充足时，这个特征谱带就会消失，取而代之的是较弱的碱性羟高铁血红素类的光谱。细胞色素不是加氧酶，因为它不易于与 CO 或者 HCN 结合。目前研究人员已经得到了细胞色素的三大组分之一——细胞色素 *c* 的

is a red substance, only slowly oxidised by molecular oxygen, readily by mild oxidising agents. It can be reduced by reducing agents or living tissues, and is an iron-porphyrin compound. Keilin found that the oxygen uptake of a system composed of oxygenase from heart muscle, cytochrome, and cysteine behaves like that of a tissue to cyanide and CO. With this system he was able to show that oxygenase is heat-labile like an enzyme, which cytochrome is not. In plants, a particular type of oxygenase, which Keilin calls catechol oxidase, and the CO compound of which, where investigated, has been found to be insensitive to light, yields $H_2O_2$ when oxidising catechol and its derivatives, as shown by Onslow[12].

We can thus give a scheme (Fig. 1) which probably covers most of the oxidation process in the average cell. In anaerobes one or more of the catalysts is absent. Oxygen is activated by oxygenase, which is reduced by cytochrome, and the latter is reduced in turn by dehydrogenases of the common or anaerobic type, that is, those which cannot reduce $O_2$ directly. This process is occasionally simplified, as in *B. coli*, where cytochrome does not seem to intervene in certain oxidations. Oxygen can also be reduced to $H_2O_2$, either by catechol oxidase or by an aerobic dehydrogenase. This $H_2O_2$ is used for further oxidation with peroxidase, or is destroyed by catalase. The latter can act as a safety-valve owing to its low affinity. Whereas peroxidase acts most rapidly in a concentration of $H_2O_2$ which may be as low as $10^{-6}$ *M.*, catalase has an optimum $H_2O_2$ concentration of about 0.2 *M.*, and at $10^{-6}$ *M.* is working at only about 0.0004 of its maximum rate. Other substances may act as intermediates. Glutathione appears to remove hydrogen from certain groupings in proteins, the reduced glutathione being later re-oxidised. St. György's[13] hexuronic acid is apparently reduced by dehydrogenases and oxidised by peroxidase. Doubtless many more similar substances will be discovered in future.

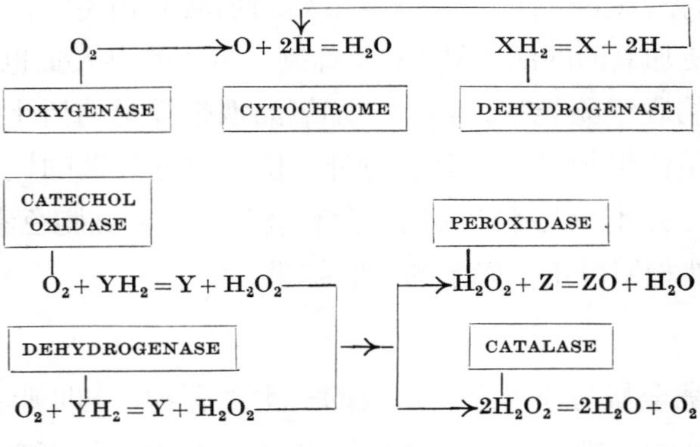


Fig. 1. The names of the catalysts are given in rectangles, the molecular species activated by each being indicated. The molecule $YH_2$ is catechol or a derivative in the case of catechol oxidase (Onslow's oxygenase) and is a purine base in the case of xanthine oxidase acting as a reducer of $O_2$. X and Z may be very varied.

高浓度溶液，它是一种红色物质，只能被分子态的氧缓慢氧化，易于被温和的氧化剂所氧化。它可以被还原剂或者活组织所还原，是一种铁－卟啉复合物。基林发现，由来自心肌的加氧酶、细胞色素以及半胱氨酸所组成的系统对氧气的摄入与一个组织对氰化物以及 CO 的摄入相似。通过这个系统，他可以说明加氧酶像多数酶一样具有热不稳定性，而细胞色素却不具有这样的特性。翁斯洛指出：在植物中有一种特殊的加氧酶，被基林称为儿茶酚氧化酶，它与 CO 的复合物对光不敏感，这种加氧酶在氧化儿茶酚及其衍生物时会生成 $H_2O_2$[12]。

因而我们可以画出一张图（见图 1），该图很可能涵盖了常规细胞内的大多数氧化过程。在厌氧微生物中会缺失其中的一个或多个催化剂。在这类体系中，氧气能被加氧酶活化，然后被细胞色素所还原，而细胞色素需要先被普通或厌氧型的脱氢酶所还原。也就是说，脱氢酶不能直接还原氧气。这个过程有时候也会被简化，比如在大肠杆菌中，细胞色素可能并不参与某些氧化过程。$O_2$ 也可以被儿茶酚氧化酶或者需氧型脱氢酶还原为 $H_2O_2$，这些 $H_2O_2$ 可以在过氧化物酶的作用下进一步氧化，或者被过氧化氢酶分解。后者因亲和力低而可以起到安全阀的作用。过氧化氢酶催化反应的最适 $H_2O_2$ 浓度为 0.2 M，当 $H_2O_2$ 浓度低至 $10^{-6}$ M 的水平时，它的反应速率只有最大反应速率的万分之四；而即使在这样低的浓度下，过氧化物酶也能快速地与 $H_2O_2$ 发生作用。其他物质可能是一些中间产物。谷胱甘肽似乎具有脱去蛋白质中某些特定基团上的氢原子的能力，被还原的谷胱甘肽随后还会重新被氧化。圣哲尔吉 [13] 的己糖醛酸就显然能被脱氢酶所还原，也可以被过氧化物酶氧化。毫无疑问，人们将会发现越来越多的类似物质。

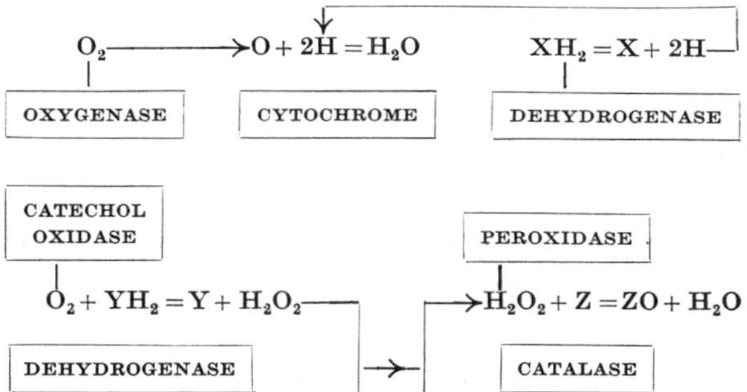


图 1. 长方格中给出的是各种催化剂的名称，图中标出了它们各自催化的分子种类。$YH_2$ 在儿茶酚氧化酶（翁斯洛加氧酶）所催化的反应中代表儿茶酚或者儿茶酚的衍生物，在黄嘌呤氧化酶催化的反应中代表的是作为氧气还原剂的嘌呤碱。X 和 Z 所代表的分子范围则可能非常广泛。

We note the great importance of metal-porphyrin compounds (Table I.). It is fairly clear that their catalytic function is primitive. They have afterwards been modified to act as stores or carriers of oxygen in higher animals. Except in chlorophyll, a magnesium compound, the metal united with the porphyrin is usually, if not always, iron. As oxygenase, catalase, and cytochrome are almost universally distributed, we need not be surprised that haemoglobin and related pigments such as chlorocruorin have often been independently evolved, a suitable protein being combined with iron-porphyrin residue.

Table I. Metal-porphyrin in Compounds found in Cells.

1. Catalysts. Chlorophyll *a* and *b*. Oxygenases. Catalases. Probably peroxidases. Cytochrome *a*, *b*, and *c*.
2. Mainly concerned in oxygen storage. *Arenicola* haemoglobin.
3. Mainly concerned in oxygen carriage. Vertebrate haemoglobins.
4. Uncertain whether in group 2 or 3. Many invertebrate haemoglobins. Chlorocruorin. Helicorubin, etc.

We know little as to the immediate source of $CO_2$. Two obvious processes are available, the dehydrogenation of formic acid, and the decarboxylation of pyruvic acid and related compounds by the enzyme carboxylase according to the equation: $R{-}CO{-}COOH = R{-}COH + CO_2$. The enzymes concerned in both processes have a wide distribution.

Still less is known of how in detail the energy made available in oxidation is passed on, or of how the rate of oxidation is controlled, though both processes are evident enough in the whole organism. The control is largely exercised on the fuel supply. Thus a rise of blood sugar in man causes an increased oxygen consumption. Hormones such as thyroxin are also concerned, but their mode of action is not understood. The energy is not generally liberated directly, but is largely employed in building up compounds of high chemical potential. These may either form new tissue or be available for rapid energy production. Thus the oxidation of sugar or lactic acid in muscle provides energy for the resynthesis of glycogen from lactic acid, and of phosphagen from creatine and phosphate.

If these processes are to be efficient, two conditions must be fulfilled. The energy of oxidation must be made available in quanta somewhat, but not greatly, larger than those required for synthesis; and the molecules undergoing oxidation and synthesis must be united with the same catalyst, which must thus have a double specificity. The significance of the complicated oxidising systems here described will remain obscure until we know what syntheses are correlated with each of them. A beginning of such an analysis has been made by Wurmser[14]. But an indispensable preliminary is a study of the total and free energy changes in the various reactions which are linked. This is still in its very early stages.

But even when we know the stages in the oxidation of different substances, and the use to which the energy thus made available is put, we shall be faced with the problem of regulation. In the living cell the activity of peroxidase or lactic dehydrogenase is doubtless governed by laws as definite as those which govern that of the heart in the living organism, laws which can be stated both in terms of chemistry and of biological function. The question of whether these two types of explanation can be reconciled, or whether one

我们注意到金属–卟啉复合物具有相当的重要性（见表 1）。相当明确的一点是它们的催化功能都很简单。后来又认为它们可以在较高等动物的体内储备和运输氧。除了叶绿素是金属镁的复合物外，在其他大多数情况下，与卟啉结合的金属都是铁。由于加氧酶、过氧化氢以及细胞色素几乎到处都有，所以我们不必对血红蛋白和相关色素如血绿蛋白往往会不受限制地转变成与铁–卟啉残基结合的蛋白而感到惊讶。

表 1. 细胞中发现的金属–卟啉复合物

1. 催化剂。叶绿素 *a* 和 *b*，加氧酶，过氧化氢酶，可能有过氧化物酶，细胞色素 *a*、*b*、*c*。
2. 主要与氧的储备有关。沙蠋的血红蛋白。
3. 主要与氧的运输有关。脊椎动物的血红蛋白。
4. 尚不确定在第 2 组或第 3 组中是否存在。许多无脊椎动物的血红蛋白，血绿蛋白，蠕虫血红蛋白等。

对于 $CO_2$ 的直接来源我们知之甚少。已知的两个显而易见的相关过程是甲酸的脱氢反应和丙酮酸及其相关化合物在羧化酶作用下的脱羧，所依据的方程式是 $R–CO–COOH = R–COH + CO_2$。这两个过程所涉及的酶都有很多种。

对于在氧化过程中所获得的能量具体是如何传递的以及怎样控制氧化的速率我们还知之甚少，尽管这两个过程在整个机体中是显然存在的。控制主要是由燃料供应实现的。因此一个人血糖升高会导致氧气的消耗量增加。另外，荷尔蒙如甲状腺素也会受到影响，不过它们的作用方式还不为人所知。氧化过程中产生的能量通常不会直接释放出去，其中很大一部分要用于合成高能化合物。这些高能化合物可能用于构成新的组织，也可能用于快速地产生能量。因此肌肉中糖或者乳酸的氧化可以为乳酸再合成糖原以及肌酸与磷酸盐再合成磷酸原提供能量。

要使这些过程都能有效运行，需要满足两个条件：氧化产生的能量必须略高于合成所需的能量；参与氧化和合成的分子必须结合在相同的催化剂分子上，因此该酶分子必须具有双重特异性。关于这里所说的复杂氧化系统，在弄清它们分别与哪些合成有关之前，人们还不清楚它们的重要性。维尔姆塞首先开展了对这方面的分析研究 [14]。但是此工作的一个必要前提是需要研究各个相互连接的反应中总能量以及自由能的变化，而这些研究尚处于刚刚起步的阶段。

不过，即使我们知道不同物质在氧化反应中所扮演的角色，也知道由此产生的能量是如何使用的，我们还将面临有关调控的问题。毫无疑问，正如机体遵守一些法则来维持心脏的正常功能一样，活细胞中过氧化物酶或乳酸脱氢酶的活性也严格遵守着某些法则，这些法则可以同时满足化学和生物学的要求，而目前这两种解释是否能统一还是其中某一种解释是多余的问题仍需要通过讨论解决。当然，这一天

of them is superfluous, will then have to be fought out. However, that day is far distant; meanwhile the biochemist can continue to accumulate knowledge without committing himself on philosophical questions.

(**128**, 175-178; 1931)

---

References:

1 Warburg, *Über die katalytische Wirkungen der lebendigen Substanz* (1926).

2 Wieland, *Ergeb. Physiol.*. **20**, 477 (1922).

3 Dixon, *Biochem. Jour.*, **20**. 703 (1926).

4 Coombs, *Biochem. Jour.*, **21**, 1259 (1927).

5 Quastel and colleagues, *Biochem. Jour.*, 1924–1928 (Bibliography in *Jour. Hyg.*, **28**, 139; 1928).

6 Cook, *Biochem. Jour.*, **24**, 1538 (1930).

7 Bertho and Glück, *Naturwiss.*, **19**, 88 (1931).

8 Zeile and Hellström, *Zeit. physiol. Chem.*, **192**, 171 (1930).

9 Warburg and Negelein, *Biochem. Zeit.*, **202**, 202 (1928).

10 Cook, Haldane, and Mapson, *Biochem. Jour.*, **25**, 534 (1931).

11 Keilin, *Proc. Roy. Soc.*, B, **98**, 312 (1925): **104**, 236 (1929).

12 Onslow and Robinson, *Biochem. Jour.*, **20**, 1138 (1926).

13 St. György, *Biochem. Jour.*, **22**, 1387 (1928).

14 Wurmser, *Oxidations et réductions* (1930).

的到来会很遥远，在此期间生物化学家们可以不断积累相关知识，而不必考虑哲学上的问题。

（高如丽 翻译；刘京国 审稿）

# Atomic Synthesis and Stellar Energy

R. d'E. Atkinson

## Editor's Note

**The source of the energy that keeps stars shining was a great mystery in the 1930s. The Welsh astronomer Robert d'Escourt Atkinson here puts forward the view that it arises from the radioactive decay of relatively heavy elements in the interiors of stars. His views were proved mistaken the following year when Hans Bethe published an account of how hydrogen atoms can fuse directly to make helium atoms by simple nuclear processes in which the existence of the neutron (also discovered in 1932) is essential.**

SOME time ago F. G. Houtermans and the present writer investigated the possibility of synthesis of elements, in stellar interiors, by the wave mechanics process of penetration of nuclei by protons.[1] The theory was not strictly correct, and various modifications have been proposed since, of which the theory of Wilson[2] is perhaps the most important; all theories, however, lead to a probability of proton penetration having the same exponential dependence on both the temperature, $T$, and the atomic number, $Z$. The importance of this factor far outweighs that of the multiplicative forefactor which alone is different in the different theories, and it seems therefore desirable to discuss somewhat more fully the consequences of the assumption that any of these theories will give the right order of magnitude for the temperature at which synthesis will occur in large amounts. The effect of the exponential is roughly to make the synthesis probability vary as $T^{20}$, or some comparable power, and thus even a change of 1,000 in the fore-factor does not seriously affect $T$. The investigation is being discussed fully in the *Astrophysical Journal*, but in view of the interest of the subject at present, and also of the comparative unfamiliarity of the line of attack, a short summary may both appeal to a wider audience and prepare the way for the more detailed treatment.

Direct synthesis of helium from hydrogen is clearly a very unsatisfactory process, but we do not need to assume its existence at all; as in the above paper, we assume that helium is produced entirely indirectly, by the spontaneous disintegration of unstable nuclei that must first themselves be formed. In addition to the known radioactive elements, Gamow's theory of nuclear stability[3] now indicates that we may expect a large number of lighter elements to be unstable if they were to be formed, and in fact we rely mainly on these. For example, if above argon the incorporation of electrons, which we clearly must suppose can occur, is somewhat difficult (and the existence of apparently permanent non-radioactive *isobars* seems to show that it can be extremely difficult), nuclei such as $Fe^{52}$, $Ni^{56}$, and $Zn^{60}$ may be formed; according to Gamow, the last of these, and quite possibly all three, should be unstable. After emitting one $\alpha$-particle, they would again collect four protons and two electrons in such order and at such intervals as they could, combine them into a fresh $\alpha$-particle, and re-emit this one also in due course. At various points in this cycle they

# 原子合成与恒星能量

罗伯特·阿特金森

## 编者按

在 20 世纪 30 年代，人们完全不清楚维持恒星不断发光的能量来源于哪里。威尔士天文学家罗伯特·阿特金森在本文中提出这种能量来源于较重元素在恒星内部的放射性衰变过程。一年后，他的观点被证明是错误的，因为汉斯·贝特发表了一篇关于氢原子可以通过简单的核反应直接聚变成氦原子的报告，当然这个结论只有在人们了解到中子的存在（也是在 1932 年发现的）之后才能得出。

豪特曼斯和本文作者曾经研究过在恒星内部，质子经由波动力学过程进入核内而引起元素合成的可能性[1]。理论并非严格正确，后来人们又提出了各种修正意见，这其中威尔逊的理论[2]应该是最为重要的；然而，所有理论一致认为质子渗透几率与温度 $T$ 和原子序数 $Z$ 有相同的指数函数关系。这一因素的重要性远远超过倍增因子，而后者也是不同理论中的唯一不同之处。所以，有必要更充分地讨论一下由“任何理论都能给出在大量合成时温度的正确数量级”这一假设所导致的结论。指数效应使合成几率大致按 $T^{20}$（或别的某个可与之比拟的幂律）变化。所以即使前面的因子改变了 1,000 倍也不会严重影响 $T$。这项研究在《天体物理杂志》上有完整的讨论，但考虑到目前人们对此课题很感兴趣，却又不太熟悉这个理论，所以一个简短的概述或许会吸引更多的读者，也能为更细致的探讨做准备。

直接由氢合成氦显然是一个非常不能令人满意的过程，但我们根本不需要假设这种过程的存在；如上一篇文章中所述，我们可以假设所有氦都是通过不稳定核的自发衰变产生的，但需要首先生成不稳定核。除已知的放射性元素外，伽莫夫的核稳定性理论[3]表明：我们现在可能要寄希望于为数众多的轻元素（如果它们能够形成的话）是不稳定的，事实上我们会主要依赖这些轻元素。例如，氩以上原子对电子的吸收是有一定困难的，虽然我们确信上述过程可以发生（而明显稳定的非放射性**同量异位素**的存在似乎表明这个过程可能极为困难），同时可能会形成类似 $Fe^{52}$、$Ni^{56}$ 和 $Zn^{60}$ 这样的核；按伽莫夫的说法，最后一种，或很可能所有三种，应该不会是稳定的。在释放掉一个 $\alpha$ 粒子之后，它们会再次按某种顺序和间隔收集四个质子和两个电子，并将其组合为一个新的 $\alpha$ 粒子，而后再次按既有程序释放掉。在这个周期的不同点，它们辐

would also have to emit a total of just as much energy as would be set free by the direct synthesis of a helium nucleus; this energy can then be used to maintain the star's radiation. This method of evading the well-known difficulty of the 6-body collision as a source of helium obviously opens up important avenues; it is, however, not at all necessary to regard helium as the final product. In fact, since small $Z$-values favour synthesis, all the helium formed will be rapidly built up again. The energy developed is roughly the same, however, *per proton consumed*, whatever the products.

Since no other theory proposes a lower temperature for an energy source than ours turns out to do, we may take it that stars will at any rate contract until this process becomes operative; they will then be unable to contract further, since even a small contraction will enormously stimulate the energy development and force them to expand again. Milne's theory seems in this way to be ruled out until such time as the hydrogen supply near the centre has run low.

Rosseland has shown that when there is no great excess of hydrogen, electrostatic forces will tend to drive it from the centre, and the centre is in any case the only place where it is being consumed. Thus in any star a time will arrive when the disappearance of hydrogen near the centre prevents the generation of energy there altogether; the star must then condense towards the degenerate state. It is known that the energy of the white dwarfs may be entirely gravitational if their lifetimes may be supposed to be only of the order of $10^{11}$ years; in addition to explaining why stars intermediate between white dwarfs and the main sequence seem to be scarce, this theory explains why heavy white dwarfs should be the commonest[4] (the minimum radius is smaller and the square of the mass larger, so that they have very much more gravitational energy available).

So long, however, as hydrogen is present, synthesis should continue. Since, now, the star's mass remains practically constant, its energy generation must remain moderately so, and it is easily seen that this involves an approximate constancy of the helium supply, but with an ever-present possibility of adding a little to it. This is the fundamental condition for stellar stability, and determines the central temperature. For a star to keep control, it must slowly decrease its central temperature, since the number of helium sources is being added to; thus, after an initial contraction to start the process, stars spend probably the greater part of their lives *expanding*. During most of their lifetime the expansion is very slow, and the central temperature at any one mass is almost determinate; this accounts for the main sequence.

The actual value for the central temperature cannot, however, be what this simple theory would indicate. If iron is to be synthesised, a temperature of perhaps 200 million degrees would be necessary, and at this temperature all the light elements would be so readily converted to heavier ones that they could not become abundant at all. With a constant helium supply we can use the ordinary equilibrium law of radioactivity theory, namely, that the amounts of the various elements should be directly as their "average lives"; the

射出的总能量正好等于直接合成一个氦核所释放的能量，而这些能量就可以用来维持恒星的持续辐射。这种方法避开了把六体碰撞作为氦核来源所遇到的著名困难，从而明显地打开了解决问题的重要思路。但也没有必要把氦核看成是最终产物，事实上，因为小的原子序数 $Z$ 更有利于合成，因此所有已形成的氦核会迅速地再次增大。而不论产物是什么，释放出的能量，即**每个质子所消耗的能量**，都是大致相同的。

因为所有其他理论要求的能量源温度都比我们的理论高，所以我们可以认为恒星无论如何都会收缩，直到这种过程开始为止；之后它们将不能继续收缩，因为即使是一个小的收缩也会极大地促进能量的释放，并使得它们再次膨胀。如此看来，在靠近中心的氢供给变低之前，米耳恩的理论就可以被排除了。

罗斯兰德已经阐述过，当没有大量氢过剩的时候，静电力会倾向于将氢从中心推出，而中心是氢得以消耗的唯一地方。所以对于任何恒星都必然会出现靠近中心处的氢不再存在的时候，这时能量产生被完全阻止，这样恒星也必然会收缩到简并态。人们知道，如果可以认为白矮星的寿命约为 $10^{11}$ 年的话，它们的能量可能会全部来自于引力，因此这个理论除了能解释为什么介于白矮星和主星序间的恒星看起来很少外，还解释了为什么大质量的白矮星应当是最常见的[4]（最小半径值越小，质量平方越大，以至于它们具有更多的引力能可以使用）。

然而，只要还存在氢，合成就应该继续。因为既然恒星的质量实际上是保持恒定的，那么它产生的能量也会保持在一个适度的值，很容易看出这关系到基本恒定的氦供给，但再增加一点的可能性是经常存在的。这是恒星稳定的基本条件，也决定了恒星中心的温度。一个恒星要想维持可控，它就必须慢慢地降低自己的中心温度，因为氦源的数量在增加；所以在经过了最初的收缩以启动这一过程之后，恒星用于**膨胀**的时间可能占去了它生命中的一大半。在它们生命的绝大部分时间里，膨胀进行得都很缓慢，并且对于任何给定的质量，中心温度几乎都是确定的，这也解释了主星序的存在。

然而，实际的中心温度值不可能由这种简单的理论给出。如果要合成铁，温度可能需要达到 2 亿度，在这种温度下，所有的轻元素都会非常容易转化成重元素，以至于它们不可能大量存在。在氦供给恒定的条件下，我们可以使用普通的放射性平衡律，即，不同元素的数量应该就相当于它们的“平均寿命”，不管我们面对的是合成过程还是分解过程都不会影响这个定律的有效性。另外，由于原子序数 $Z$ 以指

fact that we are dealing with synthesis and not disintegration does not affect the validity of the principle. Since the atomic number, $Z$, affects the synthesis probabilities, that is, the average lives, exponentially, all light elements ought to be very scarce; oxygen is, however, more abundant than anything except hydrogen, and a number of other elements near it are also at least as plentiful as iron.

In fact, it is easily seen that the most abundant element of all in a star must have an average life (until further synthesis) comparable with the past life of the star itself; otherwise some heavier element would be more abundant. If now we assume the central temperature is so low that oxygen is as long-lived as this, we find that it and the lighter elements are nevertheless abundant enough for their synthesis alone to supply enough energy, and that the actual temperature is about 16 million degrees in the sun. This is in agreement with the figure obtained on Eddington's theory for a polytrope of index about three and constitution rather above 50 percent hydrogen by weight.

At this temperature there is, however, no synthesis of iron, and thus no further supply of helium, and the process will soon exhaust itself. The difficulty may be overcome by an arbitrary assumption, and it has been found possible to make one that accounts at the same time for the permanence and actual position of the main sequence, and for the relative proportions of all the elements in main sequence stars. The assumption is that there is a second synthesis process, which is more probable than the first when $Z>8$ and has a probability that increases somewhat with increasing $Z$; it must depend about as extremely on the temperature as the other process. Even if this assumption is wrong, it is probably valuable to have the theory investigated in detail; in point of fact, it does at least lead to a number of correct results.

Oxygen will now certainly be the longest lived element, and the products of synthesis will "pile up" at and near this value of $Z$. It is, as a matter of fact, desirable to keep them from adding to the iron group which is supplying the helium, for a constant supply is wanted. The iron group itself must, however, be abundant enough to be in "equilibrium" with the lightest elements, since it must produce as many $\alpha$-particles per second as there are helium-lithium syntheses. It is found that the situation which will develop involves a marked minimum between the oxygen and the iron maxima and a marked fall after, say, zinc, in very good qualitative agreement with observation.[5] A consideration of Gamow's theory leads us to expect in addition a maximum among and below the lightest rare earths, and possibly one in the lead region; both are found. Practically the entire range of elements thus shows a qualitative agreement with what the theory requires.

The same will be true of any main sequence star; but since the age of the star at a point when it is, say, half hydrogen is much greater for small stars than for large ones, and the density is also larger in small stars, the central temperature must be smaller in them if oxygen is still to have a long enough lifetime. This is satisfactory, for Jeans's modification of Eddington's theory does involve a polytropic index varying systematically with the mass in about the right sort of way to produce this effect. Jeans's modification results from using

数方式影响着合成几率，或者说是平均寿命，所以所有的轻元素都应该非常稀少，但是氧含量比除去氢之外的所有轻元素都要多，而且邻近氧的另外一些元素也至少和铁元素一样丰富。

事实上，很容易看出，恒星中最丰富的元素一定具有与恒星目前的年龄相当的平均寿命（直到后面的合成），否则一些重元素将会更多。如果现在我们假设中心温度很低，以至于氧的寿命就这么长，那么我们就会发现它和更轻的元素仍然会非常丰富以至于仅由它们的合成就可以提供足够的能量，而太阳的实际温度约为 1,600 万度。这与从爱丁顿理论中得到的多方指数约为 3、氢的重量百分比明显超过 50% 的数字相符。

然而，在这个温度下不存在铁的合成，也就没有进一步的氦供给，并且该过程会迅速耗尽。这种困难可能会因一个任意的假设而得以克服，我们可以选择一个能同时解决主星序的持久和实际位置问题，又能给出主序星中所有元素的相对比例的假设。这个假设认为存在另一个合成过程：这个过程在 $Z>8$ 时比第一个过程更有可能发生，且发生第二个过程的可能性会随着 $Z$ 的增大而增加；它肯定与另一个过程一样与温度有很大的关系。即使这个假设是错误的，仔细地研究这个理论可能也很有价值；实际上，它至少能给出一些正确的结果。

现在，氧必定是最长寿的元素，合成的产物会在这个 $Z$ 值附近“堆积”。事实上，阻止它们增加到提供给氦的铁族元素中是可以理解的，因为需要的是恒定的供给。然而，铁族元素本身必须足够丰富以便与最轻的元素形成“平衡”，因为它每秒必须产生与氦–锂合成一样多的 $\alpha$ 粒子。这个论断将导致在氧和铁的最大值之间存在一个显著的最小值以及在锌之后出现一个明显的下降，这和观测结果在定性上是非常相符的[5]。根据伽莫夫的理论，我们认为除了在最轻的稀土元素及以下的区域会出现一个最大值以外，很可能在铅区还有一个极大值，并且这两者都被发现了。实际上从定性角度上看，元素的整个范围都和理论要求的一致。

同样的结论将适用于所有主序星；但当恒星的年龄处于某一点，比如只剩一半氢的时候，质量小的恒星的存在时间远远大于质量大的恒星，小恒星的密度也比大恒星高。如果氧此时仍然有足够长的寿命，则小质量恒星的中心温度一定会相对低一些。这是令人满意的结论，因为金斯对爱丁顿理论的修正的确包含了一个多方指数，它以一种合适的方式有规律地随质量变化从而产生了这种效应。金斯的修正来

the theoretical Kramers value for the absorption coefficient, and the main reason why it has not been more generally adopted (by followers of Eddington) than it has is probably that the absolute values obtained by Kramers' theory did not seem to fit the facts, When, however, we adopt Russell's high value for the hydrogen content of stars the discrepancy disappears.

The vast majority of the stars are thus accounted for. The main sequence consists of stars built on the Eddington-Jeans model, with central temperatures fairly sharply defined at any one mass and rising very slowly with the mass, and with a constitution very similar to that actually observed; the central temperature seems to be about 16–20 million degrees in the sun. The white dwarfs consist of a roughly parallel band of stars built nearly on the Milne degenerate model, with central temperatures up to about $3\times10^9$ degrees; they should have about the same constitution except for a shortage of hydrogen at the centre, and will be fainter for a given mass.

In addition to these two main classes we may account for the low density giants. These have a comparatively low central temperature and can only obtain their energy (*a*) if they have a large amount of free helium or unstable atoms already present, or (*b*) if some very light element can also be unstable. In case (*a*) they will not be able to live very long; but if they are very heavy their total lifetimes will be short anyway, and their life in this state may be a fairly large fraction of the total. The wave mechanics formula used shows that a star of mass 30 suns, if 10 percent of it were helium and 80 percent hydrogen, could develop enough energy for an absolute magnitude of −6 even at the density of an $M5$ supergiant, with a central temperature of only 4 million degrees. Such stars will, however, be "overstable", that is, they will be liable to develop pulsations; these are well known to be a common feature of very massive red stars. If they are not very massive, only a small fraction of their lifetimes can be spent in this state, and they would, in addition, have a very large colour index indeed; we should thus scarcely expect to see any. In case (*b*) a long life would be possible, but as synthesis would now certainly result in an immediate increase in the amount of the unstable element, the stars would have to change their central temperatures over a fairly large range during their lifetimes. The unstable element is assumed to be the isotope $Be^8$, which exists in very small quantities on the earth and probably has in fact a mass defect (referred to helium as a unit) of very nearly zero. Many beryls contain a large and otherwise unexplained amount of helium, and when the idea of the instability of $Be^8$ was first proposed, Lord Rayleigh at once pointed out the significance of this fact.[6] The "Hertzsprung gap" and its prolongation between the Cepheids and the *B* stars may be shown to follow if $Be^8$ has a long life, and its presence on the earth guarantees this. A long life is also in harmony with the $Be^8/Be^9$ ratio and the He/Be ratio.

A number of other observations may readily be fitted into the theory. We may mention in particular the absence of low density stars at medium and small masses, the occurrence of *R* and *N* types among giants but not among dwarfs, the existence of binaries in which the brighter star is the cooler and less dense, and the fact that the brightest stars in clusters are usually all red or all blue.

源于对吸收系数采用理论的克拉莫值，而这为什么没有被后人（爱丁顿的追随者们）更广泛地采纳，主要原因可能是因为由克拉莫理论得到的绝对值看起来与事实不符。然而，当我们采用罗素对于恒星中氢含量的较高的估计值时，这种不符合也就消失了。

绝大多数恒星都可以用这种方式进行解释。主星序中的恒星符合爱丁顿 – 金斯模型，这些恒星的中心温度在任一质量处都有非常明确的定义，并且中心温度随质量增加的速度很慢，它们的组成与实际观测结果非常相似，太阳的中心温度约为 1,600 万到 2,000 万度。白矮星由大体平行的恒星带组成，这些恒星基本上符合米耳恩的简并模型，其中心温度高至 30 亿度；它们与主序星应该有大体相同的组成，但在中心处氢元素较少，并且在质量一定时也会更暗一些。

除了这两个主要的类别之外，我们还知道有低密度的巨星。它们的中心温度相对较低，并且只能在两种情况下获得能量：(*a*) 如果它们有大量的自由氦或是业已存在的不稳定原子，(*b*) 如果一些非常轻的元素也是不稳定的。在情形 (*a*) 中，它们的寿命将不会很长，即使它们非常重，其总寿命仍然会很短，而处于这种状态下的时间长度或许要占总寿命中相当大的一部分。我们使用的波动力学公式显示，一个质量为太阳质量 30 倍的恒星，如果它的 10% 是氦，80% 是氢，那么即使它的密度只相当于一个 *M*5 超巨星，中心温度只有 400 万度，它也足以释放出相当于绝对星等为 – 6 的能量。然而，这样的恒星会“过于稳定”，即它们将有可能发展出脉动，这是质量非常大的红巨星广为人知的常见特性。如果它们的质量不是很大，停留在这种状态下的时间仅是整个寿命中的很小一部分，它们还将具有非常大的色指数，我们也因此很难看到这样的恒星。在情形 (*b*) 中，恒星可能会具有很长的寿命，但是因为合成肯定会导致这种不稳定元素的数量即刻增长，所以在一个相当长的寿命阶段内，恒星将不得不改变它们的中心温度。人们猜测这种不稳定的元素是同位素 $Be^8$，它在地球上只有很小的量，可能会有非常接近于零的质量缺损（以氦核为单位）。许多绿柱石中含有大量的氦，除此之外无法解释为什么有这么多氦，当 $Be^8$ 的不稳定性刚刚被提出时，瑞利勋爵立刻指出这一发现的重要性 [6]。如果 $Be^8$ 有很长的寿命，也许可以证明介于造父变星和 *B* 型星的“赫兹伯伦空隙”和它的延长线将是必然的结果，而 $Be^8$ 在地球上的存在保证了这一假设的成立。另外，较长的寿命也与 $Be^8/Be^9$ 比以及 He/Be 比相符合。

一些其他的观测结果也很容易纳入到这个理论中来。我们需要特别提到的是，不存在低密度的中小质量恒星，*R* 和 *N* 型星在巨星而不是矮星中出现，在一些双星系统中较亮的星会是密度和温度较低的星，并且星团中最亮的恒星通常全部是红的或者全部是蓝的。

The arguments that have been urged in support of the "long time scale" ($10^{13}$–$10^{14}$ years) may all be met with some plausibility. In particular the well-known theory of Jeans for the eccentricities of binaries, and similar "kinetic theory" arguments can all be reconciled with the "short time scale" ($10^{11}$ years) if the galaxy is expanding as fast as the universe in general is; this expansion (for the universe as a whole) seems to be demanded by the general theory of relativity.

It thus appears that as a result of the wave mechanics on one hand, and the general theory of relativity on the other, the universe may have developed its present complexity of stars and of atoms from an initial state consisting of a fairly dense, nearly uniform, nearly stationary mass of cold hydrogen. This comparatively simple beginning constitutes at least a pleasant ornament, if not an actual support, for our theory. It must, however, be admitted that there are still some serious difficulties; those that have been noticed are discussed in the full account which will shortly appear.

(**128**, 194-196; 1931)

R. d'E. Atkinson: Rutgers University.

References:

1 *Zeits. f. Physik*, **54**, 656 (1929).

2 *Mon. Not. R. A. S.*, **91**, 283 (1931).

3 *Proc. Roy. Soc.*, **126**, 632 (1930).

4 Russell and Atkinson, *Nature*, 661 (May 2, 1931).

5 Russell, *Astr. Jour.*, **72**, 11 (1929).

6 *Nature*, **123**, 607 (1929).

强烈支持“长时间尺度”（$10^{13}\sim10^{14}$ 年）的论证也许都是貌似正确的。尤其是如果星系膨胀得和整个宇宙一样快的话，金斯关于双星偏心率的著名理论以及与之相似的“动力学”理论都可以与“短时间尺度”（$10^{11}$ 年）相符合；而这种膨胀（对作为一个整体的宇宙来说）看起来正是广义相对论所要求的。

波动力学和广义相对论都认为，宇宙似乎是从一个相当致密、近乎均匀、近乎稳定的冷氢物质发展到现在的恒星以及原子所具有的复杂程度。这种相对简单的开端如果没有在事实上支持我们的理论，至少也是一个令人愉悦的点缀。然而，必须承认还有一些重要的问题有待于解决，已经被注意到的一些问题将会在很快就要出版的完整报告中进行讨论。

（汪浩 翻译；蒋世仰 审稿）

# Oestrus-Producing Hormones

G. F. Marrian and A. Butenandt

## Editor's Note

**In the 1930s, scientists were occupied with the identification not only of vitamins but also of hormones. The latter can be synthesised by the animal bodies in which they are essential ingredients of life, whereas vitamins are obligatory food supplements. This paper described the isolation of a hormone that induces oestrus in animals. Adolf Butenandt was one of Germany's most respected chemists of the period and was awarded a Nobel Prize in 1939. Oestrus-producing hormones and their analogues are a common route to birth-control pills.**

RECENTLY, Doisy and his co-workers (1931) have reported the isolation from the urine of pregnancy of a crystalline substance possessing oestrus-producing activity, which is distinct from the active substance theelin, previously described by them. The latter substance, to which they gave the formula $C_{18}H_{21}(OH)_2$, was shortly afterwards isolated by one of us (Butenandt, 1929)[1] and by Dingemanse and co-workers[2] (1930). It was shown afterwards (Butenandt, 1930) that this substance is represented by the formula $C_{18}H_{22}O_2$, and that it behaves either as a hydroxy ketone or as a dihydroxy alcohol.

There is no doubt that the second substance isolated by Doisy and his co-workers[3], to which they give the formula $C_{18}H_{21}(OH)_3$, is identical with that fully described earlier by one of us (Marrian, 1930)[4]. Although Prof. Doisy refers to the triol previously isolated, there is no suggestion in his papers that it had been characterised as a trihydroxy substance of the formula $C_{18}H_{21}(OH)_3$. His view that the substance described by one of us is a mixture of both active substances is apparently based solely on a difference between the *uncorrected* melting points. The evidence of the analytical data, which clearly shows this supposition to be untenable, is ignored.

A year ago when the presence in urine of two distinct oestrin-producing substances was clear to us, we were considerably puzzled over the relationship between them. The suggestion was tentatively advanced (Marrian, 1930) that the substance $C_{18}H_{22}O_2$ on treatment with hot alkali took up the elements of water to form $C_{18}H_{24}O_3$. This supposition was afterwards shown to be incorrect (Butenandt, 1930), since the former substance proved to be unchanged by such treatment. At the same time it was shown that both substances occur together in urine, and that by distillation in a high vacuum with potassium bisulphate, $C_{18}H_{24}O_3$ could be converted into $C_{18}H_{22}O_2$. Prof. Doisy has made no adequate reference to this work, and has advanced the earlier view, which has been shown to be untenable.

(**128**, 305; 1931)

G. F. Marrian and A. Butenandt: London and Göttingen, July 23.

# 催情激素

盖伊·弗雷德里克·马里安，阿道夫·布特南特

## 编者按

在20世纪30年代，科学家们不仅从事于维生素的鉴定，也进行激素的鉴定。它们是生命活动必需的基本化学物质，激素能由动物体自身合成，而维生素则必须通过食物供给。本文描述了一种诱导动物发情的激素的分离。作者阿道夫·布特南特是德国当时最受人尊敬的化学家之一，他曾于1939年获得了诺贝尔化学奖。催情激素及其类似物是计划生育药物的常规成分。

最近，多伊西及其同事（1931年）报道说他们从孕妇尿液中分离出一种具有催情活性的结晶性物质，该物质不同于他们之前提到的活性物质雌酮。之前提到的物质的化学式被他们定为$C_{18}H_{21}(OH)_2$，这种物质随后被我们中的一位作者（布特南特，1929年）[1]和帝格曼斯及其同事[2]（1930年）相继分离。后来发现（布特南特，1930年）该物质的化学式应为$C_{18}H_{22}O_2$，它的化学行为类似于羟基酮或双羟基醇。

毫无疑问，被多伊西及其同事[3]分离出来并将分子式定为$C_{18}H_{21}(OH)_3$的第二种物质与之前我们中的一位作者曾完整描述过的物质完全相同（马里安，1930年）[4]。尽管多伊西教授参考了早先分离出来的三醇，但是在其文章中没有提示它是一种化学式为$C_{18}H_{21}(OH)_3$的三羟基物质。他认为我们中的一位作者所描述的物质是两种活性物质的混合物，这一论点显然仅仅是基于两者**未经过校正**的熔点的差异。而明显证明这种观点站不住脚的分析数据却被其忽略了。

一年之前我们就已经知道尿中存在两种不同的催情物质，但对于它们之间的关系则非常困惑。有人提出假设（马里安，1930年）认为经过热碱处理的$C_{18}H_{22}O_2$因夺取水分子而形成了$C_{18}H_{24}O_3$。这个假设后来被证明是错误的（布特南特，1930年），因为已证明前者在经过这种处理后不会发生改变。另一方面，研究显示这两种物质在尿中是同时存在的，而且当在高度真空的条件下与硫酸氢钾一起蒸馏时，$C_{18}H_{24}O_3$能转变成$C_{18}H_{22}O_2$。多伊西教授并没有充分地参考这些工作，而是进一步推进其早期提出的、业已证明是站不住脚的观点。

（毛晨晖 翻译；田伟生 审稿）

References:

1 Butenandt, *Naturwiss.*, 17, 879 (1929). *Deutsch. Med. Woch.*, **55**, 2171 (1929). *Zeit. für physiol. Chem.*, **191**, 140 (1930). *Abh. d. Ges. d. Wissensch. zu Gottingen* (1931). *Math. phys.* Kl. iii. Folge, Heft 2.

2 Dingemanse *et al.*, *Deutsch. Med. Woch.*, **56**, 301 (1930).

3 Doisy *et al.*, *Proc. Soc. Exp. Biol. Med.*, **28**, 88 (1930). *J. Biol. Chem.*, **91**, 641, 647, 653, 655 (1931).

4 Marrian, *Chem. and Ind.* (June 20, 1930). *Biochem. Jour.*, **24**, 1021 (1930).

# Quantum-Mechanical Models of a Nucleus

R. H. Fowler

## Editor's Note

**By the 1930s, physicists believed they had a fair understanding of the structure of the atomic nucleus. Its mass was considered to be due to the number of protons it contained, while some of their charge was thought to be offset by the presence of negatively charged electrons involved in $\beta$-decay. But even so, it was not clear how so many protons, repelling one another, could be stably packed into so small a space. Here physicist Ralph Fowler suggests an explanation for the stability of nuclei which relies on the observation that radioactive atoms may emit $\alpha$-particles. The real explanation invokes another nuclear particle, the neutron, not discovered until 1932.**

IN their recent paper,[1] Lord Rutherford and Dr. Ellis have shown how the numerous $\gamma$-rays of radium C' can be arranged in a simple and orderly manner, which suggests, as they point out, that the multiplicity of the $\gamma$-rays is largely due to the excitation of several $\alpha$-particles into the same excited level rather than to the excitation of one $\alpha$-particle into several excited levels. Their arrangement of the lines of radium C' is probably not a unique scheme of this sort, but any reasonable scheme appears likely (they show) to present the same general features.

It seems desirable therefore to investigate theoretically in detail any simple model or models of a nucleus consisting of some fifty $\alpha$-particles, which might show such general features. The main feature brought out by Rutherford and Ellis is that the $\gamma$-rays can be expressed in the form

$$hv = pE_0 - qE_1,$$

where $p$ is an integer running from 1 to 4 and $q$ an integer running from 0 up to perhaps 10; the value of $E_1$ is about $\frac{1}{16}E_0$ for radium C' and has much the same value for radium B. For radium C' more than one value of $E_0$ may be required.

There are two models which might be investigated with some chance of success; the first is a model in which each $\alpha$-particle is considered to move independently in a central field (which is ultimately to be referred to the combined interactions with the other $\alpha$-particles), but the whole family is affected by perturbing interactions of the form $V(r_{ij})$, between each pair $i, j$ of all the $\alpha$-particles, where $r_{ij}$ is the distance between the $\alpha$-particles $i$ and $j$. Such a model is very like an atom of electrons, except that wave functions have to be symmetrical in the $\alpha$-particles instead of antisymmetrical in the electrons, and this is the

# 原子核的量子力学模型

拉尔夫·福勒

## 编者按

到 20 世纪 30 年代时，物理学家们认为他们已经对原子核的结构非常了解了：原子核的质量由所包含的质子数决定，而质子的一部分电荷被 $\beta$ 衰变中带负电的电子所中和。但是，即使这样，仍然不知道这么多相互排斥的质子怎样才能稳定地排布在一个非常狭小的空间中。在本文中，物理学家拉尔夫·福勒提出了一个能够解释这种稳定性的理论，该理论基于放射性原子会放出 $\alpha$ 粒子的实验证据。当然，正确的解释需要涉及另一种核粒子，即直到 1932 年才发现的中子。

卢瑟福勋爵和埃利斯博士在他们最近发表的文章[1]中指出，大量镭 C' 同位素放射出的 $\gamma$ 射线可以用一种简单而有序的方法进行归纳，他们指出，$\gamma$ 射线的多样性主要是由多个 $\alpha$ 粒子被激发到同一个激发态上，而不是由同一个 $\alpha$ 粒子被激发到多个激发态上造成的。他们对由镭 C' 放射出的 $\gamma$ 射线进行归纳的方法也许并不是唯一可行的，但是任何适用的方法可能都会呈现出相同的特征。

这样，我们就迫切地需要建立具有这种特征的模型并对模型进行细致的理论研究，这个模型可以是一个只有简单相互作用的模型，也可以是包含了大约 50 个 $\alpha$ 粒子的原子核模型。卢瑟福和埃利斯得出的关于 $\gamma$ 射线的最主要的特征可以用以下的形式来表示：

$$hv = pE_0 - qE_1,$$

$p$ 是一个取值从 1 到 4 的整数，而 $q$ 是一个从 0 开始的整数，最大可能只能取到 10；在镭 C' 同位素的衰变实验中，$E_1$ 的取值大约是 $E_0$ 取值的 1/16，与镭 B 同位素衰变实验中相应的 $E_1$ 值大致相当。对于镭 C' 同位素来说，我们需要选取不同的 $E_0$ 值。

我们可以研究以下两个可能成功解释原子核稳定性的模型。第一个模型认为每个 $\alpha$ 粒子都可以在中心势场中独立运动（这个中心势场指的是与其他 $\alpha$ 粒子之间的复杂相互作用），而整个原子核又受到形式为 $V(r_{ij})$ 的微扰势场的影响，其中 $V(r_{ij})$ 是每对粒子中第 $i$ 个 $\alpha$ 粒子和第 $j$ 个 $\alpha$ 粒子之间的相互作用，其中 $r_{ij}$ 是第 $i$ 个 $\alpha$ 粒子和第 $j$ 个 $\alpha$ 粒子之间的距离。这样的模型与包含电子的原子模型非常类似，不同的是 $\alpha$ 粒子的波函数是对称的，而不像电子的波函数那样是反对称的。这种本质上的

essential difference which allows of the states of reduplicated excitation, which do not occur at all in atoms. This model can be still further simplified from a three-dimensional to a one-dimensional form for a first discussion.

The second model is one in which each pair $i, j$ of $\alpha$-particles act on one another with a potential energy $\frac{1}{2}\lambda r_{ij}^2$. This model is obviously a rather poor physical approximation to the type of force, but it has the advantage that it can be studied exactly and not merely by the approximations of a perturbation method. A discussion of both these models has been begun, but has as yet only been carried through for the first model simplified to one dimension.

Confining attention only to the most general features, likely to be true of any suitable similar model, the following results have been obtained, which are to a large extent in excellent accord with the scheme of Rutherford and Ellis, but also seem to indicate clearly that a rather more elaborate scheme should be adopted. The energy levels of the model which arise from excitation of more than one $\alpha$-particle into a single excited state are of such a configuration that the corresponding $\gamma$-rays (if they could all be emitted) would be approximately of the frequencies

$$hv = p(E_0 - qE_1)$$

These frequencies agree with those of the proposed scheme of Rutherford and Ellis if the scheme is only very slightly modified, so that in place of the proposed single set of $\gamma$-rays of frequencies $2E_0 - qE_1$, we have the double set of frequencies $2(E_0 - qE_1)$ and $2(E_0' - qE_1)$ with $E_0$ and $E_0'$ nearly equal, and in place of the single set $3E_0 - qE_1$, the triple set $3(E_0 - qE_1)$, $3(E_0' - qE_1)$ , $3(E_0'' - qE_1)$ and so on. It is, moreover, clear that the reduplication of the upper levels is to be expected when we consider the three-dimensional version of the model. Further, the theory suggests that the ratio $E_0/E_1$ should be numerically somewhat less than $\frac{1}{2}n (= 26)$ in not too bad conformity with the observed value 16 for radium C'. The theory even suggests further that both $E_0$ and $E_1$, or perhaps rather $E_1$, will not vary very much between one radioactive nucleus and another. It is true that the observed values of $E_1$ (but not those of $E_0$) are much the same for radium C' and radium B. The $\gamma$-rays of other atoms have not yet been analysed in this way.

All these features are general and the conformity very reassuring. One can, however, further estimate the relative frequency of the emission of the various $\gamma$-rays corresponding to the transitions from a state of $q$-excited $\alpha$-particles to states of $q-1$, $q-2$, $q-3$... excited $\alpha$-particles. With an interaction energy of the proposed form, the transitions $q \to q-3$ should be absent, or at most very rare, and the transitions $q \to q-4$, $q \to q-5$, etc., entirely absent. The theory gives as a first approximation to $R$, the ratio of the frequency of occurrence of the transitions $q \to q-2$ and $q \to q-1$, the value

$$R\left(\frac{q \to q-2}{q \to q-1}\right) = \frac{q-1}{6.5}f$$

区别允许原子核中的粒子发生重复激发，而原子中的电子是不可能出现重复激发的情况的。在初步的讨论中，我们可以把三维情况进一步简化到一维情况。

第二个模型假设每对标记为 $i$，$j$ 的 $\alpha$ 粒子对对彼此有势能为 $\frac{1}{2}\lambda r_{ij}^2$ 的相互作用。很明显，这个模型对作用力所做的近似是一个非常不好的物理近似，但是这个近似的优点在于我们可以对其进行严格的计算而不只是用微扰理论来进行近似研究。关于以上这两个模型的研究已经开始，但到目前为止只完成了被简化到一维情况下的第一个模型。

就像任何类似的合理模型那样，我们只把注意力集中到最普遍的特征上面来，并得到了以下的结果，这些结果在很大程度上和卢瑟福、埃利斯的构想十分吻合，但是似乎也明确说明我们需要建立一个更加精细的模型。模型中由多个 $\alpha$ 粒子跃迁到同一个激发态上所产生的能级具有这样的形式，即相应的 $\gamma$ 射线（如果所有 $\gamma$ 射线都被能放射出来）的频率大致为：

$$hv = p(E_0 - qE_1)$$

如果将卢瑟福与埃利斯的构想稍加修正，由此得出的射线频率将和上式中的射线频率吻合得很好。因此我们用频率关系对应于 $2(E_0 - qE_1)$ 和 $2(E_0' - qE_1)$ 的两组 $\gamma$ 射线代替以前提出的频率关系对应于 $2E_0 - qE_1$ 的单组 $\gamma$ 射线，其中，$E_0$ 和 $E_0'$ 几乎相等。我们还用频率关系对应于 $3(E_0 - qE_1)$、$3(E_0' - qE_1)$ 和 $3(E_0'' - qE_1)$ 的三组 $\gamma$ 射线来代替频率关系对应于 $3E_0 - qE_1$ 的单组 $\gamma$ 射线，由此类推。此外，很明显地，当我们考虑三维情况下的该模型时，将会出现高能级的简并情况。并且，理论表明，比值 $E_0/E_1$ 在数值上应该略小于 $\frac{1}{2}n(= 26)$，与我们在镭 C' 同位素中观察到的 $E_0/E_1$ 值 16 相差得还不算太大。理论上还表明，不同的放射性原子核的 $E_0$ 和 $E_1$ 值（尤其是 $E_1$ 的值）不会相差太多。在镭的 C' 和 B 同位素的观测结果中，$E_1$ 的观测值的确相近，但是 $E_0$ 的值却并非如此。而其他原子核放射出的 $\gamma$ 射线还没有用这种方法分析过。

所有这些特性都是很普遍的，并且我们得到的一致性结果也很有说服力。然而我们还可以进一步估算各种不同的 $\gamma$ 射线的相对放射频率，这些不同的放射频率对应 $\alpha$ 粒子从 $q$ 激发态到 $q-1$，$q-2$，$q-3$ 激发态的跃迁。按照前面所提到的相互作用能量的表达形式，$q \to q-3$ 的跃迁过程应该不存在，即使存在也是非常罕见的，而 $q \to q-4$，$q \to q-5$ 等情况的跃迁过程也都不存在。理论上给出了 $q \to q-2$ 和 $q \to q-1$ 这两个跃迁发生几率的之比 $R$ 的第一级近似形式：

$$R\left(\frac{q \to q-2}{q \to q-1}\right) = \frac{q-1}{6.5}f$$

where $f$ is a factor certainly less than unity and probably not so small as 1/10. The absolute value of the ratio $R$ may be heavily affected by higher order terms, and we need not be concerned if the proposed scheme does not conform closely. The feature of $R$ that is almost certainly of general importance is that $R$ increases with $q$. This feature ought to be carefully borne in mind in the construction of any amended scheme. It is not yet possible to say whether these features can be incorporated in an otherwise satisfactory scheme, and a detailed re-examination must be undertaken.

The proposed scheme for radium C' is arranged to include values of $p$ up to 4 and therefore transitions of the type $q \rightarrow q-4$. These certainly do not, and the transitions $q \rightarrow q-3$ probably do not, fit into the allowed transitions of the proposed model with the simple interactions proposed. But such transitions can be present if there are terms in the interactions depending essentially on the co-ordinates of three or more particles, not reducible to sums of terms depending on the co-ordinates of only two. Such terms are to be expected in such a close configuration, though one would scarcely expect their effect to be so large. If the proposed scheme proves ultimately to be correct, one may hope to work back from the $\gamma$-ray intensities to some knowledge of the magnitude of these triple and higher interactions.

To sum up, one may say that the scheme proposed by Rutherford and Ellis, so far as it has yet been closely analysed, *that is for frequencies only*, seems likely with trivial modifications to conform completely to the requirements of a simple quantum mechanical model so far as these requirements can yet be foreseen. Such a model, however, will make fairly stringent demands on intensity ratios, and as yet no scheme has been proposed and tested with these in mind. One may hope that further work on these lines will prove fruitful.

While these models may well be able to explain the complicated spectrum of radium C', it is well to remember that the corresponding spectrum of thorium C' is very much simpler and contains no families of $\gamma$-rays—except perhaps very faint ones—corresponding to those of radium C', which have been interpreted in the scheme as transitions $q \rightarrow q-2$, $q \rightarrow q-3$, and $q \rightarrow q-4$. It has of course, in addition, a very strong isolated $\gamma$-ray of very high frequency. If therefore in attempting to proceed with this analysis, which in any event I believe to be important, one is forced finally to conclude that such models will *not* explain the facts for radium C', there is no call for surprise or disappointment. It may still be that the proposed scheme of $q \rightarrow q-1$ transitions will account properly for the important *common* features of the $\gamma$-ray spectra of radium B, radium C', thorium C', and probably other nuclei. It is more than likely that the striking *differences* between the spectra of radium C' and thorium C' should be associated with the two extra free protons in radium C', the atomic weight of which is of the form $4n+2$, while that of thorium C', is $4n$.

In the models suggested above, the effect of the protons has been ignored primarily because there seems at present no simple way of incorporating them. But it is clear that the general effect of free protons present in normal and excited states will be to cause

式中的 $f$ 因子一定小于单位 1，但可能不太会小于 1/10。高阶项对比值 $R$ 的绝对值有很大的影响，所以如果上面提到的构想中相应的 $R$ 值与实验结果不能严格一致时，我们也不必太在意。$R$ 的一个具有普遍重要性的特征是，它随着 $q$ 的增大而增大。在对任何有效模型进行修正的时候，我们都必须记住 $R$ 的这个特征。以上提到的所有特征到现在为止还不能确定是否可以整合到另一个令人满意的模型当中去，必须经过仔细地反复验证。

以上提出的关于镭 C' 同位素的构想中，$p$ 的取值可以从 1 到 4，因此，构想中包含了 $q \to q-4$ 的跃迁。在前面提到的简单相互作用模型中 $q \to q-4$ 的跃迁肯定是被禁止的，而 $q \to q-3$ 的跃迁有可能被禁止。但是，如果相互作用项是由三个或者三个以上粒子的坐标所决定的，而且不能化简成只由两个粒子的坐标所决定的两体相互作用项的总和时，上面所说的 $q \to q-3$、$q \to q-4$ 的跃迁就可能发生了。以上所讨论的相互作用项在形式上都很相近，我们想象不到这些相互作用项的影响会如此之大。如果上面提出的考虑三个粒子相互作用的构想最终被证明是正确的，那么我们也许可以回过头来，从 $\gamma$ 射线的强度出发来获知这些三重或者多重相互作用的大小。

总之，我们可以认为卢瑟福和埃利斯所提出的构想到现在为止已经被仔细地分析过了，**这是只从频率的角度进行研究的**，从这方面看，这一构想似乎经过细微的修正就可以完全符合可以预见的简单量子力学模型的要求。然而，这样的一个模型对强度比的要求非常严格，就我所知目前还没有人提出这方面的有关方案和检测方法。我们希望今后在这方面的研究工作能富有成效。

虽然这些模型也许可以很好地解释镭 C' 的复杂谱线，但不要忘记，钍 C' 的对应谱线要简单得多，而且不包括镭 C' 谱线中那些由 $q \to q-2$、$q \to q-3$、$q \to q-4$ 跃迁所产生的 $\gamma$ 射线族——除了几条非常微弱谱线以外。当然，钍 C' 的相应谱线中还包含了另外一条非常强的独立的高频 $\gamma$ 射线。如果我们试图对以上现象继续进行分析（我认为这个分析无疑重要的），我们最终不得不得出这样的结论，适用于钍 C' 的模型将**无法**用来解释镭 C' 的实验事实，对于这个结果，我们大可不必感到惊讶或失望。上面提到的 $q \to q-1$ 的跃迁方案，仍然可以很好地解释镭 B、镭 C'、钍 C'（可能还有其他的放射性原子核）衰变放射出的 $\gamma$ 射线谱中**共有**的重要特征。更有可能发生的情况是，镭 C' 和钍 C' 谱线中惊人的**差异**应该与镭 C' 比钍 C' 多出两个自由质子有关。镭 C' 的原子量是 $4n+2$，而钍 C' 的原子量是 $4n$。

在上面所提出的模型中，质子的效应从一开始就被忽略了，因为目前似乎还没有将质子效应整合到模型中的简单方法。但是可以明确的是，在正常态和激发态，

the set of low frequency transitions $q \rightarrow q-1$ to be repeated again at higher frequencies but with the same dependence on $q$, the constant shift between the two sets representing an excitation energy for a proton.

(**128**, 453-454; 1931)

R. H. Fowler: Cromwell House, Trumpington, Cambridge, Aug. 14.

---

Reference:

1 *Proc. Roy. Soc.*, A, **132**, 667 (1931).

由自由质子所引发的普遍效应会使低频跃迁 $q \rightarrow q-1$ 在高频情况下重复发生，但是高频情况下的跃迁同样依赖于 $q$，两种情况下的常数变化代表了一个质子的激发能。

（王静 翻译；李军刚 审稿）

# The Angular Momentum of Light

C. V. Raman

## Editor's Note

**Arthur Compton's pioneering work on the scattering of light by electrons showed how the process could be understood in quantum terms as a collision conserving energy and momentum. As Raman argues here, the scattering of light from molecules is considerably more complicated, since the photon may excite molecular internal degrees of freedom such as rotations or vibrations. If the intrinsic angular momentum of a photon may only take certain discrete values, this would account for a known "selection rule" governing the permitted changes in molecular angular momentum during light scattering. It also implies that any change in molecular angular momentum must be accompanied by a reversal of the circular polarisation of the photon, as confirmed by recent experiments in Calcutta.**

THE work of Compton on X-ray scattering led to the general acceptance of the idea that the scattering of radiation by a material particle is a unitary process in which energy and linear momentum are conserved. A molecule is, however, a much more complicated structure than an electron, and the conservation principles by themselves would give us an erroneous idea of what we should expect in light-scattering. This follows from the fact that a molecule has in general three degrees of freedom of rotation, several degrees of freedom of vibration according to its complexity, and various possible modes of electronic excitation, and that each of these may correspond to one or other of an extended series of quantum numbers. Restricting ourselves to the cases in which the molecule takes up a part of the energy of the quantum, the conservation principles would indicate that the spectrum of the scattered light should contain an immense number of new lines.

Actually, a remarkable simplicity characterises the observed spectra of the light scattered by polyatomic molecules, a simplicity which is in striking contrast with the complexity of their absorption and emission spectra. It is clear that the Compton principles cannot be regarded as capable of *predicting* the observed phenomena of light-scattering, and that their utility lies solely in the *interpretation* of results discovered by experiment. These remarks seem necessary to correct an impression to the contrary which finds expression in some recent publications.

We may extend Compton's principle and add angular momentum to the quantities which we should expect to find conserved in the collision between a light-quantum and a molecule. The fact that, in liquids and solids, the mutual influence of the material particles is very considerable, attaches some uncertainty to the interpretation of the results obtained with them. The recent success of Bhagavantam at Calcutta in measuring the

# 光的角动量

钱德拉塞卡拉·文卡塔·拉曼

## 编者按

阿瑟·康普顿在研究电子对光的散射时发现这个过程可以用量子力学中保持能量和动量守恒的碰撞理论来解释。就像拉曼在这里指出的那样，分子对光的散射更加复杂，因为光子可以激发分子内部的自由度，如旋转或者振动。如果一个光子的内禀角动量只能取某些不连续的值，那么这就解释了为什么普遍认可的“选择定则”能够支配分子角动量在光散射过程中可能出现的变化。最近在加尔各答的实验证明：分子角动量的任何变化都将伴随着光子圆偏振的反转。

康普顿关于 X 射线散射的研究使人们普遍地接受了以下观点，即物质粒子对辐射的散射是一种维持能量和线性动量守恒的幺正过程。然而，一个分子的结构比一个电子的结构要复杂得多，而守恒定理本身使我们在预测光散射的结果时会出现错误。这是因为一个分子通常具有三个转动自由度、几个振动自由度（数量与它的复杂程度有关）以及多种电子激发的可能模式，每一种模式都可能对应于一个或另一个来自扩展系列的量子数。如果我们局限于认为分子占据量子能量的一部分，那么根据守恒原理，散射光的谱就应该包含数量巨大的新线。

实际上我们所观察到的多原子分子散射光的谱非常简单，要比它们的吸收谱和发射谱简单很多。显然，康普顿原理不能**预言**观察到的光散射现象，它们只能用于**解释**由实验得到的结果。上述意见对于修正最近一些刊物中出现的相反看法是很有必要的。

我们可以拓展康普顿原理，并把角动量加入到我们认为在光量子与分子发生碰撞时应该保持守恒的量当中。在液体和固体中，物质粒子之间的相互影响相当可观，因而对散射结果的解释会带有某种不确定性。巴加万塔姆最近在加尔各答成功地测量了光被气体散射时的偏振性和强度，该成果为这项课题的研究开辟了新的可能性。

polarisation and intensity of light scattered by gases, however, opens up new possibilities for the development of the subject.

As a working hypothesis, we may follow Dirac and assume that the angular momentum of a photon is *plus* or *minus* $h/2\pi$, intermediate values being inadmissible. This supposition enables us to interpret very simply the known selection rule $\Delta m = 0$ or $\pm 2$ for the change of rotational quantum number of a diatomic molecule in light-scattering, which follows as a natural consequence of it. Further, it follows[1] that a change in rotational quantum number of the molecule should be accompanied by a reversal in the sign of circular polarisation of the photon, when the latter is scattered in the forward direction. This reversal has been actually observed by Bär and by Bhagavantam with the rotational wings accompanying the original mercury lines scattered in liquids, and the data obtained by Bhagavantam with hydrogen gas may also be interpreted as a confirmation of the same result.

It is remarkable that the latter result is also predicted by the classical electromagnetic theory of light for the case of a rotating anisotropic particle scattering circularly polarised radiation. Nevertheless, it is clear that the observed phenomena may be regarded as an experimental proof that radiation has angular momentum associated with it, and that it has the values $\pm h/2\pi$ for each quantum.

(**128**, 545; 1931)

C. V. Raman: 210 Bowbazar Street, Calcutta, Aug. 15.

---

Reference:

1 *Nature*, **128**, 114 (July 18, 1931).

在对这一假设进行推导时，我们可以根据狄拉克的理论假定一个光子的角动量为 $\pm h/2\pi$，中间值的存在是不允许的。这个假定能使我们很简单地解释为什么双原子分子在光散射中转动量子数的改变要遵循选择定则 $\Delta m = 0$ 或 $\pm 2$，这样选择定则的出现就成为了一个自然而然的结果。此外我们还发现 [1]：当光子向前散射时，分子转动量子数的变化应伴随着光子圆偏振符号的反向。巴尔和巴加万塔姆用伴随在液体中散射的原来汞线的旋转两翼观测到了这一反向现象，巴加万塔姆用氢气得到的数据也可以用来证明同样的结论。

值得注意的是，后一个结果也可以在旋转的各向异性并具有圆偏振散射线的粒子的情况下由光的经典电磁理论推导出来。显然观测到的现象也可以作为辐射具有相关角动量的实验证据，而每个量子所具有的角动量大小为 $\pm h/2\pi$。

（沈乃澂 翻译；张泽渤 审稿）

# Isolated Quantised Magnetic Poles

O. W. Richardson

## Editor's Note

**There were, in classical physics, no "magnetic charges"—no isolated magnetic poles without their complementary pole. But Paul Dirac suggested that quantum theory might allow the existence of such "monopoles", and here distinguished British physicist Owen Willans Richardson speculates on what their existence might entail for physics. While science focused on atoms made of electrically charged particles, a similar hierarchy of magnetic atoms might exist. Richardson argues that their properties would be unusual; in particular, the frequencies of their spectral lines would be some $10^{10}$ higher than for "ordinary" matter. Dirac had speculated that the forces between magnetic monopoles would prevent their separation in ordinary circumstances, but Richardson suggests this might happen for cosmic rays of extremely high energy.**

IN the last number of the *Proceedings of the Royal Society*, Dirac has come to the conclusion that the quantum theory requires the existence of discrete magnetic poles of a strength equal to 137÷2 times the electronic charge. If such objects were common one might expect the universe to be a good deal different from what experimenters have found it to be, so far.

There seems no a priori reason why the whole theory of atom building which has been built up for electrons and nuclei—an electrostatic problem apart from details—should not be carried over bodily into the corresponding magneto-static problem of the attractions of the oppositely charged poles. In this way we might, at first, expect to get a set of "magnetic" atoms, similar to the electric atoms of which matter is generally supposed to be built up. These atoms would be a good deal different from those we think we are familiar with. How much different depends to some extent on what the mass of a magnetic pole is. The quantum theory does not tell this, but I think its value, if it exists, can be fixed by an argument based on classical ideas at about 500 times that of the corresponding electronic object. Following this general line of argument, the dimensions of these magnetic atoms come out at $10^{-14}$ cm. to $10^{-15}$ cm. compared with $10^{-7}$ cm. to $10^{-8}$ cm. for the atoms of the periodic table. The frequencies of the "spectral" lines emitted by these magnetically constructed atoms would run about $10^{10}$ times those of the corresponding lines of the electronic spectra; for example, the first line of the Lyman series would be raised from $v=2.5\times10^{15}$ to $v=3.1\times10^{25}$ sec.$^{-1}$ if the corresponding states are capable of existence. Even if quite large changes are made in the mass of the magnetic poles, which is the doubtful element, the corresponding numbers will still remain quite wide apart.

Dirac has suggested that the reason these magnetic poles have not been observed may be that the forces between them are so much larger than those between electrons and protons

# 孤立的量子化磁极

欧文·威兰斯·里查孙

## 编者按

在经典物理学中不存在“磁荷”这个概念——没有相反磁极的孤立磁极是不存在的。但保罗·狄拉克提出量子理论也许能允许这样的“磁单极”存在。在本文中，英国著名物理学家欧文·威兰斯·里查孙认为对于物理学来说磁单极的存在也许是必然的。既然科学主要研究由带电的粒子组成的原子，就应该有相应的带磁性的一类原子存在。里查孙指出它们的性质很不一般；尤其是它们的谱线频率是“普通”物质的 $10^{10}$ 倍。狄拉克推测磁单极之间的强大作用力使它们在通常环境下无法分离，但里查孙认为在高能宇宙射线中这种现象就有可能会发生。

在最近一期的《皇家学会会刊》中，狄拉克已得出结论，量子理论要求存在强度相当于 137 ÷ 2 倍的电子电荷的单个磁极。假如这样的物质是普遍存在的，那么我们可以预期现实的宇宙与目前实验者们眼中的宇宙会有很大的不同。

似乎没有理由不能把建立在电子和原子核之上的一整套原子理论——除细节外基本属于静电问题——应用到以相反磁荷相互吸引为基础的相应的静磁问题上。按照这种方式，我们首先可以预期得到一组与带电原子类似的“磁”的原子，通常我们认为物质是由带电原子构成的。磁的原子与我们原有概念中所熟知的原子有很大的差别。差别的大小在某种程度上取决于磁极的质量。量子理论并未说明相应的具体数值，但我认为如果这个值存在，用经典方法论证则应该约为相应带电物的 500 倍。按照这个思路推算，这些磁的原子的尺度达到 $10^{-14}$ cm 至 $10^{-15}$ cm，而元素周期表中的原子尺度为 $10^{-7}$ cm 至 $10^{-8}$ cm。由这些磁性结构原子发射的“谱”线频率约为带电原子谱线相应频率的 $10^{10}$ 倍；例如，假如以上磁性结构的原子是存在的，赖曼线系中的第一条线的频率将从 $v = 2.5 \times 10^{15}\ s^{-1}$ 增加至 $v = 3.1 \times 10^{25}\ s^{-1}$。即使对数值不确定的磁极质量作很大的调整，所得的结果仍与带电原子的情况相差很大。

狄拉克指出，这些磁极尚未被观测到的原因可能是因为它们之间的力远大于电子和质子之间的力，从而使它们不能分离。我们有理由相信它们不可能接近到上述

that they cannot be separated. There is reason for believing they could not get together to the extent indicated by the preceding numbers. The number of kinds of atoms with azimuthal quantum number 1 which can be formed from these magnetic units is much less than unity. This follows from Dirac's formula for the spectral terms for hydrogen, or alternatively, from the principle of minimum time. This may be forcing the required atoms too much into the pattern of those with which we are familiar. In any event, no atom with azimuthal quantum number less than $34\frac{1}{4}$ can be made out of these elements. Otherwise the time factors in the wave functions involve real exponentials and become infinite with lapse of time. However, even with such high quantum numbers the forces would still be enormous compared with those in corresponding electronic structures and the frequencies would still be quite high.

There may be an application of these products of the quantum theory in the field of "ultra-penetrating" radiations. I have no first-hand knowledge of the process of creation, but I should suspect it would be relatively difficult to create objects with the intrinsic energy of these magnetic poles. It seems likely, therefore, that their abundance would be very small compared with that of electrons and protons, but there might be enough in the universe to account for such ultra-penetrating radiations as are not capable of being accounted for otherwise. The possible existence of such isolated magnetic poles, with properties so very different from those of electrons and protons, obviously changes the basis for discussion of a good many cosmological questions.

(**128**, 582; 1931)

O. W. Richardson: King's College, London, W.C.2, Sept. 18.

数字表示的程度。这些磁单元形成的角量子数为 1 的原子种类数远小于 1。这是根据与氢光谱项有关的狄拉克公式或者根据最小时间原理得出的。这也许是在迫使磁的原子过于符合我们所熟悉的模式。在任何情况下，磁的原子都不能构成角量子数小于 $34\frac{1}{4}$ 的原子。否则，波函数中的时间因子会含有实指数，并随时间的消逝而趋于无限大。然而，尽管有如此高的量子数，与相应的电子结构相比，磁单元之间的作用力仍然很大，频率也仍然很高。

这些量子理论的成果可能会在“超穿透”辐射领域中得到应用。我对孤立磁极的形成过程没有直接的了解，但我推测，产生这种具有磁极内能的物质是相当困难的。因此，地球上磁原子的数量似乎应该远小于电子和质子的数量，但在宇宙中磁原子的数量也许已经足以用来解释超穿透辐射这种不能用其他方法解释的现象。如果这类与电子和质子的性质差异很大的孤立磁极是存在的，那么将会使许多宇宙问题的研究思路发生明显的变化。

（沈乃澂 翻译；赵见高 审稿）

# The Biological Nature of the Viruses*

H. H. Dale

## Editor's Note

**As late as the 1930s, the properties of the viruses appeared to be a complete mystery. Although infectious diseases were an important public health problem at the time, it was clear that bacteria could explain some but not all of these infections. Common ailments such as smallpox and scarlet fever appeared to have no mechanism to account for their prevalence, but the concept of sub-microscopic entities responsible for disease was for many people a way of avoiding the problem. Sir Henry Dale was a pharmacologist and physiologist who began work as a scientist at the British drug manufacturer the Wellcome Foundation. In this talk to the British Association for the Advancement of Science, Dale firmly advocated the view that viruses were real entities and that understanding their nature should be one of the principal objectives of biological research.**

THE viruses are a group of agents, the existence of which would certainly be unknown to us but for the changes produced by their presence in the bodies of higher animals and plants. They seem to have one property at least of living organisms, in being capable, under appropriate conditions, of indefinite reproduction. We know nothing of their intrinsic metabolism: it has even been asserted that they have none. Few of them have yet been rendered visible by the microscope; it is, indeed, a question for our discussion whether any of them have yet been seen or photographed. It is a question, again, whether any of them, or all of them, consist of organised living units, cells of a size near to or beyond the lowest limits of microscopic visibility; or whether, as some hold, they are unorganised toxic or infective principles, which we can regard as living in a sense analogous to that in which we speak of a living enzyme, with the important addition that they can multiply themselves indefinitely. Some, however, would attribute this, not to actual self-multiplication, but to a coercion of the infected cells to reproduce the very agent of their own infection.

The problems presented by the nature and behaviour of the viruses cannot fail to raise questions of the greatest interest to anyone concerned with general physiological conceptions. What is the minimum degree of organisation which we can reasonably attribute to a living organism? What is the smallest space within which we can properly suppose such a minimum of organisation to be contained? Are organisation, differentiation, separation from the surrounding medium by a boundary membrane of special properties, necessary for the endowment of matter with any form of life? Or is it possible to conceive of a material complex, retaining in endless propagation its

---

* From the presidential address introducing a discussion on the subject in Section I (Physiology) of the British Association in London on Sept. 28.

# 病毒的生物学本质*

亨利·哈利特·戴尔

## 编者按

在20世纪30年代以前，病毒的本质还完全是一个未解之谜。虽然传染病在当时是一个重要的公共卫生问题，但细菌显然只是引起一部分传染病而非全部传染病的原因。人们无法解释像天花和猩红热这样的常见疾病是如何流行起来的，但对许多人来说，把亚显微物质看作是致病因素的想法可以作为回避上述问题的一种方法。亨利·戴尔爵士是一名药理学家和生理学家，他以科学家的身份在英国韦尔科姆基金会制药公司工作。在这篇对英国科学促进会的报告中，戴尔坚定地主张病毒是真实的实体，而且了解其本质应该是生物学研究的主要目标之一。

病毒是这样一群物质，要不是能够发现它们在高等动植物体内生存所造成的改变，我们必然无法知道它们的存在。病毒似乎至少具有生命的一种特征，那就是在合适的条件下能够无限繁殖。我们对它们的内部代谢一无所知：甚至有人声称它们根本就没有代谢。病毒在显微镜下几乎看不到；实际上，它们是否已经被看到或者被拍摄到仍是一个需要讨论的问题。另外，它们中的一部分或者全部是否具备有组织的生命单位，即大小接近或者低于显微可见的最小的细胞仍是一个疑问；或者正如某些人所说，它们只是无组织的毒性或者感染性物质，我们可以认为它们以一种类似于我们所说的有活性的酶的方式生存，并且还具有一个更重要的特征是它们能够无限繁殖。但是，有些人认为这不是真实的自我繁殖，而是强迫被感染的细胞产生它们自己的具有感染性的物质。

病毒的本质和行为这类难题向关注普通生理学概念的人们提出了非常有意思的挑战。我们能够合情合理地归为生命的最低组织化程度是什么？能够包含生物体最小组织的最小空间有多大？有组织、能分化以及通过一层特殊性质的界膜与周围基质分离是否是具有任何形式的生命体所必备的特征？或者是否可以设想它是一种物质复合体，保持了无穷尽地复制的生理特征，正如被感染细胞做出的高度特异性的反应一样，尽管它不是组织有序的单位，而是均匀地分散在了含水的介质中？对那

* 本文来自作者作为主席在英国科学促进会9月28日于伦敦举行的I分会（生理学分会）讨论中引入这一主题时所作的报告。

physiological character, as revealed by the closely specific reaction to it of the cells which it infects, though it is not organised into units, but uniformly dispersed in a watery medium? Among those who study the viruses primarily as pathogenic agents, these questions provide matter for debate; I suggest that they are questions with which the physiologist may properly be concerned.

I cannot deal with the history of the subject; but it is of interest to note that Edward Jenner was dealing, in small-pox and vaccinia, with what we now recognise as characteristic virus infections, long before there was any hint of the connexion of visible bacteria with disease. Pasteur himself was dealing with another typical case of a virus infection in the case of rabies. The clear recognition, however, of the existence of agents of infection, imperceptible with the highest powers of ordinary microscopic vision, and passing through filters fine enough to retain all visible bacteria, begins with Ivanovski's work in 1892 on the mosaic disease of the tobacco plant, brought to general notice and greatly developed by Beijerinck's work on the same infection some seven years later; and with Loffler and Frosch's demonstration, in the same period, that the infection of foot-and-mouth disease is similarly due to something microscopically invisible, and passing easily through ordinary bacteria-proof filters. Since those pioneer observations the study of viruses has spread, until they are recognised as the causative agents of diseases in an imposing and still growing list containing many of the more serious infections of man, animals, and plants.

If we are to discuss the biological nature of the viruses, it is obvious that we should begin by attempting some kind of definition. What do we mean by a virus? And what are the tests by which we decide that a particular agent of infection shall be admitted to, or excluded from, the group? But a few years ago I think that we should have had no difficulty in accepting three cardinal properties as characterising a virus, namely, invisibility by ordinary microscopic methods, failure to be retained by a filter fine enough to prevent the passage of all visible bacteria, and failure to propagate itself except in the presence of, and perhaps in the interior of, the cells which it infects. It will be noted that all three are negative characters, and that two of them are probably quantitative rather than qualitative.

Such a definition is not likely to effect a sharp or a stable demarcation. We shall see that its failure to do so is progressive. Nevertheless it would still be difficult to refuse the name of virus to an agent which fulfils all three criteria; and we must therefore, in consistency, apply it, on one hand, to the filtrable agents transmitting certain tumours, and, on the other hand, to the agents of transmissible lysis affecting bacteria, and now widely known and studied as bacteriophages. But the strict application of such a definition, based on negative characteristics, must obviously narrow its scope with the advance of technique. We may look a little more closely at the meaning of these different characters.

些把病毒作为主要致病因子来研究的人来说，这些问题是争论的焦点；我认为这些是生理学家更应该关注的问题。

我无法阐述有关这个话题的历史；但值得注意的是，早在有任何提示显示可见的细菌和疾病有什么联系之前，爱德华·詹纳在天花以及牛痘治疗中就研究过这个问题，这种病我们现在认识到是典型的病毒感染病。巴斯德研究的是另一个典型的病毒感染性疾病，即狂犬病。但是，真正清楚地认识到存在一种具有感染性的物质，这种物质即使用最高能力的普通显微镜也看不到，而它能够通过足以阻拦任何可见细菌的滤器，是在 1892 年伊万诺夫斯基研究烟草的花叶病之后。7 年以后贝杰林克对同一种疾病展开了研究，使这种认识得到了广泛的关注和极大的发展。同一时期，洛夫勒和弗罗施证明感染口蹄疫的原因也是某些显微镜下不可见并能轻易通过普通滤菌器的物体。自从有了这些开创性的观察结果，对病毒的研究逐渐流行，直到它们被确认为是人类和动植物多种极其严重的传染病的病因，并且列入的重大疾病还在不断增加。

很显然，如果我们要讨论病毒的生物学本质，首先应该尝试着给出某种定义。我们对病毒的定义是什么？我们通过什么检查方法能够确定一种特定的传染病原是或者不是病毒？但是数年以前，我想我们都已经毫无疑问地接受了病毒的三个基本性质，即普通显微镜下不可见；能够通过足以阻挡所有可见细菌的滤菌器；只有在受感染细胞存在的条件下才能繁殖，而且繁殖很可能是在细胞体内进行的。我们注意到所有这三条都是否定性的特征，而且其中两条很可能是可量化指标，而不是定性指标。

这样一个定义不可能给病毒划出一个清晰或者稳定的界限。我们将看到没有给出明确的界限是一种进步。然而，当某种物体满足了这三种特性后，我们仍然很难说清它不是病毒。因此，我们必须保持一致地将这个定义一方面应用到能够传播某些肿瘤且可穿过滤菌器的物体上，另一方面应用到能够传染性地裂解受感染细菌的物体，后者现在已经众所周知并被作为噬菌体研究。但是由于定义采用的都是否定性特征，想严格应用就必须利用技术的进步大大缩小其范围。我们应当更加细致地研究这几个特性的意义。

Microscopic visibility is obviously a loose term. Rayleigh's familiar formula, in which the lower limit of resolution is equal to one-half the wavelength of the light employed, divided by the numerical aperture of the objective, only gives us the smallest dimensions of an object, of which, with the method of transmitted illumination habitually used in former years, a critical image can be formed. There can be no doubt that the separate particles of practically all the agents to which the term virus would be applied fall below this limit of size. To put it in plain figures, their diameter is less than 0.2 micron. On the other hand, progress has recently been, and continues to be, rapid in the direction of bringing into the visible range minute bodies associated with a growing number of viruses. This has been effected, on one hand, by improvement in staining technique, which probably owes its success largely to increase of the natural size of the particles by a deposit of dye on their surface; and, on the other hand, by forming visible diffraction images of the unstained particles with wide-aperture dark-ground condensers, and by photographing the images formed of them with shorter invisible rays. Mr. Barnard has obtained such sharp photographic images of the bodies associated with one virus, measurements of which give their natural size by simple calculation.

The reaction of a cautious criticism to such a demonstration seems to have taken two different directions. There has been a tendency, on one hand, to exclude an agent from the group of viruses as soon as the microscope could demonstrate it with some certainty. Many have for years thus excluded the agent transmitting the pleuro-pneumonia of cattle, though the status of this organism has been compromised even more by the success of its cultivation on artificial media. Visibility seems to have rendered doubtful the position of the Rickettsia group of infections, and, if the test is logically applied, the process of exclusion can scarcely stop before the agents transmitting psittacosis, fowl-pox, infectious ectromelia, and even vaccinia and variola, have been removed from the group of viruses into that of visible organisms.

In discussing the biological nature of viruses as a whole, however, we can scarcely begin by accepting an artificial and shifting limitation of that kind. The real task before us, rather, is to discuss to what extent the evidence of these recent developments, which appear to show that some of the agents, known hitherto as viruses, consist of very minute organisms, can safely be applied to other viruses which are still beyond the range of resolution. Do these also consist of organisms still more minute, or are any of them unorganised? Another line of criticism, sound in itself, while not excluding from the virus group these agents for which microscopic visibility has been claimed, demands more evidence that the minute bodies seen or photographed are really the infective agent, and not merely products of a perverted metabolism which its presence engenders.

It is obvious that complete evidence of identity cannot be obtained until a virus has been artificially cultivated in an optically homogeneous medium. Meanwhile it is a question of the strength of a presumption, on which opinions may legitimately differ. Let us recognise that the evidence is not perfect, but beware of a merely sterilising scepticism. I suspect

显微镜下的可见性明显是一个不精确的界限。在瑞利的著名公式中，分辨率的下限等于使用的光波长的一半除以物镜的数值孔径。该公式仅仅给出了在使用前几年常用的透射照明显微镜时，能够形成临界图像所需的物体的最小尺寸。毫无疑问，实际上那些可以被称为病毒的单个粒子都在这个下限以下。用简单的数字表示就是，直径小于 0.2 微米。另一方面，最近关于将微小颗粒与数量不断增长的病毒相附着使其进入可见范围的研究已经取得了快速的进展，并且这些研究还在继续。这项研究的进展，一方面，受到染色技术进步的影响，其成功的原因很可能主要在于染料在颗粒表面沉积导致其自然尺寸变大；而另一方面，影响因素也包括通过大孔径暗视野聚光镜形成未染色颗粒的可视性衍射图像，并用更短的不可见射线拍摄下这些颗粒所形成的图像。巴纳德先生已经获得了与某个病毒相黏附的颗粒物质的清晰图像，经过测量和简单的计算可以得出病毒的自然尺寸。

针对这一论证似乎有两类不同的慎重批评。一方面，一些人倾向于将显微镜可以在某种程度上辨认出的物质从病毒种类中排除。这样，传播牛胸膜肺炎的病原就被排除了，尽管在人工基质上获得成功培养后使得这种生物更加偏离了病毒的定义。可见性似乎使得立克次氏体的定位仍存有疑问，而且如果合乎逻辑地运用此方法进行检验，排除的过程会一直继续，直到传播鹦鹉热、禽痘、传染性脱脚病、甚至牛痘和天花的病原都从病毒转移到可见生物群体中。

但是，要从整体上讨论病毒的生物学本质，我们不能从一开始就接受一个人为的还在变动的限制。最新的研究进展提供证据显示一些迄今为止被认为是病毒的物体都是由非常微小的有机组织组成，而我们真正面临的任务是要讨论这些证据到底在多大程度上能够可靠地应用到那些仍然在分辨率所及范围以外的病毒中。它们也是由更小的有机组织组成的吗？或者其中的某些是无组织的？另一个本身非常合理的批评虽然没有将这些显微镜下可见的物体排除出病毒的范畴，但要求要有更多的证据来支持这些所见的和所摄到的微小物体就是真正的传染病原，而不仅仅是由于病原的存在而造成的异常代谢所产生的代谢产物。

显然，我们不可能获得病毒的完整鉴别性证据，除非这种病毒在光学均一性培养基中可以人工培养。同时，这是一个假设程度的问题，在假设上存在不同的观点是合情合理的。我们要认识到证据并不完美，但是也要谨防打倒一切的怀疑论。我

that the attitude of some critics is coloured by past history of the search for viruses and especially by that part of it concerned with the curious objects known as "inclusion bodies", which are readily demonstrated with relatively low powers of the microscope, in the cells of animals and plants infected with certain viruses. From the earlier and admittedly hasty tendency to identify them as infective protozoa, opinion seems to have swung too quickly to the opposite extreme, of dismissing them as mere products of the infected cell. It is so comparatively simple, in some cases, to separate these bodies, that it is surprising that so few efforts have been made to test their infectivity. However, the power of such a body to convey at least one virus infection has been demonstrated; and since they have further been shown, in several cases, to consist of a structureless matrix packed with bodies looking like minute organisms, the burden of proof in other cases seems to me, for the moment, to rest on those who suggest that they consist wholly of material precipitated by the altered metabolism due to the infection.

The physical evidence, obtained by filtration through porous fabrics and colloidal membranes, and by measuring rates of diffusion, is, of course, purely concerned with the size of the units of infective material, and must be taken in conjunction with the evidence provided by the microscope. The crude qualitative distinction between the filterable and non-filterable agents of infection has long since ceased to have any real meaning. There is no natural limit of filterability. A filter can be made to stop or to pass particles of any required size. It is now realised that the only proper use of a filter in this connexion is to give a quantitative measure of the maximum size of the particles which pass it. Evidence from failure to pass must always be subject to correction for the effects of electrostatic attraction and fixation by adsorption on the fabric of the filter. A large amount of filtration evidence has, further, been vitiated by reliance on determinations of the *average* pore size of the filter. In dealing with an infective agent, the test for the presence of which depends on its propagation under suitable conditions, it is obviously the maximal pore size which is chiefly significant.

For these reasons a good deal of the evidence showing that certain viruses can be detected in the filtrates, obtained with filters which will not allow haemoglobin to pass in perceptible quantities, must be regarded at least with suspicion. Dr. Elford has recently succeeded in preparing filter-membranes of much greater uniformity, with a small range of pore-diameters. His measurements, with these, of the sizes of the particles of different viruses, show a range approaching the dimensions of the smallest recognised bacteria, on one hand, and falling as low, in the case of the virus of foot-and-mouth disease, as about three or four times the size of the haemoglobin molecule; the latter being given not only by filtration-data, but also by other physico-chemical measurements, such as those obtained by Svedberg with the ultracentrifuge. It should be noted, as illustrating the difficulties of the problem and the uncertain meaning of some of the data, that Elford has regularly found a bacteriophage to be stopped by a membrane which allows the foot-and-mouth virus to pass; while, on the other hand, recent determinations of the rate of diffusion of bacteriophage, made by Bronfenbrenner, put the diameter of its particles at 0.6 of a millimicron, that is, only about one-fifth of the accepted dimensions of the haemoglobin

猜想一些评论家的态度受到过去探索病毒的历史，尤其是与被称为“包涵体”的神奇物体有关的那部分历史的影响。“包涵体”是在受某些特定病毒感染后的动植物细胞内发现的，在分辨率相对较低的显微镜下就可以轻易观察到。最开始大家草率地倾向于把它们看作是传染性的原虫，但很快，观点转换到了另一个极端，即认为它们不是单纯的受感染细胞的产物。在一些试验中，分离这些包涵体是如此的容易，以致于很奇怪几乎没有人研究它们的感染性。但是，已经发现这样一种包涵体具有至少可以传播一种病毒感染的能力；在其他一些试验中，进一步发现它们是由无结构的基质包裹着一群看起来像是微小生物的物体。在我看来，现在从其他例子获得证据的重担似乎要落在那些认为它们完全是由感染造成的代谢异常而积聚的代谢废物的人身上。

用多孔织物和胶质膜进行过滤以及测量扩散速率获得的这些具体证据当然是完全与感染性物体组成单位的大小相关的，并且这需要和显微镜提供的证据相结合。这种对可滤过和不可滤过传染性物体的粗略定性区分早已经没有实际意义了，因为并不存在有关滤过性的自然分界线。我们能够制造出一种滤器用来阻拦或者放过任意大小的颗粒。人们现在认识到，在这种情况下滤器的最有用之处仅在于能定量测量通过它的颗粒的最大尺寸。当不能通过时，必须要修正静电吸引效应和吸附固着在滤器的织物上产生的效应。大量的滤过研究数据都因过于依赖计算滤器的**平均**孔径而失去意义。要检测某种在合适条件下能传播的传染性物体的存在，很明显具有重要意义的是最大孔径。

因为这些原因，大量的证据显示某些病毒能够在滤液中检测到，而所用的滤器在已知的范围内却不能滤过血红蛋白，这种试验结果至少应该值得怀疑。埃尔弗德博士最近成功地制备了均一性更好的滤膜，滤孔的直径变化范围很小。他用此滤膜测量了不同病毒颗粒的大小，结果显示：一方面最大的接近最小已知细菌的尺寸，而最小的病毒，如口蹄疫病毒，只有血红蛋白分子大小的 3 或 4 倍。后面的数据不仅是根据过滤试验得到的，也采用了其他的物理化学测量方法，比如斯韦德贝里提出的超速离心法。为了说明问题的难度以及一些数据的不确定意义，我们注意到埃尔弗德发现了一种能够被滤膜阻挡的噬菌体，而这种滤膜允许口蹄疫病毒通过；而在另一方面，布朗芬布伦纳最近确定了噬菌体的扩散速率，通过速率计算将噬菌体颗粒的直径锁定在 0.6 个毫微米，即大约一个血红蛋白分子大小的 1/5。如果接受了这种估计，得出的结论必须是，噬菌体不仅是无结构的，而且其分子比高分子蛋白质

molecule. If we accepted such an estimate, we should be obliged to conclude, I think, not merely that the bacteriophage is unorganised, but that its molecules are something much simpler than those of a high-molecular protein. It has even been suggested, though on very imperfect evidence, that it may be a moderately complex carbohydrate. Are we, then, to suppose that the foot-and-mouth virus is a similarly unorganised and relatively simple substance? It is difficult to do so, in view of the series of other agents, all conforming in many aspects of their behaviour to the classical type of the foot-and-mouth virus, and yet showing a range of dimensions up to that at which their units are apparently becoming clearly visible by modern microscopical methods.

It will be clear, indeed, that, if we accept the lowest estimates for the size of the units of some viruses, such as the bacteriophage and the agents transmitting some plant diseases, we cannot by analogy apply the conception of their nature, thus presented, to viruses consisting of organisms which are ceasing to be even ultramicroscopic; and we should be led to doubt the identity with the virus of the bodies which the microscope reveals. If, on the other hand, we regard the still invisible viruses, by analogy with those already seen, as consisting of even much smaller organisms, we can only do so by rejecting the conclusions drawn from some of the physical evidence. It is, of course, possible that some of the agents called viruses are organisms and others relatively simple pathogenic principles in solution; but to assume at this stage such a fundamental difference, among members of a group having so many properties in common, would be to shirk the difficulty.

The third negative characteristic of a virus, namely, its failure to propagate itself, except in the presence of living cells which it infects, may obviously again provide an unstable boundary, shifting with the advance of our knowledge and skill. We may regard it as not only possible, but even likely, that methods will be found for cultivating artificially, on lifeless media, some of those viruses at least which have the appearance of minute organisms. It would be playing with nomenclature to let inclusion in the virus group depend on continued failure in this direction. On the other hand, the dimensions assigned to the units of some viruses, representing them as equal in size to mere fractions of a protein molecule, might well make one hesitate to credit them with the power of active self-multiplication. Experience provides no analogy for the growth of such a substance by self-synthesis from the constituents of a lifeless medium; the energetics of such a process might present an awkward problem. To account for the multiplication of such a substance at all, even in cells infected by it, we should be driven, I think, to the hypothesis which has been freely used to account for the propagation of bacteriophage, on one hand, and of typical viruses like that of herpes, on the other; namely, that the presence of the virus in a cell constrains the metabolism of the cell to produce more.

Bordet has used the reproduction of thrombin by the clotting of the blood as an analogy for the suggested reproduction of bacteriophage in this manner. Another, and perhaps closer, analogy might be found in recent evidence that a culture of pneumococcus, deprived of its type-specific carbohydrate complex, can be made to take up the carbohydrate characteristic of another type, and then to reproduce itself indefinitely with this new, artificially imposed specificity. The response of the cells of the animal

还要简单。尽管证据不是很充分，有人甚至提出它可能是中度复杂的碳水化合物。那么，我们是否也可以假设口蹄疫病毒也是一种类似的无结构而且相对简单的物质？这样说恐怕很难，因为纵观这一类别的其他病原，它们行为的许多方面都和经典的口蹄疫病毒非常一致，但是其大小范围很广，其中大的病原利用现代显微技术可以清晰地观察到它们的组成单位。

很显然，如果我们接受了某些病毒单位的最小估计尺寸，比如噬菌体和传播某些植物疾病的病原，那就确实不能用类推的方法将其本质的概念应用到那些由不再是超显微结构单位组成的病毒中。我们应该怀疑那些在显微镜下看到的物体是否是病毒。另一方面，如果通过类推，我们认为这些在显微镜下不可见的病毒，和可见的病毒一样，是由更小的有机组织组成，那我们就只能推翻一些从具体证据中得来的结论。当然，有可能某些被称为病毒的物体实际上是溶液中的其他有机体或者相对简单的病原体。但是现阶段在这样一个具有如此多共同特性的类群中假设存在一个这样根本的差别是在躲避困难。

病毒的第三个否定性特征，即它不能自我繁殖，除非有受感染的活细胞的存在，这同样也是一种不确定的界限，随着知识和技术的进步会发生改变。我们会认识到，在无生命的培养基中人工培养病毒的方法不仅是也许，而且是非常可能成功的，尤其是培养那些有微小有机体外观的病毒。用这个特征来界定病毒常常会失败，也许只是玩玩命名的文字游戏。另一方面，某些病毒组成单位的大小仅相当于一部分蛋白质分子，这可能让人不敢相信它们有自我繁殖的能力。对于能否通过无生命培养基中的成分自我合成病毒类物质，我们没有任何经验；这个过程的能量学就是一个很棘手的问题。为了能够说明病毒这类物质的繁殖过程，即便是在受感染的细胞内部，我想我们也必须借助那个已有的假说，它一方面用来解释噬菌体，另一方面用来解释疱疹病毒的繁殖过程：即细胞内存在的病毒迫使细胞的代谢发生改变，使其产生更多的病毒。

博尔代使用血液的凝集产生凝血酶来类比噬菌体的繁殖方式。另一个类比，可能更贴切，是在最近的试验中发现的，即去除肺炎球菌培养液中的类型特异性碳水化合物后，该球菌能够获取另外一种类型的碳水化合物，然后以新的类型不断繁殖，这样就人为地产生了一种新的特异性类型。动物的免疫细胞在接触了外源蛋白后的

body to even a single contact with a foreign protein, by the altered metabolism producing immunity, and often persistent for the lifetime of the individual, may suggest another parallel; but here the protective type of the reaction is in direct contrast to the supposed regeneration by the cells of the poison which killed them.

Boycott, again, has emphasised the difficulty of drawing a sharp line of distinction between the action of normal cell-constituents, which promote cell-proliferation for normal repair of an injury, and the virus transmitting a malignant tumour, or that causing foot-and-mouth disease. I do not myself find it easy, on general biological grounds, to accept this idea of a cell having its metabolism thus immediately diverted to producing the agent of its own destruction, or abnormal stimulation. It is almost the direct opposite of the immunity reaction, which is not absent, but peculiarly effective in the response of the body to many viruses. It is difficult, again, to imagine that a virus like rabies could be permanently excluded from a country if it had such an autogenous origin. The phenomena of immunity to a virus, and of closely specific immunity to different strains of the same virus, are peculiarly difficult to interpret on these lines.

This conception, however, of the reproduction of a virus by the perverted metabolism of the infected cell has been strongly supported by Doerr, in explanation of the phenomena of herpes. There are individuals in whom the epidermal cells have acquired a tendency to become affected by an herpetic eruption, in response to various kinds of systemic or local injury. From the lesions so developed, an agent having the typical properties of a virus can be obtained, capable of reproducing the disease by inoculation into individuals, even of other species, such as the rabbit, and exciting, when appropriately injected, the production of an antiserum specifically antagonising the herpes infection. Such phenomena have a special interest for our discussion, in that they can be almost equally well explained by the two rival conceptions. One regards the herpes virus as a distinct ultramicroscopic organism, and the person liable to attack as a carrier, in whom the virus can be awakened to pathogenic activity and multiplication by injuries weakening the normal resistance of his cells to invasion. The other regards it as a pathogenic principle produced by cells in response to injury, and awakening other cells to further production when transmitted to them.

This forms a good example of the central difficulty in dealing with the group of agents at present classed together as viruses. They seem to form a series; but we do not know whether the series is real and continuous, or whether it is formed merely by the accidental association, through a certain similarity in effects, and through common characteristics of a largely negative kind, of agents of at least two fundamentally different kinds. If we approach the series from one end, and watch the successive conquests of microscopical technique, or if we consider the phenomena of immunity over the whole series, we are tempted to assume that all the viruses will ultimately be revealed as independent organisms. If we approach from the other end, or consider analogies from other examples of a transmissible alteration of metabolism, we may be tempted to doubt the significance of the evidence provided by the microscope, and to conclude that all viruses are

反应可能也是一种类似的机制，这种通过改变代谢产生免疫的反应经常会持续一生，但是这种保护性反应恰恰抑制了被病毒感染的细胞的复制。

博伊科特再次强调：要在能够促进细胞增殖以便修复损伤的正常细胞成分和传播恶性肿瘤或引发口蹄疫的病毒之间划一条清楚的界线是很困难的。我个人认为，在普通生物学背景下很难接受这样一个观点，即一个具有自身代谢能力的细胞会立即转向产生破坏自身的物质或者异常刺激。这几乎是免疫反应的直接反例，免疫反应在机体应对许多病毒的反应时不仅存在，而且相当有效。同样，如果狂犬病毒具有如此强大的自我繁殖能力的话，很难想象它能在一个国家被消灭。对病毒的免疫以及对同一病毒不同株系的高度特异现象，在目前尤难解释。

但是，多尔在解释疱疹病毒现象时强烈支持病毒的复制是被感染细胞异常的代谢造成的。在对各种系统的或者局部的损伤作出反应时，某些人的上皮细胞更容易受到疱疹的感染。从这些伤口中能够获得具有典型病毒特征的物体，如果接种到生物体内，即使是其他物种的生物，例如兔子体内，也可以致病，而令人兴奋的是：如果注射得当，能够产生针对疱疹感染的特异性抗血清。这种现象是我们讨论的焦点，因为以下两种相互对立的观点都能很好地解释这种现象。其中一种观点认为疱疹病毒是特殊的超显微生物，那些易于感染的人作为携带者，由于损伤减弱他们体内细胞的正常抵抗力而导致病毒被唤起进行病理性活动和复制。另一种观点认为病毒是细胞应对损伤产生的病理性物质，当传递给别的细胞时可以唤起这些细胞产生相同的物体。

这是目前在分析病毒类病原时遇到的主要难题之一。这些病原似乎形成了一个系列，但是我们不知道它们是否真实并且持续存在，或者它是否仅仅是由两种或两种以上本质不同的病原通过产生相似效应或者通过大量相同的否定性特征而偶然联系在一起形成的。如果我们从这个系列的一端入手，关注显微技术的发展，或者如果我们考虑的是整个系列的免疫现象，那么我们就会倾向于认为所有病毒最终都会被证明是独立的生物体。如果我们从另一端入手，或者考虑从传染性代谢改变的其他例子来进行类推，我们可能会怀疑显微镜所提供的证据的重要性，并得出结论所有的病毒是无结构的、自行产生的、有毒的物体。如果我们采取谨慎的态度假设两

unorganised, autogenous, toxic principles. If we take the cautious attitude of supposing that both are right, and that viruses belonging to both these radically different types exist, where are we going to draw the line? Is the test to be one of unit dimension? If so, what is the lower limit of the size of an organism? Are we to suppose that inclusion bodies can only be produced by viruses which are independent organisms? And if so, does this conclusion also apply to the "X" bodies associated with the infection of plant cells by certain viruses?

If we try to form an estimate of the lower limit of size compatible with organisation, I think we should remember that particles which we measure by filters of known porosity, or by photomicrographs, need not be assumed to represent the virus organisms in an actively vegetative condition. They may well be minute structures, adapted to preserve the virus during transmission to cells in which it can resume vegetative life. Attempts to demonstrate an oxidative metabolism in extracts containing such a virus, separated from the cells in which it can grow and multiply, and to base conclusions as to the non-living nature of the virus on failure to detect such activity, must surely be regarded as premature.

Our evidence of the vitality of its particles is, as yet, entirely due to their behaviour after transmission. They may accordingly contain protein, lipoid and other molecules in a state of such dense aggregation that comparisons of their size with that of the heavily hydrated molecules of a protein in colloidal solution may well give a misleading idea of their complexity.

Apart from their known function as the agents transmitting many of the best known among the acute infections, it is impossible, to anyone having even a slight knowledge of the recent developments which began with the work of Rous and Murphy, to doubt that in the advance of knowledge concerning the nature of the viruses in general lies the brightest hope of finding a clue to the dark secret of the malignant tumours. In unravelling what is still such a tangle of contradictions, the animal biologist needs all the help that can be given by concurrent study of the analogous phenomena in plants.

(**128**, 599-602; 1931)

者都是对的，病毒分别属于这两种完全不同的类型，那么我们如何划清这条界线？组成单位的尺寸是界定的标准吗？如果这样，一个生物的尺寸的下限是多少？我们应该假设包涵体只能由属于自主生物的病毒产生吗？如果这样，那么这个结论也能应用到与某些病毒感染植物细胞相关的“X”体上吗？

如果我们想估计出有机组织结构尺寸的下限，我认为我们应该想到，我们用已知孔隙度的滤器或者显微照相测量的颗粒不一定代表活着的病毒。它们很可能是微小的结构，用于在病毒感染细胞时保存病毒，进入细胞后，病毒可以继续植物性生活。病毒在细胞体内生长和繁殖，但试图在从细胞中分离出来的包含病毒的提取液中检测氧化代谢活性，并且基于没有检测到这种代谢活动就得出病毒不是一种生物的结论肯定是草率的。

迄今为止，我们关于病毒颗粒生命力的证据都来源于它们在传播以后的行为表现。因此，它们可能会含有蛋白质、类脂和其他分子，这些分子以一种非常紧密的方式聚集在一起，以至于如果将它们的大小和胶体溶液中高度水合的蛋白质分子大小进行对比会让我们对其复杂性产生误解。

除了知道病毒的功能是作为病原传播许多我们最熟悉的急性传染病外，任何一个对由劳斯和墨菲的工作开创的最新进展稍有一点了解的人，都不可能怀疑进一步了解病毒的本质最有可能为揭开恶性肿瘤背后深藏的秘密提供线索。为了解决这个矛盾重重的问题，动物生物学家们需要全面地借鉴在对植物学中类似现象的同步研究中得到的结果。

（毛晨晖 翻译；秦志海 审稿）

# Maxwell and Modern Theoretical Physics*

N. Bohr

## Editor's Note

**On the occasion of the Maxwell Centenary Celebrations in Cambridge, October 1931, Niels Bohr presented an address on Maxwell and Modern Theoretical Physics. Bohr notes that Maxwell's theory of electricity and magnetism had made possible developments in the understanding of atomic matter, and also provided the foundations for the discovery of quantum theory. Although this theory moved beyond Maxwell's ideas, analysis in quantum theory still required Maxwell's theory, especially through the relations for the energy and momentum of light quanta. Bohr asserts that Maxwell's theory will always play a central role in physics, as the formulation of the laws of quantum physics depends on the existence of a classical world describable in Maxwell's terms.**

I feel greatly honoured in being given this opportunity of paying a tribute of reverence to the memory of James Clerk Maxwell, the creator of the electromagnetic theory, which is of such fundamental importance to the work of every physicist. In this celebration we have heard the Master of Trinity and Sir Joseph Larmor speak, with the greatest authority and charm, of Maxwell's wonderful discoveries and personality, and of the unbroken tradition upheld here in Cambridge connecting his life and his work with our time. Although I have had the great privilege, in the years of my early studies, of coming under the spell of Cambridge and the inspiration of the great English physicists, I fear that it may not be possible for me to add anything of sufficient interest in this respect, but it gives me very great pleasure indeed to be invited to say a few words about the relation between Maxwell's work and the subsequent development of atomic physics.

I shall not speak of Maxwell's fundamental contributions to the development of statistical mechanics and of the kinetic theory of gases, which Prof. Planck has already discussed, especially as regards Maxwell's fruitful co-operation with Boltzmann. It is only my intention to make a few remarks about the application of the electromagnetic theory to the problem of atomic constitution, where Maxwell's theory, besides being extremely fruitful in the interpretation of the phenomena, has yielded the utmost any theory can do, namely, to be instrumental in suggesting and guiding new developments beyond its original scope.

I must, of course, be very brief in commenting upon the application of Maxwell's ideas to atomic theory, which in itself constitutes a whole chapter of physics. I shall just recall how successfully the idea of the atomic nature of electricity was incorporated into Maxwell's

* Address delivered on the occasion of the Maxwell Centenary Celebrations at Cambridge on Oct. 1.

# 麦克斯韦与现代理论物理*

尼尔斯·玻尔

## 编者按

1931 年 10 月，剑桥大学举行了麦克斯韦诞辰一百年纪念会，尼尔斯·玻尔在会上发表了一篇有关麦克斯韦和现代理论物理的演讲。玻尔指出麦克斯韦的电磁学理论为人类了解原子世界作出了贡献，也为创立量子理论提供了基础。虽然量子理论超越了麦克斯韦的学说，但量子力学中的分析手段离不开麦克斯韦的理论，尤其是在建立光量子能量和动量之间的关系时。玻尔认为麦克斯韦的理论在物理学中的核心地位不会丧失，因为量子物理定律中的公式都是按照麦克斯韦所描述的经典世界创建的。

我非常荣幸能有机会在此表达我对电磁学理论的创立者——詹姆斯·克拉克·麦克斯韦的敬意，因为电磁学理论对每一位物理学家的研究工作都是非常重要的。在这个纪念庆典上，三一学院院长和约瑟夫·拉莫尔爵士已经给我们作了最具权威性的精彩演讲，介绍了麦克斯韦的重要发现和伟大人格，还提到剑桥大学一直坚持把麦克斯韦的生活与工作和我们所处的时代紧密相连的传统。尽管我早年曾有幸在剑桥大学工作过一段时间，也接受过知名英国物理学家们的指点，但在这方面我恐怕讲不出更多吸引人注意的内容，不过我仍然非常高兴能应大会之邀来这里简单介绍一下麦克斯韦的研究与随后发展起来的原子物理之间的关系。

我不打算讲麦克斯韦对统计力学和气体动力学的重大贡献，因为普朗克教授已经在前面介绍过了，他还特别提到麦克斯韦和玻尔兹曼曾经一起进行过有效合作。在这里我只想谈一下如何应用电磁学理论解决原子的构成问题，在这个问题上，麦克斯韦的理论不仅很好地解释了相关的实验现象，而且已经达到了理论所能达到的极致，因为它可以启发和引导自身领域之外的研究工作的发展。

当然，我只能非常简短地介绍麦克斯韦理论在原子物理中的应用，因为仅这个问题本身就足以构成物理学中整整一章的内容。我要说洛伦兹和拉莫尔将电的原子本质与麦克斯韦理论结合在一起的思想非常成功，特别是由此可以解释包括塞曼效

---

* 这是 1931 年 10 月 1 日在剑桥举行的麦克斯韦诞辰一百周年庆祝大会上玻尔所作的演讲。

theory by Lorentz and Larmor, and especially how it furnished an explanation of the dispersion phenomena, including the remarkable features of the Zeeman effect. I would also like to allude to the important contribution to the electron theory of magnetism made by Prof. Langevin, whom we much regret not to be able to hear today. But above all, I think in this connexion of the inspiration given by Maxwell's ideas to Sir Joseph Thomson in his pioneer work on the electronic constitution of matter, from his early introduction of the fundamental idea of the electromagnetic mass of the electron, to his famous method, valid to this day, of counting the electrons in the atom by means of the scattering of Röntgen rays.

The developments of the atomic theory brought us soon, as everybody knows, beyond the limit of direct and consistent application of Maxwell's theory. I wish to emphasise, however, that it was just the possibility of analysing the radiation phenomena provided by the electromagnetic theory of light which led to the recognition of an essentially new feature of the laws of Nature. Planck's fundamental discovery of the quantum of action has necessitated, indeed, a radical revision of all our concepts in natural philosophy. Still, in this situation, Maxwell's theory continued to provide indispensable guidance. Thus the relation between energy and momentum of radiation, which follows from the electromagnetic theory, has found application even in the explanation of the Compton effect, for which Einstein's idea of the photon has been so appropriate a means of accounting for the marked departure from the classical ideas. The use of Maxwell's theory as a guide did not fail either in the later stage of atomic theory. Although Lord Rutherford's fundamental discovery of the atomic nucleus, which brought our picture of the atom to such wonderful completion, showed most strikingly the limitation of ordinary mechanics and electrodynamics, the only way to progress in this field has been to maintain as close contact as possible with the classical ideas of Newton and Maxwell.

At first sight it might perhaps look as if some essential modification of Maxwell's theory was needed here, and it has even been suggested that new terms should be added to his famous equations for electromagnetic fields in free space. But Maxwell's theory has proved far too consistent, far too beautiful, to admit of a modification of this kind. There could only be a question, indeed, of a generalisation of the whole theory, or rather of a translation of it into a new physical language, suited to take into account the essential indivisibility of the elementary processes in such a way that every feature of Maxwell's theory finds a corresponding feature in the new formalism. In the last few years, this aim has actually been attained to a large extent by the wonderful development of the new quantum mechanics or quantum electrodynamics, connected with the names of de Broglie, Heisenberg, Schrödinger, and Dirac.

When one hears physicists talk nowadays about "electron waves" and "photons", it might perhaps appear that we have completely left the ground on which Newton and Maxwell built; but we all agree, I think, that such concepts, however fruitful, can never be more than a convenient means of stating characteristic consequences of the quantum theory which cannot be visualised in the ordinary sense. It must not be forgotten that only the

应的显著特征在内的色散现象。我还想提及朗之万教授在磁性的电子理论方面所作的贡献。遗憾的是，他今天不能到场为我们作报告。但我认为最值得一提的是约瑟夫·汤姆逊爵士在物质电子结构方面的开拓性工作一直受到麦克斯韦理论的启发，从他早期引入电子电磁质量这一基本概念，到后来他发明用伦琴射线的散射计算原子中电子数的方法，这种方法一直沿用至今。

我们都知道，原子理论的迅速发展使我们现在已经不能再像原来那样直接利用麦克斯韦的理论来解决原子内部的问题。但我要强调的是，正是因为有了光的电磁学理论，我们才可能去分析辐射现象，才可能认识到自然法则的一个全新特征。的确，普朗克关于量子行为的重要发现使我们必须从根本上修正自然科学中的所有观念。但即便如此，麦克斯韦的理论仍然能为我们的研究工作提供必不可少的指导。由电磁学理论可以推出辐射能量与动量之间的关系，而我们可以利用这种关系来解释康普顿效应，虽然爱因斯坦的光子理论明确指出康普顿效应与经典理论之间存在着明显的区别。麦克斯韦的理论在原子理论后来的发展中仍然具有一定的指导意义。尽管卢瑟福勋爵对原子结构的完整描述说明普通力学和电动力学具有极大的局限性，但想在这一领域进一步拓展就必须尽可能紧密地联系牛顿和麦克斯韦的经典理论。

乍看起来，我们似乎需要从本质上对麦克斯韦的理论进行修正，甚至有人指出，应该在麦克斯韦著名的自由空间电磁场方程中加入新项。但麦克斯韦的理论高度自洽非常完美，人们无法对它进行这样的修正。实际上，我们只能对整个理论进行一致化处理，更确切地说就是把麦克斯韦的方程翻译成一种新的物理语言，这种新语言通过为麦克斯韦理论中的每一个特征找到其在新形式下的对应特征来反映基本物理过程中的不可分性。前一段时间，德布罗意、海森堡、薛定谔和狄拉克在量子力学或电动力学方面所取得的突破性进展已经在很大程度上实现了上述目标。

今天，当我们听到物理学家们谈论“电子波”和“光子”的时候，这些概念似乎已经完全脱离了牛顿和麦克斯韦建立起来的理论基础；但是我认为，大家都会同意这样一个观点：这些新观念虽然发挥了很大的作用，但它们不过是一种用来说明量子理论特殊性的便捷方法，缺乏一般意义上的形象化特征。不要忘记，只有关于

classical ideas of material particles and electromagnetic waves have a field of unambiguous application, whereas the concepts of photons and electron waves have not. Their applicability is essentially limited to cases in which, on account of the existence of the quantum of action, it is not possible to consider the phenomena observed as independent of the apparatus utilised for their observation. I would like to mention, as an example, the most conspicuous application of Maxwell's ideas, namely, the electromagnetic waves in wireless transmission. It is a purely formal matter to say that these waves consist of photons, since the conditions under which we control the emission and the reception of the radio waves preclude the possibility of determining the number of photons they should contain. In such a case we may say that all trace of the photon idea, which is essentially one of enumeration of elementary processes, has completely disappeared.

For the sake of illustration, let us imagine for a moment that the recent experimental discoveries of electron diffraction and photonic effects, which fall in so well with the quantum mechanical symbolism, were made before the work of Faraday and Maxwell. Of course, such a situation is unthinkable, since the interpretation of the experiments in question is essentially based on the concepts created by this work. But let us, nevertheless, take such a fanciful view and ask ourselves what the state of science would then be. I think it is not too much to say that we should be farther away from a consistent view of the properties of matter and light than Newton and Huygens were. We must, in fact, realise that the unambiguous interpretation of any measurement must be essentially framed in terms of the classical physical theories, and we may say that in this sense the language of Newton and Maxwell will remain the language of physicists for all time.

I do not think that this is a proper occasion to enter into further details regarding these problems, and to bring new views under discussion. In conclusion, however, I am glad to give expression to the great expectation with which the whole scientific world follows the exploration of an entirely new field of experimental physics, namely, the internal constitution of the nucleus, which is now carried on in Maxwell's laboratory, under the great leadership of the present Cavendish professor. In the fact that nobody here in Cambridge is likely to forget Newton's and Maxwell's work, we see perhaps the very best auguries for the continued success of these endeavours. Even if we must be prepared for a still further renunciation of ordinary visualisation, the basic concepts of physics which we owe to the great masters will certainly prove indispensable in this new field as well.

(**128**, 691-692; 1931)

物质粒子和电磁波的经典观念得到了实际的应用，而光子和电子波的概念还没有应用到实践中。应用受到限制的主要原因是由于存在量子效应，不可能认为观察到的现象与所用的仪器无关。作为一个例子，我想谈一下麦克斯韦理论最著名的应用，也就是在无线电传输领域中的应用。认为电磁波由光子组成只不过是形式上的说法而已，因为我们在发射和接收电磁波的时候是无法确定电磁波中包含的光子数目的。因此我们可以说，以计数为本质的光子概念已经彻底不复存在了。

为了进一步说明问题，我们可以想象一下如果严格符合量子力学规律的电子衍射和光子效应是在麦克斯韦和法拉第的工作问世之前就已经发现了，那将出现什么样的情况呢？当然，这种情况是不可能出现的，因为用来解释以上实验发现的理论是以麦克斯韦和法拉第这两人的理论成果为依据的。不过，我们还是可以发挥一下我们的想象力，问问自己，如果没有麦克斯韦和法拉第的理论，科学会处于一个什么样的水平。我想如果说我们应该在牛顿和惠更斯认为光是一种物质的理论上加以拓展，这并不为过。事实上，我们应该意识到的是，对任何测量结果的准确解释都必须建立在经典物理理论的框架之内，从这个意义上我们可以说，牛顿和麦克斯韦的语言仍将是物理学家们的通用语言。

我认为现在不是继续深入讨论这些问题并在讨论中引入新观点的最好时机。但在最后我想说的是，目前麦克斯韦实验室正在现任的卡文迪什教授的领导下开展原子核内部结构方面的研究，我希望整个科学界都去探索这一全新的实验物理领域。事实上，我相信在座的剑桥大学同仁们都不会忘记牛顿和麦克斯韦的工作，也许我们已经看到利用这些成果最有可能取得后续的成功。就算我们必须做好进一步放弃常规理论的准备，大师们为我们总结的这些基本物理观点在这个新领域中也将被证明是必不可少的。

（王静 翻译；鲍重光 审稿）

# Progressive Biology*

F. G. Hopkins

## Editor's Note

**One of the most striking features of this article by Frederick Gowland Hopkins is the breadth of what it attempts: in two pages, nothing less than a survey of the status of all of biology. It is hard to imagine such a thing being meaningfully attempted now. Hopkins ranges from the emerging understanding of genetic inheritance, made quantitative by J. B. S. Haldane and Ronald Fisher, to the study of nerve action and the biochemistry of vitamins. Hopkins alludes to the prevailing suspicion that the fundamentals of biochemistry should shed light on life's origins. And he suggests that viruses offer a glimpse of the fuzzy boundary between the living and non-living worlds, a view that is very much upheld today.**

IT is not going too far to claim that recent progress in experimental biology, though to a superficial view less impressive, has been not less significant, and indeed not less revolutionary than the progress of modern physics. I might support this claim in many ways. It is, I think, justified in that region of knowledge where cytology and genetical studies meet. The progress and the significance have become the greater since it was recognised that the material units of characters—the chromosomes and subdivisions of chromosomes—are "determinants" rather than "carriers" of genetic factors.

This domain of disinterested science is making many practical contacts. To mention but a single recent instance: Prof. R. C. Punnett, one of the original discoverers of the phenomenon of sex-linkage in inheritance, by applying his expert knowledge of that phenomenon, has produced what may be called a synthetic fowl, of which the qualities are such as to make it of extreme value to the now highly important industry of poultry breeding and egg production. The bearing of the same body of knowledge upon human affairs has been recently very ably discussed by Prof. L. T. Hogben.

The phenomena of heredity were long the stronghold of those who cling to the obscurantism of vitalistic doctrines. Infinitely complex as of course they are, we have now abundant proof that they are susceptible to analysis and that today they are yielding their secrets to well-controlled experimental studies. The results of these are becoming quantitative and are even yielding material for mathematical treatment, as the interesting writings of Dr. R. A. Fisher and Prof. J. B. S. Haldane have shown.

Another region in which accurate experimentation has removed, and is continuing to remove, inhibitions due to obscurantist assumptions is the physiology of the nervous

* Excerpts from the presidential address at the anniversary meeting of the Royal Society on Nov. 30.

# 生物学的进展*

弗雷德里克·高兰·霍普金斯

## 编者按

这篇由弗雷德里克·高兰·霍普金斯所写的文章的最突出的特点之一，是其论述内容的范围非常之广：他用 2 页纸的篇幅全面评述了生物学的所有领域。很难想象现在还有人有意去尝试这种事。霍普金斯从霍尔丹和罗纳德·费希尔最近对遗传学的定量分析开始讲起，一直讲到人们在神经活动和维生素生化性质方面的研究。霍普金斯提到了那个遭到很多人置疑的观点，即生物化学的基本原理应该能说明生命的起源问题。他还提出病毒的出现使生命体和非生命体之间的界限变得模糊不清。现在这个观点已被大家普遍接受。

毫不夸张地说，尽管从表面看并没有那么令人印象深刻，但实验生物学的最新进展在重要性甚至开创性上都毫不逊色于现代物理学的发展。我或许可以从多个方面提出证据支持这个观点。我想主要的证据来自于人们对细胞学与遗传学交叉领域的认识。由于人们认识到人类性状的物质基础——染色体及其组成部分——是遗传因子的“决定因素”而不是“载体”，从而使这些进展及其意义变得更加显著。

这个被人们忽视的科学领域具有许多实用价值。举一个最近的例子：庞尼特教授是遗传中性连锁现象的最早发现者之一，他应用自己在性连锁现象方面的专业知识发明了一种可以被称为“合成家禽”的产品，其质量如此之好使得其在当前非常重要的家禽饲养和禽蛋生产业中极具价值。最近霍格本教授非常巧妙地阐述了这个领域的知识对于人类的意义。

遗传现象很早以前就是那些信奉生机论的蒙昧主义者的大本营。尽管这些现象非常复杂，但是现在已经有足够的证据证明：它们的秘密是可以在精心设计的实验研究中被逐渐揭开的。正如费希尔博士和霍尔丹教授在生动有趣的文章中所指出的，这些研究结果正在被量化，甚而可以通过数学处理得出结论。

另一个一直在并将继续通过精确试验解除蒙昧主义假说带来的禁忌的领域是脊椎动物神经系统生理学。也许现在提出巴甫洛夫在条件反射方面的研究已经太迟了，

* 本文摘自作者作为主席在 11 月 30 日英国皇家学会的周年纪念会议上所作的演讲。

system of vertebrates. It is, perhaps, too late in the day to refer to the work of Pavlov upon conditioned reflexes, though it is justifiable to emphasise its still growing influence upon thought. The work is a supreme proof of the success of the experimental method in analysing even such apparently transcendental phenomena as those which underlie the higher functions of the brain.

The nature of the transmission of events in the nervous system is receiving much illumination from the work of the Royal Society's Foulerton professors. Prof. E. D. Adrian, having developed a most admirable experimental technique for the purpose, is studying the nerve impulse and its origin with highly profitable results. He and his colleagues are now able, with great gain, to work with single nerve fibres and single isolated end organs.

A striking circumstance, brought to light by Adrian's work and that of his colleagues, is that the nervous structures so far examined exhibit such physical regularity in their behaviour that results can often be predicted within about one percent. His experiments on animals have shown how the phenomenon of a grading in the contraction of muscles is controlled by the frequency of impulses sent out from the central nervous system, and by the number of nerve and muscle fibres involved. Moreover, he has been able to observe the activity of a single nerve cell in his own spinal cord by needle electrodes placed in his muscles, and finds human voluntary contractions are regulated in exactly the same way.

Further, Adrian has found that slow potential changes occur in nerve cells and that these are connected with their discharge of impulses; so far this work only extends to isolated nerve ganglia from insects and to nerve cells in the brain stems of fish, but the phenomena he has found are extremely significant, and it seems possible that changes of potential may be of fundamental importance in the activity of nerve cells.

Adrian has found that damaged nerve fibres set up impulses at very high frequencies, and these perhaps play an important part in sensations of pain, though his more recent work has made it clear that impulses in the smaller slowly conducting nerve fibres must also be concerned in the physical mechanism responsible for pain. A most striking feature of all this work is the general similarity of behaviour of nervous structures from whatever animal they may be taken.

Prof. A. V. Hill is studying the nerve impulse from the point of view of the thermal phenomena which accompany it. So small, of course, is the heat production in the nerve that its measurement, like that of the potential changes, calls for great refinements. It is becoming clear, though we do not yet know the details of its nature, that the nerve impulse consists of a transmitted physicochemical event, probably involving changes of ionic concentrations at membranes with consequential changes of electric potential; the whole cycle of events, comprising activity and recovery in the nerve, being supported by the energy derived from metabolic oxidative processes which, very small in scale, are associated with the cycle.

尽管怎么强调该学说对于思维日益明显的影响都不过分。该学说是利用实验方法分析诸如大脑高级功能本质等超自然现象的一个最佳成功例证。

英国皇家学会福勒敦教授们的研究使神经系统传递事件的本质越来越清晰。阿德里安教授已经为此开发出了一种最令人钦佩的实验技术，他正在研究神经冲动及其起源并且得到了非常有用的结果。他和他的同事们目前能够研究单个神经纤维和分离的单个末梢器官，并有重大收获。

阿德里安及其同事的研究工作揭示了一个引人注目的事实，即目前研究的神经结构表现出一种行为上的物理规律性以至于预测结果的误差通常在一个百分点以内。他在动物身上进行的实验显示肌肉收缩的分级现象是如何受到中枢神经系统发出的脉冲频率以及与之相关的神经纤维和肌纤维数量调控的。此外，他通过在自己的肌肉里放置针电极来观察自己脊髓中单个神经细胞的活动，并且发现了人类肌肉的自主收缩也是以完全相同的方式进行调控的。

此外，阿德里安还发现了神经细胞中发生的慢电位改变，以及这种慢电位改变与脉冲放电的关联。到目前为止，这项工作还仅限于分离的昆虫神经节和鱼脑干中的神经细胞，但是他发现的这些现象非常有价值，而且电位改变在神经细胞的活动中很可能具有根本的重要性。

阿德里安发现损坏的神经纤维能够以非常高的频率发放脉冲，而且这可能在疼痛的感觉中起着重要的作用，尽管他的最新研究结果已经清楚地表明由更细的慢传导神经纤维发出的冲动也与疼痛的自然机制有关。所有这些工作的一个最显著的特征是：任何一种动物的神经结构都会表现出大体相似的行为。

希尔教授正在根据与神经冲动相伴而生的热现象来研究神经冲动。显然，神经中的产热量是如此微小以至于其测量需要非常高的精确度，就像测量电位的变化一样。尽管我们还不知道神经冲动的细节特性，但越来越确信神经冲动是由可以传导的物理化学事件组成，很可能包括膜上离子浓度的改变和由此引发的电位改变；事件的整个周期包括神经的活化和复原，其能量来源于与这个周期相关的小规模氧化代谢过程。

When we hope for an increase in our knowledge of the nervous system we are always accustomed to look to researches from the laboratory of Sir Charles Sherrington. An extended study of reflexes has shown that the centripetal impulses do not pass straight through the spinal cord, but at central stations in the cord they are transformed into an enduring excitatory state, which may in turn set up fresh nerve impulses yielding the reflex discharges. The nature of this central excitatory state is being studied and will link up, I think, with some of Adrian's observations upon cell potentials.

It has long been suspected that when a sympathetic nerve is stimulated, adrenalin is liberated at the nerve ending, and that the observed effects are immediately due to the action of that substance. Now Dr. H. H. Dale, in conjunction with a member of his staff, Dr. Gaddum, has investigated the case of the para-sympathetic nerves, the influence of which in general opposes that of the sympathetic group, and has obtained good evidence that when one of these is stimulated, the substance acetyl-choline, previously existing in some inactive form, is liberated at the nerve ending. The action of acetyl-choline when injected into the circulation resembles in general the effect of stimulating para-sympathetic nerves, and there is every reason to believe that the physiological activity of the substance, rather than the transmitted physical impulse itself, is immediately responsible for the observed effects of stimulation. I may say that Otto Loewi, of Graz, has shown that when the heart beat is inhibited by vagus stimulation, acetyl-choline is actually formed in the organ, and the same substance, when artificially injected, is known to produce effects like those of the vagus.

In rather unexpected circumstances we have thus brought before us an example of specific physiological effects due to the influence of the specific structure of an organic molecule. Such effects and such relations are being demonstrated in increasing diversity as fundamental factors of organisation in the animal body. This is illustrated most strikingly, of course, in the domain of the control of its activities by a group of hormones. We find in the cases of adrenalin and thyroxin, the constitution of each of which is accurately known, widely different influences depending on differences of molecular structure.

I may logically pass from hormones to devote a few words to vitamins. We now possess proof that vitamin A is closely related to the carotenes, and this knowledge may well lead, without long delay, to the artificial synthesis of the vitamin itself. With respect to vitamin D, it seems probable, if not yet quite certain, that its artificial production is already accomplished. Some four years ago the constituent of animal and vegetable substances, which is converted into the antirachitic vitamin D by ultra-violet radiation, was identified as ergosterol by Rosenheim and Webster at the National Institute for Medical Research, and concurrently by Windaus in Göttingen. A team of workers at the National Institute, led by Dr. R. B. Bourdillon, appear now to have arrived at the next stage, of isolating the vitamin itself, in crystalline form, from the mixed products of irradiation; and Prof. Windaus, following with his co-workers a different route, has again arrived simultaneously at the same goal.

当我们希望丰富一些关于神经系统的知识时，我们总是习惯于去关注查尔斯·谢灵顿爵士实验室的研究工作。一项关于反射的扩展研究显示向心性的冲动不是沿着脊髓径直传导的，而是在脊髓的中心站点转换成持久的兴奋状态，随后可能会发出新的神经冲动而产生反射放电。人们正在研究这个中心站点兴奋状态的本质，而且我认为这会与阿德里安对细胞电位的一些观察结果相互联系。

很久以前就有人猜想：当交感神经被刺激时，神经末梢就会释放肾上腺素，而我们观察到的效应直接与肾上腺素的作用相关。现在，戴尔博士与为他工作的加德姆博士一起研究了副交感神经，副交感神经的作用大体上和交感神经的作用相反。他们已经获得了有力的证据证明当副交感神经受到刺激时，之前以非活性形式存在的乙酰胆碱会被神经末梢释放。乙酰胆碱在被注射到血液循环中之后，产生的效应同刺激副交感神经产生的效应十分相似，而且所有的证据都表明与观察到的刺激效应直接相关的是该物质的生理活性，而不是传导的物理冲动本身。我要提到的是：来自格拉茨的奥托·勒维已经证实了当心跳被迷走神经刺激所抑制时，心脏内确实形成了乙酰胆碱，而且已经知道在人为地将乙酰胆碱注入体内后，也可以产生类似于迷走神经刺激的效果。

在一些意想不到的情况下，我们已经展示出了由一个有机分子的特定结构能产生特定生理功能的实例。这种效应和两者之间的关系正逐渐被越来越多的证据证实为动物体组织系统的基础。认为动物的行为由一组激素所控制的思想显然是对上述观点的最好阐释。我们发现在已经明确知道分子结构的肾上腺素和甲状腺素中所表现出来的生理效应的巨大差异是由它们各自的分子结构决定的。

我希望将话题从激素合乎逻辑地转移到对维生素的简要说明上。我们现在有证据说明维生素 A 与胡萝卜素密切相关，利用这个知识很可能会在很短的时间内实现维生素的人工合成。至于维生素 D，其人工合成可能已经完成，但目前还没有完全确定。大约在四年以前，动植物原料中的某些经紫外线照射可转变成抗佝偻病的维生素 D 的成分同时被英国国立医学研究所的罗森海姆和韦伯斯特以及格丁根的温道斯鉴定出来是麦角甾醇。由鲍迪伦博士领导的国立研究所的一组研究者现在已经开始了下一阶段的研究，即以结晶的形式从照射后的混合产物中分离出维生素本身；与此同时，温道斯教授和他的同事用另一种方法也达到了相同的目的。

There is no doubt that the substance which the British group now term "calciferol", and which they have isolated as a dinitrobenzoate from the mixed product, is identical with the "vitamin $D_2$" which Windaus and Linsert obtained by a different method; and there is little doubt that this substance, as obtained in either laboratory, is the essential vitamin D in a state of practical purity. One milligramme of calciferol has an antirachitic activity corresponding to 40,000 of the newly accepted international units.

Before I close I would like to refer to a certain aspect of the chemical dynamics of living cells, concerning which progressive studies have been made during the last few years. The cell is, of course, a seat of catalysed chemical reactions and would seem to possess a multitude of catalysts each highly specific in the influence it exerts. In the case of reductions and oxidations, however, there are other agencies of less specific activity which promote the final stages of oxidation. Of great interest among these are certain combinations of metallic iron with pyrrol groupings. One such compound is concerned, possibly with the intervention of yet another, in bringing molecular oxygen into the field of activity. What, however, is specially interesting about these associations of pyrrol groupings with a metal is the wide extent of their biological functions.

We have long known, of course, of the presence of one such association in the chlorophyll molecule, where it functions as part of the trap for solar energy, and we have been long familiar with the presence of another in haemoglobin, where its function is to hold oxygen during its transference from the lungs of vertebrates to their tissues. Further, we now know that, within the tissues, two others promote oxidation, and yet a third prevents by its presence any deleterious accumulations of hydrogen peroxide. For adjustment to each separate function there is some slight modification of a fundamental structure. Compounds of the type in question are found in many of the lower organisms. Just as Nature seems to have hit upon sound principles for nerve structure early in evolution, so she seems to have satisfactorily chosen, very early, the chemical materials for life. This same suggestion is carried by all the more important constituents of living stuff; fundamentally the same throughout, yet always with minor differences underlying specific morphological differences.

To return to cell dynamics. Knowledge of enzymic catalysts which, with highly specific relations, activate in a certain sense the molecules which are to suffer oxidation, is almost daily accumulating. It is because this specific activation must precede oxidation that the indiscriminate action of oxygen on the living cell is prevented. Although an understanding of the complex organisation of chemical events in the living unit is far beyond our present powers, we are, I think, beginning to see what kind of organisation it may be.

One last word, however. We have assumed that the living cells we have best known are the ultimate units in biology. But of late years the viruses have forced themselves into our thoughts. What are viruses? Do they merely simulate some of the properties of the living? Can we conceive of them as something between the non-living and the living?

毫无疑问，这种被英国的研究小组作为一种二硝基苯甲酸酯从混合产物中分离出来并命名为“钙化醇”的物质，与温道斯和林泽特以另一种方法获得的物质——“维生素 $D_2$”十分相似。基本可以肯定，在这两个实验室中得到的物质，就是达到可应用纯度的维生素 D。一毫克钙化醇所具有的抗佝偻病活性相当于新国际单位的 40,000 倍。

在结束之前，我想提到活细胞的化学动力学这一特定领域，在过去的几年内这个领域的研究取得了一定的进展。当然，细胞是催化化学反应的温床，细胞内含有大量的催化剂，每一种催化剂的作用范围都很专一。但是，在还原和氧化的过程中，有一些专一性不是很强的物质，它们能催化氧化反应的最终步骤。其中很值得注意的是某些金属铁与吡咯基团的化合物。其中一种这样的化合物有可能在另一种化合物的作用下会将分子氧带入到活性区域。但是，就吡咯基团与一种金属的缔合来说，格外引人注目的是它们有多种多样的生物学功能。

当然，我们在很早以前就已经知道有一种这样的缔合物存在于叶绿素分子中，其功能是捕捉光能，而且我们也早已熟知在血红蛋白中还存在着另一种这样的缔合物，其功能是把氧气从脊椎动物的肺转移到各组织中去。此外，我们现在知道在组织中另有三种这样的缔合物，其中两种可以促进氧化，而第三种物质能够通过自身的存在而阻止过氧化氢的有害蓄积。为了适应每一种物质的独特生理功能，它们在基本结构上都有一些微小的修饰。这种类型的化合物在许多低等生物中也能找到。正如自然界似乎在进化早期就为神经结构找到了合理的原则一样，她似乎也很早就选定了合适的化学物质来形成生命。生命中所有更重要的组成成分都支持了这个观点。所有物质在本质上都是相同的，只不过通常在特定的形态差异下存在着微小的区别。

再回到细胞动力学。关于酶催化剂的知识几乎每一天都在增长，这些酶在某种意义上以高度专一的相关性活化了将要进行氧化反应的分子。因为在氧化之前必须进行这种有专一性的活化，所以避免了氧气对活细胞的非选择性作用。尽管我们目前还没有能力去了解生物体内各种化学作用的复杂机制，但我认为我们已经开始认识到这种机制可能会属于哪一种类型。

最后还有一句要说的话。我们已经假设我们最了解的活细胞就是生命的基本单位。但是近年来病毒迫使我们改变了想法。病毒是什么？它们仅仅是在模仿生命的某些特性吗？我们可以假设它们是介于非生命和生命之间的某种东西吗？它们是活

Are they alive? We do not yet know. Research upon them is at any rate intensely active at the moment. Its results may make it necessary to modify some fundamental biological concepts, and indeed be as revolutionary in their effects as the breaking up of the atom.

(**128**, 923-924; 1931)

的吗？我们现在还无从知晓。无论如何，目前在这方面的研究都是非常活跃的。研究结果可能导致有必要修正一些基础的生物学概念，而且由此产生的效应确实可以和原子分裂一样具有革命性的意义。

（毛晨晖 翻译；秦志海 审稿）

# The Internal Temperature of White Dwarf Stars

E. A. Milne

## Editor's Note

**With the development of quantum mechanics, astronomers began to incorporate some of its tenets into their study of the structure of stars. A prediction of quantum mechanics is that, in certain circumstances, particles and atoms will form into "degenerate" states, in which the particles all occupy a single quantum state and which are extremely dense. This happens inside white dwarf stars, formed by the collapse of ordinary stars near to the end of their life cycle, which have a Sun-like mass within an Earth-like volume. This paper by E. Arthur Milne, attempting to clarify the internal temperature of white dwarfs, refers to Subrahmanyan Chandrasekhar, who first predicted the existence of black holes and who deduced the maximum possible mass for white dwarfs.**

IT has recently been discovered by S. Chandrasekhar,[1] B. Swirles,[2] and R. C. Majumdar,[3] independently, that the opacity of a degenerate gas is very small compared with what would be computed for a classical gas at the same density and temperature, the ratio being an inverse power of Sommerfeld's degeneracy-criterion parameter. This discovery seriously affects estimates of the internal temperatures in white dwarf stars. It has previously been held that interiors of the white dwarf stars are amongst the hottest of stellar interiors; for example, Russell and Atkinson[4] remark that their internal temperatures must be of the order of 50 times those of a main sequence star built on the "diffuse" model. Again, Jeans[5] says "it appears that the central temperatures of the white dwarfs must be enormously high, while those of giant stars of large radius must be comparatively low". This has given rise to the paradox that the coolest stellar interiors appeared to be the best generators of stellar energy, the hottest the worst. To quote Jeans[6] again, "… many of the hottest and densest stars are entirely put to shame in the matter of radiation by very cool stars of low density, such as Antares and Betelgeuse".

If, however, the opacity in the interior of a white dwarf is very low, the temperature gradient in the interior must be very small. In the limit of zero opacity (assuming also small conductivity) the temperature-distribution is isothermal. The degenerate core is therefore a mass at an approximately uniform temperature, and the value of this temperature is determined purely by the observed mass $M$ and luminosity $L$ and the intrinsic opacity $\kappa_1$ of the gaseous envelope which surrounds the core. On the "generalised standard model", in which the energy-sources are uniformly distributed and the opacity takes a constant value $\kappa_1$ in the gaseous envelope, the temperature $T'$ of the approximately isothermal degenerate core is, in the standard notation:

$$T' = \frac{(R/\mu)^{\frac{5}{3}}}{(\frac{1}{3}a)^{\frac{2}{3}}K}\left(\frac{\kappa_1 L}{4\pi cGM - \kappa_1 L}\right)^{\frac{2}{3}} \qquad (1)$$

# 白矮星的内部温度

爱德华·阿瑟·米耳恩

## 编者按

随着量子理论的发展，天文学家们开始把一些量子力学的原理融入到他们对恒星构造的研究中。量子力学的一个预言是：在特定条件下，粒子和原子将形成“简并”态。在这种状态中，所有粒子都占据着一个简单的量子态，并且处于这种状态下的恒星将具有很高的密度。白矮星的内部就会出现上述情况，白矮星是由普通恒星在其生命周期的末期塌陷形成的，它和地球的体积差不多，但却具有如太阳那么大的质量。这篇由阿瑟·米耳恩撰写的文章试图对白矮星的内部温度作出解释。文中还提到了第一个预言黑洞存在的苏布拉马尼扬·钱德拉塞卡，是他推测出了白矮星的最大可能质量。

钱德拉塞卡[1]、斯怀尔斯[2]和马宗达[3]最近各自独立地发现：与同等密度和温度的经典气体相比，简并气体的不透明度是非常小的，其比值是索默菲尔德简并判据参数的倒数。这一发现对估算白矮星的内部温度影响重大。过去人们一直把白矮星的内部温度看作是恒星中最高的；例如，罗素和阿特金森[4]就认为白矮星的内部温度 50 倍于建立在“弥散”模型基础上的主序星。而且，金斯[5]也说过：“看起来白矮星的中心温度非常高，而那些大半径巨星的中心温度则会相对较低一些。”这就产生了一个悖论，温度最低的恒星内部是最好的恒星能量产生器，最热的反而最差。金斯[6]还说过：“……很多最热和最致密的恒星在辐射上远远比不上那些具有较低密度的低温恒星，比如心宿二和参宿四。”

然而，如果一个白矮星内部的不透明度很低，那么它内部的温度梯度也一定非常小。在不透明度为零的极限情况下(假设传导性也很小)，温度分布是等温的。因此，简并核就是一团温度近似恒定的物质，而这个温度的值完全取决于观测质量 $M$、光度 $L$ 和核心周围气体包络层的内禀不透明度 $\kappa_1$。在“一般标准模型”中，各能量源是均匀分布的，气体包络层的不透明度是常数 $\kappa_1$，则温度近似恒定的简并核的温度 $T'$ 用标准符号表示如下：

$$T' = \frac{(R/\mu)^{\frac{5}{3}}}{(\frac{1}{3}a)^{\frac{2}{3}}K}\left(\frac{\kappa_1 L}{4\pi cGM-\kappa_1 L}\right)^{\frac{2}{3}} \qquad (1)$$

For the observed mass and luminosity of the Companion of Sirius, $T'$ is $0.34 \times 10^6 \kappa_1^{\frac{2}{3}}$ degrees, or, even if we adopt the high value $\kappa_1 = 300$ for the gaseous envelope, the value of $T'$ is only 15 million degrees. For smaller values of the envelope-opacity it will be still smaller. For an almost completely degenerate star the internal temperature is determined by the *photospheric* opacity in the thin gaseous envelope.

According to my conclusion that all stars contain a degenerate zone surrounded by a gaseous envelope, formula (1) applies to all stars. Stars with a high value of $L/M$ have small, incompletely degenerate cores, in which the temperature gradients though small are larger than in completely degenerate cores. Formula (1) still gives the interfacial temperature between core and envelope, and is thus a lower limit to the central temperature. It follows that stars with large internal generation of energy, that is, large values of $L/M$, have very hot central cores. Such stars will not be built on the standard model, but the effect of concentrating the energy sources to the centre, keeping other parameters constant, is only to increase the central temperature. Jeans's paradox, therefore, completely disappears; the best generators of energy have the hottest cores, and this applies to stars of all types, from white dwarfs to giants.

This result is quite obvious physically. The gaseous envelope acts simply as a blanket the role of which is to keep the core warm. A high energy-generator surrounds itself with a thick blanket, which keeps it very warm; a low energy-generator with a thin blanket. The actual value of the temperature attained in the core depends naturally on the intrinsic opacity of the blanketing envelope.

The above considerations illustrate, by a particular example, my contention that we cannot discuss the internal state of a star without discussing the opacity of its outer layers. In the case of a completely degenerate white dwarf, to ignore the effect of the photospheric opacity would be to obtain an utterly false estimate of the internal temperature.

The above results were communicated to Section A of the British Association on Sept. 29, 1931, at the discussion on the evolution of the universe, but did not appear in the printed accounts. I may add that the full theory of the "generalised standard model", now fairly completely worked out, affords possible explanations of many of the observed characteristics of the stars in general, including some of those summed up in the "Russell diagram", the approximate "mass-luminosity" law for non-dense stars, the occurrence of pulsating stars and Novae, and the possible existence of several types of configurations for large $M$ and $L$ (*O*-type, giant *M*-type, *N*-type, etc.) stars.

(**128**, 999; 1931)

E. A. Milne: Wadham College, Oxford, Nov. 17.

代入天狼星伴星的观测质量和光度值后，可得 $T'$ 为 $0.34\times10^6\kappa_1^{\frac{2}{3}}$ 度，就算我们给气体包络层的不透明度取一个较高的数值，比如令 $\kappa_1=300$，$T'$ 的值也只能达到 1,500 万度。如果气体包络层的不透明度低于 300，则 $T'$ 还会更低一些。对于一个几乎完全简并的恒星而言，其内部温度是由气体包络薄层中的**光球**不透明度决定的。

我认为所有恒星都包含一个由气体层围绕的简并区域，根据这个结论，公式 (1) 可以适用于所有恒星。$L/M$ 值较高的恒星具有小的、不完全的简并核，其温度梯度虽然小，但要比完全简并核的温度梯度大。公式 (1) 还给出了核与包络层界面处的温度，这个温度是中心温度的下限。因此内部能产生大量能量的恒星，也就是 $L/M$ 值很大的恒星，其中心核的温度相当高。这样的恒星不可能建立在标准模型之上，但这种将能源积聚到中心的效应，只会提高中心的温度，而不会使其他参数发生变化。因此，金斯的悖论完全消失了；产能最大的恒星有最热的核，这对所有类型的恒星都适用，不管是白矮星还是巨星。

这个结果的物理意义也很明显。气体包络层就像毯子一样起到了给核保温的作用。一个高效能量产生器周围包着一条使它保持高温的厚毯子；而一个低效能量产生器周围包着一条薄毯子。所以核心温度的实际值当然会取决于包络层的内禀不透明度。

上述结果通过一个特别的例子说明了我的观点，即在未了解一个恒星外层的不透明度之前，我们无法讨论它的内部状态。对于一颗完全简并的白矮星来说，忽略光球层的不透明效应将使我们对其内部温度的估计完全不可信。

我已经在 1931 年 9 月 29 日讨论宇宙演化时将以上结果提交给英国科学促进会的 A 分会（译者注：数理分会），但在后来的书面记录中没有看到。我要补充说明的是:“一般标准模型”的完整理论现在已经圆满地确定下来了，它能够对许多观测到的恒星特性给出可能的解释，包括一些从“罗素图”中总结出来的规律、非致密恒星的“质量—光度”定律、脉动变星和新星的出现以及高质量高光度恒星可能存在的几种构型（*O* 型，巨 *M* 型，*N* 型等）。

（伍岳 翻译；蒋世仰 审稿）

References:

1 Chandrasekhar, S., *Proc. Roy. Soc.*, 133, A, 241 (Sept. 1931).
2 Swirles, B., *Monthly Notices, R.A.S.*, 861 (June 1931).
3 Majumdar, R. C., *Astr. Nach.*, No. 5809 (Aug. 1931).
4 Russell, H. N., and Atkinson, R. d'E., *Nature*, 661 (May 2, 1931).
5 Jeans, J. H., *Astronomy and Cosmogony*, 139.
6 Jeans, J. H., *Astronomy and Cosmogony*, 125.

# Experimental Proof of the Spin of the Photon

C. V. Raman and S. Bhagavantam

## Editor's Note

**Chandrasekhara Venkata Raman and S. Bhagavantam had recently presented experimental evidence suggesting that the photon carries one unit of intrinsic angular momentum. In subsequent weeks, great improvements in their technique led to much more accurate results, which they now report. Their experiments involved measuring the depolarisation of the light scattered in a fluid. By eliminated a source of error in the previous experiments, due to light scattered from the walls of the containing vessels, they were able to show that a theory based on photons carrying quantum-mechanical spin 1 accounted for the results far more accurately than an alternative theory for spinless photons.**

IN a paper under this title which has recently appeared,[1] we have described and discussed observations which have led us to the conclusion that the light quantum possesses an intrinsic spin equal to one Bohr unit of angular momentum. In the four weeks which have elapsed since that paper was put into print, the experimental technique has been much improved in the direction of attaining greater precision. It appears desirable forthwith to report our newer results, which confirm the conclusion stated above.

As mentioned in earlier communications,[2] the experiment we set before ourselves was to determine the extent to which the depolarisation of Rayleigh scattering of monochromatic light is diminished when it is spectroscopically separated from the scattering of altered frequency arising from the molecular rotation in a fluid. An important improvement on our previous arrangements is the use of a pointolite mercury arc, which enables an intense beam of monochromatic light to be obtained which is rigorously transverse to the direction of observation. In the case of the feeble scattering by gases, a serious source of error is the parasitic illumination from the walls of the containing vessel. We have succeeded in eliminating this by using the gas under pressure in a steel cross with suitable arrangements for securing a dark background. The depolarisation of the scattered light is determined photographically with a spectrograph and a large nicol placed in front of the slit. The use of Schwarzchild's formula for photographic blackening enables the ratio of the horizontal and vertical components of scattered light to be calculated from the times of exposure in the two positions of the nicol which give equal densities in the spectra.

Using alternately a fine slit and a very broad slit on the spectrograph, the depolarisations of the Rayleigh scattering and of the total scattering respectively are determined. The following table gives the values for the case of oxygen, carbon dioxide, and nitrous oxide gases under pressure.

# 光子自旋的实验证据

拉曼，巴加万塔姆

## 编者按

钱德拉塞卡拉·文卡塔·拉曼和巴加万塔姆最近公布的实验结果证明光子带有一个单位的内禀角动量。在随后的几周内，他们通过改进实验技术得到了更为精确的结果，本文中报告了这些结果。他们用实验测量了光散射在一种液体中的解偏振现象。他们在去除了以前实验中由于容器壁的光散射所造成的误差之后指出：用假设光子在量子力学中的自旋为1的理论来解释实验结果要比假设光子没有自旋的理论更精确。

我们在最近发表的一篇同名文章中[1]，描述并讨论了我们的实验结果，即光量子具有一个玻尔角动量单位的内禀自旋。从那篇文章发表到现在已经过去了4周，我们的实验技术在得到更高的精确度方面又有了很大改进。我们似乎有必要立即把最新的实验结果发表出来，而这新的实验结果也证实了上述结论。

如从前的文章所提到的那样[2]，用光谱法可以将单色光的瑞利散射从液体中由分子转动产生的变频散射中分离出来，我们的实验就是要确定瑞利散射解偏振降低的程度。我们对以前实验装置的一个重要改进是使用了汞弧光点光源，这样我们就可以得到一束与观察者方向严格垂直的高强度单色光。在气体散射很弱的情况下，由容器壁产生的寄生亮度将导致严重的实验误差。我们通过在钢的十字形腔中对气体加压，而这种十字形腔可用适当方式确保处于黑暗的背景中，从而成功地降低了这种误差。利用放置于狭缝前的一个大号尼科尔棱镜和光谱仪，我们可以用照相法将散射光解偏振的数值确定下来。根据底片黑度的史瓦西公式，我们可用尼科尔棱镜上产生相同光谱强度的两个不同位置的曝光次数计算出散射光横向偏振分量和纵向偏振分量的比值。

在光谱仪上交替使用窄缝和宽缝，可以分别得到瑞利散射和总散射的解偏振百分比率。下表给出了 $O_2$、$CO_2$ 以及 $N_2O$ 气在加压条件下的相关数据：

Table: Depolarisation percent

| Gas | Observed | | Calculated | |
|---|---|---|---|---|
| | Total Scattering | Rayleigh Scattering | Kramers-Heisenberg Theory | Spin Theory |
| $O_2$ | 6.5 | 4.1 | 1.7 | 4.2 |
| $CO_2$ | 10.3 | 6.3 | 2.8 | 6.7 |
| $N_2O$ | 12.0 | 7.7 | 3.4 | 7.9 |

The depolarisations of the total scattering given in column 1 thus found spectroscopically are in good agreement with the best accepted values determined by other methods. Column 2 gives the observed depolarisations of the Rayleigh scattering, column 3 the values calculated from the Kramers-Heisenberg dispersion theory, and column 4 the values calculated from the theory of the spinning photons discussed in our paper. It will be seen that the values given by the latter are strikingly supported by the experimental results.

(**129**, 22-23; 1932)

C. V. Raman and S. Bhagavantam: 210 Bowbazar Street, Calcutta, India, Nov. 29.

References:

1 *Ind. Jour. Phy.*, **6**, 353 (Oct. 1931).

2 *Nature*, **128**, 576 and 727 (1931).

表：解偏振百分比率

| 气体 | 观测值 | | 计算值 | |
|---|---|---|---|---|
| | 总散射 | 瑞利散射 | 克拉莫 - 海森堡理论 | 自旋理论 |
| $O_2$ | 6.5 | 4.1 | 1.7 | 4.2 |
| $CO_2$ | 10.3 | 6.3 | 2.8 | 6.7 |
| $N_2O$ | 12.0 | 7.7 | 3.4 | 7.9 |

我们在第一列中给出了用光谱学方法观测得到的总散射解偏振比率，其数值与用其他方法得到的最佳结果十分吻合。第二列中给出的是观测到的瑞利散射解偏振比率，第三列是根据克拉莫—海森堡色散理论计算得到的数值，而第四列中的数据是由我们文章中讨论的光子自旋理论计算出来的。可以看到，第二种理论给出的数值与实验结果非常一致。

（王静 翻译；赵见高 审稿）

# A Possible Hydrogen Isotope of Mass 2

## Editor's Note

**The idea that the simplest of all elements, hydrogen, should have isotopes—with atomic nuclei of different mass—arose in the United States as a result of work by Harold C. Urey at the University of Chicago. Because Urey submitted his paper to the American Physical Society in 1931, *Nature* had to be content with a brief abstract describing his discovery. Urey first discovered heavy hydrogen, now called deuterium, afterwards used for moderating the speed of neutrons in nuclear reactors. Tritium was recognised later as being a radioactive isotope of hydrogen. Using Chadwick's concept of the neutron, the nucleus of deuterium consists of a proton and a neutron bound together, and that of tritium consists of a proton and two neutrons. Urey was awarded the Nobel Prize for chemistry in 1934.**

THERE is some evidence from atomic weight determinations that hydrogen should have isotopes of masses 2 and 3. If they exist, it can be shown from thermodynamical reasoning that molecules of the types $H^1H^2$ and $H^1H^3$ should concentrate relative to the common $H^1H^1$ molecules in residues from the evaporation of hydrogen near the triple point, whilst it is known from simple spectroscopic theory that the heavier atoms would have a displaced Balmer spectrum. Work undertaken on these considerations is reported by H. C. Urey, F. G. Brickwedde, and G. M. Murphy in the last issue of the *Bulletin of the American Physical Society* for 1931. The atom $H^3$ has not been detected, but it has been found that the lines $H\beta$, $H\gamma$, and $H\delta$ are accompanied by weaker lines which agree within the experimental error of 0.01 A. with the positions calculated for an isotope of mass 2. The reputed isotope lines have the same width as the main lines and are definitely more intense with the treated material, although they are present when ordinary hydrogen is used.

(**129**, 101; 1932)

# 氢可能具有质量数为 2 的同位素

## 编者按

所有元素中最简单的氢应该有原子核质量不同的同位素，这一观点源自美国芝加哥大学的哈罗德·尤里的工作成果。因为 1931 年尤里将他的论文呈交给了美国物理学会，所以《自然》杂志只好用一份简短的摘要描述其发现。尤里首先发现了现在称为氘的重氢，后来它被用来减缓核反应中中子的速度。再后来发现了作为氢的放射性同位素的氚。根据查德威克的中子概念，氘核由一个质子和一个中子结合而成，而氚核是由一个质子和两个中子构成的。尤里获得了 1934 年的诺贝尔化学奖。

人们在测定原子重量时发现，氢应该具有质量数为 2 和 3 的同位素。如果它们存在的话，由热力学原理可知，相对于普通的 $H^1H^1$ 分子，$H^1H^2$ 与 $H^1H^3$ 类型的分子应该富集在三相点附近氢蒸发后的残余物中，而根据简单的光谱学原理，较重的原子将会有移位的巴耳末光谱。尤里、布里克韦德和墨菲在 1931 年最后一期的《美国物理学会通报》中报道了他们在这方面的研究成果。虽然没有检测到 $H^3$ 原子，但已经发现与谱线 $H\beta$，$H\gamma$ 和 $H\delta$ 同时存在的还有一些弱线，在 0.01 Å 的实验误差范围内，这些弱线的位置与质量数为 2 的同位素的计算值一致。这些被视为同位素特征的谱线与主要谱线有相同的宽度，尽管它们在使用普通氢气时也会出现，但在精制过的物质中强度肯定会更高。

（王耀杨 翻译；李芝芬 审稿）

# Hydrogen Liquefaction Plant at the Royal Society Mond Laboratory

P. Kapitsa and J. D. Cockcroft

## Editor's Note

**The Cavendish Laboratory at Cambridge was in the 1930s the outstanding physics laboratory in Britain. Pyotr Kapitsa was a Russian who had been trained in Moscow as a physicist and who worked with Lord Rutherford for several years at Cambridge. Rutherford went to great lengths to build a laboratory for him (called the Royal Society Mond Laboratory) with equipment for studying intense magnetic fields and the behaviour of materials at low temperatures—superconductivity in particular. This article describes the construction of a hydrogen liquefier at the Mond Laboratory. In 1935, Kapitsa returned to Moscow at the behest of the Russian government, and was able to take most of his equipment with him.**

IN the Royal Society Mond Laboratory which is now under construction at Cambridge, in addition to the apparatus required for producing intense magnetic fields, a plant for cryogenic work will be installed. We have developed as a first instalment of this apparatus a hydrogen liquefier which differs from existing liquefiers in that it allows hydrogen of a lower degree of purity than the normal to be used for liquefaction. We propose in this article to give a brief description of the liquefaction apparatus, and later to publish a more complete account.

As is well known, the only method used at present for the liquefaction of hydrogen is essentially the same as that employed originally by Dewar in 1898, and is based on the Joule-Thomson effect combined with a thermal regenerator. In order to obtain a positive Joule-Thomson effect for hydrogen a preliminary cooling with liquid air is required. The principal difficulty encountered in liquefying hydrogen in large quantities is due to the impurities present in the gas; unless extremely pure hydrogen is used, these impurities solidify at the temperature of liquid hydrogen and block the tubes in the regenerator and stop the circulation of the gas. The seriousness of this effect can be shown from a numerical example. The purest commercial hydrogen available in Great Britain is 99.5 percent pure; 3.9 cubic metres of gas are required to produce 5 litres of liquid hydrogen, and the impurities—chiefly air—when solidified have a volume of about nineteen cubic centimetres. Their deposition is thus quite sufficient to block the small bore tubes of the regenerator, and special precautions have to be taken to avoid this difficulty. In the method developed by Kamerlingh Onnes at Leyden, a preliminary purification of the hydrogen to a high degree of purity is carried out, and steps are taken to save the gas after it has been used for experiments. Another method introduced by Meissner is to make a special trap in the hydrogen circulation in such a way that in it the greater part of the impurities

# 皇家学会蒙德实验室的氢液化车间

彼得·卡皮查，约翰·考克饶夫

## 编者按

剑桥大学的卡文迪什实验室是英国20世纪30年代著名的物理实验室。彼得·卡皮查是一位俄罗斯人，他在莫斯科被培养成了一名物理学家，后来在剑桥大学与卢瑟福勋爵一起工作了很多年。卢瑟福不遗余力地为他建立了一个实验室（即皇家学会蒙德实验室），该实验室配有研究强磁场和低温下物质特性，特别是超导电性的各种设备。这篇文章对蒙德实验室中氢液化器的构造进行了描述。1935年，卡皮查在俄国政府的要求下回到了莫斯科，并且带走了他的大部分设备。

在剑桥大学正在建设的皇家学会蒙德实验室，除了配置了能产生强磁场的仪器以外，还将装备一个低温车间。我们研制了这套设备的第一个部分，即氢液化器，它与现有液化器的不同之处在于，在液化过程中可以使用纯度低于普通液化过程所需纯度的氢。在本文中我们对这种液化设备进行了简要的介绍，以后还会发表更详细的报告。

我们都知道，目前氢液化的方法只有一种，与杜瓦在1898年首先使用的方法没有本质上的区别，它是基于焦耳—汤姆孙效应和回热器原理设计的。为了使氢产生正的焦耳—汤姆孙效应，我们需要用液态空气进行预冷却。在大量液化氢的过程中遇到的主要困难是气体不纯的问题；如果使用的氢纯度不高，那么氢中的杂质就会在液氢温度下固化，堵塞回热器中的管道，导致气体循环不畅。我们可以用数字来说明这种效应的严重性。在英国，最纯的工业氢纯度可达99.5%，制备5升液氢需要3.9 $m^3$的氢气，其中的杂质（主要为空气）在固化时的体积约为19 $cm^3$。因而它们的沉积物足以堵塞住回热器中内径很小的管道，因此我们必须采取有效措施以避免这一问题。莱顿的卡默林·翁内斯发明的方法是：先将氢纯化至很高的纯度，当实验完成后，再经过一系列的步骤来回收氢气。另一种由迈斯纳设计的方法是：在氢的循环路径中设置一个特殊的冷阱，使大部分杂质在其中凝结。但每隔一定时间，液化工作就要停下来，通过一个特殊的电加热器来加热这个冷阱，清除其中的凝结物。

are condensed; the liquefaction is stopped at intervals to allow the trap to be warmed by a special electrical heater and emptied.

In our liquefier we have adopted a different principle which allows us to use the apparatus continuously even with commercial hydrogen. The method is as follows: Two hydrogen circuits are used in the liquefaction process; one circulation is similar to that used in ordinary liquefiers, but is completely closed; in it about 0.7 cubic metre of purified hydrogen is compressed to 160–170 atmospheres, and after preliminary cooling in liquid nitrogen at reduced pressure passes through a regenerator spiral and then expands to normal pressure, thereby cooling down a "condenser" to liquid hydrogen temperature, after which it returns through the regenerator to the compressor. In the second circuit we use ordinary commercial hydrogen, which is reduced to a pressure of 3–4 atmospheres by means of a reduction valve from a cylinder. This hydrogen is cooled down to the temperature of liquid nitrogen and is then passed directly into an "exchanger" cooled by the first circuit. Since the liquefaction temperature of hydrogen at 3 atmospheres pressure is a few degrees higher than at normal pressure, it liquefies in the exchanger. The whole of the cooling down process, from the temperature of liquid nitrogen to the temperature of liquid hydrogen, takes place in the exchanger, so that all the impurities condense here and do not have a chance of being deposited in the tubes. The solidified impurities are heavier than the liquid hydrogen and remain at the bottom of the exchanger, which is large enough to retain all the impurities solidified in the course of a run.

The scheme of the liquefier is shown diagrammatically in Fig. 1, and a photograph of the liquefier in Fig. 2. The hydrogen in the closed circulation enters at tube 1, passes through the regenerator spiral *A*, and enters the container *B* containing liquid nitrogen at reduced pressure, from which it passes through the second regenerator spiral *D*, and then through the expansion valve *E* to the condenser *F*, where it is partially liquefied. When the condenser *F* is about one-third full, the liquid hydrogen passes through tube 6 to a spiral which cools exchanger *G*; it then goes through the regenerator spirals *D* and *A* and passes back to the compressor through the outlet 2. The commercial hydrogen enters the tube 3 and passes only through the first regenerator circuit *A*, and the container *B*, and then passes directly into the exchanger *G*, where it meets the spiral cooled by the closed circulation and is liquefied at three atmospheres pressure. The exchanger *G* is continuously drained through the tube 4 passing through the condenser *F* as a spiral and leading to valve *H*, which controls the flow of liquid hydrogen into a Dewar receptacle. In passing through the spiral of condenser *F*, the liquid hydrogen is cooled through a few degrees from the temperature corresponding to liquefaction at three atmospheres pressure to the temperature of liquid hydrogen at atmospheric pressure. This prevents excessive evaporation when it is drawn off into the Dewar receptacle. The exchanger *G* is filled with wire gauze which helps in the liquefaction. In the actual liquefier a double container is used for the liquid nitrogen. In one part the liquid nitrogen is evaporated at slightly reduced pressure and the evaporated gas passes up tube 5 of regenerator *A* and takes up sufficient heat to cool down the incoming hydrogen of the liquefaction circulation; in the other part the liquid nitrogen evaporates at a few centimetres pressure and passes away

我们的液化器采用的是另一种原理，所以即便使用工业氢也不会影响我们连续地使用这个设备。方法是这样的：在液化过程中我们使用两个氢循环回路；第一个循环类似于普通的液化器，不过是完全封闭的；在其中，约 0.7 $m^3$ 纯化过的氢被压缩到 160~170 个大气压，随后在减压的液氮中被预冷，经过回热器螺旋管，然后膨胀到常压，从而把“冷凝器”冷却到液氢的温度，最后通过回热器再回到压缩机。在第二个循环中，我们使用普通的工业氢，由钢瓶通过一个减压阀使气压降到 3~4 个大气压。这些氢气被冷却到液氮温度后，立即进入被第一个循环冷却了的“交换器”中。因为氢在 3 个大气压下的液化温度比常压下略高几度，所以氢气在交换器中被液化。从液氮温度冷却到液氢温度的全过程都在交换器中发生，所以所有杂质都在这里凝结，也就不可能有机会沉积在管道中了。固化的杂质比液氢重，因而沉积在交换器的底部，交换器中的空间足够大，可以容纳一次生产中固化的所有杂质。

液化器构造的示意图示于图 1，液化器的照片示于图 2。封闭循环中的氢由管道 1 进入，通过回热器的螺旋管 $A$，进入装有减压液氮的容器 $B$，由此再经过第二个回热器螺旋管 $D$，然后流经膨胀阀 $E$，进入冷凝器 $F$，在 $F$ 中有一部分氢会被液化。当冷凝器 $F$ 中的液氢量接近容器高度的 1/3 时，液氢经过管 6 进入到一个螺旋管中，这个螺旋管可以冷却交换器 $G$；然后液氢经过回热器螺旋管 $D$ 和 $A$，由出口 2 返回压缩机。工业氢从管 3 进入，只经过第一个回热器管道 $A$ 和容器 $B$，而后直接进入交换器 $G$，在那里它接触到被封闭循环系统冷却的螺旋管，并在 3 个大气压下被液化。交换器 $G$ 中的液氢通过冷凝器 $F$ 的螺旋管 4 被持续地排出来，到达阀 $H$，阀 $H$ 可以控制液氢进入接收容器杜瓦瓶中的流量。在经过冷凝器 $F$ 中的螺旋管时，液氢的温度降低了几度，从 3 个大气压下氢液化的温度降低到 1 个大气压下液氢的温度。这一过程防止了液氢排入到杜瓦容器时过多的蒸发。交换器 $G$ 中装满了有助于液化的金属丝网。在实际的液化器中有一个装液氮的双层容器。在其中一层容器中，液氮在略微降低的气压下蒸发，同时吸收足够的热量使进入液化循环系统的氢冷却，而蒸发的气体则通过回热器 $A$ 的管 5 向上排出。在容器的另一层，液氮在几厘米汞柱的压强下蒸发，并直接排放到泵中。（最近我们参观了柏林西蒙博士的实验室，被告知他所使用的液化器应用着同样的两步冷却氢的原理。）

directly to the pump. (During a recent visit to Dr. Simon's laboratory at Berlin, we have been informed that the same principle of cooling hydrogen in two stages was used in his liquefier.)

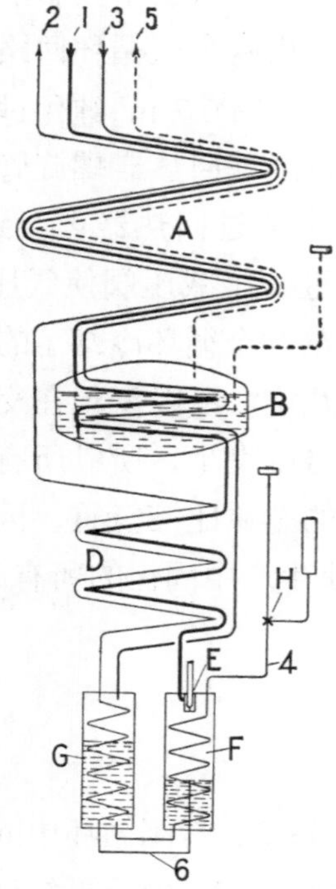

Fig. 1

Fig. 2

The tubes used in the liquefier have a small cross-section and the gas is allowed to flow with high velocity. We find, as suggested by Meissner,[1] that the heat exchange can be calculated from Nusselt's formula.[2] From this formula it appeared that a good heat exchange could be obtained by using a high velocity of the gas, and this enabled us to reduce the length of the regenerator spirals very considerably. In our case the spiral *A* was about 2.5 metres long and the spiral *D* 5 metres. The high tensile strength of the copper-nickel alloy allows the heat capacity of the regenerator spiral to be considerably reduced. The whole apparatus is soldered into a copper vessel 26 cm. in diameter by 67 cm. high, which is then evacuated. By the use of charcoal to absorb gases given off from the metal, a good vacuum can be maintained and a high degree of thermal insulation maintained without the use of glass Dewar vessels.

The new liquefier has the considerable advantage that the rate of liquefaction can be measured continuously by a flow meter placed before the inlet of tube 3. The flow meter will also indicate the moment when the gas begins to condense. An electrical flow meter is used. The hydrogen is passed through a thin-walled copper-nickel tube 20 cm. long, which is heated in the middle by a platinum wire spiral. The cooling of this spiral depends on

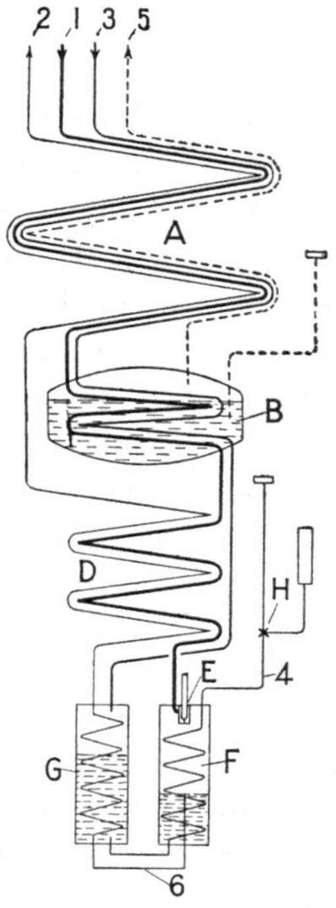


图 1

图 2

在液化器中使用的是横截面较小的管子，可以使气体高速流过。我们发现，正如迈斯纳所指出的那样[1]，热交换可以通过努塞尔特方程[2]进行计算。这个方程表明，使用高速气体也许可以得到更好的热交换效果，这使我们可以大幅度地缩短回热器螺旋管的长度。在我们设计的仪器中，螺旋管 $A$ 的长度约为 2.5 m，螺旋管 $D$ 的长度约为 5 m。铜镍合金有很高的抗张强度，从而可以使回热器螺旋管的热容量大大降低。整个装置被焊接在一个直径为 26 cm，高 67 cm 的铜桶内，然后把桶内部抽成真空。用活性炭来吸收金属中放出的气体以保持高真空，而且在不用玻璃杜瓦瓶的情况下也可以维持很高的热绝缘。

这种新型液化器的重要优势在于：只要在进入管 3 之前安装一个流量计就可以连续地测量液化速率。通过这个流量计我们还可以知道气体是在什么时间开始凝聚的。我们使用的是一个电子的流量计。氢流经一个 20 cm 长的薄壁铜镍合金管，合金管中部由一个铂丝螺旋线圈进行加热。该线圈的冷却取决于氢在管中的流动速率，

the rate of flow of hydrogen through the tube and is measured by its change of resistance. The spiral is made in two parts which form the two opposite arms of a Wheatstone bridge; the other two arms are also made of platinum, and are wound on the thick copper main tube, and thus are kept at the temperature of the inlet hydrogen. The apparatus is calibrated by separate experiments.

The liquefier has proved to be as efficient as ordinary existing liquefiers. The heat exchange is good, and the temperature of the return hydrogen and nitrogen at exit is only 10° below the temperature of the inlet hydrogen. 4–5 litres of liquid nitrogen are used for the initial cooling, and liquefaction starts 40–50 minutes after the beginning of the preliminary cooling. The liquefaction rate is 4 litres an hour, of which about twenty percent is lost when the hydrogen is drawn off. The liquid nitrogen consumption is about 1.3 litres per net litre of liquid hydrogen. We normally produce 6 litres of liquid hydrogen in a single run, using commercial hydrogen, and have not up to the present had a single stoppage due to blocked tubes. The liquefier was made in our workshop by the laboratory mechanic, Mr. H. E. Pearson.

The compressor used for the work is a compact, triple stage, high speed (600 r.p.m.) machine which was specially built for us by Messrs. Reavell and Company. The detailed design was worked out by Mr. J. Hendry. Special care was taken to ensure complete freedom from leakage; the space below the cylinders is connected to the compressor suction, and the piston rods are surrounded by oil-sealed glands which are fitted with leakage indicators. At full speed the compressor capacity is 25 cubic metres of free gas per hour; at present we are using it at reduced speeds giving a delivery of 16 cubic metres per hour.

The problem of storage of liquid hydrogen has been dealt with on new lines. It is well known that owing to the small latent heat it is difficult to store liquid hydrogen in an ordinary Dewar flask for more than a day. As described by Meissner,[3] the best containers, of a capacity of 6 litres, evaporate at the rate of 15 gm. (200 c.c.) of hydrogen an hour; these containers have a specially good vacuum and silvered surfaces to prevent radiation losses, which are the most important source of loss of cold. In order to diminish these radiation losses further, we have worked out a design for a Dewar flask which has all the advantages of the method of keeping the liquid hydrogen container immersed in liquid air, without the disadvantages and technical difficulties which occur if this method is used on a large scale. A drawing of the flask is shown in Fig. 3. It consists of a twin flask; flask 1 contains liquid air, and flask 2 liquid hydrogen. The inside of flask 1 is connected by means of a copper rod 3 to a copper shield 4 which surrounds the container of flask 2. The liquid air cools the shield 4 by thermal conductivity, and the radiation losses from the liquid hydrogen are considerably reduced. The hydrogen flask has a capacity of 5 litres and the liquid air flask holds 2 litres. The evaporation of hydrogen is about 2.5 gm. an hour, which is about seven times smaller than for ordinary flasks, and enables the liquid hydrogen not required for immediate use to remain in the flask for five days. The consumption of liquid air is about 1.7 litres per day. A picture of the flask will be seen in

这可根据线圈电阻的改变来测定。线圈由两部分组成，这两部分构成了惠斯通电桥的两个相对的臂；另外两个臂也由铂丝制成，缠绕在粗的铜主管上，这样就可以与进口处氢的温度保持一致。我们用另外的实验来校正这个仪器。

事实证明，我们设计的液化器与现有的普通液化器一样有效。它的热交换效果很好，返回的氢和氮在出口处的温度只比进口处氢的温度低 10 度。起始预冷需要 4~5 升液氮，在预冷 40~50 分钟以后开始液化。液化速率为每小时 4 升，在液氢被放出时会损失掉约 20%。每生产 1 升液氢需要消耗 1.3 升液氮。每开机一次我们用工业氢通常可生产 6 升液氢，到目前为止我们还没有遇到过一次因管道阻塞而导致的中断。这个液化器是由实验室机械师皮尔逊先生在我们的车间制造的。

本工作使用的是一台小型三级高速（600 转 / 分）压缩机，是由里维尔公司为我们特别制造的。具体的设计工作由亨德里先生完成。他在设计上的特殊考虑能够保证系统不发生泄漏；汽缸下部空间与压缩机的吸入部相连，活塞杆周围是油封的密封管，在这些密封管上都装有检漏指示器。在全速下，压缩机的能力为 25 $m^3$/h 自由气体，目前我们在较低的速度下运行，仅为 16 $m^3$/h。

我们采用新的方法解决了液氢的储存问题。大家都知道，因为液氢潜热小，所以用普通杜瓦瓶来储存液氢很难超过一天。正如迈斯纳所述[3]，就算用质量最好的 6 升容器，液氢的蒸发速率也会达到每小时 15 克 (200 毫升 ) ；这种容器有着特别高的真空度，并且在表面镀银以防止辐射损失，而辐射是冷量散失的主要原因。为了进一步减少辐射带来的损失，我们设计出一种新的杜瓦瓶，它具有把液氢容器浸于液态空气中这种方法的所有优点，而且解决了大规模使用这种方法时会遇到的不便和技术难题。这种杜瓦瓶的草图示于图 3。杜瓦瓶由一对瓶子组成，瓶 1 中装有液态空气，瓶 2 中为液氢。瓶 1 的内壁通过铜棒 3 与包围瓶 2 的铜屏 4 相连，液态空气通过热传导冷却铜屏 4，从而使液氢的辐射损失大大减少。液氢瓶的容积为 5 升，液态空气瓶的容积为 2 升。液氢的蒸发速度大约为每小时 2.5 克，约为普通杜瓦瓶的 1/7，这使得不立即使用的液氢可以在瓶中保存 5 天。液态空气的消耗量约为每天 1.7 升。在图 2 中立于液化器旁边的即为这种杜瓦瓶。

Fig. 2 standing beside the liquefier.

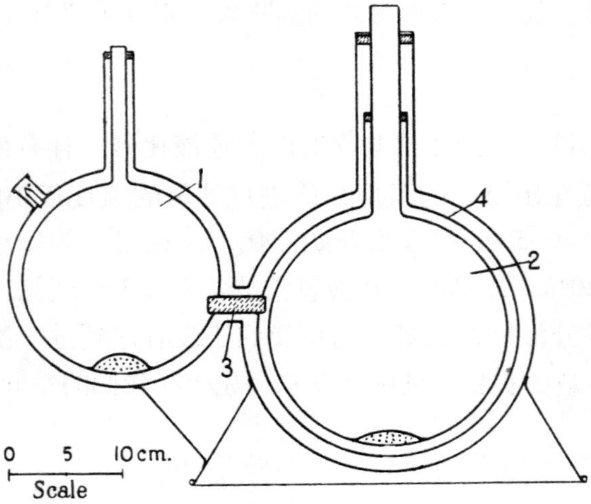


Fig. 3

Another flask is now being constructed in which the radiation will be further reduced by silvering the inner surfaces, thereby increasing the efficiency of the flask still further. The flask was manufactured for us by Messrs. Siebe Gorman and Co., Ltd.

The remaining equipment of the Laboratory is on the usual lines, and all the known precautions against explosion are employed, flame-proof mining type motors being used for the compressor drive and all open switchgear placed in a separate room. Besides the usual precautions we have introduced one more, which consists of a standard alarm lamp as used for showing the presence of coal gas in mines. This indicator is manufactured by Messrs. The W. R. Patents, Ltd. Should a leak occur, and the concentration of hydrogen in the room reach a value of more than one percent, the lamp operates a relay which automatically stops the machines, and throws the windows open at the bottom and the top of the rooms where the liquefier is in operation, thus providing a complete air circulation.

We were enabled to construct this plant by a special grant made by the Department of Scientific and Industrial Research.

(**129**, 224-226; 1932)

References:
1 *Handbuch der Physik*, **11**, 295.
2 Groeber, *Wärmeübertragung*, 84.
3 *Z. Instrumentenkunde*, **50**, 121 (1930).

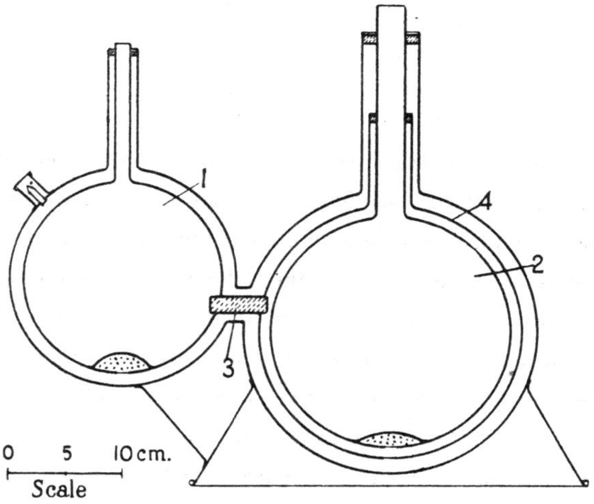


图 3

我们正在制造另一种瓶子，我们要在瓶子的内表面镀上银以便进一步减少辐射，从而更大地提高它的效率。斯西比戈曼股份有限公司承接了为我们制造这种瓶子的任务。

这个实验室中的其他设备都是常规设备，并应用了所有已知的防爆措施，驱动压缩机使用的是防火的矿用马达，所有暴露在外的接电开关都被置于一间独立的房子里。除了常规预防措施以外，我们还引进了另外一个措施，它由一个标准的报警灯组成，报警灯原本是用来显示煤矿中是否存在煤气的。这种指示器是由 W. R. 专利有限公司制造的。如果发生了泄漏，当房间内的氢气浓度超过 1% 时，报警灯就会通过一个继电器使机器自动停止运转，并打开液化器所在房间底部和顶部的窗户，使空气得到彻底的流通。

我们能建成这个车间是由于得到了科学与工业研究部的特别资助。

（李飞 翻译；陶宏杰 审稿）

# The Decline of Determinism*

A. Eddington

## Editor's Note

**Ten years ago, Arthur Eddington claims here, practically every notable physicist was a determinist, at least regarding physical processes. Physicists believed they possessed a powerful scheme of causal scientific law, embodied especially in classical mechanics, and saw the project of science as explaining ever more phenomena within this scheme. The quantum theory has now changed all this, stimulating reactions ranging from incredulity and cynicism to yawning indifference. Eddington argues, however, that the new indeterministic theory cannot be considered to be a rejection of the scientific method. He compares the older deterministic or "primary" laws to a scientific gold standard, now replaced by a "secondary" currency. Most other physicists now wonder why those primary laws were once accorded such reverence.**

DETERMINISM has faded out of theoretical physics. Its exit has been commented on in various ways. Some writers are incredulous, and cannot be persuaded that determinism has really been eliminated. Some think that it is only a domestic change in physics, having no reactions on general philosophic thought. Some imagine that it is a justification for miracles. Some decide cynically to wait and see if determinism fades in again.

The rejection of determinism is in no sense an abdication of scientific method; indeed it has increased the power and precision of the mathematical analysis of observed phenomena. On the other hand, I cannot agree with those who belittle the general philosophical significance of the change. The withdrawal of physical science from an attitude it has adopted consistently for more than two hundred years is not to be treated lightly; and it involves a reconsideration of our views with regard to one of the perplexing problems of our existence. In this address, I shall deal mainly with the physical universe, and say very little about mental determinism or freewill. That might well be left to those who are more accustomed to arguing about such questions, if only they could be awakened to the new situation which has arisen on the physical side. At present I can see little sign of such an awakening.

### Definitions of Determinism

Let us first be sure that we agree as to what is meant by determinism. I quote three definitions or descriptions for your consideration. The first is by a mathematician (Laplace):

* Presidential address to the Mathematical Association delivered on Jan. 4.

# 决定论的衰落*

阿瑟·爱丁顿

## 编者按

10年前，阿瑟·爱丁顿在《自然》杂志上发表文章声称实际上所有的知名物理学家都是决定论者，至少他们面对物理过程时都是如此。物理学家们认为他们拥有一个因果相联的庞大科学体系——最明显的例子是经典力学领域，并且人们还在利用这种模式解释更多的现象。但现在量子理论改变了所有的一切，人们对此的反应各不相同：有人将信将疑，有人冷嘲热讽，还有些人漠不关心。然而，爱丁顿指出：不能认为新出现的非决定论是一种反科学的方法。他把旧有的决定论或称“基本定律”比作科学上的金本位，现在被“第二代”货币所取代。现在，大多数物理学家都不能理解为什么这些基本定律曾经受到过如此的推崇。

在理论物理领域里，决定论的身影渐渐淡去。人们对它的退出持有各种不同的观点。有些作者对此表示怀疑，不相信决定论真的被排除了；有些则认为它仅仅是物理学领域内部的变化，对一般的哲学思想没有任何影响；另一些人认为这是对奇怪现象的合理性解释；还有一部分人冷眼旁观，等着看决定论是否会卷土重来。

摒弃决定论绝不是要放弃科学方法；在对观测到的现象进行数学分析时，它也的确提高了分析的能力和精度。从另一方面来说，我无法认同那些低估了这个变化所具有的一般哲学意义的人。我们不能轻描淡写地摆脱两百多年来被自然科学所一致采取的看法；并且这使得我们必须重新审视一个有关存在物的复杂问题。在这里，我将主要就物质世界进行探讨，而几乎不涉及思想决定论和自由意志。最好把它们留给那些更加善于探讨此类问题的人，只要他们能意识到目前在物理学方面已经出现的新情况。而我目前几乎看不出任何意识到这种情况的迹象。

### 决定论的定义

让我们首先确保我们对决定论的含义有一致的认识。我要引用三种定义或描述给你们作参考。第一种是一位数学家（拉普拉斯）的叙述：

---

* 本文是1月4日爱丁顿对数学分会所作的演讲。

We ought then to regard the present state of the universe as the effect of its antecedent state and the cause of the state that is to follow. An intelligence, who for a given instant should be acquainted with all the forces by which Nature is animated and with the several positions of the entities composing it, if, further, his intellect were vast enough to submit those data to analysis, would include in one and the same formula the movements of the largest bodies in the universe and those of the lightest atom. Nothing would be uncertain for him; the future as well as the past would be present to his eyes. The human mind in the perfection it has been able to give to astronomy affords a feeble outline of such an intelligence. ... All its efforts in the search for truth tend to approximate without limit to the intelligence we have just imagined.

The second is by a philosopher (C. D. Broad):

"Determinism" is the name given to the following doctrine. Let $S$ be any substance, $\psi$ any characteristic, and $t$ any moment. Suppose that $S$ is in fact in the state $\delta$ with respect to $\psi$ at $t$. Then the compound supposition that everything else in the world should have been exactly as it in fact was, and that $S$ should have been in one of the other two alternative states with respect to $\psi$ is an impossible one. [The three alternative states (of which $\delta$ is one) are to have the characteristic $\psi$, not to have it, and to be changing.]

The third is by a poet (Omar Khayyám):

With Earth's first Clay They did the Last Man knead,
And there of the Last Harvest sow'd the Seed:
And the first Morning of Creation wrote What the Last Dawn of Reckoning shall read.

I propose to take the poet's description as my standard. Perhaps this may seem an odd choice; but there is no doubt that his words express what is in our minds when we refer to determinism. The other two definitions need to be scrutinised suspiciously; we are afraid there may be a catch in them. In saying that the physical universe as now pictured is not a universe in which "the first morning of creation wrote what the last dawn of reckoning shall read", we make it clear that the abandonment of determinism is no technical quibble, but is to be understood in the most ordinary sense of the words.

It is important to notice that all three definitions introduce the time-element. Determinism postulates not merely causes but pre-existing causes. Determinism means predetermination. Hence in any argument about determinism the dating of the alleged causes is an important matter; we must challenge them to produce their birth certificates.

Ten years ago, practically every physicist of repute was, or believed himself to be, a determinist, at any rate so far as inorganic phenomena are concerned. He believed that he had come across a scheme of strictly causal law, and that it was the primary aim of science to fit as much of our experience as possible into such a scheme. The methods, definitions, and conceptions of physical science were so much bound up with this assumption of

我们应把目前宇宙的状态看作是它先前状态的结果和未来状态的原因。假定有这么一位天才，他在某个确定的瞬间知道了所有驱动自然界运转的力以及组成宇宙的所有实体的几个位置，如果他还具有足够的才智来收集分析这些数据的话，他就能够把从最大物体到最小原子的运动都包括在同一个公式中。对他来说，没有什么是不确定的，过去和未来全在他的掌握之中。人类的完美主义思想为天文学描绘了一个如此聪慧的人的大致轮廓……对我们刚才幻想中的这位天才而言，他为探寻到真理所做的努力几乎是不受限制的。

第二种定义来自于一位哲学家（布罗德）的观点：

“决定论”指的是下述学说：设 $S$ 为任意一个物质，$\psi$ 为任意一种特性，$t$ 为任意一个时刻。假设 $t$ 时刻特性为 $\psi$ 的物质 $S$ 实际上处于状态 $\delta$，那么认为：世界上的任意其他物质都处于实际状态，并且物质 $S$ 本来应该处于关于特性 $\psi$ 的其他两种状态中的一种的复合推断是不可能成立的。[ 这三种状态（$\delta$ 是其中一种）分别为：具备特性 $\psi$、不具备特性 $\psi$ 和正在变化的状态。]

第三种说法则是一位诗人（奥马尔·海亚姆）提出来的：

最初的泥丸捏成了最终的人形，
最后的收成便是那最初的种子：
天地开辟时的老文章写就了天地掩闭时的字句。

我选择诗人的描述作为我对决定论的理解标准。看起来这可能是个奇怪的选择，但是毫无疑问他的描述正是我们提到决定论时脑海里所浮现的想法。其他的两个定义则需以怀疑的态度仔细研究，恐怕它们之中会存在某些陷阱。当我们提到现在所描绘的物质世界时，指的并不是那种“天地开辟时的老文章写就了天地掩闭时的字句”的宇宙。我们要让人明白放弃决定论并不是一种巧妙的推托，而是用一种最平实的语言就可以理解的。

值得特别注意的是三种定义都引入了时间元素。决定论不仅仅是要假定存在的起因，而是要假定起因在早先就已经存在了。决定论意味着预先决定。因此在任何有关决定论的争论中，确定所谓起因的时间是一个非常重要的问题，我们必须让它们为自身的起源提供证明。

十年前，至少是在考虑无机系统的物理现象时，几乎所有知名的物理学家都是，或者认为他们自己是，一个决定论者。他们确信自己已经发现了一个严格的因果律体系，并且相信科学的首要目的就是尽可能地把我们的日常体验纳入到这个体系内。物理科学中的方法、定义以及概念受到这种决定论假设过多的限制，以至于人们把

determinism that the limits (if any) of the scheme of causal law were looked upon as the ultimate limits of physical science.

To see the change that has occurred, we need only refer to a recent book which goes as deeply as anyone has yet penetrated into the fundamental structure of the physical universe, Dirac's "Quantum Mechanics". I do not know whether Dirac is a determinist or not; quite possibly he believes as firmly as ever in the existence of a scheme of strict causal law. But the significant thing is that in this book he has no occasion to refer to it. In the fullest account of what has yet been ascertained as to the way things work, causal law is not mentioned.

This is a deliberate change in the aim of theoretical physics. If the older physicist had been asked why he thought that progress consisted in fitting more and more phenomena into a deterministic scheme, his most effective reply would have been "What else is there to do?" A book such as Dirac's supplies the answer. For the new aim has been extraordinarily fruitful, and phenomena which had hitherto baffled exact mathematical treatment are now calculated and the predictions are verified by experiment. We shall see presently that indeterministic law is as useful a basis for practical predictions as deterministic law was. By all practical tests, progress along this new branch track must be recognised as a great advance in knowledge. No doubt some will say "Yes, but it is often necessary to make a detour in order to get round an obstacle. Presently we shall have passed the obstacle and be able to join the old road again." I should say rather that we are like explorers on whom at last it has dawned that there are other enterprises worth pursuing besides finding the North-West Passage; and we need not take too seriously the prophecy of the old mariners who regard these enterprises as a temporary diversion to be followed by a return to the "true aim of geographical exploration". But at the moment I am not concerned with prophecy and counter-prophecy; the important thing is to grasp the facts of the present situation.

## Secondary Law

Let us first try to see how the new aim of physical science originated. We observe certain regularities in the course of Nature and formulate these as "laws of Nature". Laws may be stated positively or negatively, "Thou shalt" or "Thou shalt not". For the present purpose it is most convenient to formulate them negatively. Consider the following two regularities which occur in our experience:

(*a*) We never come across equilateral triangles whose angles are unequal.

(*b*) We never come across 13 trumps in our hand at bridge.

In our ordinary outlook we explain these regularities in fundamentally different ways. We

因果律体系的局限性（如果有的话）看作是物理科学的极限。

要了解已经出现的改变，我们仅仅需要参考最近出版的一本书——狄拉克所著的《量子力学》，它比任何人都更深层次地触及到物质世界的基本结构。我不知道狄拉克是否是一个决定论者，他很有可能一直都坚信存在着严格的因果律体系。但是值得注意的是，在这本书里他没有提及这个问题。在对已经可以确定的事物运行规律的最全面的叙述中，并没有提到因果律。

理论物理研究目标中的这样一个改变是经过深思熟虑的。如果年长些的物理学家被问及为什么科学的发展就在于把越来越多的现象纳入决定论的体系，那么他最有力的回应便是“除此之外还有什么别的办法吗？”狄拉克所写的那样一本书给出了答案。因为新的研究目标已经产生了非凡的效果，迄今仍难以给出精确数学处理的物理现象现在也可以计算出来了，并且很多预言得到了实验的验证。现在我们应该明白，非决定论的规律和决定论的规律一样有效，都可以作为实际预测的原则。所有实践都证明，我们必须把在这个新分支方向上取得的进展看作是知识的巨大进步。毫无疑问，有些人会说：“对，但为了避开障碍物，通常会绕道而行。目前我们已经越过了障碍，可以重新回到以前的老路上去了。”不过我却这样认为：我们就像那些探险家，他们最后终于意识到，除了去探寻西北通道以外，还有其他值得追求的事业。我们不需要过分看重老水手的预言，他们把这些事业当作是一种暂时性的消遣，随后还是要回到“地理大发现这个终极目标上”。但此刻我不关心那些预言和反预言的论调，重要的是把握目前的实际情况。

## 次级定律

首先，让我们了解一下物理科学中的新目标是怎样出现的。我们观察自然过程中的某些规律，然后把它们明确表达为“自然定律”。这些定律既可以用肯定句式陈述也可以用否定句式陈述，比如“你应该”或者“你不应该”。对于当前的需要，用否定句式来阐明最为方便。在我们的生活经历中会出现以上两种规律：

(*a*) 我们绝不会见到一个等边三角形具有不相等的角。

(*b*) 在打桥牌时我们绝不会碰到手中有 13 张王牌的情况。

按照我们通常的观点，我们可以用根本不同的方法来解释这些规则。我们会说

say that the first occurs because the contrary experience is *impossible*; the second occurs because the contrary experience is *too improbable*.

This distinction is entirely theoretical; there is nothing in the observations themselves to suggest to which type a particular regularity belongs. We recognise that "impossible" and "too improbable" can both give adequate explanation of any observed uniformity of experience, and the older theory rather haphazardly explained some uniformities one way and other uniformities the other way. In the new physics we make no such discrimination; the union obviously must be on the basis of (*b*), not (*a*). It can scarcely be supposed that there is a law of Nature which makes the holding of 13 trumps in a properly dealt hand impossible; but it *can* be supposed that our failure to find equilateral triangles with unequal angles is only because such triangles are too improbable.

We must, however, first consider the older view which distinguished type (*a*) as a special class of regularity. Accordingly, there were two types of natural law. The earth keeps revolving round the sun, because it is *impossible* it should run away. Heat flows from a hot body to a cold, because it is *too improbable* that it should flow the other way. I call the first type *primary* law, and the second type *secondary* law. The recognition of secondary law was the thin end of the wedge that ultimately cleft the deterministic scheme.

For practical purposes primary and secondary law exert equally strict control. The improbability referred to in secondary law is so enormous that failure even in an isolated case is not to be seriously contemplated. You would be utterly astounded if heat flowed from you to the fire so that you got chilled by standing in front of it, although such an occurrence is judged by physical theory to be not impossible but improbable. Now it is axiomatic that in a deterministic scheme nothing is left to chance; a law which has the ghost of a chance of failure cannot form part of the scheme. So long as the aim of physics is to bring to light a deterministic scheme, the pursuit of secondary law is a blind alley since it leads only to probabilities. The determinist is not content with a law which prescribes that, given reasonable luck, the fire will warm me; he admits that that is the probable effect, but adds that somewhere at the base of physics there are other laws which prescribe just what the fire will do to me, luck or no luck.

To borrow an analogy from genetics, determinism is a *dominant character*. We can (and indeed must) have secondary indeterministic laws within any scheme of primary deterministic law—laws which tell us what is likely to happen but are overridden by the dominant laws which tell us what must happen. So determinism watched with equanimity the development of indeterministic law within itself. What matter? Deterministic law remains dominant. It was not foreseen that indeterministic law when fully grown might be able to stand by itself and supplant its dominant parent. There is a game called "Think of a number". After doubling, adding, and other calculations, there comes the direction "Take away the number you first thought of". We have reached that position in physics, and the time has come to take away the determinism we first thought of.

出现第一种情况是因为**不可能**发生相反的情况；出现第二种情况是因为相反情况发生的**几率极小**。

这完全是理论上的区分。观测本身不能说明某个特定的规律属于哪种类型。我们认为“不可能”和“几率极小”都可以对在实践中观测到的一致性做出合理的解释，早期的理论非常随意地对某些一致性以一种方式做出解释，而对其他的一致性又以另一种方式做出解释。在新物理学中，我们不作这样的区分；显然地，统一应基于标准 (*b*)，而不是 (*a*)。我们无法假设存在一种使手中有 13 张王牌的情况不可能发生的自然规律，但**可以**认为找不到不等角的等边三角形是因为这样的三角形出现的几率极小。

然而，我们必须首先顾及过去的观点，即是把 (*a*) 区分出来作为一种特殊规律。因此，我们有了两类自然定律。地球持续围绕太阳运行是因为它**不可能**逃离开。热量从高温物体流向低温物体，是因为它流向相反方向的**几率极小**。我把第一种类型叫做**基本**定律，而把第二种叫做**次级**定律。对次级定律的认识有如楔子的尖端终于劈开了决定论的框架。

对于实际的目的来说，基本定律和次级定律发挥了同样严格的控制作用。在次级定律中提到的不可几性发生的几率非常大，即使出现了个别反例，也不会得到认真对待。如果热量从你身体上流向了火，你会十分惊讶，因为这样一来你站在火前就会感到寒冷刺骨，尽管在物理理论中这种情况并非不可能发生，而不过是发生的几率极小罢了。在决定论体系中，显然任何事情都不是偶然发生的；该体系中的所有定律都不可能出现任何反例。只要物理学的目标是要建立一个决定论的体系，那么我们对次级定律的研究只能走进死胡同，因为这样的研究只会得到有可能发生的结果。决定论者不会认可这样的规则：只要运气还可以我就能感到火的温暖。他承认这是一种可能出现的结果，可是他还会补充道，其物理基础应该以另一条定律来规定，即无论有没有运气，火都会使我温暖。

借用一个遗传学的相似概念，决定论可以被看作是一种**显性性状**。我们能够（事实上是必须）把次级的非决定论置于任何一个基本的决定论体系之中，非决定论会告诉我们某件事情很有可能发生，然而那些告诉我们某件事情肯定会发生的显性定律优先于非决定论的定律。因此，决定论对其内部的非决定论定律的发展泰然视之。有什么关系呢？决定论的定律仍然是占优势地位的。没有人能预料见到当非决定论定律发展成熟后会独树一帜，取代占主导地位的母体。有一个游戏，名字叫做“猜数字”。在经过各种加倍、相加和其他运算后，最终达到“去掉最初所想的数字”的目的。在物理学中，我们已经实现了这样的一个目标，现在到了把我们最初想到的决定论去掉的时候了。

The growth of secondary law within the deterministic scheme was remarkable, and gradually sections of the subject formerly dealt with by primary law were transferred to it. There came a time when in some of the most progressive branches of physics secondary law was used exclusively. The physicist might continue to profess allegiance to primary law but he ceased to utilise it. Primary law was the gold to be kept stored in vaults; secondary law was the paper to be used for actual transactions. No one minded; it was taken for granted that the paper was backed by gold. At last came the crisis, and *physics went off the gold standard*. This happened very recently, and opinions are divided as to what the result will be. Prof. Einstein, I believe, fears disastrous inflation, and urges a return to sound currency—if we can discover it. But most theoretical physicists have begun to wonder why the now idle gold should have been credited with such magic properties. At any rate the thing has happened, and the immediate result has been a big advance in atomic physics.

We have seen that indeterministic or secondary law accounts for regularities of experience, so that it can be used for predicting the future as satisfactorily as primary law. The predictions and regularities refer to average behaviour of the vast number of particles concerned in most of our observations. When we deal with fewer particles the indeterminacy begins to be appreciable, and prediction becomes more of a gamble; until finally the behaviour of a single atom or electron has a very large measure of indeterminacy. Although some courses may be more probable than others, backing an electron to do anything is in general as uncertain as backing a horse.

It is commonly objected that our uncertainty as to what the electron will do in the future is due not to indeterminism but to ignorance. It is asserted that some character exists in the electron or its surroundings which decides its future, only physicists have not yet learned how to detect it. You will see later how I deal with this suggestion. But I would here point out that if the physicist is to take any part in the wider discussion on determinism as affecting the significance of our lives and the responsibility of our decisions, he must do so on the basis of what he has discovered, not on the basis of what it is conjectured he might discover. His first step should be to make clear that he no longer holds the position, occupied for so long, of chief advocate for determinism, and that he is *unaware* of any deterministic law in the physical universe. He steps aside and leaves it to others—philosophers, psychologists, theologians—to come forward and show, if they can, that they have found indications of determinism in some other way.* If no one comes forward, the hypothesis of determinism presumably drops; and the question whether physics is actually antagonistic to it scarcely arises. It is no use looking for an opposer until there is a proposer in the field.

* With the view of learning what might be said from the philosophical side against the abandonment of determinism, I took part in a symposium of the Aristotelian Society and Mind Association in July 1931. Indeterminists were strongly represented, but unfortunately there were no determinists in the symposium, and apparently none in the audience which discussed it. I can scarcely suppose that determinist philosophers are extinct, but it may be left to their colleagues to deal with them.

在决定论体系中，次级定律的发展是引人注目的，一部分原本利用基本定律来处理的问题逐渐开始偏向使用次级定律。有一段时间，物理学中的一些最前沿的分支只采用次级定律进行研究。可能会有这样的情况，物理学家在继续宣称自己忠实于基本定律的同时已经不再使用它了。基本定律有如存放在金库中的黄金，而次级定律则是真正用于交易的纸币。没有人会介意，大家都认为纸币以黄金为基础是理所当然的事情。最终危机出现了，**物理学放弃了金本位制**。这是最近才发生的，并且对结果将怎样人们说法不一。我确信，爱因斯坦教授对这种损失惨重的通货膨胀感到担忧，他强烈要求回归到健全的货币体系——当然，要以我们能找到这种货币体系为前提。不过大部分理论物理学家都已经开始质疑为什么应该认为现在闲置着的金子具有如此神奇的特性。无论如何，事情已经发生了，其直接的结果是使原子物理学取得了一个极大的进步。

我们已经知道，非决定论定律，或者说次级定律，解释了由经验总结的规律，因此它同样可以像基本定律一样很好地预测未来。这些预测和规律与我们在大多数情况下观测到的大量粒子的平均状态相关。当我们处理数目较少的粒子时，不确定性开始变得明显起来，而预测变得更像是在冒险。直到最后，单个原子或电子的行为在很大程度上是不确定的。虽然有些过程比另一些过程更有可能发生，但是在通常情况下，预测一个电子将会怎样就如同预测一匹马一样难以确定。

人们通常会对上述观点表示反对：我们不能确定电子将会如何运动的原因不是因为非决定论而是因为无知。有人声称，在电子内部或者它的周围环境中存在着确定其未来的某些特征因素，只是物理学家还不懂得如何才能检测到它。稍后你们就会知道我是如何看待这个观点的。但是这里我要指出，如果一个物理学家要在更广泛的意义上探讨决定论对我们的生活水平以及决策可靠性的影响，他就必须以他已经发现的物理现象为论据，而不能基于他推测出的可能会发现的现象。首先他应该搞清楚的是，他已经不再拥有占据了很久的决定论主要支持者的地位，并且他对物质世界中的任何决定论定律都**毫无所知**。他将退到一边，让其他人——哲学家、心理学家、神学家站出来说明他们以其他方式发现了决定论的迹象*，如果他们能找到的话。如果没有人挺身而出，那么决定论这个假设也许会被丢弃，也就不会引出物理学是否真的与决定论相抵触的问题。寻找反对者的努力都是徒劳的，除非有人自告奋勇。

* 因为想知道反对放弃决定论的哲学家有什么想法，我参加了亚里士多德学会和哲学学会在1931年7月举办的研讨会。但不幸的是与会者都是非决定论者，研讨会上一个决定论者也没有，在听众中也没有人讨论决定论。我不敢说持决定论观点的哲学家已经不复存在了，这也许应该由哲学界人士来了断。

## Inferential Knowledge

It is now necessary to examine rather closely the nature of our knowledge of the physical universe.

All our knowledge of physical objects is by inference. We have no means of getting into direct contact with them; but they emit and scatter light waves, and they are the source of pressures transmitted through adjacent material. They are like broadcasting stations that send out signals which we can receive. At one stage of the transmission the signals pass along nerves within our bodies. Ultimately visual, tactual, and other sensations are provoked in the mind. It is from these remote effects that we have to argue back to the properties of the physical object at the far end of the chain of transmission. The image which arises in the mind is not the physical object, though it is a source of information about the physical object; to confuse the mental object with the physical object is to confuse the clue with the criminal. Life would be impossible if there were no kind of correspondence between the external world and the picture of it in our minds; and natural selection (reinforced where necessary by the selective activity of the Lunacy Commissioners) has seen to it that the correspondence is sufficient for practical needs. But we cannot rely on the correspondence, and in physics we do not accept any detail of the picture unless it is confirmed by more exact methods of inference.

The external world of physics is thus a universe populated with *inferences*. The inferences differ in degree and not in kind. Familiar objects which I handle are just as much inferential as a remote star which I infer from a faint image on a photographic plate, or an "undiscovered" planet inferred from irregularities in the motion of Uranus. It is sometimes asserted that electrons are essentially more hypothetical than stars. There is no ground for such a distinction. By an instrument called a Geiger counter, electrons may be counted one by one as an observer counts one by one the stars in the sky. In each case the actual counting depends on a remote indication of the physical object. Erroneous properties may be attributed to the electron by fallacious or insufficiently grounded inference, so that we may have a totally wrong impression of what it is we are counting; but the same is equally true of the stars.

In the universe of inferences, past, present, and future appear simultaneously, and it requires scientific analysis to sort them out. By a certain rule of inference, namely, the law of gravitation, we infer the present or past existence of a dark companion to a star; by an application of the same rule of inference we infer the existence on Aug. 11, 1999, of a configuration of the sun, earth, and moon, which corresponds to a total eclipse of the sun. The shadow of the moon on Cornwall in 1999 is already in the universe of inference. It will not change its status when the year 1999 arrives and the eclipse is observed; we shall merely substitute one method of inferring the shadow for another. The shadow will always be an inference. I am speaking of the object or condition in the external world which is called a shadow; our perception of darkness is not the physical shadow, but is one of the possible clues from which its existence can be inferred.

## 推理性的认识

现在有必要进一步审视我们对于物质世界的认识的本质。

我们对物理对象的所有认识都是通过推理获得的。我们没有办法与它们直接接触，但是它们发射或散射光波，并把压力传递给相邻的物质。它们就像广播电台一样发射我们可以接收到的信号。在传输的一个阶段信号沿着我们身体里的神经传递，最终在我们的头脑里形成视觉、触觉以及其他感觉。通过这些远程效应，我们必须反过来辨明在传输链的另一端的物质的性质。我们头脑中产生的图像并不是物质本身，尽管它是与物质相关的信息的来源；把头脑中的物质图像混同为物质的实体就等于把线索混同于罪犯。如果不存在外部世界与它在我们头脑中形成的图像之间的对应，就不可能有我们的生活。在日常生活中，自然选择（必要时需要补充精神病委员的鉴定结果）所得到的对应似乎就已经足够满足实际需要了。但是我们不能依赖这些对应，在物理领域内，我们不能接受根据图像得到的任何信息，除非经过更为精确的推理方法的确证。

物理学的外部世界就是这样一个充满**推理**的世界。这些推理只有程度上的差别，而没有本质上的区分。我手中的常见物体，与从照相底片上的模糊图像推断出的一颗遥远恒星，或从天王星运动的不规则性推出的“未知”行星一样，都可以由推论得到。有时候我们认为电子的不确定性高于恒星。但其实它们根本没有什么区别。利用一台名为盖革计数器的仪器，我们可以逐个将电子计数，犹如我们对天上的星星逐个计数一样。在上述两种情况下，计数实际上都取决于物质的远程影像。当然，对于电子错误的或根据不充分的推断会得到不正确的性质，所以对于我们所计量的对象，我们有可能得到一个完全错误的概念；然而我们在计数星星时，也同样会存在这样的情况。

在这个充满推理的宇宙里，过去、现在和未来似乎是同时存在的，需要我们用科学分析法去区分。利用特定的推理规律，即引力定律，我们可以推断出某个恒星周边在现在或过去存在一个不发光的伴星；利用这个定律我们同样可以推断，在1999年8月11日，由于太阳、地球和月亮的相对位置会出现一次日全食。1999年将要在康沃尔出现的月亮阴影已经被推算了出来。这个推算在1999年到来和日食被观测到之前是不会改变的，我们只会不断替换推断出阴影的方法。阴影将永远是一个推断。我所说的阴影是外部世界中的物体或条件；其实我们对黑暗的感知并不是物理上的阴影，而是可以从黑暗的存在推断出来的其中一种可能的线索。

Of particular importance to the problem of determinism are our inferences about the past. Strictly speaking, our direct inferences from sight, sound, touch, all relate to a time slightly antecedent; but often the lag is more considerable. Suppose that we wish to discover the constitution of a certain salt. We put it in a test tube, apply certain reagents, and ultimately reach the conclusion that it *was* silver nitrate. It is no longer silver nitrate after our treatment of it. This is an example of retrospective inference: the property which we infer is not that of "being X" but of "having been X".

We noted at the outset that in considering determinism the alleged causes must be challenged to produce their birth certificates so that we may know whether they really were pre-existing. Retrospective inference is particularly dangerous in this connexion because it involves antedating a certificate. The experiment above mentioned certifies the chemical constitution of a substance, but the date we write on the certificate is earlier than the date of the experiment. The antedating is often quite legitimate; but that makes the practice all the more dangerous, it lulls us into a feeling of security.

## Retrospective Characters

To show how retrospective inference might be abused, suppose that there were no way of learning the chemical constitution of a substance without destroying it. By hypothesis a chemist would never know until after his experiment what substance he had been handling, so that the result of every experiment he performed would be entirely unforeseen. Must he then admit that the laws of chemistry are chaotic? A man of resource would override such a trifling obstacle. If he were discreet enough never to say beforehand what his experiment was going to demonstrate, he might give edifying lectures on the uniformity of Nature. He puts a lighted match in a cylinder of gas, and the gas burns. "There you see that hydrogen is inflammable." Or the match goes out. "That proves that nitrogen does not support combustion." Or it burns more brightly. "Evidently oxygen feeds combustion." "How do you know it was oxygen?" "By retrospective inference from the fact that the match burned more brightly." And so the experimenter passes from cylinder to cylinder; the match sometimes behaves one way and sometimes another, thereby beautifully demonstrating the uniformity of Nature and the determinism of chemical law! It would be unkind to ask how the match must behave in order to indicate indeterminism.

If by retrospective inference we infer characters at an earlier date, and then say that those characters invariably produce at a future date the manifestation from which we inferred them, we are working in a circle. The connexion is not causation but definition, and we are not prophets but tautologists. We must not mix up the genuine achievements of scientific prediction with this kind of charlatanry, or the observed uniformities of Nature with those so easily invented by our imaginary lecturer. It is easily seen that to avoid vicious circles we must abolish purely retrospective characteristics—those which are never found as existing but always as having existed. If they do not manifest themselves until the moment that they cease to exist, they can never be used for prediction except by those who prophesy after the event.

在决定论问题中最重要的一点是我们对于过去的推断。严格说来，我们通过视觉、听觉、触觉直接得来的推断在时间上都有很短的滞后；但这种滞后往往是比较重要的。假如我们想知道某种盐类的构成，我们会把它放入试管内，然后加入特定的试剂，最后得到结论，原来它是硝酸银。在我们对它做了处理之后它已经不再是硝酸银了。这就是一个回顾性推理的例子：我们推出的结论不是“是 X”，而是“曾经是 X”。

我们从一开始注意到，在讨论决定论的时候，那些所谓的原因必须提供自己的出生证明，这样我们才能够知道它们是否的确是早已存在的。就此而论，回顾性推理是非常不可靠的，因为它需要提前提供证明。上面提到的实验证明了物质的化学成分，然而鉴定书上所证实的物质的存在日期要先于实验的日期。这种提前通常是非常合理的，但在实际操作中更加危险，因为它让我们产生了一种虚假的安全感。

## 回顾性的特征

为了表明回顾性的推理是如何被滥用的，假定如果不破坏物质就没有任何办法获知它的化学成分。根据这个假设，一个化学家在他进行实验前不会知道他所要测试的物质的化学成分，于是他所做的所有实验的结果都是不可预见的。那么他是否必须承认，所有的化学规律都是杂乱无章的？聪明人知道要先忽略掉这些不重要的障碍。如果他足够谨慎，从不在实验前说出自己的实验要去证明什么，那么他也许会对自然齐一性问题发表富有启发性的演讲。他把一根燃烧的火柴扔进一瓶气体中，气体燃烧起来。然后他说，“你们看，氢气是易燃的”。或者是火柴熄灭了。“这证明氮气是不能助燃的”。或者是火柴燃烧得更剧烈了。“很明显氧气是助燃的”。“你怎么知道它就是氧气呢？”“这是从火柴燃烧得更加剧烈的事实中推断出来的。”然后实验者就这样一瓶又一瓶地进行试验；火柴有时呈现出这样一种状态，有时是另一种状态，从而完美地证实了自然齐一性以及化学规律的决定论！要是提问说火柴应该怎样表现才能够表明非决定论，那将是一个很不客气的问题。

如果按照回顾性的推理，我们推断出的是较早以前的性质，然后说这些特性在以后会恒定不变地产生一种现象，而这种现象就是最初我们用来推断其性质的现象，我们就是在循环论证。这种关系并不是因果关系，而完全是在下定义。而我们也不是预言家，只是重复在使用同义词的人。我们决不能把真正的科学预言与此类骗术混同，也决不能把观察到的自然规律的一致性同那个虚构的演说家轻易编造出来的东西混同。很容易发现要避开这种恶性循环，我们就必须废除纯粹的回顾性特性——那些特性永远不是现有状态的特性，而总是曾经存在的某种状态的特性。如果这些性质在消逝的那一刻前不能表现出来，那么它们永远都不能用于预测，除非是在事后去做预测。

Chemical constitution is not a retrospective character, though it is often inferred retrospectively. The fact that silver nitrate can be bought and sold shows that there is a property of *being* silver nitrate as well as of *having been* silver nitrate. Apart from special methods of determining the constitution or properties of a substance without destroying it, there is one general method widely applicable. We divide the specimen into two parts, analyse one part (destroying it if necessary), and show that its constitution *has been X*; then it is usually a fair inference that the constitution of the other part is *X*. It is sometimes argued that in this way a character inferable retrospectively must always be also inferable contemporaneously; if that were true, it would remove all danger of using retrospective inference to invent fictitious characters as causes of the events observed. Actually the danger arises just at the point where the method of sampling breaks down, namely, when we are concerned with characteristics supposed to distinguish one individual atom from another atom of the same substance; for the individual atom cannot be divided into two samples, one to analyse and one to preserve. Let us take an example:

It is known that potassium consists of two kinds of atoms, one kind being radioactive and the other inert. Let us call the two kinds $K\alpha$ and $K\beta$. If we observe that a particular atom bursts in the radioactive manner, we shall infer that it was a $K\alpha$ atom. Can we say that the explosion was predetermined by the fact that it was a $K\alpha$ and not a $K\beta$ atom? On the information stated there is no justification at all; $K\alpha$ is merely an antedated label which we attach to the atom when we see that it has burst. We can always do that, however undetermined the event may be which occasions the label. Actually, however, there is more information which shows that the burst is not undetermined. Potassium is found to consist of two isotopes of atomic weights 39 and 41; and it is believed that 41 is the radioactive kind, 39 being inert. It is possible to separate the two isotopes and to pick out atoms known to be $K^{41}$. Thus, $K^{41}$ is a contemporaneous character, and can legitimately predetermine the subsequent radioactive outburst; it replaces $K\alpha$ which was a retrospective character.

So much for the fact of outburst; now consider the time of outburst. Nothing is known as to the time when a particular $K^{41}$ atom will burst except that it will probably be within the next thousand million years. If, however, we observe that it bursts at a time *t*, we can ascribe to the atom the retrospective character $K^t$, meaning that it had (all along) the property that it was going to burst at time *t*. Now, according to modern physics, the character $K^t$ is not manifested in any way—is not even represented in our mathematical description of the atom—until the time *t* when the burst occurs and the character $K^t$, having finished its job, disappears. In these circumstances $K^t$ is not a predetermining cause. Our retrospective labels and characters add nothing to the plain observational fact that the burst occurred without warning at the moment *t*; they are merely devices for ringing a change on the tenses.

The time of break-up of a radioactive atom is an example of extreme indeterminism; but it must be understood that, according to current theory, all future events are indeterminate in greater or lesser degree, and differ only in the margin of uncertainty. When the

化学组分并不具有回顾性的特性，尽管它总是在事后才被推断出来。硝酸银是可以被买卖的，这说明有这样一种表明它**现在是**硝酸银，而且它**曾经是**硝酸银的性质。除了一些特殊的方法可以测定物质的组成或性质而不用破坏它以外，还有一种得到广泛应用的一般方法。我们把这个样品分成两份，分析其中的一份（必要时可以去破坏它），并且表明它的成分**曾经是** $\boldsymbol{X}$；然后通常可以合理地推出，另一份的成分就是 $X$。于是时常有人认为，按照这种方式，一个可以在事后做回顾性推断得到的性质也可以实时推断出来；如果这是正确的话，那么就可以避开将回顾性推断得到的假想特性作为观测事件的原因所产生的全部危险。事实上，危险恰恰是在取样方法不再适用的情况下出现的，也就是当我们讨论能将同一个物质中单独的一个原子和另一个原子区分开的性质的时候。因为一个原子不能被分为两份，一份用于分析，另一份保留。让我们来看下面的例子：

我们知道，钾由两种类型的原子构成，一种是有放射性的，而另一种则是惰性的。我们把它们叫做 $\mathrm{K}\alpha$ 和 $\mathrm{K}\beta$。如果我们观察到一个原子以放射性的方式爆发，那么我们就推断它是 $\mathrm{K}\alpha$ 原子。我们是否可以根据爆发原子是 $\mathrm{K}\alpha$ 而不是 $\mathrm{K}\beta$ 预先断定爆炸的发生？这里提供的信息表明，根本就没有这样的道理；$\mathrm{K}\alpha$ 只是事先准备的一个标签，如果我们看见原子爆炸了就把这个标签贴在它上面。我们可以一直这样做下去，不管那个需要用到这个标签的事件是不是待定的。然而实际上，更多的信息表明爆发并不是未确定的。我们知道钾是由原子量分别为 39 和 41 的两种同位素组成的；而且我们确信原子量是 41 的那种具有放射性，而 39 的那种则是惰性的。于是可以将这两种同位素区分开，挑选出被称为 $\mathrm{K}^{41}$ 的原子。这样 $\mathrm{K}^{41}$ 就是一个实时性质，能用来合理地预测它后续的放射性爆发；因而可以用它来代替 $\mathrm{K}\alpha$ 这个回顾性的特性。

对于爆发的现象就讨论到这里，现在我们要考虑爆发的时间。我们根本不知道一个 $\mathrm{K}^{41}$ 原子会在何时爆发，除非说它或许在今后的十亿年内会爆发。然而如果我们在时刻 $t$ 观察到了它的爆炸，那么我们就可以认为这是由于此原子具有回顾性特性 $\mathrm{K}^t$ 造成的，这就表明它（自始至终）具有在时刻 $t$ 爆发的性质。现在，根据现代物理学，这个性质 $\mathrm{K}^t$ 没有以任何一种方式得到证明——甚至不能用我们对原子的数学描述来表示——直到 $t$ 时刻那个原子爆发，这个性质 $\mathrm{K}^t$ 在完成了自己的使命后销声匿迹了。在这种情况下 $\mathrm{K}^t$ 并不是一个可预测的起因。我们的回顾性的标签及特性没有给这个简单的实测现象增加任何内容，爆发毫无征兆地在时刻 $t$ 发生了；这些标签和特性只不过是变化发生时的报警装置。

放射性原子的衰变时刻就是一个极端的非决定论的例子；但是我们必须要明白，根据当前流行的理论，未来的事件，都或多或少是不可确定的，只是不确定度有所

uncertainty is below our limits of measurement, the event is looked upon as practically determinate; determinacy in this sense is relative to the refinement of our measurements. A being accustomed to time on the cosmic scale, who was not particular to a few hundred million years or so, might regard the time of break-up of the radioactive atom as practically determinate. There is one unified system of secondary law throughout physics and a continuous gradation from phenomena predictable with overwhelming probability to phenomena which are altogether indeterminate.

## Criticism of Indeterminism

In saying that there is no contemporaneous characteristic of the radioactive atom determining the date at which it is going to break up, we mean that in the picture of the atom as drawn in present-day physics no such characteristic appears; the atom which will break up in 1960 and the atom which will break up in the year 150,000 are drawn precisely alike. But, it will be said, surely that only means that the characteristic is one which physics has not yet discovered; in due time it will be found and inserted in the picture either of the atom or its environment. If such indeterminacy were exceptional, that would be the natural conclusion, and we should have no objection to accepting such an explanation as a likely way out of a difficulty. But the radioactive atom was not brought forward as a difficulty; it was brought forward as a favourable illustration of that which applies in greater or lesser degree to all kinds of phenomena. There is a difference between explaining away an exception and explaining away a rule.

The persistent critic continues: "You are evading the point. I contend that there are characteristics unknown to you which completely predetermine not only the time of break-up of the radioactive atom but also all physical phenomena. How do you know there are not? You are not omniscient."

The curious thing is that the determinist who takes this line is under the illusion that he is adopting a more modest attitude in regard to our scientific knowledge than the indeterminist. The indeterminist is accused of claiming omniscience. I will not make quite the same countercharge against the determinist; but surely it is only a man who thinks himself *nearly* omniscient who would have the audacity to start enumerating all the things which (it occurs to him) might exist without his knowing it. I am so far from omniscient that my list would contain innumerable entries. If it is any satisfaction to the critic, my list does include deterministic characters—along with Martian irrigation works, ectoplasm, etc.—as things which might exist unknown to me.

It must be realised that determinism is a positive assertion about the behaviour of the universe. It is not sufficient for the determinist to claim that there is no fatal objection to his assertion; he must produce some reason for making it. I do not say he must prove it, for in science we are ready to believe things on evidence falling short of strict proof. If no reason for asserting it can be given, it collapses as an idle speculation. It is astonishing that even scientific writers on determinism advocate it without thinking it necessary to say

差别。如果这种不确定度在测量允许的范围以内，那么这件事情就可以被看作是可以确定的；在这种意义上确定性与我们的测量精度有关。一个习惯了以宇宙尺度度量时间的人，不会觉得几亿年上下的时间有什么特别了不起，那么他也许会认为放射性原子的衰变时间其实还是非常确定的。贯穿物理学的次级定律与从有绝对把握可以预测的现象到完全不能预测的现象之间的连续渐进是一个统一的体系。

## 对非决定论的批评

当谈及没有一个实时性质可以确定放射性原子将要爆发的时间时，我们的意思是在当前物理学所描述的原子图像中不存在这种性质；对一个将要在 1960 年爆发的原子和一个将要在 150,000 年爆发的原子的描述是完全相同的。但是有人会说，那只能说明当前物理学还没有发现这种性质，在适当的时候我们总会发现这个性质，并把它添加到原子或其周围结构的理论中去。如果这种不确定性是例外情况，那么就会很自然地得到上述结论，并且这种解释完全可以被我们拿来作为摆脱困难的可靠方法。但是放射性原子并不是作为一个难点提出的，提出它是为了在一定程度上能恰当地解释所有现象。对一个例外情况做出清楚的解释和对一个规则做出清楚的解释是不一样的。

但是固执的批评家还在继续：“你在回避要点。我认为有一些你所不知道的性质不但能够完全预先确定放射性原子爆发的时间，还能够完全预先确定一切物理现象。你怎么知道没有那些性质呢？你又不是无所不知的。”

奇怪的是，持这种说法的决定论者错误地认为他们对待科学知识的态度比非决定论者更为谦虚。非决定论者因声称无所不知而受到指责。我并不打算采用完全一样的方式反击决定论者；但是可以肯定，只有自认为**接近**无所不知的人，才有胆量列举出所有（他想到的）可能存在但他自己不了解的东西。我远没有无所不知到可以列出无穷多条目的地步。如果能让那些批评家稍微满意一点的话，我承认我的列表中确实包括了一些确定性的特征，和火星灌溉工程、外质等一样，这些事物可能存在但非我所知。

必须认识到，决定论是关于宇宙性质的一个积极的论断。但是这并不足以让决定论者断言，他的论断没有致命的缺陷；他必须提出一些理由令它成立。我并不是说他必须去证明它，因为在科学上，我们宁愿去相信一些证据明显却缺乏严格证明的事情。如果无法给出其成立的理由，那么它就会成为一个空洞的想法。让人惊讶的是，即使是那些就决定论问题运用科学方法讨论的作者也认为要支持它并不必去

anything in its favour, merely pointing out that the new physical theories do not actually disprove determinism. If that really represents the status of determinism, no reputable scientific journal would waste space over it. Conjectures put forward on slender evidence are the curse of science; a conjecture for which there is no evidence at all is an outrage. So far as the physical universe is concerned, determinism appears to explain nothing; for in the modern books which go farthest into the theory of the phenomena no use is made of it.

Indeterminism is not a positive assertion. I am an indeterminist in the same way that I am an anti-moon-is-made-of-green-cheese-ist. That does not mean that I especially identify myself with the doctrine that the moon is not made of green cheese. Whether or not the green cheese lunar theory can be reconciled with modern astronomy is scarcely worth inquiring; the main point is that green-cheesism, like determinism, is a conjecture that we have no reason for entertaining. Undisprovable hypotheses of that kind can be invented *ad lib*.

## Principle of Uncertainty

The mathematical treatment of an indeterminate universe does not differ much in form from the older treatment designed for a determinate universe. The equations of wave mechanics used in the new theory are not different in principle from those of hydrodynamics. The fact is that, since an algebraic symbol can be used to represent either a known or an unknown quantity, we can symbolise a definitely predetermined future or an unknown future in the same way. The difference is that whereas in the older formulae every symbol was theoretically determinable by observation, in the present theory there occur symbols the values of which are not assignable by observation.

Hence, if we use the equations to predict, say, the future velocity of an electron, the result will be an expression containing, besides known symbols, a number of undeterminable symbols. The latter make the prediction indeterminate. (I am not here trying to prove or explain the indeterminacy of the future; I am only stating how we adapt our mathematical technique to deal with an indeterminate future.) The indeterminate symbols can often (or perhaps always) be expressed as unknown phase-angles. When a large number of phase-angles are involved, we may assume in averaging that they are uniformly distributed from 0° to 360°, and so obtain predictions which could only fail if there has been an unlikely coincidence of phase-angles. That is the secret of all our successful prophecies; the unknowns are not eliminated by determinate equations but by averaging.

There is a very remarkable relation between the determined and the undetermined symbols, which is known as Heisenberg's Principle of Uncertainty. The symbols are paired together, every determined symbol having an undetermined symbol as partner. I think that this regularity makes it clear that the occurrence of undetermined symbols in the mathematical theory is not a blemish; it gives a special kind of symmetry to the whole picture. The theoretical limitation on our power of predicting the future is seen to be systematic, and it cannot be confused with other casual limitations due to our lack of skill.

提它的优越性，只需说明新的物理理论与决定论并不抵触就可以了。如果该理论代表了决定论的观点，那么任何著名的科学杂志都不会为此浪费空间了。在缺乏足够证据的情况下妄加推测是科学的祸根，而在没有任何证据的时候就下结论则是一种暴行。就整个物理世界而言，决定论似乎没有解释任何事情；因为在深入探讨现象背后的理论的现代书籍中，没有用到决定论的观点。

非决定论并不是一个积极的论断。我是一个非决定论者，同样也是一个反对月亮是由绿奶酪做成的人。这并不是说我想要特别强调自己赞同月亮不是由绿奶酪做成的学说。至于月亮是由绿奶酪做成的理论是否能被当代天文学所接受，完全不值得去调查；关键点在于绿奶酪论就像决定论，是一个我们没有理由考虑的假设。我们可以随意创造这种无需证伪的猜想。

## 不确定性原理

对一个不确定性宇宙的数学处理和以往对一个确定性宇宙所做的处理在形式上并没有太大区别。在这个新理论中，所用的波动力学方程跟流体力学方程没有原则上的差别。事实上，既然代数符号既可以用来代表一个已知的量也可以用来代表未知量，我们就可以用同样的方式来标识一个预先完全确定的未来或者一个不可确定的未来。不同之处是：按照以往的方式，在理论上每一个符号都是由观测确定的；而在当前的理论中，会有一些符号所代表的值不能通过观测给定。

于是，如果说我们要用方程预测一个电子未来的速度，那么我们最后的表达式除了包括已知的符号外，还包括一些不可确定的符号。后者使得预测变得不可确定。(这里我并不是想证明或者解释未来的不可确定性；我只是在表述如何使用我们的数学技巧去处理不可确定的未来。）那些不可确定的符号常常（或可能总是）被表示成未知的相角。当涉及很多相角的时候，我们可以假设从平均意义上说它们从 0° 到 360° 是均匀分布的，所得预测只有在相角不太可能同时出现的情况下才会出现错误。这就是我们能够成功预言的秘密所在；不是通过确定的方程，而是通过取平均的方法来消除那些未确定的量。

在确定的符号和不确定的符号之间有一个非常值得注意的关系，那就是海森堡测不准原理。这些符号都是成对的，每个确定的符号都对应着一个不确定的符号。我想这种规律性也清楚地告诉我们，在数学理论中出现不确定的符号并不是缺陷；它为整个物理图像带来了一种特殊的对称性。这个原理认为我们在预测未来能力上所能达到的极限取决于系统上的原因，而这种限制不会与因缺乏技巧而导致的偶然性限制混为一谈。

Let us consider an isolated system. It is part of a universe of inference, and all that can be embodied in it must be capable of being inferred from the influence which it broadcasts over its surroundings. Whenever we state the properties of a body in terms of physical quantities, we are imparting knowledge as to the response of various external indicators to its presence and nothing more. A knowledge of the response of all kinds of objects would determine completely its relation to its environment, leaving only its unget-at-able inner nature, which is outside the scope of physics. Thus, if the system is really isolated so that it has no interaction with its surroundings, it has no properties belonging to physics, but only an inner nature which is beyond physics. So we must modify the conditions a little. Let it for a moment have some interaction with the world exterior to it; the interaction starts a train of influences which may reach an observer; he can from this one signal draw an inference about the system, that is, fix the value of one of the symbols describing the system or fix one equation for determining their values. To determine more symbols there must be further interactions, one for each new value fixed. It might seem that in time we could fix all the symbols in this way, so that there would be no undetermined symbols in the description of the system. But it must be remembered that the interaction which disturbs the external world by a signal also reacts on the system.

There is thus a double consequence; the interaction starts a signal through the external world informing us that the value of a certain symbol $p$ in the system is $p_1$, and at the same time it alters to an indeterminable extent the value of another symbol $q$ in the system. If we had learned from former signals that the value of $q$ was $q_1$, our knowledge will cease to apply, and we must start again to find the new value of $q$. Presently there may be another interaction which tells us that $q$ is now $q_2$; but the same interaction knocks out the value $p_1$ and we no longer know $p$. It is of the utmost importance for prediction that a paired symbol and not the inferred symbol is upset by the interaction. If the signal taught us that at the moment of interaction $p$ was $p_1$, but that $p$ had been upset by the interaction and the value no longer held good, we should never have anything but retrospective knowledge—like the chemistry lecturer to whom I referred above. Actually we can have contemporaneous knowledge of the values of half the symbols, but never more than half. We are like the comedian picking up parcels who, each time he picks up one, drops another.

There are various possible transformations of the symbols and the condition can be expressed in another way. Instead of two paired symbols, one wholly known and the other wholly unknown, we can take two symbols each of which is known with some uncertainty; then the rule is that the product of the two uncertainties is fixed. Any interaction which reduces the uncertainty of determination of one increases the uncertainty of the other. For example, the position and velocity of an electron are paired in this way. We can fix the position with a probable error of 0.001 mm. and the velocity with a probable error of about 1 km. per sec.; or we can fix the position to 0.0001 mm. and the velocity to 10 km. per sec.; and so on. We divide the uncertainty how we like, but we cannot get rid of it. If current theory is right, this is not a question of lack of skill or a perverse delight of Nature in tantalising us; for the uncertainty is actually embodied in the theoretical picture of the

让我们来考虑一个孤立的系统。那是可推理的宇宙的一部分，宇宙中出现的一切事物都必须能够从其对周围环境所施加的影响中推断出来。每当我们用物理量描述一个物体的性质时，我们正在传递的信息只不过是用不同外部指示物的响应来判断它的存在。如果知道了各类物体的响应,我们就可以完全确定它与周围环境的联系，而仅剩下它的“不能得到的”内部性质，那就是物理范畴以外的东西了。因此，如果一个系统是完全孤立的，那么它就不会与其周围的环境产生相互作用，因而它不具备任何物理性质，而只具有超出物理范畴的内部性质。因此，我们必须把条件稍微修改一下。让它在一个短暂的时间内与外部世界产生一定的相互作用，这种作用引发一连串影响并被一个观测者所感知。观测者可以通过这个信号对上述系统进行推测，换言之，确定用来表述这个系统的某个符号的值，或者确定一个方程以便判定这些符号的值。要确定更多的符号，就必须有更进一步的相互作用，每一次相互作用都可以确定一个新符号的值。看起来通过这种方法我们总有一天会确定所有的符号，于是在描述这个系统的符号中就没有哪个是未确定的了。但是，一定要记住的是，这种通过信号对外部世界产生干扰的相互作用，同样也会对这个系统产生反作用。

于是，这里就会存在两个结论：这个在外部世界产生了一个信号的相互作用告诉我们，某个符号 $p$ 在系统中的值是 $p_1$，同时它还把系统中另一个符号 $q$ 值的大小改变到一个不确定的值。如果我们已经从以前的信号得知 $q$ 的值是 $q_1$，那么我们的这个认识将不再适用，我们必须重新开始寻找符号 $q$ 的新值。不久可能有另一个相互作用告诉我们，现在的 $q$ 值是 $q_2$，但同时这个相互作用又改变了 $p_1$ 的值，于是我们不再确知 $p$ 了。预测中至关重要的问题就是：相互作用会扰动成对出现的符号，而不是那个要推断的符号。如果某个信号告诉我们：在当前的相互作用中 $p$ 为 $p_1$，但那个 $p$ 已经被相互作用所扰动，它的值不再准确，除了对先前的回顾性认识外我们绝不会得到任何东西，就和我前面提到的那个化学老师一样。事实上我们可以同时知道一半符号的值，但不会超过一半。我们就像拣包裹的喜剧演员，每拣起一个就会又丢掉一个。

这些符号可以有各种不同的变换，而条件也可以用另一种方式来表达。不采用这种其中一个完全确定而另一个完全不确定的成对符号，我们可以选取两个符号，其中每一个都带有一定的不确定性。于是就有了这样一个定律：两个不确定度的乘积是确定的。任何降低其中一个不确定度的相互作用都会增加另一个的不确定度。例如，一个电子的位置和速度以这种方式成对的。我们可以把位置的几率误差定为 0.001 mm，因而速度的几率误差大约是 1 km/s；或者我们可以把位置的几率误差定为 0.0001 mm，因而速度的几率误差是 10 km/s，依此类推。我们可以按照我们的喜好来分配这个不确定度，但却不能摆脱它。如果目前的理论是正确的，那么就不存在缺乏技巧或大自然偏偏要与我们作对的问题；这是因为这种不确定性实实在在地

electron; so that if we describe something as having exact position and velocity we cannot be describing an electron.

If we divide the uncertainty in position and velocity at time $t_1$ in the most favourable way, we find that the predicted position of the electron one second later (at time $t_2$) is uncertain to about five centimetres. That represents the extent to which the future position is not predetermined by anything existing one second earlier. If the position at time $t_2$ always remained uncertain to this extent, there would be no failure of determinism, for the thing we had failed to predict (exact position at time $t_2$) would be meaningless. But *when the second has elapsed* we can measure the position of the electron to 0.001 mm. or even more closely, as already stated. This accurate position is not predetermined; we have to wait until the time arrives and then measure it. It may be recalled that the new knowledge is acquired at a price. Along with our rough knowledge of position (to 5 cm.) we had a fair knowledge of the velocity; but when we acquire more accurate knowledge of the position, the velocity goes back into extreme uncertainty.

We might spend a long while admiring the detailed working of this cunning arrangement by which we are prevented from finding out more than we ought to know. But I do not think we should look on these as Nature's devices to prevent us from seeing too far into the future. They are the devices of the mathematician who has to protect himself from making impossible predictions. It commonly happens that when we ask silly questions, mathematical theory does not directly refuse to answer but gives a non-committal answer like $\frac{0}{0}$, out of which we cannot wring any definite meaning. Similarly, when we ask where the electron will be tomorrow, mathematical theory does not give the straightforward answer, "It is impossible to say, because it is not yet decided" , because that is beyond the resources of an algebraic vocabulary. It gives us an ordinary formula of *x*'s and *y*'s, but makes sure that we cannot possibly find out what the formula means—until tomorrow.

## Mental Indeterminism

I have, perhaps fortunately, left myself no time to discuss the effect of indeterminacy in the physical universe on our general outlook. I will content myself with stating in summary form the points which seem to arise.

(1) If the whole physical universe is deterministic, mental decisions (or at least *effective* mental decisions) must also be predetermined. For if it is predetermined in the physical world (to which your body belongs) that there will be a pipe between your lips on Jan. 1, the result of your mental struggle on Dec. 31 as to whether you will give up smoking in the New Year is evidently predetermined. The new physics thus opens the door to indeterminacy of mental phenomena, whereas the old deterministic physics bolted and barred it completely.

(2) The door is opened slightly, but apparently the opening is not wide enough; for according to analogy with inorganic physical systems, we should expect the indeterminacy

蕴涵在电子的理论图像里，所以如果我们要用精确的位置和速度来描述某个物体的话，那么这在描述电子时是行不通的。

假如在 $t_1$ 时刻，我们按照最适宜的方式把不确定度分配给位置和速度，那么我们会发现在一秒钟以后（$t_2$ 时刻）电子位置的预测值具有约 5 cm 的不确定度。这就代表着通过任何存在于一秒钟之前的事物，也不可能把对未来位置的不确定度降到这个值以下。如果 $t_2$ 时刻的位置不确定度一直保持这样的程度，那么我们可以说决定论并没有失效，因为那些我们所不能预测的事情（$t_2$ 时刻电子的精确位置）是没有意义的。**但是当这一秒钟消逝之后**我们对电子位置的测量能够精确到 0.001 mm 甚至更高。这个精确的位置并不是预先知道的，我们必须要等到时机成熟时才能对它进行测量。还要回想起获得这个新的认识是需要付出代价的。除了我们对位置（达到 5 cm）的大概了解以外，我们还对速度有着相当不错的了解。但是当我们要对位置获得更加精确的认识时，速度就变得非常不确定了。

也许我们花了很长一段时间来欣赏这种巧妙处理的精细工作原理，正是它在防止我们去寻找比我们本该知道的还要多的事情。但是我并不认为我们应该把这当作是阻止我们去探索更加遥远的未来的自然机制。它们只是数学家们用来保护自己不至做出不可能的预测的手段。当我们提出一个很愚蠢的问题时，数学理论通常不会直接拒绝回答，但会给出一个类似 $\frac{0}{0}$ 的含糊答案，根据那个答案我们得不到任何明确的意思。同样，当我们提出电子明天会在什么地方出现的问题时，数学理论也不会给出直接的回答，“这不好说，因为现在还不能确定”，因为那超出了代数语言的范畴。它所给出的是一个关于 $x$ 和 $y$ 的一般表达式，但可以肯定的是，在明天到来之前，我们不可能知道这个表达式的含义。

## 精神非决定论

似乎很幸运，我没有给自己留出时间来讨论不确定性如何影响了我们对物理世界的总体认识。接下来我很乐意把似乎可以得出的要点做一个简单的概括。

（1）如果整个物理世界是可以确定的，那么心理决策（或者至少是**有效**的心理决策）也一定可以预先确定。因为假如在物理世界里（你的身体也是其中一部分）可以预先确定 1 月 1 日你嘴上会叼着一个烟斗，那么你在 12 月 31 日为新年是否要戒烟所做的心理斗争显然已经提前有了结果。因而这个新的物理学为我们打开了一扇通向心理现象的不确定性的大门，而旧的决定论的物理学则完全把它关在门里。

（2）这个门被轻轻地打开了，但显然打开得还不够宽。因为与一个无机的物理系统类比后我们会发现人类活动的不确定性在数量上是可以被忽略的。我们必须通

of human movements to be quantitatively insignificant. In some way we must transfer to human movements the wide indeterminacy characteristic of atoms, instead of the almost negligible indeterminacy manifested by inorganic systems of comparable scale. I think this difficulty is not insuperable, but it must not be underrated.

(3) Although we may be uncertain as to the intermediate steps, we can scarcely doubt what is the final answer. If the atom has indeterminacy, surely the human mind will have an equal indeterminacy; for we can scarcely accept a theory which makes out the mind to be more mechanistic than the atom.

(4) Is the human will really more free if its decisions are swayed by new factors born from moment to moment than if they are the outcome solely of heredity, training, and other predetermining causes? On such questions as these we have nothing new to say. Argument will no doubt continue "about it and about". But it seems to me that there is a far more important aspect of indeterminacy. It makes it possible that the mind is not utterly deceived as to the mode in which its decisions are reached. On the deterministic theory of the physical world, my hand in writing this address is guided in a predetermined course according to the equations of mathematical physics; my mind is unessential—a busybody who invents an irrelevant story about a scientific argument as an explanation of what my hand is doing—an explanation which can only be described as a downright lie. If it is true that the mind is so utterly deceived in the story it weaves round our human actions, I do not see where we are to obtain our confidence in the story it tells of the physical universe.

Physics is becoming difficult to understand. First relativity theory, then quantum theory, then wave mechanics have transformed the universe, making it seem ever more fantastic to our minds. Perhaps the end is not yet. But there is another side to this transformation. Naïve realism, materialism, the mechanistic hypothesis were simple; but I think that it was only by closing our eyes to the essential nature of experience, relating as it does to the reactions of a conscious being, that they could be made to seem credible. These revolutions of scientific thought are clearing up the deeper contradictions between life and theoretical knowledge, and the latest phase with its release from determinism marks a great step onwards. I will even venture to say that in the present theory of the physical universe we have at last reached something which a reasonable man might almost believe.

(**129**, 233-240; 1932)

过某种方法，把原子较大的不确定性特征转移到人的活动上来，以代替与无机系统相比几乎可以忽略不计的不确定性。我认为这个难点不是不能克服的，但也决不能低估它。

（3）虽然我们也许不能确定中间的步骤，但我们从不怀疑最后的解决方法。如果原子具有不确定性，那么人的思维肯定也会具有同样的不确定性；因为把思维说成比原子更机械的理论是绝大多数人都不愿意接受的。

（4）如果人的决定会受到不断出现的新因素的影响，而不仅仅是遗传、培养以及其他先决条件产生的结果，那么人的意识会更加自由吗？对于这样的问题，我们没有给出任何新的答案。这个争论肯定还会无休止地进行下去。就我看来，不确定性还有一个更加重要的方面。它使我们的思想在通过某种模式作决定的时候不会完全被蒙蔽。根据物理世界中的决定论，我的手在写这个讲稿，是由数学物理方程预先确定的进程决定的，我的思想在这里并不重要——一个爱管闲事的人想出了一个与科学问题有关的不相干的故事来解释我的手在做什么——这种解释只会被认为是一种彻头彻尾的谎言。如果思想真的是完全被蒙蔽的，在这个故事中它是围绕着我们人类的行为编排出来的，那么在这个故事中，我不认为我们会有信心描述物理世界。

物理学正在变得难以理解。首先是相对论，然后是量子理论，接着是波动力学，它们已经使宇宙发生了转变，使我们眼中的宇宙变得更加奇妙。也许这还不是终点。但是这种变化还有另外一面。朴素的现实主义、唯物主义以及机械论的假设都是较简单的；但是我认为，只有当我们不去理会经验的基本性质而把它跟有意识的生命的反应联系起来的时候，它们看起来才是可信的。这种科学思想上的变革扫清了存在于生命和理论认识之间的深刻矛盾，最近它从决定论中解放出来标志着往前迈进了伟大的一步。我甚至敢说，在物理世界目前的理论中，我们终于达到了能让一个明理的人几乎可以信任的程度。

（沈乃澂 翻译；葛墨林 审稿）

# News and Views

## Editor's Note

**In the early 1930s, physicists were exploring the profound philosophical repercussions of quantum theory. Heisenberg's principle of indeterminacy apparently established clear limitations to determinism in physics. Did an absence of deterministic laws at the microscale undermine cause and effect? In a supplement to this issue, Arthur Eddington considered the "decline of determinism", insisting that indeterministic "secondary" law can still be useful for predicting the future. The author of this essay takes issue with that point, saying that Eddington proclaims the demise of determinism while at the same time supposing its implications for orderly causal links, and even the possibility of prediction, remain. But the essay applauds Eddington's statement that quantum indeterminacy does not imply a universe characterised by unrestrained caprice.**

### Determinism Defined

SIR Arthur Eddington's characteristically fascinating address on "The Decline of Determinism", which we publish as our Supplement this week, will be welcomed as a clear, unequivocal statement, by a leading authority, on a question which, even among the many revolutionary aspects of the new physics, holds a pre-eminent place for importance and interest. Such a statement is the more necessary because of the almost universal tendency for discussions of determinism to be concerned at bottom with words rather than ideas, and Sir Arthur has quite properly begun by stating definitely what he means by the determinism which he holds has declined. His thorough analysis leaves little room for disagreement, but many will wonder whether he has not achieved a Pyrrhic victory by conceding to the determinist the substance of his doctrine and destroying only the shadow. "The rejection of determinism is in no sense an abdication of scientific method", and "indeterministic or secondary law ... can be used for predicting the future as satisfactorily as primary law". In other words, Sir Arthur does not allow that the first Morning of Creation wrote what the last Dawn of Reckoning shall read, but he allows that it might have read what the last Dawn shall write. Even the most perfervid determinist will scarcely ask more. Furthermore, he acknowledges that he does not know whether Dirac, whose book "goes as deeply as anyone has yet penetrated into the fundamental structure of the physical universe", is a determinist or not. It would seem, therefore, that the determinism in question cannot be of much importance even in physics.

# 新闻与观点

## 编者按

在 20 世纪 30 年代早期，物理学家们发现量子理论中蕴藏着深刻的哲学内涵。海森堡测不准原理已经证明物理学中的决定论思想存在着明显的局限性。在微观尺度上不存在决定论难道就会有损于因果推理？在为讨论这个问题特设的增刊上，阿瑟·爱丁顿考虑到了“决定论的衰落”，但他坚信非决定论的“次级”原理仍然可以用于预测未来。这篇短文的作者不支持爱丁顿的论点，说他一边宣布决定论的死亡一边又在鼓吹仍然存在有规律的因果联系甚至预测未来的可能性。但作者在文中对爱丁顿的另一个观点表示赞同，即认为量子理论的不确定性并不意味着宇宙处于完全无序的状态之中。

### 决定论的界定

在本周《自然》杂志的增刊上刊载了阿瑟·爱丁顿爵士的一篇极具吸引力的题为“决定论的衰落”的演说词。他用清晰准确的语言阐述了一个在新兴物理学各创新领域中显得十分突出的重要问题，他的观点为主要的物理学家所接受。因为大家对决定论的讨论越来越趋向于词藻之争而不是观点的表达，所以阿瑟爵士的这篇文章就显得更加难得了，一开始他就给出了他认为已经衰落了的决定论的明确含义。他的精辟论述没有给异见者留下多少反驳的余地，但很多人怀疑他还未取得皮洛士式的胜利（译者注：指付出重大代价才取得的胜利，古希腊国王皮洛士在公元前 280 ~ 前 279 年间曾为打败罗马军队付出了惨重的代价），因为他的学说的基本内容对决定论者是认可的，仅仅否定了一些无关紧要的地方。“摒弃决定论绝不是要放弃科学方法”，“非决定论或次级定律……同样可以像基本定律一样很好地预测未来”。换言之，阿瑟爵士虽不允许在创世纪的第一个早晨就记录下在最后一次大灾难拂晓将看到的一切，但他却相信在创世纪的第一个早晨就能读到最后一次大灾难拂晓所记录下的一切。对于这一点，即使是最坚定的决定论者也不会再过分地要求什么了。阿瑟爵士还承认自己并不清楚狄拉克是不是决定论者，虽然狄拉克写了一本“比任何人都更深层次地触及到物质世界的基本结构”的书。看来决定论的观点即便在物理学中也算不上重要了。

## Physical Inference and Prediction

Apparently, however, in spite of the unqualified statement concerning prediction quoted above, Sir Arthur denies that we can predict the behaviour of electrons more certainly than that of horses, and the importance, to all but the physicist, of the "decline of determinism" therefore depends on the recognition of electrons as bodies co-equal with ordinary physical objects. To establish this he claims that since physical objects, as well as electrons and such particles, are all "inferences", they differ only in degree and not in kind. We must not, however, be deceived by words. Objects which we see and handle may be, as he says, as inferential as an undiscovered planet inferred from irregularities in the motion of Uranus, but the inferences are of different kinds; otherwise, why, when a planet was seen in a different position from that inferred from the irregularities, was it *without question* preferred to the "undiscovered" inferential planet? There was not even an instinctive estimate of the "degree" of validity to be attributed to the two "inferences". Unless Sir Arthur assigns to "direct observation" a status essentially different from that of rational deduction, it is difficult to see how his position can be "in no sense an abdication of scientific method". All this, however, does not affect determinism in relation to physical objects, and it is to be hoped that Sir Arthur's plain statement will do much to remove the widespread delusion that modern physics has revealed a universe of unrestrained caprice.

(**129**, 228-229; 1932)

## 物理推论与预测

然而，尽管上面引用了有关预测问题的无保留的阐述，但阿瑟爵士认为我们对电子行为的预测并不会比对马的行为的预测更准确。因此，对于除物理学家以外的所有人而言，“决定论的衰落”的重要性在于它使人们认识到电子可以被看作是与普通物理对象等同的实体。为了证明这一点，阿瑟爵士声称由于物理对象，包括电子和类似电子的粒子，都是由“推论”得到的，它们只会有程度上的不同，而不会有本质上的差别。然而，我们千万不要被这些文字迷惑。正如他所述，我们可以看到和触摸到的物体也许和从天王星运动的不规则性能推出一颗未知行星的存在一样可以通过推断得到，不过这些推论所属的类别并不相同；否则，为什么当观测到的一颗行星并没有处于由无规则运动推断出的位置上时，人们还是**毫无异议**地倾向于把它看作就是那颗由推论得到的“未知”行星呢？我们甚至不能直观地估计出这两种“推论”的有效“程度”。除非阿瑟爵士给“直接观测”下一个本质上不同于理性推理的定义，否则很难想象他的立场怎么会是“决不能摈弃科学的方法”。然而所有这些都不会影响到与物理对象相关的决定论，我们希望阿瑟爵士的平实论述能在很大程度上消除人们普遍存在的错觉，即认为现代物理学揭示的是一个过于变幻无常的宇宙。

（金世超 翻译；赵见高 审稿）

# Artificial Production of Fast Protons

J. D. Cockcroft and E. T. S. Walton

## Editor's Note

**To study the structure of the atomic nucleus, physicists in the early 1930s needed to accelerate probe particles to high energies. Among the first to develop such techniques were John Cockcroft and Ernest Walton in Cambridge. Here they report initial studies using a device for accelerating protons. An electrical discharge in hydrogen gas produced protons, which were then accelerated by high-voltage electrodes in a vacuum tube nearly one metre long, and detected at a fluorescent screen. Cockcroft and Walton measured proton velocities of up to $1.16 \times 10^9$ cm/s. The two physicists later used the device to achieve the first artificial splitting of the atom, or "transmutation" of the nucleus, for which they won the 1951 Nobel Prize for physics.**

A high potential laboratory has been developed at the Cavendish Laboratory for the study of the properties of high speed positive ions. The potential from a high voltage transformer is rectified and multiplied four times by a special arrangement of rectifiers and condensers, giving a working steady potential of 800 kilovolts. Currents of the order of a milliampere may be obtained at a potential constant to 1–2 percent.

Protons from a discharge in hydrogen are directed down the axis of two glass cylinders 14 in. in diameter and 36 in. long, and accelerated by the steady potentials of the rectifier. They are then passed into an experimental chamber at atmospheric pressure through a mica window having a stopping power of about 1mm. air equivalent. Luminescence of the air can easily be observed.

The ranges of the protons in air and hydrogen have been measured using a fluorescent screen as a detector. The range in air at S.T.P. of a proton having a velocity of $10^9$ cm./sec. is found to be 8.2 mm., whilst the corresponding range for hydrogen is 3.2 cm. The observed ranges support the general conclusions of Blackett on the relative ranges of protons and $\alpha$-particles, although the absolute values of the ranges are lower for both gases. The ranges and stopping power will be measured more accurately by an ionisation method.

The maximum energy of the protons produced up to the present has been 710 kilovolts with a velocity of $1.16\times10^9$ cm./sec. and a corresponding range in air of 13.5 mm. at S.T.P. We do not anticipate any difficulty in working up to 800 kilovolts with our present apparatus.

(**129**, 242; 1932)

J. D. Cockcroft and E. T. S. Walton: Cavendish Laboratory, Cambridge, Feb. 2.

# 快质子的人工产生

约翰·考克饶夫，欧内斯特·瓦耳顿

## 编者按

为了研究原子核的结构，20 世纪 30 年代的物理学家需要把探测粒子加速到很高的能量。剑桥大学的约翰·考克饶夫和欧内斯特·瓦耳顿是首先利用这类技术的人之一。本文中介绍了他们用质子加速仪所作的研究。首先让氢气放电产生质子，随后质子在近一米长的真空管中被高压电极加速，最后在荧光屏上被检测出来。考克饶夫和瓦耳顿测得的质子速度高达 $1.16 \times 10^9$ cm/s。后来这两位物理学家利用这个设备首次实现了原子的人工裂变，或称原子核的“蜕变”，他们因此获得了 1951 年的诺贝尔物理学奖。

为了研究高速正离子的性质，我们在卡文迪什实验室设立了一个高能实验室。由高压变压器输出的电压，经过特殊设置的整流器和电容器整流后，其值提高为 4 倍，最后可以得到 800 千伏的稳定工作电压。当电压的稳定度达到 1%~2% 时，我们就可以获得毫安级的电流。

我们使氢电离制得的质子沿着两个直径为 14 英寸，长为 36 英寸的玻璃圆管的轴线向下运动，质子被由整流器得到的稳定电压加速。然后它们会通过一个云母窗进入处于大气压下的实验靶室，云母片对质子的阻止作用相当于约 1 mm 厚的空气。在靶室中很容易观察到空气在质子的轰击下发出冷光的现象。

利用荧光屏作为探测器可以测量质子在空气和氢气中的射程。一个速度为 $10^9$ cm/s 的质子在处于标准温度和压强下的空气中的射程是 8.2 mm，而在相同条件下在氢气中的射程是 3.2 cm。我们测量的射程与布莱克特关于质子和 $\alpha$ 粒子相对射程的基本结论一致，但在两种气体中射程的绝对值都偏低。用电离方法测量射程和阻止本领，我们得到的结果会更精确。

目前能获得的质子的最高能量为 710 千伏，相应的速度为 $1.16 \times 10^9$ cm/s，在标准条件空气中的射程为 13.5 mm。用我们现在的设备提高到 800 千伏是完全可以做到的。

（沈乃澂 翻译；尚仁成 审稿）

# Crystal Structures of Vitamin D and Related Compounds

J. D. Bernal

## Editor's Note

**The chemical compound whose crystal structure is discussed here by J. Desmond Bernal, ergosterol, is a biological precursor to vitamin $D_2$. It is a complicated natural product with a hydrocarbon backbone that has several "chiral" centres, where the three-dimensional arrangement of atoms has two mirror-image forms. Such structures were particularly hard to unravel with X-ray crystallographic methods. Bernal's suggested structure for ergosterol is along the right lines but defective in some important respects. Yet it shows the molecular complexity that crystallographers were starting to feel able to contemplate.**

I have had the opportunity of examining by X-rays the crystals of ergosterol and certain of its irradiation products, recently described by a team working at the National Institute for Medical Research.[1] Though the results are only preliminary, they seem of sufficient interest to warrant publication at this stage. Five substances, all of composition $C_{27}H_{41}OH$ or $C_{27}H_{43}OH$, have been examined, with the results shown in the accompanying table.

| Substance | *a* | *b* | *c* | *β* | *c* sin *β* = $d_{001}$ | Space Group | No. of Mol. per Cell | No. of Mol. in Asym-metric Unit | Orders of Basal Plane, Estimated Intensities 1 | 2 | 3 | 4 | 5 | 6 | 7 | 8 | 9 | 10 |
|---|---|---|---|---|---|---|---|---|---|---|---|---|---|---|---|---|---|---|
| Ergosterol | 9.75 | 7.4 | 39.1 | 65° | *35.40* | $C_2^2$–$P2_1$ | 4 | 2 | vvs | vs | mw | a | vw | mw | s | vw | m | vw |
| *α*-Dihydroergosterol and ethyl alcohol | 30.8 | 7.4 | 43.1 | 53 | *34.5* | $C_2^3$–$C2$ | 12 | 3 | .. | vs | mw | a | vw | mw | s | a | m | .. |
| Calciferol | 20.8 | 7.15 | 38.5 | 68 | *35.65* | $C_2^2$–$P2_1$ | 8 | 4 | vvs | vs | s | a | vw | mw | ms | vw | ms | .. |
| Pyrocalciferol calciferol | 20.2 | 7.35 | 40.0 | 63 | *35.8* | $C_2^3$–$C2$ | 8 | 1 | .. | w | a | a | a | ms | w | m | w | m |
| Lumisterol | 20.3 | 7.25 | 20.4 | 60 | *17.8 =½×35.6* | $C_2^2$–$P2_1$ | 4 | 2 | .. | .. | .. | w | a | s | a | m | a | w |
| Cholesterol | 16.4 | .. | .. | .. | *33.3* | $C_1^1$–$P_1$ | .. | .. | .. | vs | a | a | a | w | ms | vw | ms | w |

*N.B.*—Letters for intensities: vs, very strong; mw, medium weak; etc.

The most striking features of the crystals are their essential similarities of properties and the simple relation between their unit cells. All the substances except lumisterol occur in platy crystals of a long-chain paraffinoid type. All are monoclinic and show a distinct tendency to elongation along the *b*-axis. (In lumisterol the crystals are fine needles with

# 维生素 D 及其相关化合物的晶体结构

德斯蒙德·贝尔纳

## 编者按

在这篇论文中，德斯蒙德·贝尔纳讨论了维生素 $D_2$ 的前体化合物——麦角甾醇的晶体结构。麦角甾醇是一种复杂的天然产物，在它的碳氢骨架上有多个“手性”中心，其原子的三维排列有两种镜像的形式。这样的结构很难用 X 射线晶体学方法拆分。贝尔纳认为麦角甾醇的原子基本上是沿直线排列的，但在一些关键位置存在缺陷。这说明晶体学家已经开始研究分子的复杂结构了。

我曾用 X 射线检测过麦角甾醇晶体和它的一些照射产物，最近英国国家医学研究所的一个小组描述了这项研究工作 [1]。虽然得到的只是一些初步的研究结果，但在此阶段它们似乎就已经具备充分的发表价值了。该小组对五种构成全部为 $C_{27}H_{41}OH$ 或 $C_{27}H_{43}OH$ 的物质进行了检测，得到的结果如下表所示。

| 物质名称 | $a$ | $b$ | $c$ | $\beta$ | $c\sin\beta = d_{001}$ | 空间群 | 晶胞中的分子数 | 不对称单元中的分子数 | 按照基面顺序排列，用光谱强度估计的强度 | | | | | | | | | |
|---|---|---|---|---|---|---|---|---|---|---|---|---|---|---|---|---|---|---|
| | | | | | | | | | 1 | 2 | 3 | 4 | 5 | 6 | 7 | 8 | 9 | 10 |
| 麦角甾醇 | 9.75 | 7.4 | 39.1 | 65° | *35.40* | $C_2^2\text{–}P2_1$ | 4 | 2 | vvs | vs | mw | a | vw | mw | s | vw | m | vw |
| $\alpha$－二氢麦角甾醇和乙醇 | 30.8 | 7.4 | 43.1 | 53 | *34.5* | $C_2^3\text{–}C2$ | 12 | 3 | .. | vs | mw | a | vw | mw | s | a | m | .. |
| 钙化醇 | 20.8 | 7.15 | 38.5 | 68 | *35.65* | $C_2^2\text{–}P2_1$ | 8 | 4 | vvs | vs | s | a | vw | mw | ms | vw | ms | .. |
| 焦钙化醇钙化醇 | 20.2 | 7.35 | 40.0 | 63 | *35.8* | $C_2^3\text{–}C2$ | 8 | 1 | .. | w | a | a | a | ms | w | m | w | m |
| 光甾醇 | 20.3 | 7.25 | 20.4 | 60 | *17.8 = ½×35.6* | $C_2^2\text{–}P2_1$ | 4 | 2 | .. | .. | .. | w | a | s | a | m | a | w |
| 胆固醇 | 16.4 | .. | .. | .. | *33.3* | $C_1^1\text{–}P_1$ | .. | .. | .. | vs | a | a | a | w | ms | vw | ms | w |

注意描述强度的字母含义：vs，非常强；mw，中等偏弱；等等

这些晶体最显著的特征就是它们的性质基本相似，而且在它们的晶胞之间存在着简单的联系。除了光甾醇以外，其他物质的晶体都是与石蜡类似的长链片状晶体。所有这些晶体都属于单斜晶系，并且在沿着 $b$ 轴方向表现出明显的延长趋势（光甾

*b* as needle axis.) All are optically positive with (010) as optic axial plane and the fast direction $\gamma$ inclined at a moderate angle to the *c* face. All have the same *b* axis of 7.2 A. and their *a* and *c* axes are simple multiples of 10 A. and 20 A. respectively. The spacing of the *c* plane is remarkably constant at 35.5 A., agreeing with the value found by K. Wejdling and E. Bäcklin.[2] It differs significantly from that of cholesterol, which was examined for comparison. Lumisterol has a halved *c* spacing, and $\alpha$-dihydroergosterol, owing to the presence of alcohol of crystallisation, deviates from the others.

From these observations certain conclusions can be drawn:

1. The unit cell of the molecular compound calciferol-pyrocalciferol contains four molecules of each kind, which is the number the symmetry demands for the space group $C_2^3$–$C2$. This proves either that calciferol is a simple substance or that it contains other substances indistinguishable by X-rays. The former conclusion is far the more probable. The association of molecules found in the other cases consequently does not show that any of them consists of more than one molecular species and is purely of geometrical intermolecular origin.

2. The molecule of ergosterol and its photo-derivatives has the approximate dimensions 5 A. × 7.2 A. × 17–20 A. These form a double layer similar to those of long-chain alcohols and acids. Such dimensions are difficult to reconcile with the usually accepted sterol formula

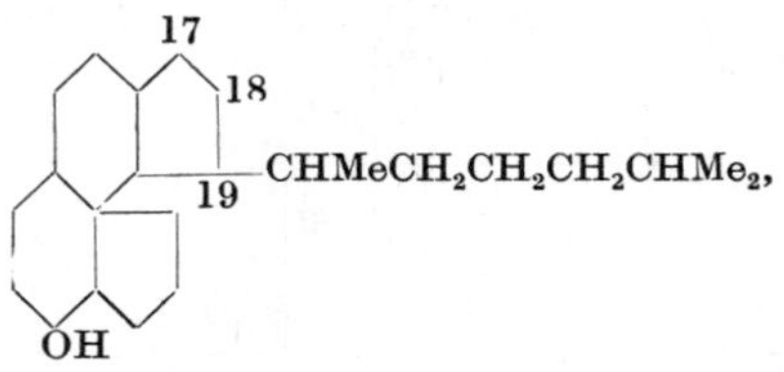


which would lead to a wider and shorter molecule, but agree much better with one where the carbon chain is attached to atom 17 in ring iv,

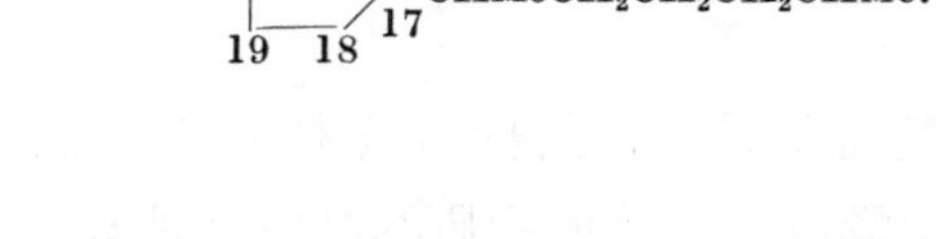

醇的晶体是细针状晶体，其 $b$ 轴即为针轴）。而且，它们都具有光学活性，以（010）为光学轴面，其速射向 $\gamma$ 与 $c$ 面成适度的斜角。它们的 $b$ 轴同样都是 7.2 Å，而 $a$ 轴和 $c$ 轴分别为 10 Å 和 20 Å 的简单倍数。它们的 $c$ 面间距明显为常量 35.5 Å，这与魏德林和贝克林得到的数值非常一致[2]。它与在检测中用于对比的胆固醇有很大的差别。同时，光甾醇的 $c$ 面间距仅为该常量的一半，而 $\alpha$– 二氢麦角甾醇因其结晶中乙醇溶剂的存在而与其他物质不同。

从上述观察研究中可以得出这样一些结论：

1. 化合物钙化醇 – 焦钙化醇的单位晶胞中含有四个分子，这也是空间群 $C_2^3$–$C2$ 的对称性所必需的分子数。这证明钙化醇要么是一种简单的物质，要么含有 X 射线所不能识别的其他物质，而前者的可能性要大得多。在研究其他几种化合物的分子排列规律时没有发现它们中的任何一个是由一种以上的分子构成的，也没有一个纯粹是源于分子间的几何结合。

2. 麦角甾醇及其光学衍生物的分子大小约为 5 Å ×7.2 Å ×（17~20）Å。它们形成了一个类似于长链的醇和酸的双层结构。这样的尺寸很难用普遍认可的甾醇结构式

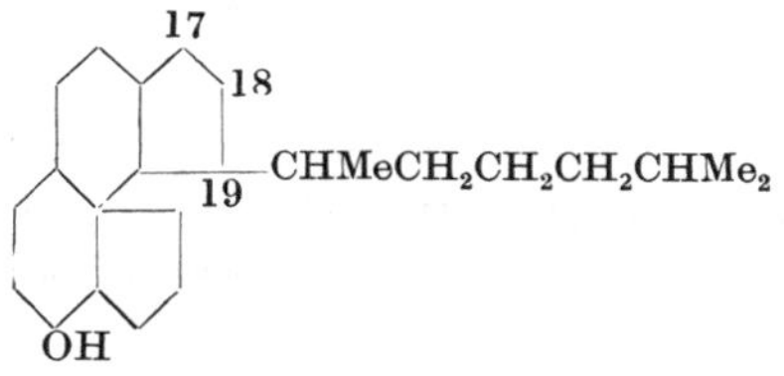


来解释，因为从公认的甾醇结构得到的应该是一个更宽更短的分子，但如果把甾醇结构上的碳链移至环 iv 的 C–17 原子上就可以很好地解释了。

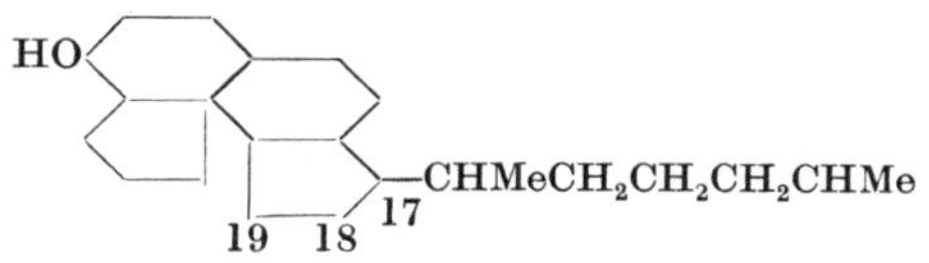

3. The rings lie approximately in the *bc* plane, that of the larger refractive indices $\beta\gamma$, and their width 7.2 is approximately constant in all the compounds. This is borne out by the observations of sterol films by N. K. Adam,[3] who finds the molecule area of 36 sq. A. for ergosterol, as against 35 sq. A. in the solid crystal.

4. The differences between the compounds is due to a differences in the side groups or linkages in the rings, leading to a different form of association in the solid and to a small but distinct redistribution of scattering matter along the chain lengths, as shown by the intensities of the *c* plane spectra. The greatest similarity is shown between ergosterol and calciferol, the chief difference being a double association of molecules in the latter case. It may be significant that while the basal plane intensities of ergosterol and dihydroergosterol are practically indistinguishable in spite of the notable difference in spacing, those of ergosterol differ from them particularly in the third and ninth orders. This would seem to indicate that the change had affected the carbon skeleton, not merely the position of double bonds in the molecule. In lumisterol and pyrocalciferol the change in intensities is so much greater that the resemblance is almost obliterated. It is doubtful, however, in view of the extreme complexity of the molecules, whether any conclusive evidence of the actual intra-molecular change can be found by X-rays alone. The most hopeful method would seem to be the examination of the ultra-violet absorption and Raman spectra of single crystals with polarised light at liquid hydrogen temperatures.

(**129**, 277-278; 1932)

J. D. Bernal: Mineralogical Museums, Cambridge, Feb. 2.

---

References:

1 Askew, F. A., Bourdillon, R. B., Bruce, H. M., Callow, R. K., Philpot J. L., and Webster, T. A., *Proc. Roy. Soc.*, B, **109**, 488 (1932). See also *Nature*, **128**, 758 (Oct. 31, 1931). I am indebted to Dr. Callow for the actual specimens and private communication giving later values.

2 *Acta Radiologica*, **11**, 166 (1930).

3 *Proc. Roy. Soc.*, A, **126**, 25 (1930).

3. 分子中的环结构基本上都位于 *bc* 平面内，*bc* 平面具有较大的折射率 $\beta\gamma$，并且在所有这些化合物中它们的宽度几乎都是 7.2 Å。这是亚当在观测甾醇薄膜时发现的 [3]，他还发现液态麦角甾醇的分子面积为 36 $Å^2$，而其固态晶体的分子面积为 35 $Å^2$。

4. 这些化合物之间的不同之处在于环上的侧链基团或键有所不同，这使得固态晶体中的结合方式各不相同，而且在链长度方向上散布的基团会出现小而明显的重排，正如 *c* 平面的光谱强度显示。麦角甾醇和钙化醇最为相似，它们的主要差别是钙化醇分子中存在双重结合。尽管麦角甾醇和二氢麦角甾醇在间距上有显著的差别，但是它们的基面光谱强度实际上没有什么区别，而麦角甾醇的基面光谱强度在第三和第九位上明显不同于其他化合物，这一点也许非常重要。它似乎说明这种改变不仅仅影响了分子中双键的位置，也影响到了碳骨架。在光甾醇和焦钙化醇中，光谱强度的变化更大以至于几乎看不出它们之间的相似性。然而鉴于这些分子的高度复杂性，不能肯定是否仅仅用 X 射线就能得到关于分子内实际变化的确切证据。看起来最有希望的方法是紫外吸收光谱检测法和在液氢温度下使用偏振光检测单晶的拉曼光谱法。

（刘振明 翻译；吕扬 审稿）

# Possible Existence of a Neutron

J. Chadwick

## Editor's Note

**Physicists had recently noted that alpha particles hitting a beryllium target produced unknown secondary radiation with great penetrating power. When directed into any material containing hydrogen, this secondary radiation had been found to produce protons. Some physicists suspected that the unknown particles might be high-energy light quanta. But here James Chadwick reports that his studies on the ionisation of nitrogen atoms by collisions with the mysterious radiation point instead to the action of a hitherto unknown particle. Chadwick suggests that the particles have atomic mass one and charge zero: they are what we now call neutrons. It took further experiments to verify the hypothesis, but for this discovery Chadwick won the Nobel Prize in physics in 1935.**

IT has been shown by Bothe and others that beryllium when bombarded by $\alpha$-particles of polonium emits a radiation of great penetrating power, which has an absorption coefficient in lead of about 0.3 $(\text{cm.})^{-1}$. Recently Mme. Curie-Joliot and M. Joliot found, when measuring the ionisation produced by this beryllium radiation in a vessel with a thin window, that the ionisation increased when matter containing hydrogen was placed in front of the window. The effect appeared to be due to the ejection of protons with velocities up to a maximum of nearly $3\times10^9$ cm. per sec. They suggested that the transference of energy to the proton was by a process similar to the Compton effect, and estimated that the beryllium radiation had a quantum energy of $50\times10^6$ electron volts.

I have made some experiments using the valve counter to examine the properties of this radiation excited in beryllium. The valve counter consists of a small ionisation chamber connected to an amplifier, and the sudden production of ions by the entry of a particle, such as a proton or $\alpha$-particle, is recorded by the deflexion of an oscillograph. These experiments have shown that the radiation ejects particles from hydrogen, helium, lithium, beryllium, carbon, air, and argon. The particles ejected from hydrogen behave, as regards range and ionising power, like protons with speeds up to about $3.2\times10^9$ cm. per sec. The particles from the other elements have a large ionising power, and appear to be in each case recoil atoms of the elements.

If we ascribe the ejection of the proton to a Compton recoil from a quantum of $52\times10^6$ electron volts, then the nitrogen recoil atom arising by a similar process should have an energy not greater than about 400,000 volts, should produce not more than about 10,000 ions, and have a range in air at N.T.P. of about 1.3 mm. Actually, some of the recoil atoms in nitrogen produce at least 30,000 ions. In collaboration with Dr. Feather, I have observed the recoil atoms in an expansion chamber, and their range, estimated visually, was sometimes as much as 3 mm. at N.T.P.

# 可能存在中子

詹姆斯·查德威克

## 编者按

物理学家们最近指出：$\alpha$ 粒子在撞击铍靶之后能够产生一种穿透力很强的未知次级辐射。他们发现当这种次级辐射射向含氢物质时会有质子生成。一些物理学家怀疑未知粒子可能就是高能光量子。但在这篇文章中，詹姆斯·查德威克报告了氮原子与这种神秘射线碰撞后所产生的离子化现象，结果表明它更像是一种迄今未知的粒子。查德威克认为这种粒子的原子量为 1，电荷数为 0：我们现在把它们称为中子。虽然要验证这一假说还需要进一步的实验，不过查德威克因此而获得了 1935 年的诺贝尔物理奖。

博特等人曾指出，当用钋元素放射产生的 $\alpha$ 粒子轰击铍元素时，铍元素会释放出一种穿透力极强的射线，铅对这种射线的吸收系数约为 0.3 $cm^{-1}$。最近，约里奥－居里夫妇发现，在一个具有薄窗的容器中测量这种铍辐射导致的电离时，如果在薄窗前放置含氢的物质，电离就会增强。这种现象似乎是由实验中有速度最大值接近于 $3\times10^9$ cm/s 的质子发射出来所致。他们认为能量是通过一个类似于康普顿效应的过程转移给质子的，并估算出这种铍辐射的量子的能量为 $50\times10^6$ eV。

为了研究从铍元素中激发出的这种射线的性质，我利用真空管计数器做了一些实验。这种真空管计数器由一个连接到放大器的小电离腔组成。质子或 $\alpha$ 粒子进入电离腔后迅速产生离子的情况可以通过示波器显示的偏转来记录。这些实验表明，该射线轰击氢、氦、锂、铍、碳、空气、氩时都能发射出粒子。从射程和致电离能力来看，氢中发射出来的粒子类似于速度高达约 $3.2\times10^9$ cm/s 的质子。其他元素中发射出来的粒子具有很高的致电离能力，看上去像是每种元素的反冲原子。

如果我们将这一质子发射过程视作能量为 $52\times10^6$ eV 的量子的康普顿反冲过程，那么在类似的过程中产生的氮的反冲原子的能量应该不大于 400,000 eV，其产生的离子数应该不多于 10,000，常温常压下这种原子在空气中的射程应该约为 1.3 mm。而事实上，一些氮的反冲原子至少产生了 30,000 个离子。在与费瑟博士合作进行的实验中，我在膨胀室中观察到了反冲原子，其在常温常压下的射程（目测）有时能达到 3 mm。

These results, and others I have obtained in the course of the work, are very difficult to explain on the assumption that the radiation from beryllium is a quantum radiation, if energy and momentum are to be conserved in the collisions. The difficulties disappear, however, if it be assumed that the radiation consists of particles of mass 1 and charge 0, or neutrons. The capture of the $\alpha$-particle by the $Be^9$ nucleus may be supposed to result in the formation of a $C^{12}$ nucleus and the emission of the neutron. From the energy relations of this process the velocity of the neutron emitted in the forward direction may well be about $3\times10^9$ cm. per sec. The collisions of this neutron with the atoms through which it passes give rise to the recoil atoms, and the observed energies of the recoil atoms are in fair agreement with this view. Moreover, I have observed that the protons ejected from hydrogen by the radiation emitted in the opposite direction to that of the exciting $\alpha$-particle appear to have a much smaller range than those ejected by the forward radiation. This again receives a simple explanation on the neutron hypothesis.

If it be supposed that the radiation consists of quanta, then the capture of the $\alpha$-particle by the $Be^9$ nucleus will form a $C^{13}$ nucleus. The mass defect of $C^{13}$ is known with sufficient accuracy to show that the energy of the quantum emitted in this process cannot be greater than about $14\times10^6$ volts. It is difficult to make such a quantum responsible for the effects observed.

It is to be expected that many of the effects of a neutron in passing through matter should resemble those of a quantum of high energy, and it is not easy to reach the final decision between the two hypotheses. Up to the present, all the evidence is in favour of the neutron, while the quantum hypothesis can only be upheld if the conservation of energy and momentum be relinquished at some point.

(**129**, 312; 1932)

J. Chadwick: Cavendish Laboratory, Cambridge, Feb. 17.

如果碰撞过程中能量和动量都是守恒的，那么如果假定铍元素中释放出的这种射线是量子化的，就很难解释上述结果以及我在这项工作中得到的其他一些结果。然而，如果假设这种射线是由一种质量为 1，电荷为 0 的粒子（中子）组成的，那么这些困难将不复存在。我们可以设想，$Be^9$ 原子核俘获 $\alpha$ 粒子后产生了一个 $C^{12}$ 原子核并释放出中子。根据这一过程的能量关系，可以得出朝前方发射的中子的速度刚好约为 $3\times10^9$ cm/s。这一中子穿过物体时与物体中的原子碰撞产生了反冲原子，通过实验对反冲原子能量进行观测得到的结果与这一观点基本吻合。此外，我还观测到，用与激发 $\alpha$ 粒子方向相反的这种射线轰击氢后发射出的质子的射程要比用正向射线轰击得到的质子的射程短得多。这一实验结果同样可以用中子假说来简单解释。

如果假设这种射线是由量子组成的，那么 $Be^9$ 原子核俘获 $\alpha$ 粒子后将形成一个 $C^{13}$ 原子核。对 $C^{13}$ 质量亏损的精确测量结果表明，这一过程中释放出的量子的能量不可能大于 $14\times10^6$ eV。因此，对于目前观测到的实验现象我们很难将其归因于这样一种量子。

可以预计，中子穿过物体时产生的很多效应都应该与高能量子产生的效应相似，因此对这两种假说的最终取舍并不容易。到目前为止，所有的证据都更倾向于中子假说，而量子假说只有在放弃能量和动量守恒原理的某些情形下才会得到人们的支持。

（曾红芳 翻译；刘纯 审稿）

# Determinism

J. B. S. Haldane

## Editor's Note

**Arthur Eddington's essay on the decline of determinism provoked strong responses. The biologist J. B. S. Haldane here criticizes Eddington's remarks about human behaviour — specifically, that if the behaviour of atoms is indeterminate, then the human mind must also be. It was then considered that behaviour may be correlated between identical twins. Haldane points out that if one such twin breaks the law during a certain period, the chance that his twin will do so may be as high as 0.875. (These data were almost certainly flawed.) Eddington was effectively claiming that no amount of extra information could turn such a prediction into a certainty. But Haldane complains that this assertion is little more than an a priori pronouncement, unsupported by evidence.**

IN his address on the decline of determinism,[1] Sir Arthur Eddington enunciates a very curious equation. "If the atom has indeterminacy, surely the human mind will have an equal indeterminacy; for we can scarcely accept a theory which makes out the mind to be more mechanistic than the atom." This statement will not bear too close an examination even from a non-quantitative point of view. Thus an attempt by myself to solve even a simple wave equation might lead to any of a large number of results; a similar attempt by Sir Arthur Eddington would lead to the correct solution with a high degree of probability. I do not think that this proves that his mind is more mechanistic than my own, whatever that may mean. Actually it is generally regarded as a compliment to describe a person as reliable, that is, to suggest that his conduct is predictable.

Fortunately, however, quantitative data exist which seem to show that, as regards moral behaviour, some minds are decidedly more determined than are some atoms as regards radiative behaviour. Consider a given man $M_1$, and the probability $p$ that between times $T_1$ and $T_2$ he will commit an action such as to lead to his imprisonment for a breach of the law. If we have no further information regarding $M_1$, $p$ is in most communities a small number, less than 0.01. If, however, $M_1$ has a monozygotic twin $M_2$ brought up in the same environment up to the age of 14, and $M_2$ is known to have been imprisoned for crime between the ages of 16 and 40, we can infer with a fairly high degree of probability that $M_1$, who has an identical nature and a similar nurture, has been or will be imprisoned between the same ages. Judging from Lange's[2] results, $p$ is about 0.875 in south Germany when we have the above amount of information. If we increase the amount of information, for example, by excluding cases where $M_2$ has suffered from head injury, the value of $p$ is raised still further. Now, if it could be shown that with sufficient information $p$ became unity in a case of this kind, we should, I take it, have proved the determinacy of some kinds, at least, of moral choice. Actually the most that scientific method can

# 决定论

约翰·波顿·桑德森·霍尔丹

## 编者按

阿瑟·爱丁顿的那篇关于决定论在衰落的短文引起了强烈的社会反响。生物学家霍尔丹批驳了爱丁顿关于人类行为的观点，尤其是他认为：如果原子的运动是不可确定的，则人类的思想也不例外。随后霍尔丹列举了同卵双生双胞胎在行为上具有相关性的例子。他说如果其中的一个在某段时间内触犯了法律，那么另一个会触犯法律的可能性高达 0.875。（这个数据肯定有问题。）爱丁顿指出这种说法缺少实际的证据。但霍尔丹辩解说爱丁顿的说法纯粹是由推理得到的结果，并没有得到实践上的验证。

阿瑟·爱丁顿爵士在他的关于决定论的衰落[1]的讲话中提到了一个非比寻常的对等关系，“如果原子具有不确定性，那么人的思维肯定也会具有同样的不确定性；因为把思维说成比原子更机械的理论是绝大多数人都不愿意接受的。”即便从非定量的角度上看，这种说法与事实也有一定的差距。比如：我在试图解一个很简单的波动方程时也许会得到众多解中的任意一个；而阿瑟·爱丁顿爵士在解同样的方程时会得到可靠性更高的解。我不会因此而认为他的思维比我的思维更机械，不管多么地像是这回事。事实上人们在说一个人可靠时通常是在称赞他，也就是说，他的行为具有可预见性。

然而，幸运的是，定量数据似乎表明，就道德行为而言，某些人的思想意识确实比一些原子的辐射行为更容易确定。对于某一个人 $M_1$，在 $T_1$ 与 $T_2$ 之间的任意时刻内，这个人付诸一个行动的几率为 $p$，比如说他会因违反法律而被监禁。如果我们不了解有关 $M_1$ 的更多情况，则 $p$ 对绝大多数人来说只是一个很小的数，小于 0.01。然而，如果 $M_1$ 有一个同卵孪生兄弟 $M_2$，他们在相同的环境下一直长到 14 岁，且已知 $M_2$ 在 16 岁至 40 岁之间曾因犯罪被监禁过，那么我们就可以认为：$M_1$ 的天性与 $M_2$ 相同，后天培养与 $M_2$ 相似，所以他很有可能在相同的年龄段内也曾被监禁过或将要被监禁。根据兰格[2]的研究结果，当我们已知以上信息时，在德国南部 $p$ 约为 0.875。如果我们能了解更多的情况，例如，知道 $M_2$ 未曾有过头部损伤，则 $p$ 的值还会更大一些。在这类情况下，如果我们了解的信息量足够多，可以把 $p$ 的值取为 1，我认为，这说明我们已经证明了某种决定论的存在，至少是在道德选择的层面上。实际上，科学研究的主要任务就是要证明 $p>1-\varepsilon$。如果阿瑟·爱丁顿爵士是正确的，

do is to prove $p>1-\varepsilon$. If Sir Arthur Eddington is correct, then no matter how complete our information, $\varepsilon$ tends to a finite limit which is not very small. Clearly no amount of observation could prove it to be zero. But if it could be shown to be less than 0.01, we could neglect it to a first approximation in ethical theory, and if it proved to be less than $10^{-6}$ we might hazard the guess that the behaviour of human beings showed no more indeterminacy than that of other systems composed of about $2\times10^{27}$ atoms.

I think that it is a legitimate extrapolation from the existing data that if we used all the available data in the above case, $\varepsilon$ would be less than 0.05. It seems unfortunate that any attempt should be made to prejudge, on philosophical or emotional grounds, the magnitude of a quantity susceptible of scientific measurement. But from the heuristic point of view the deterministic theory has the advantage that it could be disproved, and would be if $\varepsilon$ tended to a finite limit as the amount of available information increased indefinitely. On the other hand, indeterminism cannot be disproved unless its supporters state the value of $\varepsilon$, which they have so far carefully avoided. When the truth about human behaviour is discovered, it will probably appear that philosophers of all schools had failed to predict it as completely as they failed to predict Heisenberg's uncertainty principle. Human behaviour is a subject for scientific investigation rather than *a priori* pronouncements.

(**129**, 315-316; 1932)

J. B. S. Haldane: Royal Institution, Albemarle Street, London, W.

References:

1 *Nature*, 129, 240 (Feb. 13, 1932).

2 *Crime as Destiny* (1931).

则不管我们掌握的信息多么全面，$\varepsilon$ 都将是一个比较大的有限数。显然再多的观测结果也不能证明 $\varepsilon$ 为零。但如果能说明 $\varepsilon$ 的值小于 0.01，则在伦理学理论的一级近似中我们就可以把它忽略掉，如果能证明 $\varepsilon$ 小于 $10^{-6}$，我们也许可以大胆地说人类的行为不会比包含约 $2 \times 10^{27}$ 个原子的系统更难以预测。

我认为从现有数据进行的推理是合理的，如果我们利用上述事件中的所有可用信息，那么 $\varepsilon$ 的值会小于 0.05。但遗憾的是：在哲学或情感的范畴内，对所有能够用科学方法测量的量进行预测都只是一种臆断。从发现的角度上看，决定论的优点是它可以被证伪，当可获得的信息量越来越不确定，$\varepsilon$ 趋于一个有限的值时，我们就应该认为该命题不成立。从另一方面来说，非决定论是不能被证伪的，除非其支持者能够明确规定一个 $\varepsilon$ 值，而这一点正是他们一直谨慎回避的。当人类行为的真正规律性被发现时，很可能所有学派的哲学家都没能完全预测出来，就像他们没有预测到海森堡测不准原理的出现一样。人类的行为是科学研究的一门学问，而不是先验的臆断。

（沈乃澂 翻译；李淼 审稿）

# Determinism

Lewis F. Richardson

## Editor's Note

**The newly discovered principle of quantum indeterminacy inspired considerable philosophical discussion, and even a few attempts to apply it to human nature and the unpredictability of the individual human action. Here Lewis Fry Richardson writes to ridicule the latter proposition. Is it really necessary, he asks? Science is capable of making accurate predictions, as of the motion of a pendulum, for example, but only if no person interferes with it. The dynamics of something as large as the Moon can be treated with mathematical precision, precisely because no one can interfere with it. But when it comes to human action itself, we can never be sure that one person will not interfere with the workings of their own mind.**

IS it really necessary to appeal to anything so *recherché* as Heisenberg's Principle of Indeterminacy in order to justify anything so familiar as personal freedom of choice? This question arises on reading Sir Arthur Eddington's interesting address in *Nature* of Feb. 13. Consider any one of the laws of physics commonly verified in the laboratory, say $T=2\pi\sqrt{l/g}$ for a simple pendulum. If, while one student is observing the pendulum, another student were to knock it about, the observations might misfit the formula. And so in general: the accepted laws of physics are verified only if no person interferes with the apparatus. We cannot interfere with the moon, because it is so massive and so far away: and that is part of the reason why the motion of the moon is almost deterministic; the "almost" referring to the extremely small Heisenbergian indeterminacy. But there is no great mass or great distance to prevent John Doe interfering with his own brain in the act of making his decision to buy a house from Richard Roe.

(**129**, 316; 1932)

Lewis F. Richardson: The Technical College, Paisley, Feb. 13.

# 决定论

刘易斯·理查森

## 编者按

新发现的量子测不准原理引发了哲学上的大讨论，有些人甚至用它来解释人类的本性以及个人行为的不可预知性。在这篇文章中，刘易斯·弗赖伊·理查森嘲讽了后者的观点。他认为没有必要用科学来预知人的行为。对于一个钟摆的运动情况，科学是可以准确预测的，但前提是在没有人干扰的情况下。月球等大型天体的动力学也可以通过数学方法精确预测，这也是因为没有人能干涉它运动的缘故。但是当论及人类的行为本身时，我们无法保证一个人不对自己的意识施加影响。

为了说明像个人选择自由这样熟悉的事也有必要求助于学究式的海森堡测不准原理吗？这个问题是我在阅读阿瑟·爱丁顿爵士于 2 月 13 日发表在《自然》杂志上的演说词时联想到的。对于任意一个在实验室里就可以证实的物理定律，比如一个单摆的周期，$T=2\pi\sqrt{l/g}$，如果当一个学生观察单摆的时候，另一个学生撞了一下这个摆，则观测结果可能就会与公式不符。所以可以这么说：大家普遍接受的物理定律只有在没有人干扰实验设备的情况下才能被证实。我们无法干扰月球，因为它的质量很大，而且离我们又很远：这就是为什么我们基本上可以预测月球运动的一部分原因；称“基本上”是因为确实存在极小的海森堡不确定性。但是再大的质量或再远的距离也不能阻止约翰·多伊考虑是否要从理查德·罗那里买一幢房子。

（沈乃澂 翻译；李淼 审稿）

# Hexuronic Acid as the Antiscorbutic Factor

## Editor's Note

**In the 1930s, medical people first became aware that certain chemicals are essential for healthy life but cannot be made in the human body. These were called vitamins. The search for Vitamin C was led by Albert Szent-Györgyi, then at the University of Szeged in Hungary. He was awarded the Nobel Prize for medicine in 1937. This letter describes Szent-Györgyi's isolation of vitamin C, contained in citrus fruits and which famously helped prevent the development of scurvy among sailors if included in their restrictive ship-borne diet. The paper is accompanied by two others from the University of Birmingham dealing with the chemical structure of the vitamin.**

EXPERIMENTS are being carried out in order to decide whether "hexuronic acid" is the antiscorbutic factor. So far as is known, the distribution of this acid in plants follows closely the distribution of vitamin C. In the animal body it can also be found in relatively high concentration in the suprarenal cortex. Its chemical properties closely agree with the known properties of the vitamin. It was discovered and isolated several years ago at the Biochemical Laboratory, Cambridge.[1]

The hexuronic acid used in the present series was prepared in crystalline form from beef suprarenal glands two years ago at the Chemical Department of the Mayo Clinic.[2] As is known, 1.5 c.c. of lemon juice is the minimum protective dose for guinea-pigs against scurvy. This quantity of lemon juice contains approximately 0.5 mgm. of hexuronic acid. 1 mgm. of the acid has been given to our test animals daily, since, owing to the long exposure to air, some of our hexuronic acid preparation may have been decomposed.

The general procedure used in studying the antiscorbutic activity of hexuronic acid was that recommended by Sherman and co-workers.[3]

The test period in the first experiment consisted of 56 days. At the end of that time the guinea-pigs which had been receiving hexuronic acid, as well as the positive controls which received 1 c.c. of lemon juice, were chloroformed. The positive controls showed mild scurvy on autopsy, while the animals receiving hexuronic acid showed no symptoms of scurvy at all. The negative controls, which received the basal diet only, had an average survival of 26 days and had typical symptoms of scurvy. In this experiment, however, only a small number of animals were used, and the animals receiving hexuronic acid, as well as the positive controls, were losing weight continually because the basal diet employed at that time contained no milk powder (it consisted of rolled oats, bran, butter fat, and salt). For this reason we decided to repeat the experiment.

# 作为抗坏血病因子的己糖醛酸

## 编者按

20 世纪 30 年代，医学界人士首次认识到某些化学物质对于生命健康是至关重要的，但却无法在人体内合成。这些物质被称为维生素。对维生素 C 的探索始于阿尔伯特·圣哲尔吉，当时他还在匈牙利塞格德大学。他获得了 1937 年的诺贝尔医学奖。这篇快报描述了圣哲尔吉分离维生素 C 的工作，维生素 C 存在于柑橘类水果中，它非常有助于防止坏血病在只食用有限的船载食品的海员中的蔓延。此外，文后还附列了两篇来自伯明翰大学的关于维生素化学结构的文章。

我们正在进行实验以确定“己糖醛酸”是否就是抗坏血病因子。就目前的结果来看，这种酸在植物中的分布总是与维生素 C 的分布密切相关。在动物体内的肾上腺皮质中存在着相当高浓度的该物质。它的化学性质与维生素的已知性质十分吻合。这种物质是几年前在剑桥大学的生物化学实验室中被发现并分离出来的 [1]。

我们在当前一系列实验中所使用的己糖醛酸，是两年前梅奥医疗中心化学部从牛的肾上腺中制备得到的晶体 [2]。大家都知道，1.5 毫升柠檬汁是防止豚鼠患坏血病的最小剂量。这一剂量的柠檬汁中大约含有 0.5 毫克己糖醛酸。由于长期暴露于空气之中，我们制备的己糖醛酸可能已经部分发生了分解，因此在实验中我们每天给测试动物喂食 1 毫克己糖醛酸。

我们在研究己糖醛酸的抗坏血病活性时，采用了由舍曼和他的同事们推荐的基本步骤 [3]。

第一次实验的检测周期为 56 天。在这期间，测试豚鼠一直摄取己糖醛酸，而对阳性对照组的豚鼠每天供给 1 毫升柠檬汁，喂食周期结束后，对所有豚鼠进行氯仿麻醉。解剖结果表明，阳性对照组的豚鼠出现了轻微的坏血病症状，而摄取己糖醛酸的豚鼠则完全没有表现出坏血病症状。只食用基础食物的阴性对照组豚鼠的平均存活期为 26 天，并出现了典型的坏血病症状。不过，这一实验只使用了为数不多的豚鼠，而且摄取己糖醛酸的豚鼠与阳性对照组的豚鼠都发生了体重持续减轻的情况，这是因为实验所用的基础食物中没有奶粉（基础食物只包括燕麦片、糠、乳脂和盐）。因此我们决定重新进行这一实验。

In the test which is in progress at the present time the defects mentioned above have been remedied. A large number of animals has been used, and skimmed milk powder has been added to the basal diet.

The test was composed of the following groups: (1) Negative controls receiving the basal diet only, 9 animals. (2) Positive controls, receiving 1 c.c. of lemon juice daily, 8 animals. (3) Test animals receiving the basal diet and 1 mgm. of hexuronic acid daily, 10 animals. (4) Controls receiving mixed diet, 10 animals.

The negative controls all died between the time limit of 20–34 days, with an average survival of 26 days, after a continuous and big drop of weight. They all had symptoms of severe scurvy.

At the end of 55 days all the animals receiving hexuronic acid, as well as the positive controls with lemon juice or mixed diet, were living apparently in good health and were gaining weight consistently. At this time three animals which received hexuronic acid and two animals which received lemon juice were chloroformed. Mild symptoms of scurvy were present in the positive controls with lemon juice, but no signs of scurvy in the animals receiving hexuronic acid.

The test will be continued until the ninety-day period is over, and full details will be published later.

This research was supported by the Ella Sachs Plotz Foundation.

J. L. Svirbely* and A. Szent-Györgyi

* * *

At the wish and by the courtesy of Prof. A. Szent-Györgyi, I arranged to examine in my laboratory the "hexuronic acid" which he isolated while working in the Biochemical Laboratory, Cambridge. At the end of 1929 he sent me 10 grams of the substance, which had been prepared in the chemical laboratory of the Mayo Clinic, Rochester, U.S.A. Owing to the value and scarcity of this material, it has been necessary to carry out each experiment with very small quantities, and to establish with much deliberation and care the experimental conditions and controls. This work is still in progress and is being directed to the elucidation of the constitution and the achievement of the synthesis of the substance; this has involved the study of its chemical properties, and the formation of a crystalline derivative. The preliminary results now communicated show that the hexuronic acid is most probably the 6-carboxylic acid of a keto-hexose, which does not appear to be

* Holder of an America-Hungarian Exchange Fellowship, 1931-32, from the Institute of International Education, New York.

在目前正在进行的实验中，上面提到的各种缺陷都已得到了补救。实验中，我们使用了大量的豚鼠，并在基础食物中加入了脱脂奶粉。

这次实验包括以下几组动物：(1) 只摄取基础食物的阴性对照组，有 9 只豚鼠；(2) 每天摄取 1 毫升柠檬汁的阳性对照组，有 8 只豚鼠；(3) 每天摄取基础食物和 1 毫克己糖醛酸的测试组，有 10 只豚鼠；(4) 摄取混合食物的对照组，有 10 只豚鼠。

阴性对照组豚鼠在 20~34 天内全部死亡，平均存活期为 26 天，死之前体重一直在急剧下降。这组豚鼠都出现了严重的坏血病症状。

在第 55 天结束时，所有摄取己糖醛酸的豚鼠和摄取柠檬汁或混合食物的阳性对照组豚鼠都明显处于良好的健康状态，并且体重稳定增加。这次我们对 3 只摄取己糖醛酸的豚鼠和 2 只摄取柠檬汁的豚鼠进行了氯仿麻醉。解剖结果表明，摄取柠檬汁的阳性对照组豚鼠中有轻微的坏血病症状，而摄取己糖醛酸的豚鼠中则完全没有坏血病的迹象。

这次实验还将一直持续到第 90 天结束，随后我们会发表完整的详细结果。

本研究受到埃拉 · 萨克斯 · 普罗茨基金会的资助。

史文贝力*，圣哲尔吉

* * *

承蒙圣哲尔吉教授的托付和惠赠，我在自己的实验室中检测了他在剑桥大学生物化学实验室工作时分离出来的“己糖醛酸”。圣哲尔吉教授于 1929 年底寄给了我 10 克由美国罗切斯特市梅奥医疗中心化学实验室制备的该物质。由于这一物质得来不易、非常稀少，因此在进行每一次实验时只能使用很少的量，而且还必须格外小心谨慎地设定实验条件和对照物。检测工作目前还在进行中，其目标是弄清该物质的组成并找到合成该物质的方法，这就要对该物质的化学性质进行研究并且要得到一种结晶态的衍生物。对目前初步结果的讨论表明，这种己糖醛酸很可能是一种己酮糖的 6–羧酸，看起来这种己酮糖与 *d*–果糖没有什么关系，也不是相当于 *d*–半乳

* 1931~1932 年美国–匈牙利交流奖金持有者，由位于纽约的美国国际教育协会提供。

related either to *d*-fructose or to the ketose corresponding to *d*-galactose. This work has been conducted by my colleague Dr. E. L. Hirst, assisted by Mr. R. J. W. Reynolds, whose report is given in the accompanying note.

W. N. Haworth

* * *

The "hexuronic acid" prepared from suprarenal glands by Prof. Szent-Györgyi was a cream-coloured micro-crystalline powder, m.p. 184°–187° (decomp.). On recrystallisation from methyl alcohol-ether the substance was obtained in irregular aggregates of rectangular crystals, which were almost colourless. No change in m.p., analysis, or other properties was observed even after several successive crystallisations. The crystals showed brilliant colours when observed between crossed nicols in a polarising microscope. Before and after recrystallisation the same analytical figures were obtained (Found: C, 41.0; H, 4.7, $C_6H_8O_6$ requires C, 40.9; H, 4.5 percent). Neither nitrogen nor methoxyl was present. In aqueous solution the rotation $[\alpha]_D^{20^\circ}$ +23°(c. 1.1) increased slowly to +31° (3 days) and then decreased to zero (11 days).

The hexuronic acid reduced Fehling's solution, neutral silver nitrate, and neutral potassium permanganate in the cold. It gave the Molisch test and the orcinol reaction, but failed to show the naphtoresorcin colour test characteristic of glycuronic acid.

The hexuronic acid was monobasic (40 mgm. of sodium hydroxide neutralised 172 mgm. of substance—calc. for $C_6H_8O_6$, 176).

Oxidation by atmospheric oxygen in slightly alkaline solution, with a trace of copper as catalyst, introduced one carboxyl group in place of a primary alcohol group and the product reduced Fehling's solution. Oxidation to the same stage occurred with remarkable rapidity when the hexuronic acid reacted with neutral, acid, or slightly alkaline potassium permanganate. The reaction, which required two atoms of oxygen per molecule of the substance, was thereafter much less rapid but proceeded regularly in the cold until one further atom of oxygen per molecule had been absorbed. The product was now non-reducing.

When heated with phenylhydrazine in dilute acetic acid, the hexuronic acid gave intractable, dark-coloured, amorphous products which could not be purified. The action of *p*-bromophenylhydrazine in dilute acetic acid on the barium salt of the hexuronic acid (compare Goldschmiedt and Zerner, *Monatsh.*, **33**, 1217, 1912) gave a dark red micro-crystalline powder which, after recrystallisation from alcohol, had m.p. 230°–

糖的酮糖。这一工作是由我的同事赫斯特博士在雷诺兹先生的协助下进行的，本文后附有他们的报告。

霍沃思

* * *

圣哲尔吉教授从肾上腺中制得的“己糖醛酸”是一种奶油色的微晶粉末，熔点为 184℃～187℃（分解）。在甲基醇醚中进行重结晶时，可以得到该物质的矩形结晶体的不规则聚集物，这一聚集物几乎是无色的。即使是在多次连续结晶之后，也没有发现该物质的熔点、分析结果及其他性质发生变化。将晶体置于偏光显微镜的正交尼科尔棱镜之间观察时，可以看到明亮的色彩。重结晶前后得到的分析结果是一样的（分析结果是：C 占 41.0%，H 占 4.7%。而在 $C_6H_8O_6$ 中 C 占 40.9%，H 占 4.5%）。晶体中不存在氮或甲氧基。在水溶液中，比旋光度 $[\alpha]_D^{20^\circ}$ 从 + 23º（c. 1.1）缓慢增大到 + 31º（3 天），随后又下降到 0（11 天）。

这种己糖醛酸可以还原冷的斐林试剂、中性硝酸银和中性高锰酸钾。它在莫利希试验中给出阳性结果，可以发生地衣酚反应，但是在葡萄糖醛酸特征性的间萘二酚显色反应中给出阴性结果。

这种己糖醛酸是一元酸（40 毫克氢氧化钠能中和 172 毫克该物质，按 $C_6H_8O_6$ 计算需要 176 毫克）。

当在弱碱性溶液中以痕量的铜作为催化剂时，空气中的氧可以氧化伯羟基而在相应位置引入一个羧基，得到的产物能够还原斐林试剂。当这种己糖醛酸与中性、酸性或弱碱性的高锰酸钾反应时，可以非常快速地发生同样程度的氧化反应。在该反应中，每一个己糖醛酸分子需要两个氧原子，此后反应明显减慢，但是在冷溶液中反应确实依然在进行，直到每个底物分子再接受一个氧原子。此时的产物失去了还原性。

当这种己糖醛酸在稀释的乙酸中与苯肼一起被加热时，能生成难以处理又无法纯化的黑色无定形产物。在稀释乙酸中的对溴苯肼与这种己糖醛酸的钡盐反应（可以对照戈尔德施密特和策纳的工作，《化学月刊》，第 33 卷，第 1217 页，1912 年）会生成一种暗红色的微晶粉末，在用乙醇进行重结晶后，这种粉末的熔点为

235° (decomp.). Analysis showed it to be the *p*-bromophenylosazone of a hexose-uronic acid (Found: C, 40.8; H, 3.5; N, 11.1; Br, 30.3. $C_{18}H_{18}O_5N_4Br_2$ required C, 40.7; H, 3.4; N, 10.6; Br, 30.2 percent). Control experiments with glycuronic acid and galacturonic acid failed to give the above substance. With glycuronic acid Goldschmiedt and Zerner's barium salt of the *p*-bromophenylosazone of glycuronic acid was obtained, whilst the galacturonic acid gave a yellow powder which appeared to be mainly the barium salt of the corresponding galacturonic acid derivative.

The above reactions, together with Prof. Szent-Györgyi's observation that oxidation by iodine in the cold removes two atoms of hydrogen, which are easily replaced by mild reducing agents, can be understood most readily on the following basis:

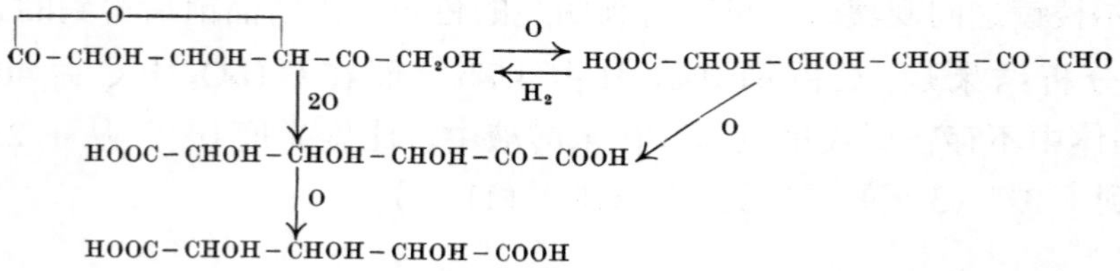


Inasmuch as the configuration and ring-structure of the lactone of the hexuronic acid have not yet been established, the structural formulae are given above in the open chain form, although the sugar-ring is most probably that of a keto-furanose.

E. L. Hirst and R. J. W. Reynolds

(**129**, 576-577; 1932)

J. L. Svirbely and A. Szent-Györgyi: Institute of Medical Chemistry, University Szeged, Hungary.
W. N. Haworth: University of Birmingham, March 28.
E. L. Hirst and R. J. W. Reynolds: Chemistry Department, University of Birmingham, March 28.

References:

1 Szent-Györgyi, A., *Nature* (May 28, 1927): *Biochem. J.*, **22**, 1387 (1928).

2 Szent-Györgyi, A., *J. Biol. Chem.*, **90**, 385 (1931).

3 Sherman, H. C., La Mer, H. K., and Campbell, H. L., *J. Am. Chem.* Soc., **44**, 165 (1922).

230℃～235℃（分解）。分析表明，它应该是某种己糖醛酸的对溴苯脎（分析结果是：C 占 40.8%，H 占 3.5%，N 占 11.1%，Br 占 30.3%。而在 $C_{18}H_{18}O_5N_4Br_2$ 中 C 占 40.7%，H 占 3.4%，N 占 10.6%，Br 占 30.2%）。用葡萄糖醛酸和半乳糖醛酸进行的对照实验不能生成上述物质。用葡萄糖醛酸进行实验得到的是葡萄糖醛酸的对溴苯脎的戈尔德施密特和策纳氏钡盐，而用半乳糖醛酸进行实验则得到了一种黄色粉末，它似乎主要是对应于半乳糖醛酸衍生物的钡盐。

另外，圣哲尔吉教授观察到在低温下这种己糖醛酸能被碘氧化而失去两个很容易被温和的还原剂取代的氢原子，这一结果和前面所述的所有反应，都可以在下面的反应关系图的基础上得到顺利的理解：

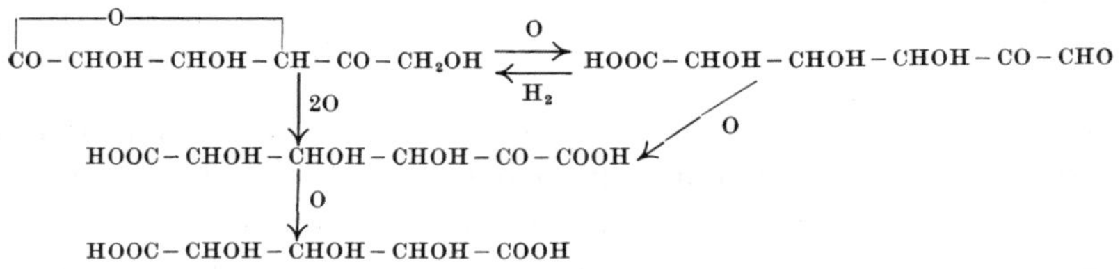


由于这种己糖醛酸中内酯的构型及其环状结构尚未确定，所以上图采用了开链形式的结构式，尽管其中的糖环很可能是一种酮基呋喃糖。

赫斯特，雷诺兹

（王耀杨 翻译；金城 审稿）

# Disintegration of Lithium by Swift Protons

J. D. Cockcroft and E. T. S. Walton

## Editor's Note

**Using their recently developed proton accelerator, Cockcroft and Walton had begun experimenting on materials placed in the path of the proton beam. Here they report experiments with lithium. Scintillations on a mica window in the side of the vacuum tube, due to particle impacts, grew more frequent with increasing acceleration voltage.The physicists deduced that these particles were alpha particles, suggesting that lithium nuclei of atomic mass 7 in the target were absorbing protons and becoming unstable nuclei of atomic mass 8, which subsequently split apart into two alpha particles. This was the first observation of the artificial transmutation of an atomic nucleus.**

IN a previous letter to this journal[1] we have described a method of producing a steady stream of swift protons of energies up to 600 kilovolts by the application of high potentials, and have described experiments to measure the range of travel of these protons outside the tube. We have employed the same method to examine the effect of the bombardment of a layer of lithium by a stream of these ions, the lithium being placed inside the tube at 45° to the beam. A mica window of stopping power of 2 cm. of air was sealed on to the side of the tube, and the existence of radiation from the lithium was investigated by the scintillation method outside the tube. The thickness of the mica window was much more than sufficient to prevent any scattered protons from escaping into the air even at the highest voltages used.

On applying an accelerating potential of the order of 125 kilovolts, a number of bright scintillations were at once observed, the numbers increasing rapidly with voltage up to the highest voltages used, namely, 400 kilovolts. At this point many hundreds of scintillations per minute were observed using a proton current of a few microamperes. No scintillations were observed when the proton stream was cut off or when the lithium was shielded from it by a metal screen. The range of the particles was measured by introducing mica screens in the path of the rays, and found to be about eight centimetres in air and not to vary appreciably with voltage.

To throw light on the nature of these particles, experiments were made with a Shimizu expansion chamber, when a number of tracks resembling those of $\alpha$-particles were observed and of range agreeing closely with that determined by the scintillations. It is estimated that at 250 kilovolts, one particle is produced for approximately $10^9$ protons.

The brightness of the scintillations and the density of the tracks observed in the expansion chamber suggest that the particles are normal $\alpha$-particles. If this point of view turns out to be correct, it seems not unlikely that the lithium isotope of mass 7 occasionally

# 由快质子引起的锂衰变

约翰·考克饶夫，欧内斯特·瓦耳顿

## 编者按

考克饶夫和瓦耳顿利用他们最近研制的质子加速器开始对放在质子束路径中的物质进行实验。他们在此报告了用锂做实验的结果。粒子的碰撞会在真空管侧面的云母窗上发出闪烁，加速电压越大，发出闪烁的次数就越多。物理学家们推测这些粒子就是 $\alpha$ 粒子。他们指出靶中原子量为 7 的锂核因吸收质子而变成原子量为 8 的不稳定核，随后分裂成 2 个 $\alpha$ 粒子。这个实验使人类第一次观测到了一个原子核的人工裂变。

在先前写给《自然》杂志的一封快报[1]中，我们描述了一种通过加高压获得能量高达 600 千伏快质子稳定流的方法，同时还描述了测量这些质子在真空管外的射程的实验。现在我们把锂片放在真空管中，与粒子束成 45º 角。然后用同样的方法测量了快质子束轰击锂片产生的效应。在真空管的端口贴有一个阻止本领相当于 2 cm 厚空气的云母窗片。锂发出的辐射可以在真空管外用闪烁方法来测量。云母窗非常厚，它在所加电压达到最高值时足以阻挡散射的质子泄漏到空气中。

当加速电压达到 125 千伏时，我们立即看到了许多明亮的闪烁光，闪烁的次数随电压迅速增加，直到所使用的最高电压，即 400 千伏。在质子流为几个微安的情况下，我们在这时每分钟可以观测到数百次的闪烁。但当质子流被阻断或当锂片被一块金属屏蔽时，任何闪烁都看不到了。我们用在辐射路径上放置的云母片来测量粒子的射程，在空气中测量到的射程为 8 cm，这个值基本上不会随加速电压的变化而改变。

为了说明这类粒子的性质，我们用清水的膨胀室做实验，发现许多粒子的径迹类似于 $\alpha$ 粒子的径迹，而射程与用闪烁法测量的数值非常接近。我们估计在加速电压为 250 千伏时，大约每 $10^9$ 个质子可以产生一个粒子。

在膨胀室中看到的闪烁亮度和径迹密度说明辐射粒子就是普通的 $\alpha$ 粒子。假如这个判断是正确的，那么质量数为 7 的锂同位素就可能俘获 1 个质子并在产生了质

captures a proton and the resulting nucleus of mass 8 breaks into two $\alpha$-particles, each of mass four and each with an energy of about eight million electron volts. The evolution of energy on this view is about sixteen million electron volts per disintegration, agreeing approximately with that to be expected from the decrease of atomic mass involved in such a disintegration.

Experiments are in progress to determine the effect on other elements when bombarded by a stream of swift protons and other particles.

(**129**, 649; 1932)

J. D. Cockcroft and E. T. S. Walton: Cavendish Laboratory, Cambridge, April 16.

---

Reference:
1 *Nature*, **129**, 242 (Feb. 13, 1932).

量数为 8 的原子核后又分裂成 2 个 $\alpha$ 粒子，每个 $\alpha$ 粒子的质量数为 4 且具有约为 $8\times10^6$ eV 的动能。按照上述观点，每次分裂将产生约 $1.6\times10^7$ eV 的能量，这与根据衰变过程中原子质量下降推算出的结果大致相等。

我们正在用实验测定快质子束和其他粒子束轰击别的元素产生的效应。

（沈乃澂 翻译；江丕栋 审稿）

# The Cry of Tin

## Editor's Note

**Tin has been long known to release a "shriek" or "cry" when bent. Here Bruce Chalmers of University College London attempts to move beyond the vague notion that the sound is caused by the grinding of crystals against one another during deformation. He proposes that it stems from the phenomenon of twinning, in which two crystals share some of the same crystal lattice points, typically with one crystal being a mirror image of the other. Chalmers, who became a celebrated crystallographer, was then working with E. N. da C. Andrade, a pioneer in the study of the crystal structures of metals. Andrade endorses Chalmer's work here, saying that it may be important for understanding the general phenomenon of twinning.**

IT is an observation of respectable antiquity that when a bar of tin is bent it emits a characteristic creaking, known as the "cry of tin". According to Mellor[1], who is one of the few authorities to refer to the subject, the cry "is supposed to be produced by the grinding of the crystals against one another during the bending of the metal", and I have been unable to find in the literature any more definite explanation of its origin. In the course of some experiments which I have been carrying out with Prof. E. N. da C. Andrade on single crystal wires I have made observations which, I think, make possible a rather more precise attribution of the sound.

I have obtained the cry with cadmium as well as with tin. When single crystal wires of these metals are stretched, the deformation takes place in two stages, a slip on the glide planes, which constitute in both cases a unique system, being succeeded by a mechanical twinning on a specified plane. The twinning does not take place until after a definite amount of glide extension has occurred, which enables the two phenomena to be studied separately.

With single crystal wires no sound is produced during the glide stage of extension, but with both metals twinning is accompanied by the characteristic creaking or tearing sound. The same sound also occurs when such wires are violently bent or twisted, a process which gives rise to the surface marking characteristic of twinning, although it does not allow the separation of twinning from other effects in the way that simple extension does.

The tin with which the phenomenon is normally observed is in a polycrystalline state. Although the cry occurs when polycrystalline cast rods of both tin and cadmium are bent, drawn wires of small diameter do not give it unless they are annealed, or, in other words, the production of the sound depends on the size of the crystallites being greater than a certain minimum—larger crystals, of course, being subjected to more severe strain when

# 锡叫

## 编者按

人们很早以前就知道金属锡在弯曲时会发出“尖叫声”或“哭泣声”。通常认为这种现象是由晶体在变形过程中的相互挤压造成的，而伦敦大学学院的布鲁斯·查默斯在这篇文章中试图给出更加清晰的解释。他认为叫声源于孪晶现象，即两个晶体共用晶格点阵上的某些点，尤其是当一个晶体作为另一个晶体的镜像存在时。当年查默斯与研究金属晶体结构的先驱者——安德雷德一起工作，后来他自己也成为了一位著名的晶体学专家。安德雷德对查默斯在这方面的研究表示认同，他说这对于认识孪晶中的普遍现象具有非常重大的意义。

这是一个相当古老的发现，当一根锡棒弯曲时会发出特有的吱吱嘎嘎声，即通常所称的“锡叫”。梅勒[1]是少数谈到过这一主题的作者之一，他认为这种声音“可能是金属在弯曲时由晶体彼此之间的相互摩擦而产生的”，但是我在文献中始终没能找到关于其起源的更为确定的解释。在我与安德雷德教授合作进行的关于单晶丝的实验过程中，曾经进行了一些我认为能够更精确地解释该声音的观测。

我发现镉也可以发出和锡一样的声音。在将这些金属的单晶丝拉伸时，变形过程分两个阶段，先是沿滑移面上滑移，这滑移存在于二个阶段中，随后是在某一特定晶面上发生机械孪生。孪生要在特定量的滑移形变出现后才会发生，这使得两种现象可以分别得到研究。

在滑移形变引起的延伸阶段，单晶丝没有产生声音，但是两种金属孪生时却伴随有特征的碾轧声或撕扯声。同样的声音在将这些金属丝强力弯曲或扭转时也出现了，这一过程产生了孪晶所特有的表面斑纹，尽管它还不足以将孪晶化与简单延伸过程中产生的其他效应相区分。

通常观测到这种效应时所用的锡处于多晶态。尽管锡和镉的多晶铸棒在弯曲时都会发出叫声，小直径的拉制金属丝却只有在退火后才能发出声音，或者换一种说法，这种声音的产生需要晶粒的尺寸大于某一特定下限——当然，较大的晶体在金属弯曲时要经受更为强烈的应变。有理由认为，在多晶态和单晶态中的发声都伴随

the metal is bent. It is reasonable to suppose that the cry is an accompaniment of twinning in the case of the polycrystalline state as well as in the single crystal state.

Preliminary measurements on cadmium indicate that whereas the heat evolved in the twinning is of the order of 0.1 calories per gram, less than one-tenth of this amount is produced during the whole extension accompanying gliding, although this extension is considerably greater than that due to the twinning. The measurements, which are being followed up with more accurate methods, give, at present, only rough approximations, but suffice to establish clearly this very much greater heating which accompanies twinning. This observation suggests that some of the mechanical energy that is supplied to the lattice to cause twinning is afterwards liberated as heat energy and, in particular cases, as sound energy, the cry of tin and cadmium being a manifestation of the latter.

It may be added that while a cry can be produced from zinc, which crystallises in the hexagonal system and twins readily, I have not been able to produce a cry with any metal crystallising in a cubic system, for which twinning does not take place.

Bruce Chalmers

* * *

The observations of Dr. Chalmers described in the above letter, which are being followed up, seem to me likely to prove of considerable importance for elucidating the problem of twinning. The generation of heat agrees with the view that, in twinning, the molecules, when sufficient energy is applied, slip from one equilibrium position to another, about which they then execute heavily damped vibrations, the energy of vibration dissipating itself in heat and probably in radiation of a frequency of the *Reststrahlen* order. The sound indicates that the twinning does not take place over the whole region of twinning simultaneously, for the sound frequency is much too low to be connected with the vibration of molecules or molecular units, but is propagated from layer to layer with a velocity or velocities of the order of sound velocity. It is possible that in the case of substances where sudden twinning is unaccompanied by audible sound, the sound exists, but is of too high a frequency to be heard.

E. N. da C. Andrade

(**129**, 650-651; 1932)

Bruce Chalmers: Physics Laboratory, University College, London, April 6.

Reference:
1 *Complete Treatise of Inorganic Chemistry*, 7, 296.

着孪生的发生。

对镉的初步观测结果，在孪生过程中所产生的热量只有 0.1 cal/g 的数量级，不足由滑移引起的整个延伸过程中所产生热量的 1/10，虽然，这种延伸明显大于孪生本身所导致的延伸。目前，以更为精确的方法进一步开展的观测只给出了粗略的近似值，但已足够清晰地确认这一伴随孪生过程而产生的较大热量。这一观测结果意味着，一些提供给晶格以产生孪晶的机械能后来以热能和（在某些特殊情况下）声能的形式释放出来，锡和镉的发声就是后一种情况的体现。

还可以补充的是，以六方晶系形式结晶并且容易形成孪晶的锌能够产生发声，但我一直无法用以立方晶系形式结晶的任何金属来产生声音，它们不产生孪晶。

布鲁斯·查默斯

*　　*　　*

上面这封信中所描述的查默斯博士即将进一步展开的观测，在我看来，很有可能会被证明对于孪晶问题的阐明具有相当的重要性。热的产生与下面的看法一致，即孪晶中的分子在外加足够能量时会从一个平衡位置滑移到另一个平衡位置，并在该位置发生强烈的阻尼振荡，振荡的能量以热的形式以及很可能以与**剩余射线**的频率相当的辐射形式消散。对声音的研究表明，孪晶化并不是在整个孪晶区域中同时发生的，因为声音的频率实在太低而无法与分子或分子单元的振动联系起来，只能以声速或具有声速水平的速度沿层间传播。有可能会有这样的情况，即突然形成的孪晶没有伴随着可听到的声音；声音是存在的，但是因其频率过高而无法被听到。

安德雷德

（王耀杨 翻译；沈宝莲 审稿）

# The Expanding Universe

## Editor's Note

**This editorial describes a recent lecture of James Jeans on developments in cosmology. Most puzzling were attempts to reconcile the apparent rapid expansion of the universe—suggested by the progressive redshift detected in more distant galaxies—with evidence on the past duration of the universe, putting its age at millions of millions of years. One possibility, Jeans suggested, is that the expansion seen today may not have continued uniformly into the past, but may have begun only after an earlier quiescent period. Jeans noted that recent calculations by Arthur Eddington, attempting to explain the expansion in theoretical terms, were rather speculative. But as Eddington intimated, the expansion really was predicted by the theory of general relativity.**

IN his Ludwig Mond lecture, delivered at Manchester on May 9, on the subject of "The Expanding Universe", Sir James Jeans began with a review of the system of galaxies, our knowledge of which has been greatly extended by recent work with the 100-inch reflector at Mt. Wilson. From these results, he concludes that some two million nebulae lie within a distance of 140,000,000 light-years—a sphere of observation which bears the same ratio to the whole of space as the Isle of Man to the whole surface of the earth. Reference was then made to the conclusions of Friedmann and Lemaître that the equilibrium of such a universe would be unstable, and if expansion started it would continue. Sir James conjectures that the initial impulse which started the expansion may have arisen in the process of the condensation of the primeval chaotic gases into nebulae. Spectrograms of the distant galaxies indicate such an expansion, the rate of recession being about 105 miles per second at a distance of a million light-years, and increasing in the same proportion as the distance, so that it attains the amount of 15,000 miles per second for the most distant nebula yet measured.

Allusion was then made to the difficulty of reconciling this rapid recession with a past duration of the universe extending to millions of millions of years. Sir James has himself given strong reasons in favour of such a past duration, but he now admits that it may be necessary to abandon it. There are, however, some alternatives; there might have been a long period before the recession got fairly started; or the spectral shift that appears to indicate recession may be due to some other cause. Allusion was made to Sir Arthur Eddington's attempt to evaluate the cosmical constant, and so obtain a theoretical value for the rate of expansion; he obtained a value quite close to the observed rate. Sir James noted that this result, while intensely interesting as linking up the largest and the smallest objects of observation, is still a matter of controversy, and cannot be accepted as certain.

(**129**, 787-788; 1932)

# 膨胀的宇宙

## 编者按

这篇社论描述了詹姆斯·金斯最近就宇宙学的发展状况所作的演讲。越遥远的星系探测到的红移越大证明了宇宙在快速膨胀，另有证据表明宇宙已经存在了成千上万亿年，调和二者之间的关系是最令人费解的事。金斯提出，一种可能是：宇宙过去并不一直都像现在所观测到的那样膨胀，膨胀可能只是在宇宙形成之初的某段静止期后才开始的。金斯认为阿瑟·爱丁顿最近对宇宙大爆炸的理论计算只不过是一种推测。但正如爱丁顿所述，由广义相对论确实可以预言宇宙的膨胀。

詹姆斯·金斯爵士 5 月 9 日在曼彻斯特的路德维格·蒙德讲座上发表了题为“膨胀的宇宙”的演讲，他首先评述了星系系统，指出最近用威尔逊山上的 100 英寸反射式望远镜进行的观测工作极大地拓展了我们对星系系统的认识。根据这些结果他推断：在距离地球 140,000,000 光年范围内大约存在着 200 万个星云——这个观测范围相对于整个宇宙空间的比例相当于马恩岛相对于整个地球表面面积的比例。然后，他引用了弗里德曼和勒梅特的结论，即宇宙的平衡是不稳定的，膨胀一旦开始就会一直持续下去。詹姆斯爵士推测使宇宙开始膨胀的最初动力可能起源于原始混沌气体凝缩为星云的过程。遥远星系的光谱证实了这种膨胀的存在，100 万光年处星系的退行速度约为 105 英里 / 秒，随着距离的增加，退行速度也会以相同的比例增加，目前能够观察到的最远的星云的退行速度可以达到 15,000 英里 / 秒。

于是就出现了这样一个困难：难道宇宙在过去的成千上万亿年中能一直保持如此快的退行速度吗？詹姆斯爵士本人曾经给出强有力的证据证明膨胀的长期存在，但他现在承认这种观点也许必须被放弃。然而，也存在着另外的可能：如在真正开始退行之前可能已经经过了很长一段时间；或者看似证明退行的谱线移动也许是由其他原因引起的。他提到阿瑟·爱丁顿爵士曾试图计算过宇宙常数，并由此得到了宇宙膨胀速率的理论值；爱丁顿的计算值与观测到的速率非常接近。而詹姆斯爵士认为：虽然这个结果能非常有趣地将观测中的最大物体和最小物体联系起来，但这一结果仍然是有争议的，不能作为确定的事实接受。

（史春晖 翻译；邓祖淦 审稿）

# The Neutron Hypothesis

D. Iwanenko

## Editor's Note

**Chadwick's hypothesis of the neutron rapidly drew attention from other physicists. Electrons were often expelled from the nucleus during radioactive decay, implying that they must reside somewhere within it. Here Russian physicist Dmitri Iwanenko suggested that electrons change their nature when inside the nucleus, losing their quantum-mechanical spin or magnetism. Inside the nucleus, they may be packed up inside neutrons or alpha particles (which were then still taken to be "elementary" particles along with protons and electrons). Indeed, beta decay involves the decomposition of a neutron into a proton and electron.**

DR. J. Chadwick's explanation[1] of the mysterious beryllium radiation is very attractive to theoretical physicists. Is it not possible to admit that neutrons play also an important rôle in the building of nuclei, the nuclei electrons being *all* packed in $\alpha$-particles or neutrons? The lack of a theory of nuclei makes, of course, this assumption rather uncertain, but perhaps it sounds not so improbable if we remember that the nuclei electrons profoundly change their properties when entering into the nuclei, and lose, so to say, their individuality, for example, their spin and magnetic moment.

The chief point of interest is how far the neutrons can be considered as elementary particles (something like protons or electrons). It is easy to calculate the number of $\alpha$-particles, protons, and neutrons for a given nucleus, and form in this way an idea about the momentum of nucleus (assuming for the neutron a moment $\frac{1}{2}$). It is curious that beryllium nuclei do not possess free protons but only $\alpha$-particles and neutrons.

(**129**, 798; 1932)

D. Iwanenko: Physico-Technical Institute, Leningrad, April 21.

Reference:

1 *Nature*, 129, 312 (Feb. 27, 1932).

# 中子假说

德米特里·伊万年科

## 编者按

查德威克的中子假说很快引起了其他物理学家的注意。在发生放射性衰变时原子核中经常会放出电子，这意味着电子肯定位于原子核内部的某个位置上。俄罗斯物理学家德米特里·伊万年科认为当电子位于原子核内部时性质会发生变化，不再具有量子力学的自旋和磁性。在原子核的内部，电子可能堆积在中子或 $\alpha$ 粒子（那时人们还以为 $\alpha$ 粒子是与质子和电子并列的“基本”粒子）里。确实在 $\beta$ 衰变中就包括一个中子分解成一个质子和一个电子的过程。

查德威克博士关于神秘铍辐射的解释[1]对于理论物理学家来说很有吸引力。难道不能认为中子在原子核的构成中也起着重要的作用，核电子**都**被包裹于 $\alpha$ 粒子或中子之中？因为缺乏关于原子核的理论，这一假设当然无法得到确认，但是如果我们记得核电子在进入核时其性质会发生根本性的变化，可以说失去了其诸如自旋和磁矩等个体特征，那么这个假设也许听起来并不是那么不可能。

我们需要关注的要点在于中子在多大程度上可以被看作是基本粒子（类似于质子或电子）。对于一种给定的核，很容易计算出其中 $\alpha$ 粒子、质子和中子的数目，并用这种方式形成一种关于核矩的概念（假定中子的核矩为 1/2）。奇怪的是，铍核并不具有自由质子而只有 $\alpha$ 粒子和中子。

（王耀杨 翻译；刘纯 审稿）

# White Dwarf Stars

## Editor's Note

**This account of a lecture by English astronomer E. Arthur Milne shows that the superdense stars that now preoccupy many astronomers were already recognised in the 1930s. Indeed, Milne suggests that the first of these, a companion to Sirius, was inferred by the nineteenth-century German astronomer Friedrich Bessel, and observed in 1862. This "Sirius *B*" was later deduced to have a tremendous density, as well as being as source of dim but bluish-white light. It was the first so-called "white dwarf" star, whose physical composition could be explained using the new relativistic quantum theory. This blend of quantum, relativistic and stellar theories is now central to our understanding of dense cosmic bodies such as neutrons stars and black holes.**

THE Halley Lecture delivered at the University of Oxford by Prof. E. A. Milne on May 19 was on the subject of the "White Dwarf Stars". He said that the discovery by Halley of the proper motion of some of the fixed stars led to a remarkable succession of researches in pure astronomy, in modern physics, and in cosmogony generally. The proper motion of one of Halley's stars, Sirius, was found by Bessel not to be uniform, but to contain a periodic element of about fifty years. This led him to suggest that Sirius was in reality double, consisting of a pair of stars, one much fainter than the other. In 1862 a faint star, Sirius *B*, was actually seen by Alvan Clark close to the place that had been theoretically assigned to the supposed companion. In 1915, W. S. Adams at Mount Wilson Observatory succeeded in obtaining a photograph of the spectrum of Sirius *B*, which led to the unexpected conclusion that the density of Sirius *B* was of the order of one ton to the cubic inch. It was shown by Eddington that this surprising density was not physically improbable, and further, that in the light of Einstein's general theory of relativity, the relative displacement of the lines of the spectrum of Sirius *A* and Sirius *B* could be estimated. The measurement when actually carried out by Adams in 1925 gave a result so near that of Eddington's estimate that the computed small radius and high density of Sirius *B* may now be accepted with confidence. A few other stars besides Sirius *B* are known in which low luminosity and abnormal blueness are combined with high density; these are known as "white dwarfs". They are all within five parsecs of the sun, but there is no reason to suppose that this is an abnormal region of space. Consideration of the phenomenon of nova-outbursts and the study of the nuclei of planetary nebulae lead to the conclusion that the list of dense objects can be largely extended. The physical state of matter at these high densities has been elucidated by R. H. Fowler in the light of the researches of Fermi and Dirac. The existence of white dwarf stars shows that it is possible for any gas to exist in either of two states or phases, the "perfect" or the "degenerate" phase; the dense state being identified with that of the second phase of a gas. It is suggested that, as foreshadowed by Bessel in regard to Tycho's nova of 1572, the system of Sirius may owe its origin to the nova phenomenon of the original Sirius; two companions

# 白矮星

## 编者按

这篇文章通过报道英国天文学家阿瑟·米耳恩的一次演讲说明现在许多天文学家潜心研究的超密恒星早在20世纪30年代就已经被发现了。米耳恩指出：第一个超密恒星是天狼星的一颗伴星，19世纪德国天文学家弗里德里希·贝塞尔推出了它的存在，这颗星于1862年被发现。人们后来发现"天狼$B$星"具有很高的密度，它是一颗暗淡的星，发出蓝白色的光。这颗星是最先被人们称为"白矮星"的恒星，其物理组成可以用相对论性量子理论来解释。现在这种融合量子力学、相对论和恒星理论的新理论在我们认识和理解像中子星和黑洞这样的致密宇宙天体时是必不可少的。

5月19日，米耳恩教授在牛津大学的哈雷讲座上发表了关于"白矮星"的演讲。他说，自哈雷发现了一些恒星的自行现象以后，人们便开始在纯天文学、现代物理学以及天体演化学方面展开一系列重大的后续研究。天狼星是其中一颗哈雷认为有自行的恒星，贝塞尔发现天狼星的自行并不是均匀的，但包含一个大约50年的周期。据此，贝塞尔提出，天狼星实际上是双星，即由一对恒星组成，其中一颗比另一颗暗很多。1862年，阿尔万·克拉克在理论给出的伴星位置附近发现了一颗暗淡的恒星，即天狼$B$星。1915年，亚当斯在威尔逊山天文台成功地得到了天狼$B$星的光谱图，由这张图推出了一个意外的结果：天狼$B$星的密度约为1吨/立方英寸。爱丁顿认为，自然界存在这么高密度的天体也不是不可能，而且由爱因斯坦的广义相对论可以估算出在天狼$A$星和$B$星光谱图中的谱线相对位移。1925年，亚当斯进行了相关的测量，测量结果非常接近于爱丁顿的估算值，以至于人们开始相信天狼$B$星真的具有计算得到的半径小和密度高的特点。天狼$B$星和其他一些恒星在具有较低光度和显示出反常蓝色的同时，也具有很高的密度；这些恒星被称为"白矮星"。它们与太阳的距离都在5秒差距以内，但不能据此就认为这一区域是宇宙中的反常区域。根据对新星爆发现象和行星状星云核的研究，我们可以认为宇宙中可能还存在着很多像这样的致密天体。福勒在费米和狄拉克研究的基础上阐明了物质在如此高密度下的物理状态。白矮星的存在表明，任何气体都可能以两种状态或相的形式存在，即"理想态"和"简并态"；致密状态就属于气体的第二种状态。这说明，正如贝塞尔在第谷1572年发现了新星之后所作的预言那样，天狼星系统可能会起源于原始天狼星的新星现象，从而产生了两颗伴星，其中一颗不断膨胀，而另一颗仍然保持致密。贝塞尔认为这些与人类探索宇宙物质组成相关的现象将会受到人们的关注，这一预

resulting, of which one re-expanded and the other remained dense. Bessel's anticipation of the interest of these phenomena in relation to our knowledge of the physical constitution of the universe has been amply justified by the course of events.

(**129**, 803; 1932)

言已经被事实充分地印证了。

（金世超 翻译；蒋世仰 审稿）

# New Evidence for the Neutron

Irène Curie and F. Joliot

## Editor's Note

**The existence of the neutron here receives support from Irène Curie and Frédéric Joliot. Experimenting with particles emitted from lithium bombarded by alpha particles, they found a penetrating power less than that of gamma rays from radioactive decay. Moreover, these particles were absorbed more readily by paraffin than by lead, ejecting protons in the process, indicating that they were not electrons or light quanta (which would not do so because of their small or zero mass). The evidence points to the particles in question being different from previously known radiation. Curie and Joliot completed some of their experiments before Chadwick's, and might have discovered the neutron first had their interpreted them properly. Their early results stimulated Chadwick's own decisive experiments.**

SEVERAL important communications dealing with the properties of rays emitted by atomic nuclei when bombarded with $\alpha$-particles have recently appeared,[1] on which we should like to make a few comments.

It has been shown by F. Joliot[2] that the rays emitted by boron under the action of $\alpha$-particles from polonium are much more penetrating than had originally been indicated. Their penetrating power, while superior to that of the most powerful $\gamma$-rays obtained from radio-active sources, is inferior to that of the rays obtained from beryllium bombarded by $\alpha$-particles from polonium. This result does not agree with Webster's findings, but agrees with the fact that the protons ejected from boron are slower than those ejected from beryllium. Secondly, we have shown that the ejection of protons is a general phenomenon. By means of the Wilson chamber, we have photographed the paths of the helium nuclei ejected by beryllium rays, and from absorption measurements were able to conclude that other atoms are also ejected. Further, our experiments showed for the first time the important part played by the nuclei in the absorption of the rays emitted by beryllium under the influence of $\alpha$-particles, a phenomenon which clearly marked them off from all previously known radiation.

J. Chadwick was led simultaneously to the same generalisation concerning the ejection of nuclei, and he put forward the view that the penetrating rays produced by the bombardment of beryllium by $\alpha$-particles from polonium are neutrons. This interpretation is necessary if energy and momentum are conserved in the collision.

Recent experiments which we have carried out with M. Savel clearly show that the rays emitted by lithium have a penetrating power, in lead, less than that of the $\gamma$-rays of polonium (they are completely absorbed by 5 mm. of lead), and that they are much more readily absorbed, at equal surface mass, by paraffin than by lead. This proves that

# 关于中子的新证据

伊雷娜·居里，弗雷德里克·约里奥

## 编者按

中子的存在被伊雷娜·居里和弗雷德里克·约里奥的实验所证实。他们用 $\alpha$ 粒子轰击锂靶使之发射出粒子，然后发现该粒子流的穿透力低于放射性衰变中的$\gamma$射线。还发现石蜡比铅更容易吸收这些粒子。吸收过程中会放出质子说明它们不是电子或光量子（因为电子和光量子的质量很小或为零）。有证据表明该粒子也不同于以前所熟知的任何辐射。居里和约里奥的实验先于查德威克，如果他们能对实验结果作出正确的解释，那他们也许会首先发现中子。正是他们得出的前期结果引出了查德威克的那个具有决定意义的实验。

最近出现了几篇颇有影响力的论文，内容是关于受 $\alpha$ 粒子轰击的原子核所发射的射线的性质[1]，对此，我们想发表一些看法。

约里奥曾指出[2]，硼在从钋中发出的 $\alpha$ 粒子的作用下发射出的射线比原来对其穿透力的预计值大很多。它们的穿透力大于由放射源得到的最强的 $\gamma$ 射线，但要低于从钋中发出的 $\alpha$ 粒子轰击铍得到的射线。这一结论与韦伯斯特的研究结果不相符，但是与硼发射的质子比铍发射的质子速度慢的现象一致。其次，我们曾说过发射出质子是普遍存在的现象。我们利用威尔逊云室拍摄了由铍辐射产生的氦核的路径，并通过吸收测量得知其他原子也会发射质子。第三，是我们的实验最先说明原子核在吸收被 $\alpha$ 粒子轰击的铍发射的射线中所起的关键作用，这一现象可以把它们与所有以前知道的辐射明确地区分开来。

查德威克与我们同时注意到了这一关于核发射的普遍现象，他还提出了以下观点，即用从钋中发出的 $\alpha$ 粒子轰击铍而产生的具有很强穿透力的射线就是中子。如果要保持能量和动量在碰撞中的守恒，就必须接受这一解释。

最近我们与萨韦尔共同完成的实验清晰地表明，由锂发射的射线在铅中具有穿透能力，但低于钋发射的 $\gamma$ 射线的穿透能力（它们能被 5 mm 厚的铅完全吸收），当表面质量相同时，石蜡对它们的吸收要远远大于铅。这说明它们不可能具有电子或

they cannot be of an electronic or electromagnetic nature. Since for various reasons it is extremely improbable that we are dealing with hydrogen nuclei or $\alpha$-particles (the energy of which would be enormous), these results prove—*independently of the ejection of nuclei and the laws of elastic collisions*—that the rays emitted by lithium under bombardment by $\alpha$-particles from polonium are different from previously known radiation and are probably neutrons. The above reasoning does not apply to the rays ejected from beryllium, boron, or to those emitted by lithium when bombarded with the $\alpha$-rays from the active residue of radium[3], because in such cases we do not have $\gamma$-rays of equivalent penetrating power, for comparison.

Our latest experiments, in collaboration with M. Savel, indicate that the protons ejected from beryllium form two groups. This suggests that there are also two groups of neutrons (each group not necessarily homogeneous); one group has a range of 28 cm. in air, and an energy of $4.5\times10^6$ electron volts; the other has a range of about 70 cm. and an energy of approximately $7.8\times10^6$ electron volts. We find it difficult to reconcile Chadwick's result of a *maximum range* of 40 cm. with the curves which we have obtained for the absorption of protons.

The mass of the neutron calculated by Chadwick[4] (based upon the experimentally estimated energy of the neutrons from boron), according to the reaction $B^{11} + \alpha = N^{14} + n$,[5] is about 1.006 (He=4), and the atomic mass of $Be^9$, based on the energy of the fast neutrons ($7.8\times10^6$ ev.), is 9.006. This suggests that the binding energy between the two $\alpha$-particles and the neutron in the $Be^9$ nucleus is relatively weak. Further, we know that the rays emitted by beryllium are composed of neutrons and photons, and we may therefore suppose that they are emitted simultaneously according to the equation

$$Be^9 + \alpha = C^{12} + n + h\nu.$$

The photons of 2 to $4.5\times10^6$ ev. energy, which we have detected, would correspond to the group of neutrons of maximum energy $4.5\times10^6$ ev. (protons having a range of 28 cm.).

(**130**, 57; 1932)

Irène Curie and F. Joliot: Institut du Radium, Laboratoire Curie, 1, Rue Pierre-Curie, Paris (5ᵉ), June 25.

---

References:

1 Webster, H. C., Chadwick, J., Feather, N., and Dee, P. I., *Proc. Roy. Soc.*, A, **136**, 428, 692, 708 and 727 (1932).

2 Joliot, F., *C.R. Ac. Sci.*, **193**, 1415 (1931).

3 Broglie, M. de, and Leprince-Ringuet, L., *C.R. Ac. Sci.*, **194**, 1616 (1932).

4 Chadwick, J., *Proc. Roy. Soc.*, A, **136**, 702 (1932).

5 Curie, I., and Joliot, F., *C.R. Ac. Sci.*, **194**, 1229 (1932).

电磁学的特征。我们有许多证据证明在实验中出现的粒子绝对不可能是氢核或 $\alpha$ 粒子（它们的能量很大），这些结果表明：**与原子核发射粒子和弹性碰撞定律无关**，用由钋衰变得到的 $\alpha$ 粒子轰击锂发出的射线与以前所知的辐射都不相同，这类射线可能是中子。上述推论不适用于由铍和硼发射的射线，也不适用于用由镭的放射性剩余物产生的 $\alpha$ 射线轰击锂而发出的射线[3]，因为在这几种情况下，我们没有用具有相同穿透力的 $\gamma$ 射线作为比照。

我们与萨韦尔合作完成的最新实验说明铍发射的质子可以分为两组。这意味着也存在两组中子（两组中子未必同质）；其中一组在空气中的射程为 28 cm，能量为 $4.5 \times 10^6$ eV；另一组射程约为 70 cm，能量约为 $7.8 \times 10^6$ eV。查德威克的结果是**最大射程**为 40 cm，而我们从质子吸收曲线得到的结论与他的结果并不一致。

查德威克根据反应式 $B^{11} + \alpha = N^{14} + n$[5] 计算出的中子质量[4]（基于实验测算出的由硼发射的中子能量）约为 1.006（He = 4），并从快中子的能量（$7.8 \times 10^6$ eV）推算出 $Be^9$ 的原子质量为 9.006。这说明 $Be^9$ 核内两个 $\alpha$ 粒子与中子之间的结合能相当弱。此外，我们还知道铍发射的射线包括中子和光子，因而我们也许可以假定它们是按照下述反应式同时发出的：

$$Be^9 + \alpha = C^{12} + n + h\nu$$

我们探测到光子的能量在 $2 \times 10^6$ eV 到 $4.5 \times 10^6$ eV 之间，它们应该对应于最大能量为 $4.5 \times 10^6$ eV 的那一组中子（质子的射程为 28 cm）。

（沈乃澂 翻译；朱永生 审稿）

# Mechanism of Superconductivity

J. Dorfman

## Editor's Note

**Superconductivity—the conduction of electrical current in cold metals without resistance—was observed in 1911, but lacked an explanation. Many suspected that some kind of coherent behaviour among the electrons must be responsible. Here Russian physicist J. Dorfman explores experimental evidence for analogies between superconductivity and magnetism. He studies the temperature dependence of the thermoelectric effect for lead (where heat creates electricity), and finds a sharp cusp near the superconducting transition temperature, leading him to suspect an analogy between the ferromagnetic and superconducting transitions. Both are now seen to belong to the same class of "critical" transitions, although magnetism per se is not involved in this kind of superconductivity.**

IT was often assumed that the transition from normal conductivity to superconductivity may be connected with a kind of "spontaneous coupling" of the conduction electrons. Some authors were even inclined to identify this phenomenon with ferromagnetism. Although this extreme point of view seems to be very improbable, some analogies with ferromagnetism must surely appear if any kind of "spontaneous coupling" between electrons is responsible for superconductivity. For example, in this case the shape of the specific heat curve near the transition temperature must be analogous to that of ferromagnetic substances in the vicinity of the Curie point. W. Keesom and J. H. van den Ende,[1] and F. Simon and K. Mendelssohn[2] attempted to discover this anomaly of the specific heat in lead near the transition temperature (7.2° K), but they could not detect any trace of the effect. This result may be interpreted in two ways: either the hypothesis of the "spontaneous coupling" of the conduction electrons in superconductors is completely wrong, or the number of the electrons which are concerned in conductivity is here so small in comparison with the number of atoms that the specific heat anomaly of the conduction electrons cannot be detected with calorimetric methods.

As our measurements have shown, the specific heat anomaly of ferromagnetic bodies at the Curie point is so well pronounced in the thermoelectric effects (Thomson effect), that in spite of some difficulties concerning the sign of this effect, the order of magnitude of the specific heat anomaly can be computed from the purely thermoelectric constants in good agreement with calorimetric measurements. It is natural to try the same method in the domain of superconductivity. The recent investigations by J. Borelius, W. M. Keesom, C. H. Johansson, and J. O. Linde[3] of the thermoelectric force for lead and tin at the lowest temperatures permit us to compute the Thomson effect for these metals and to draw conclusions concerning the specific heat anomaly. Fig. 1 represents the Thomson coefficient for lead (as calculated from the experimental data) as a function of temperature. This curve is quite analogous to that of ferromagnetic substances, and it seems quite

# 超导电性机理

多尔夫曼

## 编者按

超导电性，即某些金属在低温下无阻的传导电流，是 1911 年被首次观察到的，但没有给出解释。有不少人猜测电子之间的某种相干行为应是产生超导性的原因，在下文中，俄罗斯物理学家多尔夫曼用实验揭示了超导性与磁性之间的相似性。他研究了铅的温度与热电效应（由热生电的现象）的关系，发现在超导转变温度附近存在一个尖点，这使他猜想在铁磁和超导转变之间存在着某种相似性。在今天看来，虽然磁性本身与超导性无关，但两者都属于同种类型的“临界”转变。

人们通常假设，从正常传导性到超导性的转变可能与导电电子的某种“自发耦合”有关。某些作者甚至倾向于认为超导现象等同于铁磁现象。虽然这个极端的观点似乎不存在成立的可能，但是，如果超导性真的是由电子间的某种“自发耦合”引起的，那么它就一定会表现出与铁磁性类似的行为。例如，超导体的比热曲线在转变温度附近的形状应该与铁磁体的比热曲线在居里点附近的形状相似。凯索姆与范登恩德[1]，以及西蒙与门德尔松[2]都试图去揭露铅的比热在超导转变温度（7.2 K）附近的这种反常行为，但是他们都未能探测到这种行为的任何迹象。该结果也许可以从两个角度来解释：要么是由于超导体中导电电子的“自发耦合”假说是完全错误的，要么就是由于在传导性中计入的电子的数目较之原子的数目而言太小，以至于无法用量热法探测出由传导电子引起的比热反常。

正如我们的测量结果所表明的那样，铁磁体在居里点的比热反常表现在热电效应（汤姆孙效应）上是非常显著的，以至于尽管有关此效应的正负号确定还存在一定的困难，但由纯热电常数计算出来的比热反常的数量级与量热法的测量值还是符合得很好。人们很自然地想到将这种方法用于超导性领域。最近，博雷柳斯、凯索姆、约翰松与林德[3]研究了在对最低温度下铅和锡的温差电势，这使我们能够计算这两种金属的汤姆孙效应，并可得到关于比热反常的结论。图 1 给出了铅的汤姆孙系数（由实验数据计算得出）与温度的函数关系。这条曲线和铁磁物质的曲线十分相似，且很可能代表了与传导性效应有关的电子的比热的普遍特征。不过，我们

probable that it represents the general feature of the specific heat of the electrons concerned in the conductivity effects. It is not clear, however, why the temperature of the maximum of this specific heat curve (10.5° K) does not coincide with the transition point (7.2° K). Perhaps theory will be able to explain this discrepancy in the future.

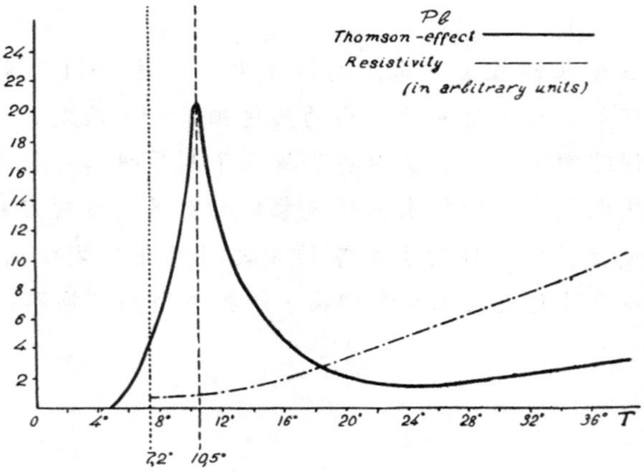


Fig. 1.

From these results two important quantities may be calculated: first, $\Delta C_\varepsilon$ (the height of the maximum of the specific heat curve), and secondly, $\Delta W_0$ (the energy difference between the normal and the superconducting state at absolute zero), both for one electron.

| | $\Delta C_\varepsilon$ cal./ degree. | $\Delta W_0$ ergs. |
|---|---|---|
| Lead | $8 \times 10^{-25}$ | $1.7 \times 10^{-17}$ |
| Tin | $\sim 10^{-25}$ | $\sim 0.6 \times 10^{-17}$ |

If the number of the electrons was equal to the number of atoms of lead, the specific heat anomaly could certainly be detected, its numerical value being of the same order of magnitude as the normal specific heat itself. The precision of the calorimetric measurements permits us to determine the upper limit of the number of the electrons involved in the conductivity effects of lead. Actually it seems that the number of the conduction electrons is less than 1/200 of the number of the atoms in this case.

It is well known that magnetic fields destroy the superconductivity, the threshold value of the field $H$ increasing as the temperature is lowered. By extrapolating the experimental data the value of $H_0$ may be found corresponding to absolute zero. We assume that the threshold value of the field is given by the condition that the magnetic energy of the electron $|\mu H_0|$ (where $\mu$ is the spin moment) is equal to $\Delta W_0$.

还不清楚为什么这条比热曲线上最大值所相应的温度(10.5 K)与超导转变温度(7.2 K)不一致。也许未来的理论可以解释这一分歧。

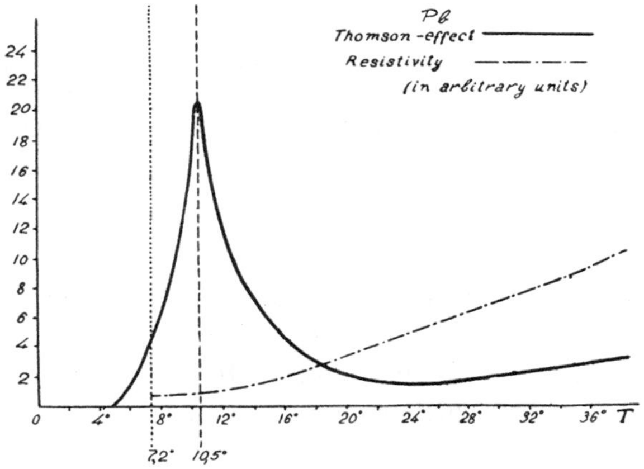


图 1

由这些结果可以计算出两个重要的物理量：首先是 $\Delta C_{\varepsilon}$（比热曲线上最大值的高度），其次是 $\Delta W_0$（绝对零度下正常态和超导态的能量差），两者都是针对一个电子。

| | $\Delta C_{\varepsilon}$ 卡/度 | $\Delta W_0$ 尔格 |
|---|---|---|
| 铅 | $8 \times 10^{-25}$ | $1.7 \times 10^{-17}$ |
| 锡 | $\sim 10^{-25}$ | $\sim 0.6 \times 10^{-17}$ |

倘若铅中的电子数目与原子的数目相等，则比热反常就一定能被探测到，因为它的数值与正常态的比热同量级。根据量热法的测量精度，我们可以确定铅中参与传导效应的电子数目的上限。实际上，导电电子的数目比此情况下原子数目的 1/200 还要少。

众所周知，磁场会破坏超导性，磁场 $H$ 的阈值随着温度的降低而增大。从实验数据可以推出：临界场 $H_0$ 的值可能与绝对零度有关。我们假设场的阈值通过电子的磁能 $|\mu H_0|$（$\mu$ 为自旋磁矩）等于 $\Delta W_0$ 来确定。

$$|\mu H_0| = \Delta W_0 \qquad (1)$$

This assumption means that the superconductivity must be destroyed when the energy of the external forces exceeds the energy of the "spontaneous coupling". Form (1) we may calculate $H_0$ for lead and tin, and compare them with the experimental results.

| | $H_0$ expt. (gauss). | $H_0$ calc. (gauss). |
|---|---|---|
| Lead | 2,000–2,500 | 2,000 |
| Tin | 560 | ~700 |

According to the recent experiments of McLennan and his co-workers,[4] superconductors cease to be superconducting for high frequency currents if the frequency $\nu$ exceeds a certain threshold value. For tin at absolute zero, $\nu \sim 10^9$ may be found by extrapolation of the experimental data obtained at higher temperatures. It is interesting to notice that by assuming

$$h\nu_0 = \Delta W_0 = |\mu H_0| \qquad (2)$$

(where $h$ is Planck's constant), we obtain for the same metal $\nu_0 = 1\times10^9$.

The remarkable coincidence between the observed and the computed data seem to support the general trend of the assumptions developed in this note. It is interesting to notice that the frequency of the Larmor precession corresponding to $H_0$ is equal to $\nu_0$; thus the correlation between the two factors destroying the superconductivity may be found either on the lines of energetics or on the lines of the short time periods. Which of these interpretations corresponds to the real mechanism remains unsolved at this moment.

(**130**, 166-167; 1932)

J. Dorfman: Physical-Technical Institute, Sosnovka 2, Leningrad (21), U.S.S.R., May 23.

References:

1 *Comm. Leiden*, 230 *d* (1930).

2 *Z. Phys. Chem.*, B **16**, H. 1 (1932).

3 *Proc. Amsterdam Acad.*, **34**, No. 10 (1931).

4 *Proc. Roy. Soc.*, A, **136**, No. 829, 52 (1932).

$$|\mu H_0| = \Delta W_0 \qquad (1)$$

这个假设意味着：当外力的能量超过“自发耦合”的能量时，超导性一定会被破坏。我们可以由式（1）计算铅和锡的临界场 $H_0$，并把它们与实验结果作比较。

| | $H_0$ 的实验值(高斯) | $H_0$ 的计算值 (高斯) |
|---|---|---|
| 铅 | 2,000~2,500 | 2,000 |
| 锡 | 560 | ~700 |

根据麦克伦南及其合作者近期的实验[4]，如果超导体中高频电流的频率 $v$ 超过了某一临界值，则超导现象就会消失。从较高温度下的实验数据可以推出，绝对零度下锡的 $v \sim 10^9$。有趣的是，通过假设

$$hv_0 = \Delta W_0 = |\mu H_0| \qquad (2)$$

（$h$ 是普朗克常数），对同一金属我们也可得到 $v_0 = 1\times10^9$。

实验值和计算值的明显致似乎支持了我们在文中提出的假设。有趣的是：对应于 $H_0$ 的拉莫尔进动频率恰等于 $v_0$；因此，两个破坏超导性的因素之间的关联既可以体现在能量的关系上，也可以体现在短周期的关系上。究竟这些解释中的哪一个对应真正的超导性机理，现在还没有答案。

（王静 翻译；陶宏杰 审稿）

# Disintegration of Light Elements by Fast Protons

J. D. Cockcroft and E. T. S. Walton

## Editor's Note

**Here Cockcroft and Walton update their studies of how high-energy protons interact with the nuclei of light elements. Since their report of artificially induced disintegration of lithium, they had improved the sensitivity of their detecting apparatus and extended their study to the element boron. Here they record a huge number of alpha particles created by proton bombardment, suggesting a nuclear reaction in which the boron nucleus boron-11 becomes boron-12 on absorbing a proton, and subsequently disintegrates into three alpha particles.**

SINCE the publication of our paper[1] on the disintegration of elements by fast protons, we have examined some of the light elements more carefully, using much thinner mica windows than we had previously employed on the high voltage tube. With the present arrangement, we can count particles which have passed through only 6 mm. air equivalent of absorber on their way from the target to the ionisation chamber.

In the case of lithium, we have found, in addition to the $\alpha$-particle group of 8.4 cm. range, another group of particles of much shorter range. The number of these is about equal to that of the long range particles and their maximum range is about 2 cm. The ionisation produced by them indicates that they are $\alpha$-particles. It will be of interest to examine whether any $\gamma$-rays are emitted corresponding to the difference of the energies of the $\alpha$-particles in the two groups, but on account of the smallness of the effect to be expected, a sensitive method will be necessary.

In the case of boron, the number of particles observed increases rapidly as the total absorption between the target and the ionisation chamber is reduced. The maximum range of these particles is about 3 cm. and in our earlier experiments we determined the number of particles only after passing through the equivalent of 2.9 cm. of air, so that we were very nearly at the end of the range. Decreasing the absorber to 6 mm. of air gives an enormous increase in the number of particles. In this way about twenty-five times as many particles have been obtained from boron as from lithium under the same conditions. We estimate that there is roughly one particle emitted per two million incident protons at 500 kilovolts. The ionisation produced by the particles suggests that they are $\alpha$-particles, and the energy of the main group would support the assumption that a proton enters the $B^{11}$ nucleus and the resulting nucleus breaks up into three $\alpha$-particles. There also seem to be present a small number of particles with ranges up to about 5 cm.

(**131**, 23; 1933)

J. D. Cockcroft and E. T. S. Walton: Cavendish Laboratory, Cambridge, Dec. 22.

---

Reference:

1 *Proc. Roy. Soc.*, A, **137**, 229 (1932).

# 快质子引起的轻元素衰变

约翰·道格拉斯·考克饶夫，欧内斯特·瓦耳顿

## 编者按

考克饶夫和瓦耳顿改进了对于高能质子与轻元素原子核之间相互作用的研究。在报告了人工引发的锂衰变之后，他们提高了探测仪器的灵敏度，并把研究范围扩展到了元素硼。他们发现硼被高能质子轰击后会产生大量的$\alpha$粒子，说明发生了这样的核反应：硼 11 核在吸收了一个质子之后生成硼 12，随后衰变成 3 个$\alpha$粒子。

在发表了关于快质子引起元素衰变的文章[1]以后，我们对一些轻元素进行了更仔细的检查，我们所用的云母窗比以前在高压管上使用的要薄很多。采用目前的装置，我们能够对从靶出发穿越阻止能力仅相当于 6 mm 厚空气的吸收层到达电离室的粒子进行计数。

我们在检测锂元素的实验中发现，除了一组射程为 8.4 cm 的 $\alpha$ 粒子以外，还有另一组射程更短的粒子。这些粒子与长射程粒子的数量大致相等，它们的最大射程约为 2 cm。由它们产生的电离现象表明，它们也是 $\alpha$ 粒子。检验是否有与两组 $\alpha$ 粒子能量差相对应的 $\gamma$ 射线产生对于我们来说是一件有趣的事，但考虑到该效应可能很微弱，所以需要一种很灵敏的方法。

在对硼元素进行实验时，如果我们减少靶与电离室之间的总吸收，则观测到的粒子数就会迅速增加。这些粒子的最大射程约为 3 cm，在早期的实验中，我们测定了穿越阻止能力相当于 2.9 cm 厚空气的粒子数，这非常接近于最大射程的终点。将吸收层厚度降至相当于 6 mm 空气时，得到的粒子数大幅增加。在相同条件下，由此方法从硼中得到的粒子约为从锂中得到的 25 倍。我们估计，当电压为 500 千伏时，大体上每 200 万个入射质子会激发出一个粒子。从这些粒子引起的电离来看它们就是 $\alpha$ 粒子，主要组 $\alpha$ 粒子的能量可以证明下面这个假设：一个质子进入 $B^{11}$ 核，而生成的核又裂变为 3 个 $\alpha$ 粒子。似乎还存在少量射程高达 5 cm 的粒子。

（沈乃澂 翻译；江丕栋 审稿）

# A Synthetic Oestrus-Exciting Compound

J. W. Cook *et al.*

## Editor's Note

**Following the isolation of estrogenic hormones a few years earlier, James Wilfred Cook and his colleagues conjecture at the chemical structure for ketohydroxy-oestrin (estrone). Acknowledging the value of being able to synthesise such estrogenic compounds to order, they test whether a related chemical can stimulate estrus in ovariectomised rats. At lower doses, it has no effect on their experimental subjects but as they increase the dose the injected chemical induces full-blown estrus. Once such hormones could be manufactured, it was only a matter of time before researchers could produce contraceptive pills and hormone replacement therapies. The authors also note that certain chemical naturally present in the environment can have estrogen-like activity, something that caused increasing alarm in the coming decades.**

IN conformity with the hypothesis, for which there is at present no experimental basis, that the ovarian hormones are formed by degradation of sterols, and in the light of recent developments in the chemistry of the sterols, ketohydroxy-oestrin is possibly represented by formula (i).

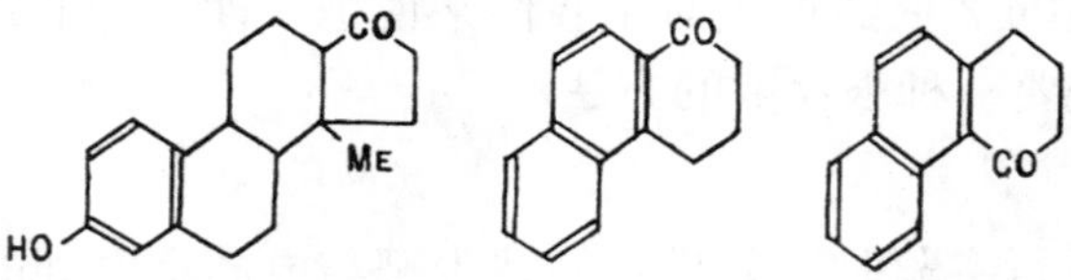


(i) (ii) (iii)

This accords with all the facts supplied by the work of Butenandt[1], Marrian[2], and others, and we decided that the arguments in favour of this formula were sufficient to justify attempts to synthesise compounds of this nature. By analogy with other physiologically active compounds, it seems likely that a whole group of substances of related chemical constitution will be found to have oestrus-exciting properties, and the synthetic production of such substances would probably be of considerable clinical value.

We have found that 1-keto-1:2:3:4-tetrahydrophenanthrene (ii), which we propose to utilise as a starting point in the synthesis of a substance of formula (i), has itself very definite oestrogenic action, although the does required is very large in comparison with oestrin. The oestrus-producing activity of the substance was examined by the Allen and Doisy procedure. The technique followed was that described by Allan, Dickens and Dodds[3]. The material was dissolved first in olive oil, and later in sesame oil. It was found that the substances were not readily soluble in olive oil, with the result that large volumes

# 一种合成的催情化合物

詹姆斯·威尔弗雷德·库克等

## 编者按

*在人们成功分离出雌激素后不久，詹姆斯·威尔弗雷德·库克和他的同事们就开始推测酮羟基雌激素（雌酚酮）的化学结构了。为了确定合成这种雌激素化合物的价值，他们对相关化学品是否能刺激摘除卵巢的大鼠发情进行了检验。低剂量药剂对试验老鼠无任何作用，加大剂量以后，注射的化学药品诱使这些动物出现明显的发情症状。一旦这样的激素被制造出来，研究人员要制作避孕药片和实施激素补充疗法就只是时间上的问题了。作者还指出：环境中某些天然存在的化学品也可能有类似于雌激素的作用，这在随后的几十年里使人们越来越感到恐慌。*

根据卵巢激素是由甾醇降解形成的假说（目前尚无实验基础）和甾醇化学的最新进展，酮羟基雌激素可能的结构式如（i）所示。

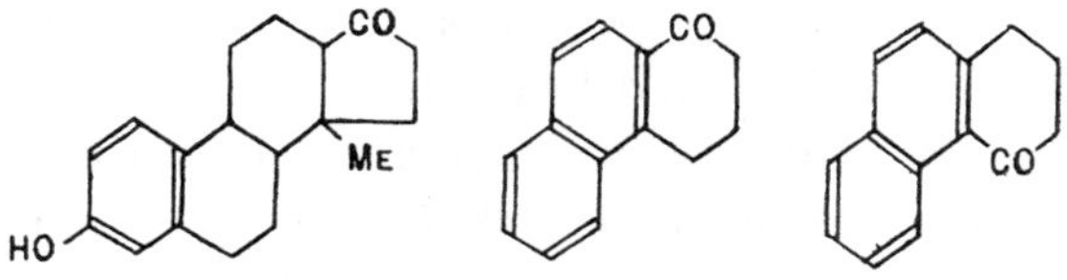

(i)　　(ii)　　(iii)

这与布特南特[1]、马里安[2]以及其他人研究得到的全部结果都很吻合。我们确信支持这个结构式的论据足以证明尝试合成具有这种特性的化合物是有必要的。类比其他生理活性物质，似乎有一大类具有相关化学组成的物质都具有催情特性，因而人工合成这类物质将会具有很大的临床价值。

我们发现我们计划用于合成结构式（i）的起始原料——1–酮–1,2,3,4–四氢菲（ii）本身就具有一定的催情功能，尽管所需的剂量比雌激素要大很多。以前曾用艾伦和多伊西的步骤检测过该物质的雌激素活性。以下是阿伦、迪肯斯和多兹所描述的检测方法[3]。起先用橄榄油溶解 1–酮–1,2,3,4–四氢菲，然后用芝麻油。我们发现该物质不易溶于橄榄油中，因此在对摘除卵巢的动物用药时只能采取大剂量皮下注

had to be administered subcutaneously to the ovariectomised animals. This proved to be unsatisfactory owing to leakage from the site of injection and intolerance to the oil, but with sesame oil the volume could be kept down to 2 c.c., and these adverse effects avoided. 25 mgm. of the substance in olive oil administered to ten ovariectomised rats produced no sign of oestrus, the animals remaining in a state of di-oestrus throughout the experiment. A batch of twenty animals injected with 50 mgm. dissolved in olive oil showed seven full oestrus responses, with three animals just short of the definition (a few leucocytes). In a series of twenty animals injected with 100 mgm. dissolved in sesame oil, a very much better response was obtained, all twenty animals going into oestrus. The oestrus in each case was complete.

In the case of the 50 mgm. dosage, oestrus appeared after 54 hours and terminated 150 hours after injection. In the case of the 100 mgm. in sesame oil, oestrus appeared after 52 hours. At the present moment, it is impossible to state the activity of the material in terms of oestrin since the relatively difficult solubility of the material together with the consequent difficulties of administration and absorption make a comparison impossible. Some form of "cross-over" method must therefore be evolved. There can be no doubt that a repetition of the standardisation experiments with 50 mgm. dissolved in a small volume of sesame oil would indicate much greater potency than a similar experiment conducted with olive oil as the vehicle.

The observations show that 1–keto–1:2:3:4–tetrahydrophenanthrene is capable when injected into castrated animals of inducing oestrus of an exactly similar type to that obtained by the injection of oestrin. This result is of importance, for 1–keto–1:2:3:4–tetrahydrophenanthrene is the first compound of known chemical constitution found to have definite oestrus-exciting activity and furthermore, its molecular structure has many points of resemblance to the structure suggested for ketohydroxy-oestrin. There is thus provided the first step in the task of defining the molecular conditions necessary for this type of physiological activity, and there are grounds for hoping that substances of a much higher order of activity will be found before very long.

The observation[4] that oestrogenic properties of a low order are possessed by suitable extracts of such a variety of materials as peat, brown coal, lignite, coal tar and petroleum is of interest, but in view of the fact that many such materials are known to contain carcinogenic constituents, the clinical use of such extracts without very stringent refinement is scarcely to be entertained.

We have also examined 4–keto–1:2:3:4–tetrahydrophenanthrene (iii) and 3–hydroxyphenanthrene; these gave no oestrus response when injected in doses of 50 mgm.

射的方法。由于药物在注射位置处泄漏和动物对橄榄油的耐受性差，这种方法的效果并不理想，但如果使用芝麻油，则注射量可降至 2 c.c. 且上述副作用可被避免。对 10 只摘除卵巢的大鼠注射 25 mg 1–酮–1,2,3,4–四氢菲橄榄油溶液，未发现有发情征兆产生，这些动物在整个实验过程中一直处于间情期。对 20 只摘除卵巢的大鼠注射 50 mg 1–酮–1,2,3,4–四氢菲橄榄油溶液，结果有 7 只表现出了充分的发情反应，还有 3 只出现了不完全的发情反应（有少量的白细胞）。在给 20 只大鼠注射了 100 mg 溶于芝麻油的 1–酮–1,2,3,4–四氢菲时，取得的效果非常明显，全部 20 只大鼠都产生了发情反应。而且每只大鼠的发情反应都是完全的。

当剂量为 50 mg 时，发情反应在 54 个小时后出现，并于 150 个小时后终止。在以 100 mg 该物质溶于芝麻油的实验中，发情反应出现于 52 个小时之后。目前，我们还不能把该物质的活性与雌激素的活性进行比较，原因是该物质溶解性较差以及由此引发的给药和吸收上的困难。因此必须引入某种“交叉”的方法。毫无疑问，重复进行将 50 mg 该物质溶于少量芝麻油的标准化实验会比以橄榄油为介质的类似实验效果更显著。

观察表明：当给阉割的动物注射催情药物时，使用 1–酮–1,2,3,4–四氢菲产生的效果与注射雌激素非常相似。这一结果意义重大，因为 1–酮–1,2,3,4–四氢菲是人们发现的第一个有明确催情活性的、已知化学结构的化合物，而且它的分子结构在很多方面都类似于酮羟基雌激素可能具有的结构。这就向解析具备此类生理活性的分子应该具有什么样的分子结构迈出了第一步，而且我们也有理由确信人们很快就会发现活性更高的催情物质。

有报告[4]显示：从诸如泥炭、土状褐煤、暗色褐煤、煤焦油和石油等多种原料中经过适当提取得到的物质具有低水平的雌激素特性，这是一个有趣的发现，但因为此类原料中大多含有致癌成分，所以在这种提取物没有经过非常严格的精炼的情况下是很少用于临床的。

我们还测试了 4–酮–1,2,3,4–四氢菲（iii）和 3–羟基菲的活性；在以 50 mg 的剂量注射后，它们都没有产生发情反应。

We are indebted to Dr. H. Allan for kindly checking over the animal experiments.

(**131**, 56-57; 1933)

J. W. Cook, C. L. Hewett: Research Institute, The Cancer Hospital (Free), London, S.W.3.
E. C. Dodds: Courtauld Institute of Biochemistry, Middlesex Hospital, London, W.1.

---

References:

1 *Z. physiol. Chem.*, **208**, 129 (1932).

2 *J. Soc. Chem. Ind.*, **51**, 277 *T* (1932).

3 *J. Physiol*, **68**, 348 (1930).

4 Schering-Kahlbaum: Fr. Pat., 710, 857.

感谢阿伦博士友好地对我们的动物实验进行了核对。

（刘振明 翻译；田伟生 审稿）

# Origin of Tektites

L. J. Spencer

## Editor's Note

**The peculiarity of the rocks known as tektites is testified by the diversity and invention of the explanations offered for them, as the influential British mineralogist Leonard James Spencer records here. Were these silica glasses relics of prehistoric glass technology, or debris from lunar volcanoes? Spencer challenges the prevailing view that tektites are meteorites, saying that they seem to be formed from molten terrestrial rocks, particularly sand. But the association with meteorites remains, for he suggests that the fusion was caused by the impact of meteorites: tektites, with their bead-like and teardrop shapes, are globules scattered far afield in the impact, solidifying in transit through the air. This is the accepted interpretation of tektites today.**

SMALL, curiously shaped pieces of green, brown, or, more usually, black glass have long been known from certain regions, and have been called moldavites from the Moldau River in Bohemia and from Moravia; australites or obsidianites from Australia; billitonites from the tin-bearing gravels in the island of Billiton, Dutch East Indies; and Darwin glass from Tasmania. They have also recently been found in some abundance in French Indo-China and in the Philippine Islands. In chemical composition they are peculiar in containing a very high percentage of silica ($SiO_2$, 70–89 percent).

Many theories have been advanced to account for the origin of these bodies, which are known collectively as tektites. Those from Bohemia and Moravia were formerly thought to be relics from a prehistoric glass factory. They have been thought to be "bombs" or bubbles shot out from volcanoes (even from volcanoes on the moon). The fusion of atmospheric dust or desert sand by lightning has been suggested. Another theory is that they are colloidal bodies formed by the action of humic acids on the underlying rock in certain climates. The view most generally accepted at the present time is that they are meteoric, although they are entirely different in all their characters from any meteorite that has been actually observed to fall.

In a recent elaborate and beautifully illustrated monograph[1] Prof. A. Lacroix gives a detailed review of the whole question. He elaborates a suggestion first made by H. Michel in 1925 that tektites have been formed in the earth's atmosphere from meteoric material consisting of the element silicon and the lighter metals (aluminium, calcium, potassium and sodium). Such material heated by friction with the air would rapidly oxidise with the production of a temperature sufficient to fuse the products of oxidation; and subsequent rapid cooling would yield a glass.

# 玻陨石的成因

伦纳德·斯潘塞

## 编者按

正如英国著名矿物学家伦纳德·詹姆斯·斯潘塞在文中所指出的那样，玻陨石的多样性以及为此设想的各种解释都印证了它的特殊性。它们到底是史前人类制造硅玻璃时留下的遗物，还是月球上火山喷发的碎片？大多数人认为玻陨石就是陨石的碎片，斯潘塞对这种看法提出了质疑，他认为玻陨石是由地球上的岩石，尤其是砂子，熔融后形成的。但他的解释仍然与陨石有关联，因为他假设熔融过程是由陨石的撞击引起的：具有类似珠状和泪滴状结构的玻陨石是陨石在撞击地面时四处飞溅的小液滴在空气中凝固而成的。这至今仍然被认为是对玻陨石成因的合理解释。

对于某些地区的一些小的、形状奇特的玻璃片人们早已熟知，这些玻璃片有的为绿色，有的为褐色，而多数为黑色，产于波希米亚的伏尔塔瓦河以及摩拉维亚时被称为绿玻陨石；产于澳大利亚时被称为澳大利亚玻陨石或似曜岩；产于荷属东印度群岛之勿里洞岛的含锡砂砾中时被称为勿里洞玻陨石；而产于塔斯马尼亚时被称为达尔文玻璃。最近人们在法属印度支那以及菲律宾群岛又发现了一些玻陨石。它们在化学组成上的特殊之处是二氧化硅所占的百分比非常高（$SiO_2$ 含量占 70%~89%）。

这些岩石被统称为玻陨石，为了解释其成因，人们提出了很多理论。以前有人认为产于波希米亚和摩拉维亚的玻陨石是史前玻璃厂的遗迹。现在它们被认为是由火山（甚至是月球上的火山）喷出的“火山弹”或岩浆球。另有一些人提出这些岩石是由大气尘埃或沙漠砂石在闪电作用下熔融形成的；还有一种理论把它们看作是下层岩石在特定气候条件下与腐殖酸作用而形成的胶质体。目前，尽管玻陨石的所有特征都与人们实际观察到的从天而降的陨石截然不同，但是认为玻陨石来自于陨石的观点还是得到了大家的广泛认可。

拉克鲁瓦教授在最近出版的一部论述精巧、插图精美的专著中[1]对这个问题作了全面而细致的总结。他详细阐述了米歇尔在 1925 年首先提出的观点，即认为玻陨石是由硅元素和轻金属元素（铝、钙、钾、钠）构成的流星体在穿过地球大气层时形成的。这些流星体与空气摩擦生热从而被迅速氧化，达到的温度足以熔化氧化后的产物；随后快速冷却形成玻璃体。

Although much has been written on the subject of tektites, the elementary fact that the material of which they are composed is really an impure silica-glass has been entirely overlooked. Pure silica-glass has a specific gravity of 2.20 and refractive index 1.46—both low values. The values for tektites are 2.27–2.51 for the specific gravity and 1.48–1.52 for the refractive index.

Now the "cinders" of the legendary city of Wabar, "destroyed by fire from heaven", which was discovered early this year by Mr. H. St. J. Philby in the Rub' al Khali, Arabia,[2] consist of such a silica-glass. The vesicular white glass contains $SiO_2$, 92.88 percent, with specific gravity 2.10 and refractive index 1.468; whilst the black glass, almost free from bubbles, contains $SiO_2$, 87.45 percent, with specific gravity 2.24 and refractive index 1.50. The black glass contains also $Fe_2O_3$, 0.28; FeO, 5.77; NiO, 0.35 percent. At this spot pieces of meteoric iron were found, the largest rusted remnant weighing 25 lb.; and also a series of craters that must have been formed by the impact of a shower of large meteorites. When a large mass of iron travelling with planetary velocity is suddenly stopped, the kinetic energy ($\frac{1}{2}mv^2$) is transformed into heat at a localised spot with the development of a very high temperature. The "bombs" of silica-glass collected by Mr. Philby at Wabar suggest there must have been a pool of molten silica in the desert sand and that this material was shot out from the craters through an atmosphere of silica, iron, and nickel vapours.

At the group of meteorite craters discovered in 1931 near Henbury in Central Australia[3] silica-glass has also been found, but in smaller quantity and only around the largest crater. Here the country-rock is a ferruginous sandstone and the glass that resulted from the fusion of this rock is black and less pure. It contains $SiO_2$, 68.88 percent and has specific gravity 2.31 and refractive index 1.545. It also contains $Fe_2O_3$, 8.46; FeO, 7.92; NiO, 0.28 percent. Nickel is not shown in analyses of tektites, probably because it was not suspected and not looked for.

The pieces ("bombs") of silica-glass from both Wabar and Henbury present many similarities to tektites; especially to the Darwin glass from Tasmania, with which some can be matched exactly in both form and appearance. Beads and tear-shaped drops are common and there are some disc-shaped pieces, but none with the perfect button-like shape of true australites. I have been much struck with this similarity, but now that I have seen pictures of the tektites from Indo-China given by Prof. Lacroix in his monograph, I have no hesitation in concluding that tektites are not meteoric, though they are connected with the fall of large meteoric masses, but that they have resulted from the fusion of terrestrial rocks, especially in sandy deserts, by the heat so developed.

Silica-glass and tektites could, of course, be formed only in very exceptional circumstances. The fall of very large meteorites on the earth's surface is fortunately not of frequent occurrence. With the possible exception of the still debatable Siberian fall on June 30,

虽然他介绍了很多关于玻陨石的知识，但是完全忽略了组成它们的物质实际上是一种不纯的硅质玻璃这一基本事实。纯硅质玻璃的比重为 2.20，折射率为 1.46——两者的值均较低。而玻陨石的比重在 2.27~2.51 之间，折射率在 1.48~1.52 之间。

菲尔比先生于今年年初在阿拉伯半岛的鲁卜哈利发现了“被天火毁灭”的瓦巴城遗址[2]，如今人们发现这座传奇城市化为的“灰烬”是由硅质玻璃组成的。这种含气泡的白色硅质玻璃含有 92.88% 的 $SiO_2$，比重为 2.10，折射率为 1.468；而黑色硅质玻璃中则几乎没有气泡，$SiO_2$ 的含量为 87.45%，比重为 2.24，折射率为 1.50。黑色硅质玻璃中还含有 0.28% 的 $Fe_2O_3$，5.77% 的 FeO 以及 0.35% 的 NiO。在这里还发现了铁陨石碎片，最大的铁锈残片重达 25 磅；还有一系列由大量流星雨撞击地球所形成的陨石坑。当以行星运行速度飞行的大块铁陨石突然停止运动时，其动能（$\frac{1}{2}mv^2$）就会在局部的一个点上转化为热能，进而达到很高的温度。菲尔比先生在瓦巴地区收集到的硅质玻璃“弹”说明：在荒漠的砂石中一定存在着一片熔融的硅层，这些硅层中的物质在陨石撞击地球时被从陨石坑中抛射出来，随后穿过充满二氧化硅、铁和镍蒸气的气团。

1931 年，人们在澳大利亚中部的亨伯里附近发现了陨石坑群[3]，在其中也发现了硅质玻璃，不过数量较少，并且仅存在于规模最大的陨石坑周围。这里的围岩是含铁砂岩，而由围岩熔融形成的硅质玻璃是黑色的并且纯度较低。它含有 68.88% 的 $SiO_2$，比重是 2.31，折射率是 1.545。这种黑色硅质玻璃还含有 8.46% 的 $Fe_2O_3$、7.92% 的 FeO 和 0.28% 的 NiO。在对玻陨石的分析中没有指出镍的含量，可能是因为人们没有想到会含有镍，所以尚未查明。

瓦巴地区和亨伯里地区的硅质玻璃碎片（“玻璃弹”）与玻陨石有很多相似之处，尤其是与塔斯马尼亚的达尔文玻璃在成分上和外观上都十分匹配。除了常见的水珠状和泪滴状之外，还有一些碟形的碎片，但真正澳大利亚玻陨石所具备的完美的纽扣状却没有在这里发现。这种相似性使我感到非常震惊，不过既然我已经看到了拉克鲁瓦教授在其专著中展示的来自印度支那的玻陨石图片，我就可以毫不犹豫地断定，尽管这些玻陨石与大量流星体的坠落有关，但它们并不是陨石的一部分，它们是由地球上，特别是沙漠中的岩石在陨石撞击地球产生的高温下熔融生成的。

当然，硅质玻璃和玻陨石只有在非常特殊的条件下才能形成。所幸的是，大块陨石坠落于地球表面这样的事并不经常发生。目前人们还在争论 1908 年 6 月 30 日

1908, none has in fact taken place during historic times. Further, the terrestrial rock at the place of fall must be of the right kind, such as sandstone or quartzite, or perhaps best of all a clean desert sand. The composition of tektites indicates that a certain amount of felspar, mica, or clayey material was present in the rock (arkose or siltstone); and no doubt these extra constituents ($Al_2O_3$, 12; CaO, 3; $K_2O$, 2; $Na_2O$, 1 percent) gave to the molten material just the right viscosity for it to assume particular shapes when spinning through the air after being shot out by the gaseous explosion from the meteorite crater. The craters, supposed to be meteoric, on the Island of Oesel in Estonia are in dolomite, while the rocks in the region of the Siberian fall are basaltic. In neither of these places could silica-glass and tektites be formed.

Silica-glass is very resistant to chemical action and it will withstand weathering processes longer than many other materials. Also, with its very low coefficient of thermal expansion, it will not be affected by changes in temperature—a very potent agent of rock disintegration in desert regions. For this reason tektites are preserved in recent deposits, such as the glacial deposits of Tasmania, the alluvial deposits of Bohemia, Indo-China, and the Philippine Islands, and in the tin-gravels of Billiton, where by slow chemical corrosion they have acquired a peculiar sculptured surface. The australites found on the surface of the Australian deserts do not show this surface sculpturing and are more perfect in form. They are therefore of more recent origin. An aerial survey of the districts where australites are found would probably reveal the presence of meteorite craters with associated large masses of meteoric iron. In the other districts, all traces of the craters would probably have been obliterated by denudation, and the meteoric iron rusted away.

(**131**, 117-118; 1933)

---

References:

1 Lacroix, A., "Les Tectites de l'Indochine.". *Arch. Mus. Nat. Hist., Paris*, **8**, 139 (1932).

2 *Nature*, **129**, 932 (June 25, 1932).

3 *Nature*, **129**, 781 (May 28, 1932).

在西伯利亚是否发生过陨石坠落事件，除了这次事件可能是个例外之外，事实上自人类有史以来还没有发生过这类现象。另外，位于陨石坠落处的地壳岩石必须属于特定的类型，例如砂岩或石英岩，最合适的或许是纯净的荒漠砂砾。从玻陨石的组成上看，这些岩石（长石砂岩或粉砂岩）中存在着一定量的长石、云母或黏土矿物；毫无疑问，这些额外成分（$Al_2O_3$，12%；CaO，3%；$K_2O$，2%；$Na_2O$，1%）使熔融物具有正好合适的黏度，以便在它们由于气体爆炸被从陨石坑里抛射出来后能在空气中旋转形成特定的形状。爱沙尼亚乌瑟岛上的坑可能就是陨石坑，坑中的岩石是白云岩；而位于西伯利亚的陨石坠落区域的岩石则为玄武岩。在这两个地方都无法形成硅质玻璃或玻陨石。

硅质玻璃极不容易发生化学反应，它所能经受的风化时间比很多其他物质都要长。此外，其热膨胀系数也很低，不受温度变化的影响——这是在沙漠地区造成岩石崩解的一个重要原因。因此，玻陨石均保留在新近的沉积层中，如塔斯马尼亚的冰川沉积层，波希米亚、印度支那和菲律宾群岛的冲积层以及勿里洞岛的含锡砂砾层，在这些地方，缓慢的化学侵蚀在玻陨石表面形成了特殊的刻蚀面。而在澳大利亚沙漠表层发现的澳大利亚玻陨石则没有这样的刻蚀面，形态也更完整。所以澳大利亚玻陨石的形成时间比较晚。如果在发现澳大利亚玻陨石的地区进行航空勘测，也许能找到若干与大块铁陨石相关的陨石坑。而在其他地区，所有能证明陨石坑存在的证据可能都已经因剥蚀作用而消失了，而铁陨石也被锈蚀掉了。

（齐红艳 翻译；张忠杰 审稿）

# Energy of Cosmic Rays

E. Regener

## Editor's Note

**Physicists had obtained increasingly accurate measurements of the ionisation created in the upper atmosphere by cosmic rays. Using this data, Erich Regener here estimates the energy flux of the cosmic rays impinging upon the Earth. He estimates that 108 pairs of ions are created per second in each square cm. As impinging cosmic rays need an energy of 32 electron-volts to trigger ionisation, this led to an estimate for the total energy flux of 5.2 × 10$^{-3}$ erg. cm.$^{-2}$ sec.$^{-1}$ As Regener notes, a body in thermal equilibrium under illumination from this flux would bear a temperature of 3.1 K, similar to Arthur Eddington's result for a body in equilibrium with the ordinary radiation coming from stars.**

IN Nature for September 3, 1932, p. 364, I published the curve of the intensity of cosmic radiation in the high atmosphere, deduced from measurements made with a self-registering electrometer. It was possible by extrapolation to find the intensity $I_\infty$ of radiation at its entrance in the atmosphere. The preliminary value given has now been corrected by the experimental determination of the factor which reduces the measurements with the ionisation chamber at 5 atmospheres to 1 atmosphere. Now the value $I_\infty$ is found corresponding to a production of 333 pairs of ions cm.$^{-3}$ sec.$^{-1}$ in air at 0° and 760 mm. mercury pressure.

The graphical integration of the curve, giving the ionisation as a function of the height, makes it possible to calculate the total number of ions, produced by total absorption of cosmic rays by a column of air of 1 sq. cm. section. The high value of $1.02 \times 10^8$ pairs of ions is found. Some time ago, Millikan and Cameron[1] made a similar calculation, which gave a value of only $1.28 \times 10^7$ pairs of ions, due to an insufficient knowledge of the intensity in the high atmosphere. Taking the energy required to produce a pair of ions in air[2] as 32 electron-volts the flux $S$ of energy coming to the earth from the cosmic rays is found to be $5.2 \times 10^{-3}$ erg. cm.$^{-2}$ sec.$^{-1}$.

From an astrophysical point of view, the great energy of cosmic rays is remarkable. A body which absorbs all the cosmic rays would be heated by them. Equilibrium will be attained when the absorbed flux $S$ of cosmic rays is equal to the heat radiation $\sigma T^4$ of that body. $T$ works out as 3.1° Kelvin. The value is equal to the temperature (3.18°) which Eddington[3] finds for a black body heated only by the heat and light radiation of stars. Eddington's calculation relates to a point in our local system of stars, but not in the neighbourhood of one of them. If at such a point the flux of energy of cosmic radiation is equal to that on the earth, the temperature of a black body, absorbing entirely the

# 宇宙射线的能量

埃里克·雷格纳

## 编者按

物理学家们一直在对宇宙射线在高层大气中产生的电离效应进行测定，所得的结果越来越精确。埃里克·雷格纳利用这些数据估算了宇宙射线在撞击地球时的能量通量。他预计每秒在每平方厘米的面积上宇宙射线将有 108 个离子对通过。因为只有能量大于 32eV 的宇宙射线才能产生电离效应，由此可以估算出宇宙射线的总能流为 $5.2 \times 10^{-3}$ erg · $cm^{-2}$ · $s^{-1}$。雷格纳指出：一个处于热平衡状态中的物体在这么高能量射线流的照射下温度将升高 3.1 K。这个值近似于阿瑟·爱丁顿从多数来自恒量的辐射对平衡态天体的影响中得到的结果。

我在 1932 年 9 月 3 日《自然》杂志的第 364 页上公布了宇宙辐射在高层大气中的强度曲线，这条曲线是根据一台自动记录静电计的测量结果推演出来的。利用外推法可以得到宇宙射线在进入大气层时的辐射强度 $I_\infty$。现在原始数据已经可以用确定的实验因子进行修正，这个因子可以把电离室在 5 个大气压下测量的结果折合成 1 个大气压下的结果。目前得到的 $I_\infty$ 值相当于在 0℃，760 mm 汞柱空气中每秒每立方厘米产生 333 个离子对。

对曲线进行图解积分，发现电离度是随高度变化的函数，这样就可以计算出在横截面积为 1 平方厘米的空气柱完全吸收宇宙射线后产生的离子对总数。我们发现这个值高达 $1.02 \times 10^8$ 对离子。早些时候，密立根和卡梅伦[1]也进行过类似的计算，但由于他们对高层大气中的射线强度缺乏充分的认识，因而给出的数值仅为 $1.28 \times 10^7$ 对离子。如果在空气中产生一个离子对所需的能量[2]为 32 eV，那么宇宙射线带到地球上的能量通量 $S$ 应该可以达到 $5.2 \times 10^{-3}$ erg · $cm^{-2}$ · $s^{-1}$。

从天体物理学的角度来看，宇宙射线的能量如此巨大是很不寻常的。一个吸收了全部宇宙射线的天体将因此而被加热。当天体所吸收的宇宙射线的总通量 $S$ 等于其热辐射 $\sigma T^4$ 时，该天体就会达到平衡，这时计算出的温度值 $T$ 为 3.1 K，这与爱丁顿[3]发现的只被恒星发出的光和热所加热的黑体所具有的温度值（3.18 K）相等。爱丁顿的计算仅关系到我们所处的局部恒星系统中的一个点，而不涉及其中某一个恒星的周边区域。如果在这样一个点上，宇宙辐射的能流与在地球上获得的能流相等，那么根据 $T^4$ 定律，一个完全吸收了这两种辐射后的黑体的温度只会升至 3.7 K。

*two* radiations, rises only to 3.7° Kelvin, according to the $T^4$ law. But at a point in space among the spiral nebulae, the ordinary radiation is very small and causes only a very small rise of temperature. Supposing that cosmic rays originate in such intergalactic space, they would produce an elevation of temperature corresponding to the flux of cosmic rays.

A more detailed report will be published shortly in the *Zeitschrift für Physik*.

(**131**, 130; 1933)

E. Regener: Physik. Inst. d. Techn. Hochschule, Stuttgart, Dec. 31.

References:
1 *Phys. Rev.*, **31**, 930 (1928).
2 Kulenkampff, H., *Phys. Z.*, **30**, 777 (1929).
3 *Internal Constitution of the Stars*, German edition, 468 (1928).

但对于处于旋涡状星云内的空间某一点来说，通常的辐射是非常小的，所以温度上升的幅度也微乎其微。假设宇宙射线起源于这样的星系际空间，它们将引发与宇宙射线通量相对应的升温现象。

更详细的结果将在近期的《物理学杂志》上发表。

（史春晖 翻译；马宇蒨 审稿）

# Helium Liquefaction Plant at the Clarendon Laboratory, Oxford

F. A. Lindemann and T. C. Keeley

## Editor's Note

**In the early 1930s, liquid helium had become precious to physicists studying the properties of matter at very low temperatures. Here the physicist Frederick Lindemann and colleagues at the University of Oxford announced the development of a new means for producing large quantities of liquid helium. Their technique used the liquefaction of hydrogen under an abrupt change in pressure to cool helium, and could produce large volumes of the liquid in continuous operation with relatively cheap apparatus. The liquid helium lasted in their laboratory for about one and one-half hours. This method and subsequent developments would enable the Russian physicist Pyotr Kapitsa to discover the phenomenon of superfluidity in liquid helium in 1938.**

THE main properties of liquid helium have been familiar to men of science for a great many years. The only object therefore in liquefying it is in order to cool other substances the characteristics of which it is desired to study in the neighbourhood of the absolute zero. It has long been known that the heat capacity of solids becomes extremely small at low temperatures. Thus the latent heat of evaporation of 20 mgm. of liquid helium is sufficient to cool 60 gm. of copper from the temperature to be attained with liquid hydrogen boiling under a reduced pressure to the boiling point of helium.

It is easy to design apparatus so that the substances the properties of which at low temperatures are under investigation, are cooled to the temperature of the surrounding liquid or solid helium and maintained at this temperature with a minimum of waste. It seemed preferable, therefore, to instal a small inexpensive apparatus requiring comparatively little liquid hydrogen, which can therefore be operated frequently or duplicated at comparatively small cost, rather than to indulge in a plant designed to produce liquid helium in large quantities. In any event, the financial resources available would have imposed this choice, even had the alternative procedure been considered desirable.

The apparatus which has been installed at Oxford is of a type developed by Prof. Simon and Dr. Mendelssohn in Berlin and Breslau. Two concentric cylinders capable of withstanding a pressure of some 150 atmospheres surround the space in which the substance under investigation is placed. Helium under a pressure of about 100 atmospheres is introduced into the space between the cylinders. The upper part of the annular space between the cylinders is separated from the lower, in which the helium is

# 牛津大学克拉伦登实验室的氦液化车间

弗雷德里克·林德曼，托马斯·基利

## 编者按

在20世纪30年代早期，液氦对于研究很低温度下物质性质的物理学家来说是十分珍贵的。在本文中，牛津大学的物理学家弗雷德里克·林德曼及其同事宣布研发出了一种能生产大量液氦的新方法。他们采用突然改变液态氦压力的方式来冷却氦，可以用这种较便宜的装置连续地得到大量的液氦。他们的实验室持续生产了1.5个小时的液氦。正是这一方法及接下来的一些发展使俄罗斯物理学家彼得·卡皮查得以在1938年发现液氦中的超流性现象。

多年以来，液氦的主要性质就已为科学界的人士所熟知。所以人们把氦液化的唯一目的，是想用它来冷却其他物质以便研究它们在绝对零度附近的性质。长期以来人们就知道，固体的热容量在低温时会变得非常小。因此，蒸发20毫克液氦吸收的潜热足以使60克铜的温度从减压液态氢沸腾的温度降低到液氦沸点的温度。

为了研究低温下物质的性质，很容易设计一个实验装置把物质冷却到与其周围的液氦或固氦温度相同的温度，并以最小的损失使物质保持在这个温度。不过，我们更喜欢对液氢需求相对较少的小型廉价装置，而不是一个能大量生产液氦的工厂，因为选择小型设备可以降低经常运转或复制它的成本。无论如何，由于财力所限，即便是还有其他令人满意的方式可供选择，也只能选择这种装置。

安装在牛津大学的设备是由柏林的西蒙教授和布雷斯劳的门德尔松博士研制的。要研究的物质被装在由两个可承受150个大气压的同心圆桶围绕的空间中。在两个圆桶之间的空间注入压强约为100个大气压的氦。圆桶之间的环状区域被一金属板分隔成上下两部分，上部分形成了一个小的金属容器，并通过一根螺线型的细铜管与纯氢的供应源相连，氦在下半部分被压缩。整个装置用一根德银管保持在一

compressed, by a metal sheet, thus forming a small metal container which is joined by a spiral of thin copper tubing to a source of pure hydrogen. The whole is held in position on a German silver tube in the centre of a larger metal vessel containing hydrogen or helium gas at low pressure which can be evacuated by means of a mercury vapour pump. This outer vessel together with the copper spirals through which the hydrogen and helium are introduced is immersed in a Dewar flask containing liquid hydrogen.

When temperature equilibrium has been attained, hydrogen is introduced into the top vessel under a pressure of two or three atmospheres. Passing through the copper spirals, this liquefies owing to the excess pressure and runs down into the metal container over the double-walled helium cylinder. A tap to the mercury vapour pump is now turned on and a high vacuum produced in the metal box, so that the helium container with its superposed pot of liquid hydrogen is thermally insulated save for the necessary connecting tubes.

The yield of liquid helium is improved if the compressed helium is further cooled by boiling the hydrogen in the inner container under reduced pressure. If the helium is now allowed to expand, about half of it liquefies and the central space with the experimental substances it contains is cooled to the temperature of the surrounding helium. By evacuating the space above the liquid, that is, causing it to boil under reduced pressure, one can, of course, reduce the temperature to within one or two degrees of the absolute zero.

In the apparatus used at Oxford the helium lasts for about an hour and a half. If the experiment is not finished in this time, one can repeat the process in a few minutes at very small cost in liquid hydrogen. The helium expands into a rubber bag and is recompressed into a cylinder so that very little gas is lost. The temperature during the experiment can be observed on a large-scale manometer connected through a fine tube to a small vessel containing helium in the liquefaction space. The apparatus cost approximately £30. Since there is no need to recompress the helium rapidly, a small cheap compressor is sufficient.

The liquid hydrogen required is produced in a plant of the standard pattern designed in the Physico-Chemical Institute in Berlin which has been in use at Oxford for some years now without giving any trouble. Impurities in the hydrogen are condensed by a preliminary expansion and continuously removed by a slow stream of hydrogen. With a compressor capable of dealing with ten cubic metres of free gas an hour and an expenditure of approximately 1.4 litres of liquid nitrogen per litre of liquid hydrogen, this plant produces some $2\frac{1}{2}$ litres of liquid hydrogen per hour. Liquefier and compressor together cost approximately £350.

The liquid hydrogen is stored in pyrex Dewar flasks silvered and exhausted in the laboratory. As their efficiency equalled that claimed for the more complicated double vessels developed by Prof. Kapitsa, they have been retained.

个更大的金属容器的中心，该容器中充有低压的氢气或氦气，可用汞蒸汽泵抽成真空。最外面的容器与输送氢和氦的铜螺线管一起浸没在一个含有液态氢的杜瓦瓶内。

当温度达到平衡时，压强为 2 或 3 个大气压的氢被注入到上部的容器中。氢气通过铜螺线管时由于所受压力过大而被液化，随后流入到在双壁氦圆桶上的金属容器中。这时打开连接汞蒸汽泵的阀门，金属容器内就会产生高真空，从而除了所需的连接管以外，氦容器与在它上面的液氢罐都与外界热绝缘。

如果通过减压使内层容器中的氢达到沸点以进一步冷却压缩状态下的氦，就可以提高液氦的产量。现在允许氦气膨胀，约一半的氦会被液化，放有实验物质的中间区域也会被冷却到与周围氦一样的温度。如果在液体上方抽真空，也就是让液体在减压的情况下沸腾，我们就可以把温度降低到距绝对零度一两度的范围之内。

牛津大学的设备能使液氦持续运转约 1.5 小时。如果在 1.5 个小时之内实验还没有做完，我们可在几分钟之内就开始重复上述过程，这只需消耗一些很便宜的液氢而已。氦气膨胀进入一个橡皮袋，然后被压缩到钢瓶内，所以丢失的气体很少。我们可以通过一个大量程的压力计观察实验时的温度，这个压力计通过一根细管子连接到液化区内的含氦气小容器上。这个设备的造价约为 30 英镑。因为不需要快速压缩氦气，所以使用一台小型廉价的压缩机就够了。

所需的液氢是用柏林物理化学研究所设计的标准设备生产的，目前这个设备已经在牛津大学无故障地运转了好几年了。氢气中的杂质先经过一次预膨胀使之凝聚，然后通过氢的低速流动继续去除杂质。使用的是每小时能处理 10 立方米自由气体的压缩机，每升液氢需要消耗约 1.4 升液氮，这个车间每小时可生产约 2.5 升的液氢。液化器和压缩机的总造价约为 350 英镑。

液氢被储存在镀银的派热克斯玻璃杜瓦瓶中并在实验室中耗尽掉。由于派热克斯玻璃杜瓦瓶与卡皮查教授研制的较复杂的双容器杜瓦具有相同的功效，所以我们一直在使用这些杜瓦瓶。

If low temperature work expands and a large number of experiments are in hand simultaneously, it may be necessary to consider the use of the continuous Linde process of liquefaction. In view of the cost of the gas and the precautions necessary for its recovery, its distribution involves considerable inconvenience, which for the time being are scarcely worth facing. The mere liquefaction, of course, offers no difficulties and there is little doubt that the Berlin type of apparatus, which is already in use in many laboratories, will prove as serviceable and efficient as the hydrogen liquefier, should it ever be necessary to change over to this system.

Finally, a word of thanks is due to Dr. Mendelssohn, who kindly brought the liquefier over from Breslau and placed all his knowledge and experience unreservedly at the disposal of the department. But for this, it would scarcely have been possible to obtain, without hitch or trouble, liquid helium within one week of the arrival of the apparatus in Oxford.

(**131**, 191-192; 1933)

如果低温工作扩展了，需要在低温下同时进行多项实验，恐怕就要考虑采用连续的林德液化过程了。考虑到气体很昂贵，以及必须仔细地回收气体，使用这一方法还有相当大的不便，所以目前还不太值得考虑。如果必须改为使用这种系统的话，仅从实现液化而言，柏林型装置当然是没有任何困难的，毫无疑问，它将被证明与氢液化器一样好用而高效，而且很多的实验室已在使用它。

最后，我要对门德尔松博士表示感谢，他慷慨地从布雷斯劳带来液化器并把自己所有的知识和经验毫无保留地贡献给这个系自由处理。否则，我们几乎不可能在设备到达牛津大学的一周之内，没有遇到任何麻烦就顺利地制备出液氦来。

（沈乃澂 翻译；陶宏杰 审稿）

# Structure and Division of Somatic Chromosomes in Allium

T. K. Koshy

## Editor's Note

**When T. K. Koshy published this account of *Allium* chromosomes separating in 1933, there were three competing theories of chromosome structure—the nuclear components were either granular, spiral or shaped like honeycombs. In order for cell division and heredity to be fully understood, Koshy knew the argument had to be resolved. So he looked at dividing cells and saw that metaphase chromosome arms were composed of two spirals coiled in opposite directions. As the spirals uncoiled, the chromosome separated and the progeny were pulled to opposite sides of the nucleus. He observed this spiral structure in all stages of mitosis, and so helped settle the debate on chromosome structure.**

THREE divergent views have been expressed regarding the structure of chromosome. Pfitzner in 1882 suggested that a chromosome is made up of a row of granules embedded in an achromatic or less chromatic matrix. About the same time, Baranetzky found a spiral structure in certain stages in the meiotic cycle of the chromosomes of *Tradescantia virginica*. Vejdovsky (1912) has termed this spiral the chromonema. The chromonema theory conceives of a continuous, filiform, spirally coiled chromatic element in an achromatic matrix. The alveolar theory foreshadowed by van Beneden and worked out by Grégoire and his pupils contemplates the homogeneous chromosomes of the metaphase becoming during the following stages a honey-combed structure by the appearance in it of numerous alveoles. The supporters of this view assume that a longitudinally aligned central series of alveoles would account for the origin of the split in each chromosome.

The exact nature of the behaviour of chromosomes both in mitosis and in meiosis, as well as their rôle in heredity, can be understood only if their real structure is known. A study of the structure of the chromosomes of *Allium* has been undertaken under the kind guidance of Prof. R. Ruggles Gates, with the view of solving some of these problems. A preliminary account of the results so far obtained by cytological observations and the use of wire models is given below.

(1) At the early metaphase each chromosome is seen to be composed of two spirally coiled chromonemata and the duality of this spiral has been observed in all stages of the mitotic cycle.

(2) The spiral is coiled in opposite directions in the two arms of the chromosome, the null

# 葱属植物体细胞染色体结构与分裂

科希

## 编者按

在科希 1933 年发表这篇葱属植物染色体分裂的研究报告时，存在着三种彼此矛盾的染色体结构理论——其争论焦点是细胞核组成元件究竟是颗粒状的，螺旋形的，还是蜂窝状的？科希知道：要全面了解细胞分裂和遗传实质就必须解决这一分歧。因此他观察了处于分裂的细胞，发现在分裂中期染色体臂是由两条反向卷曲的螺旋组成。当螺旋打开时，染色体发生分离，并被牵引到细胞核的两极。这种螺旋结构存在于有丝分裂的各个时期，他的这一发现对于解决染色体结构的分歧有着十分重要的意义。

染色体结构存在着三种不同的假说。早在 1882 年，普菲茨纳就提出染色体是由一列镶嵌在不被着色或不易染色基质上的颗粒组成的。就在此前后，巴拉涅茨基在紫露草减数分裂过程中的某些时期也发现了螺旋结构。1912 年，韦多夫斯基将这种螺旋结构命名为染色丝。染色丝理论假定在非着色基质中存在着一种连续、纤丝状且螺旋卷曲着的染色质成分。染色体泡状学说最初由范贝内登提出，随后得到了格雷瓜尔及其学生的证实。他们认为细胞分裂中期的染色体在继后的各个时期中变成了蜂窝状结构，从外形上看似许多小泡状结构凝集在一起。泡状学说的支持者们认为纵向排列的中央泡状系列组分是每一染色体分裂的起始点。

只有弄清楚染色体的真实结构，才能解释细胞有丝分裂和减数分裂过程中染色体行为的真实本质，以及它们在遗传中的作用。为解决这些问题，我们在拉各尔斯·盖茨教授的悉心指导下对葱属植物细胞染色体结构进行了研究。到目前为止，我们在细胞学观察基础上利用金属丝模型得到了初步的结论，其主要观点如下：

(1) 在有丝分裂早中期，每一染色体均由两条螺旋卷曲着的染色丝组成，而且在细胞分裂的各个时期都观察到了这种螺旋与卷曲的二重性。

(2) 每一染色体的两条臂朝着相反的方向螺旋卷曲，反向螺旋的分界点是染色体

point of the spiral being the attachment constriction of the chromosome.

(3) This form of double spiral permits of the separation of the chromosome into two by a simple uncoiling. This commences at the ends, as observed in *Allium*, but conceivably in some forms it may be initiated by the pull of the spindle fibres at the point of constriction.

(4) This unwinding causes rotation in the two arms of the chromosome; it may be possible that, as a result of this rotary motion in each arm of the chromosome, longitudinal cleavage is initiated in each chromonema at the metaphase stage.

(5) The separated chromonemata (daughter chromosomes), which now present a double spiral structure in each, remain parallel until they are finally pulled apart to the opposite poles of the spindle.

The doubleness of the anaphase chromosomes is clearly seen and the twisted appearance of these is due to slight loosening of the double spiral, which has been observed by Hedayetullah[1] in *Narcissus* and by Miss Perry[2] in *Galanthus*. The threads of this spiral retain their spiral structure in the subsequent stages of the mitotic cycle. The different appearances presented by the chromosomes in these stages are mainly due to the compact or loose nature of the double spiral. The dual threads remain closely associated together until their final separation at the next metaphase.

Further work on this subject is in progress and it is hoped that a detailed account may be published at a later date.

(**131**, 362; 1933)

T. K. Koshy: King's College, London, Feb.7.

---

References:
1 Hedayetullah, *J. Roy. Mic.* Soc., 51, 347-386.
2 Perry, *J. Roy. Mic.* Soc., 52, 344-356.

的附着缢痕。

(3) 通过简单的解螺旋作用，双螺旋染色体可以分成两部分。在葱属植物中这一过程发生在细胞分裂周期的末尾，但不难想象，在某种形式上该过程可能起始于缢痕点纺锤丝的牵引。

(4) 上述解螺旋作用使染色体的两臂发生旋转，该旋转可能导致每条染色丝在细胞分裂中期产生纵向分裂。

(5) 现在每一条分开的染色体丝（子染色体）都成为一个独立的双螺旋结构，它们在最终被牵引到纺锤体相反的两极前，一直保持着相互平行的状态。

海德亚图拉[1]和佩里小姐[2]分别观察了水仙花与雪花莲的细胞分裂周期，在细胞分裂后期，成双的染色体清晰可见；若双螺旋稍微松弛，染色体外形则呈扭曲状。这种螺旋卷曲着的染色丝在有丝分裂中期继后各阶段均保持螺旋状态，而不同时期所观察到的染色体不同形态，主要与双螺旋结构的紧缩或松弛状态有关。直到下一细胞分裂中期，紧密相连的双线结构才会分开。

关于这一主题的深入研究还在继续，希望将来还会有更详尽的研究结果发表。

（韩玲俐 翻译；程祝宽 审稿）

# Recent Researches on the Transmutation of the Elements*

E. Rutherford

## Editor's Note

**Ernest Rutherford here offers a snapshot of the rapidly advancing field of nuclear transmutation. It had been established that many atoms can be changed from one element to another by adding or subtracting any of the various particles believed to inhabit the nucleus. But so far no such reactions had been observed with heavy elements such as thallium, lead, bismuth or uranium. This might change, Rutherford says, as physicists around the world—notably Ernest Lawrence at the University of California—were developing accelerating devices of considerably higher energy. None, however, compared to the energies of cosmic rays, with which several experiments had recently found tentative evidence for a positively charged electron—later identified as the positron.**

IT is now well established that the change of one atom into another can only be effected by the addition or subtraction of one of the constituent particles of the atomic nucleus, for example, an electron, proton, neutron or $\alpha$-particle. Such a transformation was first accomplished in 1919 for the element nitrogen by bombarding it with swift $\alpha$-particles from radioactive substances. About one $\alpha$-particle in 100,000 comes so close to the nucleus that it enters and is captured by it. This violent disturbance results in the expulsion of a proton with high speed, and the formation of a new nucleus of mass 17. A number of light elements can be transformed by $\alpha$-particle bombardment in a similar way, and in most cases a proton is ejected.

A new and strange type of transformation was discovered last year by Chadwick: when $\alpha$-particles bombard the metal beryllium, uncharged particles of mass 1 called neutrons are expelled. These neutrons, which have remarkable powers of penetrating matter, are themselves very efficient agents for the transformation of atoms. Feather has shown that both nitrogen and oxygen are transformed by the capture of neutrons, with the expulsion of a fast $\alpha$-particle. The types of transformations produced by the neutron are thus very different from those observed with the $\alpha$-particle. The capture of an $\alpha$-particle in general leads to the building up of a new nucleus three units heavier than before, while the capture of a neutron leads to the formation of a nucleus three units lighter.

During the past year, Cockcroft and Walton at Cambridge made the important discovery that comparatively low-speed protons are very effective in causing the transformation of a

* Substance of the Friday evening discourse delivered at the Royal Institution on March 10.

# 关于元素嬗变的最新研究*

欧内斯特·卢瑟福

## 编者按

欧内斯特·卢瑟福在这篇文章中发表了对快速发展的核嬗变领域的简评。已经确认许多原子都可以通过增加或减少核中的任意粒子使自己从一种元素转变成另一种元素。但迄今为止人们在像铊、铅、铋和铀这样的重元素中还没有观察到这种反应。卢瑟福说：这个结论可能会有所改变，因为全世界的物理学家，尤其是美国加州大学的欧内斯特·劳伦斯，正在研制能量更高的加速器。不过所得到的能量无法和宇宙射线的能量相比，最近一些与宇宙射线相关的实验显示可能存在一种带正电的电子——后来被人们确定为正电子。

目前我们完全可以认为：仅仅通过增加或减少原子核的一个组成粒子如电子、质子、中子或 $\alpha$ 粒子就可以使一种原子变为另一种原子。这种嬗变是 1919 年用放射性物质发射的快速 $\alpha$ 粒子轰击氮元素时首次完成的。有约十万分之一的 $\alpha$ 粒子非常接近原子核以至于进入其中而被其俘获。这种强力扰动除了导致放出高速的质子，还形成了质量为 17 的新原子核。用类似的方法以 $\alpha$ 粒子轰击可以嬗变一些轻元素，而且在大多数情况下，会放出一个质子。

去年，查德威克发现了一类新奇的嬗变：当 $\alpha$ 粒子轰击金属铍时，放射出质量为 1、被称为中子的不带电的粒子。中子对于物质有极强的穿透性，是产生原子嬗变非常有效的工具。费瑟指出，氮和氧都可以通过中子俘获发生嬗变，并放出一个快速 $\alpha$ 粒子。由中子引发的这类嬗变与那些由 $\alpha$ 粒子引发的嬗变有很大的差别。通常，$\alpha$ 粒子俘获生成的新原子核比之前的质量重三个原子质量单位，而中子俘获产生的原子核要比之前轻三个原子质量单位。

去年，剑桥大学的考克饶夫和瓦耳顿作出了重要的发现，相对低速的质子在引发许多元素的嬗变中都是非常有效的。质子在氢原子放电的过程中大量产生，随后

* 本文取自作者于 3 月 10 日在英国皇家研究院所作的周五晚间演讲。

number of elements. The protons are generated in large numbers by an electric discharge through hydrogen, and then speeded up by passing through an evacuated space to which a high potential of the order of 600,000 volts is applied. Under these conditions the protons acquire high speeds comparable with that of the $\alpha$-particle from radium. When a stream of these swift protons corresponding to a micro-ampere falls on the element lithium, a large number of $\alpha$-particles are emitted of energy comparable with that of the swiftest $\alpha$-particle from radium. It seems that about one in 100 million of the protons enters a lithium nucleus of mass 7, and the resulting nucleus of mass 8 splits up into two $\alpha$-particles, each of mass 4. Cockcroft and Walton have later found that the $\alpha$-particles emitted consist of two groups differing widely in speed.

This transformation of lithium can be produced at surprisingly low voltages. With strong proton streams, the emission of $\alpha$-particles can be observed for 30,000 volts; the number of particles increases rapidly with the voltage, and the variation has been examined by different observers over a very wide range, from 30,000 to 1.5 million volts.

Protons are also remarkably effective in disintegrating the light element boron, and again $\alpha$-particles are emitted. It is possible in this case that the boron nucleus of mass 11, after capturing a proton, breaks up into three $\alpha$-particles. The radiation observed is complex, and has not yet been analysed in detail. A number of other elements have been found to be transformed, apparently in all cases with the emission of $\alpha$-particles.

In a special form of accelerating tube devised by Oliphant in the Cavendish Laboratory, a narrow, intense proton stream can be generated at voltages up to 200,000 volts. The protons, after being bent by a magnetic field, bombard a target of about one square centimetre in area. By special arrangements, it has been found possible to obtain in the detecting chamber at least a thousand times the number of particles observed by Cockcroft and Walton at the same voltage. By this method it is easy to observe the particles from very thin films of lithium and boron at comparatively low voltages, while the variation of number with voltage has been measured. For example, a number of $\alpha$-particles are emitted from lithium with voltages so low as 30,000 volts. $\alpha$-Particles from boron have been observed at 60,000 volts, but the number increases much more rapidly with voltage than in the case of lithium.

Special experiments have been made to test by this sensitive method whether the heavy elements thallium, lead, bismuth and uranium show any evidences of transformation for 200,000 volt protons, but no sign of emission of $\alpha$-particles has been observed for these elements. At first, marked effects were observed, but these were ultimately traced to a minute contamination by boron, probably originating in the discharge tube. It seems not unlikely that the effect observed for uranium and lead in the original experiments of Cockcroft and Walton may have been due to an unsuspected contamination by a minute trace of the very active element boron.

在加有 600,000 伏高电压的真空中被加速。在这样的条件下，质子获得了与从镭中放射出的 $\alpha$ 粒子相当的高速度。当这些相应于微安级电流的快速质子束流轰击元素锂时，发射出大量的 $\alpha$ 粒子，其能量与从镭中放射出的最快速的 $\alpha$ 粒子的能量相当。大约有亿分之一的质子进入质量为 7 的锂原子核，产生质量为 8 的原子核，该原子核又分裂为两个质量为 4 的 $\alpha$ 粒子。考克饶夫和瓦耳顿后来发现，所发射的 $\alpha$ 粒子由速度相差很大的两群组成。

锂的嬗变可以在特别低的电压下产生。用强的质子流，可以观测到在 30,000 伏时放射出 $\alpha$ 粒子；粒子数目随着电压的加大而快速增加，在从 30,000 伏到 1.5 百万伏这个非常宽的范围内，不同的观测者都检测到了这种变化。

质子在蜕变轻元素硼时也是非常有效的，且会再次放出 $\alpha$ 粒子。在这种情况下，质量为 11 的硼原子核在俘获一个质子后破裂为三个 $\alpha$ 粒子是可能的。所观测到的辐射很复杂，详细的分析还未完成。许多其他的元素也已被发现可以发生嬗变，当然，在所有的情况下都会放出 $\alpha$ 粒子。

在由卡文迪什实验室的奥利芬特发明的特殊形式的加速管中，细而强的质子束流可以在高至 200,000 伏的电压下产生。经过磁场偏转的质子流轰击面积约为 1 平方厘米的靶。通过特殊的装置，在检测室中可以得到的粒子数比考克饶夫和瓦耳顿在相同电压下观测到的粒子数至少大几千倍。用这种方法很容易观测到在相当低电压下从非常薄的锂和硼薄膜中放射出的粒子，还测量了粒子数随电压的变化。例如，在电压低至 30,000 伏时从锂中可以放出许多 $\alpha$ 粒子。在电压为 60,000 伏时观测到了从硼放出的 $\alpha$ 粒子，但与锂的情况相比，$\alpha$ 粒子的数量随电压增加得更快。

通过这种灵敏的方法人们已经进行了特殊的实验用以检验重元素铊、铅、铋和铀对 200,000 伏的质子是否显示任何嬗变的迹象，但并未观测到这些元素有发射 $\alpha$ 粒子的迹象。最初，观测到了明显的效应，但最终追查到这些效应是由硼的微量污染引起的，它可能来自于放电管。这似乎有可能就是考克饶夫和瓦耳顿在最初的铀和铅的实验中观测到的效应，它们可能是由微量非常活泼的元素硼的未知污染产生的。

During the last few years, much energy has been devoted throughout the world to developing methods of obtaining streams of very swift charged particles with which to bombard matter and effect its transmutation. In the apparatus of Cockcroft and Walton at Cambridge already referred to, a steady potential of 800,000 volts can be reached. A new and simple type of electrostatic generator has been designed by Van der Graaf and Atta in the Massachusetts Institute of Technology, with which they have obtained a steady potential of 1.5 million volts, and a larger apparatus is under construction with which they hope to obtain a potential of 15 million volts to apply to a large vacuum tube. Brasch and Lange have applied high momentary voltages to a discharge tube by using an impulse generator.

A new and ingenious method of multiple acceleration has been devised by Lawrence of the University of California with which he has already obtained protons of energy 1.5 million volts by using a potential less than 10,000 volts. The transformation of lithium has been examined at this high energy using a proton current of about a thousandth of a micro-ampere. It is hoped to develop this method so as to obtain protons of energy as high as 10 million volts or more.

Even if these new projects prove successful, the speeds of particles produced by their aid are much smaller than those observed for the very penetrating radiation in our atmosphere, where electrons and protons of energy from 200 million to 2,000 million volts are present. From the experiments of Anderson in Pasadena and Blackett and Occhialini in Cambridge, it seems certain that these very swift particles are very efficient in causing the transformation of nuclei, probably in novel ways. Strong evidence has been obtained of the production of a new type of positively charged particle which has a mass small compared with that of the proton. This may prove to be the positive electron, the counterpart of the well-known negative electron of light mass.

(**131**, 388-389; 1933)

在最近几年间，全世界都在投入大量精力用以发展获得快速带电粒子流的方法，以便利用这些带电粒子来轰击物质并使其发生嬗变。已经提到剑桥大学的考克饶夫和瓦耳顿的装置可以达到 800,000 伏的稳定电压。麻省理工学院的范德格拉夫和阿塔设计出了一台简单的新型静电加速器，他们用此得到了 1.5 百万伏的稳定电压。他们还在构建更大的装置，以期获得 15 百万伏的电压并将之应用到大的真空钢筒内。布拉什和兰格已将瞬时高电压通过脉冲发生器加到放电管上。

加州大学的劳伦斯发明了一种新的直接多次加速的巧妙方法，他用小于 10,000 伏的电压得到的质子能量为 1.5 百万伏。在使用约千分之一微安的质子流时，锂在这种高能下发生的嬗变得到了检验。这类方法被寄予厚望，因为它可能获得高达 10 百万伏甚至更高能量的质子。

即使这些新方案被证明是成功的，由它们产生的粒子速度仍远小于我们在大气层中观测到的穿透力很强的辐射，大气中电子和质子的能量在 200 百万伏到 2,000 百万伏之间。帕萨迪纳的安德森及剑桥大学的布莱克特和奥基亚利尼的实验似乎表明，这些非常快的粒子在引起原子核的嬗变中是很有效的，也许是新方式的嬗变。强有力的证据表明产生了一种比质子质量小且带正电的新型粒子。它可能被证明是正电子，即为人们所熟知的轻质量带负电荷的电子的反粒子。

（沈乃澂 翻译；张焕乔 审稿）

# Number of Mendelian Factors in Quantitative Inheritance

R. A. Fisher

## Editor's Note

**Ever since 1896, agricultural scientists at the University of Illinois had been selectively breeding maize for high and low protein content and for high and low oil content. In a recent publication, Illinois scientist Floyd L. Winter reported the results up to 1924. From a foundation stock of maize, he and his colleagues had created massive variation in these two traits in just under 30 years, clearly demonstrating a process of selection. Crucially, however, their different protein and oil lines were no less variable than the original stock. This, geneticist Ronald Fisher argues here, has "killed" the idea that selection of small differences will only result in small evolutionary changes and that the act of selecting reduces variation, bringing evolution to a grinding halt.**

IN a note in the current *Eugenics Review* entitled "Evolution by Selection", "Student" has directed attention to some statistical consequences of the inheritance of quantitative characters, in relation to the theory that these are due to the cumulative effect of a number of ordinary Mendelian factors.

"Student" refers in particular to the remarkable selection experiment carried out by F. L. Winter[1], in which a commercial variety of maize was exposed to mass selection from year to year in two diverging lines for high and low protein, and in two more for high and low oil content. For protein the initial value was about 11 percent with a standard deviation of a little more than 1 percent, but in the average of the last three years the mean of the high selection line is 16.82 percent while that of the low selection line is less than half that value, namely, 7.53 percent. The aggregate change produced by selection in both directions is thus 9.39 percent, or more than nine times the original standard deviation.

With respect to variability, it may be noted that the high line now varies from 13.4 to 19.8 percent, while the extremes for the low line are 5.7 and 10.5 percent; so that the two lines are now separated by a considerable gap, and therefore cannot possibly have any single genotype in common. The variability of the low selection line has shown a slight tendency to diminish, and that of the high selection line a slightly greater tendency to increase, so that no general tendency to a decrease in variability ascribable to selection is to be observed; thus, there is no reason to think that the selective potentialities of the material have been appreciably exhausted in producing the great modification which has been brought about.

"Student" contrasts these well-substantiated facts with the belief, widely held among

# 数量遗传学中孟德尔因子的数量

罗纳德·费希尔

## 编者按

自从 1896 年以后，伊利诺伊大学的农学家通过对玉米的选择育种可以得到蛋白质含量高或低和含油量高或低的玉米。伊利诺伊州的科学家弗洛伊德·温特在最近发表的一篇论文中总结了 1924 年以前的研究成果。在不到 30 年的时间里，他和他的同事从玉米的原种中培育出了蛋白质含量和含油量迥然不同的品种，这说明了选择的过程。不过最重要的是他们培育出的这些新品种可以和原种一样发生变异。遗传学家罗纳德·费希尔在本文中指出，这一点成功地“驳斥”了某些人的观点，即认为在差异小的群体中进行选种只会产生较小的进化变异，而且选种将使变异减少，使进化过程突然中断。

在近期《优生学评论》中的一篇名为《通过选择而进化》的短文中，“学生”（编者注：“学生”即为英国统计学家威廉·戈塞特）把注意力转向了数量性状遗传的一些统计结果，并认为这些结果归于多个普通孟德尔因子的累积效应。

“学生”特别提到了温特进行的受人瞩目的育种实验 [1]。该实验对一个玉米的商业变种进行年复一年的混合选择，选择方向为高蛋白质和低蛋白质两个品系，以及高油量和低油量两种类型。蛋白质含量初始值约为 11%，标准偏差略大于 1%，但在过去三年中，高蛋白质品系的均值为 16.82%；而低蛋白质品系的蛋白质含量均值还不到该值的一半，为 7.53%。于是，在两个方向上通过选择形成的累计变化为 9.39%，或者说是最初标准偏差的 9 倍多。

关于变异性，可以注意到目前高蛋白质品系在 13.4% 到 19.8% 的范围内变化，而低蛋白质品系的极端值为 5.7% 和 10.5%。因此，现在这两个品系之间相差很大，因而不可能有任何共同的单一基因型。低选择品系的变异性显示出了轻微的减少趋势，而高选择品系的变异性则出现了稍大的增长趋势，因此未能观察到因为选择而使变异性下降的总趋势；因而，没有理由认为在产生这种巨大改变时，会耗尽该材料的选择潜力。

“学生”将这些被充分验证的事实与几年前遗传学家们普遍持有的观念——即对

geneticists not so many years ago, that the selection of small differences (fluctuations) can only lead to unimportant evolutionary effects. They may also be contrasted with the oft-repeated statement that selection can do no more than select the best of the existing variety of genotypes, and with the commonly taught belief that the diversity available for selection is easily exhausted, from which it is inferred that evolutionary progress must wait upon the occurrence of mutations. It was, indeed, often represented as consisting in these occurrences.

The results obtained with oil-content have been even more striking; for the high oil line now contains nearly six times as much as the line selected for low oil content, and differs from it by more than twenty times the original standard deviation. "Student" uses these data, together with reasonable estimates of the intensity of selection, to obtain an estimate of the least possible number of factors which must be postulated to obtain the results up to the date of the report; he concludes that at least 100-300 factors would be needed; and, taking into account the complete lack of evidence that selection is nearing its limit, considers that it is more probable that the actual number of factors is measured in thousands.

Estimates of the number of factors needed to explain quantitative inheritance are beset with considerable difficulty, and "Student" has admitted to me in correspondence that his calculation fails from over-simplification. Other well-established phenomena in maize, however, such as the flood of recessive defects revealed by every plant which has been used to found a selfed line, combined with the inevitable rarity of each of these defects, taken individually, in the population from which the foundation plant was selected, force one to the conclusion that all commercial varieties must be segregating in hundreds, and quite possibly in thousands of factors influencing the normal development of the plant. This emphatic experience, has, I believe, killed among maize breeders all those doctrines concerning the supposed inefficacy of the selection of minute differences, with which the teaching of modern genetics was at first encumbered.

It should be emphasised that the result of importance for evolutionary theory is not that the number of factors must be very large, thousands for example, rather than hundreds, but the direct demonstration that selection has the exact effects that selectionists have ascribed to it, without the limitations by which its action has been supposed to be restricted, on the strength of an early misapprehension as to the number and variety of the Mendelian factors exposed to its cumulative action.

(**131**, 400-401; 1933)

R. A. Fisher: Rothamsted Experimental Station, Harpenden, Feb. 15.

---

Reference:
1 J. *Agric. Res.*, 39, 451–476 (1929).

细微差异（波动）的选择只会导致微不足道的进化效应——进行了对比。与这些事实形成对比的还有那个被再三重复的论断，即选择只能从基因型的现存变异中挑选出最好的，以及那个被普遍讲授的观点，即可供选择的多样性很容易被耗竭，因而进化过程必须等待突变的发生。实际上，在这些事件中通常是一致的。

从含油量中得到的结果更令人震惊，目前高油品系的含油量是低油品系的近 6 倍，在两个方向上通过选择形成的累计变化是最初标准偏差的 20 倍以上。“学生”利用这些数据，加之对选择强度的合理估计，得到了要想获得本报告中的结果所必需的最低可能因子数量的估计值。他认为至少需要 100~300 个因子，而考虑到没有任何证据表明进化已经接近了极限，他认为实际因子的数量很可能数以千计。

在估计解释数量遗传所需的因子数量时遇到了很大的困难。“学生”在写给我的信中承认，他的计算因过于简单而失败。然而，玉米中的其他一些已经得到确认的现象——如用来建立自交品系的所有植株都显示出大量的隐性缺陷，并且从选择建群植株的种群中单独筛选出的每一个缺陷都必定十分稀有等——迫使人们得出结论，即认为所有商业变种必然是数百个，并且很可能有数千个影响该植物正常发育的因子。我相信，这个特殊实例驳斥了在玉米育种者中流传的认为细微差异对选择无效的种种学说，而这些论点在一开始就阻碍了现代遗传学的教学。

应当强调的是，进化理论的重要结论并不在于因子数量一定要很大，比如是数千个而非数百个，而是在于它直接证明了选择具有自然选择论者所认为的确切效果，它的作用并没有受到人们一向认为会有的限制，而这些限制是由于早期人们对累积效应下孟德尔因子的数量和变化的误解所产生的。

（周志华 翻译；刘京国 审稿）

# Light and Life*

N. Bohr

## Editor's Note

**This is an address given by Niels Bohr at the International Congress on Light Therapy in Copenhagen. Bohr had been invited to discuss the beneficial effects of light in curing diseases, but he spoke instead on the potential implications of the new quantum understanding of light for the science of living organisms. Despite the inadequacy of the wave picture for detailing the behaviour of light quanta, says Bohr, there could be no question of replacing it with a purely quantum-mechanical "particle" picture. He points out that any attempt to measure the trajectories of photons precisely inevitably destroys the phenomenon of wave interference. Such problems, he suggests, compel abandonment of a complete causal description of light phenomena.**

**In the second part of his address, Bohr argues that the implications of quantum theory stretch well beyond atomic physics. The assimilation of carbon by plants surely involved the quantum nature of interactions between light and matter, and the ability of the human eye to detect only a few photons suggests that its design probes the quantum limits of optics. Bohr suggests an analogy between uncertainty in the physical and biological worlds. Attempts to study organisms closely may ultimately interfere with their vital organs, just as physicists must disturb particles in order to study them. Perhaps life and consciousness may never be explained, but must be accepted a priori much as the quantum action is axiomatic in physics.**

### Part I

AS a physicist whose studies are limited to the properties of inanimate bodies, it is not without hesitation that I have accepted the kind invitation to address this assembly of scientific men met together to forward our knowledge of the beneficial effects of light in the cure of diseases. Unable as I am to contribute to this beautiful branch of science that is so important for the welfare of mankind, I could at most comment on the purely inorganic light phenomena which have exerted a special attraction for physicists throughout the ages, not least owing to the fact that light is our principal tool of observation. I have thought, however, that on this occasion it might perhaps be of interest, in connexion with such comments, to enter on the problem of what significance the results reached in the limited domain of physics may have for our views on the position of living organisms in the realm of natural science.

---

* Address delivered at the opening meeting of the International Congress on Light Therapy, Copenhagen, on August 15, 1932. The present article, conforming with the Danish version (*Naturens Verden*, **17**, 49), differs from that published in the Congress report only by some formal alterations.

# 光与生命*

尼尔斯·玻尔

编者按

这篇文章出自尼尔斯·玻尔在哥本哈根举行的国际光疗大会上的讲话。大会本来想邀请玻尔向大家介绍一下光对于治疗疾病的好处，但实际上玻尔讲的是光在新量子理论中的概念对生命科学的潜在意义。玻尔说：虽然描述光量子行为的波动理论还不够完善，但仍可能把光看作是量子力学中的一个“粒子”。他指出：任何想精确测量光子轨迹的尝试都必然会破坏波的干涉现象。他说这一问题使人们不得不放弃对光现象的纯因果描述。

玻尔在第二部分中指出，量子理论的拓展远远超过了原子物理的范畴。植物的碳同化作用肯定包含着光与物质之间发生相互作用的量子本质，人眼只能看到几个光子说明它的结构反映了光学上的量子极限。玻尔将物理学和生物学中的不确定性进行了类比。对生物体过于精密的研究可能会对它们的重要器官产生干扰，就像物理学家为了研究粒子必须干扰它们一样。也许生命和意识是永远不能被解释清楚的，只能把它们当成不言自明的公理，物理中的量子现象也是如此。

## 第一部分

作为一个研究领域仅限于非生命物质的物理学家，在接受盛情邀请来到这个科学界人士云集的大会介绍光对于治疗疾病的有利影响时，我还是有点犹豫的。因为我无法致力于这个对造福人类有重要贡献的精彩科学分支，我至多只能对纯粹的无机光学现象发表评述，光现象对古往今来的物理学工作者来说一直有着特殊的吸引力，一个重要的原因是光是我们的主要观测手段。然而，我认为，在这样的场合谈一谈物理学范畴内的研究成果对我们认识生物体在自然科学领域中的地位具有什么样的意义也许是一件有趣的事情。

---

* 这是 1932 年 8 月 15 日玻尔在于哥本哈根召开的国际光疗大会开幕式上发表的讲话。本文与丹麦版(《自然世界》，第 17 卷，第 49 页）是一致的，但与公开出版的会议报告不完全一样，区别在于把一些口语化的文字改成了比较正式的形式。

Notwithstanding the subtle character of the riddles of life, this problem has presented itself at every stage of science, since any scientific explanation necessarily must consist in reducing the description of more complex phenomena to that of simpler ones. At the moment, however, the unsuspected discovery of an essential limitation of the mechanical description of natural phenomena, revealed by the recent development of the atomic theory, has lent new interest to the old problem. This limitation was, in fact, first recognised through a thorough study of the interaction between light and material bodies, which disclosed features that cannot be brought into conformity with the demands hitherto made to a physical explanation. As I shall endeavour to show, the efforts of physicists to master this situation resemble in some way the attitude which biologists more or less intuitively have taken towards the aspects of life. Still, I wish to stress at once that it is only in this formal respect that light, which is perhaps the least complex of all physical phenomena, exhibits an analogy to life, the diversity of which is far beyond the grasp of scientific analysis.

From a physical point of view, light may be defined as the transmission of energy between material bodies at a distance. As is well known, such an energy transfer finds a simple explanation in the electromagnetic theory, which may be regarded as a direct extension of classical mechanics compromising between action at a distance and contact forces. According to this theory, light is described as coupled electric and magnetic oscillations which differ from the ordinary electromagnetic waves used in radio transmission only by their greater frequency of vibration and smaller wave-length. In fact, the practically rectilinear propagation of light, on which rests our location of bodies by direct vision or by suitable optical instruments, depends entirely on the smallness of the wave-length compared with the dimensions of the bodies concerned, and of the instruments.

The idea of the wave nature of light, however, not only forms the basis for our explanation of the colour phenomena, which in spectroscopy have yielded such important information of the inner constitution of matter, but is also of essential importance for every detailed analysis of optical phenomena. As a typical example, I need only mention the interference patterns which appear when light from one source can travel to a screen along two different paths. In such a case, we find that the effects which would be produced by the separate light beams are strengthened at those points on the screen where the phases of the two wave trains coincide, that is, where the electric and magnetic oscillations in the two beams have the same directions, while the effects are weakened and may even disappear at points where these oscillations have opposite directions, and where the two wave trains are said to be out of phase with one another. These interference patterns have made possible such a thorough test of the wave nature of the propagation of light, that this conception can no longer be considered as a hypothesis in the usual sense of this word, but may rather be regarded as an indispensable element in the description of the phenomena observed.

As is well known, the problem of the nature of light has, nevertheless, been subjected to renewed discussion in recent years, as a result of the discovery of a peculiar atomistic

尽管生物体中的秘密难以捉摸，但这个问题在科学发展的每一个阶段都会被提出来，因为科学上的探索就是要把对复杂现象的描述还原为简单的原理。然而现在，原子理论的最新进展表明，人们对自然现象的力学描述在本质上存在着不可抹杀的局限性，这一意想不到的发现重新燃起了大家对这个古老问题的兴趣。事实上，人们最先是在对光与物体之间相互作用的全面研究中认识到这一局限性的，该现象所揭示的特性无法与迄今为止已形成的物理学理论相统一。正如我将努力向大家说明的那样，物理学家们为解决这一问题所做出的努力，在某种程度上类似于生物学家对待生命现象时多多少少有点依据直觉的方式。但我马上要说明的是，光这种在物理学中可能是最不具有复杂性的现象，只是在这一点上与多样性远远超出科学分析范畴的生命现象相似。

从物理学的观点看，光可以被定义为相隔一定距离的物体之间的能量传播。大家都知道，利用电磁学理论就可以简单地解释这样的能量传递，这也许可以被看作是对包括超距作用和接触力在内的经典力学的直接拓展。根据这一理论，光可以被描述为耦合的电磁振荡，它们与无线电广播中使用的普通电磁波一样，只不过具有较高的频率和较短的波长。事实上，我们之所以可以通过直接观察或适当的光学仪器来判断物体的位置是因为光具有直线传播的特性，而这种特性完全依赖于光的波长比相关物体和观测工具的尺度要小很多。

然而，光具有波动性的思想不仅能为我们提供解释颜色现象的依据，在光谱学中颜色能提供有关物质内部结构的重要信息，而且它对于每一种光学现象的详细分析也是必不可少的。至于代表性的例子，我只需提及干涉条纹就可以了，当从一个光源发出的光沿着两条不同的路径投射到一个屏幕上时，就会出现干涉条纹。在这种情况下，我们发现在屏幕上两列波位相一致时，也就是说两束光的电磁振动方向相同时，分开的两个光束将在这些点上产生增强，而在电磁振荡方向相反也就是说两列波彼此异相时，光强将减弱甚至有可能消失。这些干涉条纹使人们能够精确地检测光传播的波动性，因而波动概念不再是一种通常意义上的假设，而有可能被认为是描述所观察到的现象中不可或缺的要素。

尽管如此，大家都知道，近几年人们又开始讨论光的本质这个问题了，这是因为人们发现在能量传输中有一个特殊的原子性质，这个特殊性质无法用电磁理论来

feature in the energy transmission which is quite unintelligible from the point of view of the electromagnetic theory. It has turned out, in fact, that all effects of light may be traced down to individual processes, in each of which a so-called light quantum is exchanged, the energy of which is equal to the product of the frequency of the electromagnetic oscillations and the universal quantum of action, or Planck's constant. The striking contrast between this atomicity of the light phenomena and the continuity of the energy transfer according to the electromagnetic theory places us before a dilemma of a character hitherto unknown in physics. For, in spite of the obvious insufficiency of the wave picture, there can be no question of replacing it by any other picture of light propagation depending on ordinary mechanical ideas.

Especially, it should be emphasised that the introduction of the concept of light quanta in no way means a return to the old idea of material particles with well-defined paths as the carriers of the light energy. In fact, it is characteristic of all the phenomena of light, in the description of which the wave picture plays an essential rôle, that any attempt to trace the paths of the individual light quanta would disturb the very phenomenon under investigation; just as an interference pattern would completely disappear, if, in order to make sure that the light energy travelled only along one of the two paths between the source and the screen, we should introduce a non-transparent body into one of the paths. The spatial continuity of light propagation, on one hand, and the atomicity of the light effects, on the other hand, must, therefore, be considered as complementary aspects of one reality, in the sense that each expresses an important feature of the phenomena of light, which, although irreconcilable from a mechanical point of view, can never be in direct contradiction, since a closer analysis of one or the other feature in mechanical terms would demand mutually exclusive experimental arrangements.

At the same time, this very situation forces us to renounce a complete causal description of the phenomena of light and to be content with probability calculations, based on the fact that the electromagnetic description of energy transfer by light remains valid in a statistical sense. Such calculations form a typical application of the so-called correspondence argument, which expresses our endeavour, by means of a suitably limited use of mechanical and electromagnetic concepts, to obtain a statistical description of the atomic phenomena that appears as a rational generalisation of the classical physical theories, in spite of the fact that the quantum of action from their point of view must be considered as an irrationality.

At first sight, this situation might appear very deplorable; but, as has often happened in the history of science, when new discoveries have revealed an essential limitation of ideas the universal applicability of which had never been disputed, we have been rewarded by getting a wider view and a greater power of correlating phenomena which before might even have appeared as contradictory. Thus, the strange limitation of classical mechanics, symbolised by the quantum of action, has given us a clue to an understanding of the peculiar stability of atoms which forms a basic assumption in the mechanical description of any natural phenomenon. The recognition that the indivisibility of atoms cannot be

解释。事实上，所有的光效应都可以被看作是一个单独的过程，在每一个这样的过程中，发生了所谓的一个光量子交换，光量子的能量等于电磁振荡频率与基本作用量子（或称普朗克常数）的乘积。这个光的原子性与电磁理论所要求的能量传输连续性之间的明显对立使我们陷入了一个有关迄今为止在物理学中仍不清楚的性质的困境。因为尽管波动理论还明显不够完善，但是毫无疑问，我们仍可以用在经典力学思想框架下的任何其他的光传播理论来取代它。

应该特别强调的是，引入光量子这个概念决不意味着对旧思想的回归，即认为光能的载体是有明确路径的实物粒子。实际上，任何尝试追踪单个光量子路径的行为都会干扰被研究的对象，这是所有光学现象共有的特征，波动性在描述光学现象时是不可缺少的；正如如果在光源和屏幕之间有两条路径，我们为了确保光只沿着其中的一条路径传播，就应该在另一条路径上引入不透光的物质，这样干涉条纹就会完全消失。因此，一方面是光传播的空间连续性，另一方面是光效应的原子性，它们应该被看作是一件事情相互补充的两个方面，从这个意义上说，每一个方面都代表了光现象的一个重要特征，尽管从力学角度上看它们是不可调和的，但也绝对不是完全对立的，因为要用力学方法进一步分析其中一个特征或另一个特征就需要排斥对方的实验装置。

然而，这种情况使我们不得不放弃对光现象的完整因果描述而安于概率计算，原因是用电磁理论描述光的能量传输在统计学意义上仍然有效。这种计算是所谓一致论的典型应用，它显示出我们在努力通过对力学和电磁学概念的有限运用获得对原子现象的统计学描述，这似乎是经典物理理论的一个理性概括，虽然经典物理学认为必须把作用量子看成是非理性的。

这种情形也许初看起来非常令人遗憾；但正如科学史上经常发生的，当我们从新发现中察觉到一个普遍适用性从未被人置疑过的思想存在本质上的局限时，我们就已经从相关现象中得到了更广的视野和更强的能力，而这种现象或许在以前就曾作为对立的情况出现过。因此，作用量子象征着经典力学出现了前所未有的局限性，这种局限性给我们提供了理解原子具有特殊稳定性的线索，而原子所具有特殊稳定性是用经典力学理论描述所有自然现象的基本假设。经典力学理论无法理解原子是

understood in mechanical terms has always characterised the atomic theory, to be sure; and this fact is not essentially altered, although the development of physics has replaced the indivisible atoms by the elementary electric particles, electrons and atomic nuclei, of which the atoms of the elements as well as the molecules of the chemical compounds are now supposed to consist.

However, it is not to the question of the intrinsic stability of these elementary particles that I am here referring, but to the problem of the required stability of the structures composed of them. As a matter of fact, the very possibility of a continuous transfer of energy, which marks both the classical mechanics and the electromagnetic theory, cannot be reconciled with an explanation of the characteristic properties of the elements and the compounds. Indeed, the classical theories do not even allow us to explain the existence of rigid bodies, on which all measurements made for the purpose of ordering phenomena in space and time ultimately rest. However, in connexion with the discovery of the quantum of action, we have learned that every change in the energy of an atom or a molecule must be considered as an individual process, in which the atom goes over from one of its so-called stationary states to another. Moreover, since just one light quantum appears or disappears in a transition process by which light is emitted or absorbed by an atom, we are able by means of spectroscopic observations to measure directly the energy of each of these stationary states. The information thus derived has been most instructively corroborated also by the study of the energy exchanges which take place in atomic collisions and in chemical reactions.

In recent years, a remarkable development of the atomic theory has taken place, which has given us such adequate methods of computing the energy values for the stationary states, and also the probabilities of the transition processes, that our account, on the lines of the correspondence argument, of the properties of atoms as regards completeness and self-consistency scarcely falls short of the explanation of astronomical observations offered by Newtonian mechanics. Although the rational treatment of the problems of atomic mechanics was possible only after the introduction of new symbolic artifices, the lesson taught us by the analysis of the phenomena of light is still of decisive importance for our estimation of this development. Thus, an unambiguous use of the concept of a stationary state is complementary to a mechanical analysis of intra-atomic motions; in a similar way the idea of light quanta is complementary to the electromagnetic theory of radiation. Indeed, any attempt to trace the detailed course of the transition process would involve an uncontrollable exchange of energy between the atom and the measuring instruments, which would completely disturb the very energy transfer we set out to investigate.

A causal description in the classical sense is possible only in such cases where the action involved is large compared with the quantum of action, and where, therefore, a subdivision of the phenomena is possible without disturbing them essentially. If this condition is not fulfilled, we cannot disregard the interaction between the measuring instruments and the object under investigation, and we must especially take into consideration that the various measurements required for a complete mechanical description may only be made

不可分割的，而毫无疑问通常突显了原子理论的特性；这一点至今没有本质上的更改，尽管后来的物理学已经用基本带电粒子替代了不可分割的原子，而且现在认为各种元素的原子以及化合物中的分子都是由电子和原子核这些基本粒子构成的。

然而，我在这里并不想谈及这些基本粒子的固有稳定性问题，而是要探究构成这些结构所必需的稳定性。事实上，以能量存在持续传递可能性为特征的经典力学和电磁理论是不能与对元素和化合物性质的解释达成一致的。的确，我们甚至不能用经典理论来解释刚体的存在，而为了测量空间和时间中的有序现象必须有赖于刚体。但是，由于作用量子的发现，我们了解到原子或分子能量的每一次改变都必须被看作是一个单独的过程，在这样的过程中原子从它的一个定态跃迁到了另一个定态。此外，因为在一个原子发射光或吸收光的跃迁过程中只会有一个光量子产生或消失，所以我们能够通过光谱观测直接测量每一个定态的能量。人们通过对原子碰撞和化学反应中能量交换的研究已经非常有效地确证了由上述方法得到的数据。

近些年来，原子理论取得了长足的进步，它足以为我们提供计算定态能值和跃迁几率的方法，因而我们根据一致论得到的有关原子性质的结论在完整性和自洽性方面几乎与用牛顿力学解释天文观测结果的水平不相上下。虽然只有在引入新的符号处理技巧之后才有可能合理地解决原子力学的困境，但在分析光学现象时的经验对于我们评估原子力学的发展仍然有非常重要的意义。因此，确立定态概念是对用力学法分析原子内部运动的补充；同样，引入光量子概念是对电磁辐射理论的补充。任何追踪跃迁详细过程的尝试都会使原子和测量仪器之间发生不可控的能量交换，会彻底干扰我们要研究的能量转移过程。

经典意义中的因果描述只有在相互作用远大于作用量子时才可能成立，因此，在基本不干扰它们的情况下是有可能对这些现象进行细分的。而在不满足上述条件的情况下，我们就不能忽略测量仪器与被研究物体之间的相互作用，为了得到完整的力学描述，我们需要考虑使用不同的测量方法，而这些测量只有通过相互排斥的实验装置才能得到。为了充分了解用力学分析原子现象的基本局限性，我们必须清

with mutually exclusive experimental arrangements. In order fully to understand this fundamental limitation of the mechanical analysis of atomic phenomena, one must realise clearly, further, that in a physical measurement it is never possible to take the interaction between object and measuring instruments directly into account. For the instruments cannot be included in the investigation while they are serving as means of observation. As the concept of general relativity expresses the essential dependence of physical phenomena on the frame of reference used for their co-ordination in space and time, so does the notion of complementarity serve to symbolise the fundamental limitation, met with in atomic physics, of our ingrained idea of phenomena as existing independently of the means by which they are observed.

(**131**, 421-423; 1933)

## Part II

This revision of the foundations of mechanics, extending to the very question of what may be meant by a physical explanation, has not only been essential, however, for the elucidation of the situation in atomic theory, but has also created a new background for the discussion of the relation of physics to the problems of biology. This must certainly not be taken to mean that in actual atomic phenomena we meet with features which show a closer resemblance to the properties of living organisms than do ordinary physical effects. At first sight, the essentially statistical character of atomic mechanics might even seem difficult to reconcile with an explanation of the marvellously refined organisation, which every living being possesses, and which permits it to implant all the characteristics of its species into a minute germ cell.

We must not forget, however, that the regularities peculiar to atomic processes, which are foreign to causal mechanics and find their place only within the complementary mode of description, are at least as important for the account of the behaviour of living organisms as for the explanation of the specific properties of inorganic matter. Thus, in the carbon assimilation of plants, on which depends largely also the nourishment of animals, we are dealing with a phenomenon for the understanding of which the individuality of photochemical processes must undoubtedly be taken into consideration. Likewise, the peculiar stability of atomic structures is clearly exhibited in the characteristic properties of such highly complicated chemical compounds as chlorophyll or haemoglobin, which play fundamental rôles in plant assimilation and animal respiration.

However, analogies from chemical experience will not, of course, any more than the ancient comparison of life with fire, give a better explanation of living organisms than will the resemblance, often mentioned, between living organisms and such purely mechanical contrivances as clockworks. An understanding of the essential characteristics of living beings must be sought, no doubt, in their peculiar organisation, in which features that may be analysed by the usual mechanics are interwoven with typically atomistic traits in a

楚地、深刻地认识到，在物理测量中，绝不可能直接将物体和测量仪器的相互作用考虑在内。因为当仪器被用作观察手段的时候，就不能把它们包括在研究对象之中。正如广义相对论所表述的观点，物理学现象在本质上依赖于用于描述它们在空间和时间中坐标的参考系，因而原子物理学中的互补概念就用来表示基本的局限性，即我们根深蒂固的理念是现象不依赖于观测手段而独立存在。

（姜薇 翻译；张泽渤 审稿）

## 第二部分

人们对力学基本理论的修正引申出这样一个问题，即一个物理学解释可能会意味着什么，然而这不仅仅是解释原子理论中的现象所必需的，也为讨论物理学与生物学之间的相关性奠定了一个新的基础。当然，这绝不意味着我们在原子现象中发现的特征与普通的物理学效应相比更接近于生物体的性质。初看起来，原子力学所具有的基本统计学特点似乎难以与人们对所有生物体都具有的超精细组织的解释相匹配，这种超精细组织可以把本物种的所有特征植入一个微小的生殖细胞中。

然而，我们绝不能忘记：原子过程所特有的规律性不能用因果机制表示，只能借助互补模式描述，这种规律性至少在对生物体行为的描述和对无机物特性的解释上具有同等的重要性。因此，在植物的碳同化、同时也是动物养分的主要来源的生成过程中，我们正在研究的是一个现象，为了理解这个现象，必须确确实实地去考虑参与光化学反应的个体特性。另外，像在植物同化与动物呼吸作用中扮演重要角色的叶绿素和血红蛋白，它们所具有的复杂程度如此高的化合物的特性，也明显地表现出原子结构独特的稳定性。

然而，由化学知识类推解释生命体，诚然会比在古代将生命比作火更贴切，却不会强于人们常说的生命体与纯机械制造物如钟表发条之间的类比。毫无疑问，必须在特定的生物组织中探寻对生命本质特征的理解，在研究这些组织的特征时，将用普通力学进行分析并且以与无机物不同的方式交织着一些典型的原子特性。

manner having no counterpart in inorganic matter.

An instructive illustration of the refinement to which this organisation is developed has been obtained through the study of the construction and function of the eye, for which the simplicity of the phenomena of light has again been most helpful. I need not go into details here, but shall just recall how ophthalmology has revealed to us the ideal properties of the human eye as an optical instrument. Indeed, the dimensions of the interference patterns, which on account of the wave nature of light set the limit for the image formation in the eye, practically coincide with the size of such partitions of the retina which have separate nervous connexion with the brain. Moreover, since the absorption of a few light quanta, or perhaps of only a single quantum, on such a retinal partition is sufficient to produce a sight impression, the sensitiveness of the eye may even be said to have reached the limit imposed by the atomic character of the light effects. In both respects, the efficiency of the eye is the same as that of a good telescope or microscope, connected with a suitable amplifier so as to make the individual processes observable. It is true that it is possible by such instruments essentially to increase our powers of observation, but, owing to the very limits imposed by the properties of light, no instrument is imaginable which is more efficient for its purpose than the eye. Now, this ideal refinement of the eye, fully recognised only through the recent development of physics, suggests that other organs also, whether they serve for the reception of information from the surroundings or for the reaction to sense impressions, will exhibit a similar adaptation to their purpose, and that also in these cases the feature of individuality symbolised by the quantum of action, together with some amplifying mechanism, is of decisive importance. That it has not yet been possible to trace the limit in organs other than the eye, depends solely upon the simplicity of light as compared with other physical phenomena.

The recognition of the essential importance of fundamentally atomistic features in the functions of living organisms is by no means sufficient, however, for a comprehensive explanation of biological phenomena. The question at issue, therefore, is whether some fundamental traits are still missing in the analysis of natural phenomena, before we can reach an understanding of life on the basis of physical experience. Quite apart from the practically inexhaustible abundance of biological phenomena, an answer to this question can scarcely be given without an examination of what we may understand by a physical explanation, still more penetrating than that to which the discovery of the quantum of action has already forced us. On one hand, the wonderful features which are constantly revealed in physiological investigations and differ so strikingly from what is known of inorganic matter, have led many biologists to doubt that a real understanding of the nature of life is possible on a purely physical basis. On the other hand, this view, often known as vitalism, scarcely finds its proper expression in the old supposition that a peculiar vital force, quite unknown to physics, governs all organic life. I think we all agree with Newton that the real basis of science is the conviction that Nature under the same conditions will always exhibit the same regularities. Therefore, if we were able to push the analysis of the mechanism of living organisms as far as that of atomic phenomena, we should scarcely expect to find any features differing from the properties of inorganic matter.

通过研究眼睛的构造与功能，我们得到了有关这个已经发展得十分精细的组织的有用信息，也再一次地显示光现象的简单特性是非常有用的。我无需在这里详述细节，但想回顾一下眼科学是如何向我们揭示作为一种光学装置的人眼的理想特征的。实际上，由于光的波动性，干涉图像的尺寸规定了眼成像的限度，而干涉图像的尺寸与视网膜的分区相符，其中每个分区都有单独的神经与脑相连。此外，因为在这样的视网膜分区中，只要吸收几个光量子，或者也许只要吸收一个光量子就足以产生视感，有人甚至说眼睛的敏感程度已经达到了光效应的原子特性所设置的极限。在两个方面，眼睛的效能同那些连有合适放大器的高性能望远镜或显微镜一样，可以观测到单个过程。利用这样的仪器确实能从根本上提高我们的观察能力，但由于光的性质所设置的极限，在人们可以想象得出的仪器中，没有一种可以与眼睛的灵敏度相比。现在，眼睛这种只有借助物理学的最新发展才能被深刻认识的理想化结构也说明了其他的器官，不管它们的作用是接收来自周围环境的信息，还是对感觉印象做出反应，都同样会表现出与自身功能相适应的特点，在这类情况下，由作用量子所代表的个性特征以及一些放大机制起着关键性的作用。目前，我们尚无法知道除眼睛外其他器官的极限，而眼睛只取决于比其他物理现象简单得多的光现象。

然而，仅仅认识到运用原子论基本原理来说明生物体功能的必要性还不足以全面解释生物学现象。因此，我们要讨论的问题是，在我们能够用物理学观点解释生命现象之前，是否还缺少一些分析自然现象所需的基本特征。如果不去考证我们通过物理学解释而理解的内容，就很难得到这个问题的答案，更何况现实中生物现象的类别多得无法列举，这要比发现作用量子对我们的推动意义更深远。一方面，通过生理学研究不断揭示出的神奇特征与无机物的特征有着显著的差别，这使许多生物学者怀疑用纯物理学的方法是否可以真正理解生命的本质。另一方面，人们通常称为活力论的观点，不能正确地解释有一种特殊的生命力掌控着所有有机体的古老假设，在物理学中也不存在这样的力。我认为我们都赞同牛顿的观点，即科学的真正基础在于确信自然界在相同条件下会表现出同样的规律性。因此，如果我们能够把对生命体机理的分析推进到原子现象的层面，我们就不应该期待会发现任何有别于无机物的特点。

With this dilemma before us, we must keep in mind, however, that the conditions holding for biological and physical researches are not directly comparable, since the necessity of keeping the object of investigation alive imposes a restriction on the former, which finds no counterpart in the latter. Thus, we should doubtless kill an animal if we tried to carry the investigation of its organs so far that we could describe the rôle played by single atoms in vital functions. In every experiment on living organisms, there must remain an uncertainty as regards the physical conditions to which they are subjected, and the idea suggests itself that the minimal freedom we must allow the organism in this respect is just large enough to permit it, so to say, to hide its ultimate secrets from us. On this view, the existence of life must be considered as an elementary fact that cannot be explained, but must be taken as a starting point in biology, in a similar way as the quantum of action, which appears as an irrational element from the point of view of classical mechanical physics, taken together with the existence of the elementary particles, forms the foundation of atomic physics. The asserted impossibility of a physical or chemical explanation of the function peculiar to life would in this sense be analogous to the insufficiency of the mechanical analysis for the understanding of the stability of atoms.

In tracing this analogy further, however, we must not forget that the problems present essentially different aspects in physics and in biology. While in atomic physics we are primarily interested in the properties of matter in its simplest forms, the complexity of the material systems with which we are concerned in biology is of fundamental significance, since even the most primitive organisms contain a large number of atoms. It is true that the wide field of application of classical mechanics, including our account of the measuring instruments used in atomic physics, depends on the possibility of disregarding largely the complementarity, entailed by the quantum of action, in the description of bodies containing very many atoms. It is typical of biological researches, however, that the external conditions to which any separate atom is subjected can never be controlled in the same manner as in the fundamental experiments of atomic physics. In fact, we cannot even tell which atoms really belong to a living organism, since any vital function is accompanied by an exchange of material, whereby atoms are constantly taken up into and expelled from the organisation which constitutes the living being.

This fundamental difference between physical and biological investigations implies that no well-defined limit can be drawn for the applicability of physical ideas to the phenomena of life, which would correspond to the distinction between the field of causal mechanical description and the proper quantum phenomena in atomic mechanics. However, the limitation which this fact would seem to impose upon the analogy considered will depend essentially upon how we choose to use such words as physics and mechanics. On one hand, the question of the limitation of physics within biology would, of course, lose any meaning, if, in accordance with the original meaning of the word physics, we should understand by it any description of natural phenomena. On the other hand, such a term as atomic mechanics would be misleading, if, as in common language, we should apply the word mechanics only to denote an unambiguous causal description of the phenomena.

然而，当我们面临进退两难的困境时，我们必须记住，生物学和物理学的研究条件并不完全对应，因为前者要受到研究对象必须是活体的限制，而在后者中则不存在这样的限制。因此，如果我们试图对动物的器官展开研究以便描述单个原子在生命活动中的功能时，我们无疑会杀死一只动物。在对活体进行的每一次实验中，都肯定会存在因个体生理条件不同而导致的不确定性，这个观点本身说明，在这方面，即使我们允许生物体具有最低的自由度，也足以让生命体可以对我们隐藏其最根本的秘密。根据这个观点，我们应该把生命的存在看作是不能被解释的基本事实，而以此作为生物学研究的起点，这与作用量子类似，在经典机械物理学中，作用量子被看作是一种非理性的成分，而它与基本粒子一起构成了原子物理学的基础。从这个意义上说，宣称用物理或化学方法不可能解释生命体的功能就类似于用经典力学不能理解原子的稳定性。

然而，在进一步研究这个类比时，我们一定不要忘记物理学中的问题和生物学中的问题存在着本质上的不同。在原子物理学中，我们是从形式最简单的物质的性质入手的，而在生物学研究中具有根本性意义的是物质系统的复杂性，因为即便是最原始的生物也包含大量的原子。的确，经典力学的应用范围广泛，其中包括我们在研究原子物理时使用的测量仪器，要想在描述由大量原子组成的物体中应用经典力学就必须在很大程度上忽略伴随着作用量子的互补性。然而，在生物学研究中，人们通常不能像在原子物理学基础实验中那样控制单个原子所处的外部条件。实际上，我们甚至不知道哪些原子是真正属于生物体的，因为任何生命活动都伴随着物质的交换，原子不断地被构成这个生物体的组织吸入和排出。

物理学研究和生物学研究之间的这种本质不同暗示着人们无法明确地划分出在运用物理学原理解释生命现象时的界限，这也相当于因果力学描述的场和原子力学中固有量子现象之间的区别。然而，上述事实对这个类比的限制似乎从根本上取决于我们如何运用像物理学和力学这样的词。一方面，如果依照物理学这个词的原始意义，我们就应当把它理解为是对所有自然现象的描述，那么认为物理学在生物学中的运用受到限制就失去了意义。另一方面，如果在通用语言中我们用力学这个词只表示对现象的清晰的因果关系的描述，那么像原子力学这样的术语就会引起人们的误解。

I shall not here enter further into these purely logical points, but will only add that the essence of the analogy considered is the typical relation of complementarity existing between the subdivision required by a physical analysis and such characteristic biological phenomena as the self-preservation and the propagation of individuals. It is due to this situation, in fact, that the concept of purpose, which is foreign to mechanical analysis, finds a certain field of application in problems where regard must be taken of the nature of life. In this respect, the rôle which teleological arguments play in biology reminds one of the endeavours, formulated in the correspondence argument, to take the quantum of action into account in a rational manner in atomic physics.

In our discussion of the applicability of mechanical concepts in describing living organisms, we have considered these just as other material objects. I need scarcely emphasise, however, that this attitude, which is characteristic of physiological research, involves no disregard whatsoever of the psychological aspects of life. The recognition of the limitation of mechanical ideas in atomic physics would much rather seem suited to conciliate the apparently contrasting points of view which mark physiology and psychology. Indeed, the necessity of considering the interaction between the measuring instruments and the object under investigation in atomic mechanics corresponds closely to the peculiar difficulties, met with in psychological analyses, which arise from the fact that the mental content is invariably altered when the attention is concentrated on any single feature of it.

It will carry us too far from our subject to enlarge upon this analogy which, when due regard is taken to the special character of biological problems, offers a new starting point for an elucidation of the so-called psycho-physical parallelism. However, in this connexion, I should like to emphasise that the considerations referred to here differ entirely from all attempts at viewing new possibilities for a direct spiritual influence on material phenomena in the limitation set for the causal mode of description in the analysis of atomic phenomena. For example, when it has been suggested that the will might have as its field of activity the regulation of certain atomic processes within the organism, for which on the atomic theory only probability calculations may be set up, we are dealing with a view that is incompatible with the interpretation of the psycho-physical parallelism here indicated. Indeed, from our point of view, the feeling of the freedom of the will must be considered as a trait peculiar to conscious life, the material parallel of which must be sought in organic functions, which permit neither a causal mechanical description nor a physical investigation sufficiently thorough-going for a well-defined application of the statistical laws of atomic mechanics. Without entering into metaphysical speculations, I may perhaps add that any analysis of the very concept of an explanation would, naturally, begin and end with a renunciation as to explaining our own conscious activity.

In conclusion, I wish to emphasise that in none of my remarks have I intended to express any kind of scepticism as to the future development of physical and biological sciences. Such scepticism would, indeed, be far from the mind of a physicist at a time when the very recognition of the limited character of our most fundamental concepts has resulted

我不打算在这里进一步讨论这些纯逻辑学上的观点，但只想补充一点，即典型的互补性关系构成了这个类比的本质，这种关系存在于物理分析所需的细分与诸如自卫本能和个体繁殖这样的典型生命现象之间。事实上，正是由于这个原因，在力学分析中不曾有过的目的性概念，在必须考虑生命本质的领域中得到了应用。从这个方面来说，目的论在生物学中所扮演的角色使人回想起人们曾努力用对应的自变量将作用量子以一种理性模式引进到原子物理中。

在我们讨论用力学概念描述生物体时，我们对待它们和对待其他实物没有什么两样。然而，我无需强调这种生理学研究中特有的态度并没有任何对生命的心理问题的漠视。人们对力学概念在原子物理中所受限制的认识似乎更适合于理解生理学与心理学在观点上的明显对立。的确，在原子物理学中需要考虑测量仪器与研究对象之间的相互作用十分类似于在心理学分析中遇到的特定困难，该困难起源于当注意力集中在任何一个单一的功能上时，心理内容总在不断变化。

当适当考虑生物学的特性时，这个类比为阐明所谓的身心并行说提供了一个新的起点，这样说将使我们过于偏离我们要讨论的题目。然而，关于这一点，我想强调的是，这里谈到的观点完全不同于想借助在分析原子现象时因果描述受到的局限而极力推崇物质现象很可能会直接受到精神影响的看法。例如，当人们认为也许可以利用特定原子过程的规律来研究在有机体中的意志及其作用域时，原子理论只能为其建立概率的计算，我们正在谈论的这个观点与刚才提到的身心并行说水火不相容。确实，依据我们的观点，意志对自由的感受必须被看成是意识生活所特有的性质，人们必须在器官的功能中寻找与其对应的物质，既不允许力学因果描述也不能允许充分彻底地运用原子力学中的统计规律来进行物理学研究。除了形而上学的思索以外，我也许可以补充说，所有对一个解释的概念的分析都以放弃对我们自身意识行为的解释开始，也以放弃对意识行为的解释而结束。

最后，我想强调的是，我并不希望大家把我的话理解为是对未来物理学和生物学发展的怀疑。实际上，现在这个时代的物理学家绝不会抱有怀疑论的思想，因为科学已经在人们认识到最基本的概念存在局限性的基础上发生了深刻的变革。近期

in such far-reaching developments of our science. Neither has the necessary renunciation as regards an explanation of life itself been a hindrance to the wonderful advances which have been made in recent times in all branches of biology and have, not least, proved so beneficial in the art of medicine. Even if we cannot make a sharp distinction on a physical basis between health and disease, there is, in particular, no room for scepticism as regards the solution of the important problems which occupy this Congress, as long as one does not leave the highroad of progress, that has been followed with so great success ever since the pioneer work of Finsen, and which has as its distinguishing mark the most intimate combination of the study of the medical effects of light treatment with the investigation of its physical aspects.

(**131**, 457-459; 1933)

人们在生物学所有分支取得的惊人进展并没有受到放弃对生命问题本身的解释的影响，而且这些进展也相当有益于医术的发展。即使我们不能从物理学角度明确地区分健康与疾病，我们也没有理由怀疑在本次会议上所达成的对重要问题的解释，由于我们没有偏离科学发展的道路，因此从芬森的早期工作到现在已经取得了很大的进展，而此项工作明显的标志是光疗医学效应的研究和物理学研究的最紧密的结合。

（吴彦 翻译；张泽渤 审稿）

# Nuclear Energy Levels

G. Gamow

## Editor's Note

**Although physicists still lacked any clear understanding of nuclear structure—the possibility that electrons inhabited the nucleus was still widely considered, for example—quantum theory was proving useful for interpreting nuclear spectroscopy. As George Gamow here points out, one could gainfully consider nuclear constituents to be bound by unknown forces inside a square-profiled well with infinitely high sides: a model tractable to quantum theory, which could predict the energies of states of different angular momentum. Gamow shows that spectroscopic data from an isotope called radium C' revealed transitions close to 11 of the 21 predicted by the theory. Further studies might indicate how the square-well model should be altered to make the theory more accurate.**

IT is a plausible hypothesis that the forces acting on a particle inside the nucleus are comparatively weak in the internal region and increase rapidly to the boundary of the nucleus, the potential distribution being represented by a hole with more or less flat bottom and rather steep walls[1]. If we approximate this model by a rectangular hole with infinitely high walls, the energy levels of a moving particle will be determined by the roots of Bessel functions and can be easily calculated. For the real model, however, this theoretical level system will be deformed owing to the fact that the walls are neither quite steep nor infinitely high, producing compression of the upper part of the level system.

The best nucleus for testing this hypothesis is that of radium C', for which a lot of experimental evidence is available. For this nucleus we have the measurements by Rutherford[2] of long range $\alpha$-particles (nine groups) giving us approximate positions of nuclear levels. The investigations of Ellis[3] give for a number of $\gamma$-lines (nine lines) their absolute intensities and, what is most important, the values of internal conversion coefficients enabling us, as has been shown by Taylor and Mott[4], to tell the dipole transitions from quadrupole transitions.

These data are sufficient to construct the level system of the radium C' nucleus, the main part of which is represented in Fig. 1, together with the theoretical one.

# 核能级

乔治·伽莫夫

## 编者按

虽然物理学家们对核结构还缺乏明确的认识，比如很多人仍然认为电子可能存在于原子核当中，但实践证明量子理论是可以用于解释核谱的。正如乔治·伽莫夫在文中所述：可以假设原子核中的各个成分被未知的力束缚在一口无限深的方井中，这样的假设是有益的：量子理论可以通过对这个模型的计算得到不同角动量状态的能量。伽莫夫指出：在该理论预测的 21 个跃迁中有 11 个接近于从镭 C' 同位素光谱中得到的数据。接下来的研究方向可能是：对方井模型进行怎样的调整才能使该理论更为精确。

我们似乎可以合理地假设作用于核内粒子上的力在核的内部区域相当弱，随着接近核的边界而迅速增大，势能的分布可以用一个近似平底深壁的孔来表示 [1]。如果我们在模型中使用的是一个壁高为无限大的矩形孔，就可以由贝塞尔函数的根得到运动粒子的能级，计算方法非常简单。然而对于实际上的模型，由于壁并不是很陡，也不是无限高，因此理论能级系统会发生变化，能级系统的上部会被压缩。

镭 C' 的核最适于验证这个假说，因为我们有很多关于这种核的实验证据。卢瑟福通过对长程 $\alpha$ 粒子（9 组）的测量为我们提供了镭 C' 核能级的近似位置 [2]。埃利斯 [3] 的研究给出了许多 $\gamma$ 谱线（9 条谱线）的绝对强度以及内转换系数的值，后者为我们提供了非常重要的信息，正如泰勒和莫特曾经说过的那样 [4]，内转换系数值是我们分辨四极跃迁和偶极跃迁的依据。

我们用这些数据足以构建镭 C' 核的能级系统，能级的主体部分示于图 1，图中还标出了理论值。

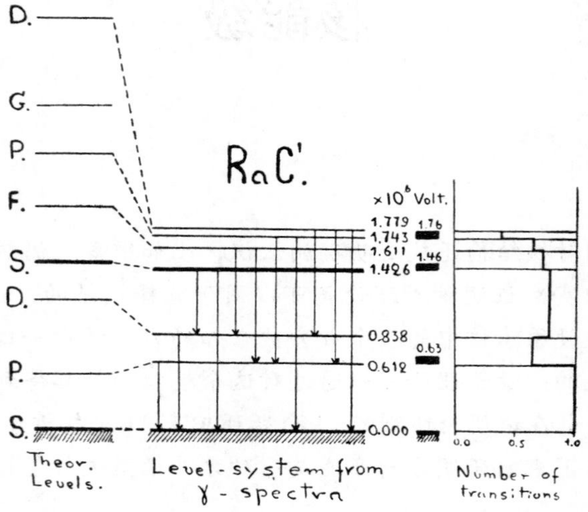


Fig. 1

We see immediately that not every level corresponds to a long range $\alpha$-group; this is, however, to be expected, as the probability of $\alpha$-disintegration from a level with large $j$ is comparatively small, due to the additional barrier of centrifugal forces (for equal energies the probability for an $\alpha$-particle escaping from *P*-, *D*-, *F*-, *G*-levels will be respectively 1.3, 4, 16 and 105 times less than for the *S*-level). The observed transitions are given in the accompanying table.

| Constructed | | Observed | | Constructed | | Observed | |
|---|---|---|---|---|---|---|---|
| $h\nu \times 10^{-6}$ volt | $\Delta j$ | $h\nu \times 10^{-6}$ volt | $\Delta j$ | $h\nu \times 10^{-6}$ volt | $\Delta j$ | $h\nu \times 10^{-6}$ volt | $\Delta j$ |
| 0.588 | 2 | 0.589 | .. | 1.131 | 0 | 1.130 | 0 ; 2 |
| 0.612 | 1 | 0.612 | 1 | 1.167 | 1 | 1.168 | .. |
| 0.773 | 1 | 0.773 | 1 | 1.426 | 0→0 | 1.426 | 0→0 |
| 0.838 | 2 | 0.839 | .. | 1.743 | 1 | 1.744 | .. |
| 0.941 | 0 | 0.941 | 0 ; 2 | 1.779 | 2 | 1.778 | 0 ; 2 |
| 0.999 | 2 | 1.000 | .. | | | | |

From twenty-one mathematically possible transitions, eleven are actually found and, as can be seen from the table, have appropriate energies and obey the exclusion principle. From the remaining ten lines, two are not to be expected corresponding to $F \rightarrow S$-transitions, four fall in a spectral region not yet investigated and four are not observed, possibly due to comparatively small intensity. It is also of interest to construct an excitation diagram, building up the sums of the intensities for all lines crossing a given level interval. From this diagram we see that there must be a $\gamma$-line $0.226 \times 10^6$ volt with absolute intensity about 0.2 which at present is not known.

The similarity of theoretical and real level systems proves the correctness of our picture of

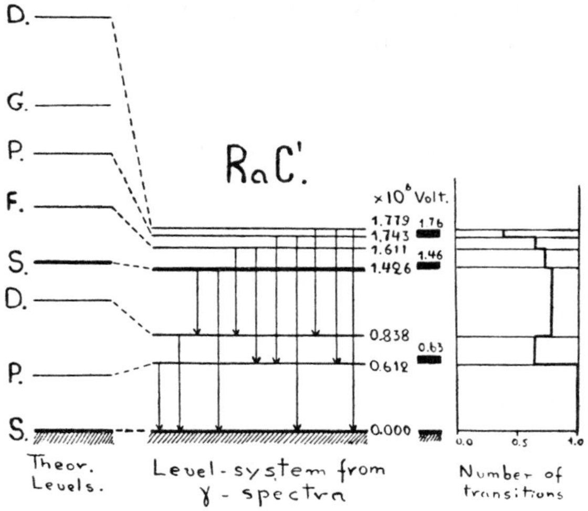


图 1

我们很快发现并不是每一个能级都对应于某个长程 $\alpha$ 粒子组；然而，这有可能是由于大 $j$ 能级的 $\alpha$ 衰变几率很小的缘故，因为离心力会产生附加势垒（如果能量相同，一个 $\alpha$ 粒子从 $S$ 能级逃逸的几率分别是从 $P$、$D$、$F$、$G$ 能级逃逸的几率的 1.3、4、16 和 105 倍）。观测到的跃迁列于下表中。

| 理论值 | | 观测值 | | 理论值 | | 观测值 | |
|---|---|---|---|---|---|---|---|
| $h\nu\times10^{-6}$ V | $\Delta j$ | $h\nu\times10^{-6}$ V | $\Delta j$ | $h\nu\times10^{-6}$ V | $\Delta j$ | $h\nu\times10^{-6}$ V | $\Delta j$ |
| 0.588 | 2 | 0.589 | .. | 1.131 | 0 | 1.130 | 0 ; 2 |
| 0.612 | 1 | 0.612 | 1 | 1.167 | 1 | 1.168 | .. |
| 0.773 | 1 | 0.773 | 1 | 1.426 | 0→0 | 1.426 | 0→0 |
| 0.838 | 2 | 0.839 | .. | 1.743 | 1 | 1.744 | .. |
| 0.941 | 0 | 0.941 | 0 ; 2 | 1.779 | 2 | 1.778 | 0 ; 2 |
| 0.999 | 2 | 1.000 | .. | | | | |

从数学的角度上看共有 21 种可能的跃迁，实际上只发现了其中的 11 种，如上表所示，能量值与理论预测相符并遵从不相容原理。至于剩下的 10 条谱线，其中 2 条 $F\rightarrow S$ 跃迁并不是预期应当有的谱线，另外 4 条处于研究范围之外的谱区，还有 4 条可能因强度太小而未被观测到。另一件有意思的事情是，我们可以通过构建跃迁图来计算穿过某个给定能级间隔的所有谱线强度之和。从这张图中我们发现了一条现在还未知的 $\gamma$ 线，这条 $0.226\times10^{6}$ V 的 $\gamma$ 线的绝对强度大约为 0.2。

理论与实际能级系统的相似性证实了我们对核内部势能的预测，而根据理论和

the potential inside the nucleus, and the deviations between these systems must permit us to calculate the real potential distribution.

(**131**, 433; 1933)

G. Gamow: Research Institute of Physics, University, Leningrad, Jan. 30.

References:

1 Gamow, *Proc. Roy. Soc.*, A, **126**, 632 (1930).

2 Rutherford, *Proc. Roy.* Soc., A, **131**, 684 (1931).

3 Ellis, *Proc. Roy. Soc.*, A, **129**, 180 (1930).

4 Taylor and Mott, *Proc. Roy. Soc.*, A, **138**, 665 (1932).

实测能级系统之间的偏差，我们一定能计算出实际的势能分布。

（沈乃澂 翻译；尚仁成 审稿）

# New Evidence for the Positive Electron

J. Chadwick *et al.*

## Editor's Note

**Here James Chadwick, along with Patrick Blackett and Giuseppe Occhialini, confirms the existence of a positively charged anti-particle of the electron, initially reported by Carl Anderson from cloud-chamber experiments. Chadwick and colleagues placed pieces of polonium and beryllium just outside a cloud chamber, and near a lead target placed just inside the chamber. Alpha particles from the polonium excited neutrons or gamma rays from beryllium that in turn stimulated the emission of particles from lead. These left tracks in the cloud chamber with the properties expected for a positively charged electron. Further experiments strongly suggested that the unknown particles had the same mass as electrons, but a positive charge. They were later called positrons, the first known example of antimatter.**

THE experiments of Anderson[1] and of Blackett and Occhialini[2] on the effects produced in an expansion chamber by the penetrating radiation strongly suggest the existence of positive electrons—particles of about the same mass as an electron but carrying a positive charge.

Some observations of the effects produced by the passage of neutrons through matter, and the experiments of Curie and Joliot[3] in which they observed retrograde electron tracks in an expansion chamber, led us to consider the possibility that positive electrons might be produced in the interaction of neutrons and matter, and we have recently obtained evidence which can be interpreted in this way.

A capsule containing a polonium source and a piece of beryllium was placed close to the wall of an expansion chamber. On the inside of the wall was fixed a target of lead about 2.5 cm. square and 2 mm. thick. This lead target was thus exposed to the action of the radiation, consisting of $\gamma$-rays and neutrons, emitted from the beryllium. Expansion photographs were taken by means of a stereoscopic pair of cameras. A magnetic field was applied during the expansion, its magnitude being usually about 800 gauss.

Most of the tracks recorded in the photographs were, from the sense of their curvature, clearly due to negative electrons, but many examples were found of tracks which had one end in or near the lead target and showed a curvature in the opposite sense. Either these were due to particles carrying a positive charge or they were due to negative electrons ejected in remote parts of the chamber and bent by the magnetic field so as to end on the lead target. Statistical examination of the results supports the view that the tracks began in the target and therefore carried a positive charge.

# 有关正电子的新证据

詹姆斯·查德威克等

## 编者按

在这篇文章中，詹姆斯·查德威克、帕特里克·布莱克特和朱塞佩·奥基亚利尼证实了一种带正电的粒子的存在，它是电子的反粒子，这种粒子是卡尔·安德森在云室实验中首先发现的。查德威克和同事把一小块钋和铍放在云室外面靠近云室内铅靶的地方。钋发射的$\alpha$粒子从铍中激发出中子或$\gamma$射线，随后又使铅发射出粒子。这些粒子在云室中留下的径迹显示出了一个带正电的电子所具有的性质。更多的实验表明这种未知粒子的质量和电子相同，但带正电。后来它们被命名为正电子，是人们发现的第一种反物质。

安德森[1]以及布莱克特与奥基亚利尼[2]利用贯穿辐射在膨胀云室中产生的效应有力地证明了正电子的存在——一种与电子质量大致相等但带有正电荷的粒子。

人们在中子穿过物质时观察到的一些现象以及居里和约里奥[3]在膨胀云室中观察到反向电子径迹的实验使我们想到，正电子可能是在中子与物质发生相互作用时产生的，而且我们最近得到了可以用这种想法来解释的实验证据。

将装有钋放射源和铍金属片的密封容器放在靠近膨胀云室外壁的地方。在云室的内壁上固定一个面积为2.5 cm见方，厚2 mm的铅靶。这个铅靶会受到从铍中辐射出的一种由中子和$\gamma$射线组成的射线的照射。膨胀时的照片是利用立体像对照相机拍摄的。在膨胀过程中给云室外加一个磁场，强度通常为800高斯。

从弯曲方向来看，照片上记录的大多数径迹明显是由负电子产生的，但在实验中多次发现，有一些径迹的一端位于铅靶或铅靶附近并且向相反方向弯曲。之所以会出现这种现象，或许是因为产生这些径迹的粒子带正电荷，又或许是因为产生于云室远端的负电子在磁场作用下发生偏转，从而使它们的径迹最终在铅靶处结束。对该结果的统计分析支持了径迹始于铅靶的观点，所以产生该径迹的粒子是带正电的。

Strong evidence for this hypothesis was acquired by placing a metal plate across the expansion chamber so as to intercept the paths of the particles. Only a few good photographs have so far been obtained in which a positively curved track passes through the plate and remains in focus throughout its path, but these leave no doubt that the particles had their origin in or near the lead target and were therefore positively charged. In one case the track had a curvature on the target side of the plate, a sheet of copper 0.25 mm. thick, corresponding to a value of $H\rho$ of 12,700; on the other side the curvature gave a value $H\rho$ =10,000. This indicates that the particle travelled from the target through the copper plate, losing a certain amount of energy in the plate. The change in the value of $H\rho$ in passing through the copper is roughly the same as for a negative electron under similar conditions. The ionising power of the particle is also about the same as that for the negative electron. These observations are consistent with the assumption that the mass and magnitude of the charge of the positive particle are the same as for the negative electron.

The manner in which these positive electrons are produced is not yet clear, nor whether they arise from the action of the neutron emitted by the beryllium or from the action of the accompanying $\gamma$-radiation. It is hoped that further experiments now in progress will decide these questions.

Our thanks are due to Mr. Gilbert for his help in the experiments.

(**131**, 473; 1933)

J. Chadwick, P. M. S. Blackett, G. Occhialini: Cavendish Laboratory, Cambridge, March 27.

---

References:

1 Anderson, *Science*, 76, 238 (1932).

2 Blackett and Occhialini, *Proc. Roy. Soc.*, A, 139, 699 (1933).

3 Curie and Joliot, *L'Existence du Neutron* (Hermann et Cie, Paris).

我们通过在膨胀云室中横放一块金属板以阻挡粒子路径的方法得到了支持这个假说的有力证据。虽然到目前为止，我们仅得到了几张效果较好的照片，照片上有一条明显弯曲的径迹穿过金属板，并且整条路径都比较清晰，但上述实验结果清清楚楚地说明这些粒子产生于铅靶或铅靶附近，因而带正电。在使用 0.25 mm 厚的铜板进行的一次实验中，我们在有铅靶的那一侧发现径迹出现弯曲，相应的 $H\rho$ 值为 12,700 ；而在铜板的另一侧，相应的值为 $H\rho$=10,000。这表明粒子从靶出发穿过铜板时，在铜板内损失了一部分能量。在穿过铜板前后粒子 $H\rho$ 值的变化与类似情况下负电子产生的结果大致相等。这种粒子的致电离能力也与负电子大致相同。以上实验结果都说明认为这种带正电的粒子与负电子质量相同且电荷数相同的假说是成立的。

我们现在还不清楚这些正电子是怎么产生的，也不知道它们是在铍发射的中子还是在随之发射的 $\gamma$ 辐射的作用下产生的。希望正在进行的后续实验能够解决这一问题。

感谢吉尔伯特先生在实验中给予我们的帮助。

（王锋 翻译；李军刚 审稿）

# The Physical Nature of the Nerve Impulse*

A. V. Hill

## Editor's Note

**Following a lecture he had recently given at the Royal Institution in London, Nobel Prize-winning physiologist Archibald Hill here explains the nature of nerve impulses. This is one of the earliest examples of a biological problem the understanding of which demanded a strong degree of knowledge in physics. Hill ends by reflecting on an extremely hot topic of the period that promised to revolutionize the study of nerve cell function: Russian scientists had recently produced evidence that living organisms give off radiation, particularly when active, that will induce mitosis (cell division) in other cells. As Hill suspects, however, the phenomenon of "mitogenic radiation" was not borne out by further research.**

ALL our sensations, all our movements, most of the activities of our nervous system, depend upon a certain transmitted disturbance which we call the nervous impulse: this, in the study of nerve activity, is what the atom, the electron and the quantum are to chemistry and physics. A rapid reaction to events occurring at a distance is necessary for efficient working. Special nerve cells, therefore, have been developed in all the larger animals: from these the axon or nerve fibre runs out, which is only 3 $\mu$ to 25 $\mu$ in diameter but may be many metres in length. Along these fibres wave-like messages are sent.

The velocity of a nerve impulse varies greatly according to the fibre in which it runs and to the conditions affecting the fibre. In the medullated nerve of a mammal the velocity is of the order of 100 metres per second. (Compare this with 330 metres per second, the velocity of sound.) In the medullated nerve of the frog at 20°C. it is about 30 metres per second. In the non-medullated nerve of a mammal it is said to be about one metre per second; in the non-medullated nerve of the pike and of *Anodon* respectively it is stated to be 0.2 metre and 0.05 metre per second. The velocities in this list are in the ratio of 2,000 to 1.

The nerve impulse is an event, a wave, a propagated disturbance, not a substance or a form of energy. It is transmitted along a thread of protoplasm which, in medullated nerve, is surrounded by a protecting or "insulating" sheath. Its passage can be detected in several ways: (*a*) by its physiological effect on the organ to which it runs, (*b*) by the electric change which accompanies its transmission, (*c*) by a production of heat, and (*d*) by a consumption of oxygen and a liberation of carbon dioxide.

* Friday evening discourse delivered at the Royal Institution on Feb. 10.

# 神经冲动的物理学本质*

阿奇博尔德·希尔

## 编者按

最近诺贝尔奖得主生理学家阿奇博尔德·希尔在伦敦的英国皇家研究院作了一场报告，随后他在《自然》杂志上发表了一篇解释神经冲动本质的文章。这是其中一个用大量物理学知识来解释生物学问题的早期例子。希尔以反思当时一个有希望使神经细胞功能的研究发生革命性变化的热门话题作为结尾——俄罗斯科学家最近发现生物体可以放出辐射，而且在辐射时会引发其他细胞的有丝分裂（细胞分裂）。然而，正如希尔所料，这种“导致有丝分裂的辐射”效应并没有被后续的实验所证实。

我们所有的感觉、行为以及神经系统的大部分活动都依赖于一种特定的可以传递的扰动，我们称之为神经冲动：神经冲动之于神经活动的研究就如同原子、电子和量子之于化学和物理学。对远程事件作出快速反应是高效工作所必需的。因此，所有大型动物都进化出了特殊的神经细胞，从其上延伸出直径只有 3~25 微米、而长度可达数米的轴突或神经纤维。信息像波一样沿着这些纤维进行传递。

神经冲动传递的速度在很大程度上受到传递它的纤维以及纤维所处环境的影响。在哺乳动物的有髓鞘神经纤维中，传递速度的数量级可达 100 米 / 秒（可以将这个速度与 330 米 / 秒的声速进行比较）。温度 20℃时在青蛙有髓鞘神经中的传递速度约为 30 米 / 秒。据说在哺乳动物无髓鞘神经中的传递速度为 1 米 / 秒；而在梭子鱼和无齿蚌的无髓鞘神经中，传递速度分别是 0.2 米 / 秒和 0.05 米 / 秒。在上面列出的数据中，最快速度与最慢速度的比值为 2,000:1。

神经冲动是一个事件、一束波、一种可传递的扰动，而非一种物质或能量形式。它沿着原生质丝进行传递，在有髓鞘神经中，原生质丝外面包围着保护性的或“绝缘”的鞘。神经冲动的传递可以用多种方式进行检测：(*a*) 途经器官的生理响应，(*b*) 与传播过程相伴的电位变化，(*c*) 产生的热效应，(*d*) 氧气的消耗和二氧化碳的释放。

* 本文取自希尔于 2 月 10 日在英国皇家研究院所作的周五晚间演讲。

No difference of electrical potential can be detected in an uninjured resting nerve. If, however, the nerve be injured, for example, by cutting, a potential difference is found of the order of a few hundredths of a volt between the injured and the uninjured parts, in the sense that positive current runs in an external circuit towards the former. The injury does not *produce* the potential difference; it merely allows its normal presence across the fibre boundary to be manifested.

If two electrodes be placed on a nerve and the nerve be stimulated, a momentary change of potential travels along it which can be recorded with an oscillograph. At any given instant a certain length of the nerve of the order of a few centimetres is found to be the site of a wave of negative potential. We are probably right in thinking that the impulse itself, whatever that be, occupies the same region and moves at the same speed as its electrical accompaniment.

## Properties of the Nerve Impulse

Let us consider the properties of the impulse which is transmitted, or transmits itself, in nerve. The single impulse in the single fibre is the basis of nerve activity. Until recently, this individual impulse could not be separately examined and deductions had to be made from the results of stimulating many fibres in parallel. Of late, however, through improvements in electrical recording, it has become possible to register the form and movement of the electric change resulting from a single impulse in a single fibre.

(*A*) A single impulse has an "all-or-none" character. Its size cannot be varied by changing the strength of the stimulus which produces it: it makes no difference to the magnitude of the discharge how hard the trigger is pulled. (*B*) An absolute "refractory" period follows the passage of an impulse, a period during which no stimulus, however strong, can evoke a second response. In frog's nerve at 20°C. this absolute refractory period is about 0.001 sec. (*C*) As a consequence of (*B*), two nerve impulses going in opposite directions in the same fibre come each into the refractory region of the other and both are abolished. "One way traffic" alone is possible: separate sensory and motor systems are required. (*D*) After the absolutely refractory stage a relatively refractory stage persists, during which a stronger stimulus than usual is required to start an impulse, and the second impulse, measured by electric change or heat, is smaller than the first one. Discharge can take place before recharge is complete. (*E*) As a result of the refractory phase, the frequency of transmission is limited. Prof. H. S. Gasser of New York recently informed me that he had made mammalian nerve carry 1,500 impulses per second, and that at 1,000 per sec., impulses were not greatly subnormal. In the normal functioning of the nervous system nearly all messages consist of trains of impulses of varying frequency. (*F*) The impulse at any instant occupies a few centimetres of the fibre. This length is not much altered by a change of temperature and it is approximately proportional to the diameter of the fibre. There must be some simple physical reason for these facts, as also for the next one. (*G*) The velocity of the impulse is also approximately proportional to the diameter of the fibre. Consequently in a given nerve trunk which consists of fibres of various diameters, a

在未经损伤的处于静息状态的神经上是检测不到电位差别的。但是，如果神经受到损伤，比如被切割，在损伤部分和未损伤部分之间就会有几十毫伏数量级的电位差，从这个意义上来说，正向电流是沿着一个外部的环路流向损伤部分的。损伤并不是电位差**产生**的原因；它仅仅是让正常情况下就存在的跨纤维边界的电位差显现出来而已。

如果将两个电极接在一根神经上，神经就会受到刺激，可以用示波器记录沿神经传播的瞬间电位变化。研究发现：一段长度为几厘米的神经在任意一个瞬间都是负电位波的位点。我们认为神经冲动本身，无论其本质是什么，都和伴随它的电位处于同一个位置并以同样的速度进行传播，这个观点很可能是正确的。

## 神经冲动的特性

让我们来谈一谈在神经中传播的冲动或传播过程本身的特性。单个纤维中的单个冲动是神经活动的基础。直到最近，人们仍然不能单独检测这种单个的冲动，而只能根据刺激多个平行纤维得出的结果进行推算。但是现在随着电位记录技术的进步，人们已经有可能记录由单个纤维中单个冲动引发的电变化以及它的传播。

(*A*) 单个冲动具有“全或无”的特点。冲动的大小不会随刺激强度的变化而变化：无论刺激多么强烈，也不会在放电量上产生差别。(*B*) 在一个神经冲动通过后会出现一段绝对的“不应”期，在这个时期内无论多强的刺激都不能引发第二次响应。20℃时青蛙神经的绝对不应期约为 0.001 秒。(*C*) 根据 (*B*)，两个在同一纤维中沿相反方向传播的神经冲动会使对方进入不应区而一起消失。只有“单向传播”是允许的：传播需要独立的感知和运动系统。(*D*) 绝对不应期之后会有一个相对不应期，需要比平时更强的刺激才能在这个阶段产生冲动，而且第二个冲动的电位变化或热效应要小于第一个冲动。放电可以在充电完成之前发生。(*E*) 由于存在不应期，所以冲动传播的重复频率是有限的。最近，纽约的盖瑟教授告诉我，他已经能让哺乳动物的神经在每秒内传递 1,500 个冲动，而且当达到每秒 1,000 个时，神经冲动并没有明显变弱。在功能正常的神经系统中，几乎所有的信息都是由一个个不同频率的神经冲动组成的。(*F*) 神经冲动在任意一个瞬间仅占据神经纤维中数厘米的范围。这个长度基本上不随温度的改变而改变，并与神经纤维的直径大致成正比。用简单的物理学原理一定能解释这些现象，下一条也是如此。(*G*) 冲动传播的速度也与神经纤维的直径大致成正比。因此，在给定的由不同直径神经纤维组成的神经干中，电波从一端向另一端传播时会表现为对应于频率曲线上若干极点的一系列波。

wave started electrically at one end gradually spreads out and appears as a series of waves corresponding to the several maxima in a frequency curve. (*H*) When the temperature is raised or lowered by 10°C. the velocity of transmission is increased or diminished in the ratio of 1.7 to 1. (*I*) The passage of an impulse is associated with a liberation of heat to which some special attention is necessary.

## Heat Production of Nerve

No work is performed, no force is developed, no movement at all occurs in a nerve when it is active, and for long it was believed that in the transmission of nerve impulses no heat is evolved. Many attempts were made to measure the heat, all unsuccessful until 1925. Today, when the heat production of nerve can be measured almost as well as that of muscle could in 1920, it is hard to believe that for many years we argued as though there was no heat at all associated with nerve activity. It is true that the amount is small, that the *total* heat (which takes thirty to fifty minutes to appear) in a single impulse in a gram of nerve is only about one millionth of a calorie, and it is true still that we must have several impulses before we can measure the heat properly, but with that provision and with present-day arrangements, the measurement is comparatively simple and accurate. The sensitivity is such (i) that a galvanometer deflection of 1 mm. (readable to 0.1 mm.) corresponds to a rise of temperature of about three millionths of a degree, and (ii) that during a steady state of heat production one millimetre of steady deflection corresponds to a rate of heat production of about $2\times10^{-8}$ calorie per second.

The heat is produced not only during the passage of the impulse *but for a long time afterwards*; some kind of breakdown occurs, presumably as the wave goes by. This breakdown has then to be reversed, the nerve allowed to recover, in a re-charging process of some kind which takes place afterwards. The fact that heat is produced, and the manner of its production, dispose of the possibility that the nerve impulse is, to use Bayliss's words, a "reversible physico-chemical process".

At 20°C. the initial heat in a single isolated impulse in a frog's medullated nerve lies between $10^{-7}$ calorie and $3\times10^{-8}$ calorie per gram of nerve. The recovery heat, which continues for a long time after the impulse has passed, is about ten to thirty times as much. During continual stimulation, say of fifty shocks per second, a steady state is gradually reached in which recovery balances breakdown, the recovery heat in any given interval representing the process of restoration from all the impulses which passed in the preceding forty minutes. During the steady state, which is possible only in oxygen, the total heat production may occur at the rate of about 25 microcalories per gram per second. At a higher frequency the total heat rate may, for a time, be rather greater, but a genuine steady state is not possible; fatigue progressively sets in. It is striking that the *resting* rate of heat production of the same nerve is about $70\times10^{-6}$ calorie per gram of nerve per second, so that moderate activity only increases the metabolism of a nerve by a comparatively small amount, even extreme activity does not double it. The mere maintenance of the machine in working order requires more energy than the excess required when it goes full speed during activity.

($H$) 如果温度升高或者降低 10℃，传播速率会以 1.7:1 的比例增加或减小。($I$) 冲动的传播伴随着放热，这一点需要特别注意。

## 神经的放热

当神经具有活性时，既没有做功，也没有产生力，更没有移动位置，长期以来人们一直认为在神经冲动的传播过程中没有热量放出。在 1925 年之前，人们多次试图对神经冲动传播过程中可能产生的热量进行测量，但是都失败了。而现在，人们对神经放热的测量已经能够达到 1920 年对肌肉放热的测定水平，难以想象这么多年来我们一直相信神经活动中根本不会放热。当然这个热量非常小，1 克神经单次冲动产生的**总**热量（耗时 30~50 分钟）大约只有 $1 \times 10^{-6}$ 卡路里，而且必须在有若干个神经冲动之后我们才能够准确地测定这种热量，但在满足上述条件并运用现有技术手段的情况下，测量还是比较简单和准确的。其灵敏度是（i）检流计偏转 1 mm（最小刻度是 0.1 mm）对应于温度升高约百万分之三摄氏度；（ii）在稳定放热阶段，1 mm 的稳定偏移对应于约 $2 \times 10^{-8}$ 卡路里 / 秒的放热速率。

热量的产生不仅发生在冲动传过的瞬间，**在冲动传过之后很长一段时间内**也会发生；人们推测当电波通过时会造成某种程度的击穿，为了对击穿进行修复，神经会在之后的时间里进行某种形式的再充电过程以便恢复原状。放热现象本身以及其产生的方式说明：神经冲动很可能，用贝利斯的话讲，是一个“可逆的物理化学过程”。

20℃时，单个冲动在每克青蛙有髓鞘神经中产生的初始热量大约在 $10^{-7}$ 到 $3 \times 10^{-8}$ 卡路里之间。恢复热在冲动传过之后很长一段时间内都会持续存在，其大小约为以上数值的 10~30 倍。在持续的刺激，比如 50 次 / 秒的电击下，就能逐渐达到恢复和击穿取得平衡的稳定状态，任何一段给定时间间隔内的恢复热代表了在之前 40 分钟内传过的所有冲动的复原过程。在这种必须有氧参与才可能存在的稳定状态下，整个放热过程的放热速率大约为每克每秒 25 微卡路里。当频率较高时，总的放热速率可能会突然变大，但在这种情况下真正的稳定状态是不可能发生的；因为神经会渐渐疲劳。令人惊讶的是：在**静息**状态下同一条神经的放热速率约为每克神经每秒 $70 \times 10^{-6}$ 卡路里，所以中等程度的活动只会使神经代谢增加很少一部分，即便是强度最大的活动也不能使其翻倍。刚好能维持机器正常运转所需的能量要高于开足马力时所需要的额外能量。

This initial heat is the result presumably of some chemical reaction involved in, or immediately after, the transmission of the impulse. If we suppose the reaction to occur throughout the substance of the axis cylinder, its heat is so small that it is difficult to picture any mechanism by which the change could be propagated. There are other grounds—for example, the relation between speed and diameter—for supposing that the reaction, whatever it be, is somehow connected with the surface of the fibres. It can be calculated that the area of the surface in a gram of nerve is of the order of 2,000 sq. cm., and that the energy in the transmission of a single effective impulse is from $5\times10^{-3}$ to $2.5\times10^{-4}$ erg per sq. cm. of fibre surface. This is still a very small quantity, the smallness of which can be realised by the statement that it is 1/4,000 to 1/80,000 of the surface energy of a water-olive oil interface.

One naturally asks, may not the initial heat be really due to the electrical disturbance transmitted in nerve? If we take the observed potential differences along the nerve and assume that these cause currents to flow through the conducting media inside and outside the sheath, then the Joule's heat of the currents can be calculated. The result is only a small fraction, less than one percent, of the observed initial heat. There is another possibility, however, namely, that the nerve is to be regarded as a charged electrical condenser which is discharged as the wave passes by. The energy of a condenser of capacity $F$ microfarads, charged to $V$ volts, is $5FV^2$ ergs. Taking $V$ as 0.05 we should require a capacity of the order of half a microfarad per square centimetre of nerve fibre surface to give us the observed initial heat. There is some evidence that capacities of this size may possibly exist at the surface of living cells. If so, we should not need to look for a chemical reaction to explain the initial heat—the electrical discharge would be sufficient. Other evidence, however, makes it unlikely that this is really the source of the heat.

The recovery process by which the nerve is restored to its initial condition is of an oxidative nature, though deprival of oxygen does not immediately cause it to fail. Apparently the nerve possesses, maybe as a safeguard against asphyxiation, a store of oxygen in some form other than molecular. A nerve may go on functioning and carrying out its usual recovery for hours, or even days (depending on the temperature) before all its oxygen store is used up. Then, and only then, it fails. If a nerve asphyxiated by lack of oxygen is given oxygen once more, recovery rapidly occurs and excitability returns.

## Other Effects of Oxygen

The difference of potential between an injured and an uninjured point of a crab's nerve is maintained for a long time in the presence of oxygen and the absence of stimulation. Stimulation rapidly reduces it, so to speak "depolarises" the nerve surface. The potential rises again to its full value if, and only if, oxygen be present. In the absence of oxygen it falls still further. The potential difference across the surface of a nerve depends for its maintenance on the continued presence of oxygen.

据推测，这些初始热量可能来源于传播神经冲动的过程或者紧随其后发生的化学反应。如果我们假设该反应是在整个轴突中发生的，那么这些热量就太小了以至于很难描述变化得以传播的机制。还有其他一些证据，比如传播速度和直径的关系，证明了化学反应不管怎么样都会在某种程度上与神经纤维的表面有关。计算表明：1 克神经的表面积大约为 2,000 $cm^2$ 数量级，而单次有效冲动传播的能量为每平方厘米神经纤维表面 $5 \times 10^{-3} \sim 2.5 \times 10^{-4}$ 尔格。这个值仍然是非常小的，仅仅是水–橄榄油之间界面能的 1/4,000～1/80,000。

有人很自然地会问：这些初始热量难道不是由神经中传播的电扰动引起的？如果我们测量出沿神经的电位差，并假设电位差就是使电流在鞘内外传导介质中流动的原因，那么我们就能计算出电流的焦耳热。这个结果只占初始热测量值的很小一部分，还不到 1%。然而，还存在另一种可能性，即神经可以被看成是一个带电的电容器，当波通过时会发生放电。一个电容为 F 微法、充电到 $V$ 伏特的电容所具有的能量为 $5FV^2$ 尔格。假设 $V$ 等于 0.05，则电容的数量级要达到 0.5 微法每平方厘米神经纤维表面才能得到与观察到的初始热量相符的结果。有一些证据表明：在活细胞表面有可能存在这么大的电容。如果事实真的如此，那么我们就不再需要寻找化学反应来解释初始热量了，电容放电已经足以说明一切。不过其他证据否认了电容放电是热量来源的观点。

神经恢复到初始状态的复原过程是一种氧化过程，而去除氧气不会马上使其终止。显然，神经储存了大量非分子形式的氧，这也许是抵御窒息现象发生的一种手段。在它储备的氧耗尽之前，神经可以在数小时乃至数天内（取决于温度）继续发挥功能并且像往常一样进行复原。之后，也只有在氧气耗尽之后，神经才会失效。如果再次恢复对缺氧神经的氧气供应，它会很快复原并恢复活性。

## 氧气的其他作用

蟹神经损伤部位和未损伤部位之间的电位差在有氧但没有刺激的环境下能够保持很长一段时间。刺激可以使之很快降低，这就是所谓的神经表面“去极化”。当且仅当氧气存在时该电位才能再次达到最大值。没有氧气它就会降得更低。跨神经表面电位差的保持依赖于氧的持续存在。

Stimulation and lack of oxygen, however, are not the only means by which the potential difference can be reduced. There is normally a ratio of about 10 to 1 between the inside and the outside of a crab's nerve fibre in respect of potassium ion concentration. If we suppose that potassium is the only substance capable of penetrating the fibre surface of the crab's nerve, then this concentration ratio should lead to a potential difference of $\frac{RT}{F}\log_e 10$ which is about 58 mv. Values of 30 mv. in freshly dissected nerve are commonly observed, and sometimes more, and since a certain amount of short-circuiting must occur in the strongly conducting fluid between the fibres, the real value may well approximate to the 58 mv. required by the formula. If the hypothesis is right, the potential difference would be reduced by increasing the potassium ion concentration on the outside of the fibre. Cowan has found this to be the case. By soaking a nerve for a few seconds in sea-water to which potassium has been added, the potential difference may be varied from 30 mv. or 40 mv. down to nearly nothing as desired. The potential difference is clearly determined by the potassium ion concentration, and yet it is dependent also on the presence of oxygen. This paradoxical dependence on two such different factors has not yet been resolved: perhaps the oxygen is used in maintaining the normal properties of the surface membrane.

Another, and a most curious effect of oxygen, has recently been observed in the action of veratrine, a plant alkaloid, on frog's nerve. Applied to a muscle, this drug causes a prolonged response to a single impulse: applied to a nerve it has little effect, the action current is not greatly lengthened, the heat production is not largely increased, by soaking the frog's nerve for an hour in 1 in 50,000 veratrine solution. If, however, after the nerve has been soaked it be then asphyxiated for three or four hours until it is completely inexcitable, and if it be then revived by admitting oxygen, it shows in a striking manner a typical veratrine effect. The action current lasts hundreds of times as long, the heat production is thousands of times as great, as in the normal response of a nerve to a single shock.

Apparently the drug is usually unable to penetrate the nerve fibre sheath. When, however, the nerve has been asphyxiated, the condition of the surface has somehow been altered so that the substance which was previously held out is now able to penetrate. Oxygen is necessary for the maintenance of the normal impenetrable condition of the surface of the fibre. One naturally associated this effect with the presence of a thick sheath around the axis cylinder, and asked whether the veratrine effect could be manifested in other nerves in which no medullary sheath is present. The experiment was made by Cowan, and showed that in crab's nerve a typical veratrine effect is produced without any asphyxiation, and that the concentration of the drug required is only one thousandth of that for frog's nerve. Veratrine apparently can penetrate normally the very thin surface of a non-medullated nerve, but it is held out almost indefinitely, until the nerve is asphyxiated, by the sheath normally covering the axis cylinder of a medullated nerve.

This strange result suggested that the effect of curare should be similarly tested. Curare

然而，刺激和缺氧并不是使电位差下降的唯一方法。在正常情况下，蟹神经纤维内部与外部的钾离子浓度比为 10:1。如果我们假设钾是唯一能够透过蟹神经纤维表面的物质，那么这个浓度比将产生 $\frac{RT}{F}\log_e 10$ 的电位差，其大小约为 58 毫伏。人们在新鲜剥离的神经上测得的数值通常为 30 毫伏，有时会高一些，因为在纤维与纤维之间导电性很强的流体中必然会发生一定程度的短路，实际值可能刚好接近于由公式推算出来的 58 毫伏。如果这个假设是正确的，那么提高神经纤维外部的钾离子浓度就会降低电位差。考恩已经证实了这一点。他将一根神经浸泡在添加了钾离子的海水中，几秒钟后电位差从 30 或 40 毫伏降低到几乎为 0，这与预期是相符的。电位差明显取决于钾离子的浓度，并与氧气是否存在有关。人们至今也说不清为什么电位差会依赖于这两种完全不同的因素：也许氧气的作用是用来维持膜表面的正常特性。

最近人们在研究藜芦碱（一种植物碱）对青蛙神经的作用时发现了氧气的另一个非常奇怪的特性。把藜芦碱作用到肌肉上可以延长单个冲动的响应时间；但该药物对神经几乎没有什么影响，把青蛙神经放在 1:50,000 的藜芦碱溶液中浸泡 1 小时，动作电流并没有明显延长，放热也没有大幅增加。但如果使浸泡后的神经缺氧 3 小时或 4 小时直至完全失活，然后再供氧使其恢复活性，典型的藜芦碱效应就会以一种不同寻常的方式表现出来。此时的动作电流比一根神经对单个刺激的正常响应时间长几百倍，放热也增加了几千倍。

显然，药物在通常情况下是不能通过神经纤维的髓鞘的。但是当神经缺氧时，表面状态发生了某种变化，所以本来不能透过的物质现在可以透过了。氧气对于维持神经纤维表面在正常情况下的非通透性是非常必要的。人们会很自然地将这种效应与轴突外面包裹的厚鞘联系起来，并怀疑藜芦碱效应是否也能在没有髓鞘的神经中表现出来。考恩进行了这方面的实验，他发现即使不缺氧，蟹神经也能表现出典型的藜芦碱效应，而且所需药物的浓度仅为进行青蛙神经实验所需浓度的千分之一。在正常情况下，藜芦碱显然能够穿透很薄的无髓神经表面，但是几乎永远不可能穿透有髓鞘神经轴突外面的髓鞘，除非该神经经过了缺氧处理。

这个奇特的结果使人联想到应该用同样的方法研究一下箭毒的效应。箭毒能通

paralyses a muscle, in respect of impulses coming to it along its motor nerve. It was formerly thought to attack the neuro-muscular junction, though recently, on the strength of Lapicque's theories, it has been supposed to produce its effect by changing the "time scale of excitation" of the muscle fibre, putting it out of tune so to speak with its nerve. Recent work by Rushton has shown that this hypothesis of Lapicque's is untenable, so that the manner of action of the drug was still unsolved. It was possible that curare might be a potent nerve poison but normally unable to penetrate except at the neuro-muscular junction. At this point the medullary sheath is absent. Perhaps a nerve dosed with curare but apparently unaffected, might be found effectively poisoned after asphyxiation.

The experiment was performed by Fromherz: a muscle nerve preparation was paralysed by soaking in curare, the nerve was removed and still showed a normal action current: it was then asphyxiated in hydrogen and after asphyxiation allowed to recover (if it could) in oxygen. An unpoisoned nerve treated in this way immediately gives a large action current on readmission of oxygen. The curarised nerve gave only a small one and recovered very slowly. Curare, therefore, may render a nerve incapable of responding, once it is able—as during a state of asphyxia—to get in. This may be the solution of the problem: the effect of curare is not on the "chronaxie" of muscle, but on the part of the nerve which is exposed to the action of the drug, namely, its ending where the medullary sheath is absent.

## Time Relations of Excitation

All living animals, organs, or organisms, have a certain characteristic scale of time. The fibres of the wing muscle of a fly can contract hundreds of times a second, those of the leg muscle of the tortoise, differing from the fly's in no other very obvious way, may take several seconds to give a single twitch. The mouse and the man differ greatly in many of their characters and the difference is largely that of the scale of time on which respectively they live. This difference of time scale is a necessary accompaniment of a difference of size: a very small motor may do 10,000 revolutions per minute, a large one must be content with a few hundreds. One of the most important problems of physiology, and it is a problem of general, almost of philosophical interest, is what determines the scale of time of an animal or cell.

In nerve, the time required at any point for the action current to go through its cycle, the time taken in the transmission of the impulse, and the time-scale (to which I will refer later) of electric excitation, all can be varied together as we alter the condition of the cell or pass from one cell to another. These are different aspects of the same phenomenon—the transmission of the impulse. At the end of the last century it was shown by Waller, employing stimulation by condenser discharge, that there is an "optimal" stimulus for any given tissue, in the sense that the energy in it is a minimum. He showed, and Keith Lucas following him showed, that the effectiveness of a condenser stimulus of given energy depends upon the rate of discharge of the condenser. If $F$ be the capacity and $R$ the resistance through which discharge takes place, the time of discharge is proportional to

过沿运动神经传入肌肉组织的冲动麻痹肌肉。之前人们认为它攻击神经与肌肉的结合部，但是按照拉皮克的最新理论，改变肌纤维“兴奋的时间尺度”使之不能与支配它的神经的时间尺度相匹配才是箭毒的作用机制。而拉什顿最近的研究成果表明拉皮克的这一假设是站不住脚的，所以该药的作用机制仍然没有解决。箭毒可能是一种潜在的神经毒剂，不过在一般情况下它不能穿透除神经肌肉接合部以外的部位。因为神经肌肉接合部不存在髓鞘。原本对箭毒没有明显反应的神经也许在缺氧后就会中毒。

弗朗姆荷茨进行了如下的实验：将一条肌肉神经样本浸泡于箭毒中使之麻痹，然后取出神经，仍然可以观测到正常的动作电流；再将其置于氢气环境中进行缺氧处理，随后在氧气中使之恢复（如果可以恢复的话）。一条没有经过箭毒处理的神经在重新供氧后会马上出现明显的动作电流。而用箭毒处理过的神经只会出现很小的动作电流并且恢复得很慢。因此一旦箭毒能够渗入，比如在缺氧条件下，它或许就能使神经丧失响应能力。这也许就是上述问题的答案：箭毒效应与肌肉的“时值”无关，而与暴露在药物中的那部分神经，即与没有髓鞘的神经末梢部位有关。

## 兴奋的时间关系

所有活的动物、器官或组织都具有特征性的时间尺度。苍蝇翅膀的肌肉纤维每秒能收缩数百次，除了需要几秒钟才能收缩一次以外，乌龟腿部的肌肉与苍蝇的肌肉没有太大的差别。小鼠和人类在许多特征上都有很大的不同，主要区别在于它们生存的时间尺度不同。时间尺度不同是体型大小不同的必然结果：一个非常小的马达也许每分钟能转 10,000 圈，而大马达只能转数百圈。生理学上的一个最重要的问题，同时也是一个具有普遍意义和哲学意味的问题，就是到底是什么决定了动物或细胞的时间尺度。

在神经中，如果我们改变细胞存在的环境或者从一个细胞传入另一个细胞，则动作电流完成整个回路所需的时间、传播冲动所需的时间以及电兴奋的时间尺度（我将在后面提到）都会发生改变。这些都是同一现象——冲动传播的不同表现形式。上个世纪末，沃勒在利用电容器放电的刺激实验中发现，对于任何特定的组织都有一个“最佳”的刺激条件，此时电容内的能量最小。他以及他之后的基思·卢卡斯都发现：特定能量电容器的放电刺激效率依赖于电容器的放电速度。如果 $F$ 是电容器的容量，$R$ 是放电时的电阻，则放电时间正比于 $FR$ 的乘积，因此对于给定的刺激能量 $\frac{1}{2}FV^2$，其响应依赖于乘积 $FR$。

the product $FR$, and for given energy $\frac{1}{2}FV^2$ in the stimulus, the response depends on the product $FR$.

The use of condensers is very convenient and is generally adopted in studying the time relations of the excitatory process. The relation, however, is clearer if excitation be produced with the aid of a constant current of variable duration. If a constant current be led into an excitable tissue by two non-polarisable electrodes, in order that a stimulus of very short duration may be effective its intensity must be great, while if it lasts for a long time its intensity may be small. In the case of medullated nerve the times involved are very short, so that rather special methods of determining the duration of the constant current employed must be adopted. The relation between the duration of a constant current and the least strength required for excitation (the so-called strength-duration curve) is shown in Fig. 1.

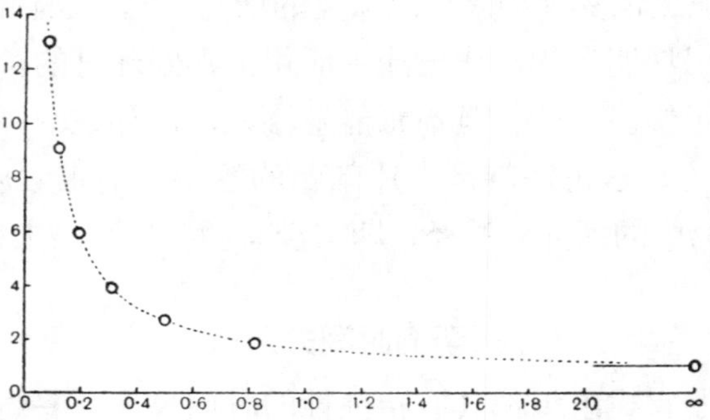


Fig. 1. "Strength duration curve" for nerve excitation. Horizontally, duration in $\sigma$ (0.001 sec.): vertically minimum strength required.—From "Chemical Wave Transmission in Nerve", by A. V. Hill (Cambridge University Press, 1932).

In the case of nerve this curve is always approximately of the same form and may be defined by two parameters, the scale of time and the scale of current. The latter is of no particular interest, since most of the current is short-circuited in the fluids between the excitable elements and no strictly standard conditions for comparison can be defined. The scale of time, however, *is* important, and is very constant for a given nerve under given conditions, and the usual method of expressing it is by means of the minimum duration of a current of twice the threshold strength. This duration was called by Keith Lucas the "excitation time" and by Lapicque the "chronaxie", the latter term in its derivation meaning no more than the time scale of the process or tissue in question.

The excitation time of nerve depends upon many factors: (*a*) the nature of the nerve itself; it varies greatly from one fibre to another, in the same kind of way as the velocity of propagation of the impulse referred to earlier; (*b*) it is increased by a fall, decreased by a rise of temperature; (*c*) it is considerably affected by the nature of the ionic constituents in the solution around the nerve, particularly by the concentration of the calcium, and to a less extent of the potassium ion; (*d*) it depends upon the size of the fibre, being smaller in a fibre of greater diameter.

利用电容器研究兴奋过程的时间相关性是非常便利的，而且已经得到了广泛的认可。但如果使用持续时间不同的恒定电流来引发兴奋，其时间相关性会更加清晰。如果通过两个非极化电极将恒定电流引入可兴奋的组织中，为了使持续时间非常短的刺激能够产生效果，强度必须很大；而对于持续时间较长的刺激，强度可以小一些。在有髓鞘神经纤维中，这个时间非常短，以至于需要采用特殊的办法才能测定稳态电流的持续时间。稳态电流持续时间和兴奋所需最小强度之间的关系（被称为强度 – 时间曲线）如图 1 所示。

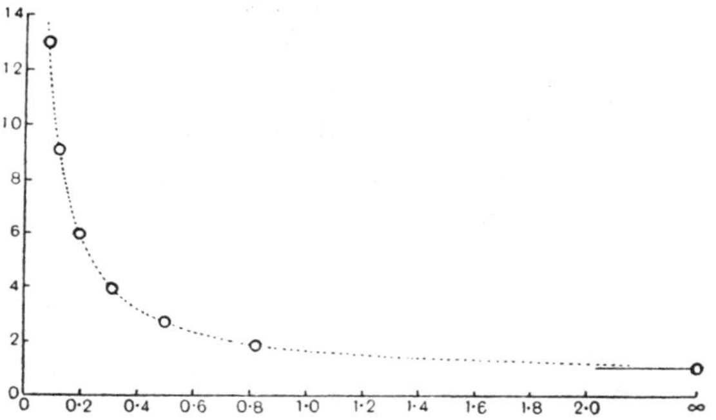


图 1. 神经兴奋的“强度 – 时间曲线”。横轴，持续时间 $\sigma$（0.001 秒）；纵轴，所需的最小强度。——摘自《化学波在神经中的传播》，希尔著（剑桥大学出版社，1932 年）。

就神经而言，这条曲线的形状基本上是大致相同的，也许用两个参数就可以对其进行定义，即时间尺度和电流尺度。后者的意义不是很大，因为大部分电流都会在可兴奋部件之间的基质液中发生短路，无法定义严格的比较标准。重要的是时间尺度，对于给定条件下的特定神经，时间尺度是非常恒定的，人们通常用强度是临界强度两倍的电流的最小持续时间来描述它。基思·卢卡斯把这个持续时间定义为“兴奋时间”，而拉皮克称之为“时值”，后面这个术语的引申意义指的是不超过所研究过程或者组织的时间尺度。

神经的兴奋时间取决于多个因素：(*a*) 神经本身的性质；一根纤维和另一根纤维之间差别很大，这同之前提到的冲动传播速率受神经纤维的影响类似；(*b*) 温度降低，兴奋时间增加；温度升高，兴奋时间减少；(*c*) 神经周围溶液的离子组成对兴奋时间影响很大，尤其是钙离子浓度，钾离子的影响程度略低于钙离子；(*d*) 取决于神经纤维的大小，兴奋时间随纤维直径的增大而减少。

The form of the strength–duration curve leads us to a discussion of the nature of electrical excitation. A constant current passed through an excitable tissue excites twice, once at the cathode at make, once at the anode at break. Unless the current be too strong, when secondary effects (for example, electrolysis and polarisation) occur, no propagated impulse is started off during the passage of a constant current. With an alternating current, however, of not too high a frequency the case is different. An impulse starts off from the cathode for each positive phase of the current, another from the anode for each negative phase. This is true up to, say, 300 a second for a frog's nerve, 700 a second for a mammalian nerve. When, however, we consider the case of a much higher frequency, say, of 100,000 to 1,000,000 per second, a different result is found. Such currents produce no response even though they be so strong that considerable warming occurs. This is commonly imagined to be due to the so-called "skin effect", but it can readily be shown that with the high specific resistance of living tissues the skin effect does not come in until a frequency is reached far higher than that we are considering.

Let us suppose that excitation occurs, that an impulse is started, when the current outwards through the sheath of a nerve fibre in the region of the cathode attains more than a certain density (Fig. 2). When the outward current is large enough something is rendered unstable, and the state of instability is propagated as a wave. We suppose that the sheath of a fibre possesses the properties of a dielectric of high but not infinite specific resistance. The first effect of a difference of potential applied along the nerve is to charge the capacities at the anode and the cathode. The nerve, in fact, acts like a cylindrical condenser, the sheath being the dielectric between the plates.

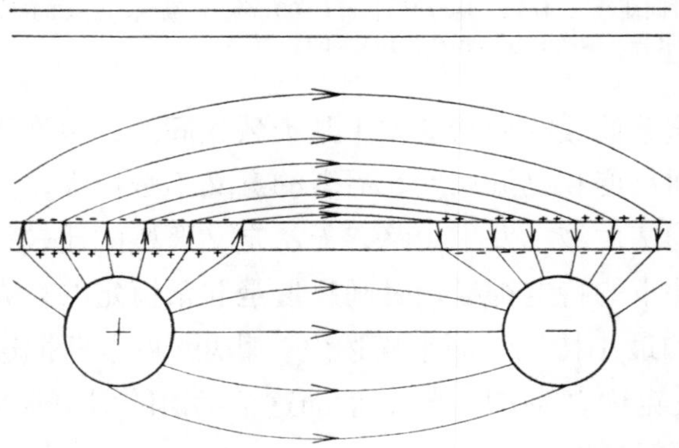

Fig. 2. Nerve fibre with two electrodes; current flow outside, inside and through sheath.

When an alternating current of high frequency is applied between electrodes resting on the nerve the effect of each cycle is to charge, alternately in opposite directions, the condensers lying near the electrodes. Unless the current be very strong, these condensers absorb it and prevent a potential difference from arising across the dielectric of sufficient intensity to drive any considerable current through the latter. With a lower frequency, however, or with a constant current, while the first effect is still to charge the condensers,

我们可以根据强度－时间曲线的形状来讨论电兴奋的本质。恒定电流通过可兴奋组织时会对它产生两次刺激，一次是当电路接通时在阴极发生，另一次是当电路断开时在阳极发生。除非电流太强，否则当有副反应（比如电解和极化）发生时，在恒定电流通过期间不会引发冲动的传播。但是如果换成频率不太高的交流电，情况就不同了。当电流处于正相位时会有一个冲动从阴极开始传播，而当电流处于负相位时会有一个冲动从阳极开始传播。对青蛙神经而言，频率要达到 300 次每秒才能出现这种情况；在哺乳动物的神经中，频率要达到 700 次每秒。然而，当我们考虑更高的频率时，比如 100,000~1,000,000 次每秒，就会发现不同的结果。尽管电流已经强到足以造成可观的加热效应，但不会产生任何响应。通常认为这一现象源于所谓的“趋肤效应”，但因为我们知道生物组织有很高的电阻，所以趋肤效应是不可能出现的，除非频率远远高于我们的预期。

我们可以假设当阴极区中通过神经髓鞘向外传播的电流超过一定量时，冲动会产生，兴奋也会出现（图 2）。当外向电流大到足以出现某种不稳定时，这种不稳定状态就会以波的形式传播开来。我们假设神经髓鞘具有很高的介电性，但电阻率没有达到无穷大。将电位差加到神经上后出现的第一个效应就是对阳极和阴极处的电容进行充电。实际上，神经就像一个圆柱形的电容器，髓鞘就是两个极板之间的电介质。

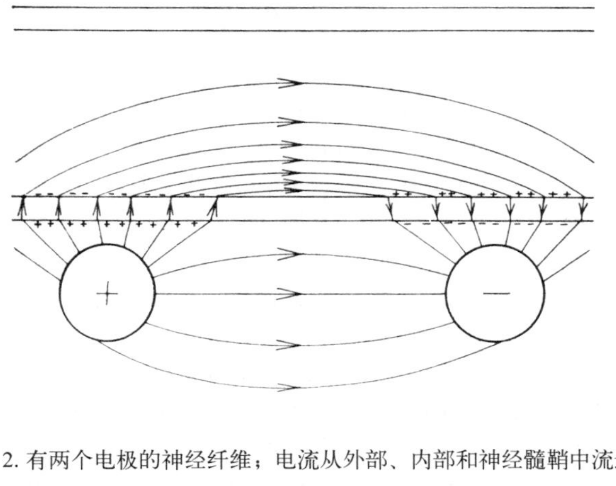

图 2. 有两个电极的神经纤维；电流从外部、内部和神经髓鞘中流过

当高频交流电加到神经上的两个电极之间时，其效果就是每一个周期都会交替地从相反的方向给电极附近的电容器充电。在电流不太强的情况下，电容器会吸收电流并阻止在足够强的电介质中产生电位差和可观的电流。但在频率较低或电流恒定时，尽管第一个效应还是使电容器充电，但在充电进行时会产生跨电介质的电位差，并最终导致电流通过电介质。当电流在阴极外达到足够高的强度时，就会产生不稳

as these are charged a difference of potential arises across the dielectric by which a current is caused to pass. When this current reaches a sufficiently high density outwards at the cathode, instability is produced and excitation occurs.

With constant currents, the shorter the duration the greater the current has to be to produce an excitatory effect. With a current of great duration the capacities in the surface of the fibre have ultimately no influence. With very short durations, however, the first effect is to charge the condensers and so to reduce the E.M.F.'s available across the dielectric. If then the applied current is cut off before the condensers are charged, the potential difference across it will be less than that which would ultimately be attained, and for excitation to occur the applied E.M.F. must be greater.

From this model an equation for the strength-duration curve can be deduced as follows:

$$C = \frac{R}{1 - e^{-t / \frac{Fr(r_o + r_i)}{2r + r_o + r_i}}}$$

Here $C$ is the current, $t$ its duration, $R$ a constant, $F$ the capacity and $r$ the resistance per sq. cm. of the sheath in the neighbourhood of the electrodes, $r_i$ the resistance of the inside, $r_0$ that of the fluids on the outside, of the nerve between the electrodes.

For the case of electrodes very far apart where $(r_0 + r_i)$ is large compared with $r$, this equation approximates to

$$C = \frac{R}{1 - e^{-t/Fr}}$$

The important term in deciding the form of the relation is the product $Fr$, which is obtained by multiplying together the capacity and the resistance per square centimetre of the surface of the fibre. The relation experimentally observed in the strength-duration curve (Fig. 1) is fitted with sufficient accuracy by this equation.

If the excitation time be determined by the product of the capacity and the resistance per square centimetre of nerve fibre surface, then we should seek to explain the differences between different fibres, or between the same fibre under different conditions, by changes in the product $Fr$. The thinner the sheath the greater will $F$ be, and the greater the excitation time: the lower the resistance, the shorter will be the excitation time. A rise of temperature presumably alters the excitation time by diminishing $r$. The absence of calcium causes a large increase in the excitation time, possibly through an increase in the resistance of the surface of the nerve. Such a change of resistance might be brought about by an alteration in the state of the emulsion of oil in water, or water in oil, of which it is possible that the sheath of the nerve is composed.

There are complications, however, in this story. It seems certain that the potassium ion

定性并出现兴奋。

就恒定电流而言，持续的时间越短，恒定电流就要越大才能产生兴奋效果。长时间的电流最终不能对神经纤维表面的电容产生影响。但在持续时间很短时，电容器会首先充电，从而降低了跨介电质的有效电动势。如果在电容充分充电之前将加在上面的电流切断，其产生的电位差就会小于最终能达到的电位差，此时需要使用更大的电动势才能产生兴奋。

根据这个模型，我们可以推导出如下的强度 – 时间曲线公式：

$$C = \frac{R}{1 - e^{-t/\frac{Fr(r_o + r_i)}{2r + r_o + r_i}}}$$

其中：$C$ 是电流，$t$ 是持续时间，$R$ 是常数，$F$ 是电容，$r$ 是电极附近每平方厘米鞘的电阻，$r_i$ 是两电极间神经的内部电阻，$r_0$ 是两电极间神经外部液体的电阻。

如果两个电极相距很远，$(r_0+r_i)$ 远大于 $r$，则上述公式可以近似表示为如下形式：

$$C = \frac{R}{1 - e^{-t/Fr}}$$

乘积 $Fr$ 对于决定这个关系式的形式起着重要的作用，它是电容与在每平方厘米纤维表面积中的电阻的乘积。由实验得到的强度 – 时间曲线（图 1）中的关系与这个公式的拟合结果非常一致。

如果兴奋时间由电容与在每平方厘米纤维表面积中的电阻的乘积决定，那么我们就应该试着用乘积 $Fr$ 的变化去解释不同纤维之间的差别或者同一条纤维在不同情况下的差别。髓鞘越薄 $F$ 越大，兴奋时间也就越长；电阻越低，兴奋时间越短。人们推测升温过程可以通过减少 $r$ 来改变兴奋时间。缺钙会明显延长兴奋时间，这可能与增加了神经表面的电阻有关。这种电阻的变化也许是由于改变了油在水中或水在油中的乳化状态造成的，因为神经髓鞘有可能是由乳液组成的。

不过情况还很复杂。钾离子对神经纤维内外的电位差和电波传播时的动作电流

has some specific function in determining the potential difference which exists between the inside and outside of a fibre and the action current by which the wave is propagated. Possibly potassium has some specific solubility in the lipoidal substances of the nerve sheath, some specific power of penetrating which other ions have not. The current outward at the cathode by which we suppose excitation to occur is probably carried by potassium ions.

This may explain a phenomenon on which I have not yet touched, that of the gradual adaptation to a slowly increasing current. It has long been known that a current which would normally be strong enough to produce excitation may not do so if its full value be reached not suddenly but slowly. If potassium be the only means of carrying current through the sheath, its continued transfer outwards at the cathode would have the effect of depleting the inside and raising its concentration on the outside, so that a back E.M.F. would be generated (determined by $\frac{RT}{F} \log \frac{C_2}{C_1}$): this might effectively prevent the further transfer of current at a time when the externally applied E.M.F. at last reached the value at which, if suddenly applied, it would excite.

Similarly, we may explain the stimulus occurring at the anode at break of a long-continued constant current. During the prolonged passage of the current the potassium ions on the outside at the anode have been depleted by carriage through the sheath until either so few are available, or the back E.M.F. is so great, that no current can run. Breaking the circuit of the applied E.M.F., the constraint at the anode is released, the unusually high ratio (potassium inside) : (potassium outside) immediately tends to right itself by the back transfer of potassium ions outwards through the membrane. This constitutes a current similar to that which occurs normally at excitation at the cathode; consequently, when the back rush of potassium ions is rapid enough, excitation occurs and an impulse starts off.

The normal function of motor nerves is to transmit impulses to the muscles, and for many years physiologists have discussed how the impulse in the nerve gets across to, and produces its effect in, the muscle fibre. Motor end-plates have been described by histologists, but their functions, and even their existence, are doubtful. It has been supposed that the electric change in the nerve which is an accompaniment of the impulse, starts the process of excitation in the muscle fibres, just as in the laboratory an impulse is started by an electric shock. This idea has led to the view that the muscle fibre and its motor nerve are normally "isochronous", that is to say, have the same "excitation time"; a muscle was supposed to respond to the impulse in a nerve if the latter was in tune with it, but not otherwise.

Some years before the War, Keith Lucas showed that in muscle there are two different excitable substances which he supposed were the muscle fibres themselves and the nerve twigs running to them. Lucas's experimental demonstration was denied by Lapicque who, employing different electrodes, found that the excitation time of both tissues was the same. Lucas's observations, however, have been reinstated by Rushton, and it seems

起着特殊的作用，这一点似乎是肯定的。也许钾离子在神经髓鞘的脂质成分中具有特殊的溶解能力以及其他离子所不具备的穿透能力。由阴极向外流动的电流很可能是由钾离子传输的，我们认为兴奋就是由这个电流引起的。

上述假设可以解释一个我尚未提及的现象，即对缓慢增加的电流的适应性现象。很久以前人们就知道：通常情况下强度足够产生兴奋的电流在缓慢而非很快达到最大值时是不能产生兴奋的。如果钾离子是使电流流向神经髓鞘的唯一方法，那么钾离子在阴极的持续外流就会耗尽鞘内的钾离子同时使外部的浓度增加，因而会产生一个反向电动势（大小由 $\frac{RT}{F}\log\frac{C_2}{C_1}$ 决定）；这个反向电动势也许会有效地阻止当从外部快速施加的电动势达到足以产生兴奋的值时进一步的电流外流。

我们也可以用类似的方法解释当持续的恒定电流中断时在阳极处产生的刺激。在电流持续通过的情况下，阳极处位于鞘外的钾离子会一直被向内输送，直到浓度远远不够或者反向电动势足够大以至于没有电流能够通过时为止。如果取消外加的电动势，阳极处的约束条件就解除了，这种不寻常的高浓度比（内部钾离子：外部钾离子）会立即引发钾离子跨膜向外输运从而使体系恢复到初始状态。这就形成了一种类似于在通常情况下处于兴奋状态时阴极处的电流；因此，当钾离子的回流速度足够快时，也会出现兴奋并开始冲动的传播。

运动神经的正常功能就是传递冲动到肌肉，多年来生理学家们一直在讨论神经中的冲动是如何通过肌肉纤维并在其中产生作用的。组织学家们提出了运动终板，但是运动终板的功能乃至它们的存在都还不能完全确定。人们假设神经中伴随着冲动的电变化引发了肌肉纤维中的兴奋过程，就像在实验室中冲动可以由电击产生一样。这个观点使我们联想到：肌肉纤维和它的运动神经在通常情况下是“同步”的，也就是说它们的“兴奋时间”相同；肌肉会对神经中与之同步的冲动作出响应，否则就不会有响应。

在第一次世界大战之前，基思·卢卡斯发现肌肉中有两种不同的可兴奋组织，他猜想这些组织可能是肌纤维本身以及延伸其中的神经分支。卢卡斯的实验结果被拉皮克否定，拉皮克在测试时使用了不同的电极，他发现两种组织的兴奋时间是相同的。但拉什顿重复出了卢卡斯的实验结果，这样拉皮克认为肌肉和神经在通常情况下同步的观点是否站得住脚就值得怀疑了。拉皮克理论的一个最精彩的应用是解释箭毒、

doubtful whether Lapicque's claim of normal isochronism between muscle and nerve can stand. The most beautiful application of Lapicque's theory, one which was perhaps just a little too convincing because of its beauty and because it appeared to explain so much, was that of the mechanism by which paralysis is caused by curare or other drugs or by such agencies as fatigue. Normally, the impulse from the nerve passes over into the muscle. A small dose, however, of curare, or the onset of fatigue, somehow breaks the connexion, and Lapicque maintained that this was due to the fact that the curare, or the other paralysing agency, had increased the excitation time of the muscle fibre until it was no longer isochronous with its motor nerve and therefore the impulse from the latter failed to affect it. The case was like that of two tuned electric circuits, sending and receiving—if the receiver were put out of tune with the transmitter, messages were not received.

Various experiments were adduced in support of this theory, and for a time it was accepted and was in danger of becoming a dogma. Unfortunately its experimental basis seems to be at fault. The experiments on which it was founded have been repeated by Rushton and their results denied. Other experiments have been made by which the "heterochronism" theory of curarisation has been made untenable. It is a strange thing in science to find a theory, so directly based upon apparent experimental facts, displaced by a direct denial of the facts: but so it seems to be.

## The Propagated Disturbance

We have considered the manner in which excitation by an electric current occurs. With every adjustment made to get the most efficient stimulus, the energy in it is still very large when compared with that set free by the nerve itself as an impulse runs along it. Electrical stimulation is very wasteful compared with the natural stimulation from point to point by which an impulse is propagated. This is not difficult to understand. The chief part of the energy of an artificial stimulus is wasted in the fluid between the electrodes outside the active region of the nerve fibres. Only that fraction of the current which, according to our hypothesis, crosses the cathode region of the surface, is effective as a stimulus. In natural stimulation, that is from point to point in the propagation of the wave, there are no electrodes and there can be no short-circuiting in the different fluids: the stimulating current, therefore (if propagation be by means of the current), is far more efficiently used.

There is a tendency to assume, as I have assumed here, that propagation of the impulse from point to point occurs through the agency of the action current which can be detected at an active point. There is no doubt that the action current has the time relations of an efficient stimulus and, properly applied, it should have the magnitude requisite for excitation. We have no picture of the manner in which the excitatory disturbance is propagated, except that which supposes that the action current at any given point "stimulates" a neighbouring point, where in its turn a further action current is produced, which again stimulates a neighbouring point, and so on. The fact that the velocity of propagation runs parallel with the speed of development of the action current at a given point, and also inversely with the time scale of the process of excitation, strongly suggests that these three factors are linked together in some relation of cause and effect.

其他药物或者诸如疲劳等作用所导致的肌肉麻痹的产生机制，由于拉皮克的理论本身很完美，也似乎解释了很多现象，以至于这个理论有点太深入人心了。在通常情况下，冲动会从神经传到肌肉。但小剂量的箭毒或疲劳的出现也许会在某种程度上阻断它们的联系，拉皮克认为是箭毒或者其他可以导致麻痹的因素延长了肌肉纤维的兴奋时间，使之不再与它的运动神经同步，因此来自后者的冲动就不能在肌肉纤维中生效了。这就像两个调谐的电路，一个发送信号一个接收信号——如果接收方的频调与发送方不一致，就收不到信号了。

很多实验结果都证明了拉皮克的理论，在一段时间内它曾经被人们接受并差点成为公认的真理。不幸的是该理论的实验基础是错误的。拉什顿重复了证实该理论的实验，但得到的结果却是负面的。其他一些实验也说明了箭毒中毒的“异时性”理论是站不住脚的。这样一个直接建立在明确实验基础上的理论却因与事实完全不符而被取代，这在科学上是一桩怪事：但事实似乎就是如此。

## 传播出去的扰动

我们已经讨论了电刺激产生兴奋的方式。尽管为了达到最有效的刺激，人们对各个方面都进行了调整，但所需的能量仍比神经自身在冲动传播时释放的能量大很多。就传播冲动而言，电刺激的耗费要远远大于点对点的自然刺激。这一点并不难理解。人工刺激的大部分能量都浪费在了神经纤维活性区域之外两电极之间的液体中。根据我们的假设，只有跨过表面阴极区的那部分电流才会形成有效的刺激。自然刺激在以波的形式传播时是点对点的，没有电极，也不会在不同液体中出现短路，因此刺激电流（如果传播是通过电流进行的）的利用效率是非常高的。

正如我所设想的，人们倾向于假设冲动的点对点传播是在动作电流的作用下进行的，而这个动作电流可以在活动位点被检测到。毫无疑问，动作电流和有效刺激之间具有时间上的相关性，并且如果能够适当施加有效刺激，它可以达到产生兴奋所需的强度。我们不知道兴奋性扰动的传播方式，但可以假设任意给定点上的动作电流“刺激”了临近的点，随后产生了新的动作电流，后者又刺激了临近的点，如此反复进行。在任一给定位置，扰动的传播速度和该处动作电流产生的速度成正比，与兴奋过程的时间尺度成反比，这充分说明在这三个因素之间存在着某种因果关系。

It must not be imagined that this self-perpetuating electro-chemical wave is analogous to those waves in physics in which no new energy is required from point to point for the transfer of the wave. In sound, or in light, energy is forced into the medium at the source but no further energy is required for the propagation. Unquestionably in nerve, as the initial heat shows, energy is liberated at each point as the impulse passes by, and, moreover, in the next thirty or forty minutes several times as much energy is set free in restoring completely the *status quo*. With this qualification, however, we can think of the propagated disturbance as some type of self-transmitting electro-chemical wave.

The problem, therefore, of its nature ultimately resolves itself into two: one is that of the change which is produced at the cathode when a current of sufficient intensity causes conditions to become unstable and some mechanism to be fired off; the other is of the physico-chemical basis of the action current itself. If we could understand these two effects we could make a clearer picture of how the impulse is propagated. It seems likely that as the result of "excitation" an unstable state is reached, in which the potential difference normally held at the surface of the fibre is for a moment released. It discharges until some change sets in by which the instability is reversed and the initial condition realised once more. Looked at in this way, the action current is nothing more than a momentary discharge of the resting potential, which is normally to be seen between an injured and an uninjured point of a nerve. Our problem, therefore, comes to this, what is the nature of the instability which is produced by a sufficient outward current through the nerve surface, and how is this instability rapidly reversed and the nerve surface restored to its normal state?

The chemical reactions occurring in muscle are largely those of recovery. Lactic acid formation is involved in the restoration of creatine phosphoric acid which breaks down in activity; oxidation and the combustion of food-stuffs are involved in the restoration of the lactic acid. In nerve we know that in any case nine-tenths of the energy liberated is involved in recovery. It is not going very much further to suppose that the remaining tenth is involved in the immediate recovery process by which the instability produced by stimulation is reversed. I should picture the primary effect as a physico-chemical one transmitting itself along the surface. The surface is rendered somehow unstable by the passage of a current outwards across it, and the instability is propagated by means of the current it releases. The return of the surface to its normal state is the result of some chemical reaction involving the liberation of free energy. Without this return no further impulse could be propagated.

## Mitogenetic Radiation in Nerve

The facts I have described so far are reasonably certain, though their explanation is not. I wish now shortly to refer to some others, of great importance if they are confirmed, but of which the evidence is as yet not quite convincing. During the last few years a number of papers have appeared from Moscow and Leningrad on the subject of so-called "mitogenetic radiation". The name implies that the radiation in question is able to cause mitosis in cells, and the approved method of detecting and measuring it is to determine the increase

千万不能认为这种持续不断的电化学波类似于物理学中的波，在物理学中，波的点对点传播不需要另外增加能量。虽然声波或者光波的产生需要能量，但在传播过程中并不需要额外补充能量。毫无疑问，在神经中，正如初始热所显示的，在冲动传过的每一点上都有能量释放出来，而且在之后的 30 或者 40 分钟内，数倍于此的能量将在体系复原时被释放。而按照这种分析方法，我们可以把传播的扰动看作是一种自动传播的电化学波。

因此，关于神经冲动本质的问题最终归结为了两个问题：其一是当电流强度大到足以引起状态不稳定时在阴极处发生的变化以及它的恢复机制；其二是动作电流本身的物理化学基本原理。如果我们能够弄明白这两个机制，我们就能更加清晰地认识到冲动是如何传播的。也许“兴奋”的结果就是达到一种不稳定态，这时通常存在于纤维表面的电位差会突然释放出来。放电过程会一直持续，直到这种不稳定态得到逆转并再次恢复到初始状态。从这个角度上看，动作电流不过是静息电位的暂时性放电而已，静息电位通常位于神经的损伤处和未损伤处之间。因此我们的问题就是：由足量的经过神经表面的外向电流导致的不稳定性的本质到底是什么，以及这种不稳定性是如何快速逆转并使神经表面恢复到正常状态的？

肌肉中发生的大部分化学反应都是可逆的。活动过程中分解的磷酸肌酸在重新生成时会导致乳酸的产生；而在乳酸的复原过程中会出现氧化和养分的燃烧。我们知道，在神经释放的总能量中，有 9/10 是在复原过程中释放的。由此很容易联想到剩下的 1/10 是由刺激产生的不稳定态在逆转后的快速复原过程中被消耗掉的。我认为初始作用应该来自于沿神经表面传播的物理化学波。因为有向外流动的电流通过，神经表面变得有些不稳定，而这种不稳定会通过神经释放的电流传播开来。一些释放自由能的化学反应将使神经表面恢复到正常状态。在这种恢复完成之前，冲动无法继续传播。

## 神经中促进有丝分裂的辐射

至此为止我描述的事实都是确定的，尽管它们的解释并不确定。现在我想简单地讨论一下另外的几个问题，如果它们能够被证实，其意义是非常重大的，但目前证实这些问题的证据还不是很有说服力。近几年，在许多来自莫斯科和列宁格勒的文章中都提到了所谓的“促进有丝分裂的辐射”。这个名字意味着该辐射可以引起细胞的有丝分裂，而检测和测量它的有效方法是测定放置在辐射下的悬液中酵母细

in the number of yeast cells in a suspension subjected to the radiation. Living organisms themselves are said to give out this radiation, particularly when active, and the analysis of the radiation is held to indicate the type of chemical reaction involved in the activity.

The yeast cells prepared in a special manner are held in a suspension which is placed in two tubes, an experimental and a control. The experimental tube is exposed through its open end to the radiation in question, the control is kept without radiation. At the end of the exposure, samples are taken and incubated, and after three or four hours the cells are killed and counted; the excess of cells in the experimental suspension is expressed as a percentage of the control.

The radiation stated to be given out by living cells is in the ultra-violet region, chiefly between 1900 A. and 2500 A. Its amount is so relatively large that it can be split up by a quartz spectrograph into bands 10 A. wide and each band examined separately for its effect in producing the division of yeast cells.

This is not the occasion to deal with the general question of mitogenetic radiation, but a few months ago a series of papers appeared from the laboratory in Leningrad in which various results obtained from nerve are discussed. If it be true that excited nerve gives out a characteristic radiation which can be used to identify the chemical reactions involved in its activity, then indeed a new day has dawned in the very difficult problem of the physical nature of nerve activity.

In a figure in a recent paper by Kalendaroff (*Pflügers Arch.*, 231), successive spectra, analysed by a quartz spectrograph and the yeast cell indicator, refer to (1) a resting nerve, (2) ground up nerve, (3) mechanical stimulus, radiation from the point of stimulation, (4) electrical stimulus, between the electrodes, (5) injury, radiation 20 mm. from the place of injury, (6) electrical stimulus, radiation 20 mm. away, (7) mechanical stimulus, 20 mm. away. In the lower half of the figure there are spectra for (1) oxidation of pyrogallol in air, (2) glycolysis, (3) action of phosphatase, (4) splitting of creatine-phosphoric acid, (5) splitting off of ammonia from protein.

When we remember that maximal continuous stimulation of nerve does not double its resting metabolism, the variety and strength of the radiation emitted from active nerve, under the comparatively mild stimuli administered to it, are rather astonishing. A vague suspicion that the results are almost too good to be true is a little increased by a subsequent paper by Schamarina which shows an evident misunderstanding of the nature of nerve activity. It is known, and it is an obvious consequence of the existence of a refractory period following the passage of an impulse, that when two nerve impulses start at opposite ends of a nerve and meet in the middle they are unable to pass one another and both are wiped out. When a single impulse traverses the nerve the whole of the nerve goes through a phase of activity. When two impulses start at opposite ends of the nerve they meet in the middle and stop, but again the whole of the nerve has gone through the active phase.

胞数目的增加。据说活的生物体本身可以放出这种辐射，尤其是在它们活动的时候，而对辐射的分析则能够显示出该活动包含的化学反应类型。

将用特殊方法制备的酵母细胞置于悬液中，它们被分别装在两个试管内，一个是实验管，另一个是对照管。实验管的开口端暴露于辐射中，对照管则不受辐射。辐射结束后取出样品并进行孵育，3~4 个小时后杀死细胞并计数。实验悬液中增加的细胞数以相对于对照样品中细胞数的百分比来表示。

上述由活细胞发出的辐射位于紫外区，主要在 1900 Å 到 2500 Å 之间。该辐射强度很大，可以被石英摄谱仪分裂成一系列 10 Å 宽的谱峰，人们可以分别检测每一个谱峰对酵母细胞分裂的影响。

现在不是解决与促进有丝分裂的辐射的相关问题的时候，不过几个月前，来自于列宁格勒实验室的一系列论文都讨论了从与神经相关的实验中得到的不同结果。如果兴奋的神经能够放出特征辐射，这种辐射可被用于鉴定在兴奋过程中发生的化学反应，那么人们就可以在新的起点上研究关于神经活性的物理本质这一非常困难的问题了。

在卡伦达洛夫最近的一篇论文（《欧洲生理学杂志》，第 231 卷）中有一幅图，图中有若干张用石英摄谱仪分析得到、以酵母细胞为指示剂的连续光谱，其中（1）静息状态的神经，（2）破碎的神经，（3）机械刺激状态下，刺激点发出的辐射，（4）电刺激状态下，电极间的辐射，（5）损伤状态下，距损伤点 20 mm 处的辐射，（6）电刺激状态下，距刺激点 20 mm 处的辐射，（7）机械刺激状态下，距刺激点 20 mm 处的辐射。在图的下半部分是下列反应的图谱：（1）焦酚在空气中氧化，（2）糖酵解作用，（3）磷酸酶的作用，（4）磷酸肌酸分解，（5）从蛋白中放出氨的反应。

我们知道即使是神经中最大的持续刺激也不能使它的静息代谢加倍，那么在比较温和的刺激下，从激活的神经中发出的辐射种类如此之多，强度如此之高是非常令人惊讶的。有人怀疑这些结果过于完美以至于很难让人相信是真的，沙玛丽娜后来发表的文章加深了人们对这些结果的怀疑，她所论述的内容其实是对神经活性本质的误解。我们知道：如果两个神经冲动分别从一条神经的两端开始相向传播并在中间汇合，它们将不能穿过对方而导致两者都消失掉，这显然是因为在冲动传过后存在一个不应期。当单个冲动传过神经时，整条神经都会经历一个兴奋期。当两个冲动从一条神经的两端开始相向传播并在中间汇合而终止时，整条神经同样也会经历一个兴奋期。如果发出的辐射是神经兴奋的结果，那么在上述两种情况下发出的

If radiation is given out as the result of nerve activity, its emission should occur equally in the two cases. Schamarina, however, expecting that because the two impulses destroy one another, therefore there should be no radiation from the point where they meet, has described experiments in support of the expectation. If the results are true, we need a new picture of the propagated disturbance in nerve.

The suspicion is strengthened by a further paper by Brainess describing the use of the same technique for the study of human fatigue. At the beginning of this remarkable paper it is stated that modern methods for investigating the phenomena of fatigue in man leave much to be desired, and that the author therefore took up the method of mitogenetic radiation in order to find a new and more accurate means of describing the state of fatigue in a factory worker. One hundred girls working in an electrical factory were examined, samples of their blood being taken at eight in the morning, at three in the afternoon and at five in the afternoon. The blood was dried on filter paper, then dissolved in distilled water and finally allowed to give out its radiation, which was measured as usual by the yeast cells. At eight in the morning the mean value of the radiation coming from their blood was 28, as measured by the percentage increase, over the control, of the number of cells in the yeast suspension. After seven hours work the girls were apparently completely exhausted, for their blood gave out no radiation at all, except in a few isolated cases. After two hours rest the radiation had risen to 28 again.

Of the social and industrial importance of these results, supposing them to be true, I need not speak, though I wonder if there are many British factory operatives who would be found completely exhausted, even of "radiation", after seven hours work. An even stranger result follows. Not only did haemolysed blood emit radiation which was abolished by seven hours work in a factory, but also the cornea and the conjunctiva did the same. The girls apparently had only to look at the yeast cells to set them dividing! At eight in the morning the radiation from the girls' eyes had a mean value of 24, after seven hours work it had a mean value of 4, after two hours recovery a mean value of 20. Finally—and most unromantically—it is stated that the spectrum analysis of the radiation given out by the girls' eyes showed that its only important component is that due to glycolysis!

It is not easy, in the case of the paper describing the results of the two nerve impulses meeting one another, to avoid the feeling that the expectation of a certain result has had something to do with its appearance, and it is difficult not to draw the same conclusion from the paper describing the new test for fatigue. The claims made are clearly most important if they can be verified, and one hopes that verification may soon be at hand. The difficulty in understanding nerve is largely that the changes in it are too small for ordinary chemical methods to detect. If the new methods elaborated by our Russian colleagues can throw real light on the subject, then we shall be deeply indeed in their debt. At present, however, one cannot stifle suspicion that the phenomena described may have more to do with the enthusiasm of those who describe them than with the physical nature of the nerve itself.

(**131**, 501-508; 1933)

辐射应该是相等的。但沙玛丽娜认为由于这两个冲动都破坏了对方，所以在它们汇合的地方应该没有辐射放出，她在文中描述了证实这一假设的实验。如果这个结论是正确的，那么我们就需要用新的方法来解释在神经中传播的扰动了。

布瑞内斯的一篇论文也加深了这个疑点，他把同样的方法应用于研究人类的疲劳。他在这篇著名文章的开头指出：目前用于研究人类疲劳现象的方法还有许多需要改进的地方，作者为了找到一种能够更加准确地描述工厂工人疲劳状态的新方法而采用了促进有丝分裂的辐射的方法。他对在电子工厂工作的 100 名女孩进行了测试，分别在早上 8 点、下午 3 点和下午 5 点采集她们的血液。血液在滤纸上吸干，然后溶解在蒸馏水中，使之能够放出辐射，并按常规用酵母细胞测定辐射强度。早上 8 点她们血液中辐射的平均强度值是 28，平均强度值用实验样本悬液中酵母细胞的数量相比于对照样本中增加的百分比表示。在工作了 7 个小时以后，女孩们显然已经疲惫不堪了，因为除了个别的几个人例外以外，大部分人的血液都不再发出任何辐射了。经过 2 个小时的休息后，辐射强度再次增加到 28。

尽管我怀疑是否有很多英国工厂的工人在工作了 7 个小时之后都会筋疲力尽，即使是仅仅表现在“辐射”上，但如果上述结果是正确的，那么这些结果对社会和工业的重要性我就不必赘述了。之后一个更加奇怪的结果出现了：不仅溶血的血液能够发出在工厂工作 7 小时后可能会消失的辐射，角膜和结膜也会产生同样的效果。女孩们只需看着这些酵母就可以使它们发生分裂！早上 8 点，从女孩们眼睛中发出的辐射平均值为 24，工作了 7 小时后平均值变成 4，休息 2 小时后平均值又达到 20。最后，也是最实际的结果是：对女孩眼睛中发出的辐射进行光谱分析后发现其唯一重要的成分来自于糖酵解！

人们很自然地希望能从描述两个神经冲动相遇的文章中发现某种结论以解释一些现象，对于这篇描述疲劳检测新方法的文章也是一样。显然，如果前面提出的观点被证明是正确的，它们将变得非常重要，人们希望相关的验证工作能马上开始进行。在认识神经的过程中遇到的主要困难是其中的变化过于微小，用普通化学方法难以检测。如果俄罗斯同行们提出的新方法确实能够为这一领域的研究带来一线曙光，那我们真不知道要如何感谢他们才好。但是目前我们不能不怀疑他们所描述的现象在很大程度上是出于实验者的热情，而不是与神经本身的物理本质相关。

（毛晨晖 翻译；刘力 审稿）

# A New Alloy, "Stainless-Invar"

K. Honda

## Editor's Note

**Precision-engineered mechanical devices such as watches rely on metal allows that will not expand significantly when warmed, which might otherwise cause jamming. Such low thermal expansion is rare, but was discovered in 1896 by Charles Edouard Guillaume in an alloy of iron and nickel, christened Invar because of its invariance. The discovery won Guillaume the 1920 Nobel Prize in physics. Here Kotaro Hondo explains how his theory of the Invar phenomenon—the first real attempt at such a thing—led him to new, improved formulations for Invar alloys: one with a very low thermal expansion, another that contracts slightly when heated. Honda became one of Japan's foremost metallurgists, and invented a new type of permanently magnetic steel called KS steel.**

INVAR, invented by Ch. Ed. Guillaume in 1896, has a small coefficient of thermal expansion, about $1.2 \times 10^{-6}$. Since then, no better invar has been obtained. I have, for the last six years, been engaging in the investigation of alloys having a small coefficient of expansion and obtained in June, 1929, an alloy[1] containing about 63.5 percent iron, 31.5 percent nickel and .5 percent cobalt, which has a smaller coefficient of expansion than that of fused silica.

Several explanations of the small expansibility of invar have been proposed, but none can be considered to be satisfactory. I also tried to explain this phenomenon and developed a new theory[1] by which the small expansibility of invar can be satisfactorily explained from magnetic data. Following up this theory, I began to investigate the thermal expansion of the ternary alloys of iron-cobalt-chromium and found that an addition of a small quantity of chromium to iron-cobalt alloys containing more than 50 percent cobalt considerably reduces their expansibility. In July, 1931, I obtained an alloy having a much smaller coefficient of expansion than that of fused silica. For example, the coefficient of linear expansion at ordinary temperature of an alloy containing about 36.5 percent iron, 54.5 percent cobalt and 9 percent chromium is less than $10^{-7}$ in the annealed state, and that of another alloy having a very similar composition to the above has even a negative coefficient amounting to $-1.2\times10^{-6}$. These alloys are so resistant to corrosion that polished surfaces can be left for several months in a moist atmosphere, water, sea water, etc., without showing any rust spots; they have been called "stainless-invar" (Hakar Masumoto).

(**131**, 587; 1933)

Kotaro Honda: Research Institute for Iron, Steel and Other Metals, Sendai, Japan, March 10.

Reference:

1 *Sci. Rep. Tôhoku Imp. Univ.*, **20**, 101 (1931).

# 一种新型合金——“不生锈的因瓦合金”

本多光太郎

## 编者按

像手表这样的精密机械要求所用的金属材料在受热时不会明显膨胀，否则就会出现故障。这种热膨胀系数极低的金属非常少见，但在1896年查尔斯·爱德华·纪尧姆发现了一种膨胀率很低的铁镍合金，由于它非常恒定所以被正式命名为因瓦合金。这一发现使纪尧姆赢得了1920年的诺贝尔物理奖。本多光太郎利用纪尧姆的因瓦合金理论研制出了几个改进后的新配方：其中一个具有非常低的热膨胀系数；另一个在加热时反而会出现很小的收缩，他在本文中记录了这些在因瓦合金方面的初次尝试。后来本多光太郎成为日本最著名的冶金学家之一，他发明了一种被称为KS钢的永磁钢。

因瓦合金是纪尧姆于1896年发明的，它的热膨胀系数很小，大约为$1.2\times10^{-6}$。此后人们再也没有得到过比它更好的因瓦合金。在过去的6年里，我一直致力于研究小膨胀系数的合金，并于1929年6月得到了一种约含63.5%的铁、31.5%的镍和0.5%的钴的合金[1]，它的热膨胀系数比熔融石英还要小。

对于因瓦合金的小膨胀性人们已经提出了若干种解释，但都不尽如人意。我也曾试着解释过这种现象，并建立了一种新理论[1]，该理论认为可以利用磁学数据合理地解释因瓦合金的小膨胀性。根据这一理论，我开始研究铁–钴–铬三元合金的热膨胀性，并发现向钴含量超过50%的铁–钴合金中添加少量的铬会使它们的膨胀性显著降低。1931年7月，我得到了一种膨胀系数比熔融石英小很多的合金。比如在常温下，一种约含36.5%的铁、54.5%的钴和9%的铬的合金在退火状态下的线性膨胀系数会小于$10^{-7}$，而另一种组成与之非常类似的合金的线性膨胀系数甚至为负数，达到$-1.2\times10^{-6}$。这些合金都是高度耐腐蚀的，其抛光表面可以在潮气、水、海水等环境下放置几个月而不出现任何锈斑；它们已经被人们称为“不生锈的因瓦合金”(Hakar Masumoto)。

（王耀杨 翻译；沈宝莲 审稿）

# Amino-Acids, Proteins and Proteolytic Enzymes*: I

M. Bergmann

## Editor's Note

**In 1932, German biochemist Max Bergmann and a colleague had devised a method for stringing together any two amino acids into a dipeptide—the benzylcarbonate method of peptide synthesis. Here, he outlines the steps of this reaction before describing how he is using it to study the subtleties of the peptide bonding. By recording how the same enzyme performs on the bond between different synthetic amino acid combinations, he finds "surprising differences of behaviour between closely related compounds". Such experiments allowed him to begin to work out the effect of the individual amino acids on the nature of the bond between them, and also the influence of the bond on the structure of the amino acids themselves.**

APPROXIMATELY twenty-five amino-acids are generally recognised at the present time as constituents of proteins. It is usually assumed that the amino-acids are liked together in the protein molecule by condensation of the carboxyl group of one amino-acid with the amino group of the next with elimination of water to form an amide or peptide linkage; of such linkages the protein molecule contains very large numbers.

It has been calculated that the number of known amino-acids is fully sufficient to account, by variations in the order in which they are combined, for the existence not only of the clearly differentiated fundamental types of protein but also of the enormous number of individual proteins which are required by biological and immunological theory.

Such an arithmetical calculation is, however, no longer satisfying; we desire to know more precisely what is the influence of the nature of the component amino-acids and of the order in which the latter are combined upon the properties of the protein as a whole. One might anticipate, for example, that the action of proteolytic enzymes on a given peptide linkage would be determined by the properties and arrangement of the amino-acids of which the peptide is built up; it is impossible, however, to regard the properties of a protein as a simple summation of those of its constituent amino-acids.

The remarkable stability of the amino-acids is usually ascribed to their zwitterionic nature, from which results their capacity to form internal salts; the immediate neighbourhood

---

* Substance of three lectures on "The Chemistry of Proteins" delivered at University College Hospital Medical School, London, on January 20, 23 and 24, 1993.

# 氨基酸、蛋白质和蛋白质水解酶* I

马克斯·伯格曼

## 编者按

1932年，德国生物化学家马克斯·伯格曼与他的一位同事一起设计了一种方法可以将任何两个氨基酸串在一起形成二肽——即多肽合成的苯甲基碳酸法。在本文中，他先简要介绍了反应的步骤，然后描述了他如何利用这种方法来研究肽键特征的细微之处。通过记录同一种酶对不同人工合成氨基酸结合而成的不同肽键的作用情况，他发现"极其相似的化合物之间令人吃惊的行为差异"。这样的实验结果使他能够开始揭示每一种特定氨基酸对所参与形成的肽键性质的影响，以及这样的肽键反过来对所参与的氨基酸自身结构的影响。

目前，大约有25种氨基酸被广泛认为是蛋白质的组成成分。通常的假设是，在蛋白质分子中，氨基酸之间是通过一个氨基酸的羧基与另一个氨基酸的氨基脱水缩合成酰胺键（也被称为肽键）而连接在一起的；一个蛋白质分子中包含了大量这样的连接。

计算结果表明：通过组合顺序的变化，已知数量的氨基酸不仅足以形成已经被明确区分的那些基本类型的蛋白质，而且也足以满足生物学以及免疫学理论所需要的数目庞大的特异蛋白质分子。

然而，这样的算术计算已不再令人满意；我们期望更为精确地了解所含氨基酸组分的本质以及它们相互结合的顺序对于所形成的蛋白质整体性质的影响。例如，有人可能会预测，蛋白质水解酶对于特定肽键的特异作用可能取决于构成肽链的氨基酸的性质以及排列的顺序；但一种蛋白质的性质不能认为就是组成它的氨基酸性质的简单叠加。

氨基酸的超常稳定性通常被归因于它们的两性离子特性，这使它们具备了形成内盐的能力。那些带相反电荷的解离基团之间的毗邻肯定会对氨基酸的行为施以决

* 本文内容根据作者分别于1933年1月20日、23日和24日在伦敦大学学院附属医院的医学学校所作的关于"蛋白质化学"的三次演讲整理而成。

of oppositely charged ionised groups must indeed exercise a dominating influence on the behaviour of the amino-acids. It is therefore to be expected that we shall modify the properties of the amino-acids, and in particular their chemical behaviour, if we combine the ionisable groups in peptide linkage and thereby alter their mutual electro-chemical effects.

The outstanding problem of modern protein chemistry is thus twofold in nature: What effect does combination in peptide linkage exercise upon the different amino-acids? And how is the nature of the peptide linkage itself influenced by the character of the amino-acids which take part in its formation? Although work on both aspects of this question is still in an elementary stage, a number of facts have already been revealed which are significant both from a chemical and a biochemical point of view.

In the first place, I should like to show by a few examples that we can reveal a new series of chemical properties of the amino-acids if we convert the latter, by simple acylation of the amino group, into a condition analogous with that in which they exist in peptides. The simplest case is that of acetylation; if we acetylate the amino group of an optically active amino-acid, we find that contact with a small amount of acetic anhydride at the ordinary temperature is sufficient to catalyse the rapid racemisation of the acetylated amino-acid[1]. The striking ease with which this racemisation occurs must be ascribed to an intermediate enolisation:

$$R.CH(NH.OC.CH_3).COOH \longrightarrow R.C.(NH.OC.CH_3){:}C(OH)_2$$

In this reaction, therefore, different parts of the same molecule which are not directly connected with one another, namely, the peptide linkage and the $\alpha$-hydrogen atom, exhibit a definite mutual influence. A similar mutual influence but in the opposite sense is shown by the complete absence of racemisation when chloroacetylated amino-acids are treated with acetic anhydride under the same conditions. Such remote actions of different parts of the molecule upon one another are of special importance in enzymic processes; their investigation in model experiments makes it possible to expose properties of the amino-acids and peptides which would otherwise remain hidden and to draw conclusions therefrom as to the processes which these compounds may undergo in metabolism.

A particularly surprising example is provided by pyridylacetylphenylalanine, which is a dipeptide closely related to glycylphenylalanine; this compound, when treated with acetic anhydride and pyridine at the ordinary temperature, is converted into acetyldehydropheny lalanine with liberation of pyridine and water:

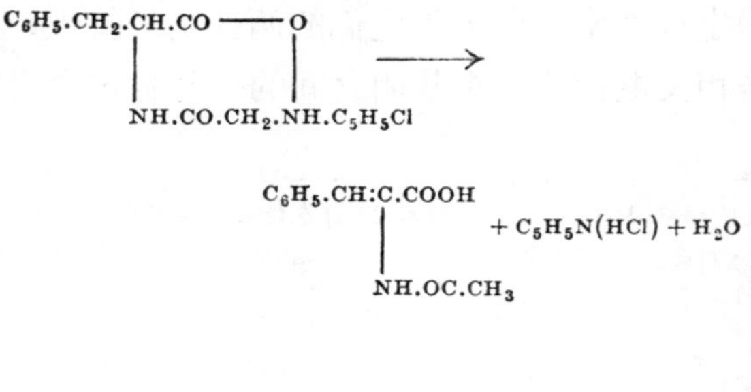

定性的影响。因此可以期许的是，如果我们把通过肽键连接的可解离基团组合在一起并因此而改变它们各自的电化学效用的话，那么我们也就必然会改变这些参与形成肽键的氨基酸的性质，特别是它们的化学行为。

因此，现代蛋白质化学的突出问题在于其两重性本质：肽键的形成对所参与的氨基酸施加何种影响？反过来，肽键自身的特性又是如何受到直接参与形成它的氨基酸的性质影响的？尽管人们对与该问题有关的这两个方向的研究尚处于起步阶段，但已经取得了不少进展，无论从化学角度还是从生物化学角度看，这些进展都非常重要。

首先，我想通过一些例子来说明的是，如果我们通过对氨基进行简单的酰基化处理，使其转变成与它在多肽中相类似的状态，那么我们就能够揭示氨基酸的一系列新的化学性质。最简单的例子就是乙酰化反应，如果我们对一种具有旋光活性的氨基酸的氨基进行乙酰化处理的话，就会发现在常温下，只要与少量的乙酸酐接触，就足以催化乙酰化氨基酸发生快速的外消旋过程[1]。这种外消旋过程之所以能够如此容易就发生，肯定是因为产生了烯醇化中间体。

$$R.CH(NH.OC.CH_3).COOH \longrightarrow R.C.(NH.OC.CH_3){:}C(OH)_2$$

因此，在此反应过程中，同一分子中并不直接相连的不同部分，如肽键与 $\alpha$– 氢原子之间，表现出了确凿无疑的相互影响。一种类似的但表现相反的相互影响是，当在同样条件下用乙酸酐处理氯乙酰化氨基酸时，结果完全不发生外消旋化。分子内不同部分之间的这种远程相互作用对于酶的催化过程就显得特别重要了。通过这样的模拟实验所进行的研究使我们能够揭示出那些否则仍将处于隐蔽状态的氨基酸和多肽的性质，并进而认识氨基酸和多肽在代谢过程中所发生的变化。

令人吃惊的是，一种非常类似于甘氨酰苯丙氨酸的二肽——吡啶乙酰苯丙氨酸，当在常温下用乙酸酐和吡啶处理时，被转变成了乙酰脱氢苯丙氨酸，同时产生吡啶和水：

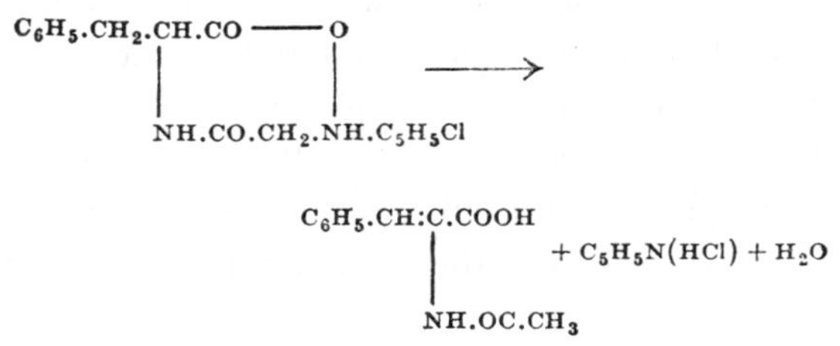

The phenylalanine is thus dehydrogenated and the liberated hydrogen is employed to hydrogenate the pyridylacetic acid to pyridine and acetic acid[2]. Here, therefore, we have in one half of the molecule the first example of the direct transformation of an amino-acid into a fatty acid, accompanied by simultaneous unsaturation of the amino-acid constituting the other half to give a dehydroamino-acid. According to the theory of Wieland, a dehydrogenation of this character would require the activation of the amino-acid and the presence of an acceptor for the liberated hydrogen; the activation of the phenylalanine is brought about by its combination in peptide linkage with transient formation of a cyclic anhydropeptied whilst the pyridylacetic acid residue serves as hydrogen acceptor.

According to the prevailing view, the biological degradation of an amino-acid to a keto-acid begins with a dehydrogenation, and conversely the biological synthesis of an amino-acid from a keto-acid ends with a hydrogenation. It is possible to combine examples of both these processes in a single experiment[3] *in vitro*. The introduction of the dehydrophenylalanyl residue into aspartic acid yields a cyclic anhydride; dissolution of the latter in normal sodium hydroxide causes transference of two hydrogen atoms from the aspartic acid to the dehydrophenylalanine:

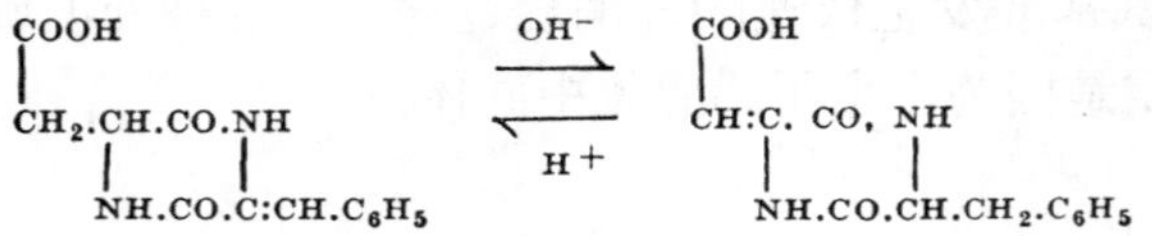


whilst in acid solution the reverse transformation may be accomplished. In the first case, therefore, degradation of the aspartic acid has begun and in doing so has completed the synthesis of phenylalanine from its unsaturated precursor. These experiments show that the hydrogenation : dehydrogenation potentials of the individual amino-acids are different; in metabolism there must indeed exist among the amino-acids a constant competition for hydrogen, the outcome of which will vary with circumstances.

By similar facile reactions it is possible to convert serine with elimination of water and cysteine with elimination of hydrogen sulphide into dehydroalanine and thence into pyruvic acid; serine and cysteine are thus brought into genetic relationship with the simple amino-acids and their nitrogen-free transformation products[4].

Of all the amino-acids, the most widely distributed is arginine, which occupies a special position also by virtue of its guanido group. Arginine can be converted into a peculiarly reactive condition by complete acetylation with simultaneous elimination of water. The triacetylanhydroarginine so formed has a strong tendency, in presence of water and of hydroxy or amino compounds in general, to lose the cyanamide residue, which is itself transferred to the accompanying compound; a mixture of sarcosine with triacetylanhydro-arginine, for example, yields creatine together with a derivative of ornithine[5].

在此过程中苯丙氨酸发生了脱氢反应，释放出来的氢进而促使吡啶乙酸发生氢化反应而转变成吡啶和乙酸[2]。因此在这里，我们第一次将分子的一半直接从氨基酸转化成了脂肪酸，同时使氨基酸分子的另一半发生不饱和化，转变为脱氢氨基酸。根据维兰德的理论，这样的脱氢反应需要在氨基酸先被活化，并存在一种氢受体的条件下才可发生。苯丙氨酸的活化要通过参与肽键连接和瞬时性地形成一个环化的脱水肽，此时吡啶乙酸残基担当了氢的受体。

根据目前被大家接受的观点，氨基酸通过生物降解生成酮酸的过程起始于脱氢作用，反之，从酮酸生物合成氨基酸的过程是以一步氢化作用结束。人们可以通过一个单一的体外实验使上述两个过程同时发生[3]。将一个脱氢苯丙氨酰残基引入到一个天冬氨酸分子内，就会产生一个环化酐；将后者溶解于正常的氢氧化钠溶液中后，就会导致天冬氨酸分子中的两个氢原子转移至脱氢苯丙氨酸上。

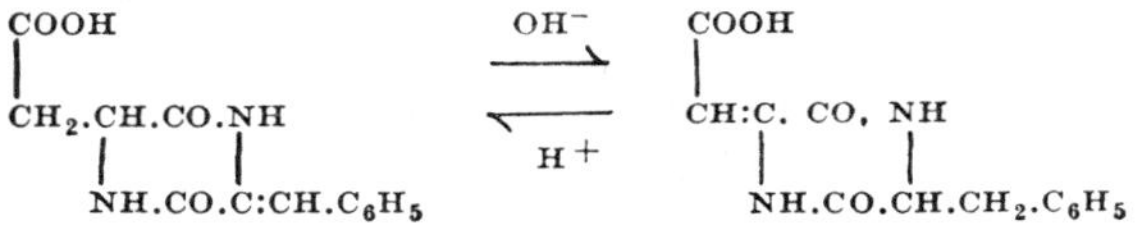


但在酸溶液中，转化可能沿反方向进行。因此，在氢氧化钠溶液里发生的反应中，天冬氨酸的降解过程开始了，这同时也完成了从苯丙氨酸的不饱和前体到苯丙氨酸的合成过程。这些实验结果表明，特定氨基酸的氢化和脱氢潜力是不同的。在代谢过程中，不同氨基酸之间对于氢的竞争自然是一直在发生着的事件，最终结果随所处环境不同而异。

通过类似的简单化学反应，也可以使丝氨酸通过脱水、半胱氨酸通过脱硫化氢而转化成脱氢丙氨酸，并进而转化成丙酮酸。这样人们就可以将丝氨酸和半胱氨酸与简单的氨基酸以及它们的无氮转化产物丙酮酸之间建立起一种遗传关联了[4]。

在所有氨基酸中，分布最广泛的是精氨酸，它也因为带有胍基而地位特殊。精氨酸可以通过伴随脱水过程的彻底乙酰化反应而转变成一种具有相当反应活性的状态。如此形成的三乙酰脱水精氨酸，在有水、羟基或者氨基化合物存在的条件下，通常会具有很强的去除氰胺残基的倾向，其自身转化为其伴生化合物。例如，将肌氨酸（即 N–甲基甘氨酸）和三乙酰脱水精氨酸混合，可以得到肌酸以及一种鸟氨酸衍生物[5]。

The latter result is of interest in relation to two physiological processes: (1) the creatine synthesis *in vitro* shows how creatine-nitrogen can be derived from two different amino-acids; it is probable that in the course of metabolism creatine is formed in a similar manner from two amino-acids of which one is arginine; (2) the conversion of arginine into ornithine by the enzyme arginase demands that the latter be attached to the arginine molecule in such a manner that the arginine is activated and hydrolysed to ornithine even by cold water; this process is imitated by the case of hydrolysis of triacetylanhydroarginine to acetyl derivatives of ornithine and of urea.

There remains to be discussed yet another noteworthy transformation of arginine which has long caused confusion in the literature; if arginine be esterified with methyl alcohol, the resulting ester passes spontaneously into ornithine methyl ester and *bis*guanidovaleric acid:

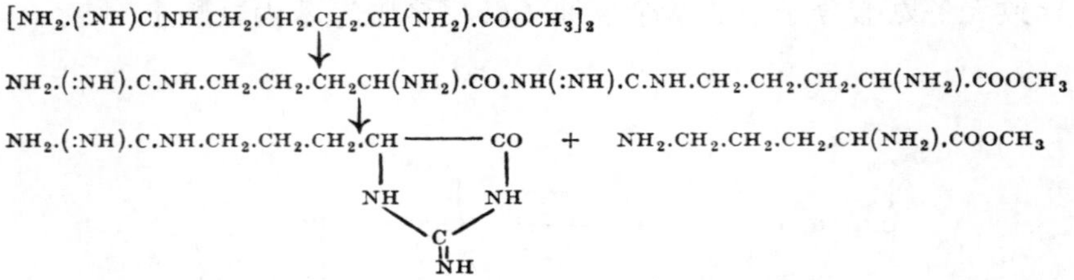


This reaction must occur in the metabolism of those shell-fish from which Kutscher, Ackermann and Flössner[6] have isolated arcaine (1:4-diguanidobutane).

The few examples which have been given indicate what an abundance of unsuspected reactions can be elicited from the amino-acids if their zwitterionic character is destroyed by combination in peptide linkage. Almost every amino-acid is affected differently in this respect; conversely, therefore, every amino-acid must have a different influence on the peptide bond.

In order to be able to study this influence on representative material, it is necessary to prepare different peptide combinations artificially and to test the action of enzymes upon them. To carry this task to its logical conclusion would be a formidable undertaking; fortunately, however, it suffices to prepare peptides containing representative members of the most important types of amino-acids.

Chemists have striven for more than thirty years to discover suitable methods for the synthesis of peptides containing the more complex amino-acids, but until recently only isolated successes have been obtained[7]. Quite lately, however, a general method has been developed[8], the essential feature being the nature of the acid residue used to block the amino group.

上一段里描述的后面一种结果因与下面两个生理过程相关而引起了人们的兴趣：(1) 这样的肌酸体外合成结果暗示，肌酸分子中的氮是如何衍生自两种不同氨基酸的。可以推测的是，在代谢过程中，肌酸就是以类似的方式利用两种不同氨基酸前体合成的，其中之一可能就是精氨酸。(2) 在精氨酸酶催化作用下精氨酸转变为鸟氨酸的过程，需要酶被通过这样一种方式连接到精氨酸分子上，使得即使在冷水中精氨酸也可以被活化和水解而产生鸟氨酸；这样的一个过程可以通过三乙酰脱水精氨酸水解生成鸟氨酸和尿素的乙酰化衍生物来模拟。

下面我们要讨论的是精氨酸分子的另一种值得注意的转变，文献对此的报道长期以来一直很混乱；如果精氨酸被甲醇处理而酯化的话，所得到的产物酯就会自发转变为鸟氨酸甲酯和二胍基戊酸。

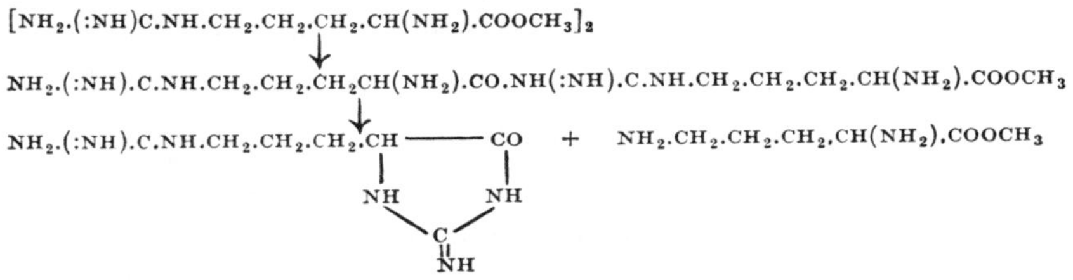


该反应在甲壳类动物的代谢中必然会发生。库切尔、阿克曼和弗勒斯纳[6]就曾经从甲壳类动物中分离出了蛸碱（1:4 – 二胍基丁烷）。

上述几个例子显示：由于形成肽键时破坏了氨基酸的两性离子特性，使得氨基酸能够发生那么多人们从未想象到的化学反应。在此方面，几乎每一种氨基酸所受到的影响都是不同的。反之，每一种氨基酸对肽键的影响也肯定是相异的。

为了能够利用有代表性的材料来研究这种影响，我们需要人工制备各种不同的多肽样品，并检验酶对这些多肽的作用是否存在差异。希望执行此任务并得到合乎逻辑的结论自然是极其困难的。然而，幸运的是，我们只需制备含有各种重要代表性类型氨基酸的多肽样品就够了。

三十多年来，化学家们一直在努力寻找适当的方法来合成包含更为复杂氨基酸的多肽，但直到最近也只有少数几个案例是成功的[7]。不过，就在不久前人们总算成功地建立了一种通用的方法[8]，其关键之处在于用来封闭氨基的酸性残基的选择方面。

The acid chloride of benzylcarbonic acid is readily obtained by the interaction of benzyl alcohol and phosgene and can be condensed with any amino-acid to yield the corresponding benzylcarbonato derivative. The benzylcarbonato-amino-acids are beautifully crystalline substances which can be easily transformed into their acid chlorides or azides and these in turn can be condensed with other amino-acids to yield benzylcarbonatopeptides. Most important, however, is the fact that the benzylcarbonato residue can be split off without the employment of a hydrolytic agent, so that it can be eliminated from a benzylcarbonatopeptide without danger of scission of the peptide bond. The removal of the benzylcarbonato residue is accomplished by catalytic hydrogenation in presence of palladium black, under which conditions the benzyl residue is eliminated as toluene and the resulting carboxy-amino derivative loses carbon dioxide spontaneously to give the free peptide. The last step of the process proceeds not only with ease but also in most cases almost quantitatively:

$$C_6H_5.CH_2.O.CO.Cl + NH_2.CHR.COOH \longrightarrow C_6H_5.CH_2.O.CO.NH.CH.R.COOH$$

$$C_6H_5.CH_2.O.CO.NH.CHR.COCl + NH_2.CHR^1.COOH \longrightarrow C_6H_5.CH_2.O.CO.NH.CHR.CO.NH.CH.R^1.COOH$$

$$C_6H_5.CH.O.CO.NH.CHR.CO.NH.CHR^1.COOH + H_2 \longrightarrow NH_2.CHR.CO.NH.CHR^1.COOH + C_6H_5.CH_3 + CO_2$$

A further advantage of the benzylcarbonato method is that it involves no risk of racemisation; with its aid, in fact, the preparation of many optically active peptides, which have hitherto been practically inaccessible, becomes a trivial matter.

A complete picture of the possibilities of the new method of peptide synthesis cannot be given here, but it is possible to indicate some of the new lines of research which it opens up; in particular it may be of interest to mention certain hitherto unobtainable peptides which have been prepared by the benzylcarbonato method and to describe their behaviour towards enzymes.

As representative peptides we may mention: d-*Glutamyl*-d-*glutamic acid*, a substance with three carboxyl groups and one amino group and therefore strongly acidic in character; d-*Lysyl*-d-*glutamic acid*, the first example of a dipeptide of a diamino-acid and an amino-dicarboxylic acid; d-*Lysyl*-l-*histidine*, a dipeptide of two strongly basic amino-acids; l-*Asparagyl*-l-*tyrosine* and d-*glutamyl*-l-*tyrosine*, two closely related dipeptides which, however, differ remarkably in their behaviour towards enzymes (see below); l-*Tyrosyl*-l-*tyrosine*, a dipeptide containing two phenolic groups; *Glycyl*-l-*proline* and d-*alanyl*-l-*proline*, which occupy a distinctive position owing to the nature of the peptide linkage:—

苯甲基碳酸酰基氯可以很容易通过苯甲醇和碳酰氯（光气）的相互作用而获得，并可以与任意一种氨基酸缩合形成相应的苯甲基碳酸衍生物。苯甲基碳酸－氨基酸是一种可以形成漂亮结晶的物质，也很容易被转化成它们的酰基氯或叠氮化衍生物，后面两种物质又进而可以与其他氨基酸进行缩合，产生苯甲基碳酸多肽。然而最为重要的是，苯甲基碳酸残基在不使用水解试剂的条件下就能够被去除掉，因而它可以被从苯甲基碳酸多肽中去除而不会产生肽键断裂的危险。苯甲基碳酸残基的去除是通过钯黑催化下发生的氢化反应实现的，在这种条件下，苯甲基以甲苯形式被消除，剩下的羧基－氨基衍生物自发脱去二氧化碳而生成自由的多肽。这个过程的最后一步不仅非常容易发生，而且在大多数情况下几乎都是按照定量关系进行的：

$$C_6H_5.CH_2.O.CO.Cl + NH_2.CHR.COOH \longrightarrow C_6H_5.CH_2.O.CO.NH.CH.R.COOH$$

$$C_6H_5.CH_2.O.CO.NH.CHR.COCl + NH_2.CHR^1.COOH \longrightarrow C_6H_5.CH_2.O.CO.NH.CHR.CO.NH.CH.R^1.COOH$$

$$C_6H_5.CH.O.CO.NH.CHR.CO.NH.CHR^1.COOH + H_2 \longrightarrow NH_2.CHR.CO.NH.CHR^1.COOH + C_6H_5.CH_3 + CO_2$$

苯甲基碳酸法的另一个优点在于，它不会带来消旋化的危险；事实上，正因为有了这种方法，制备许多迄今为止被认为是无法得到的光学活性多肽已经不是什么难事了。

因为空间有限，在这里我无法对这种多肽合成新方法的可能应用进行全方位的描述，但可以指出它所开辟的一些新的研究方向；我想提及某些迄今为止无法制备但已经可以利用苯甲基碳酸法获得的多肽并描述它们作为酶的作用对象的行为也许会引起大家的兴趣。

作为代表性的多肽，我们可以提及的包括：*d*–谷氨酰–*d*–谷氨酸，一种具有三个羧基和一个氨基，因而表现出强酸性特征的物质；*d*–赖氨酰–*d*–谷氨酸，是人们获得的第一个由一种二氨基氨基酸（赖氨酸）和一种氨基二羧酸（谷氨酸）连接而成的二肽；*d*–赖氨酰–*l*–组氨酸，由两种强碱性氨基酸组成的二肽；*l*–天冬酰胺酰–*l*–酪氨酸及*d*–谷氨酰–*l*–酪氨酸，两种高度相似的二肽，但在它们作为酶的作用对象时，行为明显有所不同（参见下文）；*l*–酪氨酰–*l*–酪氨酸，一种含有两个苯酚基团的二肽；甘氨酰–*l*–脯氨酸和*d*–丙氨酰–*l*–脯氨酸，因所含肽键的特殊性而受到人们的特别关注：

For comparison with these proline peptides another dipeptide in which the nitrogen of the peptide linkage is tertiary in character, namely, glycylsarcosine, has been prepared.

In the following table, the behaviour of these dipeptides is shown towards dipeptidase, towards aminopolypeptidase, and towards trypsin (that is, a mixture of proteinase and carboxypolypeptidase):

| | Dipeptidase | Aminopolypeptidase | Trypsin (Carboxypolypeptidase+proteinase) |
|---|---|---|---|
| *d*-Glutamyl-*d*-glutamic acid | + + | – | – |
| *d*-Lysyl-*d*-glutamic acid | + | – | – |
| *d*-Lysylglycine | + + | – | – |
| *d*-Lysyl-*l*-histidine | + + | – | – |
| *l*-Asparagyl-*l*-tyrosine | – | – | – |
| *d*-Glutamyl-*l*-tyrosine | + + | – | – |
| *l*-Tyrosyl-*l*-tyrosine | + + | – | + |
| *d*-Tyrosyl-*d*-arginine | – | – | + |
| Glycyl-*l*-proline | – | + + | – |
| *d*-Alanyl-*l*-proline | – | + + | – |
| Glycylsarcosine | – | 0 | – |

With glutamylglutamic acid the result is as one would expect; this dipeptide, in spite of its strongly acidic character, is hydrolysed by dipeptidase after suitable buffering.

Lysylglutamic acid on the other hand is attacked only with difficulty by dipeptidase; lysylglycine is readily hydrolysed by this enzyme and the same is true of the strongly basic lysylhistidine. These examples show that the preponderance of acidic or of basic groups does not interfere with dipeptidase action, since the most strongly acidic and most strongly basic dipeptides are both attacked by the enzyme. Surprising differences of behaviour between closely related compounds are exemplified by asparagyl- and glutamyl-tyrosine, of which the first is resistant to all intestinal proteolytic enzymes whilst the second is readily hydrolysed by dipeptidase.

*l*-Tyrosyl-*l*-tyrosine presents an anomaly inasmuch as it is hydrolysed not only by dipeptidase but also by trypsin, whilst *d*-tyrosyl-*d*-arginine is actually not affected by dipeptidase but is hydrolysed by carboxypolypeptidase.

The behaviour of the proline peptides towards proteolytic enzymes is especially illuminating. Neither glycylproline nor alanylproline is attacked by dipeptidase whilst both are hydrolysed by aminopolypeptidase; here therefore we have two dipeptides for

为了能与这些含有脯氨酸的多肽进行比较，人们制备了另外一种二肽——甘氨酰肌氨酸，其参与肽键形成的氮为叔氮。

下面的表格展示了这些二肽在被二肽酶、氨基多肽酶以及胰蛋白酶（即蛋白质水解酶与羧基多肽酶的混合物）作用时的行为。

| | 二肽酶 | 氨基多肽酶 | 胰蛋白酶（羧基多肽酶+蛋白质水解酶） |
|---|---|---|---|
| *d*-谷氨酰-*d*-谷氨酸 | ++ | − | − |
| *d*-赖氨酰-*d*-谷氨酸 | + | − | − |
| *d*-赖氨酰甘氨酸 | ++ | − | − |
| *d*-赖氨酰-*l*-组氨酸 | ++ | − | − |
| *l*-天冬酰胺酰-*l*-酪氨酸 | − | − | − |
| *d*-谷氨酰-*l*-酪氨酸 | ++ | − | − |
| *l*-酪氨酰-*l*-酪氨酸 | ++ | − | + |
| *d*-酪氨酰-*d*-精氨酸 | − | − | + |
| 甘氨酰-*l*-脯氨酸 | − | ++ | − |
| *d*-丙氨酰-*l*-脯氨酸 | − | ++ | − |
| 甘氨酰肌氨酸 | − | 0 | − |

对于谷氨酰谷氨酸而言，结果正如人们所预期的那样；尽管此二肽具有强酸性特征，在合适的缓冲溶液中也可被二肽酶所水解。

另一方面，赖氨酰谷氨酸被二肽酶水解是相当困难的，而赖氨酰甘氨酸却很容易被该酶水解，同样很容易被水解的还有碱性很强的赖氨酰组氨酸。这些例子表明，多个酸性或碱性基团的存在均不会干扰二肽酶的作用，因为最强酸性和最强碱性的二肽均能被二肽酶进攻。表明密切相似的化合物在行为上可以存在惊人差异的例子是，天冬酰胺酰酪氨酸和谷氨酰酪氨酸，前者能抵抗肠道来源的所有蛋白质水解酶的作用，而后者却非常容易被二肽酶水解。

*l*–酪氨酰–*l*–酪氨酸是一个表现反常的例子，因为它不仅可以被二肽酶水解，也可以被胰蛋白酶水解；而 *d*–酪氨酰–*d*–精氨酸却不能被二肽酶作用，但可以被羧基多肽酶水解。

含脯氨酸的多肽作为蛋白质水解酶的作用对象所表现出来的行为特征对我们特别具有启发性。甘氨酰脯氨酸和丙氨酰脯氨酸均不受二肽酶的攻击，但两者都可

which dipeptidase is not the appropriate enzyme, and it becomes clear that the accepted definitions of dipeptidase and aminopolypeptidase are unsatisfactory. More important still is the conclusion which emerges from the experiments with the proline peptides that "dipeptidase" can only attack a normal peptide linkage (.CONH.), whilst at least one constituent of "aminopolypeptidase" can hydrolyse a peptied linkage in which the nitrogen atom is tertiary. This view is confirmed by the fact that glycylsarcosine is also resistant towards dipeptidase.

(**131**, 662-664; 1933)

---

References:

1 Bergmann and Zervas, *Biochem. Z.*, **203**, 280 (1928).

2 Bergmann, Zervas and Lebrecht, *Ber. deutsch. Chem. Ges.*, **64**, 2315 (1931).

3 Bergmann and Ensslin, *Z. physiol. Chem.*, **174**, 76 (1928); Bergmann and Stern, *Liebigs Ann.*, **448**, 20 (1926); Bergmann, Kann and Miekeley, *Liebigs Ann.*, **449**, 137 (1926); Bergmann and Miekeley, *Liebigs Ann.*, **458**, 40 (1927).

4 Bergmann and Delis, *Liebigs Ann.*, **458**, 76 (1927); Bergmann and Stather, *Z. physiol. Chem.*, **152**, 190 (1926).

5 Bergmann and Köster, *Z. physiol. Chem.*, **159**, 179 (1926); Bergmann and Zervas, *Z. physiol. Chem.*, **172**, 277 (1927); **173**, 80 (1928).

6 Zervas and Bergmann, *Ber. deutsch. chem. Ges.*, **61**, 1195 (1928); also *Z. physiol. Chem.*, **201**, 208 (1931); Kutscher, Ackermann, Flössner and Hoppe-Seyler, *Z. physiol. Chem.*, **199**, 273 and 277 (1931).

7 Bergmann, Stern and Witte, *Liebigs Ann.*, **449**, 277 (1926); Bergmann and Köster, *Z. physiol. Chem.*, **167**, 92 (1927); Bergmann, Zervas and du Vigneaud, *Ber deutsch. chem. Ges.*, **62**, 1905 (1929).

8 Bergmann and Zervas, *Ber. deutsch. chem. Ges.*, **65**, 1192 (1932); Bergmann, Zervas and Greenstein, *Ber. deutsch. chem. Ges.*, **65**, 1692 (1932); Bergmann, Zervas, Schleich and Leinert, *Z. physiol, Chem.*, **212**, 72 (1932).

以被氨基多肽酶水解；因此在这里我们观察到了两种在二肽酶作用下不发生水解的二肽，这表明现在人们给二肽酶和氨基多肽酶所下的定义是不能令人满意的。更为重要的问题还不在这里，而是在那些利用含有脯氨酸的多肽所做的实验中得到的结论，即“二肽酶”只能进攻正常的肽键（–CONH–），而至少有一种“氨基多肽酶”可以使含有叔氮原子的肽键水解。这一观点也被以下观察所证实，即甘氨酰肌氨酸也能抵抗二肽酶的水解作用。

（刘振明 翻译；吕增益 审稿）

# Amino-Acids, Proteins and Proteolytic Enzymes: II

M. Bergmann

## Editor's Note

**Following on from an earlier article that shed light on the complexities of the peptide bond, here Max Bergmann reflects on the action of proteolytic enzymes. His work made significant contributions to the study of enzyme specificity, building upon the work of his more famous mentor, the Nobel-prize winning chemist Emil Fischer. Just days after the series of lectures in London on which these two papers are based, Adolf Hitler became Chancellor of Germany. Later in 1933, Jewish-born Bergmann fled to the United States, where he continued his research into protein chemistry at Rockefeller University in New York.**

THIS is perhaps a suitable moment at which to assess our knowledge of the proteolytic enzymes. It remains a fact that dipeptidase, aminopolypeptidase and carboxypolypeptidase are three distinct enzymes; for the present, we may retain these names, but only so long as we bear in mind that they do not truly express the characteristic properties of the enzymes. We have seen that there is a dipeptide of naturally occurring amino-acids (asparagyltyrosine) which is not attacked by any intestinal proteolytic enzyme; there is a dipeptide (tyrosyltyrosine) which is hydrolysed not only by dipeptidase but also by carboxypolypeptidase; finally there are dipeptides (glycyl- and alanyl-proline) which are resistant to dipeptidases but are attacked by polypeptidase. It is therefore clearly not the number of amino-acids in the molecule of a peptide which determines its susceptibility to a particular peptidase. The presence of free amino and carboxyl groups adjacent to the peptide linkage does not necessarily render the compound open to attack by dipeptidase, nor will aminopolypeptidase hydrolyse all peptides in which the peptide linkage adjoins a free amino but no free carboxyl group. On the other hand, the action of the latter enzyme is not always inhibited by the proximity of a free carboxyl group to the peptide linkage.

It is evident that we must take further circumstances into consideration before we can hope to define rigidly the conditions of action of the various peptidases; in particular, careful attention must be given to electro-chemical effects and to such structural features as the secondary or tertiary nature of the nitrogen participating in the peptide bond. The accumulation of facts bearing on this question will be a major object of future work; this work can be undertaken hopefully now that the benzylcarbonato method affords a means of obtaining almost any peptide which may be desired.

From still another point of view, it has been possible to gain an insight into the structural and electro-chemical conditions which regulate the enzymic hydrolysis of peptides, namely, by experiments concerning the transformation of proteins into non-nitrogenous compounds. Hitherto, it has been thought that this transformation could only take place

# 氨基酸、蛋白质和蛋白质水解酶 II

马克斯·伯格曼

## 编者按

马克斯·伯格曼曾在之前发表的一篇文章中阐述了肽键的复杂性，而本文反映了作者对蛋白质水解酶作用机制的认识。他的工作对酶专一性的研究做出了重要贡献，而这些贡献都建立在其知名度更高的导师——著名化学家、诺贝尔奖获得者埃米尔·费歇尔的工作基础之上。就在作者以这两篇论文为基础开展伦敦系列讲座之后没几天，阿道夫·希特勒成了德国的总理。后来在1933年，具有犹太血统的伯格曼被迫逃往美国，在纽约的洛克菲勒大学继续开展他在蛋白质化学方面的研究。

现在可能是评估我们对蛋白质水解酶认识的一个恰当时期。目前人们仍然认为，二肽酶、氨基多肽酶和羧基多肽酶是三种性质截然不同的酶，尽管目前我们仍然可以保持这些称谓，但同时我们心里也应该明白，上述名称并没有真正表述出这些酶的特性。我们已经看到，有一种由天然存在的氨基酸合成的二肽化合物（天冬酰胺酰酪氨酸）不会成为任何肠道内蛋白质水解酶的攻击对象；而另一种二肽化合物（酪氨酰酪氨酸），不仅可以被二肽酶水解，还可以被羧基多肽酶水解；最后还有一些二肽化合物（如甘氨酰脯氨酸和丙氨酰脯氨酸）不能被二肽酶作用，但却可以被多肽酶作用。因此非常清楚的是：多肽分子中氨基酸的数目决定不了其对特定肽酶的敏感性。与肽键毗邻的自由氨基和羧基并不一定会使其更易遭受二肽酶的进攻；而氨基多肽酶也不会水解在肽键附近存在自由氨基但缺乏自由羧基的所有多肽。另一方面，氨基多肽酶的水解作用也不总会因为有自由羧基位于肽键附近而被抑制。

显然，在我们希望能够严格定义不同肽酶发生作用的条件之前，我们必须考查更多的不同情形。特别需要仔细分析其中的电化学效应，以及像参与形成肽键的氮原子的仲氮和叔氮结构特性等方面的情况。围绕这个问题的数据积累将是我们未来工作的主要目标。现在我们有望开展这样的研究，因为苯甲基碳酸法为我们提供了这样一条途径，使我们几乎能够获得任何希望获得的多肽。

再换个角度看，我们已经具备条件来探究调节多肽酶水解能力的多肽的结构和电化学条件了，这主要通过旨在将蛋白质转化为无氮化合物这样的实验来开展。迄今为止，人们认为这种转化只能由每一种氨基酸以自身独特的方式发生，这被假想

by way of the individual amino-acids themselves, which were supposed to undergo dehydrogenation and subsequent hydrolytic loss of nitrogen with formation of a ketonic acid.

At the time when we began experiments bearing on this point, no enzyme had been discovered which was capable of dehydrogenating amino-acids. For reasons which need not be discussed here, the idea occurred to us that such a dehydrogenation might be accomplished at the peptide stage. In order to test this hypothesis, a number of unsaturated di- and tri-peptides were synthesised and a search was made for an enzyme which might be capable of hydrolysing these compounds. An enzyme was in fact obtained from kidney[1] which attacked glycyldehydrophenylalanine with the production of glycine, phenylpyruvic acid and ammonia; the same enzyme also attacked glycyldehydroalanine with analogous results:

$$C_6H_5.CH{:}C(NH.CO.CH_2.NH_2).COOH \longrightarrow$$

$$CH_2.NH_2.COOH + C_6H_5.CH_2.CO.COOH + NH_3$$

Glycyldehydrophenylalanine is completely resistant towards dipeptidases of plant and animal origin, amino- and carboxy-polypeptidase, trypsin and pepsin. On the other hand, the kidney enzyme is quite unable to attack glycylphenylalanine. It is clear therefore that the kidney enzyme is no ordinary dipeptidase but is indeed specifically adapted to the hydrolysis of unsaturated peptides.

The fact that glycylphenylalanine and glycyldehydrophenylalanine, two peptides which differ only by two hydrogen atoms, should require distinct enzymes for their hydrolysis, is of great importance in relation to the conditions of action of the various peptidases; it indicates that a compound may possess all the characteristics (a normal peptide linkage adjacent to free amino and carboxyl groups) hitherto regarded as essential to a substrate for dipeptidase and may still fail to be hydrolysed by this enzyme.

The existence and properties of the kidney dehydrodipeptidase have also important physiological implications, since they demonstrate a possible mechanism of deamination of protein degradation products in the body; moreover, the process involves the simultaneous formation in the kidney of keto-acids and ammonia, which are well known to occur in the urine in considerable quantities under certain conditions. It appears that the kidney, through its possession of this enzyme, may play a definite part in protein metabolism, particularly if we may assume that unsaturated peptides or related compounds of unsaturated amino-acids are produced in the course of renal metabolism. The likelihood of the latter assumption is indicated by the work of Krebs[2] who has shown that the kidney is capable of dehydrogenating amino-acids and peptides; in these experiments, however, the action of the kidney was not confined to the naturally occurring amino-acids but extended to their optical enantiomorphs, and it is therefore too early to say whether the results are of true biological significance.

是通过先脱氢然后再水解脱氮这样的过程而发生的，最后形成一种酮酸。

当我们实验室开始进行有关这方面的研究时，还没有任何酶被发现可以催化氨基酸发生脱氢作用。基于无需在此讨论的原因，我们当时的想法是，这样一种脱氢过程可能是在多肽阶段完成的。为了检测这一假说，我们合成了多种不饱和的二肽和三肽化合物，并试图寻找可以水解这些化合物的酶。实际上我们从肾脏中获得了这样一种酶[1]，它可以进攻甘氨酰脱氢苯丙氨酸，生成甘氨酸、苯基丙酮酸和氨。该酶也能进攻甘氨酰脱氢丙氨酸而得到类似的结果：

$$C_6H_5.CH{:}C(NH.CO.CH_2.NH_2).COOH \longrightarrow$$
$$CH_2.NH_2.COOH + C_6H_5.CH_2.CO.COOH + NH_3$$

甘氨酰脱氢苯丙氨酸完全不被植物和动物来源的二肽酶、氨基和羧基多肽酶、胰蛋白酶以及胃蛋白酶所作用。另一方面，从肾脏获得的这种酶对于甘氨酰苯丙氨酸也相当的无效。因此，很清楚的是，肾脏中的这种酶并非常见的二肽酶，它实际上是一种特异演化出来的能使不饱和多肽水解的酶。

只相差两个氢原子的两种肽——甘氨酰苯丙氨酸和甘氨酰脱氢苯丙氨酸——竟然需要不同的酶才能使其水解，该结果对于理解不同肽酶的作用条件而言，的确意义非凡。它表明，虽然一种化合物可能具备迄今为止被认为是二肽酶底物所应具备的一切特征，即一个附近存在自由氨基和自由羧基的正常肽键，但它可能仍然无法被这种酶催化水解。

肾脏脱氢二肽酶的存在和其所表现出来的特性，在生理学上也具有很重要的含义，因为这揭示了体内蛋白质降解产物脱氨的一种可能机制；而且此过程涉及肾脏中酮酸和氨的同时生成，而它们在某些条件下以相当的量出现于尿液中是一个众所周知的事实。通过拥有这种酶，肾脏似乎在蛋白质代谢中发挥着独特的作用，尤其是如果我们可以假设在肾脏的蛋白质代谢过程中的确产生了不饱和多肽或相关的不饱和氨基酸化合物的话。后一种假设的可能性被克雷布斯的工作所印证[2]，他发现肾脏能够使氨基酸和多肽发生脱氢反应。但在这些实验中，肾脏的作用并没有只限于那些天然氨基酸，也延伸到了它们的非天然光学对映体，因此现在就去判断这些结果是否的确具有生物学意义还为时过早。

Up to the present point, we have been dealing with the synthesis of new peptides and their behaviour towards enzymes. We must now pass on to consider the various conclusions, which experiments of this type enable us to draw, concerning the structure of the natural proteins themselves. This matter can best be exemplified by a consideration of the position occupied by proline in the natural proteins in the light of the behaviour of synthetic proline peptides of known structure[3].

The process of enzymic hydrolysis of a protein must be pictured as the successive scission of peptide linkages; this being so, it is natural to assume that every such scission will involve the liberation of an amino and a carboxyl group. The carboxyl groups liberated during digestion can be readily determined by titration in alcoholic solution by the method of Willstätter and Waldschmidt–Leitz, and the amino groups by the method of van Slyke. The course of enzymic digestion of many proteins has been followed with the aid of these methods and it has invariably been found that amino and carboxyl groups are liberated in equivalent amounts; in spite of the fact therefore that various authors, for example, Emil Fischer himself, have discussed at different times the possible occurrence of other than normal peptide linkages in proteins, no analytical evidence of the existence of such other linkages has been obtained, and the liberation of amino and carboxyl groups in equivalent amounts has indeed been taken as a criterion of true proteolysis.

Now we have already discussed two synthetic proline peptides, glycyl- and alanyl-proline, which are peculiar in that they are hydrolysed by amino-polypeptidase but not by dipeptidase; moreover, the hydrolysis of such a peptide, when it does occur, will give rise to liberation of a free carboxyl group but not of an amino group; in this case, therefore, the accepted rule of equivalent liberation of amino and carboxyl groups evidently does not apply. This fact can be utilised to throw light upon the mode of combination of proline and hydroxyproline in gelatin.

Proline can clearly occupy three distinct positions in the peptide chain of gelatin: (1) it may be attached through its carboxyl group to the amino end of the chain; (2) it may be attached through its imino group to the carboxyl end; (3) it may lie inside the chain and be linked through its carboxyl and imino groups. The second and third of these possibilities involve the existence of linkages similar to that of glycylproline, and it is therefore possible, by comparing the action of proteolytic enzymes on gelatin and glycylproline, to decide whether this type of linkage is indeed present in gelatin or whether the proline is combined in the protein molecule entirely through its carboxyl group.

In order to test this question, gelatin has been submitted to digestion with trypsin followed by intestinal peptidase. Tryptic digestion causes rapid and equivalent increases in free amino and carboxyl groups whilst the peptidases cause a predominant increase in free carboxyl. Reference to the results obtained in the enzymic hydrolysis of the proline peptides will make it clear, therefore, that a large part at any rate of the proline (and perhaps also of the hydroxyproline) of gelatin must be combined through its imino group.

本文到此一直在讨论新的多肽分子的合成以及它们作为酶的作用对象的行为等问题。现在我们要接着讨论这类实验能让我们对天然蛋白质的自身结构所下的不同结论。在此方面，最好的例子是基于人工合成的、结构已知的含脯氨酸的多肽的行为来推测脯氨酸在天然蛋白质中所占据的位置[3]。

蛋白质的酶催化水解过程必然会被看作是肽键连接的连续断裂过程。如果的确是这样的话，人们自然会假设每一次这样的断键过程都将涉及一个氨基和一个羧基的释放。降解过程中所释放出来的羧基利用维尔斯泰特和瓦尔德施密特－莱茨建立的在乙醇溶液中进行滴定的方法很容易就能测定，而氨基则可以通过范斯莱克法进行测定。利用这些方法，人们分析了多种蛋白质的酶催化降解过程，发现氨基和羧基总是被等量释放。因此，尽管有一些作者，如埃米尔·费歇尔本人，曾在不同场合讨论过在蛋白质中可能存在除常规肽键之外的其他化学键，但到目前为止仍没有获得这样的其他连接方式的确存在的分析证据。基于这些考量，等量释放氨基和羧基就被人们当成了判断蛋白质是否真正发生了酶催水解的标准。

我们已经讨论过两种人工合成的脯氨酸多肽：甘氨酰脯氨酸和丙氨酰脯氨酸。它们的特别之处在于可以被氨基多肽酶水解，但不能被二肽酶水解。此外，当这样一种多肽发生水解时，会释放出一个自由的羧基，但不释放氨基。因此，在这种情况下，等量释放氨基和羧基的公认原则显然不再适用。但这样的结果可以用于揭示脯氨酸和羟基脯氨酸在明胶中的结合方式。

在明胶的多肽链上，脯氨酸很明确地可能占据三种不同的位置：(1) 它可以通过自身的羧基连接在肽链的氨基末端；(2) 它可以通过自身的亚氨基连接在肽链的羧基末端；(3) 它可以通过自身的羧基和亚氨基进行连接而处于肽链的内部。在第二种和第三种可能性中涉及类似于甘氨酰脯氨酸中的连接方式，因此我们就可以通过比较蛋白质水解酶作用于明胶和作用于甘氨酰脯氨酸的结果，来确定在明胶中这种类型的连接到底是存在的，还是说，蛋白质分子中的脯氨酸全部是通过其羧基而结合的。

为了回答此问题，明胶被先用胰蛋白酶降解，之后再用肠肽酶处理。胰蛋白酶降解导致了自由氨基和自由羧基的快速等量增加，而肽酶只导致了自由羧基的显著增加。因此，这样的酶催化水解脯氨酸多肽的结果很清楚地表明：明胶中的脯氨酸（也许还包括羟基脯氨酸）至少大部分是通过其亚氨基与其他氨基酸连接的。

These experiments provide an example of a protein digestion in which free amino and carboxyl groups are not liberated in equivalent amounts; such equivalence can therefore no longer be regarded as an essential characteristic of proteolysis. Furthermore, they show in a convincing manner the importance of the individual constituent amino-acids in determining the behaviour of a protein towards enzymes; owing to the structure of proline the peptide chain is heterogeneous at those positions where proline is linked through its imino group, and this heterogeneity forces the process of enzymic degradation of the protein to follow a certain course.

We may now pass from the amino-acids, peptides and peptidases to a brief consideration of the enzymic degradation of complete proteins. Very little is known of the enzymes (proteinases) which are able to attack proteins of high molecular weight, but the action of these enzymes is of great importance; not only are they responsible for the first stages of the digestion of all protein taken in the food, but also there are industrial processes of the first importance which depend on the enzymic digestion of proteins.

A serious difficulty in the investigation of proteinase action is that these enzymes often have to work in heterogeneous systems, since the substrate may be largely undissolved, and hence the simple rules of mass action cannot be applied; the variable magnitude of the surface of the protein exposed to enzymic attack complicates the situation so that the curves representing the course of action of proteinases on undissolved proteins are not susceptible of simple interpretation.

In the case of gelatin the problem can be simplified to some extent by using the protein in the form of films of uniform size and thickness, so that the surface of protein remains practically constant during digestion; moreover, the course of the digestion can be conveniently followed optically if a black insoluble substance be previously distributed evenly through the gelatin, so that it gradually passes into the aqueous phase as digestion proceeds. With the aid of this method it has been found that the course of digestion of gelatin is represented by the simple formula: $x = kt\sqrt{E}$, where $x$ = digestion (percent); $k$ = constant, $t$ = time, $E$ = enzyme concentration (percent).

This formula is valid during the whole of the process of digestion, and for concentrations of enzyme varying from 0.0001 to 0.1 percent and more. Thus apart from variations in the surface exposed, it may be stated that the rate of digestion of a protein is proportional to the time and to the square root of the enzyme concentration, but is not affected by the total amount of enzyme or of protein[4].

The same rule applies to the digestion of fibrous collagen, at least during the first third of the digestion period, provided that precautions are taken to prevent the inactivation of the

上述实验提供了一个自由氨基和自由羧基并非等量释放的蛋白质降解的例子。因此这种等量关系不能再被看作是蛋白质水解的关键特征了。此外，这些实验以一种令人信服的方式证明，蛋白质中的每一种特定的氨基酸在决定其被蛋白质水解酶作用行为方面的重要性；由于脯氨酸的结构特点，多肽链在脯氨酸通过其亚氨基而连接的位置是不均一的，这种不均一性使特定蛋白质的酶催化降解过程必须按照某种特定的方式才能发生。

我们现在应该可以将话题从对氨基酸、多肽和肽酶的研究中转移到对完整蛋白质的酶催降解过程的简单介绍方面来了。对于能够进攻分子量很高的蛋白质的酶(即蛋白质水解酶)，我们还知之甚少，但这些酶的作用是极其重要的，因为它们不仅负责了我们从食物中所摄取的所有蛋白质发生降解的第一步，而且一些非常重要的工业过程也要依赖于蛋白质的酶催降解。

研究蛋白质水解酶作用过程的极其困难之处在于，这些酶经常需要在不均质的体系中去发挥其作用，因为它们的底物可能有一大部分处于非溶解状态。这就使得我们无法简单地将质量作用定律应用于这样的研究工作中。底物蛋白质暴露给水解酶进攻的表面大小不一，这就使得情况复杂化了，因此对代表蛋白质水解酶作用于未溶解底物蛋白质进程的曲线就不能仅进行简单的解释。

在明胶这个例子中，通过将其制备成大小和厚度都均一的膜可以使问题得到一定程度的简化，这样，底物蛋白质的表面就会在被降解过程中基本保持恒定状态。另外，如果事先将一种不能溶解的黑色物质均匀地撒在明胶中的话，那么明胶被降解的进程就能够很方便地利用光学方法进行跟踪，这样的话，这些黑色物质就会随着降解过程的进行而逐渐地进入到水相之中。通过借助于这种方法，人们发现明胶的降解进程可以用以下简单公式来描述：$x = kt\sqrt{E}$，这里 $x$ 代表降解的百分比；$k$ 是常数，$t$ 代表时间，$E$ 是酶的百分比浓度。

该公式对整个降解过程都有效，条件是酶浓度在 0.0001% 到 0.1% 或者更高之间。因此，如果不考虑底物蛋白质所暴露的表面的差异的话，我们可以认为蛋白质的降解速率与时间和酶的浓度的平方根成正比，但却不受酶的总量或者底物蛋白质的总量的影响[4]。

同一规则也适应于胶原纤维的降解，至少在整个降解过程的前三分之一是这样的，但前提条件是必须采取预防酶失活的措施。这个公式能被用于描述胶原蛋白的

enzyme. The validity of the formula in the case of collagen is at first sight surprising, since it might be expected that the fibres would become thinner during the digestion and that the surface would then be altered. The only explanation of the constancy of the rate of digestion actually observed seems to be that digestion of the collagen fibres proceeds only from their ends. That this is indeed the case is shown by the fact that the rate of digestion of true skin is proportional to the area of the external surface in which the ends of the collagen fibres lie.

The key to present-day and future protein chemistry lies in the development of new synthetic methods, and this is the justification for the expenditure of so much time and labour on the improvement of such methods. In these lectures I have described technical advances made during the last few years in my laboratory, which have thrown some new light on the specificity of the proteolytic enzymes, at the same time extending our knowledge of normal and pathological protein metabolism. With the aid of the combined efforts of enzyme chemistry and organic synthesis, we may reasonably hope that these advances will be continued.

(**131**, 698-700; 1933)

---

References:

1 Bergmann and Schleich, *Z. physiol. Chem.*, **205**, 65 (1932): **207**, 235 (1932): Bergmann and Grafe, *Z. physiol. Chem.*, **187**, 187 (1930): Bergmann, Schmitt and Miekeley, *Z. physiol. Chem.*, **187**, 264 (1930).

2 Krebs, *Klin. Woch.*, **11**, 1744 (1932).

3 Bergmann, Zervas and Schleich, *Ber. deutsch. chem. Ges.*, **65**, 1747 (1932).

4 Bergmann and Föhr, *Biochem. Z.*, **250**, 568 (1932).

降解这一事实，初看令人颇为意外，因为人们可能预期的是，在降解过程中纤维将会变细，从而导致表面发生变化。对于实际观测到的降解速率保持恒定的结果，唯一的解释是，这似乎表明胶原纤维的降解过程只从它们的末端开始。以下事实表明，这的确如此：真实皮肤的降解速率与胶原纤维末端所占的外表面积成正比。

现在及未来的蛋白质化学研究的关键在于新的人工合成多肽方法的建立。这也表明，在改进这样的方法上花费那么多的时间和精力的确都是非常值得的。我已经在这几次的演讲中讲述了我所在的实验室在最近几年里所取得的技术进步，我们的研究为认识蛋白质水解酶的特异性带来了新的曙光，同时也拓展了我们对于正常和病理状态下蛋白质代谢的认识。只要依靠酶化学和有机合成这两方面研究工作者的共同努力，我们就有理由期望研究工作还将取得更大进展。

（刘振明 翻译；昌增益 审稿）

# Nature of Cosmic Rays*

A. H. Compton

## Editor's Note

**This address by Arthur Compton to a meeting of the American Physical Society describes recent studies of the geographical distribution of cosmic rays, and their variation with altitude. A marked increase in cosmic-ray intensity in temperate and polar latitudes, compared with tropical zones, could be explained if the primary cosmic rays were electrons arriving in two energy ranges, the higher-energy particles being largely unaffected by the Earth's magnetic field while those in the lower-band are strongly deflected and therefore unable to reach the tropics. The data argue against the particles being photons, but cannot distinguish between ordinary electrons, "positively charged electrons", or protons or alpha particles. Today we know that most primary cosmic rays are protons.**

THERE are three kinds of experiments which seem to afford direct evidence regarding the nature of cosmic rays. These are: (1) the Bothe-Kolhörster double counter experiment, which compares the absorption of the particles traversing the counters with the absorption of cosmic rays; (2) measurements of the relative intensity of cosmic rays over different parts of the earth, designed to show any effect due to the earth's magnetic field; and (3) studies of the variation of cosmic ray intensity with altitude, which should follow different laws according as the rays are electrons or photons.

(1) The Bothe-Kolhörster experiment serves to measure the absorption in a block of gold or lead of the high-speed electrified particles that produce coincident impulses in two neighbouring counting chambers. It is found that this absorption is surprisingly small, about the same, in fact, as that of the cosmic rays themselves.

The simplest interpretation of this similarity in absorption is to suppose that the high-speed particles in question are the cosmic rays. There is, however, the alternative possibility that the primary cosmic rays are photons which eject high-speed electrons as recoil electrons when the photons are stopped, and that these recoil electrons are absorbed at about the same rate as the primary rays themselves. Theoretical calculations indicate that the recoil electrons should be absorbed five or ten times as rapidly as the photons which give rise to them. These calculations are somewhat uncertain because of extrapolation far beyond the wave-length region where the existing formulae have been tested. For this reason, the equal absorption coefficients of the cosmic rays and the high-speed particles

* Substance of an address presented at a symposium on cosmic rays, held by the American Physical Society at Atlantic City on December 30, 1932.

# 宇宙射线的性质*

阿瑟·康普顿

## 编者按

这是阿瑟·康普顿在美国物理学会的一次会议上就宇宙射线的地理分布以及它们的强度随高度变化的问题所作的演讲。与热带地区相比，宇宙射线的强度在温带和极区纬度上会有明显增强，这也许可以通过以下方式进行解释：如果初级宇宙射线是电子，它们以两个能量范围到达地球，那么高能粒子流几乎不会受到地球磁场的影响；而较低能段的粒子流会发生很大的偏转，因而根本无法到达赤道地区。这些数据表明构成宇宙射线的粒子不是光子，但不能区分是普通电子、“带正电的电子”、质子还是 $\alpha$ 粒子。今天我们知道大多数初级宇宙射线都是质子。

能够直接说明宇宙射线性质的实验有三类。它们是：(1) 博特–柯尔霍斯特的双计数器实验，可以用于比较穿过计数器的粒子的吸收和宇宙射线的吸收；(2) 测量宇宙射线在地球上不同地区的相对强度，目的是想了解地球磁场对其造成的影响；(3) 研究宇宙射线强度随海拔高度的变化，根据宇宙射线是电子或是光子而采用不同的定律。

(1) 博特–柯尔霍斯特实验用于测量金块或铅块对高速带电粒子的吸收，带电粒子可在两个相邻计数室中产生同步脉冲。实验发现，这类吸收出奇地小，实际上与宇宙射线自身的吸收大致相同。

对两者在吸收性质上相似的最简单的解释是假定宇宙射线就是高速运动的粒子。然而，还存在另外一种可能性，即认为初级宇宙射线是光子，当光子停止时会打出高速电子作为反冲电子，这些反冲电子以与初级宇宙射线本身大致相同的速率被吸收。理论计算表明，反冲电子被吸收的速度应该是产生它们的光子的吸收速度的 5 倍到 10 倍。这些计算结果不是很准确，因为外推远远超过了被现有公式检验过的波长范围。由于这个原因，虽然宇宙射线和高速粒子具有相同的吸收系数并不足以排除这些粒子就是宇宙射线激发的反冲电子。不过，这仍然难以想象，公式的误差会大

* 这是在专题讨论会上的一篇有关宇宙射线的演讲稿，该讨论会是由美国物理学会于 1932 年 12 月 30 日在大西洋城举办的。

does not necessarily rule out the possibility that the particles in question may be recoil electrons excited by the cosmic rays. It would, nevertheless, be surprising if the formulae were in error by so large a factor as five or ten, as would be implied if the coincidences are due to secondary electrons.

(2) If the cosmic rays consist of electrified particles coming into the earth's atmosphere from remote space, the earth's magnetic field should affect their geographical distribution. This effect has been investigated theoretically by Størmer, Epstein, and recently much more completely by Lemaître and Vallarta. It appears that for energies less than $10^9$ electron volts, electrons approaching the earth can reach it only at latitudes north of about 60°. For energies greater than about $5 \times 10^{10}$ volts the geographical distribution is not affected by the earth's magnetic field. For intermediate energies, there will be a difference in intensity with latitude according to the distribution of energy of the incoming electrons.

Experimental studies of the relative intensity of cosmic rays in different parts of the world have been made by J. Clay, who made several trips between Java and Holland, and found consistently a lower intensity near the equator; Millikan and Cameron, who found but slightly lower intensity in the lakes of Bolivia than in the mountain lakes of California, and no difference between Pasadena and Churchill close to the north magnetic pole; Bothe and Kolhörster, who carried a counting tube from Hamburg (53° N.) to Spitsbergen (81° N.) and back, and detected no variations in the cosmic rays larger than their rather large experimental error; Kennedy, who, under Grant's direction, carried similar apparatus from Adelaide, Australia, to Antarctica, and likewise found no measurable change; and Corlin, who on going from 50° N. to 70° N. in Scandinavia found some evidence of a maximum at about 55° N. The prevailing opinion regarding the significance of these measurements has thus been expressed by Hoffman in a recent summary: "The results so far have on the whole been negative. Most of the observers conclude that within the errors of experiment the intensity is constant and equal, and those authors who do find differences give their results with certain reservations."

During the past eighteen months, Prof. Bennett of the Massachusetts Institute of Technology, Prof. Stearns of the University of Denver, and I have organised a group of ten expeditions, with some sixty physicists, and we have attempted to make as extensive a study of the geographical distribution of cosmic rays as could be done in a limited period of time. Fig. 1 shows the position of the eighty-one stations in different parts of the world at which measurements have been made. These stations are about equally divided between the northern and southern hemispheres. They have extended from latitude 46° S. to latitude 78° N., and from sea level to about 20,000 ft. (Figs. 2 and 3). When these data are brought together, they show a marked difference in intensity between the cosmic rays at temperate and polar latitudes, as compared with the tropical latitudes. At sea level the difference in intensity is about 14 percent, at 2,000 metres about 22 percent, and at 4,400 metres about 33 percent. The change between the intensity for tropical as compared with that for temperate latitudes occurs rather sharply between geomagnetic latitudes 25° and 40°.

到 5~10 倍，以至于认为吸收系数的符合是由次级电子引起的。

（2）如果宇宙射线是从遥远太空进入地球大气的带电粒子，那么地球磁场应该会影响它们的地理分布。斯托默和爱泼斯坦曾对此进行过理论上的研究，最近勒梅特和瓦拉塔又大大完善了这一理论。他们的研究表明：对于能量小于 $10^9$ 电子伏特的电子，它们在接近地球时只能到达纬度约 60° 以北的地方；对于能量大于约 $5\times10^{10}$ 电子伏特的电子，其地理分布不受地球磁场的影响；如果能量介于两者之间，入射电子的强度将会按照其能量分布随纬度而异。

克莱在世界各地进行了宇宙射线相对强度的实验研究，他在爪哇与荷兰之间往返了好几次后发现赤道附近的强度总是比较低；密立根和卡梅伦也发现在玻利维亚湖附近的宇宙射线强度略低于加州山湖，而在帕萨迪纳与靠近北极的丘吉尔港之间的宇宙射线强度并无差别；博特和柯尔霍斯特带着一支计数管往返于汉堡（北纬 53°）和斯匹次卑尔根群岛（北纬 81°）之间，他们用误差较大的仪器没有检测到宇宙射线强度的变化；肯尼迪在格兰特的指导下，带了同样的装置从澳大利亚的阿得雷德到南极洲，同样没有测量到强度的变化；但科林在测量了斯堪的纳维亚半岛上从北纬 50° 到 70° 之间的宇宙射线强度后发现在大约北纬 55° 处有一个极大值。最近，霍夫曼总结了人们对这些测量结果的普遍看法：“迄今为止得到的结果从总体上说是负面的。大多数观测者认为，在实验误差范围内，宇宙射线的强度恒为一个常数，而那些发现强度确实存在差别的作者在公布结果时带有某种保留。”

在过去的 18 个月内，麻省理工学院的贝内特教授、丹佛大学的斯特恩斯教授和我组织了一组有 60 余位物理学家参加的 10 次考察，我们试图在限定的时间内对宇宙射线的地理分布进行尽可能大范围的研究。图 1 中标出了分布在世界各地的 81 个观察站的位置，在这些位置我们都进行了测量。这些观察站在南北半球上基本上是平均分布的。从南纬 46° 延伸到北纬 78°，从海平面一直到海拔约 20,000 英尺处（图 2 和图 3）。当把这些数据汇总在一起时，我们发现在温带和两极处的宇宙射线强度与赤道地区明显不同。在海平面上，强度差约为 14%；在海拔 2,000 米处，约为 22%；在海拔 4,400 米处，约为 33%。在地磁纬度 25° 和 40° 之间，赤道地区宇宙射线强度与温带地区宇宙射线强度之间的差别会格外明显。

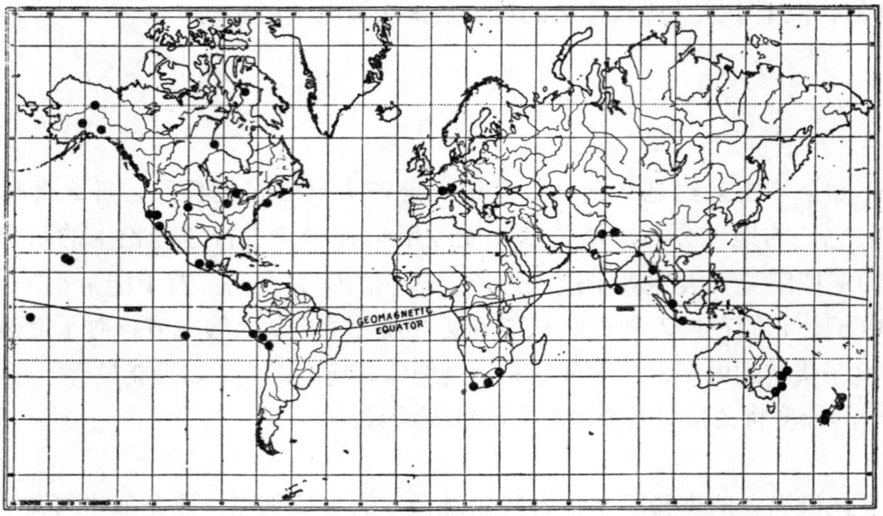


Fig. 1. Map showing major stations at which associated expeditions have made cosmic ray measurements during 1932.

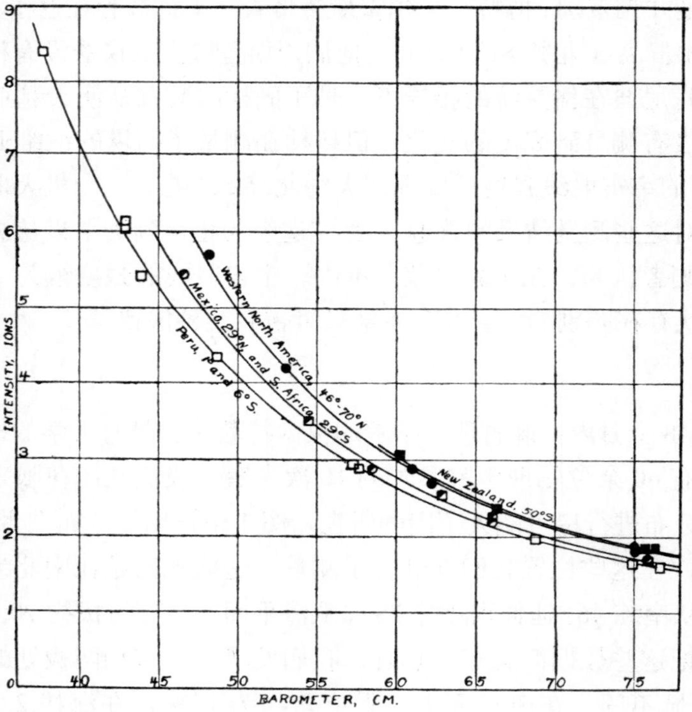


Fig. 2. Typical intensity-barometer curves, showing variation of intensity with altitude in different parts of the world. Circles, northern hemisphere; squares, southern hemisphere.

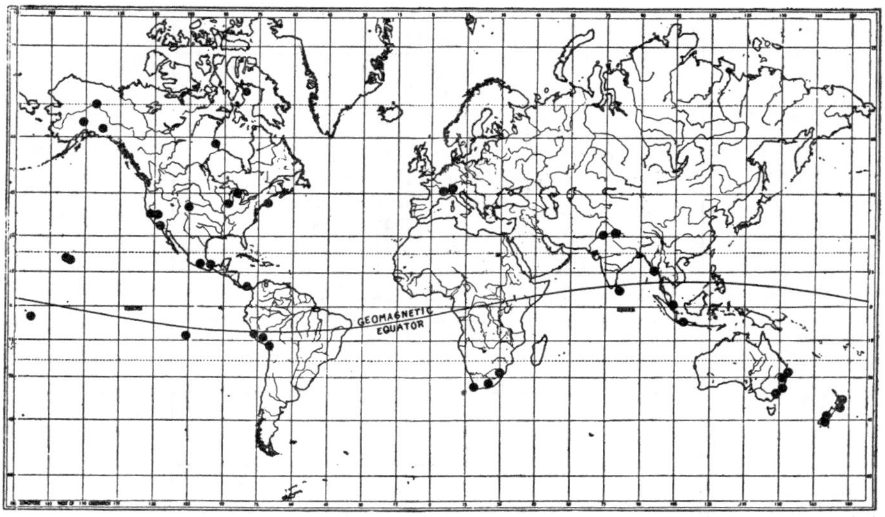


图 1. 考察队 1932 年在全球测量宇宙射线的主要站点分布图

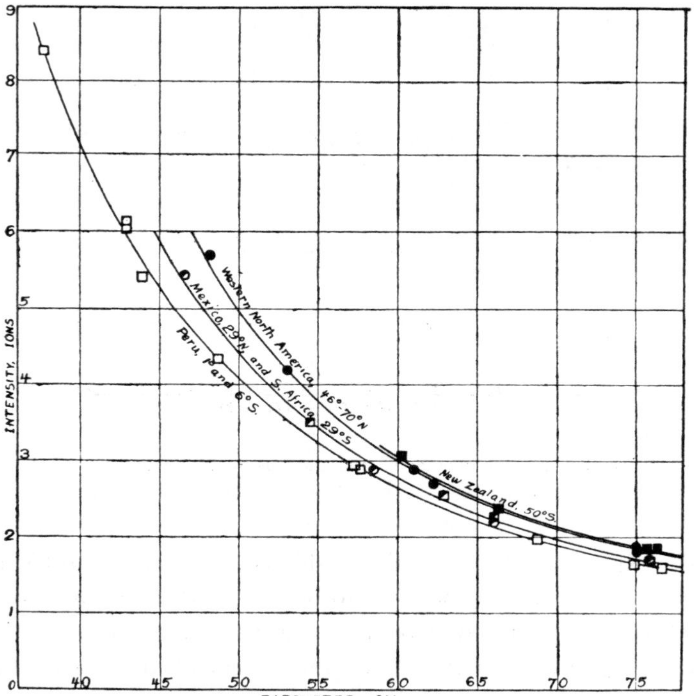


图 2. 典型的强度－气压曲线，这张图说明在世界上纬度不同的地区，宇宙射线的强度是不相同的。圆形，北半球；方块，南半球。

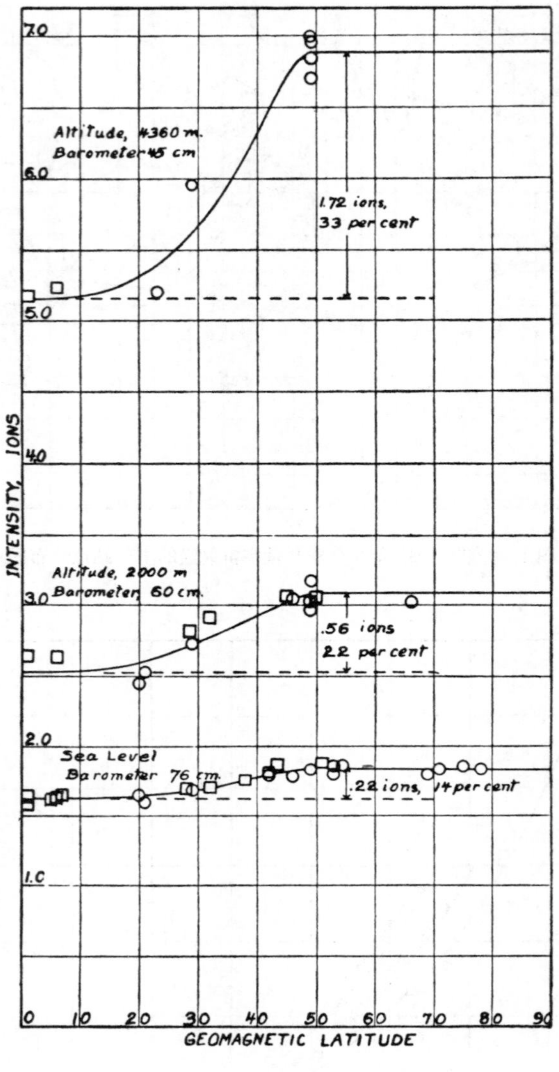


Fig. 3. Variation of cosmic ray intensity with geomagnetic latitude, as found for three different altitudes. The variation is more prominent at high altitudes. Curves calculated from Lemaître-Vallarta theory.

Comparison of the experimental data with the theory of Lemaître and Vallarta shows that the distribution of cosmic rays is about that to be expected if the rays consist of electrons entering the earth's atmosphere in two energy groups. One of these is of such great energy that it is not appreciably affected by the action of the earth's field. This group comprises in the temperate zone 88 percent of the total radiation at sea level, and might, so far as these experiments are concerned, be classified as photons. At 4,400 metres this component constitutes 75 percent of the total radiation. The second component is less penetrating and represents particles with an energy, if they are electrons, of about $7 \times 10^9$ electron volts. It is these particles which reach the earth at temperate latitudes but fail to reach it near the equator.

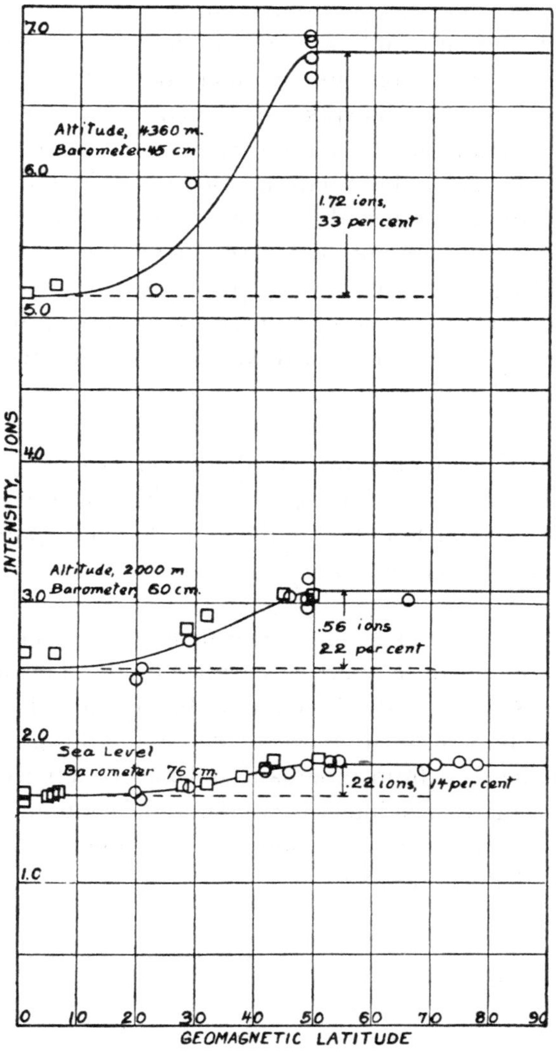


图 3. 宇宙射线强度随地磁纬度的变化，包括在海拔高度不同的三个地点测量得到的结果。海拔越高，变化越明显。曲线是根据勒梅特 – 瓦拉塔的理论计算出来的。

对这些实验数据与勒梅特和瓦拉塔理论的比较说明：如果进入地球大气层的宇宙射线由两个能量组的电子组成，则宇宙射线的分布就与人们预期的大体一致。其中的一组电子具有很高的能量，以至于基本不受地球磁场的影响。在温带地区的这组电子的能量占海平面处宇宙射线总辐射量的 88%，这组电子是迄今为止的实验所关注的可以看作是光子的那一类。在海拔 4,400 米处该成分占总辐射量的 75%。第二组成分穿透力稍差并表现为有相近能量的粒子，如果它们是电子，将具有约 $7\times10^9$ 电子伏特的能量。这些粒子可以进入地球的温带地区，但不能进入靠近赤道的地区。

It may be remarked that even these less-penetrating cosmic rays have energies which are much larger than those that could be accounted for as recoil electrons resulting from photons, if these photons were to constitute the main body of the cosmic rays. According to Millikan, measurements of the absorption of the cosmic rays at sea level indicate that their energy, if they are photons, is of the order of $2 \times 10^8$ electron volts. This is so much less (a factor of 35) than that of the electrons responsible for the difference in intensity between temperate and tropical zones, that we would seem to be safe in concluding that the particles reaching the earth are not of the recoil type. On the other hand, the energy of $7 \times 10^9$ electron volts demanded by the Lemaître–Vallarta theory for these particles would mean a range taken along the particle's trajectory of about three times the thickness of the earth's atmosphere. This is in accord with the fact that these rays penetrate the earth's atmosphere, but with difficulty.

This geographical study of the cosmic rays thus indicates that the less penetrating part of the cosmic rays, at least, consists of high-speed electrified particles. Regarding the more penetrating component, we conclude that if they are electrified particles, they must have an energy of $3 \times 10^{10}$ electron volts or more.

(3) During the past two years, extensive experiments have been carried out studying the variation in the intensity of cosmic rays with altitude. The highest altitudes have been those reached by Regener with his sounding balloon and Piccard with his famous stratosphere balloon. We have also paid especial attention to this problem in our mountain experiments. In Fig. 4 the data from mountain and balloon observations are compared. These data show a rapid increase in intensity with altitude, continuing nearly exponentially to an altitude of 15 km., and from there approaching a limiting value as the apparatus is carried close to the top of the atmosphere.

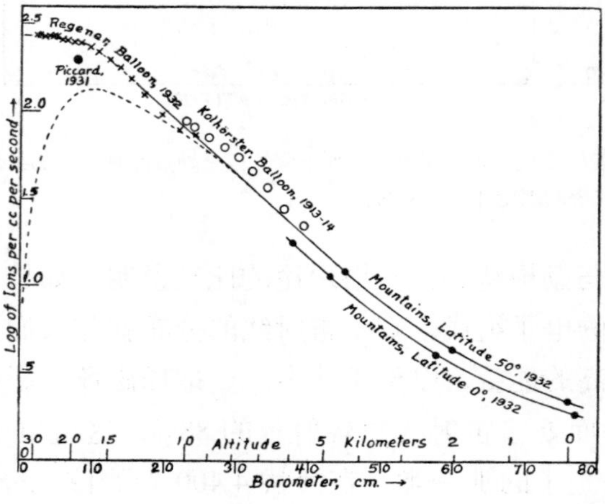


Fig. 4. Combined balloon and mountain data on intensity as function of altitude. Broken line, anticipated values for photons.

可以说，如果光子是组成宇宙射线的主体，那么即使是穿透性较差的那些宇宙射线所具有的能量也要远远高于由光子产生的反冲电子的能量。密立根认为，在海平面处对宇宙射线的吸收的测量表明：如果宇宙射线是光子，那么它们的能量就会达到 $2 \times 10^8$ 电子伏特数量级。这比使温带和热带地区宇宙射线强度产生差异的电子的能量小很多（相差 35 倍），以至于我们似乎可以肯定到达地球的粒子不是反冲电子。另一方面，勒梅特－瓦拉塔的理论要求粒子的能量应达到 $7 \times 10^9$ 电子伏特，这意味着粒子的射程约为地球大气层厚度的三倍。这一点符合这样的事实，即这些射线可以穿透地球大气，但是有一定的困难。

对宇宙射线地理分布的研究表明，宇宙射线中穿透力较差的部分起码会包含高速带电粒子。对于穿透性较强的成分，我们的结论是：如果它们是带电粒子，那么它们的能量就必须达到或超过 $3 \times 10^{10}$ 电子伏特。

（3）在过去的两年内，人们已经进行了大量的实验以研究宇宙射线强度随海拔高度的变化。目前以雷格纳的探空气球和皮卡德的著名平流层气球到达的高度最高。我们在山上做实验时也特别关注这个研究课题。在图 4 中，我们对山上的实验数据与气球观测的结果进行了比较。这些数据表明：随着高度的增加，宇宙射线的强度很快上升，持续呈指数型增长直至 15 km 高度，从那儿起，当测试仪器接近大气层顶部时，强度达到极限值。

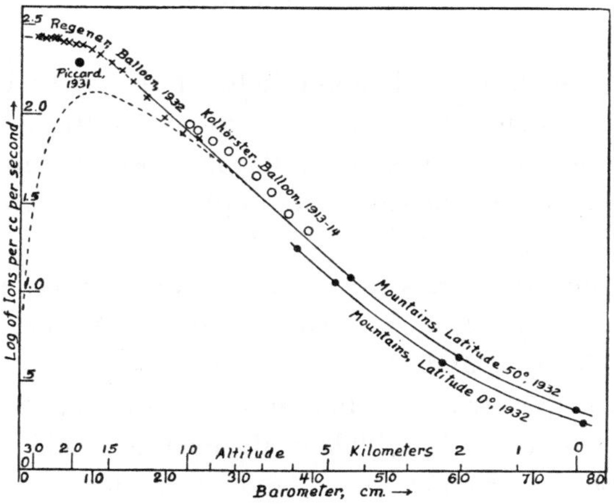


图 4. 综合气球实验和在山上所作的实验得到的宇宙射线强度随海拔高度的变化曲线。虚线是把宇宙射线看成光子后的预期值。

If we suppose that the cosmic rays enter the earth's atmosphere as photons, any secondary electrons that may have been associated with them in space will have been removed by the action of the earth's magnetic field. We should thus have a beam of pure photons entering the atmosphere. At the surface of the atmosphere these photons will produce very little ionisation, for the ionisation results directly from the secondary electrons that pass through the chamber. The secondary electrons, however, arise only at the absorption of the primary photons, and will not approach their normal intensity until the photons have traversed a thickness of air about equal to the range of the electrons. This means that at very high altitudes the ionisation due to a beam of photons entering the earth must be almost zero. The ionisation current should rather approach a maximum at a depth in the atmosphere at which the cosmic rays are somewhat less than half absorbed, and should then gradually diminish in intensity as sea level is approached. Our high mountain experiments confirm the recent balloon experiments as indicating that no such high altitude maximum exists. This would seem to rule out the possibility that the cosmic rays can be photons entering the earth's atmosphere from remote distances.

If we suppose, on the other hand, that the cosmic rays are electrons entering the atmosphere from above, we should expect very much the kind of intensity-altitude curve that the present experiments show. It is well known that the ionisation per unit path by high speed electrons remains almost constant over a wide range of energies. Thus, if a beam of such electrons enters the atmosphere, it will produce nearly uniform ionisation down to such depths that an appreciable number of the electrons are stopped by the air. If the initial electrons were all travelling downward, there would be a rather definite limit or range where there would be a rapid reduction in the ionisation by the cosmic rays. If, however, the initial electrons entered in all directions, some of them would be stopped even in the upper layers of the atmosphere. Thus, supposing that the cosmic rays consist of electrons entering the earth's atmosphere from outer space, the general characteristics of the intensity-altitude curve can be readily accounted for.

If Regener's measurements from his balloon flights during the past summer are reliable, it appears that there is no detectable decrease in ionisation as the top of the atmosphere is approached. This would mean, in accord with the above reasoning, that no appreciable portion of the cosmic rays enters the earth's atmosphere in the form of photons.

On the other hand, if the cosmic rays enter the atmosphere as electrons, they will produce photons just as cathode rays striking a target produce X-rays. Accordingly, at lower altitudes a mixture of electrons and photons will be present, and it may be expected that the photons will have the greater penetrating power. It is thus not impossible that the very penetrating cosmic rays observed by Millikan, Regener, and others at great depths under water may be such photons excited by the incoming electrons.

Although we have discussed the problem as if the electrified particles which seem to constitute the cosmic rays are electrons, it will be understood that the experiments that have been cited do not serve to distinguish between negatively and positively charged

假如我们把进入地球大气层的宇宙射线看作是光子，那么在太空中可能与这些光子相关联的次级电子都将因地球磁场的作用而偏离地球。因而我们应该有一束纯光子束进入大气层。在大气层表面，这些光子几乎不会发生电离，因为电离直接由穿过计数室的次级电子产生。然而，这些次级电子只有在吸收了初始光子的能量后才能产生，它们在光子穿越大气层的厚度小于电子的射程时是不会达到其正常强度的。这意味着在海拔很高的地方，由进入地球的光子束引起的电离应该接近于零。当到达大气层某一深度处的宇宙射线有将近一半的量被吸收时，电离电流将达到极大值，而在不断接近海平面的过程中，宇宙射线的强度应逐渐减小。我们在高山上所作的实验与最近的气球实验结果相同，都没有发现在高海拔处出现极大值。这似乎可以排除从遥远太空进入地球大气层的宇宙射线是光子的可能性。

另一方面，如果我们假设宇宙射线是从上方进入地球大气层的电子，我们应该能够很好地预期由现有实验得到的那类强度 – 高度曲线。众所周知，高速电子产生的每单位路径的电离在很宽的能量范围内几乎保持为一个常数。因此，如果一束这样的电子进入大气层，它们将产生几乎完全相同的电离直到这样一个深度，在这个深度上有数量相当可观的电子被空气阻止。如果初始的电子都是向下运动的，那么宇宙射线的电离发生快速下降的高度界线或范围将是非常明确的。然而，如果初始电子是从各个方向进入大气层的，则其中的某些电子会停止在大气层的上部。于是，假定宇宙射线是由外层空间进入地球大气层的电子所组成，实验的强度 – 高度曲线的总体特征就能很容易地得到解释。

如果雷格纳去年夏天用他的气球飞行实验得到的结果是可靠的，那么在接近大气层顶部时就不存在可探测的电离度下降。这意味着按照上述推理，在进入地球大气层的宇宙射线中，绝大部分都不是光子。

另一方面，如果宇宙射线以电子形式进入大气层，则它们也会生成光子，就像轰击靶子的阴极射线能产生 X 射线一样。于是，在海拔高度较低的地方将出现电子和光子的混合，可以预期光子将有更强的穿透能力。而密立根、雷格纳和其他研究者在水下很深处观测到的穿透力超强的宇宙射线并非不可能存在，它们也许就是被入射电子所激发的光子。

虽然我们推断组成宇宙射线的带电粒子可能是电子，但我们知道前面提到的那些实验都无法判断粒子带的是正电还是负电。这些实验结果同样可以用于说明宇宙

particles. The experiments are equally consistent with the view that the rays consist of protons or high speed $\alpha$-particles. I find no way of reconciling the data, however, with the hypothesis that any considerable portion of the primary cosmic rays consist of photons.

(**131**, 713-715; 1933)

射线是由质子或高速 $\alpha$ 粒子组成的。然而，如果假设初级宇宙射线的主要成分是光子，我认为上述数据就没办法得到解释了。

（沈乃澂 翻译；马宇蒨 审稿）

# Structure of Alloys*

W. L. Bragg

## Editor's Note

**One of the first sciences to reap the benefits of the Braggs' work on the technique of X-ray crystallography was metallurgy. Here Lawrence Bragg summarizes the current state of understanding of alloy structure. One particular puzzle was why, even for apparently randomly arranged mixtures of the atoms of two metals, the ratios tend to be simple whole numbers. This fact was empirically explained by William Hume Rothery in terms of a requirement for simple ratios of atoms to generate a complement of "free" or valence electrons—an intimation of the modern view that metals have "bands" of electrons that are free to move throughout the crystal lattice, with strict limitations on the electron capacity of each band.**

WHEN one metal is alloyed with another, in a series of varying relative proportions, generally several new alloy structures (phases) appear which are different from each other and from the structures of either pure metal. In the usual type of diagram, the composition of the alloy is represented along a horizontal scale starting with the pure metal $A$ on the left side and ending with the pure metal $B$ on the right side; temperatures are plotted vertically. In a typical case, the addition of small quantities of the metal $B$ to the metal $A$ does not alter its characteristic structure, the atoms remaining in the same relative arrangement. Atoms of $B$ replace a corresponding number of atoms of $A$ in an apparently random manner, and the only observable change is a uniform contraction or expansion of the $A$ lattice. There is thus a more or less extended single phase region on the left of the diagram. As the proportion of $B$ is increased, a limit is reached at which the $A$ structure can no longer absorb $B$ atoms in this way, and beyond this point a new phase appears. The new phase, which is richer in the $B$ constituent, has a different atomic arrangement, as has been confirmed by X-ray analysis. Throughout a certain range of composition the two phases co-exist and each is constant in composition, the amount of the first phase decreasing and of the second phase increasing in passing through the two-phase region from left to right. The first phase finally disappears, and a new region of single phase is entered, to be succeeded by two-phase regions and single phase regions alternately. The last single phase region on the right hand side includes as a limiting case the pure metal $B$.

Such phase diagrams have been worked out for many alloys by metallurgical methods. The boundaries between single phase and two-phase regions are determined by examining polished and etched surfaces under the microscope, and thermal and electrical

* Friday evening discourse delivered at the Royal Institution on March 17.

# 合金的结构*

威廉·劳伦斯·布拉格

## 编者按

冶金学是最早应用布拉格父子的X射线晶体学技术的领域之一。劳伦斯·布拉格在这篇文章中总结了目前人们对合金结构的理解。一个特别令人困惑的问题是：为什么即便是两种金属原子的任意混合物，它们之间的比例也倾向于一个简单的整数？威廉·休姆·罗瑟里给出的经验解释是原子之间需要保持简单的比例关系以形成对“自由”电子或价电子的补偿——这暗示了现代理论中的一个观点，现代理论认为金属“能带”中的电子可以在晶格内自由运动，而每个能带中的电子数量又受到严格的限制。

当一种金属与另一种金属以各种不同的相对比例形成合金时，通常会出现一些新的合金结构（相），它们不但彼此之间结构不一样，与两种纯金属的结构也都不相同。在通常的相图中，合金的组成标在水平轴上，左端最开始表示纯金属 $A$，最右端表示纯金属 $B$；而垂直轴则代表温度。在一般情况下，向金属 $A$ 中添加少量的金属 $B$ 不会改变它的特征结构，$A$ 原子保持着原有的相对排布方式，$B$ 原子以表观随机的方式替换掉了对应数量的 $A$ 原子，唯一可观察到的变化是 $A$ 晶格的均匀收缩或膨胀。因而在相图左侧的单相区会有所扩大。当 $B$ 的比例增加到某一极限时，$A$ 的结构不能再以上述方式吸收 $B$ 的原子，在超越了这一极限之后就会有新相形成。这个含更多 $B$ 原子的新相具有与原来不同的原子排布方式，这一点已被X射线分析所证实。接下来是一段两相共存的区域，这两相中各自都有恒定的组成结构，当从左至右穿过两相区时，第一个相的含量逐渐减少，而第二个相的含量则逐渐增加。第一个相最终消失，从而进入到一个新的单相区，接着是交替出现的两相区和单相区。右端最后一个单相区是作为极限情况的纯金属 $B$。

人们利用冶金学方法已经完成了很多种合金的相图。通过在显微镜下检查抛光和刻蚀的表面，人们可以确定单相区和两相区之间的边界，热学和电学的测量结果

* 本文取自作者于3月17日在英国皇家研究院所作的周五晚间演讲。

measurements aid in outlining the diagram. The single phase regions are bounded on each side by lines of which the departure from the vertical shows that the extent of the phase is, to some extent, dependent upon temperature. The liquidus and solidus boundaries above each phase region show at what temperatures solidification from the melt begins and ends.

In recent years, X-ray methods have played an important part in the construction of phase diagrams, the "powder method" being particularly suitable for this purpose. Westgren's name will always be associated with this field of inquiry, in which he was a pioneer. Several methods differing in their experimental detail have been used. In one method the alloy in the form of a fine powder is placed in a Debye-Scherrer camera, and irradiated with monochromatic X-rays of suitable wave-length. The diffracted beams form a pattern of lines upon a strip of photographic film, which is in the form of a cylinder with the powder at its axis. The pattern is characteristic of the alloy structure, and if not too complex, the structure can be completely analysed by studying the pattern it produces. In a single phase region the character of this pattern remains the same throughout the range of composition, the only change being a shift in the positions of the lines due to the expansion or contraction of the lattice. When the boundary of the single phase region is passed and the two-phase region is entered, the photographs show the pattern of both constituent phases superimposed. The lines of one become fainter, and of the other stronger, as the region is traversed. Since in this region each phase is constant in composition, the lines, though altering in intensity, do not shift their positions. If the lattice dimensions of a phase as determined by the powder photograph are plotted against composition, a sloping line is obtained in the single phase region and a horizontal line in the two-phase region. The composition at which the two lines intersect is a highly accurate index of the position of the phase boundary.

## X-Ray Technique

The wave-length of the radiation used in making the photographs must be adapted to the alloy which is being examined. It must not be absorbed too heavily by the alloy powder, both because the diffracted lines are then weak, and because the absorption implies a re-scattering of radiation in all directions with consequent darkening of the background. For example, cobalt, iron and chromium $K\alpha$ radiations are excellent for examining iron alloys, since they are of lower frequency than the iron "absorption edge" and hence are little absorbed. A cobalt radiation gives a large absorption of cobalt $K\beta$ rays in the specimen if these waves have not previously been filtered out. Copper radiation is extremely inefficient owing to the very large absorption, which produces a blackened film on which scarcely any lines are discernible.

It is possible to obtain powder photographs which at the same time give the pattern of lines throughout the complete circle, and enable the lattice dimensions to be worked out with high accuracy. The latter are most useful indices in elaborating the phase diagram. A recent design of camera by Bradley, combined with an ingenious method of evaluating the results, enables spacings to be compared with an accuracy approaching 1/50,000 when

对相图的绘制也有很大的帮助。单相区的边界线并不是垂直的，这表明相的存在范围在某种程度上取决于温度。各个相区上方的液相线和固相线表明熔融态开始凝固和完全凝固时的温度。

近些年来，X 射线法在相图的绘制中发挥了重要的作用，“粉末照相法”尤其适合于相图的绘制。在这项研究中人们经常会提到韦斯特格伦的名字，他是该领域的先驱。现在有几种实验细节不尽相同的方法。其中的一种方法，是将极细的合金粉末置于德拜－谢尔照相机中，并用适当波长的单色 X 射线照射样品。照相底片呈圆筒状，粉末就放在圆筒的轴上，衍射光束会在照相底片上形成谱线的图案。由衍射图案可以看出合金结构的特征，对于一些不太复杂的结构，研究其产生的衍射图案就完全可以分析出与之对应的结构了。在单相区的整个范围内，衍射图案保持相同的特征，唯一的变化只不过是因晶格膨胀或收缩而导致的谱线位移。当从单相区的边界处进入两相区时，照片中显示出两种相成分的衍射图案叠合在一起。在横越这一区域的过程当中，一个相的谱线逐渐变暗，另一个相的谱线则逐渐加强。由于这个区域内的每一个相都有恒定的组成，所以谱线虽然会有强度上的变化，但位置是不会改变的。如果以由粉末照相法确定的一个相的晶格尺寸为纵坐标，以组成为横坐标绘图，那么在单相区就会得到一条斜线，而在两相区会得到一条水平线。两条线相交之处的组成高度精确地指示出了相边界的位置。

## X 射线技术

照相时选用的辐射波长必须适用于所检测的合金。绝对不能让合金粉末对辐射有过强的吸收，这不仅是因为衍射线会随之变弱，还因为强吸收意味着辐射的再次被散射，从而导致衍射图的背景过暗。例如，钴、铁和铬的 K$\alpha$ 辐射对于铁合金的检测是非常合适的，因为它们的频率低于铁的“吸收边”的频率，因此基本不会被吸收。如果不对波长进行预先过滤的话，钴的辐射会在样品中产生显著的钴 K$\beta$ 吸收。而由于非常显著的吸收，铜的辐射会产生背景黑暗的相片，从而效果极差，很难在相片上辨认出任何谱线。

人们可以在得到粉末衍射图的同时获得由整个衍射环得到的谱线图，进而能够非常准确地计算出晶格的尺寸。后者是精确绘制相图时最有用的参数。最近，布拉德利设计出了一种照相机，在与精巧的计算方法相结合后，只要晶体材料合适，就可以使晶格间距的测量值达到接近于 1/50,000 的精度，而该方法使用的相机只不过

the crystalline material is suitable, while at the same time the camera is of the ordinary circular type utilising short exposures and including the complete pattern. All "precision methods" of measuring spacing depend upon the useful feature that rays diffracted backwards through nearly 180° enable a very accurate comparison of spacing with wave-length to be made. The particular feature of the method referred to above is the way in which errors due to incorrect placing of the specimen, absorption in the specimen, film shrinkage, and uncertainty as to camera-radius, are automatically eliminated.

Powder cameras must be calibrated by taking in each camera a photograph of a crystal with known spacings. Quartz is very suitable for this purpose. It is constant in composition, has a small temperature coefficient, and gives a large number of very clear lines. The quartz photograph may become as important in X-ray work as the comparison iron spectrum in spectroscopy.

## Nature of a "Phase"

The determination of phase boundaries by X-rays is merely the application of a new method to a problem already dealt with by well-established metallurgical technique. The particular contribution of X-ray analysis is its determination of the atomic arrangement in the alloy. It is found that each phase has a characteristic geometrical pattern of atomic positions. This is in accord with the findings of analysis in other crystalline bodies such as inorganic and organic compounds, but there is a new feature in alloy structures which is peculiar to them. The phase is an absolutely definite arrangement of "sites" for atoms, if one may put it in that way, but in many cases the way in which the atoms are distributed amongst these sites turns out to be of secondary importance, and may vary widely. Such a feature is foreign to the typical inorganic or organic compound, where the atoms of various kinds have each their appointed positions.

An example of this peculiar feature is given by the structures of two closely related alloys the compositions of which approach the ideal formulae $Cu_5Zn_8$ and $Cu_5Cd_8$. These alloys, which appear as phases in the copper-zinc and copper-cadmium systems, are obviously similar in nature. They are hard and brittle with a characteristic fracture and sheen. X-ray analysis by Bradley has determined their complex structure, in which there are 52 atoms in the unit cube, the "$\gamma$ structure". From the similarity in atomic ratio and the correspondence in chemical properties of zinc and cadmium, it would be expected that the arrangement of zinc atoms in one and of cadmium atoms in the other would precisely correspond. The sites for atoms in the two alloys are indeed almost identical, but Bradley has been able to show that the distribution of zinc atoms amongst these sites in the one alloy is entirely different from the arrangement of cadmium atoms in the other. Clearly the peculiar complex $\gamma$ structure is determined by something apart from the distribution of the atoms; the latter is a secondary feature influenced by the relative sizes of zinc and cadmium atoms.

We find similar phases, or arrangements of atomic sites, in different alloys. For example,

是普通的环形相机，具有曝光时间短并能包括完整衍射图案的特点。所有测量间距的“精确方法”必须具有这样的有效特征，即衍射线以接近 180º 的角度返回，从而使晶格间距与波长可以进行极为精确的比较。上述方法的特别之处在于可以自动消除由样品摆放错误、样品吸收、胶片收缩以及相机半径的不确定性而导致的偏差。

粉末照相法中所使用的相机必须用一种已知晶格间距的晶体的衍射图进行校准。石英非常适合这一要求，它具有恒定的组成和很小的温度系数，并能产生许多条非常清晰的谱线。石英的衍射图在 X 射线研究中的重要位置或许可以与铁谱图在光谱学中的地位相比拟。

## “相”的性质

用 X 射线法确定相的边界，只不过是在应用一种新方法处理早已被成熟的冶金学技术解决掉的问题。X 射线分析的特殊贡献在于它能确定合金中原子的排布方式。人们发现在每一个相中，原子的位置都具有一种特征的几何构型。这与其他晶体，如无机化合物和有机化合物的晶体的分析结果是一致的，但在合金结构中有一种新特性是它们所独有的。如果可以这么说的话，则相是原子“位置”的一种完全确定的排布形式，但在很多情况中，不同原子在这些位置中的分配是次要的，而且可能有很大差异。典型的无机化合物和有机化合物不具备这样的特性，因为在这些物质中，不同类型的原子各自有自己确定的位置。

我们可以用两种密切相关的合金结构作为上述特性的一个实例，它们的组成可近似用化学式 $Cu_5Zn_8$ 和 $Cu_5Cd_8$ 表示。这两种合金也是存在于铜 – 锌和铜 – 镉体系中的相，其性质明显相似。它们又硬又脆，具有特征的断面和光泽。布拉德利通过 X 射线分析确定了它们的复杂结构——“$\gamma$ 结构”，其晶胞中有 52 个原子。考虑到这两种合金中原子比例相近且锌与镉的化学性质基本一致，因而可以预期锌原子在第一种合金中的排布与镉原子在第二种合金中的排布应该完全一致。事实上，在两种合金中原子的位置几乎相同，而布拉德利指出，处于这些位置上的锌原子在一种合金（$Cu_5Zn_8$）中的分布方式完全不同于镉原子在另一种合金（$Cu_5Cd_8$）中的分布方式。很明显，这种独特的复杂 $\gamma$ 结构是由原子分布以外的因素决定的；而原子分布只是受锌原子和镉原子相对大小所影响的次要特征。

我们在各种合金中都发现了类似的相或类似的原子位置排布方式。例如，铜、银、

the alloys of copper, silver, gold with metals of the *B* subgroups such as zinc, cadmium, aluminium, gallium, tin form an $\alpha$ face-centred cubic phase like that of copper, silver, gold themselves, a body-centred $\beta$ phase, and a complex $\gamma$ phase with 52 atoms in the unit cell. All $\gamma$ phases have similar physical characteristics such as their extreme hardness. Since the geometrical arrangement of atomic sites in each phase appears to be quite definite, while at the same time independent of the atomic distribution, by what is it determined?

## Hume-Rothery's Law

The answer to this question is provided by a brilliant hypothesis which we owe to Hume Rothery, the truth of which has now been verified by a large number of examples. Hume-Rothery's law states that each phase appears when the ratio of valency electrons to atoms has a value characteristic of that phase. For example, the $\beta$ phase, which is body-centred cubic, is found when there are three valency electrons to every two atoms, examples being the alloys CuZn, $Cu_3Al$, $Cu_5Sn$. Assigning one valency electron to copper, two valency electrons to zinc, three to aluminium, and four to tin, it will be seen that in the first of these compounds there are three electrons to two atoms, in the second six electrons to four atoms, and in the third nine electrons to six atoms. An even more striking example is found amongst the $\gamma$ structures to which reference has already been made. Here the electron-atom ratio is 21:13, examples being $Cu_5Zn_8$, $Cu_9Al_4$, $Cu_{31}Sn_8$. A hexagonal, close-packed $\varepsilon$ structure which appears in many of the alloy systems has a ratio 7:4, as evidenced by $CuZn_3$, $Cu_3Sn$, $AgZn_3$, $Ag_5Al_3$, $AuCd_3$. A very large number of alloys obeying this law is now known, and it will no doubt be added to as other systems are examined.

There are exceptions to the rule. It must further be borne in mind that an alloy phase is not definite in composition but extends over a range in the phase diagram which may be broad or narrow. The composition which gives one of the above ideal electron-atom ratios may be towards one side of the single phase region, or even just outside it. It is justifiable to say, however, that the electron-atom ratio is a main factor in determining the arrangement of atomic sites in the phase. The range of the phase is modified by other factors, which make it broad or narrow and displace it one way or the other, but they are of secondary importance. Starting with copper, silver, or gold and alloying them with other metals, we run through a similar series of phases. The higher the valency of the second metal, the smaller is the amount of it which has to be added in order to produce each new phase. Quantitatively this may be expressed by saying that its contribution is to be reckoned in terms of added valency electrons, according to Hume-Rothery's law.

It is an interesting feature that the metals of the triads iron, cobalt, nickel; ruthenium, rhodium, palladium; osmium, iridium, platinum; form similar phases of the $\beta$ and $\gamma$ types. In these alloys the valency *zero* must be assigned to the transition metals; for example,

3:2 phase FeAl, CoAl, NiAl
21:13 phase $Fe_5Zn_{21}$, $Co_5Zn_{21}$, $Ni_5Zn_{21}$, $Rh_5Zn_{21}$, $Pt_5Zn_{21}$.

金与副族金属锌、镉、铝、镓、锡的合金可以形成一种与铜、银、金本身一样的面心立方 $\alpha$ 相，也可以形成一种体心立方 $\beta$ 相或一种晶胞中有 52 个原子的复杂 $\gamma$ 相。所有 $\gamma$ 相都有相似的物理性质，比如有极高的硬度。由于在每一个相中原子位置的几何排布都是非常确定的，但又与原子的具体分布无关，那么这是由什么决定的呢？

## 休姆－罗瑟里定律

休姆·罗瑟里提出的一个高明的假说提供了解决这一问题的答案，该假说的正确性已经得到了大量实例的证实。休姆－罗瑟里定律称：只有在原子与价电子的比例满足某一相的特征值时，该相才会出现。比如，体心立方的 $\beta$ 相在每 3 个价电子对应于 2 个原子时出现，例如合金 CuZn，$Cu_3Al$ 和 $Cu_5Sn$。其中铜有 1 个价电子，锌有 2 个价电子，铝有 3 个而锡有 4 个，可以看出，第一个化合物的价电子与原子之比为 3:2，第二个为 6:4，第三个则为 9:6。有人提到在 $\gamma$ 相中有一个令人惊奇的实例。其价电子与原子之比为 21:13，这样的例子有 $Cu_5Zn_8$，$Cu_9Al_4$ 和 $Cu_{31}Sn_8$。一种出现在很多合金体系中的六方密堆积 $\varepsilon$ 结构具有 7:4 的比例，例如 $CuZn_3$，$Cu_3Sn$，$AgZn_3$，$Ag_5Al_3$，$AuCd_3$。现在已经知道有很多合金都遵循这一原理，毫无疑问，在检验其他体系时这样的实例还会增加。

该规律也是有反例的。我们必须牢记，一个合金相的组成并不是固定的，而是在相图中占据一个或宽或窄的区域。满足上述理想的价电子与原子之比的组成可能靠近单相区内的某个边界，也可能刚好落在单相区之外。不过，我们有理由认为，价电子与原子之比是决定相中原子位置的排布方式的主要因素。其他因素也会改变相区的大小，令其变宽或变窄或者使其发生这样或那样的移位，但是这些都是次要的。以铜、银或者金作为第一种金属，用其他金属与它们形成合金，我们会观察到一系列相似的相。第二种金属的价态越高，为形成新相所需加入的该金属的量就越少。根据休姆－罗瑟里定律，定量关系可以用下面的方式表达：金属的贡献是以其加入的价电子数来衡量的。

这是一个有趣的现象：金属的三元系合金——铁钴镍、钌铑钯和锇铱铂会形成类似的 $\beta$ 或 $\gamma$ 类型的相。在这些合金中，必须认为这些过渡金属的价态为零；例如，

3:2　相 FeAl，CoAl，NiAl

21:13 相 $Fe_5Zn_{21}$，$Co_5Zn_{21}$，$Ni_5Zn_{21}$，$Rh_5Zn_{21}$，$Pt_5Zn_{21}$。

To sum up, the arrangement of atomic sites in an alloy phase appears to be due not to the interaction between the metals of one kind and those of another kind, but to the interaction between all the metal atoms on one hand, and the common electronic structure, to which they join in contributing their valency electrons, on the other hand. The metal atoms can be shuffled about between the phase-sites without a profound alteration of the nature of the phase, as if the structure were almost indifferent to the nature of the atoms in the various sites so long as they provided the quota of valency electrons. It has been shown by Bradley, for example, that ternary alloys and presumably alloys of any complexity assume the $\gamma$ phase if the total electron-atom ratio is 21:13.

## Segregation of Atoms into Phase-Sites

Two aspects of the problem of alloy structure may thus be distinguished. The first concerns the geometrical arrangement of the sites for atoms, characteristic of each type of phase. Its elucidation must be sought for in the electron-atom interaction as part of the problem of metallic structure in general. The second concerns the way in which the atoms distribute themselves amongst these sites. It has been known for some time that this distribution may vary in a given phase. On one hand, atoms of each kind may segregate into certain positions in a symmetrical way, so as to build a crystal structure of definite pattern like those found in inorganic and organic compounds. In some of the $\gamma$ alloys, for example, similar atoms occupy certain sets of the sites which are related by the crystal symmetry, and the other atoms occupy the remainder.

Alternatively, we may find the formation of a *super-lattice*. In a simple $\beta$ structure of the body-centred cubic type, for example, there are two atomic positions in each unit cubic cell, at corners and centres, which are crystallographically identical. In such structures as CuZn, or FeAl, one atom occupies the corners and the other the centres. In $\beta$ alloys of more complex composition, however, the unit of pattern repeats in a larger distance, so that it is necessary to stack several cubes together and select symmetrically certain positions from the large unit for one of the atoms, in order to represent the unit of pattern. An X-ray photograph of such an alloy shows as a primary feature the lines due to the body-centred cubic arrangement characteristic of all $\beta$ phases. In addition, subsidiary lines due to the super-lattice appear, which indicate that the unit of pattern is upon a larger scale. The segregation of the atoms into preferred positions may be followed by studying these lines.

As opposed to the formation of a super-lattice or of a regular crystalline segregation, we find in other cases that the X-ray diagram indicates merely the arrangement of the atomic sites, as if the atoms were arranged in an absolutely random manner amongst these sites. Such a random arrangement would affect the X-ray diffraction pattern as if each site were occupied by an identical unit of mean composition. Many examples might be quoted, a very striking one being given by Westgren. The alloy $Cu_5Si$ has a complex structure in which there are twenty atoms in the unit cube. This $\beta'$ structure is assumed instead of the simple $\beta$ structure by certain alloys with a 3:2 electron ratio, and is similar to one form of the element manganese, the $\beta$-manganese structure. An X-ray photograph of $Cu_5Si$ gives

总而言之，在一种合金相中原子位置的排布方式似乎与一类金属和另一类金属之间的相互作用无关，而是在一方面取决于所有金属原子之间的相互作用，在另一方面取决于它们以贡献自身价电子而形成的共用电子结构。金属原子可以在相结构中杂乱排布而不会导致相性质发生显著变化，好像只要它们能提供一定量的价电子，相的结构就几乎不会受到处于各个位置上的原子性质的影响。例如，布拉德利曾指出，如果总的价电子与原子之比为21:13，那么三元合金就会出现 $\gamma$ 相，其他具有复杂结构的合金也可能会出现 $\gamma$ 相。

## 原子在相结构中的占位

因此合金结构问题可以划分为两个方面。第一个方面涉及原子位置的几何排布方式，这也是每一种相的特征。要解释这一点通常必须把价电子与原子之间的相互作用看作是影响金属结构的一部分原因。第二个方面涉及原子在这些位置上的分布。人们已经知道这种分布在一个给定的相中是可以变化的。一方面，各种原子能够以对称的方式分布在某些位置上，从而构造出有特定模式的晶体结构，就像无机化合物和有机化合物的晶体一样。例如，在一些 $\gamma$ 合金中，相似的原子占据着与晶体对称性相关的一系列位置，其他原子则占据剩余的位置。

另一方面，我们可能观察到了一种**超晶格**的形成。例如，在一种属于体心立方类型的简单 $\beta$ 结构中，每个立方体晶胞内有两个位置——顶点和中心，它们在结晶学上是等同的。例如 CuZn 或 FeAl 就具有这样的结构，一个原子占据顶点，另一个原子占据中心。然而在组成更为复杂的 $\beta$ 合金中，该模型单元是在更大的尺度上重复出现的，因此为了描述这时的模型单元，必须将若干个立方体叠在一起，并从这个更大的单元中选取对应于某个原子的对称的位置。这种合金的 X 射线衍射图显示，作为所有 $\beta$ 相共同特征的体心立方排布所产生的谱线是最主要的特征。此外，由于超晶格的存在还会出现一些附加谱线，这些附加谱线表明该模型单元具有更大的尺度。通过研究这些谱线，我们也许可以了解原子在最适位置中的分布情况。

与形成超晶格或者通常的晶相偏析的状况相反，我们发现在另一些情况下，X 射线图仅仅显示出了原子位置的排布，好像原子是以完全随机的方式排布到这些位置上的。这种随机排布会影响到 X 射线的衍射图案，每个位置就像是被具有平均组成的同一单元所占据一般。可能有很多这方面的例子，韦斯特格伦就给出了一个非常令人吃惊的例子。合金 $Cu_5Si$ 的结构非常复杂，每个晶胞中有 20 个原子。它是 $\beta'$ 结构，而非某些满足 3:2 电子比的合金所具有的简单 $\beta$ 结构，这种结构类似于元素锰的一种结构——$\beta$– 锰结构。在 $Cu_5Si$ 的 X 射线照片中出现了与 $\beta$– 锰结构的排布

lines identical in arrangement and relation in intensity with those of $\beta$-manganese, in which, of course, all atoms have the same scattering power, so that the scattering by each atomic site must be that of a mean effective atom. Further, it may be noted that the six atoms of $Cu_5Si$ cannot be distributed in any regular way between twenty atomic positions, since 6 is not a factor of 20. Structures which give such an effect are said to be structures of *random replacement.*

The transition between the two extremes of regular and random replacement may be observed in one and the same alloy. Alloys at high temperatures or which have been rapidly quenched from high temperatures show random arrangement, whereas alloys subjected to prolonged annealing have a regular or super-lattice structure. The potential energy of the symmetrical structure must be less than that of the disordered structure, and hence it is the stable structure at low temperatures. At high temperatures, however, the thermal movements are causing the atoms constantly to change places, a disordered arrangement having a higher entropy than an ordered arrangement.

The study of these changes in arrangement is of great interest and importance, because they affect the physical properties of the alloy. It is to be emphasised that we are not concerned here with a phase change, since the phase remains the same throughout. We are dealing with continuous changes from order to disorder within the same phase structure.

The segregation of atoms into regular positions was surmised by Tammann in 1919 as an explanation of the changes in resistance of annealed alloys. One of the most fully examined cases is that of the gold copper alloy AuCu studied by Johannson and Linde. In this case we are dealing not only with regular and irregular distribution of atoms, but also with an alteration of crystalline form. The alloy of perfect arrangement is tetragonal in symmetry, and the symmetry passes by change of axial ratio into the cubic type as the temperature is raised. A similar but simpler case will be discussed here, where the arrangement of the atomic sites remains the same throughout. This is the case in the iron aluminium alloys examined in detail by Bradley.

The alloy of composition FeAl is a structure of the $\beta$ type, with iron atoms and aluminium atoms at corners and centres of the unit cube. Iron has itself a body-centred cubic structure, and it is found that, when aluminium is dissolved in iron, there is a very wide continuous range of this body centred cubic phase extending from pure iron to FeAl. The added aluminium atoms simply replace iron atoms. Two types of super-lattice are built up. When the composition is FeAl, iron atoms at the centres of the cubes are entirely replaced by aluminium atoms, so that the structure is of the type known as a "CsCl" structure. It may be noted that there is no crystallographic distinction between corners and centres, so that we might equally well describe the arrangement as one of aluminium atoms at corners and iron atoms at centres. When the composition is $Fe_3Al$, and the alloy is carefully annealed, one half of the cube centres chosen in a symmetrical way are occupied by aluminium and the other half remain iron atoms.

方式和强度关系都一样的谱线；当然，在 $\beta$− 锰中，所有原子都具有相同的散射能力，因此每个原子位置处的散射肯定都等于一个平均有效原子的散射。另外，可以看出 $Cu_5Si$ 的 6 个原子不可能以任何规则的方式分配到 20 个原子位置中去，因为 6 不是 20 的因数。人们把能够产生这种效应的结构称为**随机取代**结构。

在同一种合金中可能会观测到在规则与随机替换这两个极端之间的过渡情况。处于高温下的合金或者从高温经过快速淬火的合金表现为随机分布方式，而退火时间比较长的合金则具有规则结构或超晶格结构。对称结构的势能势必小于无序结构的势能，因而对称结构是低温条件下的稳定结构。但在高温下，热运动使原子不断地改变位置，无序分布状态的熵要高于有序分布状态的熵。

研究排布的变化非常有趣也很重要，因为它们会影响合金的物理性质。需要强调的是，在这里我们并没有涉及相变，因为相并没有发生变化。我们是在同一种相结构中处理有序到无序的连续变化问题。

塔曼在 1919 年推测，原子向规则排布的转化可以解释合金在退火时出现的电阻变化。约翰尼森和林德研究的金铜合金 AuCu 就是一个经过充分检验的例子。在这个例子中，我们不仅要讨论原子的有序和无序分布，而且要讨论晶型的变化。完美排布的合金具有四方晶系的对称性，随着温度的升高，对称性在经过轴比的变化之后过渡为立方晶系。这里要讨论的是一种与之类似但要简单一些的情形，即原子位置的排布保持不变的情形，这就是布拉德利曾详细考查过的铁铝合金中的情况。

组成为 FeAl 的合金具有 $\beta$ 型结构，铁原子和铝原子位于立方晶胞的顶点和中心。铁本身就具有体心立方的结构，人们发现当铝溶入铁时，这种体心立方相的延续范围非常宽，其跨度从纯铁到 FeAl。加入的铝原子只是取代了部分铁原子而已。有两种类型的超晶格形成。当组成为 FeAl 时，所有位于立方体中心的铁原子都被铝原子取代，成为人们所熟知的“CsCl”结构。可以看到，此时顶点和中心在晶体学上已不再有分别，我们同样可以把这种排布描述为，铝原子位于顶点而铁原子位于中心。当组成为 $Fe_3Al$ 的合金被小心地退火后，立方体中心的位置非常对称地一半由铝原子占据，而另一半仍由铁原子占据。

By observing the super-lattice lines in the photographs, Bradley has been able to follow out the process of replacement at all compositions between pure iron and FeAl. Taking first annealed alloys, the first aluminium atoms to enter the structure replace iron atoms at random. At a certain concentration, the aluminium atoms desert cube corners and one set of cube centres, and tend to concentrate in the remaining set of cube centres, finally at $Fe_3Al$ occupying it entirely. Past this point, since one set of cube centres is now full, the further aluminium atoms start filling up the remaining set of cube centres. At a certain point, in order to equalise the distribution between the two sets of centres, these two share the available aluminium until finally at FeAl they are completely filled. The quenched alloys show a curious phenomenon. Up to 25 percent atomic aluminium they have apparently random replacement. Past that point, within less than 1 percent change in composition, they change over into a distribution in which all corners are occupied by iron, and centres by a random replacement of iron by aluminium.

## Random Replacement

When an X-ray photograph shows an apparently random replacement, are we to interpret this as meaning that the atomic sites are occupied by iron and aluminium as if they were the "black and white balls" of a problem in probabilities? On physical grounds this is not to be expected. The $Fe_3Al$ and FeAl structures show us that aluminium atoms under conditions of ideal equilibrium tend in the first place to avoid being nearest neighbours by segregating into cube centres, leaving the corners for iron, and further to avoid being in cubes which are side by side ($Fe_3Al$ structure). We must postulate a slight increase in potential energy when aluminium atoms are at centres of contiguous cubes, and a larger increase when two find themselves at a corner and centre of the same cube. I am indebted to Dr. Williams for calculations concerned with this effect. If we suppose a small increase $V$ of potential energy to be produced by one of these undesirable contacts, it is then possible to calculate the proportion of atoms in "disorder" as opposed to "order" at a series of temperatures.

The calculation shows that it is impossible to account for the whole range between complete order (which we know to exist by the evidence of super-lattice lines) and complete disorder, in any range of temperature experimentally available. The difference between annealing and quenching could at the most produce a slight disorder. The conditions we have set are, however, not true to actualities. As the structure becomes more disordered, the contrast between the ordered position and disordered position for a given atom becomes less, and so $V$ must be supposed to diminish, until finally one can picture a state where no criterion is possible—the atom is completely demoralised by the corrupt state of society in which it finds itself.

It is possible, however, that what appears to be random replacement is not really a purely fortuitous distribution. We may suppose that within each small crystallite of the metal there is for the most part an ordered distribution, but that this ordered distribution is frequently getting "out of step". To take a simple case of a linear row, we may suppose an alternation

通过观察照片中的超晶格谱线，布拉德利研究了所有介于纯铁与 FeAl 之间的组分的取代过程。对于初退火合金，首批进入结构的铝原子将随机地取代铁原子。达到一定浓度后，铝原子放弃了立方体的顶点和一组立方体的中心位置，而倾向于集中在剩余立方体的中心位置，最终当组成变为 $Fe_3Al$ 时这些位置也被完全占据了。当浓度超过这个值之后，由于有一组立方体的中心已被占满，更多的铝原子开始填充到剩下的那组立方体的中心位置。达到某一个特定的浓度值时，为了使这两组中心在分布上达到平衡，两组位置分享所得的铝原子，直到它们完全被填满，最终成为 FeAl。淬火合金则呈现出一种奇异的现象。在铝原子占总数的 25%以下时，表现为随机取代。超过以上比例之后，在组成变化不到 1%的范围之内，它们的分布就发生了改变，所有的顶点均被铁原子占据，而中心位置的铁则被铝随机取代。

## 随机取代

当可以从 X 射线衍射图中看到明显的随机取代时，我们是否该将其解释为原子位置被铁和铝随机占据，就如同它们是概率问题中的“黑球和白球”呢？在物理学中不能这么认为。$Fe_3Al$ 和 FeAl 的结构告诉我们，在理想的平衡条件下，铝原子首先倾向于分散到立方体的中心而将顶点留给铁以避免处于最近邻的位置，还要避免处于相邻的立方体之中（$Fe_3Al$ 结构）。由此我们必须假定，当两个铝原子位于相邻立方体的中心时，势能会略微增加；而当两个铝原子位于同一立方体的顶点和中心时，势能会有更大的增加。我要感谢威廉博士对这种效应所做的计算。如果我们假设上述不利于系统能量的情况会使势能产生一个微小的增量 $V$，那么就可以计算出一系列温度下处于“无序状态”的原子相对于“有序状态”下的原子的比例。

计算表明，在实验可以达到的温度范围内实现了完全有序（关于这一点我们已经用超晶格谱线证实了）到完全无序的整个变化过程，我们无法对此作出解释。退火和淬火的差别至多只在于少量无序态的产生。不过我们在这里提出的情况并不符合现实。随着结构变得越来越无序，有序位置与无序位置对于某一个给定原子来说差异越来越小，因此 $V$ 必然会变小，直到最后达到了一种再也找不到有序判据的状态——原子已完全陷入了混乱无序的状态之中。

然而，看似随机的替换不一定真的就是纯粹的偶然分布。我们可以假设，在金属中的每一个微晶内，有序分布占大部分，但这种有序分布经常会出现“步调不一致”。对于一种简单的线性排列，我们可以假设排列中的一部分是交替出现的

Al-Fe-Al-Fe to take place for a part of the row, and that then owing to an excess of iron, two iron atoms follow, so that when the alternation recommences, aluminium and iron atoms have changed places. This process may be frequently repeated. Since the effects of all atoms in crystal planes are summed when the X-rays are diffracted by the crystallite as a whole, the result as regards diffraction would be an apparently random replacement of iron by aluminium. A kind of structural twinning within the crystal, which does not alter the orientation of its axes but only the succession of its atomic planes, is possible.

The behaviour of the quenched iron aluminium alloys suggests some such explanation. So long as aluminium is present in quantities less than 25 percent in atomic proportions, there is apparent random replacement. Beyond this point the segregation suddenly appears by which aluminium goes into cube centres alone. May not this be because below 25 percent the excess of iron causes the structure to get "out of step", two successive layers of iron atoms causing a part of the crystallite with aluminium at centres of cubes to continue as a pattern in which the same atoms go to corners? Beyond 25 percent aluminium, each cube must have contiguous cubes containing aluminium at centres, so that there is no question as to what is a centre and what is a corner. The plan of iron at corners and aluminium at centres is therefore carried out throughout the crystallite

Though so many problems of alloy constitution are still to be solved, an important step forward has been made by the recognition that the arrangement of atomic sites and the segregation of atoms into these sites are separate problems, and by the discovery of similar phase-structures in alloy series of different metals. There is promise of reducing to order the vast array of hitherto uncorrelated data.

(**131**, 749-753; 1933)

Al–Fe–Al–Fe 结构，接着由于铁过量，两个铁原子连续出现，于是当再次出现交替情况时，铝原子和铁原子已经交换了位置。这一过程可以频繁地重复发生。当微晶作为一个整体使 X 射线发生衍射时，由于晶面中所有原子的效应叠加在了一起，所以从衍射结果上看就好像是铝原子在随机地替换铁原子。在原子内有可能出现不改变轴方向只改变原子平面次序的结构性孪晶。

淬火铁铝合金的行为也证实了上面的解释。只要铝的含量少于原子比例的 25%，就会出现随机替换现象。超过该值后会突然出现规则的分布，铝原子只进入立方体的中心。这会不会是因为在铝的含量低于 25%时，铁的过量使结构产生“步调不一致”，两个相继的铁原子层使接下来的一部分原本铝位于立方体中心的晶体如同铝位于顶点的形式呢？铝超过 25%后，每个立方体的周围必定有包含铝原子在中心的立方体，因而不再存在哪一个在中心、哪一个在顶点的问题。从而在整个晶体中实现了铁位于顶点而铝位于中心的布局。

尽管有许多关于合金构造的问题还有待解决，然而，通过认识到原子位置的排布与原子在这些位置中的分配是两个独立的问题，以及发现了在不同金属的合金序列中存在相似的相结构，我们已经向前迈出了重要的一步。简化处理大量目前仍找不到关联的数据是有可能实现的。

（王耀杨 翻译；沈宝莲 审稿）

# A Possible Property of the Positive Electron

W. Elsasser

## Editor's Note

**The curious similarity of the neutron and proton, coupled with the discovery of the positron, suggested some intriguing possibilities for structures within the atomic nucleus. Some physicists had suggested that the proton might be a composite particle formed from a neutron and positron. Walter Elsasser suggests here that the hypothesis might also help explain recent discoveries about the proton's magnetic moment—a measure of its magnetic behaviour. He says the idea might account for why positrons seem to be found only in nuclei. Elsasser's suggestions were well motivated, but would soon be proven off the mark, especially by experiments showing the positron to have spin (a quantum property related to angular momentum) of 1/2, just like the electron.**

THE detection of the positive electron (called positron) by Blackett and Occhialini[1] and by Anderson[2] makes it very probable that the positron has a great importance in the building up of nuclei. Anderson[2] suggests that the proton may consist of a neutron and a positron. In favour of this hypothesis we may mention the experiments of Stern (still unpublished), who found that the magnetic momentum of the proton is three times greater than it should be if the proton were to behave like an elementary particle in Dirac's theory. Following Heisenberg[3], both the proton and the neutron obey Fermi statistics and have a half integral spin momentum. This leads at once to the conclusion that, if the hypothesis of Anderson is true, the positron should obey Bose statistics and have an integral spin momentum (0 or 1). If this view should be confirmed by other experimental evidence we should understand better why the positrons can only be found in nuclei; for, since positrons have symmetrical wave functions, they can always be placed in the deepest energy levels. It seems to be an advantage of the proposed hypothesis, that contrary to Dirac's theory of "holes"[4] an essential asymmetry between positive and negative electricity is introduced into the laws describing the behaviour of elementary particles. Since the light-quanta also have whole number momenta, it seems that it may be a general rule, that symmetrical wave functions are combined with integral momenta and anti-symmetrical wave functions with half integral momenta.

(**131**, 764; 1933)

W. Elsasser: Physikalisches Institut, Technischen Hochschule, Zürich, April 25.

---

References:

1 *Proc. Roy. Soc.*, **139**, 699 (1933).

2 *Phys. Rev.* (March, 1933).

3 *Z. Phys.*, **77**, 1 (1932).

4 *Proc. Roy. Soc.*, **126**, 360 (1932).

# 正电子可能具有的性质

沃尔特·埃尔萨瑟

## 编者按

中子和质子的惊人相似以及正电子的发现使人们对原子核的内部结构浮想联翩。一些物理学家认为质子可能是由中子和正电子合成的。沃尔特·埃尔萨瑟在这篇文章中指出上述假说也许有助于解释最近的一项与质子磁矩有关的发现——一种对质子磁行为的测量。他说这个观点或许可以说明为什么正电子似乎只出现于原子核中。埃尔萨瑟的这种提法绝对不是空穴来风，但他的假设很快就被证明是错误的，实验证明正电子的自旋（一种与角动量相关的量子特性）为 1/2，和电子没有什么两样。

布莱克特、奥基亚利尼[1]和安德森[2]探测到了带正电的电子（被人们称为正电子），这很有可能意味着正电子是原子核的重要组成部分。安德森[2]指出，质子可能是由一个中子和一个正电子组成的。为了证明这个假说，我们要提到斯特恩的实验（尚未发表），他发现：根据狄拉克的理论，如果质子是基本粒子，那么它的磁矩应该是现在的 3 倍。按照海森堡[3]的说法，质子和中子都遵循费米统计规律并具有半整数自旋动量。由此我们马上可以得到这样的结论：如果安德森的假说成立，那么正电子应该遵守玻色统计规律并且具有整数自旋动量（0 或 1）。如果这个观点能够被其他实验现象所证实，那么我们就可以更好地理解为什么正电子只出现在原子核当中；因为正电子具有对称的波函数，所以它们可以一直处在最低的能级上。这似乎支持了上面提出的假说，但却与狄拉克的“空穴”理论[4]相反，狄拉克理论在描述基本粒子行为的物理规律中引入了正负电子之间重要的不对称性。由于光量子也具有整数自旋，看起来总的规律是：对称波函数与整数自旋动量并存，反对称波函数与半整数自旋动量并存。

（王静 翻译；李军刚 审稿）

# Crystals of the Living Body*

W. H. Bragg

## Editor's Note

**This summary of the crystallography of biological molecules was presented by William Bragg at the Royal Institution in London. Bragg points out that biological tissues achieve their function largely from the organisation of the component molecules, which in fibrous materials such as hair and silk involve a near-crystalline arrangement of chain-like molecules. Bragg suggests, using wooden models, how this ordering might be related to the flexible backbones of the constituent protein molecules. These were the first steps towards an understanding of the hierarchical (many-levelled) structure that is now known to confer superior mechanical properties on biological materials such as silk.**

IT is obvious that the atoms and molecules of a living body are not thrown together in a haphazard fashion. There is in the first place a certain preferential disposal of the various kinds of atoms. While carbon, oxygen, hydrogen are widely and plentifully distributed throughout the body, the bones and teeth are comparatively rich in phosphorus and calcium, the hair contains sulphur and nitrogen, and so on. But these and other special occurrences are not enough to serve the body's purposes. There is a greater differentiation in the distribution of the molecules into which the atoms are grouped. There are, for example, many kinds of protein molecules which have their several parts to play as constituents of the different organs, and help to endow each organ with its peculiar function. But again this is not enough. There is a further requisite, namely, order in the arrangement of the molecules; which gives directive action to the various composite masses. A hair, for example, is largely composed of a species of the proteins known as the keratins. These are long, narrow, molecular arrangements which we shall presently consider more in detail. The molecules are fastened together, somewhat loosely it would seem, into little bundles, in which the molecules all point nearly in the same direction. The bundles are so disposed that this direction is nearly the same as that of the axis of the hair.

This order in the arrangement of the long molecules would seem to us, now that we have discovered it, to be in accordance with what we might have expected. The long molecules are an important part of the hair, and indicate a disposition of its components which must give to it directional properties. The hair grows in a particular direction to which also its various mechanical properties are related. If the molecules lay in all directions, there would be no reason why the hair should be long, narrow, flexible and yet strong.

---

* Friday evening discourse delivered at the Royal Institution, January 20.

# 活生物体中的结晶*

威廉·亨利·布拉格

## 编者按

这份对生物分子晶体学的总结来自于威廉·布拉格在伦敦英国皇家研究院所作的报告。布拉格指出：生物组织主要是通过将组成它们的分子予以组装来实现它们的功能的，在毛发和蚕丝这样的纤维类物质中就涉及链状分子的近晶形排列。布拉格用木质模型来表明他的建议，即这种排序方式有可能是怎么与组成蛋白质分子的柔性骨架相联系的。这是我们向了解多层次结构迈出的第一步，现在已经知道，这种多层次结构可以赋予像蚕丝这样的生物材料非常好的力学性能。

显然，活生物体中的原子和分子不是随意地堆放在一起的。首先，在不同类型的原子间存在着某种优势排列。虽然碳、氧和氢广泛和大量地分布于生物体的各个部分，但磷和钙在骨骼和牙齿中含量相对较多，硫和氮存在于头发中等等。但是以上这些以及其他特殊的存在并不足以满足机体的功效，由原子组合而成的分子在分布状态上存在的差别更大。例如，有很多种蛋白质分子作为不同器官的组成部分发挥着几项作用，并且帮助每个器官实现它的独特功能。但这些仍然是不够的，还有更进一步的需求，即分子排布要有一定的顺序，这使各种组分原料表现出具有方向性的效应。例如，毛发主要是由一种被称为角蛋白的蛋白质组成的，它们的分子具有又长又细的排布形式，我们会在后面更详细地讨论。这些分子会栓连在一起（表面看起来有点松散）成为小的捆束，其中的每个分子都指向大致相同的方向，这些捆束的摆放方向与毛发的轴向大致相同。

现在我们已经发现，这种细长分子的排布方向似乎与我们的预期可能相一致。长分子是毛发的一个重要组成部分，它表明其组成的取向必然使毛发具有方向性质。此外，毛发的种种机械性质也与它朝一个特定的方向生长有关，如果分子是朝各个方向排布的，那就没有理由说明为什么毛发会既长又细，外柔内刚。

---

* 本文取自作者于 1 月 20 日在英国皇家研究院所作的周五晚间演讲。

All growth in Nature implies extensions in particular directions. Function is connected with orientation, and there can be no orientation without method in the molecular arrangements; for it has never yet been found that a process in a living body moves in contradiction to the laws of physics and chemistry as observed in the laboratory. This does not, of course, imply that any artificial arrangement of atoms and molecules has ever been endowed with life. A mass of molecules so indiscriminately arranged that no particular direction can be distinguished from any other, cannot be expected, even though it is part of a living body, to extend and grow in one direction more than in another.

We have taken a hair as an example, but other parts of the body would have served equally well. Nerves, muscles and tendons all possess arrangement; the bones are not merely shaped externally as an engineer would shape them, but show also in the internal arrangement of their molecules an orientation for a definite purpose which the engineer must envy.

Clearly, if arrangement of the molecules is so necessary to enable the body to function and to live, the actions of the body cannot be fully understood without taking it into account. The new methods of analysis by radiation of very short wave-length, including, we may now say, electrons as well as X-rays, have provided us with means of examination of structure which are of much greater power than any that we possessed previously. These latter have been indeed very few and indirect. Furthermore, catalytic actions depend on the arrangements of the atoms and molecules on the surface of the catalysing solid; but though this fact may have been appreciated, the details of the arrangement have been out of reach. In fact the new methods open up possibilities which are also new.

Our chemical methods, it must be pointed out, do not reveal the nature and details of molecular arrangements. When we employ them for the analysis of a material, we begin by pulling the material to pieces and so destroying that very arrangement of molecules which we should be glad to examine. We knock the house down, and discover the numbers and natures of its components; so many bricks, so many slates, so many planks and so on; but we have lost the plan of the house. We must differentiate between the arrangement of atoms in the molecule, and of the molecules with respect to one another. The former has long been the study of the chemist, and especially of the organic chemist. In such studies the molecules are free and approachable from all round, being either the constituents of a liquid or in solution in a liquid. A liquid has no permanent directional properties except, possibly, at its surface. On the other hand, the mutual arrangement of the molecules in the solid is fundamentally concerned in those directive properties which are characteristic of the solid; it is this arrangement which is now open to our examination.

As illustrations of the effects of mutual arrangement among the molecules, we may first consider the case of two soap bubbles, which may be rubbed together—not too violently—without coalescing. The material of the film is contained between two surface borders of

自然界中的所有生长都意味着在特定方向上的伸展。功能是与取向相联系的，而没有分子排布的特定方式就不可能存在任何取向性，因为迄今还没有人发现活生物体中的某一个过程以与在实验室中观察到的物理和化学定律相矛盾的方向运行。当然，这并不意味着生命已经被赋予了人工排列的原子和分子。如果将大量分子不加区别地排布，以至于无法从中区分出特定的指向，就不可能预期分子能在一个方向上比在另一个方向上更好地伸展和生长，即使它也是活生物体的组成部分。

虽然我们举的例子是毛发，但机体的其他部分也同样可以很好地说明这一问题，神经、肌肉和腱都有其特定的分子排布方式。骨骼不仅在外形上像是被一位工程师塑造出来的，而且其分子的内部排布也体现出一种目的明确的取向性，这足以使工程师自愧不及。

很明显，如果分子的独特排布方式是使机体行使功能和维持生存所必需的，那么若不能对其加以解释，就无法完全理解机体的作用。新的分析方法是利用波长非常短的辐射，现在可以认为有电子和 X 射线两种，这种方法对结构的检测威力远远高于我们以往所拥有的任何一种方法。原来的检测方法确实很有限而且得到的结果还是间接的。此外，催化作用依赖于催化固体表面上原子和分子的排布方式，虽然这个事实或许已得到了认可，但关于排布方式的细节仍然不可知。实际上这些新方法也为我们开辟了新的可能性。

我们必须要指出的是，化学方法无法揭示出分子排布方式的本质和细节。当我们用化学方法来分析一种物质时，我们是从把该物质拆解开始的，这样就破坏了我们原本希望研究的分子排布方式。就像我们将房子推倒，然后看清了房子中各种构件的数目和性质，有很多砖、很多石板，还有很多板材等等，但我们无法了解房子的整体布局。我们必须区分分子中原子的排布方式与分子间的相互排列方式。前者长期以来一直是化学家特别是有机化学家的研究课题，在这类研究中分子是自由的，可以从周围各个方向靠近，因为这些分子要么是组成液体的成分，要么处于液态的溶液中。液体没有固定的方向性性质，除了在它的表面有可能是个例外。与此相反，固体中分子的相互排布方式基本上与那些作为固体特征的方向性质相关联，现在我们正是要考察这种分子的排布方式。

为了说明分子间相互排布方式的影响，我们可以首先考虑两个肥皂泡的情况，它们可能会相互摩擦，如果不是很剧烈就不会汇合到一起。薄膜材料的两个表面边界之间的长链分子会把它们的甲基（$CH_3$）端基排列在薄膜的外侧，于是一个泡的

long chain molecules which are arranged so as to present their methyl ($CH_3$) terminals to the outside of the film. Thus a "methyl face" of one bubble rubs against a similar face on the other. There is very little action between methyl groups, and so the films remain separated. The active ends of the molecules are all turned inwards, and so are kept out of each other's reach.

The solid crystal naturally gives the readiest examples of molecular arrangement, since the arrangement is the cause of the crystalline form. Every face presents only some selected part of a molecule to the external world. Zinc-blende may be looked on as an assemblage of molecules composed each of one atom of zinc and one of sulphur, all lying parallel to one another. Two opposing faces, both perpendicular to the direction in question, and forming parts of the crystal boundaries, differ in their behaviour because one is associated with zinc atoms in the same way as the other with sulphur. It is well known that if the crystal is heated, one such face is electrified positively and the other negatively. There are four such directions in each crystal of zinc-blende and four corresponding methods of picturing the assemblage of molecules.

Resorcinol possesses the same property to a high degree. The molecule is unsymmetrical, being a benzene ring in which two of the hydrogens at points 120° apart are replaced by hydroxyl (OH) groups. The arrangement of the molecules in the crystal has not been determined exactly, but we know that it is at any rate insufficient to give the crystal a high order of symmetry. The symmetry is certainly higher than that of the molecule itself, as is usually the case. There still remains a strong polarity which is revealed by the form of the crystal. The upper end of the crystal is very different from the lower; the faces that form naturally at one end are not those which form at the other. The polarity can be very simply demonstrated by suspending a couple of crystals in liquid air, whereupon they develop opposite electrical charges at their ends, so strong that the two behave to one another like small magnets. The strong electrification of resorcinol and similar bodies is sometimes used to clear liquid air of foreign particles.

The behaviour which is thus exhibited is the behaviour of the unit of pattern in the crystal. The unit can be shown by the X-ray methods to contain four molecules: arranged in a way which, as the term "unit of pattern" implies, is repeated indefinitely in the structure of the crystal. Mere multiplication cannot alter the properties of the crystal: whatever is true of the crystal as a whole is true of the single unit as it lies embedded in the crystal. That does not mean, necessarily, that the single unit would behave in the same way as it does in the crystal if it were free of its environment.

This is an extremely important point. We obtain from observation on the crystal information respecting the properties of a certain small company of molecules, generally not more than two, three or four. These properties are various: magnetic, electric, optical, thermal and so on. If we determine the arrangement of the molecules in the unit, and of the atoms in the molecule, we may correlate properties and arrangements and so contribute to the solution of one of the great problems of physics, namely, the connexion between the properties of

“甲基表面”与另一个泡的相似的表面互相摩擦。甲基基团之间很少有相互作用，因此薄膜会保持分离。而分子的活性端基全都朝向里面，因此它们互不接触。

固态晶体当然是最便于说明分子排布方式的实例，因为结晶形式取决于分子的排布方式。每个晶面只选择性地向外部世界呈现分子的某些部分。闪锌矿可以被看作是一个分子聚集体，每个分子由一个锌原子和一个硫原子组成，分子与分子彼此平行排列。两个相对的晶面都与分子的方向相垂直，并且形成晶体边界的一部分。它们具有彼此不同的行为，因为一个晶面是与锌原子相关联的，而另一个则以同样的方式与硫原子相关联。大家都知道，当晶体被加热时，上述一个面将带正电荷，而另一个则带负电荷。在闪锌矿的每个晶体中有四个这样的方向以及对应的四种描绘分子聚集体的方法。

间苯二酚晶体在更高的水平上具有与闪锌矿类似的性质。它的分子是不对称的，因为它是一个苯环，其中两个相隔 120º 的氢被羟基（OH）所取代。目前尚未准确地测定出分子在晶体中的排布方式，但是我们知道这种分子无论如何也不能使晶体具有高度的对称性。因为在通常情况下，晶体的对称性无疑要比分子本身的对称性高。这种晶体的外形说明它仍具有极强的极性：晶体的上端与下端颇为不同；在一端自然形成的晶面不同于在另一端形成的晶面。可以非常简单地证明它的极性：在液态空气中悬挂一对晶体，它们会逐渐在自己的末端带上相反的电荷，其强度之大足以使它们像小磁体一样相互作用。间苯二酚和类似物质的强起电作用有时被用来清除液态空气中的杂质粒子。

以上列举的行为是晶体中模式单元的行为。用 X 射线法可以证明该单元中含有四个分子，它们的排布方式如同“模式单元”这个词所暗示的那样，在晶体结构中是无限重复的。只靠增殖不能改变晶体的性质，整个晶体的性质就是组成晶体的单一单元的性质，因为每个单元都是包埋于晶体之中的。当然，这并不必然意味着单一单元在脱离其周围环境时的行为会表现得同其在晶体中时一样。

这是极为重要的一点。我们从观察中得到的有关晶体学方面的信息只与少数几个特定分子的性质相关，通常不超过两个、三个或四个分子。这些性质各种各样，有磁学的、电学的、光学的和热学的等等。如果我们确定了单元中的分子排布方式以及分子中的原子排布方式，就可以将性质和排布方式联系起来，这就为物理学中的一个重大难题提供了解决方案，这个难题就是物质的性质与构成物质的原子之间

a substance and the atoms of which it is built. Conversely, knowing relations between the properties of one or more unit and the details of their structures, we may use our knowledge for the determination of the structures of other units by the examination of the properties of the crystals of which such other units form part.

To sum up what I have said so far, the positions of the various atoms in the molecule determine the characteristic of the molecule: this is well known and has been widely studied. The positions of the molecules in the solid are equally important, especially if there is any regularity in their arrangement, in other words, if there is any attempt at crystallisation. In a living body there must be arrangements of various kinds to various extents. We want to know what these arrangements are and their effects.

The X-rays demonstrate to us any such arrangements. It is now well known that a pencil of X-rays which passes through any substance where molecular arrangement exists gives some sort of diffraction pattern, which may be examined photographically or electrically. From the character of the pattern, information can be obtained as to the nature of the arrangement. When there is much arrangement and great regularity, the pattern is sharply defined. As an example, we may take the photograph of the mineral kaliophilite (Fig. 1) obtained by F. A. Bannister of the British Museum (Natural History). When the arrangement is less regular, the photograph is less definite. When the first photographs were obtained from silk and wool, nerve and muscle, they were in comparison exceedingly vague and it seemed that it would be difficult to make any useful deductions from them. However, both technique and skill in interpretation have increased materially and conclusions can now be drawn which are of great interest. The two photographs of proteins in Figs. 2 and 3 were obtained respectively from silk and from the quill of a sea-gull's feather. These are due to W. T. Astbury and Miss Marwick. The detail is sufficiently pronounced to give valuable information to the experienced observer.

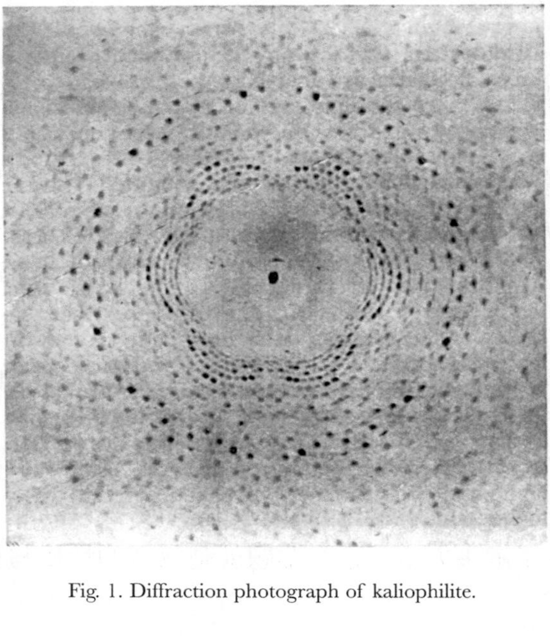

Fig. 1. Diffraction photograph of kaliophilite.

的关系。反过来，知道了一个或多个单元的性质与其具体结构细节之间的关系，我们就可以应用这些知识，通过考察由其他单元组成的晶体的性质，来确定其他单元的结构。

综上所述，各种原子在分子中的位置决定了分子的特性：这是众所周知的，并且人们已经在这方面进行了大量的研究。分子在固体中的位置也具有同样的重要性，尤其是当它们的排布具有某种规律性时，换句话说，就是当要努力得到晶体的时候。活的生物体中必定存在着程度不同的各类分子排布方式。我们想知道这些排布方式是什么样的以及它们所造成的影响。

X 射线为我们描述了所有的排布方式。现在人们已经熟知，一束 X 射线在穿过存在着分子排布的任何物质之后会形成某种类型的衍射图案，并且可以用照相方法或电学方法来检测。根据这些图案的特征，可以获得有关排布性质方面的信息。当排布较多并且具有高度规律性时，图案的界限很分明。以大英博物馆（自然历史馆）班尼斯特拍摄的矿物钾霞石的照片（图 1）为例，当排布的规律性较低时，照片会比较模糊。最早拍摄的 X 射线照片取自丝毛、神经和肌肉，相比之下这些照片是极为模糊的，很难从中得到任何有用的推论。但是，现在解释照片用到的技术和技能都已得到实质性的改善，因而能够从中得出很有意义的结论。图 2 和图 3 中的两张蛋白质照片分别来自于丝和海鸥羽毛的翎管，它们是由阿斯特伯里和马威克小姐拍摄的。照片中的细节已经足够清晰，经验丰富的观测者可以从中发现有价值的信息。

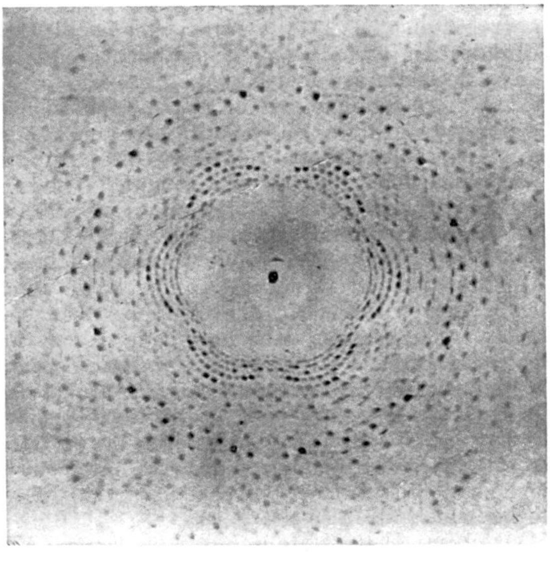

图 1. 钾霞石的衍射照片

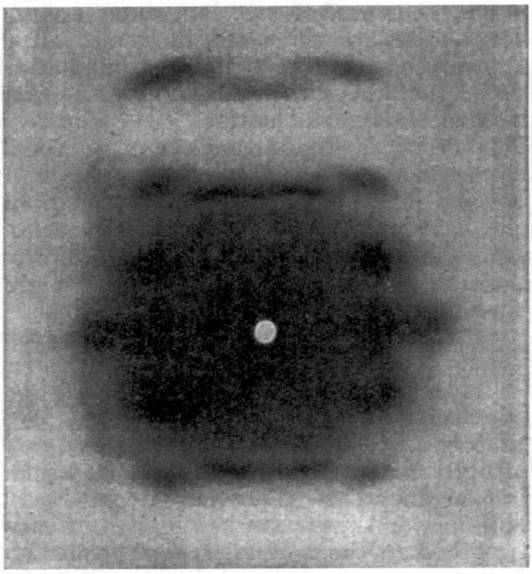

Fig. 2. Diffraction photograph of silk.

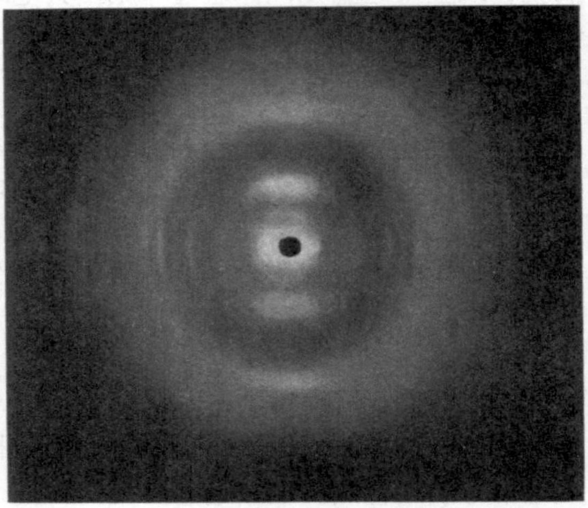

Fig. 3. Diffraction photograph of sea-gull's quill.

In the first place, it is clear that there must be quite a considerable amount of arrangement in both cases. The silk is largely composed of a protein known as fibroin. It is remarkable that similar photographs are obtained from a great number of proteins, drawn from different sources; there is in fact a characteristic protein photograph which implies that there are elements of structure common to protein forms. Fig. 3 is an example of the diffraction pictures obtained from a peculiar class of proteins known as the keratins; their connexion with the main body has recently been beautifully demonstrated by Astbury.

It has continually happened during the recent development of X-ray analysis that its first results have been confirmations of the conclusions of the organic chemist, and have been followed immediately by closer definitions and fuller knowledge. The chief feature of the structure of proteins has been supposed, on chemical grounds, to be a chainlike arrangement of amino-acids. These bodies may be obtained in the laboratory by breaking up the natural proteins. There are many kinds of them, and they can be separated and examined in detail. Two of the simplest are glycine and alanine.

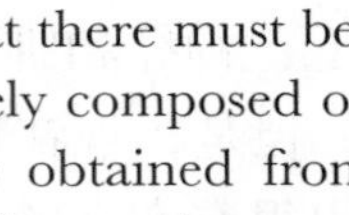

Glycine.

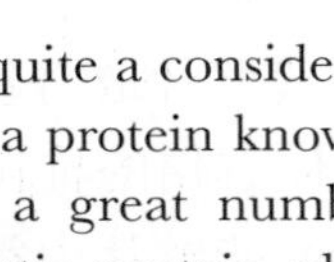

Alanine.

They are characterised by the presence of an amino-group, $NH_2$, on one side of a certain carbon atom and of a carboxyl group, COOH, on the other. One has a positive character, the other a negative: the two groups have not only a general attraction for one another, but can also be made to combine in the manner shown below:

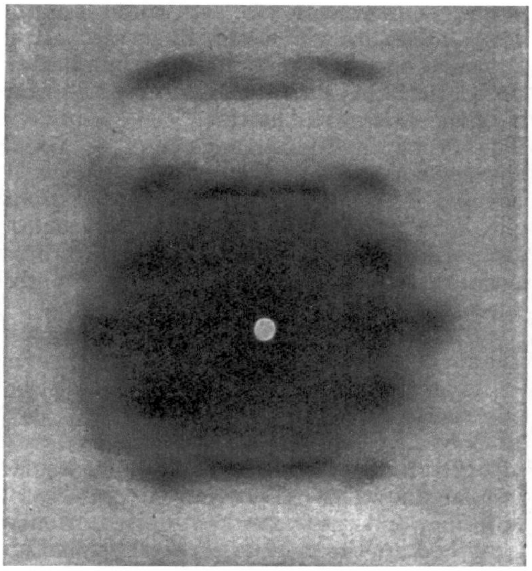

图 2. 丝的衍射照片

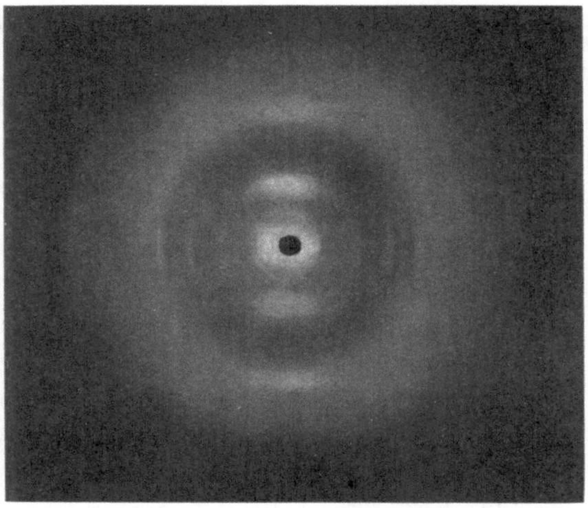

图 3. 海鸥羽毛翎管的衍射照片

首先，很显然在两种情况中必定存在着相当可观的排布。丝的主要成分是一种被称为丝心蛋白的蛋白质。值得注意的是，从大量不同来源的蛋白质中得到的 X 射线照片是相似的，事实上存在一张特征性的蛋白质照片，能够体现各种蛋白质形式共有的结构要素。图 3 是一个衍射照片的实例，它来源于一类被称为角蛋白的特殊蛋白质，阿斯特伯里最近对它们与主要机体之间的关系进行了精确的阐述。

在 X 射线分析的近期进展中不断发生的事情是，它的最初结果确认了有机化学家的结论，而且紧随其后就会出现更精密的定义和更全面的认识。从化学的角度上看，蛋白质结构的首要特征被认为是氨基酸的链状排列。在实验室中通过分解天然蛋白质可以得到氨基酸。它们的种类繁多，可以把它们分离并进行详细的检验，其中最简单的两种是甘氨酸和丙氨酸。

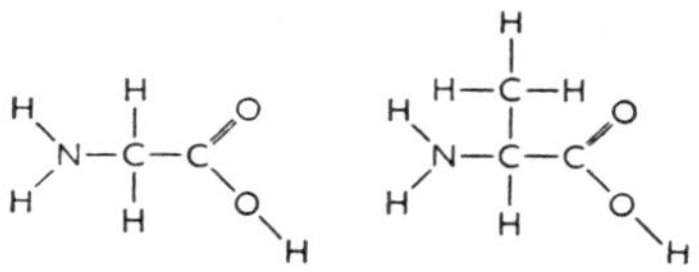

甘氨酸　　丙氨酸

氨基酸的特征是在某个碳原子的一侧连有一个氨基 $NH_2$，而在另一侧连有一个羧基 COOH，其中一个带正电，另一个带负电。这两个基团不仅具有一般意义上的相互吸引，而且还能以下列方式进行结合：

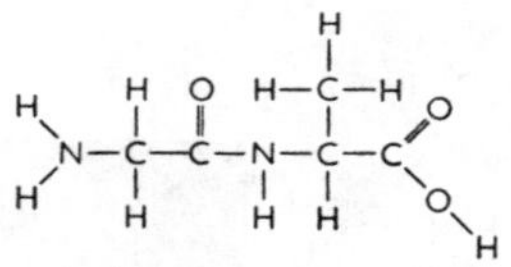

**Glycine and Alanine.**

Two hydrogen atoms and one oxygen have dropped out. Willstätter supposed that such combinations could take place in regular alternations of the two amino- acids, thus forming a chain of indefinite length. Now alanine and glycine can be obtained from the decomposition of natural silk. If this regular structure is the cause of the X-ray photograph of silk, the numerical details that can be obtained from an examination of the photograph must fit in with the structure proposed by the chemist. This is remarkably verified. Previous X-ray work has shown that a chain composed of two carbons and one nitrogen in regular succession would probably take the zig-zag form well known as a characteristic of long chain compounds. The following formula shows how the silk protein would be represented.

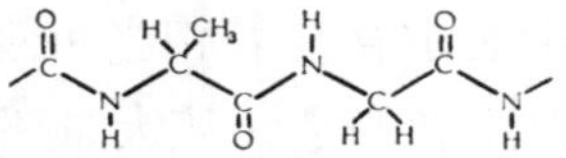

From the X-ray analysis of many organic compounds, we have learnt the dimensions of the atoms of carbon and nitrogen, and we can assert that the distance along the chain at which the pattern (two carbons and one nitrogen) repeats itself should be about 3.6 A. Now the interpretation of the X-ray picture, though hazy in some respects, is exceedingly precise in one at least. It shows that some arrangement exists along the fibre, based on a pattern which repeats itself at intervals of 3.5. The coincidence is striking. The X-rays show not only that there is arrangement among the molecules in the silk, but also that there is agreement with chemical theory as to the existence of a repeat in each chain. They show also that the chains—this also is one of the details which can be examined in the picture—are arranged more or less parallel to one another and to the direction of the fibre. This is the sort of arrangement which we should expect.

Silk fibroin is one of the simplest of the proteins. There are innumerable other possible combinations, because there are many different amino-acids and kindred bodies which can be strung on to the chain in various ways. There is, for example, cystine, which clearly can be inserted into the chain by either of its ends. This group contains the sulphur which occurs in hair.

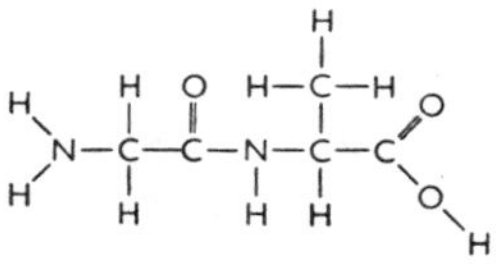

甘氨酸和丙氨酸

结合过程中脱去了两个氢原子和一个氧原子。维尔施泰特提出：由两种氨基酸的不断规则交替就可以产生这样的合成物，由此形成了一条不限长度的链。现在可以通过分解天然丝得到丙氨酸和甘氨酸。如果正是这种规则结构产生了丝的 X 射线照片，那么通过分析照片所得到的数字细节信息就必然会与化学家提出的结构相吻合，这已得到了惊人的证实。此前的 X 射线研究已经表明，由两个碳原子和一个氮原子规则连接构成的链，可能会具有被认为是长链化合物特征的“之”字型形式。下列结构式表示的是丝蛋白可能具有的形式。

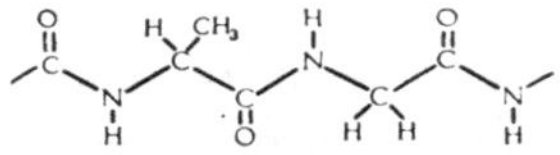

根据对多种有机化合物的 X 射线分析，我们已经知道了碳原子和氮原子的大小，并且可以断言，这种单元（两个碳原子和一个氮原子）沿着链重复自身的距离应该是约 3.6 Å。现在就对 X 射线图的解释而言，尽管照片中的某些方面还很模糊，但至少有一点是极其精确的。照片显示沿着纤维方向存在着某种排布方式，根据是有一种以 3.5 Å 间隔重复自身的图案，这种一致性是突出的。X 射线不仅能说明丝里面的分子间存在着某种规则的排布，还与认为每条链中存在重复单元的化学理论相吻合。它们还表明，链（这也是能从图中检测到的细节之一）的排布基本上是彼此平行的，并且与纤维的方向一致，这正是我们应该期望到的排布方式。

丝的丝心蛋白是最简单的蛋白质之一，还有无数种其他可能的化合物，因为多种不同的氨基酸和类似物能够以各种方式排列在链上。例如，胱氨酸显然可以用它的任意一端插入到链中去。这种氨基酸中含有硫，它存在于头发中。

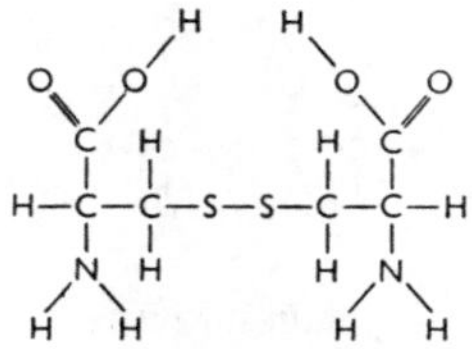

Cystine.

To return now to the keratins which, as I have said, do not give the same diffraction pattern as silk and other proteins. Hair, feathers, horn and the like give photographs which are comparable with each other. Astbury has made the surprising discovery that a hair when stretched gives a picture resembling that of silk. The stretching alters the arrangement of the molecules. If the hair is allowed to resume its former length, which it readily does if the operations are carried on in warm water, the first form of picture is again obtained, so that the effect is reversible. Silk does not possess any capacity for complete recovery after extension. Hair recovers completely after 30 percent of extension; beyond that there is only a partial recovery though it will stand an extension of 70 percent before breaking.

Astbury has pointed out that these effects can be readily accounted for by supposing that the chain which forms the backbone of all the proteins is similar to that of silk. But in the keratins the chain is somewhat crumpled up. Tension pulls the chains straight without breaking them, so that the contractile forces, whatever they may be, can restore the chain to its old form, and the process of extension and contraction may be repeated indefinitely. Beyond the 30 percent of elastic extension there is a possibility of further extension by means of the slipping of molecules past one another. This is practically the only form of extension possible in silk: it is not reversible.

A comparison of the two kinds of X-ray photographs supports this conception. The distance of repeat along the chain in stretched wool is only a very little less than that of silk, which is correct if the stretching of the wool is due to the stretching of the chains, while the repeat in the unstretched hair is 30 percent shorter than in the stretched. Other geometrical deductions from the photographs, some very definite, others less definite, are also in general agreement with the hypothesis.

But why should some keratin chains tend to crumple up while others do not? A plausible explanation can be readily given. The amino-acids and other pendants of the chain have a certain attraction for each other, at least if there are some which contain acid groups, while others have a basic character. All such attractions tend to shorten the chain.

A rough model can be made to illustrate this point by stringing a number of wooden bars along a piece of flexible material (see Fig. 4). Elastic threads join the ends of the bars as shown and tend to draw them together. The attractions simulated by the elastic links tend

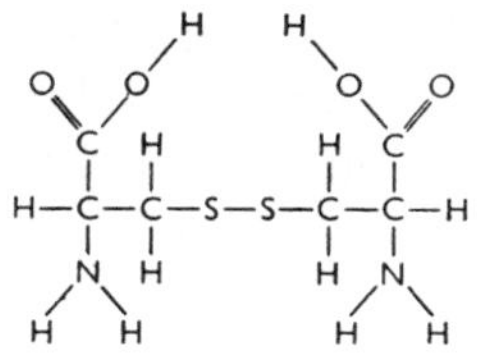

胱氨酸

现在回到角蛋白，我曾经提到过，它的衍射图案与丝和其他蛋白质并不相同，而头发、羽毛和角等会给出彼此类似的照片。阿斯特伯里发现了一个令人吃惊的现象：一根拉紧的头发给出与丝类似的照片，拉伸改变了分子的排布方式。如果令头发恢复其初始长度，这在温水中很容易实现，则又会得到原来的图案，因此该效应是可逆的。丝在伸展后不能完全恢复原状。头发在伸展 30% 之后能完全恢复，超过这个限度之后就只能恢复一部分，不过在断裂前它能被伸展 70%。

阿斯特伯里曾指出，如果假定构成所有蛋白质骨架的链都与构成丝的链类似，就可以很顺利地解释这些效应。但在角蛋白中链略有一点皱曲，张力将链拉直而没有使它发生断裂，因此无论什么样的收缩力都能够使链恢复到原来的状态，而且这种伸展和收缩的过程可以不限次地重复。超过 30% 的弹性伸展后，通过分子相互之间的滑移还存在进一步伸展的可能性。这实际上是丝中唯一可能的伸展形式，它不是可逆的。

比较两种类型的 X 射线照片可以证实上述观点。如果羊毛的伸展确是由链的伸展所引起，那么在拉伸的羊毛中沿着链方向的重复距离只比在丝中的重复距离略小一点，而在未拉伸头发中的重复距离比拉伸头发中的重复距离短 30%。从照片中得到的其他几何推论，有一些非常确定，另一些不那么确定，但都与该假说大体一致。

但是为什么有一些角蛋白链易于皱曲而另一些则不会呢？其实很容易给出一个较为合理的解释。氨基酸和链上的其他附属物会在某种程度上相互吸引，至少在有些含酸性基团而另一些含碱性基团的情况下会如此，所有这些吸引作用都倾向于使链缩短。

我们可以制作出一个粗略的模型来说明这一点，方法是沿着一条柔软的材料穿上很多木棒（见图 4）。如图所示，弹性的线连接木棒的末端并倾向于将它们拉拢。

to shorten the chain, but an applied tension may break the connexions so formed and give the chain its full length. This sort of thing cannot be expected to happen in the case of silk, because glycine and alanine have no attraction for each other, built as they are into the chain.

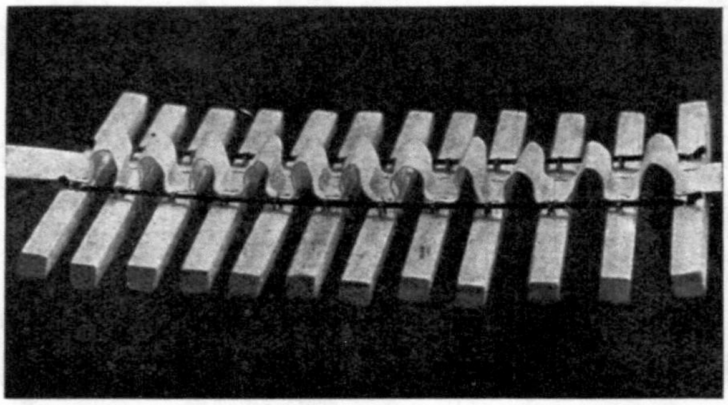

Fig. 4

The same hypothesis gives a good explanation of the fact that hair and other keratin structures are so very resistant to chemical actions such as the attacks of enzymes. The crumpled chain protects itself in several ways. Its susceptible points are masked, partly by its compactness, partly by the previous satisfaction of tendencies to combination either in respect to groups belonging to the same chain or to different chains. Thus hair, horn and similar materials acquire a peculiar permanency often illustrated by the state of the remains in ancient tombs.

All these facts are illustrative of the statement with which I began, namely, that not only does the arrangement of the atoms in the molecule decide the characteristics of the molecule but also the arrangement of the molecules with respect to each other in the solid decides the behaviour of the solid. Arrangement of the protein molecules among themselves is essential to their function in the living body.

These general deductions regarding protein structure are only an earnest of what may be expected to follow from the precise measurements of position which we are now able to make. They are no more than indications of the directions in which knowledge of living structure may be able to advance as a consequence of the new methods of inquiry. Like any other new tool, X-ray analysis has to be in use for a certain time before its capacities are understood.

Besides the direct applications of X-rays which I have been describing, there are certain other ways in which the substances of the living body have been studied by their aid. A most interesting example is the examination by J. D. Bernal and his colleagues of the crystal structure of the separate amino-acids, of the vitamins and similar bodies. When such bodies can be crystallised, valuable hints can be obtained as to the arrangement

弹性连接用于模拟吸引作用，这种作用倾向于使链缩短，但是一个外加张力可能会破坏现有的连接方式，并使链充分伸展。对于丝，就不能期望有这样的情况发生，因为链中的甘氨酸和丙氨酸不会相互吸引。

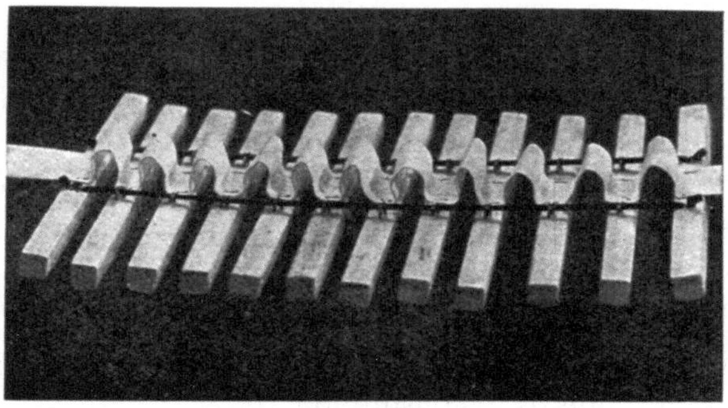

图 4

同一假说还为下面的事实提供了很好的解释，即头发和其他角蛋白结构为什么对诸如酶的攻击等化学作用具有很强的抵抗性。皱曲的链能够以多种方式保护自己，其敏感位置被遮蔽起来，其中一部分原因是其致密性，另一部分原因是同一条链上或不同链上的基团所具有的结合趋势已经事先被满足。因此头发、角和类似的物料能保存特别长久的时间，古墓中遗存物的状态通常可以说明这一点。

所有这些事实都证明了我最初的陈述，即不仅原子在分子中的排列方式决定了分子的特性，而且固体中分子与分子之间的排列方式也决定了固体的行为。蛋白质分子自身之间的排列方式对于它们在活生物体中的功能是至关重要的。

上述关于蛋白质结构的一般性推论仅仅是我们现在能对位置进行精确测量后可以期望得到的结论。它们只不过表明：在使用新的研究方法之后，可能会给活生物体结构的认识带来新的发展方向。X 射线分析像任何其他新工具一样，先要经过一段时间的使用，然后它的威力方能被充分认识。

除了我已经描述过的对 X 射线的直接应用之外，还有其他一些方式可以令 X 射线法对活生物体物质的研究有所帮助。一个最为有趣的实例是贝尔纳及其同事对于单个氨基酸、维生素及其类似物的晶体结构的考察。当这些物质能够结晶时，即使无法完全确定其结构，我们也可以得到关于其中原子和分子排列方式的有价值的线

of the atoms and molecules, even if the structure cannot be fully determined. Chemical considerations suggest various possible arrangements, the choice from which may be narrowed down by the result of X-ray measurement. Thus, for example, Bernal showed that the formula proposed for sterol must be incorrect: in consequence, a search for the proper formula was instituted and has seemingly been successful.

Bernal's investigations of the structure of these compounds are an example of one of the two lines along which, broadly speaking, X-ray work is advancing. A series of like compounds is examined, and the various members are compared with each other. Information is derived from observations of the changes as the composition is varied step by step. In this particular research some twenty different substances have been compared. They are all members of a family of the greatest importance biologically. Their X-ray pictures show that they possess certain common characteristics of a structural nature, and the comparison of gradually changing quality with corresponding changes in certain dimensions gives important hints as to constitution.

A new method often gives new force to older methods, and this is happening now. The optical, magnetic and other constants of a crystal show remarkable dependencies on the crystalline form. When we are able, as in this case, to determine the contents of the unit of pattern, and sometimes are able to go so far as to find the position of the atoms and molecules in the unit, the constants in question can be connected directly with the contents of the unit. Several years ago, W. L. Bragg showed how the refractive indices of calcite could be calculated in terms of the refractivities of the atoms and the arrangement in the calcite crystal which had just been discovered. So also, electrical displacement takes place with much greater ease in the plane of the aromatic benzene ring than normal to it. Consequently, the velocity, within the crystal, of light in which the vibrations are perpendicular to the ring is greater than that of light in which the vibrations lie in any other direction. This principle can be used to help in the determination of the arrangement of the molecules in the crystal.

There is a second line of advance which is being followed; and the two modes of research support each other. In this other method the arrangement of the atoms in very simple crystals is worked out to the bitter end. The method is very laborious and cannot at present be applied to complicated cases. Molecules are chosen for investigation containing the atomic groupings which occur so widely, hydroxyl, carboxyl, benzene linkings and so on. Experiment shows, so far as it has gone, that the relative positions and orientations of the atoms in these common groupings are always the same or nearly so. If they are exactly determined from the examination of particular cases, the resulting rules can obviously be very helpful in the determination of structure, and also we may confidently hope, in the discovery of the *why* of a particular structure as well as the *how*.

On these lines several detailed investigations have been completed recently. One of the results has been a better understanding of the details of the linkages between carbon atoms. It is of especial interest in the study of organic compounds, and will serve as an

索。从化学角度可以提出多种可能的排列方式，利用X射线的观测结果或许可以缩小选择的范围。例如，贝尔纳发现甾酮现有的结构式一定是错误的，于是人们开始追究其正确的结构式，并且看来已经取得了成功。

大体上说，X射线研究有两条发展路线，贝尔纳对这些化合物结构的研究是其中一条路线的实例。先对一系列类似化合物进行检验并对不同成员加以比较，然后观察在组分逐步变动时发生的变化以获得信息。在这项特殊的研究中，大约有20种不同的物质被比较过，它们都是生物学上一个最具重要性的家庭中的成员。X射线图表明，它们拥有一种结构方面的某些共同特性。通过比较那些伴随某个维度中的变化所产生的性质的逐渐变化，我们可以得到关于其构造的重要线索。

一种新方法往往能赋予老方法以新的力量，现在这种情况又发生了。晶体的光学常数、磁学常数以及其他常数对晶型有惊人的依赖性。在目前的这种情况下，如果我们能确定模式单元中的成分，甚至有时还能找出原子和分子在单元中的位置，那么上述常数就能与单元中的成分直接联系起来。几年以前，威廉·劳伦斯·布拉格展示了如何通过原子的折射能力和新发现的方解石晶体的排布方式计算出方解石的折射率。由此还能算出，在芳香苯环平面内比在与其垂直的平面内更容易发生电位移。因此，晶体内振动方向垂直于苯环的光要比苯环内各个振动方向上的光有更快的传播速度。这个原则可以用来辅助测定晶体中的分子排列方式。

X射线研究还有第二条发展路线，也正在被人采用，这两种研究模式是彼此支持的。人们利用第二种方法把极简单晶体中的原子排布研究得非常透彻。这种方法非常繁琐，目前还无法应用于复杂情况。被选来研究的分子中包含广泛存在的羟基、羧基和苯基等原子团，目前已进行的实验表明，原子在这些常见基团中的相对位置和取向总是相同或大体相同的。如果它们是在分析特殊样品时精确测定的，那么所得的规律显然会对结构的确定帮助很大，并且我们也许可以满怀信心地希望在发现一种特定结构是**怎样的**同时还能知道**为什么**会是这样的。

最近人们在两条发展路线上完成了几项细致的研究。其中的一项结果有助于我们更好地认识碳原子间的连接细节。它在有机化合物的研究中具有特殊的意义，并

illustration. It is well known that carbon linkages are not all the same; we speak of a single bond, a double bond, and so on. According to the measurements we are now able to make, there are at least two kinds of carbon linkage differing primarily in the closeness of approach. There is the diamond linkage in which each carbon atom is at a distance of 1.54 A. from its four neighbours: and the graphite linkage where the distance is 1.42 A. between each atom and its three close neighbours. The difference between these is far greater than can be put down to experimental error. The former kind occurs also in the fatty acid chains, where each carbon also has four neighbours, two carbons and two hydrogens. The latter is found in anthracene and naphthalene, the basis of these substances being the benzene ring: in these the carbon has three neighbours as in graphite. It may prove to be the case that the former kind of bond is peculiar to the aromatic substances and the latter to the aliphatic. The heats of combustion of diamond and graphite are very nearly the same: so that it takes as much energy to break down the four bonds in the diamond as the three in the graphite. In such a comparison the heat spent on breaking the weak bonds between the network layers of graphite is taken to be negligible.

Such accurate measurements as these encourage the hope that there are exact rules as to distances apart of the atoms, and very probably as to their mutual orientation. Knowledge of these rules will greatly facilitate the determination of structure.

What has been said above may serve to show how eagerly the new powers of detecting molecular arrangement in the solid are being used. With the knowledge gained in this way we may learn more of the forces which bind all atoms and molecules together, and in particular consolidate and give form and function to the various constituents of the living body.

(**132**, 11-13 & 50-53; 1933)

且可以作为一个例证。人们已经知道碳原子间的键合并不完全相同，我们指的是单键和双键等方式。根据我们现在所能进行的测量，碳的键合至少有两种类型，两者的主要不同在于接近的程度。在金刚石型键合中，每个碳原子与四个相邻原子的距离为 1.54 Å；而在石墨型键合中，每个碳原子与三个近邻原子的距离是 1.42 Å。这二者之间的差异远不能归因于实验误差。前一类情况还出现在脂肪酸链中，它的每个碳原子也有四个相邻原子——两个碳和两个氢。蒽和萘属于后一类，这些物质的基础在于它们都有苯环，其中每个碳有三个相邻原子，就像在石墨中一样。这也许可以证明：前一种类型的键是芳香族物质所特有的，而后者是脂肪族物质所特有的。金刚石和石墨的燃烧热非常接近，因此破坏金刚石中的四个键与破坏石墨中的三个键所需的能量差不多。在上述比较中，打破石墨网状层之间的弱键所需要的热被认为可以忽略不计。

诸如此类的精确测量促进我们认为：原子之间的距离有准确的规则，它们的相互取向很可能也有准确的规则。对这些规则的认识将极大地加快确定结构的进程。

上面所讲的这些也许可以说明，我们正在如何急切地使用这种检测固体中分子排列方式的新方法。利用以这种方法获得的知识，我们可以更多地了解使所有原子和分子结合在一起的力，尤其是使活生物体中各种成分结合且赋予其形式和功能的力。

（王耀杨 翻译；顾孝诚 审稿）

# Date and Place of Priestley's Discovery of Oxygen

## Editor's Note

**This letter from Robert Marin Caven and response from Philip Hartog provide a footnote to the controversial issue of "who discovered oxygen". Together they offer a salutary reminder of the difficulties of reconstructing historical events. The point at issue—whether the English chemist Joseph Priestley conducted his synthesis of oxygen in the town of Calne in Wiltshire or in London—seems relatively trivial. But Priestley's famous descriptions of his experiments in respiration of the new "air", conducted on a mouse and on himself, are rendered more vivid by knowing where to place them. Hartog's response to Caven's question issues a plea, now commonly overlooked, that Priestley's "discovery" not be too firmly affixed to the date of 1 August 1774, and hints also at Priestley's prevarications about whether he had sufficiently interpreted his experiments.**

IN *Nature* of March 11, Mr. H. G. Wayling states that "At Lansdowne House on August 1, 1774, Priestley discovered oxygen"; and a similar statement is made by Sir Philip Hartog in the "Dictionary of National Biography".

Sir Edward Thorpe in his "Joseph Priestley" says, however, that "the course of inquiry which he began at Leeds was continued by him with characteristic assiduity and conspicuous success at Calne", and again, "The years which Priestley spent at Calne constitute the most fruitful period of his scientific career", and "it cannot be maintained that during the subsequent period he added many first-rate facts to our knowledge, or indeed discovered any facts at all comparable in importance with those he ascertained during his life in Wiltshire".

Moreover, Lord Shelburne, when he became Priestley's patron, was, Thorpe tells us, "living in retirement at Bowood" which was near to Calne; and provided for Priestley "a pleasant house at Calne in the summer and a house in town during the winter".

Further, on p. 34 of vol. 2 of "Experiments and Observations on Different Kinds of Air", Priestley says: "Mr. Warltire, a good chymist, and lecturer in natural philosophy, happening to be at that time in Calne, I explained my views to him, and was furnished by him with many substances which I could not otherwise have procured. With this apparatus, after a variety of other experiments, an account of which will be found in its proper place, on the first of August 1774 I endeavoured to extract air from *mercurius calcinatus per se*; and I presently found that, by means of this lens, air was expelled from it very readily."

# 普里斯特利发现氧气的日期和地点

## 编者按

罗伯特·马林·卡文发表的快报和菲利普·哈尔托赫对他的回应是对“谁发现了氧气”这一有争议问题的补充说明，这些资料有益于提醒人们在再现历史事件原貌时会遇到的困难。本文要说明的是一个看起来很琐碎的问题：英国化学家约瑟夫·普里斯特利到底是在威尔特郡的卡恩还是在伦敦合成了氧气。不过，要是我们知道普里斯特利在老鼠和自己身上进行的呼吸新型“空气”的实验是在哪里完成的，就会使他对此的著名描述更加生动。哈尔托赫在回答卡文的质疑时为自己辩白，他认为普里斯特利“发现”氧气的日期不能完全确定就是1774年的8月1日，虽然现在人们已经不在意这些细节了，他还含蓄地指出：普里斯特利对于自己是否充分解释了这个实验也是搪塞不清的。

威林先生在3月11日的《自然》杂志中称“1774年8月1日，普里斯特利于伦敦的兰斯唐宅发现了氧气”；而菲利普·哈尔托赫爵士在《英国人物传记辞典》中也给出了类似的描述。

但是，爱德华·索普爵士在他的《约瑟夫·普里斯特利》中写道，“普里斯特利的探索过程始于利兹，而后他经过孜孜不倦的努力最终在卡恩取得了显著的成果”，而“普里斯特利在卡恩度过的岁月也是他科学生涯中最硕果累累的时期”，我们“不能断定他是否在随后的日子里为我们的知识增添了头等要紧的事实，也不知道后来他是否真的发现了一些重要性可以和他在威尔特郡时的成就相比拟的现象”。

另外，索普还告诉我们，谢尔本勋爵在成为普里斯特利的赞助人时，就“隐居在威尔特郡的博伍德”，而博伍德就在卡恩附近；勋爵为普里斯特利提供了“一所位于卡恩的适合夏天居住的住宅，还有一所位于市内适合过冬的住宅”。

在《不同类型气体的实验与观测》第2卷第34页中，普里斯特利说：“沃尔泰拉先生是一位优秀的化学家，也是一位自然哲学的讲演者，当时他恰好也在卡恩，我向他解释了我的想法，于是他给了我很多在别处得不到的东西。后来我利用这种装置又作了许多次实验，终于发现了对这个问题的适当解释，1774年8月1日，我从**汞的焙烧产物**中提取出了气体；当时我发现利用这种透镜形的装置可以很快地排出气体。”

Soon after this, Priestley visited the Continent with his patron, and met Lavoisier in Paris; but in the following March he was back again in Calne. This is shown by an autograph letter which I have been privileged to see amongst a collection in Dr. Williams's library in Gordon Square. In this letter, Priestley, after referring to his indifferent health—he was suffering, he says, from painful boils—states that when able he hoped to continue his experiments on the new air, which he was now able to prepare in larger quantity; and at the foot of this letter, on the left hand side, occurs the single word "Calne".

In view of this evidence one would not doubt that Priestley discovered oxygen in Wiltshire rather than in London, were it not for the categorical statement in the "Dictionary of National Biography". Is there any evidence to support this statement? I have found none.

R. M. Caven

* * *

I am obliged to the Editor of *Nature* for having communicated to me the foregoing letter by Prof. Caven.

I wish at the outset to say, after looking through the voluminous notes on which my article on Priestley was based, that I cannot confirm my statement that Priestley's experiment of August 1, 1774, on *mercurius calcinatus per se* was made at Lansdowne House, and I think Prof. Caven is probably right in suggesting that it was made at Calne. But the matter does not end there. My error must, I think, have been due to the following passage (of which I have been reminded by Sir Harold Hartley) in a letter of Priestley of April 1, 1775:

"By the heat of the flame of a candle ... I get *the pure air I discovered in London* in great plenty from a variety of cheap materials; not only from red lead, but many earthy substances moistened with spirit of nitre and dried," etc.*

This should be read in connexion with the following well-known passage from the "Experiments and Observations on Different Kinds of Air", vol. 2 (1775), p. 40, in which, after referring to his experiment of August 1, 1774, Priestley says:

"In this ignorance of the real nature of this kind of air, I continued from this time (November) to the 1st March following."

* *Phil. Trans.*, 65, 390; 1775. (The italics are mine.—P. J. H.)

此后不久，普里斯特利与他的赞助人一起访问了欧洲大陆，并在巴黎见到了拉瓦锡；但在接下来的三月份中，他再次返回了卡恩。有一封亲笔签名的信可以说明这一点，我曾获准在戈登广场的威廉斯博士图书馆的藏品中看到过它。在信中，普里斯特利先是谈到自己的健康状况很差——他说他正被疔疮苦苦折磨，接着便称，如果病情好转，他希望能继续进行有关这种新发现气体的实验，现在他已经能大量地制备这种气体了；在这封信末尾的左手边只出现了一个单词——“卡恩”。

如果不是因为《英国人物传记辞典》中的记载很明确，在有这封信作证的情况下大家都会相信普里斯特利发现氧气的地点是威尔特郡而不是伦敦。是否存在着支持该陈述的任何证据呢？到现在我也没有找到。

卡文

* * *

我要感谢《自然》杂志的编辑将卡文教授的前述信件转交于我。

我想首先声明，在审核了我在撰写关于普里斯特利的文章时所参照的大量记录之后，我无法确认我的描述，即普里斯特利 1774 年 8 月 1 日用**汞的焙烧产物**所做的实验是在兰斯唐宅进行的，卡文教授提出该项实验的地点是卡恩，我认为他的观点很可能是正确的。不过问题到这里并没有结束。我想我的失误想必与普里斯特利在 1775 年 4 月 1 日的信中所写的这段内容（经哈罗德·哈特利爵士提醒）有关：

“利用蜡烛火焰的热……我从很多种廉价原料中获取了大量**我在伦敦时发现的纯净气体**；不仅是从铅丹中，而且还从很多用硝精（译注：历史名词，即硝酸。）浸润后再干燥过的土样物质中，”等等。*

以上文字应该和摘自《不同类型气体的实验和观测》第 2 卷（1775 年）第 40 页的这个有名段落结合起来阅读，普里斯特利在其中谈到了 1774 年 8 月 1 日的实验，然后他说：

“在从当时（11 月）到来年 3 月的这段时间里，我一直不知道那种气体到底是什么。”

* 摘自《自然科学会报》第 65 卷，第 390 页；1775 年（英文斜体是我加的——哈尔托赫）

The comparison of these two passages indicates clearly that for Priestley himself the date of the "discovery of oxygen" was March 1, 1775, and the place, London.

That Priestley's experiments in London were made in the house now called Lansdowne House (but which was then called Shelburne House, presumably until Lord Shelburne became Marquis of Lansdowne in 1784)* is shown by a passage in his "Philosophical Empiricism" (1775), p. 4, where he speaks of having shown some of his experiments (on oxygen) at that house to friends on May 23, 1775, the day before he wrote his third letter on the subject to the Royal Society. (I owe this reference to Prof. A. N. Meldrum.)

An undue importance has, as I have always thought, been attached to the date August 1, 1774, since, as Priestley himself pointed out†, he "was in possession of", that is, had isolated, the new gas in his laboratory "before the month of November 1771"—though he did not recognise the fact either then or in August 1774. It is to be hoped that the statement that Priestley "discovered oxygen on August 1, 1774" may now disappear from our textbooks.

An examination of the letter-books of the Royal Society and of the Journal Book has revealed certain slight inaccuracies in the text of Priestley's three letters on the discovery of oxygen published in the *Philosophical Transactions* (vol. 65, pp. 384—394; 1775); and together with the letter in Dr. Williams's library of March 25, 1775, addressed to Rev. Theophilus Lindsey (the letter to which Prof. Caven refers), these MSS. enable one to trace Priestley's movements at the time. Letter I to Sir John Pringle, president of the Royal Society, is in Priestley's own handwriting and is dated "London, March 15, 1775"; that letter was read on March 23, 1775; and this must be taken as the date of Priestley's first public announcement of the discovery of oxygen. Letter II is not printed in full but is in reality an extract from a letter of April 1, 1775 to the Rev. Dr. Richard Price; it is in Price's handwriting; it is definitely stated in it that the letter was dated Calne, April 1; and it was read on April 6, 1775. It was quite natural that Priestley should refer in it to the gas which he "had discovered in London" as Price, his intimate friend, and himself a fellow of the Royal Society, would have known about the gas and also that he had recently gone from

---

* Lord Lansdowne, to whom I sent a copy of this letter, confirms my statement that Shelburne House and Lansdowne House were the same. He adds that the room at Bowood (Lord Shelburne's country seat near Calne) in which Priestley conducted his experiments is to this day known as "The Laboratory", though it has certainly not been used as such since Priestley's, and, following him, Ingenhousz's time. Lord Lansdowne thinks that the experiment of August 1, 1774, was in all probability made in this room, though it may have taken place at the private house (on "the Green" at Calne) where Priestley lived when he was in Lord Shelburne's employ.

† See "Experiments and Observations on Air", vol. 1, pp. 155—157; 1774; and "Expts. and Obsns. relating to ... Natural Philosophy", vol. 1, pp. 194—198; 1779. In these early experiments Priestley obtained oxygen from saltpetre.

通过对比以上这两段文字，我们可以很清楚地看到，普里斯特利本人认为“发现氧气”的时间是 1775 年 3 月 1 日，而地点是伦敦。

普里斯特利在伦敦的实验是在现称为兰斯唐宅（不过那时叫作谢尔本宅，估计这个名字应该一直保持到谢尔本勋爵 1784 年成为兰斯唐侯爵时为止）的地方进行的*，他所著的《哲学经验主义》（1775 年）一书可以证明这一点，他在该书第 4 页中谈到：1775 年 5 月 23 日，他在兰斯唐宅中向朋友们展示了自己的一些实验（关于氧气的），这一天就是他就该主题第三次写信给皇家学会的前一天。（以上参考信息是由梅尔德伦教授提供的。）

我一直认为 1774 年 8 月 1 日这一天的重要性被人们过分地夸大了，因为，正如普里斯特利本人所指出的那样†，他“在 1771 年 11 月之前”就已“拥有”或者说已经分离出了那种新气体——尽管不论在当时还是在 1774 年 8 月他都没有认可这一事实。现在看来，普里斯特利“在 1774 年 8 月 1 日发现氧气”的说法也许可以从我们的教科书中消失了。

在对皇家学会的书信备查簿和日志进行考证之后发现：从普里斯特利就发现氧气这一主题发表在《自然科学会报》（第 65 卷，第 384~395 页；1775 年）上的三封信中可以看出某些细微的不一致；还有威廉斯博士图书馆中收藏的那封 1775 年 3 月 25 日普里斯特利写给西奥菲勒斯·林赛牧师的信（就是卡文教授谈到的那封信），这些手稿可以使我们追溯普里斯特利在当时的活动。信件 I 是普里斯特利写给皇家学会主席约翰·普林格尔爵士的亲笔信，落款为“伦敦，1775 年 3 月 15 日”；该信被宣读的时间为 1775 年 3 月 23 日；因而这一天应该作为普里斯特利首次公开宣布发现氧气的日期。信件 II 并未全文出版，实际上只是从 1775 年 4 月 1 日普里斯特利写给牧师理查德·普赖斯博士的信中摘录出来的一部分；为普赖斯的笔录；信中的落款明确为卡恩，4 月 1 日；它被宣读的时间是 1775 年 4 月 6 日。普里斯特利自然会在信中提及他“在伦敦时发现”的气体，因为普赖斯是他的亲密朋友，且他自己是皇家学会的一名会员，普赖斯肯定知道这种气体，也知道他刚刚从伦敦来到卡恩。（给林赛的信说明普里斯特利在 3 月 25 日时就已经在卡恩了。）信件 III 是普里斯特利写

---

* 我把这封信的副本交给兰斯唐勋爵，他确认兰斯唐宅和谢尔本宅是同一个地方。他还说，普里斯特利曾经在博伍德（谢尔本勋爵在卡恩附近的乡间别墅）做过实验的地方现在已经被人们称为“实验室”了，虽然自普里斯特利和英格豪斯之后不曾有人在那里做过实验。兰斯唐勋爵认为 1774 年 8 月 1 日的实验很可能就是在这个房间里作的，但也有可能是在普里斯特利的私人住所（在卡恩的格林）完成的，那时普里斯特利正在为谢尔本勋爵工作。

† 见《关于空气中的实验和观察》，第 1 卷，第 155~157 页；1774 年；以及《实验和观察关于……自然哲学》，第 1 卷，第 194~198 页；1779 年。在这些早期的实验中，普里斯特利从硝石中得到了氧气。

London to Calne. (The letter to Lindsey shows that he was already in Calne on March 25.) Letter III was from Priestley to Pringle and is dated London, May 24, 1775; it was read on May 25, 1775. The *Philosophical Transactions* wrongly give the date of Letter III as May 25, and an inset at the beginning of the communications wrongly suggests that all three letters were read on that day.

To complete the matter, it may be added that the MSS. show that Priestley asked Price to show Letter II to Pringle, so that, if he chose, it might be "read to the Royal Society, but not to be published", but that he withdrew his objection to publication. Letter I has endorsed on it "Withdrawn by the President through mistake, believing that such was Dr. Priestley's inclination". But the words are crossed out, perhaps to avoid their being reproduced by the printer. Obviously the passage in Priestley's Letter II made Pringle doubt if he wished his Letter I to be published. It is probable that Priestley only hesitated about the publication of Letter II because he wished to continue his experiments before publishing them. I am afraid that some of these details may seem meticulous; only the importance of the discovery to which they refer justifies my taking up so much space. The points of chief importance are the place and date which Priestley himself assigns to his great discovery.

P. J. Hartog

(**132**, 25-26; 1933)

R. M. Caven: The Royal Technical College, Glasgow, C.1.
P. J. Hartog: 5 Inverness Gardens, W.8.

给普林格尔的，落款为伦敦，1775 年 5 月 24 日；它被宣读的时间是 1775 年 5 月 25 日。《自然科学会报》误将信件 III 的写作日期定为 5 月 25 日，还在这些信件开始处的插入段落中错误地把所有三封信的宣读时间都当成了 5 月 25 日。

作为这个问题的结束，还可以补充一点，这些手稿表明普里斯特利曾请普赖斯将信件 II 呈交给普林格尔，如果普林格尔同意，这封信可以“在皇家学会内宣读，但不要发表”，不过他收回了对发表信件的反对。信件 I 上面签署着“误被主席退回，以为这是普里斯特利博士本人的意向”。但是这些文字被划掉了，可能是为了避免印刷工把它们复制上去。很明显，信件 II 中的这段话使普林格尔怀疑普里斯特利是否希望发表信件 I 中的内容。也许普里斯特利只是在是否发表信件 II 的问题上犹豫不决，因为他希望在公开这些信件之前继续自己的实验。恐怕这些细节太过琐碎；只是因为它们所谈及的发现十分重要才使我占用了这么大的篇幅。最要紧的是这一伟大发现的地点和时间是由普里斯特利本人指定的。

菲利普·哈尔托赫

（王耀杨 翻译；李芝芬 审稿）

# Chemical Test for Vitamin C, and the Reducing Substances Present in Tumour and Other Tissues

L. J. Harris

## Editor's Note

**In the 1930s, chemists and physiologists were able to define and characterise chemicals known as vitamins, which are necessary for human well-being but which are not synthesised in the human body. Early in the decade, very little was known about these compounds, as papers from the time amply illustrate. This paper suggests how vitamin C can be recognised in foodstuffs by the change in the colour of an oxidation-reduction indicator.**

IN previous communications a method has been described for estimating the hexuronic (ascorbic) acid content of foodstuffs, based on titration in acid solution with the oxidation-reduction indicator 2-6-dichlorophenolindophenol after preliminary extraction with trichloracetic acid[1,2,3]. Judging from the fact that this method when applied to some forty common sources—mostly fruit and vegetable materials—enabled the "minimal antiscorbutic doses" to be calculated to give results in excellent agreement with the values determined directly by biological tests, it is evident that the method has a considerable range of specificity. A number of necessary conditions and provisions were set out, which unfortunately there seems to have been some tendency to overlook, and it would appear advisable therefore to direct attention to certain considerations which must be borne in mind if the possibility of misleading conclusions is to be avoided.

As we have already pointed out[3], the reagent does not possess an *absolute* degree of specificity. Notably, free cystein (which may be present in stale or autolysed materials) was found to reduce it as readily as did the vitamin itself: this could easily be allowed for by a separate determination for cystein by the Sullivan method. Adrenalin also reduced the indicator, but much less intensely, so that in practice no ordinary natural source contains sufficient to interfere seriously. Products obtained by heating solutions of certain sugars, especially in alkaline media, tended to reduce the indicator; and we find that a number of proprietary baby foods and similar preparations give suspiciously high readings. Mr. A. L. Bacharach, of the Glaxo Research Laboratory, has titrated a series of specimens of malt-extracts by our method and found some of them to reduce the indicator strongly[4]. Among other materials of vegetable origin we found that the following also react appreciably with the indicator: yeast[3]; whole oats[3]; incubated pea mush[7]. Since these materials have not hitherto been regarded as sources of vitamin C, it would appear advisable to suspend judgment as to the precise nature of the reducing substance in such

# 肿瘤以及其他组织中所含的维生素C等还原性物质的化学检测

莱斯利·哈里斯

## 编者按

*在 20 世纪 30 年代，化学家和生理学家已经能够定义和描述维生素这种化学物质了，维生素是人体维持健康所必需的物质，但人体自身不能合成。在那个年代，极少有文章会详细描述这类物质。而这篇文章就是其中之一，本文讲述了如何通过氧化还原指示剂的颜色变化来鉴别食物中是否存在维生素 C。*

在以前的文章中，我们介绍了一种估算食物中己糖醛酸（抗坏血酸）含量的方法，即经三氯乙酸 [1,2,3] 初步萃取后用氧化还原指示剂 2,6–二氯酚靛酚在酸溶液中进行滴定的方法。当这种方法被应用到约 40 种常见的含抗坏血酸的物质——主要是水果和蔬菜中时，计算出的“抗坏血病的最小剂量”与直接利用生物学实验得到的值十分吻合，很显然，该方法的特异性仍具有一定的局限性。而且，需要具备许多必要的前提条件。不幸的是，这些前提条件很容易被忽略。因此，我们应该注意一些需要考虑的事项，以免得出误导性的结论。

正如我们所指出的那样 [3]，这种指示剂并没有**绝对**的特异性。值得注意的是，自由的半胱氨酸（可能存在于不新鲜或自溶的物质中）可以像维生素一样轻易地还原指示剂，但用沙利文法可以很容易地单独测定半胱氨酸。肾上腺素也可以还原这种指示剂，但作用远没有那么强烈，实际上自然界中天然存在的物质，其还原性还不足以强烈干扰指示剂的作用。如果加热某种糖溶液，尤其是在碱性条件下加热得到的产物能还原指示剂。此外，我们还发现许多婴儿专用食品以及类似的制剂都给出了可疑的高还原性数值。葛兰素研究实验室的巴卡拉克先生用我们的方法测定了一系列麦芽提取物样品，发现其中一些可以很强烈地还原指示剂 [4]。在其他植物来源制品中我们发现以下几种物质也可以与指示剂发生明显的反应：酵母粉 [3]、全燕麦 [3]、孵育豌豆粥 [7]。由于至今还没有人认为这些物质含有维生素 C，所以我们最好等到目前进行的生物学试验有了结果，再来判断这些特殊条件下的还原性物质的确切本质。

special cases until the biological tests, now in progress, are concluded.

Turning to the animal kingdom, it might have been anticipated that the specificity of the test would be less certain. Nevertheless we found that the suprarenal gland (not hitherto recognised as an antiscorbutic) was very potent, the biological activity agreeing with the value determined chemically; and the same is true, approximately at least, for liver. A systematic survey of various animal tissues, initiated in this laboratory by Messrs. Birch and Dann[6], showed that many of them gave very substantial titres, often accounting for a large fraction of the total iodine-reducing value, hitherto held to be a measure solely of the glutathione content. In the case of one of these materials, the aqueous humour of the eye, the very surprising indication of the presence of large amounts of vitamin C has already been confirmed biologically[7].

Another material giving a high iodine value and of very obvious interest in this connexion is tumour tissue. Dr. E. Boyland of the Cancer Hospital Research Laboratory approached us for details of our method to apply to tumours. We are indebted to him for permission to refer here to his results, which show that tumour tissues of various kinds likewise reduce the indicator[8]. Our own independent observations confirmed this finding, although our experiences were limited only to the Jensen rat sarcoma. This we find to give a very constant titre, equivalent in terms of hexuronic acid to 0.4 mgm. per gm. of wet tissue. Biological tests have so far given somewhat inconclusive results as to whether the titre is due wholly to vitamin C. The freshly excised sarcoma (rendered available by the collaboration of Mrs. B. Holmes) was fed to a series of five guinea pigs in curative tests at the level of 3.5 gm. per day. If the indophenol titre were due *entirely* to vitamin C, 2.5 gm. per day would suffice as the minimal dose. However, the experimental animals receiving 3.5 gm. lost weight as rapidly and survived no longer than the negative controls, although at death the degree of scurvy appeared less severe. In such tests a complicating factor due to the possible toxic effect of relatively large amounts of animal tissue fed to a herbivorous species like the guinea pig has always to be borne in mind. Further assays by several alternative methods are in progress. In any case the presence in the tumour tissue of such high concentrations of an intensely reducing substance, hitherto unrecognised, seems of special significance, bearing in mind the distinctive character of the cell respiration of tumours. Furthermore, observations in another connexion with Dr. E. W. Fish seem to indicate that vitamin C is needed primarily for the maintenance of certain actively functioning cells, so that its apparent presence in tumour tissue seems additionally suggestive. It is proposed to investigate the effect of deprivation of vitamin C on tumour growth.

Returning to the question of the applicability of the chemical test, it may be concluded that, on all fours with the now well-known and extensively used antimony trichloride test for vitamin A, it furnishes a valuable if not absolutely infallible guide. Certainly for fruits and vegetables as ordinarily dealt with, the test seems to give perfectly reliable results

对于动物界，可以预测到上述检测方法的特异性就会更加不确定了。然而，我们发现肾上腺（至今还未被认为是一种抗坏血病的物质）有着较高的还原值，它的生物学活性与用化学方法测定的完全相符，其他组织也是一样，至少肝脏的情况大致如此。由我们实验室的伯奇先生和丹恩先生发起的一项关于各种动物组织还原性物质的系统调查[6]显示，许多动物组织都有很高滴度的还原性，并常常占全部碘还原值的大部分。而碘值法也是到目前为止测定谷胱甘肽含量的唯一方法。这些组织之一的眼球房水中含有大量的维生素C的奇怪现象，已经在生物学上得到了证实[7]。

在这项研究中，另一种具有很高还原值并具有重要意义的是肿瘤组织。肿瘤医院研究实验室的博伊兰博士在向我们咨询后，已尝试将这种方法应用到肿瘤研究上。非常感谢他允许我们在这里引用他的研究结果。其结果显示各种肿瘤组织同样可以还原指示剂[8]。尽管我们仅仅观察了詹森大鼠肉瘤，但我们的独立观察结果也可以证实上述结论。我们发现这种肿瘤有一个非常恒定的滴定度，相当于每克湿组织中有0.4毫克己糖醛酸。至于这一滴定度是否完全源自于维生素C，生物学试验至今未能给出明确的结论。我们把新切的肉瘤（由霍姆斯夫人协助提供）以每天3.5克的量喂给五只患坏血病的豚鼠以进行治疗试验。如果靛酚滴定度**完全**源自于维生素C，那么每天2.5克就足以作为试验抗坏血病的最小剂量。意外的是，尽管死亡时所患坏血病的程度看起来要轻一些，这些每天食用3.5克肉瘤的实验动物和阴性对照组一样很快地消瘦，而且并没有活的更长。在上述试验中，一定要始终牢记喂给像豚鼠这样的食草类动物相对大量的动物组织有可能会产生毒性反应这一复杂因素。因此，人们还在利用另外几种方法进行进一步的检测。无论如何，考虑到肿瘤细胞呼吸的显著特性，在肿瘤组织中存在如此高浓度的、至今尚未被探明的强还原性物质看起来具有特殊的意义。此外，菲什博士的另一项观察似乎表明，维生素C主要用于维持某些功能活跃的细胞，所以它在肿瘤组织中的存在似乎还有其他暗示。有人建议研究维生素C缺失对肿瘤生长的作用。

总之，考虑到化学试验的适用性问题，可以得出以下结论：与众所周知且广泛应用的利用三氯化锑测定维生素A的试验一样，这种方法即使不算绝对可靠，至少也有价值。当然，对于通常涉及的水果和蔬菜，这种试验似乎不需要进一步的检验

without further elaboration; when unusual types of material are under investigation, the test must be used with due understanding.

(**132**, 27-28; 1933)

Leslie J. Harris: Nutritional Laboratory, Cambridge, June 20.

---

References:

1 Birch, T. W., Harris, L. J., and Ray, S. N., *Nature*, **131**, 273 (Feb. 25, 1933).

2 Harris, L. J., and Ray, S. N., *Biochem*. J., **27**, 303 (1933).

3 Birch, T. W., Harris, L. J., and Ray, S. N., *Biochem. J.*, **27**, 590 (1933).

4 Bacharach, A. L., private communication.

5 Harris, L. J., and Ray, S.N., *Biochem. J.*, **26**, 2067 (1932);

6 Birch, T. W., and Dann, W. J., *Nature*, **131**, 469 (April 1, 1933).

7 Birch, T. W., and Dann, W. J., unpublished work.

8 Boyland, E., private communication; *Biochem. J.*, in the press.

就可以得到可靠性很高的结果；而当研究某些特殊物质时，这种试验只能在具备足够相关知识的前提下才可使用。

（李世媛 翻译；秦志海 审稿）

# Mitosis and Meiosis

C. L. Huskins

## Editor's Note

**How chromosomes are partitioned when cells divide was still unclear in the 1930s. Here Canadian geneticist Charles Leonard Huskins from McGill University, Montreal, presents a unified theory of mitosis and meiosis (cell division that retains or halves, respectively, the number of chromosomes) that overcomes the pitfalls of its main predecessor, the so-called precocity theory of meiosis. English geneticist Cyril Dean Darlington had suggested that meiosis was precocious because the first stage (prophase) begins before chromosomes have divided into two identical parts (chromatids). Huskins neatly side-steps the problems associated with that idea by suggesting that the chromosome threads are attracted in pairs at all stages of meiosis and mitosis, but that pairs of pairs repel one another.**

FROM observations made in this laboratory by S. G. Smith, E. Marie Hearne, Jane D. Spier, J. M. Armstrong, A. W. S. Hunter, and me on meiosis and both haploid and diploid mitosis in *Trillium*, *Matthiola*, a number of cereals and grasses, and in grasshoppers, it can be shown that, at all stages of mitosis and meiosis chromosome threads are attracted in pairs and that pairs of pairs are repulsed. A unified theory of chromosome behaviour thereby arises which seems adequately to explain the mechanism of both mitosis and meiosis, including the varied behaviour of univalents in the latter. Fig. 1 illustrates essential features, broken lines indicating stages during which splitting of the chromosomes can be seen to be occurring. (Throughout this note it is "effective" lateral splitting which is referred to; if Nebel's, unpublished, observations in *Tradescantia reflexa* are confirmed for other material the initiation of the split occurs one division cycle earlier.)

These observations were stimulated by Darlington's precocity theory of meiosis (which Dr. A. H. Sturtevant in his recent review in *Nature* of January 7, p. 5, states that he favours) and the new unified theory has, of course, features in common with it as well as with more generally accepted accounts. Briefly, according to our observations, chromosome behaviour in mitosis and meiosis is as follows: at the earliest prophase stage of mitosis the chromosomes are double; in meiosis they are single. The single threads pair in meiotic zygotene; during pachytene the "secondary" split occurs. Repulsion between pairs of chromatids begins with the "secondary split" but in *most* organisms the pairs are held together by changes of partner or chiasmata. So far we agree with Darlington, except that he has attributed universality to the chiasma mechanism. As I have pointed out

# 有丝分裂与减数分裂

查尔斯·伦纳德·赫斯金斯

## 编者按

20 世纪 30 年代，人们还不清楚细胞分裂时染色体是如何分开的。在这篇文章中，来自蒙特利尔麦吉尔大学的加拿大遗传学家查尔斯·伦纳德·赫斯金斯提出了一种关于有丝分裂和减数分裂（分别是指染色体数目保持不变或者减半的细胞分裂）的统一理论，这一理论克服了它的主要前任，即所谓的减数分裂早熟论的缺陷。此前，英国遗传学家西里尔·迪恩·达林顿提出，减数分裂是早熟的，因为在染色体分成完全相同的两部分（染色单体）之前，减数分裂的第一阶段（前期）就开始了。赫斯金斯提出，在减数分裂和有丝分裂的所有阶段，染色体丝都是配对相连的，不过这些配对的染色体丝再成对后，两组染色体丝配对之间则是互相排斥的，这样，赫斯金斯就巧妙地避开了与早熟理论相关的一些困难。

史密斯、玛丽·赫恩、简·施皮尔、阿姆斯特朗、亨特和我在实验室中对减数分裂以及延龄草、紫罗兰、大量谷物与草类和蝗虫中的单倍体与双倍体有丝分裂进行了研究，结果表明，在有丝分裂和减数分裂的所有阶段，染色体丝因相互吸引而配成对，但对与对之间是相互排斥的。因此就可以用一个统一的染色体行为理论来圆满解释有丝分裂和减数分裂的机制，包括在减数分裂过程中单价染色体表现出的各种行为。图 1 中的例子解释了有丝分裂和减数分裂的基本特征，间断的线说明该阶段是可以看到染色体发生分离的阶段。（图中所示的均为“有效”的横向分离；如果尼贝尔尚未发表的关于紫露草的观察结果对其他生命体也成立，那么分离过程应开始于一个分裂周期之前。）

因为我们是在达林顿的减数分裂早熟论的启发下开始这项研究的（斯特蒂文特博士在他最近发表于 1 月 7 日《自然》杂志第 5 页上的评论文章中表明了自己对该理论的支持），所以我们提出的新理论理所当然地与减数分裂早熟论以及更为广泛接受的理论有共同的特征。简言之，根据我们的观察，染色体在有丝分裂和减数分裂中的行为如下：在有丝分裂前期的最开始，染色体是双链的；而在减数分裂前期，染色体是单链的。两条单链染色体丝在减数分裂的偶线期配成对；到了减数分裂的粗线期，又会发生“第二级”分离。在“第二级”分离时，成对染色单体之间开始相互排斥，但在**大多数**生物体中，成对的染色单体通过互换链或交叉而聚集在一起。到此阶段为止，我们的观察结果与达林顿的理论是一致的，但我们不认同他认为交叉机制具有普适性的看法。我曾在另一篇文章中指出 [1]：威尔逊和施拉德斯的研究

elsewhere[1], the work of Wilson and the Schraders shows conclusively that it has not universal application, and almost equally certainly Darlington is wrong in applying it to *Drosophila*.

From diplotene on, our observations differ from previous accounts. As demonstrated at the Sixth International Congress of Genetics[2], a "tertiary" split develops before meiotic metaphase. (This was discovered independently and simultaneously by Nebel[3].) At a parallel stage of mitosis we find, in both root tips and the haploid pollen grains, a split occurring, as reported by Sharp[4], Hedayetuallah[5] and others in root tips. Darlington rejected Sharp's observations as "optical illusions". Some of ours being end-views of chromosomes cannot thus be disposed of. The "tertiary" split initiates a repulsion within the 4-partite daughter chromosomes, at anaphase causing their arms to separate widely and preparing them for the second meiotic division, in which we find the pre-metaphase split omitted. Omission of a split in one division is, of course, essential to reduction. It follows as a mechanical consequence of the preceding stages as here described. The splitting of univalents in both divisions, which occurs chiefly when there are many of them, is apparently due to their delaying the second division and thus permitting the ordinarily omitted premetaphase split to occur. It is inexplicable on Darlington's view that splitting occurs during the resting stage.

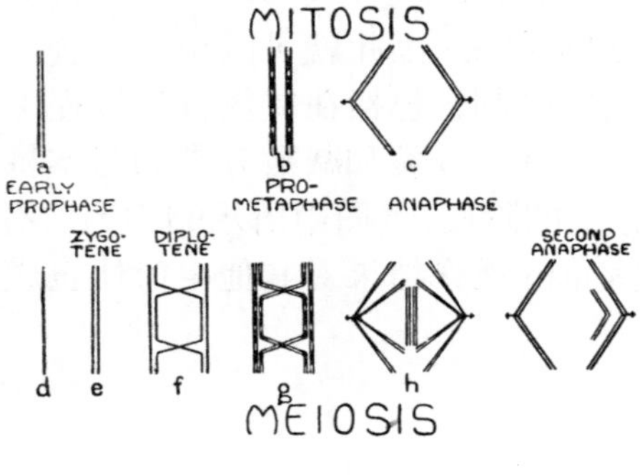


Fig. 1. Diagram of mitosis and meiosis. A univalent is included in h and i.

It is from this view that practically all the contradictions in Darlington's precocity theory arise. From it he is forced to assume that though at prophase single threads attract one another, they repulse one another at anaphase. To get around this duality of principle, he suggests[6] (p. 48) "It may be that the ... spindle attachment ... has not the property which the chromatids have, of associating in pairs". Again (p. 300) he assumes that though the chromosomes divide during the resting stage, their attachments divide at metaphase. Both these assumptions are theoretically inadequate and, according to us, observationally invalid. Finally, though the object of his precocity theory is to homologise mitosis and

已经证明交叉机制并不具有普适性，并同样明确地指出达林顿将交叉机制应用于果蝇是错误的。

从双线期开始，我们的观察结果就与达林顿的理论有了偏差。正如我在第六届国际遗传学大会上声明的[2]，“第三级”分离在减数分裂进入中期以前就已经形成了。（内贝尔在同一时间也独立地发现了这个现象[3]。）我们注意到，在有丝分裂中的对应阶段，根尖和单倍体花粉粒都发生了染色体的分离，这与夏普[4]和海德亚图拉[5]等人所报道的在根尖中发生的分离一样。达林顿不承认夏普的观察结果，认为它们是“视觉上的错觉”。但不能因此而否认我们观察到的一些染色体端视图。“第三级”分离开始于四分体中子染色体之间的相互排斥，在分裂后期排斥会引起染色体臂的大幅度分离，并为减数第二次分裂做准备，我们发现在减数第二次分裂时没有出现前中期的分离过程。当然，在一次减数分裂中省去一次分离过程是产生减数所必需的。正如本文所描述的，分离的缺省是前一步分裂过程自然发展的结果。在两次分裂中单价染色体的分离都主要发生在存在大量单价染色体的时候，这种分离的产生显然是由于减数第二次分裂的延迟，因而发生了在通常情况下不会出现的前中期分离。达林顿认为分离发生在分裂间期的观点是解释不通的。

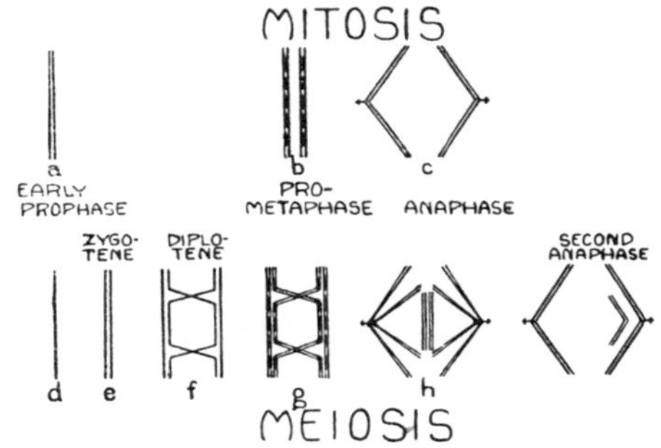


图 1. 有丝分裂和减数分裂示意图。在 h 和 i 中含有一个单价染色体。

这个观点可以让达林顿早熟论中几乎所有的矛盾都暴露出来。他不得不因此而假设尽管在分裂前期单链染色体丝之间是相互吸引的，但在后期它们又会相互排斥。为了避免在理论中出现二重性，达林顿指出[6]（第 48 页），“也许是因为……纺锤体着生区……不具备染色单体所具有的可以连接成对的属性。”他还假设（第 300 页）虽然染色体会在分裂间期分离，但它们的纺锤体着生区却在分裂中期才分开。上述两点假定都缺乏理论上的依据，也与我们的观察结果不符。最后的结论是，尽管达林顿提出早熟论的目的在于统一有丝分裂和减数分裂的机制，但他的基本原理在最

meiosis, Darlington is left at the end (p. 305) with a basic duality of principle: "Perhaps all nuclear division, *apart from the first division of meiosis* [my italics], is determined by division of the chromosomes."

The observations here summarised show this duality to be non-existent; the principle of attraction between single threads and repulsion between pairs of pairs, postulated by Darlington for the prophase only and denied by him at anaphase, really applies at all stages of mitosis and meiosis.

(**132**, 62-63; 1933)

C. Leonard Huskins: McGill University, Montreal.

References:
1 Huskins, C. L., *Trans. Roy. Soc. Canada*, **26** (Sect. V), 17-28 (1932).
2 Huskins, C. L., Smith, S. G., *et al.*, Proc. Sixth Internat. Cong. Genetics, **2**, 95-96, 392-393 and 396 (1932).
3 Nebel, B. R., *Z. Zell. Micro. Anat.*, **16**, 251-284 (1932).
4 Sharp, L. W., *Bot. Gaz.*, **88**, 349-382 (1929).
5 Hedayetullah, S., *J. Roy. Micro. Soc.*, **51**, 347-386 (1931).
6 Darlington, C. D., "Recent Advances in Cytology" (Churchill and Co., London) (1932).

后部分（第 305 页）出现了二重性："也许所有的细胞核分裂，**除了减数第一次分裂以外** [ 英文斜体是我加上的 ]，都是由染色体的分离决定的。"

根据本文中介绍的观察结果，这种二重性是不存在的；单链染色体丝之间相互吸引以及成对染色体之间相互排斥的原理完全可以应用于有丝分裂和减数分裂的所有阶段，而达林顿却错误地认为该原理只适用于分裂前期，不适用于分裂后期。

（管冰 翻译；刘京国 审稿）

# Positrons and Atomic Nuclei

G. W. Todd

## Editor's Note

**Walter Elsasser had recently suggested that the proton might be a composite of neutron and positron, and that this hypothesis might help explain the positive charge of nuclei. Here George Todd criticizes that idea, and suggests another. He notes, however, that a particular transmutation of uranium can be understood in Elsasser's picture if the process involves the spontaneous creation of an electron and positron from nothing—a process that is now known to happen, although not here. Todd's proposed nuclear constitution leads to the conjecture that isotopes differ only by the number of neutrons in the nucleus, another prescient suggestion.**

IN *Nature* of May 27, Dr. W. Elsasser offers evidence in favour of the suggestion that the proton consists of a neutron and a positron. Examining the question from a different point of view, I put forward the following as evidence against the suggestion.

If we allow that an atomic nucleus may contain $\alpha$-particles, protons, neutrons, electrons and positrons, the number of possible structures for a nucleus of atomic mass $P$ and atomic number $Z$ increases rapidly with increase of $P$ and $Z$, and for the heavy atoms it may run into hundreds. If we exclude the possibility of unattached electrons and positrons in the nucleus, then the structure becomes unique and is given by

$$\tfrac{1}{2}(Z-p)\ \alpha\text{-particles} + (P-2Z+p)\ \text{neutrons} +\ p\ \text{protons} \quad (1)$$

where $p = 0$ or 1, whichever value makes $\frac{1}{2}(Z-p)$ an integer.

It is also possible to get a unique structure by excluding the possibility of unattached electrons but allowing the possibility of positrons. The structure is then

$$\tfrac{1}{2}(Z-p')\ \alpha\text{-particles} + (P-2Z+2p')\ \text{neutrons} +\ p'\ \text{positrons} \quad (2)$$

where again $p' = 0$ or 1 as before. This is practically the suggestion which Elsasser supports.

Using these expressions, we can trace the changes which take place in the nuclei of radioactive elements during $\alpha$- and $\beta$-ray transformations. The accompanying table shows a typical set of transformations.

# 正电子和原子核

乔治·托德

## 编者按

沃尔特·埃尔萨瑟最近指出质子可能是中子和正电子的合成物，而且这一假说很可能有助于解释原子核为什么带正电。在这篇文章中，乔治·托德反驳了这一观点，并提出了另外一个观点。不过托德指出：有一种特殊的铀嬗变也许可以用埃尔萨瑟的理论来解释，如果在这个过程中会凭空自发产生一个电子和正电子——现在我们知道这样的反应是存在的，虽然当时还不知道。由托德提出的核结构理论可以推出同位素之间的差别仅仅是原子核中的中子数不相同，这是托德的又一个真知灼见。

在 5 月 27 日的《自然》杂志上，埃尔萨瑟博士提出证据证明质子是由一个中子和一个正电子组成的。我从不同的角度出发用以下证据来反驳这一观点。

如果我们承认原子核有可能是由 $\alpha$ 粒子、质子、中子、电子和正电子组成的，那么对于一个原子质量为 $P$、原子序数为 $Z$ 的原子来说，它可能具有的结构个数将随着 $P$ 和 $Z$ 的增加急剧上升，而重原子可能具有的结构或许会达到数百种。如果我们排除原子核中存在独立正、负电子的可能性，那么就可以认为核结构只能有以下一种形式：

$$\frac{1}{2}(Z-p)\text{ 个 }\alpha\text{ 粒子}+(P-2Z+p)\text{ 个中子}+p\text{ 个质子} \tag{1}$$

式中 $p$ 取 0 或 1，看哪一个值可以使 $\frac{1}{2}(Z-p)$ 为整数。

如果只排除独立负电子，而允许独立正电子存在，也可以得到唯一的结构。此时原子核结构为：

$$\frac{1}{2}(Z-p')\text{ 个 }\alpha\text{ 粒子}+(P-2Z+2p')\text{ 个中子}+p'\text{ 个正电子} \tag{2}$$

和前面一样，$p'$ 取 0 或 1。事实上这就是埃尔萨瑟所支持的观点。

利用这些表达式，我们可以探索放射性元素的原子核在 $\alpha$ 和 $\beta$ 射线衰变过程中发生的变化。下表中给出了一系列典型的衰变：

| | Nucleus from (1) | Nucleus from (2) | Radiation |
|---|---|---|---|
| Ur I | $46\alpha + 54n + 0p$ | $46\alpha + 54n + 0p'$ | |
| ↓ | | | $\}\ \alpha$ |
| Ur $X_1$ | 45 54 0 | 45 54 0 | |
| ↓ | | | $\}\ \beta$ |
| Ur $X_2$ | 45 53 1 | 45 54 1 | |
| ↓ | | | $\}\ \beta$ |
| Ur II | 46 50 0 | 46 50 0 | |
| ↓ | | | $\}$ |
| Io | 45 50 0 | 45 50 0 | |

The explanation of the $\alpha$-ray changes is obvious. The $\beta$-ray changes in a radioactive series generally occur in pairs and the pair above shows changes identical with all other pairs of $\beta$-ray transformations. If the nuclear contents are expressed by (1), the changes take place in the following reasonable manner:—

$1n \rightarrow 1p + 1\beta$ the proton remaining in the nucleus,

and $3n + 1p \rightarrow 1\alpha + 1\beta$ the $\alpha$- particle remaining in the nucleus.

On the other hand, if expression (2) gives the nuclear contents, then the changes which take place are

$0 \rightarrow 1p' + 1\beta$, a positron appearing in the nucleus,

and $4n + 1p' \rightarrow 1\alpha + 1\beta$, the $\alpha$-particle remaining in the nucleus.

But where do the electron and positron come from in the first change, and how is the alteration in charge to be accounted for in the second change?

It is interesting to note that the expressions (1) and (2) give lower limits to the mass of an isotope. The minimum value from (1) is $P \geqslant 2Z - p$ and from (2) it is $P \geqslant 2Z - 2p'$. It will also be observed that isotopes only differ from each other in the number of neutrons in their nuclei.

(**132**, 65; 1933)

George W. Todd: Armstrong College, Newcastle-upon-Tyne, June 3.

| | 式（1）中的原子核 | 式（2）中的原子核 | 辐射 |
|---|---|---|---|
| Ur I | $46\alpha + 54n + 0p$ | $46\alpha + 54n + 0p'$ | |
| ↓ | | | $\}\ \alpha$ |
| Ur $X_1$ | 45　54　0 | 45　54　0 | |
| ↓ | | | $\}\ \beta$ |
| Ur $X_2$ | 45　53　1 | 45　54　1 | |
| ↓ | | | $\}\ \beta$ |
| Ur II | 46　50　0 | 46　50　0 | |
| ↓ | | | $\}$ |
| $I_0$ | 45　50　0 | 45　50　0 | |

关于产生 $\alpha$ 射线的转变的解释是显而易见的。而产生 $\beta$ 射线的转变在放射系中一般成对出现，上表中出现的那对表现出与所有其他 $\beta$ 射线转变对相同的变化。如果原子核的构成可以表示为式（1），那么发生转变的合理方式应该是这样的：

$1n \rightarrow 1p + 1\beta$，质子留在原子核中；$3n + 1p \rightarrow 1\alpha + 1\beta$，$\alpha$ 粒子留在原子核中。

另一方面，如果原子核的构成可以表示为式（2），那么发生的转变则是：

$0 \rightarrow 1p' + 1\beta$，一个正电子出现在原子核中；$4n + 1p' \rightarrow 1\alpha + 1\beta$，$\alpha$ 粒子留在原子核中。

然而，在第一种转变中，电子和正电子从何而来？在第二个转变中，又如何解释电荷变化？

有趣的是，我们注意到式（1）和式（2）给出了同位素质量的下限。由式（1）推出的最小值为 $P \geqslant 2Z - p$ 而由式(2)推出的最小值为 $P \geqslant 2Z - 2p'$。我们还发现，同位素之间的区别仅仅在于其原子核中的中子数不相同。

（王静 翻译；李军刚 审稿）

# Liquid Crystals

## Editor's Note

**This anonymous report on a meeting at London's Royal Institution to discuss liquid crystals suggests that the conference helped to establish a consensus on this hitherto controversial state of matter. The idea, suggested by experiments in the late 1880s, that a material could be simultaneously liquid and ordered at the molecular scale seemed initially puzzling. In 1924 Daniel Vorländer, an attendee at the London meeting, explained the behaviour as that of liquids composed of rod-like molecules, which can become aligned while still mobile. William Bragg pointed out how defects in the alignment could create the striking visual appearance of liquid crystals. Manipulations of the alignment in layers of material using electric fields now form the basis of liquid-crystal display devices.**

BY holding a conference on "Liquid Crystals and Anisotropic Melts" at the Royal Institution on April 24–25, the Faraday Society has rendered a service not only to the cause of international science but particularly to science in Great Britain, for it has long been a regrettable fact that this interesting and important subject has been practically unknown here. So much so, that in the symposium volume on liquid crystals published by the *Zeitschrift für Krystallographie*, there was not one contribution from an English worker in the field. In part, this neglect has been due to the apparent multiplicity and complexity of the phenomena of liquid crystals, and in part to the prolonged and violent controversies to which their interpretation gave rise. This is a situation to which the holding of the Faraday Society conference has definitely put an end. We now have, as a result of the discussions, a fairly coherent picture of the nature and importance of liquid crystals: and though differences still remain, they will now, far more than in the past, lead to fresh fields of research rather than to controversy.

Since their discovery by Reinitzer in 1888, and the pioneer work of Lehmann, Friedel, and Vorländer—of whom the last was present at the conference—liquid crystals have been intensively studied chemically, physically and mathematically, and their essential nature is now well established. The great majority of known chemical substances on melting pass abruptly at a sharp temperature from a crystalline solid with well-defined anisotropic properties to a mobile liquid in every way—optically, magnetically, electrically—isotropic. In some substances, however, a number of intermediate states are interposed between these ultimate ones.

The properties of these states are just as definite as those that distinguish the crystalline and liquid states, but they partake, in different degrees, of the nature of both. Their most striking character, though by no means an essential one, is their optical anisotropy, which betrays itself in their spontaneous turbidity in thick layers, and by the colours they

# 液晶

## 编者按

这份匿名报告的内容是关于研究人员在伦敦英国皇家学院的一次会议上对液晶的讨论结果，这次会议使大家就物质的这一迄今为止尚存争议的状态达成了共识。19 世纪 80 年代晚期，有人在实验中发现某些液态材料在分子尺度上也具有规整的排列，这在当时引起了人们的质疑。1924 年，丹尼尔·福伦德出席了当时在伦敦举行的会议，他在会上解释说，这些液体材料是由棒状分子组成的，它们在移动时也能保持准直排列。威廉·布拉格指出了排列上的缺陷是如何使液晶产生惊人的视觉效果的。用电场控制材料层中分子的排列就是目前液晶显示装置的工作原理。

4 月 24~25 日法拉第学会在皇家研究所举办了关于“液晶和各向异性熔体”的讨论会，通过这次会议，法拉第学会为国际科学事业，尤其是为英国的科学事业做出了贡献，因为长久以来人们一直对英国人不了解这项有趣而重要的课题而感到遗憾。这种无知的程度很深，以至于在《晶体学杂志》有关液晶的专题论文集中竟然没有一篇是英国学者在该领域发表的文章。他们对这个问题的忽视，一方面是由于液晶现象非常复杂多样，另一方面也与各种解释所引发的漫长而激烈的争论有关。显然，法拉第学会的会议打破了这种局面。讨论的结果是人们对液晶的性质和重要性达成了相当一致的认识：尽管分歧仍然存在，但与过去相比，它们更倾向于将人们引向崭新的研究领域，而不是导致争论。

自 1888 年莱尼茨尔发现液晶，以及莱曼、夫里德耳和福伦德（他们中的最后一位出席了本次会议）对此开展了早期探索之后，人们从化学、物理和数学层面上对液晶进行了深入的研究，现在已经完全确认了它的本质特征。绝大多数已知的化学物质在熔融时都会经过一个突变温度，在此温度下物质从具有高度确定的各向异性性质的结晶态固体转变为在各个方面——光学、磁学和电学等都呈各向同性的流动性液体。不过，在某些物质中还存在着许多介于这两种极端状态之间的中间状态。

这些中间态的性质非常明确，如同那些用于区分结晶态和液态的性质一样，但它们多多少少会带有与结晶态以及液态相同的性质。它们最显著的特性，虽然并不是本质的特性，就是光学各向异性，体现为在厚层中自动变混浊，以及在交叉尼科

show between crossed nicols. Another significant property is the possession of a variety—bewildering at first—of internal structures, threads, rods, cones, stepped and faceted drops, oily streaks and iridescent colours, recalling the appearance of biological rather than physical objects.

Direct observation early established two principal types of liquid crystal. The first, apart from optical anisotropy, behaves like a normal liquid of high mobility, with convection currents and Brownian motion. This phase, characterised by the appearance of mobile threads in the body of the liquid, due to lines of optical discontinuity, was called by Friedel *nematic* (from νῆμα, a thread; Fig. 1). The second type, called *smectic* by Friedel, is much more oily in consistency, and shows only limited internal mobility, but a great complexity of internal structure. When in bulk, it consists entirely of the characteristic focal conic structure (see Fig. 2), but when spreading on surfaces or in small free drops it tends to form flat terraces, the terraces of Grandjean, of unequal thickness and rounded outline (see Fig. 3)*.

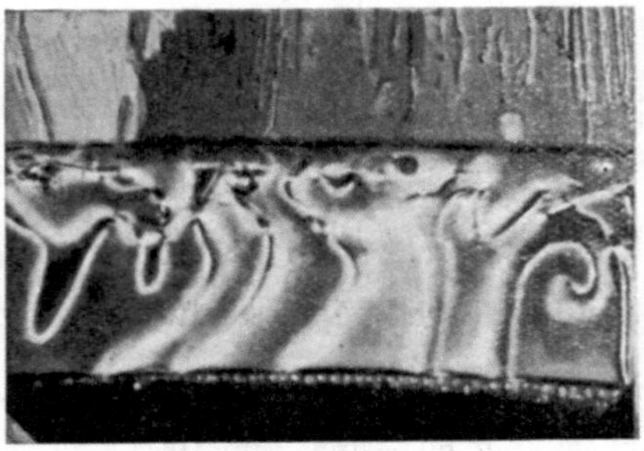

Fig. 1. Anisaldazine showing solid crystals, nematic liquid crystals with singular points, and isotropic liquid.

* The photographs reproduced as Figs. 1, 2 and 3, were taken by Dr. Lawrence at the Colloid Physics Department, Cambridge.

尔棱镜之间显现色彩。另一个重要性质就是拥有各式各样起先令人困惑不解的内部结构——线形、杆形、锥形、有阶梯和面的滴状、油状条纹以及斑斓的色彩，这使人联想到这是生物学而非物理学的研究对象。

早期的直接观察确定了液晶的两种基本类型。第一类的行为类似于流动性很高的普通液体，但具有光学各向异性，并且可以进行对流和布朗运动。这个以在液体内存在游动细丝为特征的相，被夫里德耳称之为向列相（来自 $\nu\widehat{\eta}\mu\alpha$，细丝；见图 1)，而这种“细丝”源自于光学上呈不连续的线。第二类被夫里德耳称为近晶相，在稠度上更接近油，而且只表现出有限的内部流动性，但其内部结构非常复杂。在体积大时，它完全由特征的焦锥结构态构成（见图 2)，但是当在表面展开或成小的自由液滴状时，它倾向于形成平面阶地——具有不等厚度和圆形轮廓的格朗让阶地(见图 3) *。

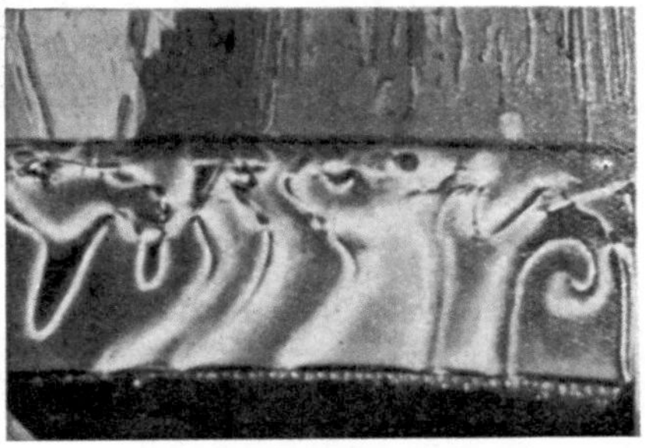

图 1. 茴香醛连氮表现为固态晶体、具有奇点的向列相液晶以及各向同性液体

* 图 1、图 2 和图 3 中复制的照片是由剑桥大学胶体物理系的劳伦斯博士拍摄的。

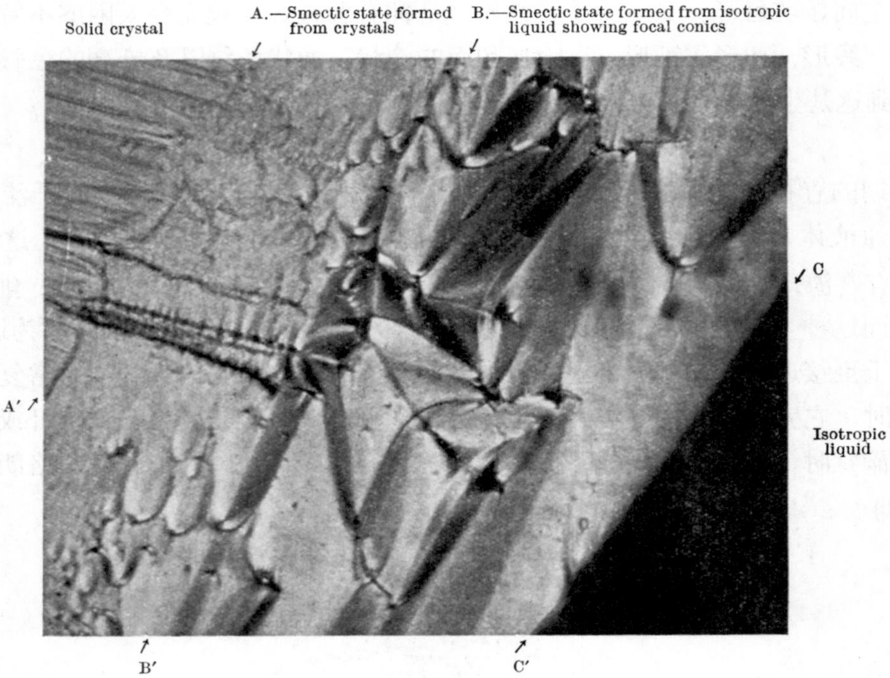


Fig. 2. Ethylazoxybenzoate showing smectic structures.

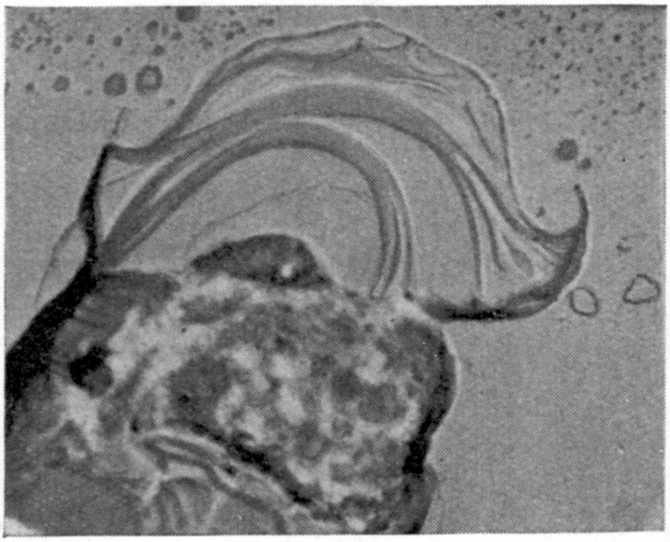

Fig. 3. Drop of thallium stearate showing Grandjean planes.

The physical explanation of these two types is now fairly clear. In the first place all liquid crystals have very anisotropic molecules, usually—as emphasised by Prof. Vorländer—with one dimension much greater than the others, for example, the classical p-azoxyanisol

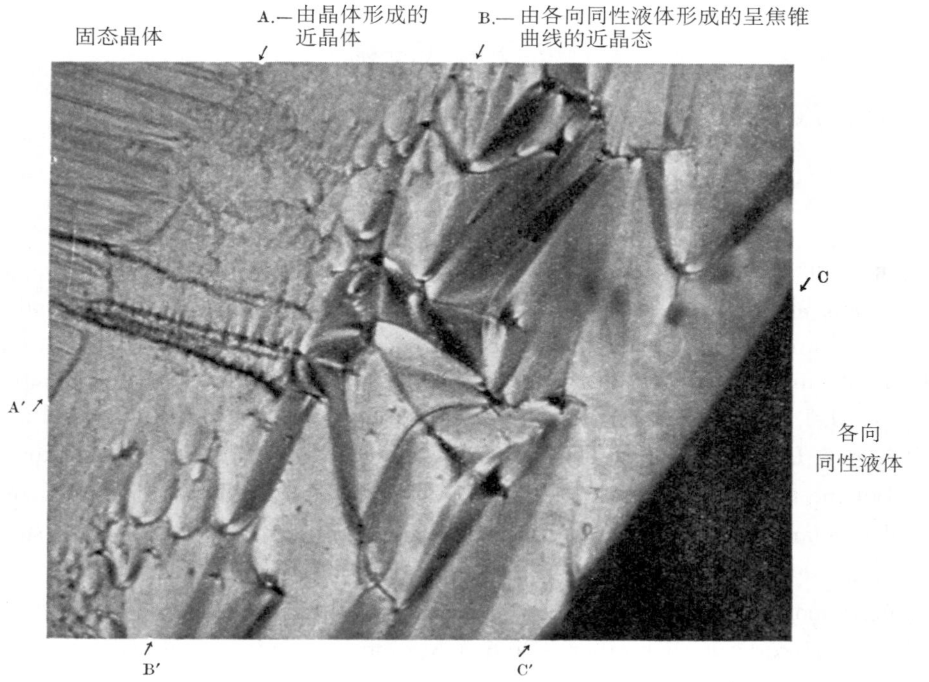


图 2. 表现为近晶相结构的氧化偶氮基苯甲酸乙酯

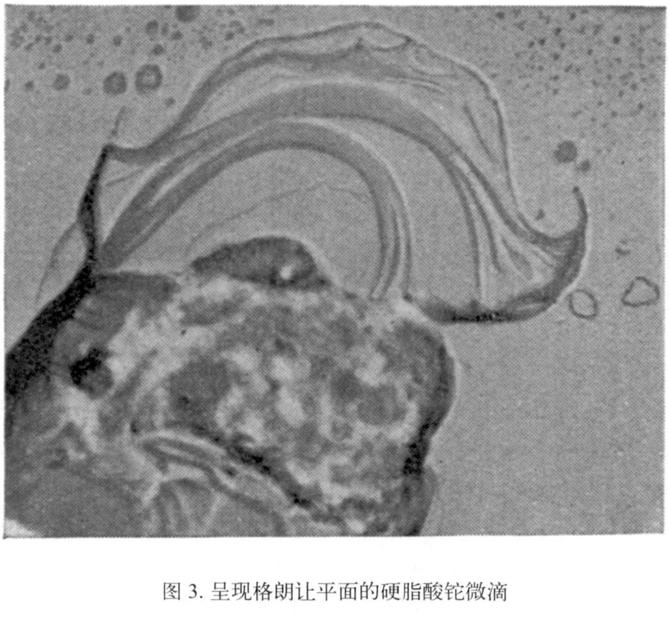

图 3. 呈现格朗让平面的硬脂酸铊微滴

目前对这两类液晶的物理解释已经相当清楚。首先，所有液晶都有高度各向异性的分子，正如福伦德教授所强调的那样，通常在一个维度上要比在其他维度上大很多，例如，经典的对 – 氧化偶氮苯甲醚

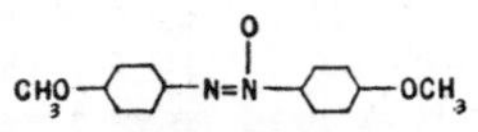

or the diethyl-*p*-xylylidene-bisamino cinnimate

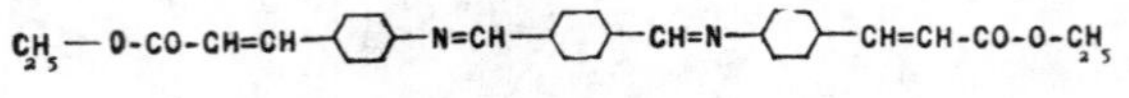

This leading dimension determines the mutual relation of neighbouring molecules to a greater or less extent, according to the temperature. If we limit our consideration to a very small volume, the following main cases will arise (see Fig. 4): In I the molecules are completely at random: this is the case for the normal isotropic liquid. In II all the molecular axes are parallel, but the centres of the molecule are as irregularly arranged and as free to move as in case I. This corresponds to the *nematic* state. In III as in II the molecular axes are parallel, but the molecular centres have lost one degree of freedom, and are now restricted to a set of regularly spaced parallel surfaces. This corresponds to the typical *smectic* state. In V, which is the case for the crystal, the molecules are parallel, and their centres form a regular three-dimensional network. (Two cases may arise here: either (*a*) the molecules are arranged in planes, or (*b*) interleave each other. The first type (smectogenic crystal) tends to give rise to smectic and the second (nematogenic crystal) to nematic.)

That these explanations are essentially correct is proved by the examination of liquid crystals by X-rays; particularly by the work of K. Hermann and Kast, where sharp Bragg reflections are obtained in the smectic case, but only liquid haloes in the nematic.

A question discussed at the Conference was that of the existence of further liquid crystal states. One other has long been recognised, that typical of cholesterol esters, but which in fact occurs whenever optically active substances form liquid crystals and is called the *cholesteric*. Friedel considers it a variant of the *nematic* type, but it has many properties also of *smectic* states. It is characterised by the production of spectral colours by reflection, with the peculiarity that only right- (or left-) handed circularly polarised light is reflected. This Friedel considers to be Bragg reflection from Grandjean planes regularly spaced, 1,000–10,000 A. apart in different cases together with a spiral arrangement of molecules. Oseen, in a paper to the Conference, attempted to prove, by rigorous use of electromagnetic theory, that the latter assumption is sufficient to account for all the phenomena, and that the Grandjean planes are in this case an optical illusion. Friedel maintains that there are no liquid crystal phases apart from nematic, smectic and cholesteric: however, Vorländer has long claimed that he has produced substances with no less than four intermediate states between solid and liquid, and more recently K. Hermann

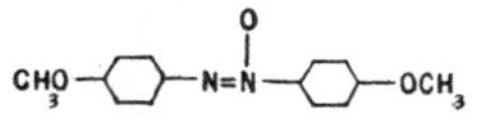

或对 – 苯二甲二亚胺基肉桂酸二乙酯

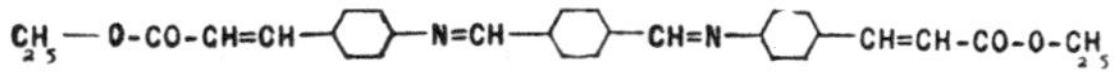

随温度变化相邻分子之间相互关系或多或少取决于分子的主要尺寸。如果我们只考虑很小的体积，那么将出现下列几种主要的情况（见图 4）：在 I 中分子完全是随意排列的，这就是普通的各向同性液体的情况。在 II 中所有分子的轴都是平行的，但是分子中心的无规则排布和自由移动情况与 I 中一样。这相当于**向列相**状态。在 III 中分子的轴也像在 II 中一样是平行的，但是分子中心失去了一个自由度，此时分子被约束于一组等间隔的平行平面内。这相当于典型的**近晶相**状态。在 V 中画出了与晶体对应的情况，分子是平行的，而它们的中心构成了一个规则的三维网络。（这里可能有两种情况：(a) 分子排布于平面内；(b) 分子彼此交错。第一类（近晶生成型晶体）倾向于产生近晶相，而第二类（向列生成型晶体）则倾向于产生向列相。）

X 射线对液晶的检测证明了上述解释在本质上是正确的，特别是赫尔曼和卡斯特在这方面所做的工作，他们发现近晶相给出了尖锐的布拉格反射，而向列相则只有液体的晕。

本次会议的议题之一是讨论是否存在更多的液晶状态。另一种液晶态很早以前就得到了承认，即典型的胆固醇酯，但实际上每当光学活性物质形成液晶时它就会出现，被称为**胆甾相**。夫里德耳认为它是**向列相**的一种变体，但它也具有**近晶相**的很多性质。它的特征是通过反射产生光谱色，特别是只反射右（或左）旋圆偏振光。夫里德耳认为这种现象源于来自间隔相等（间距在不同情况下为 1,000~10,000 Å）且分子呈螺旋排布的格朗让平面的布拉格反射。在一篇提交给会议的论文中，奥森试图通过严格运用电磁理论来证明后一种假设足以解释所有的现象，这样格朗让平面就只是一种光学幻觉。夫里德耳坚持认为除了向列相、近晶相和胆甾相之外不存在其他液晶相；然而，福伦德则一直宣称他制备出的物质在固液态之间具有不少于四种的中间态。最近，赫尔曼确认其中除了普通的近晶相之外，还存在着以有面微滴为特征的相，由它们产生的反射不同于由主要平面间隔所导致的反射，这说明分子在近晶相物质的每一层中都是规则排布的（见图 4 中的第 IV 种情况）。

has established that among them there exist, besides normal smectic states, some characterised by faceted drops, showing sharp reflections other than those due to the main plane spacing, and indicating regular arrangement of molecules in each layer of the smectic substance (case IV in Fig. 4).

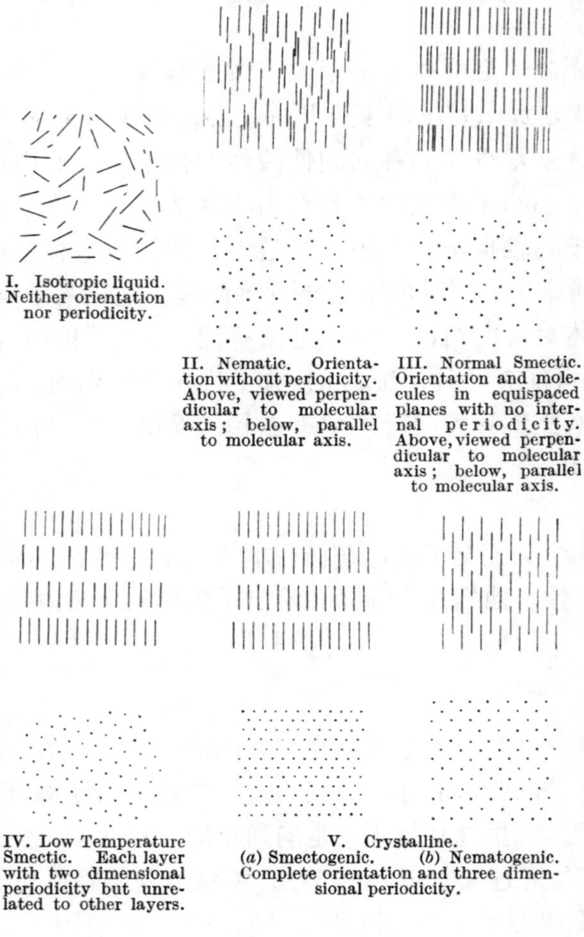

I. Isotropic liquid. Neither orientation nor periodicity.

II. Nematic. Orientation without periodicity. Above, viewed perpendicular to molecular axis; below, parallel to molecular axis.

III. Normal Smectic. Orientation and molecules in equispaced planes with no internal periodicity. Above, viewed perpendicular to molecular axis; below, parallel to molecular axis.

IV. Low Temperature Smectic. Each layer with two dimensional periodicity but unrelated to other layers.

V. Crystalline. (*a*) Smectogenic. (*b*) Nematogenic. Complete orientation and three dimensional periodicity.

Fig. 4

Such arrangement is geometrically possible; in fact, it is one of C. Hermann's theoretically derived eighteen intermediate forms between crystal and liquid, but whether it should be called "liquid crystal" may well be only a matter of convention, as it is difficult to draw the line sharply between a liquid with some regular arrangement of molecules and a crystal with some freedom of molecular movement.

The chief business of the Conference was not, however, the discussion of the intermolecular structure of liquid crystals, on which moderate agreement already exists, but the more intricate problem of explaining the texture of liquid crystals, particularly

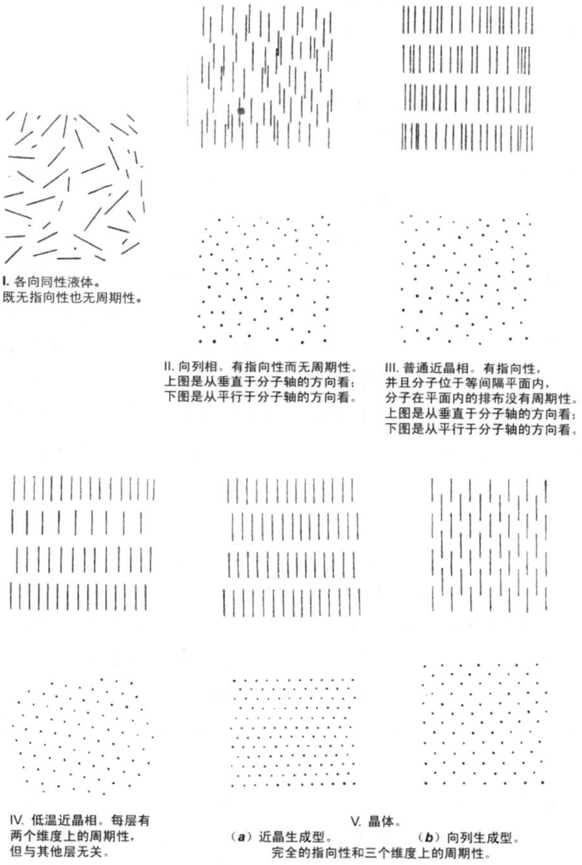
I. 各向同性液体。
既无指向性也无周期性。
II. 向列相。有指向性而无周期性。
上图是从垂直于分子轴的方向看；
下图是从平行于分子轴的方向看。
III. 普通近晶相。有指向性，
并且分子位于等间隔平面内，
分子在平面内的排布没有周期性。
上图是从垂直于分子轴的方向看；
下图是从平行于分子轴的方向看。
IV. 低温近晶相。每层有
两个维度上的周期性，
但与其他层无关。
V. 晶体。
（a）近晶生成型。
（b）向列生成型。
完全的指向性和三个维度上的周期性。

图 4

这种排布在几何学上是有可能的；实际上，它就是赫尔曼从理论上推导出来的 18 种晶体与液体之间的中间状态之一，但是否应称其为“液晶”可能只是习惯上的问题，因为在分子具有某种规则排布的液体与分子运动具有某种自由度的晶体之间很难划出一条清晰的界限。

不过，会议的主要任务并不是讨论液晶的分子间结构，关于这一点大家已经基本上达成了一致，而是讨论更为复杂的问题，即解释液晶的织构，特别是在有表面

under the action of surface forces and that of magnetic and electric fields. Two rival views were upheld with some vigour, with the aid of a wealth of experimental and theoretical material. The upholders of the "swarm" theory—Ornstein and Kast—consider that in nematic substances the strictly parallel arrangement of molecules only holds for groups of about $10^{15}$ molecules, which form independent swarms in the free interior of the liquid with their axes arranged at random, but can be oriented in parallel by surface or electromagnetic forces. Where such forces are not present, any considerable volume (greater than 0.001 cub. mm.) is considered on this theory to resemble a polycrystalline solid, and thus to appear translucent instead of transparent.

The other view, of which the chief protagonist was Zocher, recognises also the limited range of the parallelism of molecules due to their interaction, but considers that the molecular orientation varies continuously from point to point, due not to any intrinsic cause, but to convection currents and Brownian motion in the fluid. The two theories are formally analogous to the ideas of turbulence or stream line motion in hydrodynamics, or to those of mosaic structure or continual deformation in overstrained solids. These are certain ranges of experiment that seem to be more simply explained by one or the other theory. In particular, Kast's work on orientation of pazoxyanisol in alternating electric fields points to the existence of critical frequencies of $10^5$–$10^6$ per sec., above which parallel orientation of the molecules is impossible. This frequency is much too low for simple molecular movement which is usually of the order of $10^{10}$ per sec., and certainly suggests the existence of swarms.

As Foëx points out, there is an extremely close parallel between the phenomena of orientation in liquid crystals and those of magnetism, a nematic liquid corresponding to a ferromagnetic, and a normal liquid to a paramagnetic substance, with the transition point between the two corresponding to the Curie point. The basis for this comparison is plainly geometrical and not physical, and depends on the existence in both cases of blocks in parallel orientation, such as in magnetism give rise to a Barkhausen effect.

On the other hand, the deformation theory is more suited to account for the phenomena in the neighbourhood of surfaces. Liquid crystals in all their phases exhibit the range of influence of surface forces to a far greater extent than either true liquids or crystalline solids, a range of $10^{-2}$ instead of $10^{-6}$ cm. In general, there is a strong tendency to orientation of molecules parallel to the surface, or further, in the case of crystal or rubbed glass surfaces, to certain directions in it. The strength of this force can be measured by opposing to it magnetic or electric forces, as has been done particularly in the beautiful and ingenious experiments of Freedericksz and Zolina. The theoretical treatment of these cases by Zocher shows that they can be explained by continuous distortion up to a point beyond which the structure breaks down sharply as in an overloaded pillar. It became plain as the Conference progressed that the swarm and distortion theories were merely apparently antagonistic, and needed only an effort of synthesis to weld them into a more comprehensive theory.

张力和磁场、电场作用时的织构。在大量实验和理论材料的基础上，两种对立的观点都得到了有力的支持。奥恩斯坦和卡斯特是“攒动”理论的支持者，他们认为，在向列相物质中，分子的严格平行排布只适用于约含 $10^{15}$ 个分子的分子群，分子在液体内部的自由空间形成独立的大群，它们的轴是随意排列的，但在表面张力或电磁力的作用下可以变成平行排列。当这些作用力不存在时，该理论认为任何体积较大（大于 0.001 立方毫米）的向列相物质都类似于多晶固体，从而表现为半透明而不是透明。

另一种观点的主要倡导者是措赫尔，他也承认分子平行性的有限范围是由它们之间的相互作用造成的，但认为分子的定向是从点到点连续变化的，其原因并非来自于内部，而是由于流体内的对流和布朗运动。这两种理论在形式上类似于流体动力学中的湍流和流线运动，或者类似于应变过度固体中的镶嵌结构和连续变形。有些实验用这种理论解释更简单，而另一些实验则可能用那种理论解释更简单。特别值得一提的是卡斯特对对－氧化偶氮苯甲醚在交流电场中定向性的研究，他发现存在一个在 $10^5$~$10^6$ 每秒左右的临界频率，超过该频率后分子就不可能平行指向了。这一频率对于数量级通常为 $10^{10}$ 每秒的简单分子运动来说就太低了，因而说明大群是肯定存在的。

正如福埃所指出的那样，液晶中的定向现象与磁学中的取向极为相似，向列相液体对应于铁磁性物质，而普通液体则对应于顺磁性物质，两者之间的转变点为居里点。这一比较明显是基于几何曲线，与物理意义无关，并且在两种情况下都取决于平行指向时团块的存在，例如在磁现象中会引起巴尔克豪森效应。

另一方面，形变理论更适于解释液晶表面附近的现象。表面张力对各种相液晶的影响范围要比真正的液体或结晶态固体大很多，可以达到 $10^{-2}$ 厘米而不是 $10^{-6}$ 厘米。一般来说，分子的指向有着强烈的平行于表面的倾向，进而在晶体或磨砂玻璃的表面上，分子也有平行于其中某个特定方向的倾向。通过给它施加相反的磁力或电力可以测定这个力的强度，特别值得一提的是，弗雷德里克兹和佐里纳用精巧的实验已经测定了这个力的强度。措赫尔对此作出的理论解释是：当连续形变超过临界点时，其结构会像负载过度的支柱一样迅速倒塌。随着大会的不断进行，人们越来越清楚地认识到：大群理论和变形理论的对立仅仅是表面现象，只需要努力将它们融合成一种综合性更强的理论就可以了。

The nature of smectic structures was not discussed in any paper presented, but the Conference was delighted by the unexpected intervention of Sir William Bragg, who in a few words, explained the *raison d'être* of the focal conic structures which has so long remained a puzzle to students of liquid crystals. These structures consist in general of a pair of cones inclined to a common elliptical base, and having as a singular line a hyperbola in a plane at right angles to the ellipse, each conic having its focus at the vertex of the other (Figs. 2 and 5). Friedel had shown that the molecular axes lay on lines joining the ellipse to the hyperbola, and that the smectic planes lay in surfaces normal to these lines, the so-called cycloids of Dupin. Sir William now showed that this arrangement is a structure that combines minimum surface and minimum inclination of molecular axes, avoiding the great divergence that would occur at the centre of a simple sphere of radial molecules, by spreading it along the two singular lines of ellipse and hyperbola. Such structures will not, of course, fill space, but the interstices are filled with smaller and smaller focal conics, down to submicroscopic dimensions.

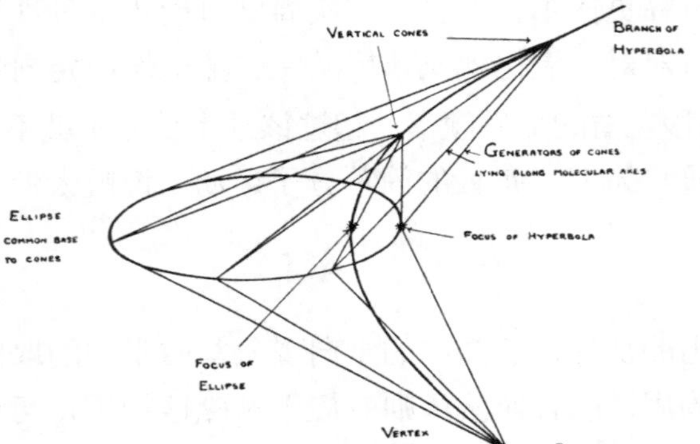


Fig. 5. Focal conic structure. The ellipse and hyperbola must be imagined in planes at right angles. Each cone has its vertex on the hyperbola and its base on the ellipse.

The behaviour of such smectic liquids in motion is naturally quite different from that of true liquids. It is misleading in this case to speak of a viscosity. As Lawrence has shown, the distribution of velocity follows a law much more complicated than that of Newton, in some cases even elastic forces coming into play. The practical values of such studies are obviously great, as many lubricants approximate to liquid crystal conditions.

It remains to point out the widespread importance of liquid crystals in Nature. This was considered in a paper by Prof. Rinne, whose recent lamented death overclouded the proceedings at the beginning of the Conference. The liquid crystals mostly studied are provided by melts of pure substances: far more, however, are to be found in two-component systems, where greater or less concentration in a solvent is equivalent to a rise in temperature. Such liquid crystals show all the phenomena observed in melts, besides

在会议的所有论文中，没有一篇讲到了近晶相结构的性质，但威廉·布拉格爵士出人意料的发言为大会带来了惊喜，他用寥寥数语解释了焦锥结构态存在的理由，而这个问题长期以来一直困扰着研究液晶的学者。该结构一般是由一对倾斜于一个共用椭圆底面的锥体组成的，并在垂直于椭圆所在平面内有一条双曲线，它作为唯一的一条线使其中每条圆锥二次曲线的焦点都落在另一条的顶点上（见图 2 和 5)。夫里德耳曾指出，分子的轴位于连接椭圆和双曲线的直线上，而近晶相平面则处于垂直于这些直线的表面之中，这些直线也就是我们所说的迪潘摆线。现在，威廉爵士指出这种排布构成了一种具有最小表面积和最小分子轴倾斜度的结构，通过将其沿椭圆和双曲线的两条奇线展开而避免了在简单放射状分子球体中心处可能发生的巨大发散现象。当然，这种结构不会充满空间，但是其间隙为逐级减少的焦点圆锥所填充，直至达到亚显微尺度。

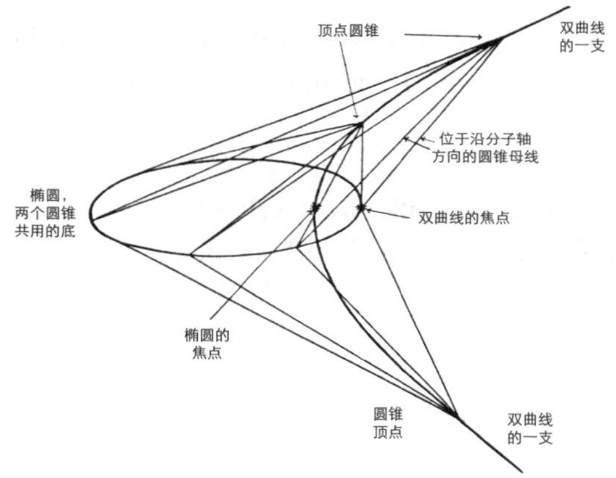


图 5. 焦锥结构态。必须想象椭圆和双曲线位于彼此成直角的平面中。每个锥体的顶点都在双曲线上，而它们的底面在椭圆上。

这种运动中的近晶相液体的行为自然与真正液体的行为颇为不同。在这种情况下谈及黏度会令人误解。正如劳伦斯所指出的那样，其速度分布遵循的规律要比牛顿定律复杂得多，在某些情况下甚至需要考虑弹性力的影响。这些研究的实际价值非常大，因为有很多润滑剂都近似处于液晶状态。

我们仍需指出液晶在自然界中是普遍存在的。林内教授在一篇论文中谈到了这一点，他于不久前去世的消息在会议一开始就给大会笼罩上了悲伤的气氛。人们用于研究的液晶大部分是通过纯净物质的熔融来制备的：然而，在双组分体系中发现的液晶要比在单组分中多得多，在双组分的情况下，溶剂中溶质浓度的增大或减小等价于温度的升高。除了其他一些与分散特性有关的现象以外，这些液晶还可以表

others due to their disperse nature, and are widespread, indeed universally found in biological structures.

Most of the protein, fat and myelinic substance of living bodies exists in liquid crystals, but this is only directly visible as such when all the molecules are oriented in definite directions, as in spermatozoa, muscles, nerves and their myelinic sheaths. Indeed the liquid crystal state seems the most suited to biological functions, as it combines the fluidity and diffusibility of the liquid while preserving the possibility of internal structure of crystalline solids.

The spontaneous structures—threads, cones, etc.—of liquid crystals have dimensions intermediate between those of molecules and those of living cells, so that we may say that the liquid crystal has as much right as the colloid to be considered the basis of vital activity.

The existence of this virtually new state of matter will have to be taken into account in any modern comprehensive picture of the material world, whether physical, chemical or biological.

The Faraday Society Conference will have well fulfilled its purpose if it succeeds in provoking further research in the field of liquid crystals.

(**132**, 86-89; 1933)

现出人们在熔融体中观察到的所有现象，而且双组分体系中的液晶分布广泛，普遍存在于各种生物结构中。

生物体中大多数蛋白质、脂肪和髓鞘物质都以液晶形式存在，但是只有当所有分子都定向于确定的方向时才能直接看到这一点，如在精子、肌肉、神经和神经髓鞘中的情况。实际上，液晶态似乎最适合于生物体的功能，因为它不但兼有液体的流动性和扩散性，同时还可能保留结晶态固体的内部结构。

液晶的自发性结构，如细丝和锥体等具有的尺寸介于分子和活细胞之间，因此我们可以说，液晶与胶体一样都可以被看作是生命活动的基础。

现在，任何关于物质世界的综合性图像，无论是物理学的、化学的还是生物学的，都必须考虑到这种并不新的“新”物态的存在。

如果法拉第学会举办的这次会议能成功地推进人们对液晶领域的深入研究，那么它的目标就圆满地达到了。

（王耀杨 翻译；赵见高 审稿）

# Magnetic Moment of the Proton

I. Estermann *et al.*

## Editor's Note

**Paul Dirac's theory of the electron predicted that it has a quantum-mechanical spin of 1/2 and a magnetic moment equal to 1 Bohr magneton. As the theory would seem to apply to any elementary particle of spin 1/2, physicists in the early 1930s expected the proton to behave similarly, having a magnetic moment smaller by the inverse ratio of their masses (1/1,840). But here Immanuel Estermann and colleagues announce a very surprising result: the magnetic moment of the proton is around 2.5 times larger than that. The result indicated that Dirac's theory failed in some important respects for the proton, and supplied the first experimental evidence that nuclear particles (nucleons) have internal structure.**

THE spin of the electron has the value $\frac{1}{2}\cdot\frac{h}{2\pi}$, and its magnetic moment has the value $2\frac{e}{m_e c}\cdot\frac{1}{2}\cdot\frac{h}{2\pi}$, or 1 Bohr magneton. The spin of the proton has the same value, $\frac{1}{2}\cdot\frac{h}{2\pi}$, as that of the electron. Thus for the magnetic moment of the proton the value $2\frac{e}{m_p c}\cdot\frac{1}{2}\cdot\frac{h}{2\pi} = 1/1{,}840$ Bohr magneton $=$ 1 nuclear magneton is to be expected.

So far as we know, the only method at present available for the determination of this moment is the deflection of a beam of hydrogen molecules in an inhomogeneous magnetic field (Stern-Gerlach experiment). In the hydrogen molecule, the spins of the two electrons are anti-parallel and cancel out. Thus the magnetic moment of the molecule has two sources: (1) the rotation of the molecule as a whole, which is equivalent to the rotation of charged particles, and leads therefore to a magnetic moment as arising from a circular current; and (2) the magnetic moments of the two protons.

In the case of para-hydrogen, the spins of the two protons are anti-parallel, their magnetic moments cancel out, and only the rotational moment remains. At low temperatures (liquid air temperature), practically all the molecules are in the rotational quantum state 0 and therefore non-magnetic. This has been proved by experiment. At higher temperatures (for example, room temperature) a certain proportion of the molecules, which may be calculated from Boltzmann's law, are in higher rotational quantum states, mainly in the state 2. The deflection experiments with para-hydrogen at room temperature allow, therefore, the determination of the rotational moment, which has been found to be between 0.8 and 0.9 nuclear magnetons per unit quantum number.

# 质子的磁矩

伊曼纽尔·埃斯特曼等

## 编者按

保罗·狄拉克的电子理论预言：电子的自旋量子数为1/2，磁矩为1玻尔磁子。因为该理论似乎适用于所有自旋量子数为1/2的基本粒子，所以20世纪30年代早期的物理学家们认为质子也有类似的特征，它的磁矩大小与其质量成反比，是电子磁矩的1/1,840。但是，伊曼纽尔·埃斯特曼及其同事在这篇文章中报告了一个非常令人惊奇的结果：质子的磁矩大约是这一预计值的2.5倍。这一结果说明狄拉克的理论无法解释质子的一些重要特征，而且这也是证明核粒子（核子）具有内部结构的第一例实验证据。

电子自旋角动量为$\frac{1}{2}\cdot\frac{h}{2\pi}$，它的磁矩为$2\frac{e}{m_e c}\cdot\frac{1}{2}\cdot\frac{h}{2\pi}$，或者1玻尔磁子。质子的自旋角动量和电子具有相同的值$\frac{1}{2}\cdot\frac{h}{2\pi}$。由此，我们猜想质子磁矩为$2\frac{e}{m_p c}\cdot\frac{1}{2}\cdot\frac{h}{2\pi}$ =1/1,840玻尔磁子 =1核磁子。

据我们所知，目前能够确定这一磁矩的唯一有效方法就是氢分子束在非均匀磁场中偏转的实验（斯特恩–盖拉赫实验）。在氢分子中，两个电子的自旋是反平行的，所以互相抵消了。这样，分子磁矩就有两种来源：(1) 分子作为一个整体的旋转，这等价于带电粒子的旋转，因此可以产生由环形电流引发的磁矩；(2) 两个质子的磁矩。

在仲氢分子中，两个质子的自旋是反平行的，因此它们的磁矩相互抵消，只有转动力矩存在。在低温下（液化空气温度），几乎所有的分子都处于转动量子态为0的状态，所以是非磁性的。这一点已经被实验所证实。在较高的温度下（例如室温），可以用玻尔兹曼定律算出有一定比例的分子处于更高的转动量子态上，以2态为主。因此，室温下仲氢分子的偏转实验可以用来确定其转动力矩，我们已经得到的转动力矩为每单位量子数0.8到0.9核磁子之间。

In the case of ortho-hydrogen, the lowest rotational quantum state possible is the state 1. Therefore, even at the lowest temperatures, the rotational magnetic moment is superimposed on that due to the two protons with parallel spin. Since, however, the rotational moment is known from the experiments with pure para-hydrogen, the moment of the protons can be determined from deflection experiments with ortho-hydrogen, or with ordinary hydrogen consisting of 75 percent ortho- and 25 percent para-hydrogen. The value obtained is 5 nuclear magnetons for the two protons in the ortho-hydrogen molecule, that is, 2.5 (and not 1) nuclear magnetons for the proton.

This is a very striking result, but further experiments carried out with increased accuracy and over a wide range of experimental conditions (such as temperature, width of beam, etc.) have shown that it is correct within a limit of less than 10 percent.

A more detailed account of these experiments will appear in the *Zeitschrift für Physik*.

(**132**, 169-170; 1933)

I. Estermann, R. Frisch, O. Stern: Institut für physikalische Chemie, Hamburgischer Universität, June 19.

在正氢中，可能存在的最低转动量子态是 1 态。因此，即便是在最低的温度下，由于两个质子的自旋平行，转动磁矩也会叠加。然而，因为转动力矩已经由纯仲氢的实验测得，所以质子的磁矩可以从正氢或者从含 75% 正氢和 25% 仲氢的普通氢的偏转实验中得到。结果是，正氢分子中两个质子的磁矩是 5 核磁子，也就是说，质子的磁矩是 2.5（而不是 1）核磁子。

这是一个非常惊人的结果，但我们在后来的实验中提高了精度，并尝试了各种不同的条件（例如，不同温度，不同分子束宽度等），实验仍表明，这个结果的误差小于 10%。

我们将在《物理杂志》上发表有关这个实验的更多细节。

（王静 翻译；赵见高 审稿）

# Interaction between Cosmic Rays and Matter

B. Rossi

## Editor's Note

**Italian physicist Bruno Rossi had recently shown that cosmic rays passing through matter often generate secondary particles. He had developed a sensitive technique to investigate the secondary "particle showers" by detecting the near-simultaneous passage of particles at three different detectors. Here he reports that showers seems to be more abundant in materials of higher atomic number, and that the particles penetrate lead for shorter distances than primary cosmic rays. Rossi's technique spurred the further development of "coincidence-detection" devices for high-energy and nuclear physics. Rossi himself later showed that cosmic rays near the Earth's surface have two components. The first component was ultimately identified as electrons and photons, the second with a new type of particle called the muon.**

LAST year I showed by means of a coincidence method that a secondary corpuscular radiation is generated when cosmic rays pass through matter[1]. From the beautiful experiments of Blackett and Occhialini we know now that these secondary particles are produced in so-called "showers". This can also be shown by the method of coincidences; moreover, if a coincidence is observed between counters arranged in a triangle, we may conclude with a high degree of certainty that we have to do with a shower originating from a point in the neighbourhood of the counters[2]. The method of triple coincidences therefore offers a very useful means for investigating the frequency of occurrence of the showers.

Up to the present, the following results have been obtained:

(1) The showers occur more frequently in elements of high atomic number; the ratio of the numbers of coincidences caused by thin layers of lead, iron, aluminium of the same weight per cm.$^2$ is 4:2:1 approximately[3].

(2) The number of showers emerging from a layer of lead, as a function of the thickness of this layer, increases at first, reaches a maximum at a thickness of about 20 gm./cm.$^2$ and then decreases very rapidly; at 100 gm./cm.$^2$, for example, the frequency of the coincidences is less than one half of the maximum value. We conclude that the radiation which causes the showers has a mean range of a few centimetres in lead. It follows that this radiation cannot be identical with the primary cosmic rays.

(3) When the thickness of the layer is further increased, the frequency of the emerging showers decreases very slowly. The most probable hypothesis to explain this seems to be

# 宇宙射线与物质之间的相互作用

布鲁诺·罗西

编者按

意大利物理学家布鲁诺·罗西前不久指出，宇宙射线在穿过物质时经常会产生次级粒子。他还发展了一种很灵敏的技术，通过探测三个不同的探测器上几乎同时达到的粒子流来研究这些次级“粒子簇射”。在这篇文章中他指出，在较高原子数元素的物质中，簇射会更多，并且与初级宇宙射线相比，次级粒子在铅中的穿透距离更短。罗西的技术促进了高能物理和核物理学中所使用的“符合探测”装置的进一步发展。罗西本人后来发现，地球表面附近的宇宙射线中存在两种组分，其中一种组分最终被确定是电子和光子，而另一种组分中包含一种被称为 μ 介子的新型粒子。

去年，我用符合法证明了当宇宙射线穿过物质时会产生次级微粒辐射[1]。现在，我们根据布莱克特和奥基亚利尼的精巧实验得知这些次级粒子是在所谓的“簇射”中产生的。这一点也可以用符合法来证明；此外，如果我们看到排列成三角形的计数器同时触发信号，那么就可以非常确定地得出以下结论：这种符合一定与这些计数器附近某一点上产生的簇射有关[2]。因此，三重符合法对于研究簇射出现的频率是非常有效的。

到目前为止，我们已经得到了以下这些结论：

（1）簇射在高原子数元素的物质中出现得更频繁；由每平方厘米重量相同的铅、铁、铝薄层引发的符合次数比率大约为 4:2:1[3]。

（2）铅层中产生的簇射数是该层厚度的函数，随着厚度的增加，簇射数一开始增加，在厚度约为 20 克 / 平方厘米时达到最大值，然后迅速减少；例如，当厚度为 100 克 / 平方厘米时，符合出现的频率不到最大值的一半。我们的结论是：引发簇射的辐射在铅中的平均射程为几个厘米。由此可以肯定这种辐射不同于初级宇宙射线。

（3）当薄层的厚度继续增加时，簇射出现的频率减小得非常慢。对这一现象最有可能的解释是假设引起簇射的射线是在层中进一步产生的；因而这些射线被认为

to assume that a further production of the rays which cause the showers takes place in the layer; these rays are therefore to be regarded as a secondary radiation of the primary cosmic rays, the equilibrium value of which is roughly three to four times greater in air than in lead.

(4) The shower-producing rays are more readily absorbed by elements of higher atomic number. When 24.5 gm./cm.[2] of lead is placed over the counters, 70±3 coincidences per hour are observed; this number was reduced to 36.7±1.4 by a further sheet of lead of 39 gm./cm.[2] on top of the first one but only to 52.3±1.7 by a sheet of aluminium of the same weight per cm.[2] and in the same position. From this and from (1) we conclude that the absorption of these secondary rays by an element and the number of showers which they produce depend in the same way on the atomic number. Thus it seems that the production of showers must be the main reason for their absorption. This is in agreement with the consideration that these rays should have an energy of at least some milliards of electron-volts, which could not be absorbed by a few centimetres of lead in the ordinary way.

(5) That the equilibrium value of the secondary radiation is lower in elements of high atomic number may be explained by their greater absorption, if we assume that the rate of production is roughly the same in all elements; which seems plausible from the experiments on the absorption of the primary rays.

(**132**, 173-174; 1933)

Bruno Rossi: Physical Institute, University of Padova, Italy, July 3.

---

References:

1 Rossi, B., *Phys. Z.*, **33**, 304 (1932).

2 Rossi, B., *Atti. R. Acad. Naz. Lincei* (in the press).

3 Rossi, B., *Z. Phys.*, **82**, 151 (1933).

是初级宇宙射线的次级辐射，它们在空气中的平衡常数是在铅中的 3~4 倍左右。

（4）产生簇射的射线更容易被较高原子数的元素所吸收。当把 24.5 克 / 平方厘米的铅置于计数器上时，每小时可以观察到 $70 \pm 3$ 次符合；如果在原有铅层上再放置一层 39 克 / 平方厘米的铅，这个值就会减小到 $36.7 \pm 1.4$，但当在同一位置放置每平方厘米重量相同的铝层时，这个值只减小到了 $52.3 \pm 1.7$。根据这一现象和（1），我们可以得出这样的结论：元素对次级射线的吸收以及次级射线产生的簇射数以同样的方式取决于原子数的大小。由此看来簇射的产生一定是射线吸收的主要原因。这与认为这些射线至少具有数十亿电子伏特的能量，在通常情况下不可能被几厘米厚的铅层吸收的论点是一致的。

（5）如果我们假设簇射在所有元素中的产生率大致相同，那么就可以把原子数高的元素次级辐射平衡常数较小的原因归于原子数高的元素具有较强的吸收；从初级射线吸收实验的结果来看，这样的解释看上去是合理的。

（王静 翻译；刘纯 审稿）

# The Genetics of Cancer*

J. B. S. Haldane

## Editor's Note

**Cancer is a genetic disease, resulting from mutations that cause a cell to become malignant. An individual's risk of developing cancer also has a strong genetic element, sometimes due to a pathogenic version of a single gene, or, more commonly, to the cumulative effect of many genes, which together influence the body's response to environmental carcinogens and ageing. In this paper the geneticist and evolutionary biologist J.B.S Haldane discusses all these factors. He concludes that "our knowledge is not sufficient to warrant interference with human breeding". This referred to the notion of using eugenics to control the incidence of "bad genes"; but the ability to genetically screen embryos is now forcing the question of other forms of intervention.**

THE statement is occasionally made, and as frequently denied, that cancer is hereditary. It is, of course, clear that environmental influences can play a leading part in determining the production of cancer.

The question is whether nature, as well as nurture, is of importance. By far the most satisfactory evidence on this point comes from a study of genetically homogeneous populations of mice. By brother-sister mating for many generations (more than fifty in certain cases) pure lines can be built up in which the individuals are all homozygous for the same genes, apart from rare cases of mutation. By crossing two pure lines we obtain a population which is also genetically uniform, but not homozygous. Their progeny, however, is not genetically uniform.

In such a population, we can study three types of cancer:

(1) due to transplantation of a tumour from another animal.

(2) due to a carcinogenic agent. These include tar, the hydrocarbons shown to be carcinogenic by Kennaway and his colleagues, certain parasitic worms, and X-rays.

(3) spontaneous tumours; that is, tumours arising for no, at present, assignable cause.

Now the order of ease of study is the above. An inoculated tumour can be judged as a "take" or otherwise within a month. Tar painting may produce tumours within six months; but spontaneous tumours in many lines do not reach their maximum incidence until an age of eighteen or more months. Hence our knowledge of tumour etiology is in the above order,

* Substance of lectures delivered at the Royal Institution on February 2 and 9, 1933.

# 肿瘤遗传学*

约翰·伯登·桑德森·霍尔丹

## 编者按

癌症是一种遗传性疾病，是由细胞内基因的恶性突变造成的。遗传因素使一个人患癌症的危险大大增加；有时由于单个基因的突变，但更常见的是多个基因的累积突变影响了人体对环境中致癌物质和机体老化的反应。遗传学家和进化生物学家霍尔丹在这篇文章中讨论了所有的影响因素。他总结道："我们所掌握的知识尚不足以使我们敢于干预人类生育。"这一说法涉及利用优生学控制"不良基因"；但现有的大规模测试胚胎基因的能力正促使人们提出其他形式的干预手段相配合。

少数人认为癌症具有遗传性，而这一说法常常受到质疑。因为很明显环境因素在癌症发生中可以起到主导作用。

问题是，先天因素和后天因素是否同样重要。目前回答这个问题最令人满意的证据来源于对基因同源性小鼠群的研究。通过多代（在某些情况下要超过 50 代）的兄妹交配，能够建立起一个纯系种群，除了偶发的几个突变外，所有个体都是基因相同的纯合子。再将两个纯系种群进行杂交，我们可以得到一个基因完全一致的杂合子鼠群。而它们的后代，基因就不再完全一样了。

在这样一个种群中，我们能研究三种类型的肿瘤：

(1) 从另外一个动物中移植过来的肿瘤。

(2) 由致癌剂诱发的肿瘤。这些致癌剂包括焦油、由肯纳韦和同事发现的具有致癌性的烃类化合物、某些寄生虫和 X 射线。

(3) 自发性肿瘤。即根据目前所知，诱因不明的肿瘤。

上面的顺序也反映了研究工作的难易程度。用一个月时间就可以判断接种过去的肿瘤能否"生长"。涂抹焦油在 6 个月内可以诱发肿瘤。而在许多品系的小鼠中，自发性肿瘤的发生率到第 18 个月或者更晚才会最高。所以我们对于肿瘤病因学的知识是通过以上顺序的研究获得的，但在临床实践中，就这些知识的重要程度来说，

* 本文取自 1933 年 2 月 2 日和 9 日作者在英国皇家研究院所作的报告。

though the order of practical importance for medicine is clearly the reverse.

It may be said at once that there are enormous differences between different lines as regards all three types of cancer. The genetics of reaction to transplantable tumours have been very fully worked out by Little and his colleagues. The laws disclosed are precisely similar to those which govern the transplantation of normal tissue or the transfusion of blood or of leukaemic corpuscles. A tumour arising spontaneously in one member of a pure line can be transplanted into all other members of it (actually more than 99 percent of successful "takes" can be achieved). Further, it can be transplanted into every $F_1$ mouse one of whose parents belonged to the pure line, but if these are mated together or outcrossed, only a minority of their offspring are susceptible. This at once suggests that susceptibility is due to the possession of certain dominant genes. This theory is fully confirmed by experiment. Supposing that a line $X$ carries $n$ pairs of genes *AABBCC* . . . . which are needed for tumour growth, and are not found in a line $Y$, then the $F_1$ will be *AaBbCc* . . . . , and 100 percent susceptible. Of the back-cross from mating of the $F_1$ with $Y$, only $\left(\frac{1}{2}\right)^n$ will carry all $n$ genes, and of the $F_2$, $\left(\frac{3}{4}\right)^n$ will carry them, and thus be susceptible. In a number of cases, Cloudman[1] found that the two values of $n$ so calculated were in agreement. The number of genes ranged from 2 to about 12.

Similarly, a tumour arising spontaneously in a $F_1$ individual, between two pure lines, in general requires in its host $m$ genes contributed by one parent, and $n$ contributed by the other. In such cases the tumour will grow in all the $F_1$, in $\left(\frac{1}{2}\right)^m$ of one back-cross, $\left(\frac{1}{2}\right)^n$ of the other, and $\left(\frac{3}{4}\right)^{m+n}$ of the $F_2$ . Thus Bittner[2] found in one case $m=4$, $n=1$, while the observed value of $m+n$ was 5.

Occasionally a tumour in the course of transplantation changes its character, so that it becomes transplantable into a larger proportion of a mixed population ($F_2$ or back-cross). It is then found that one or more genes less are required for susceptibility in the host.

These facts can be explained if the host only reacts to a transplanted tumour so as to destroy it as the result of foreign antigens in that tumour, just as a recipient agglutinates the corpuscles of a donor if they carry foreign isoagglutinogens. On this hypothesis each gene is responsible for the manufacture of a particular antigen, as in the case of the red corpuscles. However, the genetical facts are quite independent of this hypothesis.

A thorough study of these phenomena is under way in Little's laboratory. The genes required for susceptibility to different tumours are being compared. Thus it was found that a number of tumours arising in the same line required the same basic gene for susceptibility, but each demanded a different assortment of extra genes. Some of these genes have been located, by means of linkage studies, in the same chromosomes as genes responsible for colour differences.

顺序显然是相反的。

需要立即指出的是在不同的品系中，这三种类型的肿瘤有很大的不同。利特尔和他的同事，已经把机体对移植肿瘤反应的遗传学机制进行了透彻的研究。他们发现调控移植肿瘤和调控那些正常组织移植、输血和输白血病细胞的机制非常相似。纯系种群中一个个体上自发发生的肿瘤能够被移植到该系所有的其他个体身上（实际上成功“接受率”能够超过99%）。此外，该肿瘤还能够被移植到任何一个 $F_1$ 代小鼠身上，这些小鼠的亲本之一必须为上述纯系种群的成员。但是如果这些 $F_1$ 代小鼠相互交配或者与品系之外的小鼠交配，它们的后代只有一小部分能够接受这些移植的肿瘤。这就暗示移植肿瘤的接受程度由是否拥有特定的显性基因所决定。这个理论完全被实验所证实了。假设一个品系 $X$ 带有 $n$ 对肿瘤生长所必需的基因 $AABBCC$ ……，而在品系 $Y$ 中没有这些基因，那么 $F_1$ 的基因型将是 $AaBbCc$ ……，它们将100%能接受移植肿瘤。如果将 $F_1$ 和 $Y$ 进行回交，那么只有$\left(\frac{1}{2}\right)^n$的个体会携带所有 $n$ 个肿瘤生长所必需的基因，而对 $F_2$ 来说，$\left(\frac{3}{4}\right)^n$的个体会携带这些基因，因而能够接受移植的肿瘤。在多次试验中，克劳德曼[1]发现如此计算出来的两个 $n$ 值是相同的，这些基因数在2到12之间波动。

与此类似，两个纯品系杂交后的 $F_1$ 代个体要产生自发性肿瘤，总体来说，需要其亲本一方提供 $m$ 个基因，另一方提供 $n$ 个基因。这种情况下，这个肿瘤可以在所有 $F_1$ 代个体、$\left(\frac{1}{2}\right)^m$的 $F_1$ 与带 $m$ 个基因的亲本一方的回交后代、$\left(\frac{1}{2}\right)^n$的 $F_1$ 与带 $n$ 个基因的亲本一方的回交后代和$\left(\frac{3}{4}\right)^{m+n}$个 $F_2$ 代个体中生长。这样，比特纳[2]发现在这个试验中 $m$=4，$n$=1，而观察到的 $m$+$n$ 值正好是5。

偶尔的情况下，肿瘤在移植过程中发生了性质的改变，以至于该肿瘤能被移植到一个混合种群（$F_2$ 或者回交种群）的更多个体中去。人们这时发现，肿瘤移植时宿主基因的要求会少一个或者多个。

这些现象可以这样解释，宿主只有在识别移植肿瘤中的外源性抗原后，才产生对移植肿瘤的排斥，正像如果供体的血细胞含有外源的同种凝集原，受体就会产生抗供体的凝集反应。根据这个假说可知，如同在红细胞中一样，每个基因负责编码一种特定的抗原。但是，遗传学的实际情况与这一假说并不相符。

在利特尔的实验室，一项针对这个现象的深入研究正在进行。实验室的工作人员正在对照不同肿瘤易感性所需的决定基因。他们发现对于在同一品系发生的多种类型的肿瘤，其易感性都需要相同的基本基因。但是每一种肿瘤的生长又需要不同种类的额外基因。通过连锁研究的分析方法，他们发现其中一些基因与决定肤色差异的基因定位于同一条染色体上。

The tendency to develop cancer as the result of tarring varies greatly in different lines. Thus Lynch[3] compared two lines *A* and *B* which differed in their spontaneous tumour rates, *A* having a higher incidence of spontaneous lung cancer than *B*. These tumours, however, never appeared before the age of 15 months. By tarring a large area of skin between the ages of 2 and 6 months, she induced lung tumours before the age of 13 months in 85 percent of line *A*, and 22 percent of line *B*. The difference was 6.3 times its standard error. On crossing *A* and *B* she found 79 percent susceptibility. The back-cross to *A* gave 81 percent susceptibility, while that to *B* gave 39 percent. These figures suggest that susceptibility is determined, among other things, by a number of dominant genes. Other workers have obtained essentially similar results. Their importance for non-genetical workers on cancer is considerable. It is clear that in comparing the efficacy of two different carcinogenic agents, far fewer mice need be used in a pure line than in a mixed population, and it is worth nothing that the variance in a mixed population is only about halved when litter mates instead of individuals taken at random are used as controls.

In the same way, Curtis, Dunning and Bullock[4] state that in the rat they have found that susceptibility to cancer, on infection with the cestode *Cysticercus*, is strongly inherited.

The problem of spontaneous cancer presents much greater difficulties. In no line can one obtain 100 percent of deaths from cancer, because over the long period necessary, deaths from other causes cannot be prevented. But some idea of the conditions in a highly cancerous line can be obtained from the work of Murray[5] . In a particular inbred line, 1,938 females lived to be more than 7 months of age. Of these, 65 percent died of mammary carcinoma, or were killed when severely affected with it. Above 80 percent of deaths in females more than twelve months old were due to this cause. None survived for 23 months and probably none would have reached two years without cancer had all deaths from other causes been prevented.

In such a line we can observe the effects on spontaneous cancer of prophylactic measures. Thus of 198 females ovariotomised at 7 months, only 40 percent died of mammary cancer, and one of these reached the age of 30 months. Still more striking is the fact that not a single operated female living beyond 22 months developed mammary cancer. It follows that in this stock the ovary plays an important part in the causation of mammary carcinoma. It is clear that a pure line (or the $F_1$ hybrids of two pure lines) furnish ideal material for the determination of factors in the environment favourable or otherwise to the development of cancer.

In contrast with such lines are others with an extremely low susceptibility to spontaneous tumours under ordinary laboratory conditions. A cross between such lines generally gives a hybrid generation with a cancer mortality nearly so high as that of the more susceptible line. Indications of linkage with colour genes have been obtained in one case.

It is important that the location of tumours is highly specific. One line has a high

焦油诱发性肿瘤发生的倾向，在不同品系中有很大的差异。因此林奇[3]对比了$A$和$B$这两个不同品系诱发性肿瘤发生的情况：它们自发性肿瘤的发生率不同，$A$自发性肺癌发生率要高于$B$。然而，这两个品系中的自发性肿瘤都是在小鼠15月龄后才出现。在2到6月龄小鼠的皮肤上大片涂抹焦油，到小鼠13月龄时$A$品系85%的个体中诱导出了肺癌，而$B$品系只有22%。差异是标准差的6.3倍。在$A$和$B$的杂交后代中，发现79%的个体有肿瘤易感性。子代与$A$回交的群体中，81%有易感性，而与$B$回交则只有39%。这些数据表明肿瘤易感性除了受其他因素影响之外，也受大量显性基因的影响。其他研究者也得到了基本类似的结果。对于那些不从事基因学的肿瘤工作者来说，他们的结论具有十分重大的意义。如果对比两种不同致癌物质的致癌效果，很明显，所需要的纯系小鼠比混合种群小鼠要少得多。当我们选择同窝出生的混合种群个体代替随机个体作为对照时，得到的数据应小心对待，变化仅为一半时，其意义可能并不大。

用同样的方法，柯蒂斯、邓宁和布洛克[4]宣称已经发现大鼠在感染囊尾蚴后可以诱发肿瘤，而肿瘤易感性在很大程度上是遗传因素决定的。

自发性肿瘤的研究面临更大的困难。没有一个品系会因癌症而100%死亡，因为在肿瘤发生的漫长过程中，其他原因导致的死亡是不可避免的。但是，默里[5]的工作提到了利用高致癌品系小鼠解决这个问题的观点。在一个特别近亲繁殖的品系中，1,938只雌鼠的生存时间超过了7个月。其中65%死于乳腺癌，或者由于乳腺癌严重影响生活而被杀掉。在生存超过12个月的雌鼠中，有80%以上死于乳腺癌。没有一只生存时间超过23个月。即使避免其他死因，这些小鼠也不可能无癌生存到2年。

在这个品系中，我们可以观察避孕措施对自发性肿瘤的作用。在长到7月龄时被切除卵巢的198只雌鼠中，只有40%死于乳腺癌，而且其中一只生存到了30月龄。更令人瞩目的是没有一只被切除卵巢的小鼠在生存超过22月龄时发生乳腺癌。这证明卵巢在该品系小鼠乳腺癌的发病中起重要作用。很明显，纯系动物（或者是两个纯系的$F_1$杂交后代）为确定环境中的各种因素是否有利于肿瘤的发生提供了理想的材料。

相对于这些易感品系来说，在正常实验室条件下，其他品系的动物对自发性肿瘤的易感性极低。但是这些品系之间的杂交后代常常具有与易感品系的后代同样高的肿瘤死亡率。在这项研究中，人们发现肿瘤基因可能与肤色基因有关。

肿瘤发生的部位具有高度的特异性，这一点非常重要。其中一个品系只是在雌

deathrate from mammary carcinoma in females only, and few tumours elsewhere. Another line has a heavy incidence of primary lung carcinomata in both sexes, and little mammary carcinoma. A third has few carcinomata of any kind, but sarcoma is not very rare. The genetics of spontaneous cancer will clearly be very complicated, and it is quite ludicrous to ascribe it to the activity of one gene, dominant or recessive.

Besides the work described above, a good deal has been done on stock which was not genetically homogeneous. From this work it is clear that, while a tendency to spontaneous cancer is hereditary, it is not due to a single gene, dominant or recessive, and also that a particular localisation of cancer may be hereditary. Thus Zavadskaia[6] found 13 out of 45 tumours in the occipital region in one particular line, and only 1 out of 212 in other lines. But all work with genetically heterogeneous material is unsatisfactory, because any individual may die before reaching the cancer age, and no other individual will be of just the same genetical make-up. Hence really exact work is impossible.

In the same way, human cancer tends to "run in families" to some extent, but precise analysis is only possible where, as with retinoblastoma and some sarcomata, its victims are attacked early in life. Here there is reason to believe that a single dominant gene is mainly responsible for the cancerous diathesis, though environmental and possibly other genetic factors may be concerned as well.

A particularly clear case of the interaction of nature and nurture in cancer production is found in the case of human xeroderma pigmentosum, almost certainly a recessive character. Here the skin becomes inflamed, and ultimately cancerous, under the influence of light. We could speak with equal logical propriety of the recessive gene or the light as the "cause" of the cancer, but as the former is rare, and the latter universal, it is more natural to regard the cancer as genetically determined.

Thus we have evidence of many different types of genetical predisposition to cancer, and although the data available on mice suggest that this predisposition is generally due to multiple dominant genes, it would certainly be incorrect to apply this theory to all human types of malignant disease.

The theory has been held by Boveri, Strong, and others, that the difference between a cancer and a normal cell is of the same character as that between the cells of two different varieties, that is to say, due to chromosomal aberration or gene mutation. This theory cannot of course be proved or disproved by genetical methods, as cancer cells do not reproduce sexually, and it is only by sexual reproduction that the geneticist can distinguish nuclear changes from plasmatic changes or virus infections.

The geneticist is concerned with the differences of "nature" (in Galton's sense of the word) which play their part, along with environmental differences, in determining whether a given animal will or will not develop cancer. He is not particularly qualified to determine whether the difference between a normal cell and a cancer cell is analogous to that

性动物中有很高的乳腺癌死亡率，而其他肿瘤则很少。另一个品系的动物无论雌雄均有很高发生率的原发性肺癌，而乳腺癌非常少见。第三个品系任何肿瘤的发生都很少，但是肉瘤却较常见。很明显，自发性肿瘤的遗传学机制是非常复杂的，绝对不可能完全归因于某一个显性或者隐性基因的作用。

除了上面所述的研究，还有大量的研究以基因不同源的动物为对象。这些研究结果很清楚地表明，尽管自发性肿瘤的倾向是有遗传性的，但不能归因于单个显性或者隐性基因，而特定的肿瘤发生部位可能也是遗传的。加瓦兹卡亚[6]在研究特定品系的动物中发现，45只动物中有13只患有枕部肿瘤，而在其他品系，212只动物中仅一只患有此病。但是所有以基因异源性动物为对象的研究都不能令人满意，因为任何个体都可能在达到癌症发病年龄之前死亡，而没有其他个体会有与其完全相同的基因组成。因此不可能获得真正准确的结果。

同样，人类肿瘤在一定程度上倾向于具有“家族聚集性”，尽管只有在例如视网膜母细胞瘤和某些肉瘤这些常常在生命早期发病的肿瘤中才有可能进行精确的分析。在此有理由相信，单个显性基因对肿瘤易感性起主要作用，尽管环境因素以及其他基因因素也有可能参与其中。

人类的着色性干皮病（该病几乎都是隐性遗传的）是一个能清晰说明在肿瘤发生过程中先天和后天因素如何相互作用的特殊例子。在光的影响下，皮肤会发炎并最终癌变。我们可以说这个隐性基因和光在逻辑上都能作为肿瘤的“起因”。但是由于这个隐性基因十分罕见，而光普遍存在，所以认为肿瘤是由先天基因决定的会显得更加自然。

这样，我们有大量关于各类肿瘤遗传易感性的证据，而且在小鼠身上得到的这些数据显示这种遗传易感性常常由多个显性基因决定，当然将这个理论运用到所有的人类恶性肿瘤中显然是不正确的。

博韦里、斯特朗和其他人提出的理论认为，癌细胞和正常细胞之间的差异与两个不同细胞变种之间的差异在本质上是相同的，也就是说，都是由染色体畸变或者基因突变引起的。这个理论当然不能被遗传学方法证实或者证伪，因为癌细胞不是通过性生殖的方式传代的，而遗传学家只能通过个体交配的方法将核改变与胞质改变或者病毒感染鉴别开。

遗传学家所关注的是，在决定一个特定动物是否会发生肿瘤的因素中，“先天”（以高尔顿的用词方式来说）因素和环境因素所起作用的不同。遗传学家们并没有特殊能力来确定正常细胞与癌细胞之间的差别，是否与减数分裂时产生的姐妹配子之

between sister gametes produced at meiosis, or to the difference which comes about at other cell divisions in the course of differentiation. The recognition of the importance of genetics for the study of cancer need not lead to any decision on this point.

To sum up, we can devise conditions under which either nature or nurture will play a predominant part in determining the incidence of cancer. Neither factor can possibly be neglected in a comprehensive survey. Except in a few cases, such as retinoblastoma, our knowledge is not sufficient to warrant interference with human breeding on eugenic grounds. Nevertheless, it is probable that in the ultimate solution of the problem of human cancer, eugenical measures will play their part.

(**132**, 265-267; 1933)

References:

1 Cloudman, A. M., *Amer. J. Cancer*, **16**, 568 (1932).

2 Bittner, J. J., *Amer. J. Cancer*, **15**, 2202 (1931).

3 Lynch, C. J., *J. Exp. Med.*, **46**, 917 (1927).

4 Curtis, Dunning and Bullock, *Amer. Nat.*, **67**, 73 (1933).

5 Murray, W. S., *Science*, **75**, 646 (1932).

6 Zavadskaia, *J. Genetics*, **27**, 181 (1933).

间的差别，或者与分化过程中细胞分裂的产物之间的差别一样。认识到遗传学在肿瘤研究中的重要性并不一定能对此有所帮助。

总体来说，我们能设计出各种不同的情况，在这些情况下，先天因素和后天因素中的一个会对肿瘤发生起主要决定作用。在一个综合性的调查中，两个因素都不能被忽略。除了视网膜母细胞瘤等少数例子以外，我们的知识不足以在保证优生的前提下干预人类生殖的过程。但要从根本上解决人类肿瘤的问题，很可能仍需要采取优生学的手段。

（毛晨晖 翻译；秦志海 审稿）

# Vertical Distribution of Ozone in the Atmosphere

F. W. P. Götz *et al.*

## Editor's Note

**The Swiss scientist Paul Götz, along with two British colleagues, here reports new measurements of the vertical distribution of ozone in the atmosphere. Their earlier measurements had placed the centre of mass of atmospheric ozone (in essence, an "ozone layer") at roughly 40–50 km. Now a more accurate method gives a different result of only 20 km above sea level, which is still in the stratosphere. The paper notes that some ozone is also present at lower levels. Researchers later discovered that stratospheric ozone plays a helpful role in filtering dangerous ultraviolet radiation and preventing it from reaching the Earth's surface; in contrast, ozone at lower levels has harmful health effects and is regarded as a pollutant.**

PREVIOUS estimates of the height of the ozone in the atmosphere, including our own measurements at Arosa[1], agreed in giving the centre of gravity of the ozone layer at about 40–50 km. above sea-level. These estimates were based on measurements of the intensity of the spectrum of direct sunlight as the sun was rising or setting, and—as we were careful to point out—it was necessary in deducing the height to assume that there was no regular diurnal variation in the amount of ozone through the day.

Recently it has been found possible to deduce, not only the centre of gravity of the ozone layer, but also the general character of the vertical distribution of the ozone in the atmosphere. This new method is based on observations of the spectrum of the light received from the clear blue zenith sky as the sun is rising or setting. The results of the new method are much more reliable than those of the former method, and measurements on different days give values for the average height of the ozone which agree within a few kilometres. The average height at Arosa now appears to be about 20 km., which is much below the former estimates.

The recent measurements also confirm the results obtained by an entirely different method by Götz and Ladenburg[2] and by Buisson[3] that there is an appreciable amount of ozone in the lower layers; though the main amount seems to be situated between 15 km. and 50 km. and to be distributed in a manner similar to that deduced theoretically by Chapman. So far as we can tell at present, the changes in the total amount of ozone which are associated with changes in the meteorological conditions seem to take place mainly in the upper region.

(**132**, 281; 1933)

# 大气中臭氧层的垂直分布

保罗·戈茨等

编者按

在本文中，瑞士科学家保罗·戈茨和两位英国同事报告了他们最近对大气臭氧层垂直分布的测量结果。他们以前测量的大气臭氧质心（本质上就是一个“臭氧层”）约在 40~50 km 处。现在他们用更精确的方法给出了一个完全不同的结果：臭氧层只是在海拔 20 km 的高度上，这仍然在平流层之内。这篇文章还指出大气的较低层也有臭氧。研究人员后来发现平流层中的臭氧有助于过滤有害的紫外辐射，防止其到达地球表面；反之，较低层的臭氧因为对人体的健康不利而被视为是一种污染物。

之前对大气中臭氧层高度的估算，包括我们自己在阿罗萨的测量结果[1]都说明：臭氧层的重心大约位于海拔 40~50 km 处。这些估算值是基于日出或日落时对直射太阳光光谱强度的测量而获得的，我们曾谨慎地指出过，在推断臭氧层高度时需假定一天中的臭氧含量不会发生规则的昼夜变化。

最近发现，我们不仅能够推导出臭氧层重心的位置，还能了解臭氧层在大气中垂直分布的一般特征。这种新方法基于在日出或日落时对湛蓝晴空中天顶光光谱的观察。新方法得到的结果比以前的方法要可靠得多。在不同日期测量臭氧层平均高度所得的结果仅仅相差几公里。现在我们知道臭氧层在阿罗萨地区的平均高度大约为 20 km，这要比之前的估算值低得多。

新测得的结果还证实了戈茨和拉登堡[2]以及比森[3]用完全不同的方法获得的结果，即在低层大气中也存在一定量的臭氧；虽然大部分臭氧仍然位于 15~50 km 之间，其分布也符合查普曼从理论上推导出来的结果。我们目前认为，臭氧总量的变化中与气象条件变化相关的部分似乎主要发生在高层。

（齐红艳 翻译；王鹏云 审稿）

F. W. P. Götz: Lichtklimatisches Observatorium, Arosa, Switzerland.
G. M. B. Dobson and A. R. Meetham: Boar's Hill, Oxford.

References:

1 Götz and Dobson, *Proc. Roy Soc.*, A, **120**, 252 (1928); **125**, 292 (1929).

2 Götz and Ladenburg, *Naturwiss.*, **19**, 373 (1931).

3 Buisson, Janssevan and Rouard, *Revue d'Optique*, 12 (1933).

# Vitamin A in the Retina

G. Wald

## Editor's Note

**The primary biological role of vitamin A is as the light-absorbing molecule retinol in the light-sensitive cells of the eye's retina. Here American biochemist George Wald reports a major step in the understanding of that function: the discovery of vitamin A in the retina of several animals. This association was not wholly unexpected, in view of the fact that a dietary lack of vitamin A was known to be linked to visual disorders. But Wald later went on to reveal the biochemistry involved: the presence of retinol in the light receptor protein rhodopsin and the different colour sensitivities of different forms of this protein in cone cells. For that work he was awarded a Nobel Prize in 1967.**

I have found vitamin A in considerable concentrations in solutions of the visual purple, in intact retinas, and in the pigment-choroid layers of frogs, sheep, pigs and cattle. The non-saponifiable extracts of these eye tissues display in detail all of the characteristics of vitamin A-containing oils.

The blue antimony trichloride coloration given by retinal and choroid layer extracts, when observed spectroscopically, exhibits the sharp, strong band at 620 mμ specific for vitamin A. More concentrated preparations also display the characteristic fainter band at 580 mμ, recently shown to be due to a foreign material which in natural oils always accompanies vitamin A in varying concentrations[1]. Both bands fade rapidly after mixing with antimony trichloride, while a secondary absorption at about 500 mμ appears which is responsible for the red coloration in later stages of the reaction. This last phenomenon also is characteristic of impure vitamin A preparations.

Absorption spectra have been measured of the chloroform solutions of oils from the retinas and pigment layers of sheep and oxen, and from pig retinas. The extinction coefficient (log $I_0/I$) rises without inflection from 500 mμ to a single broad maximum between 320 mμ and 330 mμ. This is the characteristic vitamin A band. The smoothness of the absorption curves between 500 mμ and 400 mμ is an indication that no other carotenoids are present in these extracts, since all the other known carotenoids possess one or more absorption bands in this region[2].

Feeding experiments on rats suffering from avitaminosis have been performed at the Pharmacological Institute of Hoffmann - La Roche et Cie., Basle, using an extract of ox retinas, from which the sterins had been frozen. The results of these experiments with a first preparation have now been received. This oil, tested with antimony trichloride, had shown in the Lovibond tintometer a colour intensity of 20 c.l.o. units. The purest vitamin A preparations test at about 10,000 c.l.o. units. Therefore this oil contained

# 视网膜中的维生素A

乔治·沃尔德

编者按

维生素 A 在生物上的主要作用是作为视网膜上感光细胞中的光吸收分子。美国生物化学家乔治·沃尔德在本文中报导了理解这一功能的一个关键点：在几种动物的视网膜中发现了维生素 A。这种关联的存在并不十分出人意料，因为人们通常把饮食中缺乏维生素 A 与视觉疾病联系起来。但沃尔德又揭示出了其中包含的生物化学机理：维生素 A 存在于光受体蛋白视紫红质上，这种蛋白在视锥细胞中有不同的种类，不同种类的光受体蛋白具有不同的光敏感性。由于这项工作他获得了 1967 年的诺贝尔奖。

我已经发现在青蛙、羊、猪和牛的视紫红质溶液、完整视网膜以及色素脉络膜层中都含有相当高浓度的维生素 A。这些眼组织的非皂化提取物明确地显示出含维生素 A 油所具有的全部特性。

视网膜和脉络膜层的提取物能与三氯化锑发生显色反应呈现蓝色，如果用光谱法进行检测，会发现在 620 nm（维生素 A 的特征吸收）处有尖锐、强烈的吸收带。浓度更高的提取物还会在 580 nm 处出现较弱的特征吸收带，最近的研究表明这是因为提取物中有一种外来物质，无论浓度如何变化它在天然油中总是与维生素 A 同时存在 [1]。在与三氯化锑混合后，两条谱带迅速减弱，同时在 500 nm 附近出现了一个次级吸收，它是造成反应后期出现红色着色的原因。最后这个现象也说明维生素 A 的提取物中含有杂质。

我们已经测量了羊、牛视网膜和色素层提取物以及猪视网膜提取物在氯仿溶液中的吸收光谱。其消光系数（log $I_0/I$）从 500 nm 开始直线上升，一直到 320~330 nm 之间的一个宽谱带最高点。这就是维生素 A 的特征谱带。吸收曲线在 500 nm 和 400 nm 之间没有什么起伏，这说明提取物中不存在其他的类胡萝卜素，因为所有已知的类胡萝卜素在这个区域都会有一条或多条吸收谱带 [2]。

在巴塞尔的霍夫曼–罗氏公司的药理学研究所中，有人进行了一项用牛视网膜提取物（其中的硬脂酸甘油酯已经被冷冻）喂养患有维生素缺乏症的大鼠的实验。由首次提取物取得的实验结果已经得到了人们的认可。用三氯化锑检测此提取物，并用洛维邦德色辉计测量其颜色强度，结果为 20 个 c.l.o. 单位。而最纯的维生素 A 制备物的颜色强度约为 10,000 个 c.l.o. 单位。因此，该提取物约含有 0.2% 的维生素

about 0.2 percent vitamin A. Rats displaying the symptoms of avitaminosis were cured by administering a daily ration of 1 mgm. of the oil; 0.3 mgm. was found to be inadequate. By the antimony trichloride test, 1 mgm. of the oil contained $2\gamma$ vitamin A. The purest preparations of Karrer and his co-workers are capable of maintaining growth in rats when fed in a daily dosage of $0.5\gamma$[3]. Since the vitamin requirement is appreciably greater for curing diseased rats than for maintaining growth in normal animals, the agreement is adequate.

Some time after these experiments had been begun, I learned of work from two other sources which, to a degree, anticipates the present results. Holm[4] has found that fresh calf retinas fed to rats suffering from avitaminosis are capable of curing xerophthalmia and restoring normal growth. Smith, Yudkin, Kriss and Zimmerman[5] have obtained similar results with dried pig retinas; choroid tissue proved ineffective. In neither contribution is the presence of vitamin A exclusively indicated. Of the other known carotenoids, carotene possesses all of the described characteristics. It is also not clear in the light of the present work why the latter authors found choroid tissue without effect; or why alcohol extracts of their preparations did not respond to the arsenic trichloride test, since alcohol is a good solvent for vitamin A.

The physiological significance of the presence of considerable quantities of vitamin A in the eye tissues will be discussed in detail in a more complete communication elsewhere. Most interesting is the relation of the presence of the vitamin in the eye to the optic disorders which are the specific symptoms of its absence from the diet: xerophthalmia, keratomalacia and—most pertinent to the present work—night-blindness.

(**132**, 316-317; 1933)

George Wald (National Research Fellow in Biology): Chemical Institute, University of Zurich, Aug. 6.

---

References:

1 Karrer, P., Walker, O., Schöpp, K., and Morf, R., *Nature*, 132, 26 (July 1, 1933).

2 Von Euler, H., Karrer, P., Klussmann, E., and Morf, R., *Helv. Chim. Acta*, 15, 502 (1932).

3 Karrer, P., Morf, R., and Schöpp, K., *Helv. Chim. Acta*, 14, 1036 (1931).

4 Holm, E., *Acta Ophthal.*, 7, 146 (1929).

5 Smith, Yudkin, Kriss and Zimmerman, *J. Biol. Chem.*, 92, *Proc.*, xcii (1931).

A。患有维生素缺乏症的大鼠只要每天食入 1 mg 这样的提取物，就可以得到治愈；每天服用 0.3 mg 是不够的。根据三氯化锑试验，1 mg 的提取物中含有 2$\gamma$ 维生素 A。如果用卡勒及其同事制备的最纯的维生素 A 以每天 0.5$\gamma$ 的剂量喂食大鼠，就足以维持它们的生长[3]。由于治愈患病大鼠所需的维生素剂量要略微大于维持健康动物生长所需的剂量，所以这与事实是相符的。

在这些实验开始后不久，我了解到其他两项研究工作在某种程度上预言了现在的结论。霍尔姆[4]发现：用新鲜的小牛视网膜喂养患有维生素缺乏症的大鼠，就可以治愈干眼症并能够恢复其正常的生长。史密斯、尤德金、克里斯和齐默尔曼[5]用干燥的猪视网膜也得到了类似的结果；但脉络膜组织被证明是无效的。上述两个文献并没有专门提到维生素 A 的存在。在其他已知的类胡萝卜素中，胡萝卜素具有上述的所有特性。以目前的研究成果而论，我们还不清楚为什么史密斯等人会认为脉络膜组织是无效的；抑或既然乙醇是维生素 A 的良溶剂，为什么他们制备的乙醇提取物对三氯化砷的检测却没有反应。

我将在其他论文中以更完整的形式详细地讨论大量维生素 A 存在于眼组织中的生理学意义。维生素在眼睛中的存在与因饮食中缺乏维生素而引起的视障碍疾病之间的关系最惹人注目：干眼症，角膜软化症以及与目前工作联系最紧密的夜盲症。

（刘振明 翻译；刘力 审稿）

# Disintegration of Light Atomic Nuclei by the Capture of Fast Neutrons

W. D. Harkins *et al.*

## Editor's Note

**Observations of nuclear disintegration induced by neutrons provoked suspicions that such nuclear processes play a role in the Sun and other stars. Here William Draper Harkins and colleagues report experiments on the disintegration of nitrogen and several other nuclei by high-energy neutrons. They noticed that the incident neutrons must possess a certain threshold energy, which is converted to a mass increase in the product particles. For nitrogen this threshold is equivalent to the energy of particles in a gas with average temperature of about $10^{10}$ K. A small fraction of particles in a gas at typical solar temperatures would also have such velocities, suggesting that light atoms may undergo such disintegrations in stars.**

ABOUT thirteen disintegrations of neon nuclei have been obtained in 3,200 pairs, and approximately 100 disintegrations of nitrogen nuclei in 7,600 pairs of photographs of a Wilson chamber through which neutrons were passing. The source of the neutrons consisted of beryllium powder intimately ground with a mixture of mesothorium and thorium-X. The neutron source used was on the average more powerful in the experiments with neon than with nitrogen. If all the factors are taken into account, it is found that with identical atomic concentrations of neon and of nitrogen in the chamber, the neon nuclei are disintegrated much less often than those of nitrogen.

The average energies of the neutrons which have been found to disintegrate light nuclei are, in millions of electron volts, 5.8 for nitrogen, 7.0 for oxygen, and 11.6 for neon. Here the value for oxygen is taken from the work of Feather. The mass data indicate that the energy needed to supply mass increases in just this order, and is respectively $-1.4\times10^6$, 0 and $+2\times10^6$ electron volts, if the mass of the neutron is assumed to be that given by Chadwick, 1.0067, which is probably too high. Obviously the value assumed does not affect the differences between the energy values.

In a gas, ethylene, which consists of hydrogen and carbon, three disintegrations were obtained in 3,200 pairs of photographs. If carbon (12) is disintegrated by capture of the neutron the reaction is

$$C^{12} + n^1 \rightarrow C^{13} \rightarrow Be^9 + He^4$$
$$12.0036+1.0067\rightarrow 9.0155+4.00216$$

# 轻核俘获快中子产生的核衰变

威廉·德雷珀·哈金斯等

## 编者按

在观察到由中子引发的核衰变之后，人们猜测这样的反应可能会存在于太阳和其他恒星之中。在本文中，威廉·德雷珀·哈金斯和他的同事们报告了氮及其他原子核在高能中子诱发下产生的衰变。他们发现入射中子必定有一个能量阈值，这个能量转化为反应产物粒子的质量增加。对于氮来说，这一阈值等价于粒子处于气体平均温度约为 $10^{10}$ K 时的能量。在太阳所处的温度下，气体中有一小部分粒子可以达到这样的速度，这说明恒星中的轻原子可能确实经历了这样的核衰变过程。

观察中子穿过威尔逊云室所得到的照片，在 3,200 对氖核照片中得到了大约 13 次核衰变，而在 7,600 对氮核照片中则大概得到了 100 次核衰变。中子源是由铍粉末与新钍和钍 –X 的混合物充分研磨而成。平均而言，所使用的中子源在用氖进行实验时比用氮进行实验时强。如果考虑到所有的因素，我们就会发现当云室中的氖和氮具有相同的原子浓度时，氖核的衰变数通常会显著地少于氮核的衰变数。

我们已经知道能使轻核发生衰变的中子的平均能量，若以百万电子伏特计，对于氮是 5.8，对于氧是 7.0，对于氖则是 11.6。上述关于氧的数值是从费瑟的研究成果中得到的。质量数据表明：如果假定中子的质量等于查德威克给出的数值 1.0067——这个值有可能偏高，那么供给反应产物粒子的质量增加所需的能量也恰好按这个顺序增加，分别为 $-1.4\times10^6$，0 和 $+2\times10^6$ 电子伏特。显然，假定的中子质量大小并不影响能量之间的差值。

在由氢和碳组成的乙烯气体中，我们从 3,200 对云室照片中得到了 3 次衰变。如果碳 (12) 通过捕获中子而发生了衰变，则其反应为：

$$C^{12} + n^1 \rightarrow C^{13} \rightarrow Be^9 + He^4$$
$$12.0036 + 1.0067 \rightarrow 9.0155 + 4.00216$$

or, if the mass assumed for the neutron is correct, $\Delta m = 0.0074$, which is equivalent to $6.9 \times 10^6$ electron volts.

This corresponds to a velocity of $3.6 \times 10^9$ cm. per sec., so only neutrons of a velocity higher than this should be effective in disintegrating carbon of mass 12. The smallness of the yield of disintegrations which we have obtained with carbon is thus to be expected, especially since probably less than one-fifth of the neutrons have velocities higher than this.

A remarkable relation which has been found to hold without exception is: in disintegrations by capture of a neutron the kinetic energy almost always decreases, is sometimes conserved, but in no case increases.

It has been pointed out previously by Harkins that the values for the energy which disappears suggest definite energy values for the $\gamma$-rays into which this energy is converted, but the accuracy of the work is not yet sufficient to prove that this is true.

It may be assumed that the neutrons in the stars are scattered by the atomic nuclei and thus take part in the temperature distribution of velocities of the atoms. If the neutrons of higher velocity are captured much more often than those of lower velocity, the distribution will be affected. Our experiments give no information concerning the capture of neutrons without disintegration, but only for those cases in which the capture is revealed by the accompanying disintegration.

It is of interest in this connexion to consider the minimum energy of the neutron which has been found to give a disintegration. The values, in millions of electron volts, are 1.9 for nitrogen, and 7.8 for neon. The corresponding maximum values are 16.0 and 14.5, the lower maximum for neon being due to the smallness of the number of disintegrations which have been obtained in this gas. An energy of $1.9 \times 10^6$ corresponds to a mean temperature of the order of $10^{10}$ degrees, but at $10^8$ degrees a considerable number of neutrons should have this energy, and a moderate number even at $10^7$, so it is not unreasonable to suppose that nitrogen nuclei are disintegrated by this process in the stars.

A part of this work was presented by Harkins on June 23 at a symposium on nuclear disintegration under the auspices of the Century of Progress Exposition, Chicago. Other papers were presented by Cockcroft, Lawrence and Tuve, and a general discussion of the theory was given by Bohr.

(**132**, 358; 1933)

William D. Harkins, David M. Gans and Henry W. Newson

也就是说，如果我们采用的中子质量是正确的，则 $\Delta m$=0.0074，相当于 $6.9\times10^{6}$ 电子伏特。

这对应于 $3.6\times10^{9}$ cm/s 的速度，所以只有速度超过这个值的中子才能有效地使质量为 12 的碳发生核衰变。所以我们就可以理解为什么碳的衰变率比较低了，因为很可能只有不到五分之一的中子具有高于这个值的速度。

一个至今没有出现过例外情况的、值得注意的关系是：在俘获中子的核衰变过程中，动能几乎总是在减少，有时候会保持恒定，但绝不会增加。

哈金斯以前曾指出：反应中消失的能量值就是由该能量转变成的 $\gamma$ 射线的确切能量值，但是目前该项实验的精确度还不足以证明这种说法是正确的。

我们也许可以假设恒星中的中子被原子核散射，因而参与了原子速度的温度分布。如果具有较高速度的中子比具有较低速度的中子更容易被俘获，那么上述分布情况就会受到影响。我们的实验没有给出与未引起核衰变的中子俘获相关的信息，而只涉及了那些伴随着核衰变的俘获现象。

与此相关，我们有兴趣了解目前已发现的能导致核衰变的中子所具有的最小能量。以百万电子伏特计，该值对于氮是 1.9，对于氖是 7.8。与两者对应的最大值分别为 16.0 和 14.5，氖的最大值偏低是因为在这种气体中得到的核衰变数较少。当平均温度的数量级达到 $10^{10}$ 度时，对应的能量值为 $1.9\times10^{6}$，不过在 $10^{8}$ 度时就会有相当数量的中子具有这一能量，甚至在 $10^{7}$ 度时就会有一些，所以假定在恒星中氮核可以通过这一过程实现核衰变没有什么不合理。

哈金斯于 6 月 23 日在芝加哥世纪进步博览会主办的关于核衰变的研讨会上介绍了该项研究中的一部分内容。考克饶夫、劳伦斯和图夫宣读了另外一些论文，对理论进行全面阐述的则是玻尔。

（王耀杨 翻译；朱永生 审稿）

# Extremely Low Temperatures

W. J. de Haas

## Editor's Note

**Physicist Wander Johannes de Haas of the University of Leiden reports here on recent experiments reaching extremely low temperatures using the method of "adiabatic demagnetisation." In this method, a material magnetised by being held in a strong magnetic field can grow much colder if the field is abruptly removed. De Haas describes experiments with cerium fluoride. Preliminary tests were able to achieve a temperature of 0.27 K, and de Haas's team had more recently reduced this to 0.085 K. With the same apparatus, de Haas suggests, much lower temperatures should be possible. Given these extremes, he notes, current methods for measuring temperatures have reached their limits, and further progress will require new thermometers suited to very low temperatures.**

IN 1926 Debye pointed out that temperature must decrease when a magnetised body is demagnetised adiabatically. Giauque made the same remark in 1927; and still earlier the same idea was expressed by Langevin for oxygen. Debye calculated the predicted effect for the case of gadolinium sulphate. His calculation was based upon the following considerations: a magnetisable body contains a great number of small elementary magnets. When such a body is magnetised these magnets are directed. The part of the entropy belonging to this order is decreased and, the process being supposed isentropic, the part of the entropy connected with the statistical movement must necessarily increase. When, on the contrary, the disorder of the elementary magnets is increased by demagnetisation, the part of the entropy connected with the magnetisation is increased and the part belonging to the statistical movement is decreased, so that the body is cooled down.

If we wish to obtain easily seen results, the following points require special attention: (1) the elementary magnets shall not exert a directing influence upon each other (no ferromagnetic body); (2) the elementary magnets shall have a moment as large as possible, subject to the restriction of (1); (3) at low temperatures the effect will be greatest, as here the part of the entropy belonging to the magnetisation becomes comparable with the other part, while at the same time the order strongly increases.

The condition to be fulfilled by the experimental arrangement in order to obtain extremely low temperatures is that the exchange of heat with the surroundings both by radiation and by connexion is cut down. In our experiments this condition is satisfied. The substance that is cooled down is at the same time used as a thermometer.

The experiments were made with cerous fluoride (a weakly paramagnetic salt of one of the rare earths) as suggested by Prof. Kramers, of Utrecht (see "Leipziger Vorträge",

# 极低温

万德·约翰尼斯·德哈斯

编者按

荷兰莱顿大学的物理学家万德·约翰尼斯·德哈斯在下文中描述了他最近利用“绝热退磁”法达到极低温的实验。在这一方法中，先使一种材料在强磁场中被磁化，然后突然去除磁场，则材料会变得更冷。德哈斯介绍了他用氟化铈所作的实验。最初实验，温度只能达到 0.27 K，近来德哈斯领导的团队已经把温度降低到 0.085 K。德哈斯认为，用这一装置还可以得到更低的温度。在给出这些极限值之后他注意到，在这么低的温度之下，当前的测温手段都已经达到了它们的极限，下一步的进展要求适用于很低温度的温度计。

1926 年德拜指出，被磁化了的物体在绝热去磁时其温度一定会降低。吉奥克在 1927 年也提出了同样的观点；在更早之前，朗之万就曾提到氧有这样的性质。德拜以硫酸钆为例，对预期效应进行了计算。他的计算基于以下几个原则：一种可磁化的物体中含有大量小的单元磁体。当该物体被磁化时，这些磁体会发生定向排列。属于这一有序的那部分熵会减少，而该过程被认为是一个等熵的过程，与统计运动相关的那部分熵就一定会增加。反过来，当单元磁体的无序度由于退磁而增加时，与磁化有关的那部分熵就会增加，而与统计运动相关的那部分熵则会减少，从而使物体的温度降低。

如果我们想得到显而易见的结果，就需要特别注意以下几点：(1) 单元磁体彼此之间不应该存在直接的相互作用（非铁磁体）；(2) 由于第 (1) 点的限制，单元磁体应具有尽可能大的磁矩；(3) 这种效应在低温时将达到最大，因为这时与磁化对应的那部分熵变得与另一部分熵大小差不多，与此同时，有序剧烈地增加。

为了获得极低的温度，在实验中必须保证完全切断与环境之间通过辐射或传导而进行的热交换。在我们的实验中这个条件是满足的。被冷却的物质同时也被用作温度计。

实验是用乌得勒支大学的克拉默斯教授建议的三氟化铈（一种稀土弱顺磁盐）（参见《莱比锡演讲》，1933 年）进行的。图 1 简单画出了我们所用的实验装置。棒

1933). Fig. 1 very diagrammatically represents the experimental arrangement. The rod $A$ is fixed to a balance. It carries a small Dewar flask, which contains a small tube filled with cerous fluoride and suspended by a central carrier $B$. The whole apparatus is placed between the poles of the large electro-magnet of the Kamerlingh Onnes Laboratory in such a way that the salt occupies the spot of maximum $H.dH/dx$ ($x$=vertical co-ordinate). The lower extremity of the rod $A$ together with the small Dewar flask is surrounded by liquid helium boiling at 1.26°$K$. The thermal insulation of the cerous fluoride is so good, that after 4–5 hours only a very small quantity of salt of exceedingly low heat capacity (the latter is inversely proportional to $T^3$) is cooled down to 1.26°$K$.

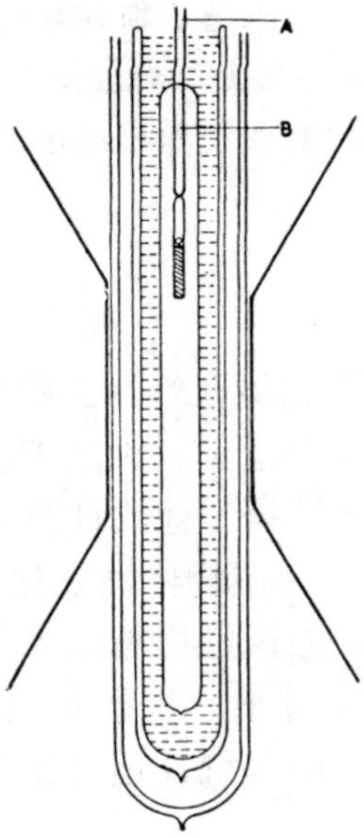


Fig. 1

We know that finally this temperature has been reached, because the salt is the indicator of its own temperature. This paramagnetic body is drawn into the field (31 k. gauss) by a force $K=M.dH/dx$, where $M$ is the total moment of the body. As $M=\varphi(H, T)$ and as $H$ remains constant, we easily see, by measuring $K$, when $T$ has become constant.

As soon as this is the case the body is demagnetised by lowering the field to 2.7 k. gauss in the first experiments, to 1,000 or 500 gauss in later experiments.

In this weak field the force $K$ is measured as a function of the time. In this way we obtain a curve as shown in Fig. 2.

$A$ 固定在一平衡物上。它连着一个小的细长杜瓦瓶，杜瓦瓶中的小试管装有三氟化铈，小试管由中间导管 $B$ 悬挂着。整个装置被置于卡默林·昂内斯实验室的大型电磁铁的两磁极之间，并确保顺磁盐样品处于 $H.dH/dx$ 最大值的位置（$x$ 为垂直坐标）。棒 $A$ 的最下端以及整个小杜瓦瓶都浸没在沸点为 1.26 K 的液氦中。三氟化铈的热绝缘非常好，以至于 4~5 个小时之后只有极少量的这种具有极低热容量（与 $T^3$ 成反比）的盐被冷却到了 1.26 K。

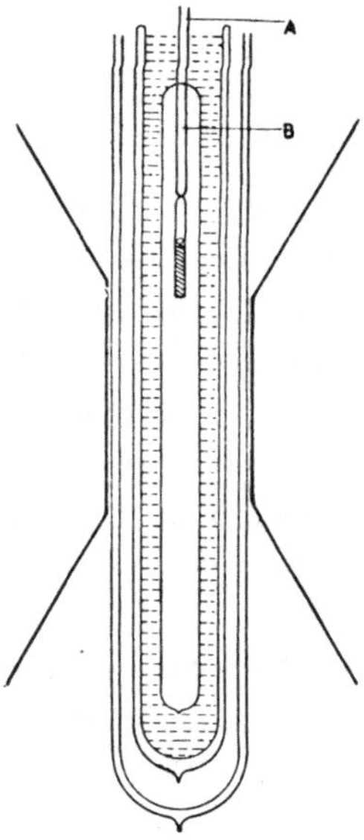


图 1

由于这种盐是其自身温度的指示器，我们知道最终被冷却到了 1.26 K。力 $K=M.dH/dx$ 将顺磁体吸入磁场中（强度为 31,000 高斯），其中 $M$ 是顺磁体的总磁矩。由于 $M=\varphi(H, T)$，且 $H$ 是保持不变的，我们很容易通过测量 $K$ 而看出 $T$ 是何时变为恒定的。

一旦满足了以上所说的情况，就通过降低磁场给顺磁体退磁，在头几次实验中把磁场降至 2,700 高斯，而在以后的实验中降到了 1,000 或 500 高斯。

在这种弱场中，测量了作为时间的函数的力 $K$。这样，我们得到了图 2 所示的曲线。

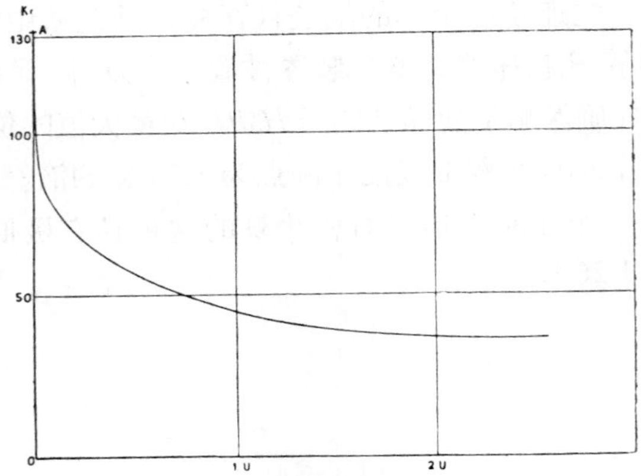

Fig. 2

The point $A$ on the curve corresponds to the force at the lowest temperature, while the asymptote after a long time corresponds to the force at 1.26°$K$. The steep fall of the curve in the beginning is due to the fact that in the vacuum of the small Dewar flask a trace of helium ($10^{-7}$ mm.) has been left intentionally for thermal contact. This helium gas is condensed under development of the heat of condensation. When the pressure of the helium gas is still lower, the curve has a different form and heating up with the time goes extremely slowly. The cold has been caught in a trap. The vacuum becomes practically absolute and heat is no longer transmitted.

The forces are directly proportional to the moments and the only thing we have to find out is to which temperatures these moments correspond. The connexion between temperature and moment has been determined between 7.2°$K$. and 1.3°$K$. The curve representing this connexion was extrapolated linearly, though this gives a stronger increase of the moment than the curve itself does. That is why we can only give an upper limit of the temperature reached.

The first experiments were made in March and April of this year with cerium fluoride and gave as the upper temperature limit 0.27°$K$. More recent experiments with dysprosium ethyl sulphate gave the upper limit 0.17°$K$. Finally, the experiments of July last made with cerium ethyl sulphate gave as the upper temperature limit 0.085°$K$.

It is possible that with the same experimental arrangement much lower temperatures can be reached. The choice of the right substance will decide further results. I am convinced that with the above-described arrangement the theoretical limit can be reached.

Up to the present, the lowest temperatures had been reached with the aid of liquid helium, boiling under very low pressures. The results of this method evidently depend upon the capacity of the pumps used and upon the perfection of the thermal insulation.

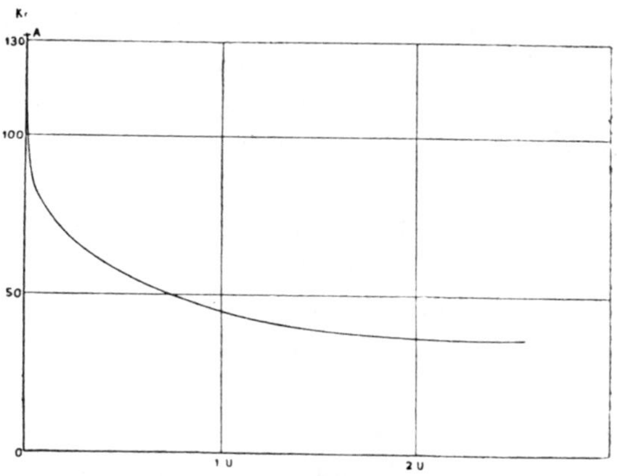


图 2

曲线上的 $A$ 点对应于最低温度时力的值，而长时间后的渐近线趋近于温度为 1.26 K 时力的值。曲线在开始时急剧下降是因为在抽成真空的小杜瓦瓶中，为了保证热接触而有意留下了少量的氦（$10^{-7}$ mm）。这些氦气在放出凝聚热的过程中被凝聚。当氦气的压强更低时，曲线具有不同的形式，随时间而升温的速度十分缓慢。低温被维持在阱里。这时的真空实际上变成绝对真空，而且不再有热传输了。

力正比于磁矩，因而我们唯一需要确定的是这些磁矩对应什么温度。在 7.2 K 到 1.3 K 之间，温度与磁矩的关系已经确定了。代表这一关系的曲线被线性外推，尽管这样做给出的磁矩随时间增加的幅度比实际曲线上增加的幅度还要大一些。这就是为什么我们只能给出所能达到的温度的上限的原因。

最初的实验是在今年 3 月和 4 月用氟化铈进行的，得到的温度上限为 0.27 K。较近期实验是用硫酸乙基镝进行的，给出的温度上限为 0.17 K。最后一次实验是在今年 7 月用硫酸乙基铈进行的，给出的温度上限为 0.085 K。

用同样的实验装置有可能达到更低的温度。正确地选用顺磁物质将决定未来的结果。我确信用上述装置可以达到理论的极限。

目前人们已经可以用在极低压强下沸腾的液氦达到最低的温度了。这一方法的最终结果很明显地取决于所用泵的排量，以及热绝缘的理想程度。

With this method Kamerlingh Onnes reached in October, 1921, a temperature of 0.82°$K$. Keesom worked with diffusion pumps of a capacity fifteen times higher than that of the pumps Kamerlingh Onnes had. In 1929 he reached a temperature of 0.71°$K$. It is, however, difficult to proceed much further in this way.

The conception of temperature is based upon the properties of the ideal gas. The temperature is determined with the aid of the helium thermometer (several corrections being applied). At the extremely low temperatures reached recently no gas thermometric measurement of the temperature is possible, so far as I can see.

A thermometric scale based upon another process must be fitted to the absolute temperature scale; only a magnetic scale can be used for this purpose.

Just as was done in gas thermometry, we shall have to find some substances, which within a considerable range of temperature show the same behaviour; a highly developed theory will then enable us to fix the temperature with the same accuracy by means of magnetic thermometry as by the use of gas thermometric methods.

A reservation must be made, however, for the case that at very low temperatures the substances used might become ferro-magnetic or might show a new kind of ferro-magnetism. In this case little might be said about the temperature.

Another great difficulty is this: if by means of the magnetic method we wish to cool down other substances, the question of the thermal contact becomes urgent. The radiation is negligible, and also the vapour pressure of the helium becomes so small that thermal contact by means of gaseous helium can scarcely be considered.

The experiments were made in collaboration with Dr. E. C. Wiersma, conservator of the Laboratory, to whom I express my warmest thanks for his help and for many suggestions. To Prof. H. A. Kramers of Utrecht I am indebted for his valuable theoretical assistance.

(**132**, 372-373; 1933)

1921 年 10 月，卡默林·昂内斯利用这种方法达到了 0.82 K 的低温。基桑使用的扩散泵排量是卡默林·昂内斯所用的 15 倍。他在 1929 年实现了 0.71 K 的低温。不过，这个方向的研究已经很难再有更大的进展了。

温度的概念是以理想气体的性质为基础的。我们是借助氦温度计（已进行过多次校正）来测定温度的。在我看来，在最近所达到的极低温度下，没有一种气体温度计的测温方法是可行的。

基于其他过程的温标必须拟合到绝对温标；为此目的，只有磁学标度是可用的。

正如在气体测温术所做的那样，我们必须找到某种在相当宽的温度范围内呈现同一行为的物质；然后，已经高度发展了的理论将使我们能够用磁测温术得到与气体测温法同样精确的温度。

但是我们必须有所保留，因为在极低的温度下，所使用的物质可能会变成铁磁性或者表现出新型的铁磁性。在这种情况下，就很难谈什么温度了。

另一个巨大的困难是：如果我们希望利用磁学方法来冷却其他物质，那么热接触就变成了非常紧迫的问题。辐射是可忽略的，而且氦的蒸汽压也变得非常小，以至于几乎不能考虑通过气态氦进行热接触。

实验是在实验室管理员威尔斯玛博士的协作下进行的，我要对他的帮助和诸多建议表示最真诚的谢意。我还要感谢乌得勒支的克拉默斯教授在理论方面所提供的有价值的帮助。

（王耀杨 翻译；陶宏杰 审稿）

# Some Chemical Aspects of Life

F. G. Hopkins

## Editor's Note

**Scientific speculations about the origins of life go back at least as far as Charles Darwin. By the time of this address from Frederick Hopkins, a 1929 Nobel laureate for his work on vitamins, the question had received serious if tentative attention. Yet Hopkins' assertion that most biologists agreed on life's origin being both singularly important and singularly improbable very much remained true decades later. Hopkins' aim here is not to outline any explicit theories of how life began, but to provide a context for such discussions by describing life as a chemical process, for example in terms of enzyme catalysis and metabolism. After the later focus on genetics, biochemical energetics is today enjoying a revival as a fundamental aspect of living systems.**

### I

THE British Association returns to Leicester with assurance of a welcome as warm as that received twenty-six years ago, and of hospitality as generous. The renewed invitation and the ready acceptance speak of mutual appreciation born of the earlier experience. Hosts and guests have today reasons for mutual congratulations. The Association on its second visit finds Leicester altered in important ways. It comes now to a city duly chartered and the seat of a bishopric. It finds there a centre of learning, many fine buildings which did not exist on the occasion of the first visit, and many other evidences of civic enterprise. The citizens of Leicester on the other hand will know that since they last entertained it the Association has celebrated its centenary, has four times visited distant parts of the Empire, and has maintained unabated through the years its useful and important activities.

In 1907 the occupant of the presidential chair was Sir David Gill, the eminent astronomer who, unhappily, like many who listened to his address, is with us no more. Sir David dealt in that address with aspects of science characterised by the use of very exact measurement. The exactitude which he prized and praised has since been developed by modern physics and is now so great that its methods have real aesthetic beauty. In contrast, I have to deal with a branch of experimental science which, because it is concerned with living organisms, is in respect of measurement on a different plane. Of the very essence of biological systems is an ineludable complexity, and exact measurement calls for conditions here unattainable. Many may think, indeed, though I am not claiming it here, that in studying life we soon meet with aspects which are non-metrical. I would have you believe, however, that the data of modern biochemistry which will be the subject of my remarks were won by quantitative methods fully adequate to justify the claims based upon them.

# 生命的某些化学面貌

弗雷德里克·戈兰德·霍普金斯

## 编者按

人们对生命起源的探索可以一直追溯到查尔斯·达尔文时代。当因在维生素方面的研究而荣获 1929 年诺贝尔奖的弗雷德里克·霍普金斯发表这篇演说的时候，世人已经开始认真考虑生命起源的问题了，但也许只是尝试性的。然而霍普金斯指出：多数生物学家都认为生命起源问题非常重要也非常难以想象，在几十年后的今天仍然如此。霍普金斯这次演讲的目的不是为了总结任何一种能够清晰阐述生命如何起源的理论，而是为了引导大家去探讨生命过程的化学本质，例如，从酶催化和新陈代谢的角度上进行分析。生物学研究在后来的一大段时间内转向了遗传学，而如今生物化学能量学作为生命系统的基本特征又一次得到了复兴。

### I

英国科学促进会这一次重返莱斯特必定会受到和 26 年前一样的隆重欢迎和盛情款待。在新一次的邀请与爽快的答复之中都谈及了双方在此前的交往经历中萌生出的相互欣赏。今天，主宾双方均有理由相互祝贺。在英国科学促进会的第二次来访中，我们发现莱斯特发生了一些重要的变化。如今，她已变成一座获得正式特许权的城市，成为主教辖区的中心。在这里，我们看到了一所研究中心、许多在初次来访时还不存在的精美建筑以及其他很多显示出城市进取心的标志。另一方面，莱斯特的市民也将发现，自从他们上一次招待科学促进会之后，该协会已经度过了自己的百年诞辰，还曾四次出访大英帝国的边远地区，并且在这些年中一直毫无懈怠地坚持开展那些有益而重要的活动。

在 1907 年，当时协会的主席是杰出的天文学家戴维·吉尔爵士，遗憾的是，他和很多曾聆听他讲演的人一样，如今已不在我们身边了。戴维爵士在那次演讲中谈到了用非常精确的测量方法所表征的科学现象。他所看重和称许的精确性此后被现代物理学发扬光大，现在更是达到了登峰造极的程度，其方法甚至已具备了真正的美学意义。与之相对，我必须要讨论的是实验科学的一个分支，由于它所涉及的是活的有机体，因此在实验观测方面还处于不同的层次。生物学体系的一个特定本质就是无法回避的复杂性，而精确观测所要求的条件是这里所不具备的。事实上，尽管我没有在这里宣称，但很多人也许都会认为在对生命的研究中我们很快就会遇到不可测量的现象。不过，我会让你们相信，在我将要谈论到的主题中，以定量方法测得的现代生化数据足以去证实基于它们的论断。

Though speculations concerning the origin of life have given intellectual pleasure to many, all that we yet know about it is that we know nothing. Sir James Jeans once suggested, though not with conviction, that it might be a disease of matter—a disease of its old age! Most biologists, I think, having agreed that life's advent was at once the most improbable and the most significant event in the history of the universe, are content for the present to leave the matter there.

We must recognise, however, that life has one attribute that is fundamental. Whenever and wherever it appears, the steady increase of entropy displayed by all the rest of the universe is then and there arrested. There is no good evidence that in any of its manifestations life ultimately evades the second law of thermodynamics, but in the downward course of the energy-flow it interposes a barrier and dams up a reservoir which provides potential for its own remarkable activities. The arrest of energy degradation in this sense is indeed a primary biological concept. Related to it and of equal importance is the concept of organisation.

It is almost impossible to avoid thinking and talking of life in this abstract way, but we perceive it, of course, only as manifested in organised material systems, and it is in them we must seek the mechanisms which arrest the fall of energy. Evolution has established division of labour here. From far back the wonderfully efficient functioning of structures containing chlorophyll has, as is well known, provided the trap which arrests and transforms radiant energy—fated otherwise to degrade—and so provides power for nearly the whole living world. It is impossible to believe, however, that such a complex mechanism was associated with life's earliest stages. Existing organisms illustrate what was perhaps an earlier method. The so-called autotrophic bacteria obtain energy for growth by the catalysed oxidation of materials belonging wholly to the inorganic world; such as sulphur, iron or ammonia, and even free hydrogen. These organisms dispense with solar energy, but they have lost in the evolutionary race because their method lacks economy. Other existing organisms, certain purple bacteria, seem to have taken a step towards greater economy, without reaching that of the green cell. They dispense with free oxygen and yet obtain energy from the inorganic world. They control a process in which carbon dioxide is reduced and hydrogen sulphide simultaneously oxidised. The molecules of the former are activated by solar energy which their pigmentary equipment enables these organisms to arrest.

Are we to believe that life still exists in association with systems that are much more simply organised than any bacterial cell? The very minute filter-passing viruses which, owing to their causal relations with disease, are now the subject of intense study, awaken deep curiosity with respect to this question. We cannot yet claim to know whether or not they are living organisms. In some sense they grow and multiply, but, so far as we yet know with certainty, only when inhabitants of living cells. If they are nevertheless living, this would suggest that they have no independent power of obtaining energy and so cannot represent for us the earliest forms in which life appeared. At present, however, judgment on their biological significance must be suspended. The fullest understanding of all the methods by

尽管关于生命起源的思考已经给很多人带来了智力上的愉悦，但我们关于这个问题所知道的一切就是我们一无所知。詹姆斯·金斯爵士曾经提出，虽然并非断言，这可能是一种病症——一种年深日久的病症！我觉得，大多数生物学家都同意，生命的出现随即成为宇宙历史中可能性最小和意义最深远的事件，而且他们都对目前暂且任这个问题自然发展的现状感到满意。

然而，我们必须承认，生命有一种根本性的属性。无论它出现于何时何地，宇宙中所有其余地方所呈现的熵的稳定增长都在此时此地被终止。没有可靠的证据能表明，生命的任何一种表现形式会最终超越热力学第二定律，但是它在能量流向下流动的过程中设置了一道势垒用于截流以储存能量，为自己的非凡活动提供势能。实际上以这种方式停止能量的消耗是一个基本的生物学概念。与之相关联并且具有同等重要性的是组织的概念。

要回避以这种抽象方式对生命进行思考和讨论几乎是不可能的，但是，显然，我们只有在有组织的物质系统中才能明确地感受到这一点，而且，我们必须要在这些系统中寻找遏止能量降低的机制。这里，进化导致了劳动的分化。我们都知道，早在很久以前，含叶绿素结构的极为有效的机能就已经为截留和转化辐射能提供了一个势阱——否则它便注定要消耗掉——从而为几乎整个生物世界供应了动力。但是，令人无法相信的是，这样一种复杂的机制竟与生命的最早期阶段相关联。现存有机体表现出一种可能是早期的方法。通常所称的自养型细菌通过将完全属于无机世界的原料催化氧化来获取生长所需的能量；例如硫、铁或者氨，甚至还有游离态氢。这些有机体不需要太阳能，但是它们在进化中被淘汰了，因为它们的方法缺乏效率。其他现存有机体，如某些紫色细菌，看来是向提高效率的方向前进了一步，但没有达到绿色细胞所拥有的程度。它们不需要游离态氧，但从无机世界获取能量。它们控制一个还原二氧化碳并同时将硫化氢氧化的过程。前者的分子靠太阳能来活化，它们的色素系统使这些有机体能够吸收太阳能。

我们是否应该相信，在那些由比任何细菌细胞简单得多的方式组织起来的系统中仍然存在生命呢？极为微小的滤过性病毒强烈地唤起了人们对于这一问题的好奇心，由于它们与疾病之间的因果关系，这些病毒如今已成为深入研究的主题。我们还不能确定地知道它们是否就是活的有机体。但是，我们现在可以断言：从某种意义上说，它们只有在寄生于活细胞中时才会进行生长和复制。如果这样它们也算是活的，那么这就意味着它们没有独立获取能量的能力，因而也就无法为我们展示出生命出现时的最初形式。但是，目前对它们生物学意义的判断必定还是悬而未决的。关于

which energy may be acquired for life's processes is much to be desired.

In any event, every living unit is a transformer of energy however acquired, and the science of biochemistry is deeply concerned with these transformations. It is with aspects of that science that I am to deal, and if to them I devote much of my address, my excuse is that since it became a major branch of inquiry, biochemistry has had no exponent in the presidential chair I am fortunate enough to occupy.

As a progressive scientific discipline, it belongs to the present century. From the experimental physiologists of the last century it obtained a charter, and, from a few pioneers of its own, a promise of success; but for the furtherance of its essential aim, that century left it but a small inheritance of facts and methods. By its essential or ultimate aim, I myself mean an adequate and acceptable description of molecular dynamics in living cells and tissues.

## II

When the British Association began its history in 1831, the first artificial synthesis of a biological product was but three years old. Primitive faith in a boundary between the organic and the inorganic which could never be crossed, was only just then realising that its foundations were gone. Since then, during the century of its existence, the Association has seen the pendulum swing back and forth between frank physico-chemical conceptions of life and various modifications of vitalism. It is characteristic of the present position and spirit of science that sounds of the long conflict between mechanists and vitalists are just now seldom heard. It would almost seem, indeed, that tired of fighting in a misty atmosphere, each has retired to his tent to await with wisdom the light of further knowledge. Perhaps, however, they are returning to the fight disguised as determinist and indeterminist respectively. If so, the outcome will be of great interest.

In any event, I feel fortunate in a belief that what I have to say will not, if rightly appraised, raise the old issues. To claim, as I am to claim, that a description of its active chemical aspects must contribute to any adequate description of life is not to imply that a living organism is no more than a physico-chemical system. It implies that at a definite and recognisable level of its dynamic organisation, an organism can be logically described in physico-chemical terms alone. At such a level, indeed, we may hope ultimately to arrive at a description which is complete in itself, just as descriptions at the morphological level of organisation may be complete in themselves. There may be yet higher levels calling for discussion in quite different terms.

I wish, however, to remind you of a mode of thought concerning the material basis of life, which though it prevailed when physico-chemical interpretations were fashionable, was yet almost as inhibitory to productive chemical thought and study as any of the claims of vitalism. This was the conception of that material basis as a single entity, as a definite though highly complex chemical compound. Up to the end of the last century and even

对生命过程赖以获得能量的所有方法的最完整理解，是我们极为渴望获得的。

无论如何，每个活着的个体都是一个能量转换器——不管它是怎样做到的，而生物化学这门科学就是要深入考察这些转化过程。我将要讨论的就是科学的这些方面，而如果我的讲演过多地集中在这里的话，我的解释是，自从生物化学成为一个主要的研究分支以来，还没有一个像我这样有幸占据主席位置的人来阐释过。

作为一个不断发展的学科，它属于当前这个世纪。从上世纪的实验生理学家那里，生物化学获得了作为学科的认可，又从它自身的几位先驱者那里获得了成功的希望；但是就对其根本目标的促进而言，那个世纪留给它的遗产只是少许的事实和方法。而它的根本目标或者说最终目标，我本人认为，是对活细胞和组织中的分子动力学行为进行充分和可接受的描述。

## II

当英国科学促进会于 1831 年成立时，第一个人工合成的生物制品只有三岁。人们就是在那个时候才认识到了，最初关于有机与无机之间存在着无法跨越的界限的信条，其根基已经不复存在。从那以后，在它存在的整个世纪中，协会一直在单纯利用物理－化学概念解释生命与各种修正形式的生机论之间摇摆不定。当代科学之立场与精神的特征表现为：机械论者与生机论者之间长期以来的争论如今已经很少听到了。实际上，基本上可以看出来，每个人都已厌倦了在蒙昧气氛下的争执，各自返回营帐，明智地等待着更为先进的知识的指引。不过，也许他们将会分别伪装成决定论者和非决定论者重新加入战团。如果是这样的话，结果将会非常有趣。

无论如何，如果正确评价的话，我都会因如下信念而感到幸运——我将要讲述的内容不会是老调重弹。正如我即将谈到的，认为对生物化学面貌的描述必定会有助于充分地理解生命，这并不是要暗示一个活的有机体仅仅是物理－化学系统。它意味着，在一个明确的和可认知的动力学组织水平上，可以只用物理－化学术语对一个有机体进行合乎逻辑的描述。事实上，在这样一个水平上，我们可以希望最终形成一种完全自洽的描述，正如对组织的形态学水平上的描述可以是完全自洽的那样。也许在更高的水平上会需要用相当不同的术语进行讨论。

不过我希望能提醒你们，一种考虑生命之物质基础的思考模式，尽管它在物理－化学解释流行时占据上风，却如同生机论的所有主张一样，对于诸多基于化学的思想与研究而言几乎是抑制性的。这种观念认为物质基础是一种单一实体，是一种尽管高度复杂但明确的化合物。直到上个世纪末甚至更晚些时候，“原生质”这个词

later, the term "protoplasm" suggested such an entity to many minds. In his brilliant presidential address at the British Association's meeting at Dundee twenty-one years ago, Sir Edward Sharpey-Schafer, after remarking that the elements composing living substances are few in number, went on to say: "The combination of these elements into a colloid compound represents the physical basis of life, and when the chemist succeeds in building up this compound it will, without doubt, be found to exhibit the phenomena which we are in the habit of associating with the term 'life'." Such a compound would seem to correspond with the "protoplasm" of many biologists, though treated perhaps with too little respect. The presidential claim might have seemed to encourage the biochemist, but the goal suggested would have proved elusive, and the path of endeavour has followed other lines.

So long as the term "protoplasm" retains a morphological significance as in classical cytology, it may be even now convenient enough, though always denoting an abstraction. In so far, however, as the progress of metabolism with all the vital activities which it supports was ascribed, in concrete thought, to hypothetical qualities emergent from a protoplasmic complex in its integrity, or when substances were held to suffer change only because in each living cell they are fires built up, with loss of their own molecular structure and identity, into this complex, which is itself the inscrutable seat of cyclic change, then serious obscurantism was involved.

Had such assumptions been justified, the old taunt that when the chemist touches living matter it immediately becomes dead matter would also have been justified. A very distinguished organic chemist, long since dead, said to me in the late eighties: "The chemistry of the living? That is the chemistry of protoplasm; that is super-chemistry; seek, my young friend, for other ambitions."

Research, however, during the present century, much of which has been done since the British Association last met in Leicester, has yielded knowledge to justify the optimism of the few who started to work in those days. Were there time, I might illustrate this by abundant examples; but I think a single illustration will suffice to demonstrate how progress during recent years has changed the outlook for biochemistry. I will ask you to note the language used thirty years ago to describe the chemical events in active muscle and compare it with that used now. In 1895, Michael Foster, a physiologist of deep vision, dealing with the respiration of tissues, and in particular with the degree to which the activity of muscle depends on its contemporary oxygen supply, expounded the current view which may be thus briefly summarised. The oxygen which enters the muscle from the blood is not involved in immediate oxidations, but is built up into the substance of the muscle. It disappears into some protoplasmic complex on which its presence confers instability. This complex, like all living substance, is to be regarded as incessantly undergoing changes of a double kind, those of building up and those of breaking down. With activity the latter predominates, and in the case of muscle the complex in question explodes, as it were, to yield the energy for contraction. "We cannot yet trace," Foster comments, "the steps taken by the oxygen from the moment it slips from the blood into

对于很多人来说还是指这样一种实体。在 21 年前英国科学促进会于敦提召开的会议上，时任主席的爱德华·沙比 – 谢弗爵士发表了精彩的演讲，他首先谈到构成有生命物质的元素数量很少，接着说道："由这些元素结合成的胶体化合物是生命的物理基础，一旦化学家成功地合成出这种化合物，毫无疑问，就可以发现它会表现出我们通常与'生命'这一术语联系在一起的现象。"这样一种化合物似乎对应于很多生物学家所说的"原生质"，尽管它可能只得到了很有限的关注。主席的这一断言似乎鼓励了生物化学家，但是他提出的目标却被证明是难以把握的，而努力的方向也已改弦易辙。

现在"原生质"这个名词被更加方便地保持着在古典细胞学中那样的字面意思，尽管它也会经常表示抽象意义。但是，如果新陈代谢和它所维持的所有生命活动的进行，在实际思想中被归因于一种原生质复合物在其完整状态下所呈现出来的假定属性，或者认为，物质经历转变只是因为它们在每个活细胞中都要以自身分子结构与特性的丧失为代价合成这种复合物，其本身是发生循环变化的神秘场所，那么就会深深地陷入到蒙昧主义之中。

如果上述假设被证明是合理的，那么以往认为化学家一旦接触生命物质就会把它变成死物的讥讽就也是合理的了。一位已故去多年的杰出有机化学家，曾在他快 90 岁的时候对我说："研究生命的化学？那就是研究原生质的化学；那是超级化学；我年轻的朋友，去追寻其他的抱负吧。"

但是，在当前这个世纪所进行的研究中有很大一部分是在英国科学促进会最后一次访问莱斯特之后所完成的，由这些研究得到的知识印证了在那些日子里开始研究的少数人的乐观是有道理的。如果时间允许，我可以通过充足的实例来阐明这一点；但我相信只要一个例证就足以说明近年来的进展如何改变了生物化学的前景。我将请你们注意一下 30 年前在描述运动肌肉中的化学事件时所使用的语言，并且将之与现在所用的相比较。在 1895 年，一位富有洞察力的生理学家迈克尔·福斯特研究了组织的呼吸作用，尤其是肌肉运动对当时氧气供应情况的依赖程度。他详细阐述了当时流行的看法，这里可以简要概述一下。从血液进入肌肉的氧并不参与直接氧化，而是转变成肌肉物质。它消失在某些原生质复合物之中，以自己的出现为原生质带来了不稳定性。如同所有活体物质一样，这种复合物应该被看作是在持续地经历着一种具有合成和分解双重特性的转变。运动时分解是主要的，而在肌肉中，我们所讨论的复合物发生分解以产生收缩所需的能量。"我们还不能描绘——"福斯特谈道，"氧从血液进入肌肉物质直到与碳结合生成碳酸排出之间所经历的各个步骤。生命的全部奥秘就隐藏在这个过程之中，而目前我们必须满足于只知道开始

the muscle substance to the moment when it issues united with carbon as carbonic acid. The whole mystery of life lies hidden in that process, and for the present we must be content with simply knowing the beginning and the end."

What we feel entitled to say today concerning the respiration of muscle and of the events associated with its activity requires, as I have suggested, a different language, and for those not interested in technical chemical aspects the very change of language may yet be significant. The conception of continuous building up and continuous breakdown of the muscle substance as a whole, has but a small element of truth. The colloidal muscle structure is, so to speak, an apparatus, relatively stable even as a whole when metabolism is normal, and in essential parts very stable. The chemical reactions which occur in that apparatus have been followed with a completeness which is, I think, striking. It is carbohydrate stores, as distinct from the apparatus (and in certain circumstances also fat stores), which undergo steady oxidation and are the ultimate sources of energy for muscular work. Essential among successive stages in the chemical breakdown of carbohydrate which necessarily precede oxidation is the intermediate combination of a sugar (a hexose) with phosphoric acid to form an ester. This happening is indispensable for the progress of the next stage, namely, the production of lactic acid from the sugar, which is an anaerobic process.

The precise happenings to the hexose sugar while in combination with phosphoric acid are from a chemical point of view remarkable. Very briefly stated they are these. One half of the sugar molecule is converted into a molecule of glycerin and the other half into one of pyruvic acid. Now with loss of two hydrogen atoms glycerin yields lactic acid, and, with a gain of the same, pyruvic acid also yields lactic acid. The actual happening then is that hydrogen is transferred from the glycerin molecule while still combined with phosphoric acid to the pyruvic acid molecule, with the result that two molecules of lactic acid are formed*. The lactic acid is then, during a cycle of change which I must not stop to discuss, oxidised to yield the energy required by the muscle.

The energy from this oxidation, however, is by no means directly available for the mechanical act of contraction. The oxidation occurs indeed after and not before or during a contraction. The energy it liberates secures, however, the endothermic resynthesis of a substance, creatin phosphate, of which the breakdown at an earlier stage in the sequence of events is the more immediate source of energy for contraction. Even more complicated are these chemical relations, for it would seem that in the transference of energy from its source in the oxidation of carbohydrate to the system which synthesises creatin phosphate, yet another reaction intervenes, namely, the alternating breakdown and resynthesis of the substance adenyl pyrophosphate.

The sequence of these chemical reactions in muscle has been followed and their relation in time to the phases of contraction and relaxation is established. The means by which

* Otto Meyerhof, *Nature*, Sept. 2, p.337 and Sept. 9, p.373.

和结束的情况。”

如同我曾提议的那样，我们需要一种不同的语言来谈及目前已确知的有关肌肉和与其活动相关的事件的呼吸作用，而且对于那些对技术性化学内容不感兴趣的人来说，在语言上的这种转变也许还是很重要的。肌肉物质作为一个整体连续合成与分解的概念只含有很少量的真实成分。可以说，凝胶状肌肉结构，即使作为一个整体在新陈代谢正常时也是相对稳定的系统，而且其核心部分的稳定性极高。在我看来，该系统中发生的化学反应具有令人惊叹的完整性。与在系统中不同，碳水化合物储备（在某些情况下还有脂肪储备）进行的是稳定的氧化反应，并成为肌肉运转的最终能量源。碳水化合物在氧化之前必然要先发生化学分解，这个过程能够连续进行的关键在于由一分子糖（己糖）和磷酸形成一种酯类的中间化合作用。这件事对于下一个阶段，即从糖产生乳酸这一厌氧过程的进行来说是必不可少的。

从化学的角度上看，己糖在与磷酸结合时所发生的具体变化是很值得关注的。极为简略地讲，过程是这样的。糖分子的一半转变成一分子甘油，而另一半则转变成一分子丙酮酸。然后甘油失去两个氢原子，产生乳酸；而丙酮酸则得到两个氢原子，也生成乳酸。接下来的实际过程是，氢原子从仍与磷酸相连接的甘油分子转移到丙酮酸分子中，结果是形成了两分子乳酸*。接着，在一个我不能停下来去讨论的变化过程中，乳酸发生氧化，产生了肌肉所需的能量。

但是，这一氧化过程所产生的能量还无法被机械性的收缩动作直接利用。实际上，氧化发生在收缩过程之后而不是之前或其间。不过，它释放出来的能量使重新合成磷酸肌酸的吸热反应得以进行，对于收缩过程来说，其能量更为直接的来源是磷酸肌酸在这一系列变化的较早阶段中的分解。这些化学反应甚至更为复杂，因为当能量从碳水化合物发生氧化的源头向合成磷酸肌酸的体系传输时，似乎还有另一个反应参与其间，即三磷酸腺苷交替进行的分解与重新合成。

我们已经知道了肌肉中上述化学反应的发生顺序，并且建立起它们与收缩阶段和伸展阶段的时间关系。目前尚不清楚能量从一个反应体系向另一个反应体系传输

* 奥托·迈耶霍夫，《自然》，9 月 2 日第 337 页和 9 月 9 日第 373 页。

energy is transferred from one reacting system to another has until lately been obscure, but current work is throwing light upon this interesting question, and it is just beginning (though only beginning) to show how at the final stage the energy of the reactions is converted into the mechanical response. In parenthesis, it may be noted as an illustration of the unity of life that the processes which occur in the living yeast cell in its dealings with sugars are closely similar to those which proceed in living muscle. In the earlier stages they are identical and we now know where they part company. You may be astonished at the complexity of the events which underlie the activity of a muscle, but you must remember that it is a highly specialised machine. A more direct burning of the fuel could not fit into its complex organisation. I am more particularly concerned to feel that my brief summary of the facts will make clear how much more definite, how much more truly chemical, is our present knowledge than that available when Michael Foster wrote.

Ability to recognise the progress of such definite ordered chemical reactions in relation to various aspects of living activity characterises the current position in biochemistry. I have chosen the case of muscle, and it must serve as my only example, but many such related and ordered reactions have been studied in other cells and tissues, from bacteria to the brain. Some prove general, some more special. Although we are far indeed from possessing a complete picture in any one case, we are beginning in thought to fit not a few pieces together. We are on a line safe for progress.

I must perforce limit the field of my discussion, and in what follows, my special theme will be the importance of molecular structure in determining the properties of living systems. I wish you to believe that molecules display in such systems the properties inherent in their structure even as they do in the laboratory of the organic chemist. The theme is no new one, but its development illustrates as well as any other, and to my own mind perhaps better than any other, the progress of biochemistry.

Not long ago a prominent biologist, believing in protoplasm as an entity, wrote: "But it seems certain that living protoplasm is not an ordinary chemical compound, and therefore can have no molecular structure in the chemical sense of the word." Such a belief was common. One may remark, moreover, that when the development of colloid chemistry first brought its indispensable aid towards an understanding of the biochemical field, there was a tendency to discuss its bearing in terms of the less specific properties of colloid systems, phase-surfaces, membranes, and the like, without sufficient reference to the specificity which the influence of molecular structure, wherever displayed, impresses on chemical relations and events. In emphasising its importance, I shall leave no time for dealing with the nature of the colloid structures of cells and tissues, all important as they are. I shall continue to deal, though not again in detail, with chemical reactions as they occur within those structures. Only this much must be said. If the colloid structures did not display highly specialised molecular structure at their surface, no reactions would occur; for here catalysis occurs. Were it not equipped with catalysts every living unit would be a static system.

时所采用的方式，但是最近的研究为这个有趣的问题提供了解释，而这只是表明在最后阶段反应能量是如何转变成力学响应的开始（虽然仅仅是开始）。插一句话，我们也许可以从以下过程中发现生命活动的统一性，即糖在活酵母细胞中发生的反应与在活体肌肉中发生的反应是高度相似的。在更早的阶段中，它们是完全相同的，而且我们现在知道它们是在哪里分道扬镳的。你们可能会惊讶于肌肉活动机理的复杂性，但是你们别忘了，这是一种高度专门化的机械装置。燃料更直接的燃烧不可能适合于它的复杂组织形式。我非常希望我对于这些事实的简要概述能使大家清楚，从明确性和纯化学性角度考虑，我们现在的知识到底在多大程度上超越了迈克尔·福斯特写作时所能达到的认识。

我们认识这些明确而有序的化学反应与活体行为诸多方面的关联性的能力标志着生物化学当今的发展状况。我曾选择肌肉作为案例，它也必定会成为我仅有的例子，但是很多这样有关联又有序的化学反应都在包括从细菌到脑在内的其他细胞和组织中得到了研究。有些结果被证实是普适的，另外一些则比较特殊。尽管我们实际上远远不能完整地解释任何一个案例，但还是在考虑将为数不少的碎片拼合在一起。我们正处在一条可以稳步发展的路线上。

我必须强行限定自己的讨论范围，下面我要讲的是一个特殊的主题，即分子结构对于决定生命体系之性质的重要性。我希望你们能相信，分子在这些体系中所表现出来的性质是由它们的结构决定的，甚至就像它们在有机化学家的实验室中所表现的那样。这并不是一个新主题，但是它的发展和其他方面的发展一样能说明生物化学的进步，我个人认为，它的发展比其他方面的发展更能说明这种进步。

不久之前，一位深信原生质是一种实体的著名生物学家这样写道："但似乎可以确定的是，活的原生质并不是一种普通的化合物，因此它不可能具有化学意义上的分子结构。"这种观点是大家所熟悉的。此外，有人会说，当胶体化学的发展第一次使其将对生物化学领域的理解作为自己的重要目标时，就有一种倾向，即根据胶体体系、相表面和膜等不那么专业的特性讨论结果，而没有充分考虑一旦发挥作用就会影响化学关系及化学反应的分子结构的特殊性。由于要强调它的重要性，我也就留不出时间来讨论细胞和组织中胶体结构的本质了，尽管它们都是重要的。接着我将继续讨论发生在这些结构中的化学反应但不会再那么详细了。这就是全部必须要说的。如果胶体结构并未在其表面呈现出高度优化的分子结构，就不会有化学反应发生；因为催化作用是在这里进行的。如果不具备催化剂的话，每个活体单元都将是一个静止的体系。

It is well known that a catalyst is an agent which plays only a temporary part in chemical events which it nevertheless determines and controls. It reappears unaltered when the events are completed. The phenomena of catalysis, though first recognised early in the last century, entered but little into chemical thought or enterprise, until only a few years ago they were shown to have great importance for industry. Yet catalysis is one of the most significant devices of Nature, since it has endowed living systems with their fundamental character as transformers of energy, and all evidence suggests that it must have played an indispensable part in the living universe from the earliest stages of evolution.

The catalysts of a living cell are the enzymic structures which display their influences at the surface of colloidal particles or at other surfaces within the cell. Current research continues to add to the great number of these enzymes which can be separated from, or recognised in, living cells and tissues, and to increase our knowledge of their individual functions.

A molecule within the system of the cell may remain in an inactive state and enter into no reactions until at one such surface it comes in contact with an enzymic structure which displays certain adjustments to its own structure. While in such association, the inactive molecule becomes (to use a current term) "activated", and then enters on some definite path of change. The one aspect of enzymic catalysis which for the sake of my theme I wish to emphasise is its high specificity. An enzyme is in general adjusted to come into effective relations with one kind of molecule only, or at most with molecules closely related in their structure. Evidence based on kinetics justifies the belief that some sort of chemical combination between enzyme and related molecule precedes the activation of the latter, and for such combinations there must be close correlation in structure. Many will remember that long ago Emil Fischer recognised that enzymic action distinguishes even between two optical isomers and spoke of the necessary relation being as close as that of key and lock.

There is an important consequence of this high specificity in biological catalysis to which I invite special attention. A living cell is the seat of a multitude of reactions, and in order that it should retain in a given environment its individual identity as an organism, these reactions must be highly organised. They must be of determined nature and proceed mutually adjusted with respect to velocity, sequence, and in all other relations. They must be in dynamic equilibrium as a whole and must return to it after disturbance. Now if of any group of catalysts, such as are found in the equipment of a cell, each one exerts limited and highly specific influence, this very specificity must be a potent factor in making for organisation.

Consider the case of any individual cell in due relations with its environment, whether an internal environment as in the case of the tissue cells of higher animals, or an external environment as in the case of unicellular organisms. Materials for maintenance of the cell enter it from the environment. Discrimination among such materials is primarily determined by permeability relations, but of deeper significance in that selection is the

众所周知，催化剂是一种只暂时性地参与化学反应却对化学反应起着决定和控制作用的试剂。反应完成后，它又恢复了原状。尽管催化现象早在上个世纪就已经被首先认识到，但很少有人对它进行化学上的研究和探索，直到几年前人们发现催化对于工业的重要意义之后。催化是自然界最重要的机制之一，因为它把能量转换者这一基本特征赋予了生命体系，而且所有的证据都表明，它从进化的最早阶段起到现在一直在生命体系中起着不可或缺的作用。

活细胞的催化剂是酶结构，它在胶体颗粒表面或在细胞中的其他表面上发挥着自己的作用。当前的研究使我们可以从活细胞和组织中分离出来的酶或者可以在其中识别出来的酶的庞大数目继续增加，同时还增加了我们对单个酶的功能的认识。

在细胞系统内的一个分子可以保持惰性状态而不参与任何反应，直到它在某个表面上与一种表现出根据其自身结构作出相应调整的酶结构相接触。而在这种结合中，惰性分子变成（用一个现在的词）“活化的”，接着便按照某种确定的路径发生变化。为我的主题考虑，我希望强调的有关酶催化的一个特性是它的高度专一性。一般地说，一种酶会调整到只对唯一一类分子或至多对与它结构密切相关的一类分子具有有效联系的状态。基于动力学的证据使我们有理由相信，酶与相应分子之间的某种化学结合会先于后者的活化过程，并且这种结合是与结构密切相关的。很多人会记得，很久以前埃米尔·费希尔就认识到酶在发生作用时甚至可以区分出两种光学异构体的不同，并指出它们之间必定有如锁和钥匙般密切的关系。

我要提请大家特别注意的是，在生物催化中的这种高度专一性有一个重要后果。一个活细胞是很多反应的发生地，而为了使它在给定的环境之中保持作为一个有机体的个体性特征，这些反应必须是高度有组织的。它们必须具有确定的性质而且要能够针对速率、反应次序以及所有其他关系进行相互调整。它们必须作为一个整体处于动力学平衡之中，并且必须在受到干扰后恢复平衡。那么，如果现在有任何一组催化剂，比如在一个细胞的器件中所发现的催化剂，其中的每一个都发挥着有限的并且是高度专一性的作用，这种特别的专一性必定是导致组织化的有利因素。

无论是在高等动物组织细胞中的内环境，还是在单细胞生物中的外环境，都应考虑与所处环境具有适当关系的任意个体的情况。维持细胞所需的原料从环境中进入细胞。对这些物质的分辨主要是靠渗透性的不同，但是在这个选择的过程中更为重要的是细胞催化剂的专一性。人们经常说，活细胞与所有无生命系统的不同在于

specificity of the cell catalysts. It has often been said that the living cell differs from all non-living systems in its power of selecting from a heterogeneous environment the right material for the maintenance of its structure and activities. It is, however, no vital act but the nature of its specific catalysts which determines what it effectively "selects". If a molecule gains entry into the cell and meets no catalytic influence capable of activating it, nothing further happens save for certain ionic and osmotic adjustments. Any molecule which does meet an adjusted enzyme cannot fail to suffer change and become directed into some one of the paths of metabolism.

It must here be remembered, moreover, that enzymes as specific catalysts not only promote reactions, but also determine their direction. The glucose molecule, for example, though its inherent chemical potentialities are, of course, always the same, is converted into lactic acid by an enzyme system in muscle but into alcohol and carbon dioxide by another in the yeast cell. It is important to realise that diverse enzymes may act in succession and that specific catalysis has directive as well as selective powers. If it be syntheses in the cell which are most difficult to picture on such lines, we may remember that biological syntheses can be, and are, promoted by enzymes, and there are sufficient facts to justify the belief that a chain of specific enzymes can direct a complex synthesis along lines predetermined by the nature of the enzymes themselves. I should like to develop this aspect of the subject even further, but to do so might tax your patience. I should add that enzyme control, though so important, is not the sole determinant of chemical organisation in a cell. Other aspects of its colloidal structure play their part.

## III

It is surely at that level of organisation, which is based on the exact coordination of a multitude of chemical events within it, that a living cell displays its peculiar sensitiveness to the influence of molecules of special nature when these enter it from without. The nature of very many organic molecules is such that they may enter a cell and exert no effect. Those proper to metabolism follow, of course, the normal paths of change. Some few, on the other hand, influence the cell in very special ways. When such influence is highly specific in kind, it means that some element of structure in the entrant molecule is adjusted to meet an aspect of molecular structure somewhere in the cell itself. We can easily understand that in a system so minute the intrusion even of a few such molecules may so modify existing equilibria as to affect profoundly the observed behaviour of the cell.

Such relations, though by no means confined to them, reach their greatest significance in the higher organisms, in which individual tissues, chemically diverse, differentiated in function and separated in space, so react upon one another through chemical agencies transmitted through the circulation as to coordinate by chemical transport the activities of the body as a whole. Unification by chemical means must today be recognised as a fundamental aspect of all such organisms. In all of them it is true that the nervous system has pride of place as the highest seat of organising influence, but we know today that

它有从异质环境中选取正确的物质以维持自身结构与活性的能力。不过，不是生命行为而是它的专属催化剂的性质决定了它将有效“选取”的对象。如果一个分子获准进入细胞，并且没有受到能活化它的催化过程的影响，那么除了对某些离子和渗透进行调节之外，不会发生什么。当遇到一个适当的酶时，任何分子都不能免于变化，从而进入到某一条新陈代谢的路径之中。

这里必须还要记得，酶作为专属催化剂不仅促进了反应的发生，还决定了反应进行的方向。例如葡萄糖分子，尽管其固有的化学反应能力通常应该是一样的，但是它通过肌肉中的酶系统就会转化成乳酸，而通过酵母细胞中的另一个酶系统则会转化成酒精和二氧化碳。重要的是要认识到不同的酶可以依次起作用，并且专属催化性不仅具有选择性还具有导向性。即使是对于最难用这些路线来描述的细胞内的合成，我们也要记得，生物合成可以并且事实上也是由酶促进的，而且有充分的事实可以证明下述观点，即由专属酶构成的一条链能够沿着由酶自身性质所预先决定的路线引导一个复杂的合成过程。我还想更进一步谈谈本主题的这个方面，但是这样做可能会让你们的耐心经受很大的考验。我要补充的是，尽管酶控制是如此重要，但它并不是细胞内化学组织化的唯一决定因素。细胞胶体结构中的其他方面也各有其作用。

## III

可以确定，在基于细胞内诸多化学反应精确协作的组织水平之上，一个活细胞对从外部进入自身的具有特定性质的分子表现出独特的敏感性。而很多有机分子所具有的属性使它们可以进入一个细胞却不产生任何影响。那些专属于新陈代谢过程的分子当然会遵循正常的变化路径。另一方面，还有少数分子则以极为特殊的方式影响细胞。如果这种影响是高度专属性的，那就意味着新进入的分子中的某些结构特征发生了调整并与细胞自身某处的分子结构的某一特点相适应。我们可以很容易理解，在这样小的一个体系中，即便是少量这种分子的侵入也能改变现有的平衡，从而在很大程度上影响了我们所观测到的细胞的行为。

这些关系，尽管绝不仅限于它们，在高等有机体中具有最重要的意义；在高等有机体中，单个组织虽然化学组成不同，功能有所区别，在空间中也是分离的，却能通过在循环中传输的化学物质而彼此影响，从而通过化学运输协调机体作为一个整体的活动。我们今天必须认识到，统一借助化学手段是所有这一类有机体的一个根本方面。在它们之中都有如下事实，神经系统作为组织化影响的最高场所具有首要地位，但是今天我们知道，即使是这种影响也经常（如果并非总是如此的话）通

even this influence is often, if not always, exerted through properties inherent in chemical molecules. It is indeed most significant for my general theme to realise that when a nerve impulse reaches a tissue the sudden production of a definite chemical substance at the nerve ending may be essential to the response of that tissue to the impulse.

It is a familiar circumstance that when an impulse passes to the heart by way of the vagus nerve fibres the beat is slowed, or, by a stronger impulse, arrested. That is, of course, part of the normal control of the heart's action. Now it has been shown that, whenever the heart receives vagus impulses, the substance acetyl choline is liberated within the organ. To this fact is added the further fact that, in the absence of the vagus influence, the artificial injection of minute graded doses of acetyl choline so acts upon the heart as to reproduce in every detail the effects of graded stimulation of the nerve.

Moreover, evidence is accumulating to show that in the case of other nerves belonging to the same morphological group as the vagus, but supplying other tissues, this same liberation of acetyl choline accompanies activity, and the chemical action of this substance upon such tissues again produces effects identical with those observed when the nerves are stimulated. More may be claimed. The functions of another group of nerves are opposed to those of the vagus group; impulses, for example, through certain fibres accelerate the heart beat. Again a chemical substance is liberated at the endings of such nerves, and this substance has itself the property of accelerating the heart. We find then that such organs and tissues respond only indirectly to whatever non-specific physical change may reach the nerve ending. Their direct response is to the influence of particular molecules with an essential structure, when these intrude into their chemical machinery.

It follows that the effect of a given nerve stimulus may not be confined to the tissue which it first reaches. There may be humeral transmissions of its effect, because the liberated substance enters the lymph and blood. This again may assist the coordination of events in the tissues.

From substances produced temporarily and locally and by virtue of their chemical properties translating for the tissues the messages of nerves, we may pass logically to consideration of those active substances which carry chemical messages from organ to organ. Such in the animal body are produced continuously in specialised organs, and each has its special seat or seats of action where it finds chemical structures adjusted in some sense or other to its own.

I shall here be on familiar ground, for that such agencies exist, and bear the name of hormones, is common knowledge. I propose only to indicate how many and diverse are their functions as revealed by recent research, emphasising the fact that each one is a definite and relatively simple substance with properties that are primarily chemical and in a derivate sense physiological. Our clear recognition of this, based at first on a couple of instances, began with this century, but our knowledge of their number and nature is still growing rapidly today.

过化学分子所固有的性质显现出来。对于我的一般主题来说，实际上最重要的是意识到，当一个神经脉冲到达组织时，位于神经末端处的一种确定化学物质的突然生成对于该组织对冲动的反应来说可能是至关重要的。

下面的情况是常见的：当一个脉冲通过迷走神经纤维到达心脏时，心跳减慢，或者因更强的脉冲而停止。当然，这是心脏动作正常控制的一部分。现在发现，只要心脏接收到迷走神经脉冲，乙酰胆碱这种物质就会在器官中被释放出来。进一步的事实对此给出了佐证，在没有迷走神经影响时，人工注射分级的小剂量乙酰胆碱也能对心脏起作用，以至于在每个细节上都能重现对神经进行分级刺激的效果。

此外，逐渐累积的证据表明，在与迷走神经属于相同形态族但供应其他组织的其他神经的情况下，活动时也同样会释放出乙酰胆碱，而且这种物质对于那些组织的化学作用会产生与神经在接受刺激时所观测到的效应相同的结果。还有一些可以说明的是，另外一组神经的功能与迷走神经族相对立；例如，通过某些纤维的脉冲加快了心脏跳动。也有一种化学物质在这些神经的末端被释放出来，而且该物质自身具有加速心跳的性质。接着我们发现，这些器官和组织对于凡是能到达神经末端的非专属性物理变化只有间接的反应。它们会在侵入者进入其化学系统时对具有基本结构的特定分子所造成的影响作出直接的反应。

由此可知，一种给定的神经刺激的作用可以不限于它最先到达的组织。它可能会传到肩部，因为释放出来的物质进入了淋巴和血液。这也会有利于组织内各种反应的协作。

根据临时在小范围内生成的物质和它们所具有的为组织转译神经信息的化学性质，我们可以合理地推测出那些携带着化学信息从一个器官到另一个器官的活性物质。在动物体内，它们在专门的器官中持续地产生，并且都有各自专属的一个或多个作用位点，在作用位点上它们能找到以这样或那样的方式适合于自身的化学结构。

下面我将来到熟悉的领域中，因为这种物质的存在以及被称为激素是大家都知道的常识。我只想说明最近的研究揭示出它们有多少种不同的新功能，并强调下面的事实，即每一种都是确定的并且相当简单的物质，具有主要是化学的而在衍生意义上还是生理学的性质。我们从本世纪就开始对这一点有了清晰的认识，最初的根据来源于一组实例，但我们关于它们的数量与性质的知识直到今天还在快速增长。

We have long known, of course, how essential and profound is the influence of the thyroid gland in maintaining harmonious growth in the body, and in controlling the rate of its metabolism. Three years ago a brilliant investigation revealed the exact molecular structure of the substance—thyroxin—which is directly responsible for these effects. It is a substance of no great complexity. The constitution of adrenalin has been longer known and likewise its remarkable influence in maintaining a number of important physiological adjustments. Yet it is again a relatively simple substance. I will merely remind you of secretin, the first of these substances to receive the name of hormone, and of insulin, now so familiar because of its importance in the metabolism of carbohydrates and its consequent value in the treatment of diabetes. The most recent growth of knowledge in this field has dealt with hormones which, in most remarkable relations, coordinate the phenomena of sex.

It is the circulation of definite chemical substances produced locally that determines, during the growth of the individual, the proper development of all the secondary sexual characters. The properties of other substances secure the due progress of individual development from the unfertilised ovum to the end of foetal life. When an ovum ripens and is discharged from the ovary a substance, now known as oestrin, is produced in the ovary itself, and so functions as to bring about all those changes in the female body which make secure the fertilisation of the ovum. On the discharge of the ovum new tissue, constituting the so-called *corpus luteum*, arises in its place. This then produces a special hormone which in its turn evokes all those changes in tissues and organs that secure a right destiny for the ovum after it has been fertilised. It is clear that these two hormones do not arise simultaneously, for they must act in alternation, and it becomes of great interest to know how such succession is secured. The facts here are among the most striking. Just as higher nerve centres in the brain control and coordinate the activities of lower centres, so it would seem do hormones, functioning at, so to speak, a higher level in organisation, coordinate the activities of other hormones. It is a substance produced in the anterior portion of the pituitary gland situated at the base of the brain which, by circulating to the ovary, controls the succession of its hormonal activities. The cases I have mentioned are far from exhausting the numerous hormonal influences now recognised.

For full appreciation of the extent to which chemical substances control and coordinate events in the animal body by virtue of their specific molecular structure, it is well not to separate too widely in thought the functions of hormones from those of vitamins. Together they form a large group of substances of which every one exerts upon physiological events its own indispensable chemical influence.

Hormones are produced in the body itself, while vitamins must be supplied in the diet. Such a distinction is, in general, justified. We meet occasionally, however, an animal species able to dispense with an external supply of this or that vitamin. Evidence shows, however, that individuals of that species, unlike most animals, can in the course of their metabolism synthesise for themselves the vitamin in question. The vitamin then becomes a hormone. In practice the distinction may be of great importance, but for an understanding of

当然，我们很久以前就知道，甲状腺对于保持机体内激素数量以及控制机体新陈代谢速率有着多么重要而深刻的影响。三年前，一项出色的研究揭示了甲状腺素的精确分子结构，该物质是出现这种效应的直接原因。这是一种并不怎么复杂的物质。我们在更早以前就已了解到肾上腺素的组成以及它对于维持多种重要生理调节过程的显著影响。但是它也是一种相当简单的物质。我只需再提醒你们注意的是分泌素，它是第一种获得激素之名的物质，还有胰岛素，我们现在对它如此熟悉是因为它在碳水化合物代谢过程中的重要性以及随之产生的在糖尿病治疗中的价值。关于这个领域的最新研究进展体现在对与协调性别现象密切相关的激素的研究上。

局部生成的确定的化学物质的循环在个体生长过程中决定了所有第二性征的适当发育。其他物质的性质保证了从未受精卵到胎儿期末期之间个体发育的应有进度。当一个卵子成熟并且从卵巢中释放出来时，一种现在我们称为雌激素的物质在卵巢内生成，并且发挥作用，导致能确保卵子受精的雌性机体出现所有相应的变化。随着卵子的释放，由通常所说的**黄体**组成的新组织在自己的位置上出现。接着，这里产生出一种特殊的激素，它的任务是唤起组织和器官中的所有相关变化，以保证了卵子在受精后的正确命运。很显然，这两种激素不会同时出现，因为它们必须轮流起作用，所以知道如何才能保证这种交替就成了一件非常值得关注的事情。此中真相是极为令人吃惊的。正如脑中的高级神经中枢控制并协调低级中枢的活动一样，可以这么说，在高级组织水平上起作用的激素也会这样去协调其他激素的活动。由位于脑基部的脑垂体的前部所产生的一种物质，通过到卵巢的循环，控制着卵巢激素活性的交替。我所提到的这些例子远没有穷尽现在已认识到的数量繁多的激素的作用。

要完整把握化学物质通过其特有的分子结构来控制与协调动物体内发生响应的程度，最好在考虑激素的功能时不要把它与维生素的功能过分地割裂开。它们一起构成了一大类物质，其中每一种都通过化学作用对生理反应施加着自己必不可少的影响。

激素是机体自身产生的，而维生素则必须要靠饮食来供应。这种区分方式在通常情况下是合理的。不过，偶尔我们也会遇到某种动物能够不需要外部供应这种或那种维生素。但是有证据表明，与大多数动物不同，这类物种的个体能够在新陈代谢过程中为自己合成该维生素。合成的维生素随即变成一种激素。在实践中这种区分可能是有重要意义的，但是从理解新陈代谢的角度来看，这些物质的功能比它们

metabolism the functions of these substances are of more significance than their origin.

The present activity of research in the field of vitamins is prodigious. The output of published papers dealing with original investigations in the field has reached nearly a thousand in a single year. Each of the vitamins at present known is receiving the attention of numerous observers in respect both of its chemical and biological properties, and though many publications deal, of course, with matters of detail, the accumulation of significant facts is growing fast.

It is clear that I can cover but little ground in any reference to this wide field of knowledge. Some aspects of its development have been interesting enough. The familiar circumstance that attention was directed to the existence of one vitamin ($B_1$ so called) because populations in the East took to eating milled rice instead of the whole grain; the gradual growth of evidence which links the physiological activities of another vitamin (D) with the influence of solar radiation on the body, and has shown that they are thus related, because rays of definite wave-length convert an inactive precursor into the active vitamin, alike when acting on foodstuffs or on the surface of the living body; the fact again that the recent isolation of vitamin C, and the accumulation of evidence for its nature started from the observation that the cortex of the adrenal gland displayed strongly reducing properties; or yet again the proof that a yellow pigment widely distributed among plants, while not the vitamin itself, can be converted within the body into vitamin A; these and other aspects of vitamin studies will stand out as interesting chapters in the story of scientific investigation.

In this very brief discussion of hormones and vitamins I have so far referred only to their functions as manifested in the animal body. Kindred substances, exerting analogous functions, are, however, of wide and perhaps of quite general biological importance. It is certain that many microorganisms require a supply of vitamin-like substances for the promotion of growth, and recent research of a very interesting kind has demonstrated in the higher plants the existence of specific substances produced in special cells which stimulate growth in other cells, and so in the plant as a whole. These so-called auxines are essentially hormones.

It is of particular importance to my present theme and a source of much satisfaction to know that our knowledge of the actual molecular structure of hormones and vitamins is growing fast. We have already exact knowledge of the kind in respect to not a few. We are indeed justified in believing that within a few years such knowledge will be extensive enough to allow a wide view of the correlation between molecular structure and physiological activity. Such correlation has long been sought in the case of drugs, and some generalisations have been demonstrated. It should be remembered, however, that until quite lately only the structure of the drug could be considered. With increasing knowledge of the tissue structures, pharmacological actions will become much clearer.

I cannot refrain from mentioning here a set of relations connected especially with the

的来源更要紧。

目前在维生素这一领域中的研究活动多得惊人。本领域中原创性研究论文发表量已达到每年约一千篇。目前已知的每一种维生素都得到了大量研究者的关注，关注点既包括其化学性质也包括生物学性质，而且，尽管许多出版物中所讨论的无疑都是一些细节问题，但重要事实的积聚量仍在迅猛增长。

很明显，关于这一宽广的知识领域，我只能够谈到其中很少的一部分。某些发展方向也一直是颇为有趣的。下列情况是我们所熟悉的：人们开始关注一种维生素（被称为 $B_1$）的存在，这是因为东方人习惯于吃去壳的而不是整粒的米；证明另一种维生素（D）的生理学活性与太阳辐射对机体的影响有关联的证据逐渐增多，这些证据说明它们之间确实是相关的，因为特定波长的射线可以将一种惰性前体转化成活性的维生素，作用于食物就如同作用于生物体表面一样；还有最近对维生素 C 的分离，人们从观察到肾上腺皮层呈现出强烈的还原性质开始不断积累有关维生素 C 性质方面的证据；或者还有下面的证据，有一种广泛分布于植物之中的黄色色素，虽然自身不是维生素，却能在体内转化成维生素 A ；维生素研究中的这些和那些方面将会构成科学探索故事中趣味十足的篇章。

以上是我对激素和维生素的简短评述，到目前为止我只谈到了它们在动物体内所表现出来的功能。但是，能实施类似功能的同类物质是很多的，而且可能具有更为普遍的生物学价值。可以肯定，很多种微生物需要类似于维生素的物质以促进其生长发育，最近，有一类极为有趣的研究表明，高等植物中存在着某些由特殊细胞产生的能刺激其他细胞的生长，从而也能促进植物作为一个整体的生长的特殊物质。这种物质被称为生长素，本质上就是激素。

知道下面这件事对于我当前的主题来说格外重要，它也是我们得到极大满足的原因：我们对激素与维生素的实际分子结构的了解正在快速增多。我们已经对为数不少的物质有了确切的了解。实际上，我们有理由相信，在几年之内，这些知识就会拓展到足以使我们充分了解分子结构与生理学活性之间关系的程度。多年以来，人们一直在药物研究中寻找着这样的关联，而且某些推论也已得到阐明。但是应该记得，直到最近的时候，我们仍然只能考虑药物的结构。随着对组织结构的认识不断深入，药理作用将会逐渐变得更加清晰。

我在这里不可避免地要谈到一组与受到格外关注的组织发育现象有特殊联系

phenomena of tissue growth which are of particular interest. It will be convenient to introduce some technical chemical considerations in describing them, though I think the relations may be clear without emphasis being placed on such details. The vitamin, which in current usage is labelled "A" , is essential for the general growth of an animal. Recent research has provided much information as to its chemical nature. Its molecule is built up of units which possess what is known to chemists as the isoprene structure. These are condensed in a long carbon chain which is attached to a ring structure of a specific kind. Such a constitution relates it to other biological compounds, in particular to certain vegetable pigments, one of which, a carotene, so called, is the substance which I have mentioned as being convertible into the vitamin. For the display of an influence upon growth, however, the exact details of the vitamin's proper structure must be established.

Now turning to vitamin D, of which the activity is more specialised, controlling as it does the growth of bone in particular, we have learnt that the unit elements in its structure are again isoprene radicals; but instead of forming a long chain as in vitamin A they are united into a system of condensed rings. Similar rings form the basal components of the molecules of sterols, substances which are normal constituents of nearly every living cell. It is one of these, inactive itself, which ultra-violet radiation converts into vitamin D. We know that each of these vitamins stimulates growth in tissue cells.

Next consider another case of growth stimulation, different because pathological in nature. It is well known that long contact with tar induces a cancerous growth of the skin. Very important researches have recently shown that particular constituents in the tar are alone concerned in producing this effect. It is being further demonstrated that the power to produce cancer is associated with a special type of molecular structure in these constituents. This structure, like that of the sterols, is one of condensed rings, the essential difference being that (in chemical language) the sterol rings are hydrogenated, whereas those in the cancer-producing molecules are not. Hydrogenation indeed destroys the activity of the latter. Recall, however, the ovarian hormone oestrin. Now the molecular structure of oestrin has the essential ring structure of a sterol, but one of the constituent rings is not hydrogenated. In a sense, therefore, the chemical nature of oestrin links vitamin D with that of cancer-producing substances. Further, it is found that substances with pronounced cancer-producing powers may produce effects in the body like those of oestrin.

It is difficult when faced with such relations not to wonder whether the metabolism of sterols, which when normal can produce a substance stimulating physiological growth, may in very special circumstances be so perverted as to produce within living cells a substance stimulating pathological growth. Such a suggestion must, however, with present knowledge, be very cautiously received. It is wholly without experimental proof. My chief purpose in this reference to this very interesting set of relations is to emphasise once more the significance of chemical structure in the field of biological events.

Only the end results of the profound influence which minute amounts of substances with

的关系。用一些技术性化学的知识来描述它们会很便利，尽管我认为不强调这些细节该关系也可以是清晰的。当前被标记为“A”的维生素对于动物的一般发育是至关重要的。最近的研究提供了大量与这种维生素的化学本质相关的信息。它的分子由具有化学家们已知的异戊二烯结构的单元搭建而成。它们聚集在与一种特殊类型的环结构相连的长碳链上。这样的结构使它与其他一些生物化合物相关联，尤其是与某些植物色素相关联，其中一种被称为胡萝卜素，是我曾提到过的可以转化为维生素的物质。但是，要说明它对发育过程的影响，就必须了解维生素合理结构的精确细节。

现在转向维生素D，它的作用更具专属性，尤其是在控制骨骼发育时更是如此，我们已经了解到它的结构单元也是异戊二烯基；但是不像在维生素A中那样形成一个长链，而是结合成一个稠环体系。类似的环构成了甾醇分子的基本结构，后者几乎是每个活细胞中的正常组分。甾醇是一种自身无活性但是能被紫外辐射转化为维生素D的物质。我们知道，这些维生素中的每一种都会刺激组织细胞的生长。

接下来考虑另一个刺激发育的例子，不同之处在于它的本质是病理学的。众所周知，长期与焦油接触会导致皮肤癌变的扩大。最近有一些极为重要的研究表明，焦油中的特定组分能独立地产生这种效果。进一步的结果显示，致癌能力与这些组分中的一种特殊类型的分子结构有关。这种结构与甾醇的结构相似，是一种稠环结构，其根本差别在于（用化学语言来说）甾醇环是氢化了的，而致癌分子中的环结构则不是。氢化作用实际上破坏了后者的活性。但是，回忆一下卵巢激素，雌激素。虽然雌激素的分子结构中含有甾醇的基本环结构，但是其结构中的一个环是没有氢化的。因此，在某种意义上，雌激素的化学本质将维生素D与致癌物质的化学本质联系起来。此外，目前已发现，具有显著致癌能力的物质在体内可以产生与雌激素相似的效果。

当面对这种关系时，很难不去猜测在正常情况下可以产生一种刺激生理发育的物质的甾醇代谢，是否会在极为特殊的环境中异常到足以使活细胞内产生一种刺激病变发育的物质。不过，用现在的知识来看，这样一种提法一定要十分谨慎地对待。它完全没有实验上的证据。我在此谈到这组极为有趣的关系的主要目的，是想再次强调化学结构在生物学活动领域中的重要性。

只有当具有适当结构的少量物质为活细胞和组织带来很大的影响时，我们才能

adjusted structure exert upon living cells or tissues can be observed in the intact bodies of man or animals. It is doubtless because of the elaborate and sensitive organisation of chemical events in every tissue cell that the effects are proportionally so great.

It is an immediate task of biochemistry to explore the mechanism of such activities. It must learn to describe in objective chemical terms precisely how and where such molecules as those of hormones and vitamins intrude into the chemical events of metabolism. It is indeed now beginning this task, which is by no means outside the scope of its methods. Efforts of this and of similar kind cannot fail to be associated with a steady increase in knowledge of the whole field of chemical organisation in living organisms, and to this increase we look forward with confidence. The promise is there. Present methods can still go far, but I am convinced that progress of the kind is about to gain great impetus from the application of those new methods of research which chemistry is inheriting from physics: X-ray analysis; the current studies of unimolecular surface films and of chemical reactions at surfaces; modern spectroscopy; the quantitative developments of photochemistry; no branch of inquiry stands to gain more from such advances in technique than does biochemistry at its present stage. Especially is this true in the case of the colloidal structure of living systems, of which in this address I have said so little.

## IV

As an experimental science, biochemistry, like classical physiology, and much of experimental biology, has obtained, and must continue to obtain, many of its data from studying parts of the organism in isolation, but parts in which dynamic events continue. Though fortunately it has also methods of studying reactions as they occur in intact living cells, intact tissues, and, of course, in the intact animal, it is still entitled to claim that its studies of parts are consistently developing its grasp of the wholes it desires to describe, however remote that grasp may be from finality. Justification for any such claim has been challenged in advance from a certain philosophic point of view. Not from that of General Smuts, though in his powerful address which signalised our centenary meeting he, like many philosophers today, emphasised the importance of properties which emerge from systems in their integrity, bidding us remember that a part while in the whole is not the same as the part in isolation. He hastened to admit in a subsequent speech, however, that for experimental biology, as for any other branch of science, it is logical and necessary to approach the whole through its parts. Nor again is the claim challenged from the point of view of such a teacher as A. N. Whitehead, though in his philosophy of organic mechanism there is no real entity of any kind without internal and multiple relations, and each whole is more than the sum of its parts. I nevertheless find *ad hoc* statements in his writings which directly encourage the methods of biochemistry.

In the teachings of J. S. Haldane, however, the value of such methods have long been directly challenged. Some will perhaps remember that in an address to Section I, twenty-five years ago, he described a philosophic point of view which he has courageously maintained in many writings since. Dr. Haldane holds that to the enlightened biologist a

在完好无损的人或动物体内观测到最终的结果。毫无疑问，由于每个组织细胞内的化学反应具有精细且敏感的组织性，所以效果相应地也会非常显著。

生物化学的一项当务之急是探索这些活动的机制。必须要学会用客观的化学术语精确地描述维生素和激素等分子是如何以及从哪里闯入新陈代谢的化学过程的。事实上人们正在开展这方面的研究，但所使用的方法绝对没有超出这项研究本身的范畴。这方面的工作以及类似的其他工作不可避免地会和活有机体中整个化学组织领域知识的稳定增长相关，我们对这一增长的前景充满信心。这是我们的承诺。目前的方法还能更进一步，但是我确信，如果化学可以从物理学中借鉴一些方法，那么对这些新研究方法的运用将会极大地推动该项工作的进展，这些方法是：X 射线分析；当前对于单一分子表面薄膜和在表面发生的化学反应的研究；现代光谱学；光化学的定量研究。没有一个研究分支会比现阶段的生物化学从这些技术进步中获得的收益更多。尤其是对于生物系统的胶体结构更是如此，关于这一点我在本次演讲中很少涉及。

## IV

作为一门实验科学，生物化学类似于古典生理学，并在很大程度上与实验生物学一样，其已经获得的大量数据均来自对有机体各分离部分的研究，而不是动力学反应继续进行的那些部分，并且必将继续通过这种方式获得大量属于自己的数据。尽管幸运的是，还有一些方法可以研究发生在完好无损的活细胞、完好无损的组织，以及完好无损的动物体内的反应，但是我们仍然有权宣称，生物化学对局部的研究仍在不断地扩充着它对想要去描述的整体的认识，无论这种掌握距离最终目的会多么遥远。类似于这样的说法曾经受到过某种哲学观点的抨击。这并非来自于斯穆茨将军，不过在那次庆祝我们协会成立一百周年会议上所发表的强有力的演讲中，他像很多今天的哲学家一样，强调系统在处于完整状态时所具有的性质的重要性，他要我们记住，一个部分在处于整体中时并不等同于被分离开时的那个部分。不过，他很快便在后来的一次演讲中承认，对于实验生物学来说，如同科学的任何其他分支一样，通过部分到达整体是合乎逻辑的也是必需的。对这种说法的抨击也并非来自于像怀特海那样的一位教师的观点，尽管在他的“有机哲学”中不存在任何一类没有内在和多重关系的真正的实体，而且每个整体都大于其各部分之和。但我还是在他的著作中找到了直接鼓励生物化学方法的专门陈述。

但是，在霍尔丹的教诲中，这种方法的价值却一直受到直接的质疑。可能有人会记得，在 25 年前的一次面向 I 分会的演讲中，他描述了一种其后他在多部著述中仍勇敢坚持的哲学观点。霍尔丹博士坚持认为，对于一位开明的生物学家，一个活

living organism does not present a problem for analysis; it is, *qua* organism, axiomatic. Its essential attributes are axiomatic; heredity, for example, is for biology not a problem but an axiom. "The problem of Physiology is not to obtain piecemeal physico-explanations of physiological processes" (I quote from the 1885 address), "but to discover by observation and experiment the relatedness to one another of all the details of structure and activity in each organism as expressions of its nature as one organism."

I cannot pretend adequately to discuss these views here. They have often been discussed by others, not always perhaps with understanding. What is true in them is subtle, and I doubt if their author has ever found the right words in which to bring to most others a conviction of such truth. It is involved in a world outlook. What I think is scientifically faulty in Haldane's teaching is the a priori element which leads to bias in the face of evidence. The task he sets for the physiologist seems vague to most people, and he forgets that with good judgment a study of parts may lead to an intellectual synthesis of value. In 1885 he wrote: "That a meeting-point between Biology and Physical Science may at some time be found there is no reason for doubting. But we may confidently predict that if that meeting-point is found, and one of the two sciences is swallowed up, that one will not be Biology." He now claims indeed that biology has accomplished the heavy meal, because physics has been compelled to deal no longer with Newtonian entities but, like the biologist, with organisms such as the atom proves to be. Is it not then enough for my present purpose to remark on the significance of the fact that not until certain atoms were found spontaneously splitting piecemeal into parts, and others were afterwards so split in the laboratory, did we really know anything about the atom as a whole.

At this point, however, I will ask you not to suspect me of claiming that all the attributes of living systems or even the more obvious among them are necessarily based upon chemical organisation alone. I have already expressed my own belief that this organisation will account for one striking characteristic of every living cell—its ability, namely, to maintain a dynamic individuality in diverse environments. Living cells display other attributes even more characteristic of themselves; they grow, multiply, inherit qualities and transmit them. Although to distinguish levels of organisation in such systems may be to abstract from reality, it is not illogical to believe that such attributes as these are based upon organisation at a level which is in some sense higher than the chemical level. The main necessity from the point of view of biochemistry is then to decide whether nevertheless at its own level, which is certainly definable, the results of experimental studies are self-contained and consistent. This is assuredly true of the data which biochemistry is now acquiring. Never during its progress has chemical consistency shown itself to be disturbed by influences of any ultra-chemical kind.

Moreover, before we assume that there is a level of organisation at which chemical controlling agencies must necessarily cease to function, we should respect the intellectual parsimony taught by Occam and be sure of their limitations before we seek for super-chemical entities as organisers. There is no orderly succession of events which would seem less likely to be controlled by the mere chemical properties of a substance than the

的有机体不会呈现出任何可供分析的问题；作为有机体，这是不言自明的。它的基本属性是自明的；例如，遗传对于生物学来说不是一个问题而是一个公理。“解决生理学问题不在于获得对生理过程的支离破碎的物理解释”（引自1885年的演讲），“而在于通过观察和实验来发现每个有机体中的结构与活动之全部细节彼此间的关联性，作为一个有机体来描述它的性质。”

我不能如此斗胆在这里讨论这些观点。它们经常为其他人所论及，也许不总是在足够理解的情况下。其中的真实部分是微妙的，而且我怀疑提出上述观点的人是否曾经找到过恰当的字眼来使大多数其他人确信它的真实性。它涉及世界观的问题。我认为在霍尔丹的教论中所存在的在科学意义上有缺陷的内容，正是面对证据时导致偏见的先验因素。他为生理学家安排的任务对于大多数人来说似乎是含糊的，而且他忘记了，基于准确的判断，对于局部的研究可以合乎理性地拼合成有价值的信息。在1885年他写道：“可能在某些时候会发现生物学与物理科学之间的交汇点是无可置疑的。但是我们可以满怀信心地预言，如果找到了那个交汇点，并且两门科学中的一门要被吞并掉，那么被吞并的将不会是生物学。”现在他宣称，生物学实际上已经啃掉了硬骨头，因为物理学已经被迫不再处理牛顿式实体，而是像生物学家一样，处理像原子一样的有机体。我现在还不足以去评论这件事的重要意义，只有在我们发现某些原子能够自发破裂成几个部分，随后发现另外一些原子在实验室中也能这样分裂之后，我们才能真正了解到原子作为一个整体的所有情况。

然而就这一点而言，我希望你们不要猜测我会宣称：生物系统的所有属性乃至于其中较为明显的部分必定只能建立在化学组织的基础之上。我已经表达过我自己的观点，化学组织足以解释每个活细胞所具有的惊人特性——即在各种环境中保持其动态个性的能力。活细胞还呈现出其他更具自身特性的属性；它们生长、繁殖、继承品性并将其传承下去。尽管要在这样的系统中区分组织水平可能要对现实加以抽象，但我们仍然有理由相信，这些属性是基于在某种意义上高于化学水平的组织水平之上的。于是从生物化学的角度来看，主要任务就是要确定实验研究结果是否在其自身水平之上仍然是自成体系和前后一致的，这一点显然可以说清楚。生物化学现在所获得的数据肯定满足这一条件。化学一致性在其发展过程中从未表现出它会受到任何超化学因素的干扰。

此外，在我们假定存在某种高级别的组织使得化学控制试剂必定会停止作用之前，我们应该遵从奥卡姆关于理智节俭性的教诲，并且在寻找超化学实体作为组织者之前先要明确它的局限。在所有有序的连续变化中，介于受精卵与完整胚胎之间的细胞分裂与细胞分化最不可能只被一种物质的化学性质所控制。不过看起来，一

cell divisions and cell differentiation which intervene between the fertilised ovum and the finished embryo. Yet it would seem that a transmitted substance, a hormone in essence, may play an unmistakable part in that remarkable drama. It has for some years been known that, at an early stage of development, a group of cells forming the so-called "organiser" of Spemann induces the subsequent stages of differentiation in other cells. The latest researches seem to show that a cellfree extract of this "organiser" may function in its place. The substance concerned is, it would seem, not confined to the "organiser" itself, but is widely distributed outside, though not in, the embryo. It presents, nevertheless, a truly remarkable instance of chemical influence.

It would be out of place in such a discourse as this to attempt any discussion of the psychophysical problem. However much we may learn about the material systems which, in their integrity, are associated with consciousness, the nature of that association may yet remain a problem. The interest of that problem is insistent and it must be often in our thoughts. Its existence, however, justifies no pre-judgments as to the value of any knowledge of a consistent sort which the material systems may yield to experiment.

## V

It has become clear, I think, that chemical modes of thought, whatever their limitation, are fated profoundly to affect biological thought. If, however, the biochemist should at any time be inclined to overrate the value of his contributions to biology, or to underrate the magnitude of problems outside his province, he will do well sometimes to leave the laboratory for the field, or to seek even in the museum a reminder of that infinity of adaptations of which life is capable. He will then not fail to work with a humble mind, however great his faith in the importance of the methods which are his own.

It is surely right, however, to claim that in passing from its earlier concern with dead biological products to its present concern with active processes within living organisms, biochemistry has become a true branch of progressive biology. It has opened up modes of thought about the physical basis of life which could scarcely be employed at all a generation ago. Such data and such modes of thought as it is now providing are pervasive, and must appear as aspects in all biological thought. Yet these aspects are, of course, only partial. Biology in all its aspects is showing rapid progress, and its bearing on human welfare is more and more evident.

Unfortunately, the nature of this new biological progress and its true significance is known to but a small section of the lay public. Few will doubt that popular interest in science is extending, but it is mainly confined to the more romantic aspects of modern astronomy and physics. That biological advances have made less impression is probably due to more than one circumstance, of which the chief, doubtless, is the neglect of biology in our educational system. The startling data of modern astronomy and physics, though of course only when presented in their most superficial aspects, find an easier approach to the uninformed mind than those of the new experimental biology can hope for. The primary

种本质上属于激素的传导物质可以在这出引人关注的大戏中扮演明白无误的角色。若干年前我们就知道，在早期的生长阶段，一组被施佩曼称为“组织者”的细胞能诱导其他细胞进入分化的后续阶段。最近的研究似乎表明，从无细胞的提取物中也可以得到能实现同样功能的“组织者”。看起来，我们所说的这种物质并不只限于“组织者”本身，而是广泛地分布在胚胎的外部而不是内部。不过，它确实仍是化学影响中的一个典型例子。

在这样的演讲中尝试对心理物理学问题进行讨论恐怕是不恰当的。无论我们对于这个在其完整状态时与意识相关的物质系统了解多少，这种关系的本质可能仍然是一个问题。对这一问题的关注是持久的，并且必定会经常出现在我们的思考中。但是，它的存在使我们不能预先判断该物质系统可以给实验提供的一致性知识的价值。

## V

我认为，现在已经清楚，无论其局限在哪里，化学的思维模式都注定要深刻地影响生物学的思维。但是，如果生物化学家要在任何时候都倾向于高估他对生物学贡献的价值，或者低估自己所在领域之外的问题的重要性，那他不如为了这个领域暂时离开实验室，或者索性到博物馆去寻找关于生命所能具有的无限适应性的提示。这样他就会以谦卑的心态来工作，不管他认为自己的方法有多么重要。

但是，下面的宣称肯定是正确的：通过从早期关注死的生物产物过渡到当前关注活有机体内的活动过程，生物化学已经真正成为前进中的生物学的一个分支。它开启了在一代人以前还根本无法想象的关于生命具有物理基础的新型思维模式。这样的数据和它现在所提供的这种思维模式是渗透性的，而且必定会在生物学研究的所有方面都呈现。当然，目前这些方面中还只有部分受到了影响。生物学的所有方面都显示出快速的发展趋势，而且它对于人类福利的意义也越来越明显。

遗憾的是，这些生物学新进展的本质及其真正意义只为一小部分一般公众所认识。很少有人会怀疑，大众对科学的兴趣日益增长，但却主要局限于现代天文学与物理学中更为浪漫的方面。生物学进展的影响较小，这可能是由多种原因造成的，其中最主要的原因无疑是我们的教育系统对于生物学的漠视。现代天文学和物理学为未受教育的人了解它们的惊人成就找到了一条更为省力的方式，尽管肯定只能限于最表层的一些方面，但这也是新兴实验生物学所望尘莫及的。与之相互矛盾的是，现代天文学和物理学中涉及的主要概念却不那么令人熟悉。此外，作家们一直在以

concepts involved are paradoxically less familiar. Modern physical science, moreover, has been interpreted to the intelligent public by writers so brilliant that their books have had a great and stimulating influence.

Lord Russell once ventured on the statement that in passing from physics to biology one is conscious of a transition from the cosmic to the parochial, because from a cosmic point of view life is a very unimportant affair. Those who know that supposed parish well are convinced that it is rather a metropolis entitled to much more attention than it sometimes obtains from authors of guide-books to the universe. It may be small in extent, but is the seat of all the most significant events. In too many current publications, purporting to summarise scientific progress, biology is left out or receives but scant reference. Brilliant expositions of all that may be met in the region where modern science touches philosophy have directed thought straight from the implications of modern physics to the nature and structure of the human mind, and even to speculation concerning the mind of the Deity. Yet there are aspects of biological truth already known which are certainly germane to such discussions, and probably necessary for their adequacy.

## VI

It is, however, because of its extreme importance to social progress that public ignorance of biology is especially to be regretted. Sir Henry Dale has remarked that "it is worth while to consider today whether the imposing achievements of physical science have not already, in the thought and interests of men at large, as well as in technical and industrial development, overshadowed in our educational and public policy those of biology to an extent which threatens a one-sided development of science itself and of the civilisation which we hope to see based on science." Sir Walter Fletcher, whose death during the past year has deprived the nation of an enlightened adviser, almost startled the public, I think, when he said in a national broadcast that "we can find safety and progress only in proportion as we bring into our methods of statecraft the guidance of biological truth". That statecraft, in its dignity, should be concerned with biological teaching, was a new idea to many listeners.

A few years ago the Cambridge philosopher, Dr. C. D. Broad, who is much better acquainted with scientific data than are many philosophers, remarked upon the misfortune involved in the unequal development of science; the high degree of our control over inorganic Nature combined with relative ignorance of biology and psychology. At the close of a discussion as to the possibility of continued mental progress in the world, he summed up by saying that the possibility depends on our getting an adequate knowledge and control of life and mind before the combination of ignorance on these subjects with knowledge of physics and chemistry wrecks the whole social system. He closed with the somewhat startling words: "Which of the runners in this very interesting race will win it is impossible to foretell. But physics and death have a long start over psychology and life!" No one surely will wish for, or expect, a slowing in the pace of the first, but the quickening up in the latter which the last few decades have seen is a matter for high

极为美妙的方式将现代物理学介绍给受过教育的公众，他们的书籍起到了很大的启蒙作用。

罗素勋爵曾大胆地表达了以下论点：从物理学到生物学，人们经历了从整个宇宙到局部地区的转换，因为从宇宙的角度看来，生命只是一件无关紧要的事。那些熟悉某个指定区域的人相信，比起偶然从宇宙指南手册的作者那里所获得的关注来说，大都市其实是一个更有资格被关注的领域。它的范围也许很小，但所有最重要的事件都在这里发生。在太多号称概述了科学进展的现行出版物中，生物学都被排除在外，或者只是被略有提及。如果要对现代科学与哲学相交的领域可能遇到的所有内容进行精辟的说明，就必须将思考从现代物理学的推论引向人类思维的本质与结构，甚至引向对于神性思维的思索。还有一些目前已知的生物学现象，它们与这次演讲无疑也是密切相关的，而且就恰当性而言可能是必要的。

## VI

然而，由于生物学对于社会发展极其重要，所以公众对它的漠视就更加令人感到遗憾。亨利·戴尔爵士曾经谈到“今天值得考虑的是：就普通人的思维方式和关注点以及对技术和工业发展的意义而言，物理科学的卓越成就是否并未在我们的教育与公共政策中掩盖了生物学的成果，以至于达到了科学自身以及我们希望建筑在科学基础之上的文明有可能出现片面发展的程度。”沃尔特·弗莱彻爵士在去年的离世使这个国家失去了一位贤明的导师，他生前曾在一次面向全国的广播中讲了一句在我看来几乎使公众震惊的话，他说“只有我们越来越将生物学真理的指导引入治国方法时，才能找到安全与进步”。高高在上的治国之术会与生物学理论有关系，这对于很多听众来说是一种新观念。

几年之前，剑桥哲学家布罗德博士——他对科学领域的熟悉程度远远超过许多其他的哲学家——曾评论过科学的不平衡发展会带来的灾难；我们对于无机自然界的控制程度之高与对于生物学和心理学的相对无知形成了鲜明的对比。在一次关于全球思想水平持续发展之可能性的讨论的结尾，他用下面的话作出总结：在对这些学科的无知与物理和化学知识的结合破坏整个社会系统之前，这种可能性取决于我们对充足知识的把握以及对生命和思维的控制。他用多少有点令人震惊的话作为结束：“很难预言在这场极为有趣的竞争中哪位奔跑者能够获胜。但是物理学和死亡在起跑时就已大大领先于心理学和生命！”当然，没有人会希求或者期望在比赛一开始就落后一步，但是后者在最近几十年中的奋起直追令人非常满意。不过，要重复说明的是，有必要认识到生物学真理对于个人行为乃至于治国之术与社会政策都是

satisfaction. But, to repeat, the need for recognising biological truth as a necessary guide to individual conduct and no less to statecraft and social policy still needs emphasis today. With frank acceptance of the truth that his own nature is congruent with all those aspects of Nature at large which biology studies, combined with intelligent understanding of its teaching, man would escape from innumerable inhibitions due to past history and present ignorance, and equip himself for higher levels of endeavour and success.

Inadequate as at first sight it may seem when standing alone in support of so large a thesis, I must here be content to refer briefly to a single example of biological studies bearing upon human welfare. I will choose one which stands near to the general theme of my address. I mean the current studies of human and animal nutrition. During the last twenty years—that is, since it adopted the method of controlled experiment—the study of nutrition has shown that the needs of the body are much more complex than was earlier thought, and in particular that substances consumed in almost infinitesimal amounts may, each in its way, be as essential as those which form the bulk of any adequate dietary. This complexity in its demands will, after all, not surprise those who have in mind the complexity of events in the diverse living tissues of the body.

My earlier reference to vitamins, which had somewhat different bearings, was, I am sure, not necessary for a reminder of their nutritional importance. Owing to abundance of all kinds of advertisement, vitamins are discussed in the drawing-room as well as in the dining-room, and also, though not so much, in the nursery, while at present perhaps not enough in the kitchen. Unfortunately, among the uninformed their importance in nutrition is not always viewed with discrimination. Some seem to think nowadays that if the vitamin supply is secured the rest of the dietary may be left to chance, while others suppose that they are things so good that we cannot have too much of them. Needless to say, neither assumption is true. With regard to the second indeed it is desirable, now that vitamin concentrates are on the market and much advertised, to remember that excess of vitamin may be harmful. In the case of that labelled D at least we have definite evidence of this. Nevertheless, the claim that every known vitamin has highly important nutritional functions is supported by evidence which continues to grow. It is probable, but perhaps not yet certain, that the human body requires all that are known.

The importance of detail is no less in evidence when the demands of the body for a right mineral supply are considered. A proper balance among the salts which are consumed in quantity is here of prime importance, but that certain elements which ordinary foods contain in minute amounts are indispensable in such amounts is becoming sure. To take but a single example: the necessity of a trace of copper, which exercises somewhere in the body an indispensable catalytic influence on metabolism, is as essential in its way as much larger supplies of calcium, magnesium, potassium or iron. Those in close touch with experimental studies continually receive hints that factors still unknown contribute to normal nutrition, and those who deal with human dietaries from a scientific point of view know that an ideal diet cannot yet be defined.

必不可少的指导，这一点到今天仍应加以强调。如果坦诚地接受下面的事实，即人类自身的本性与生物学所研究的整个自然界的所有方面是大体一致的，再加上对生物学理论的深刻理解，那么人类将会从源于对以往历史和当今的无知的无数压抑中解脱出来，并且为了更高水平上的努力和成功而武装自己。

尽管乍看起来，这样做似乎不足以独立支撑如此宏大的一个主题，但在这里我必须满足于只简要地介绍一个关于生物学造福于人类的例子。我将选择一个与今天演讲的主要论题相接近的例子。我指的是当前关于人类与动物的营养的研究。在过去的 20 年中，也就是说，自从采用对照实验的方法以来，人们对营养的研究表明，机体的需求远比以前所认为的要复杂得多，尤其是那些消耗量极微的物质可能会，以各自的方式，和那些构成足量食谱中主要部分的成分一样重要。说到底，这种需求上的复杂性并不会使那些知道机体内不同组织中的反应非常复杂的人感到惊讶。

之前我对于维生素的讨论多少有点偏重于其他方面，我知道它们对于强调维生素的营养价值来说并不是必要的。由于有大量各种各样的广告，维生素会在客厅和饭厅之中被人们谈起，尽管不是那么经常但有时在托儿所中也会听到这种讨论，不过到目前为止，可能在厨房中还是讨论得不够。遗憾的是，在未受教育的人那里，它们在营养中的重要作用并不总是能分辨明晰。现在似乎还有一些人认为，如果保证了维生素的供应，那么食谱中的其他成分就可以听之任之了，而另外一些人则认为，它们是那种我们无论吃多少都不过分的好东西。毋庸赘言，这两种想法都不是正确的。就第二点来说，由于市场上有维生素提取物出售而且做了很多广告，所以确实需要提醒大家，维生素过量可能是有害的。至少对于标记为 D 的维生素来说，我们有关于这一点的明确证据。不过，越来越多的证据证明：每种已知的维生素都有极为重要的营养功能。有可能但也许还不能完全确定的是，人体需要所有已知的维生素。

在考虑到机体对一定矿物质的需求时，细节的重要性也是明显的。最重要的是，被大量消耗的各种盐分之间的适当平衡，但是对于在普通食物中只含微量的某些元素，它们的数量也是必不可少的，这一点逐渐得到了确认。只举一个例子——痕量铜元素的必要性，它在机体中的某处行使对于新陈代谢过程不可或缺的催化功能，与需要量更大的钙、镁、钾或铁的一样，它们都是必不可少的。那些与实验研究有密切接触的人不断地得到这样的暗示，即，仍有某些未知因素会影响正常的营养；而那些从科学角度考虑人类食谱的人则知道，目前还不能界定出一种理想的饮食。

This reference to nutritional studies is indeed mainly meant to affirm that the great attention they are receiving is fully justified. No one, I think, need be impressed with the argument that, because the human race has survived until now in complete ignorance of all such details, the knowledge being won must have academic interest alone. This line of argument is very old and never right.

One thing I am sure may be claimed for the growing enlightenment concerning human nutrition and the recent recognition of its study. It has already produced one line of evidence to show that nurture can assist nature to an extent not freely admitted a few years ago. That is a subject which I wish I could pursue. I cannot myself doubt that various lines of evidence, all of which should be profoundly welcome, are pointing in the same direction.

Allow me just one final reference to another field of nutritional studies. Their great economic importance in animal husbandry calls for full recognition. Just now agricultural authorities are becoming acutely aware of the call for a better control of the diseases of animals. Together these involve an immense economic loss to the farmers, and therefore to the country. Although, doubtless, its influence should not be exaggerated, faulty nutrition plays no small share in accounting for the incidence of some among these diseases, as researches carried out at the Rowett Institute in Aberdeen and elsewhere are demonstrating. There is much more of such work to be done with great profit.

## VII

In every branch of science the activity of research has greatly increased during recent years. This all will have realised, but only those who are able to survey the situation closely can estimate the extent of that increase. It occurred to me at one time that an appraisement of research activities in Great Britain, and especially the organisation of State-aided research, might fittingly form a part of my address. The desire to illustrate the progress of my own subject led me away from that project. I gave some time to a survey, however, and came to the conclusion, among others, that from eight to ten individuals in the world are now engaged upon scientific investigations for every one so engaged twenty years ago. It must be remembered, of course, that not only has research endowment greatly increased in America and Europe, but also that Japan, China, and India have entered the field and are making contributions to science of real importance. It is sure that, whatever the consequences, the increase of scientific knowledge is at this time undergoing a positive acceleration.

Apropos, I find difficulty as today's occupant of this important scientific pulpit in avoiding some reference to impressive words spoken by my predecessor which are still echoed in thought, talk and print. In his wise and eloquent address at York, Sir Alfred Ewing reminded us with serious emphasis that the command of Nature has been put into man's hand before he knows how to command himself. Of the dangers involved in that indictment he warned us; and we should remember that General Smuts also sounded the

在这里提及营养学研究的主要目的实际上是为了证实该研究得到的深切关注是合理的。我认为，不需要向任何人强化这样的论点：由于人类已经在完全不了解所有这些细节的情况下存活到了今天，所以我们获取的知识必定只具有学术上的意义。这种论点是非常陈旧的，也是绝对错误的。

由于从人类食物以及最近对营养学研究的认识中得到了越来越多的启发，我能确定有一件事是可以说的。一系列证据表明：营养品对人类的辅助程度已经达到了几年前没有得到普遍认可的程度。那是一个我希望自己能够去追求的主题。我本人毫不怀疑来自多方的证据都会指向同样的方向，它们全部都应该是深受欢迎的。

请允许我最后一次谈及营养学研究的另一个领域。它们在畜牧业中的巨大经济价值还有待于全面的了解。农业专家在不久之前开始敏锐地认识到有必要对动物疾病进行更好的控制。动物染病会给农场主带来巨大的经济损失，也会给国家带来损失。无疑地，尽管不该夸大它的影响，根据阿伯丁郡洛维特研究所以及在其他地方所进行的研究，不合理的食物对于引发某些疾病起着不小的作用。还有更多能带来巨大效益的工作有待于进行。

## VII

在最近这些年里，每个科学分支中的研究活动都明显增加了。所有的人都会认识到这一点，但只有那些能够仔细考察局势的人才能估计出增长量的大小。我曾想到有一份关于在英国进行的研究活动，尤其是有关国家资助的研究组织的评估，它也许很适合作为今天演讲的一部分。但想描述自己工作进展的欲望使我放弃了这个打算。不管怎样，我还是花了一些时间来考察并且得到了结论，其中包括，现在全世界参与科学研究的独立团体数量是 20 年前的 8 到 10 倍。当然我们必须要记得，不仅美国和欧洲大幅增加了研究基金，日本、中国和印度也已加入了这一领域，并且正在为科学作出真正有价值的贡献。可以确定，无论结果会是什么，目前科学知识的增长速度在明显地加快。

顺便说一句，今天，作为这个有重要影响的科学讲坛的主讲者，我很难避免提到一些我的前任曾说过的惊人词句，它们至今仍在思想、言谈和出版物中反复出现。那次在约克所作的智慧而生动的演讲中，艾尔弗雷德·尤因爵士非常严肃地提醒我们，人类在知道如何掌控自己之前，已经得到了对自然界的掌控权。他就这种指控中隐含的危险对我们提出了警示；而且我们应该记得，斯穆茨将军在伦敦也提出了

same note of warning in London.

Of science itself it is, of course, no indictment. It may be thought of rather as a warning signal to be placed on her road: "Dangerous Hill Ahead", perhaps, or "Turn Right"; not, however, "Go Slow", for that advice science cannot follow. The indictment is of mankind. Recognition of the truth it contains cannot be absent from the minds of those whose labours are daily increasing mankind's command of Nature; but it is due to them that the truth should be viewed in proper perspective. It is, after all, war, to which science has added terrors, and the fear of war, which alone give it real urgency; an urgency which must of course be felt in these days when some nations at least are showing the spirit of selfish and dangerous nationalism. I may be wrong but it seems to me that, war apart, the gifts of science and invention have done little to increase opportunities for the display of the more serious of man's irrational impulses. The worst they do perhaps is to give to clever and predatory souls that keep within the law, the whole world for their depredations, instead of a parish or a country as of yore.

But Sir Alfred Ewing told us of "the disillusion with which, now standing aside, he watches the sweeping pageant of discovery and invention in which he used to make unbounded delight". I wish that one to whom applied science and Great Britain owe so much might have been spared such disillusion, for I suspect it gives him pain. I wonder whether, if he could have added to "An Engineer's Outlook" the outlook of a biologist, the disillusion would still be there. As one just now advocating the claims of biology, I would much like to know. It is sure, however, that the gifts of the engineer to humanity at large are immense enough to outweigh the assistance he may have given to the forces of destruction.

It may be claimed for biological science, in spite of vague references to bacterial warfare and the like, that it is not of its nature to aid destruction. What it may do towards making man as a whole more worthy of his inheritance has yet to be fully recognised. On this point I have said much. Of its service to his physical betterment there can be no doubts. I have made but bare reference in this address to the support that biological research gives to the art of medicine. I had thought to say much more of this, but found that if I said enough I could say nothing else.

There are two other great questions so much to the front just now that they tempt a final reference. I mean, of course, the paradox of poverty amidst plenty and the replacement of human labour by machinery. Applied science should take no blame for the former, but indeed claim credit unfairly lost. It is not within my capacity to say anything of value about the paradox and its cure; but I confess that I see more present danger in the case of "Money versus Man" than danger, present or future, in that of the "Machine versus Man"!

With regard to the latter, it is surely right that those in touch with science should insist that the replacement of human labour will continue. Those who doubt this cannot realise the meaning of that positive acceleration in science, pure and applied, which

同样的警告。

当然，科学自身是无可指责的。它可以被更恰当地认为是放置于科学道路上的一个警示信号：也许是“前方有险坡”，或者是“右转”；但不会是“减速”，因为科学不会采纳这个建议。指责是针对人类的。那些每天都在以自己的劳动增加人类对自然的支配能力的人不可能不认可其中所含的事实；但正是因为有了他们，那些事实才会被正确地对待。毕竟，科学增加了战争的恐惧，而只有对战争的畏惧才能真正给科学带来紧迫感；总会有一些国家在正表现出自私倾向和危险的民族主义时要感受到这种紧迫感。可能我是错的，但在我看来，除了通过战争，科学和发明的馈赠几乎不会为人类表现其更为严重的非理性冲动增加多少机会。也许它们所做的最糟糕的事情也就是使一些狡猾而贪婪的人能够在法律允许的范围内对整个世界进行掠夺，而不是像以往那样仅限于一个教区或者一个国家。

但是艾尔弗雷德·攸英爵士告诉我们，“带着幻想的破灭，他站在一旁，看着过去常常带来无限喜悦的发现和发明的大规模庆典”。我希望那些应用科学并且为英国做出过很大贡献的人也许可以免受这种幻灭的伤害，因为我猜想这会给他带来痛苦。我很好奇，如果他能在生物学家的视角之上叠加“一个工程师的视角”，这样的幻灭是否还会出现。作为一个刚刚还在为生物学谋取权利的人，我很想知道。不过可以确定，工程师对于全人类之赠予要远远超过他可能给予破坏力量的帮助。

关于生物科学我们可以这样讲，尽管隐约听到有诸如细菌战这类的提法，但助纣为虐毕竟不是它的本质。我们现在还没有充分认识到生物学可以为使人作为一个整体配得上大自然的馈赠做些什么。关于这一点我已经说过很多。而在生物学对人类体质改善的贡献方面，是不存在什么疑问的。在这次演讲中，我曾经但只是大略提及生物学研究给予医学技术的支持。我原本想说的比这多得多，但我发现若是充分论述这个问题，就没有时间再说别的了。

还有两个最近非常引人注目的大问题使我在演讲的最后不得不提到。当然，我指的是富足中的贫穷悖论与机械对人力的代替。应用科学应该不会因前者而遭受指责，但实际上却不公平地失去了应得的荣誉。关于这一悖论及其解决方案，我没有能力说出什么有价值的东西；但我承认，我从“猴子 vs 人类”中看到的眼前的危机要比“机器 vs 人类”会在当下或未来造成的危机更多！

关于后者，必定正确的是那些与科学打交道的人会坚持认为对人力的替换还将继续。那些怀疑这一点的人无法认识到科学发展的积极作用，不管是纯粹科学还是

now continues. No one can say what kind of equilibrium the distribution of leisure is fated to reach. In any event an optimistic view as to the probable effects of its increase may be justified.

It need not involve a revolutionary change if there is real planning for the future. Lord Melchett was surely right when some time ago he urged on the Upper House that present thought should be given to that future; but I think few men of affairs seriously believe what is yet probable, that the replacement we are thinking of will impose a new structure upon society. This may well differ in some essentials from any of those alternative social forms of which the very names now raise antagonisms. I confess that if civilisation escapes its other perils I should fear little the final reign of the machine. We should not altogether forget the difference in use which can be made of real and ample leisure compared with that possible for very brief leisure associated with fatigue; or the difference between compulsory toil and spontaneous work.

We have to picture, moreover, in Great Britain the reactions of a community which, save for a minority, has shown itself during recent years to be educable. I do not think it fanciful to believe that our highly efficient national broadcasting service, with the increased opportunities which the coming of short wave-length transmission may provide, might well take charge of the systematic education of adolescents after the personal influence of the schoolmaster has prepared them to profit by it. It would not be a technical education but an education for leisure. Listening to organised courses of instruction might at first be for the few; but ultimately might become habitual in that part of the community which it would specially benefit.

In parenthesis allow me a brief further reference to "planning". The word is much to the front just now, chiefly in relation with current enterprises. But there may be planning for more fundamental developments; for future adjustment to social reconstructions. In such planning the trained scientific mind must play its part. Its vision of the future may be very limited, but in respect of material progress and its probable consequences, science (I include all branches of knowledge to which the name applies) has at least better data for prophecy than other forms of knowledge.

It was long ago written, "Wisdom and Knowledge shall be stability of Thy times". Though statesmen may have wisdom adequate for the immediate and urgent problems with which it is their fate to deal, there should yet be a reservoir of synthesised and clarified knowledge on which they can draw. The technique which brings governments in contact with scientific knowledge in particular, though greatly improved of late, is still imperfect. In any case the politician is perforce concerned with the present rather than the future. I have recently read Bacon's "New Atlantis" afresh and have been thinking about his Solomon's House. We know that the rules for the functioning of that House were mistaken because the philosopher drew them up when in the mood of a Lord Chancellor; but in so far as the philosopher visualised therein an organisation of the best intellects bent on gathering knowledge for future practical services, his idea was a great one. When

应用科学，这种发展趋势仍在继续。没人能说清楚闲暇时间的分布最终将达到什么样的平衡。无论如何，乐观地对待闲暇时间增加可能带来的影响也许是有道理的。

如果对于未来有一个真正的计划的话，其实并不需要涉及革命性的变化。梅尔切特勋爵前一阵子在上议院呼吁现在的思考应该为未来做打算当然是正确的；但是我认为，很少有务实的人会真的相信我们正在考虑的机器对人力的取代有可能会使社会产生新的结构。在某些关键环节上，这可能会大大不同于任何可供选择的社会形态，这些社会形态的名字增加了目前的对立。我承认，如果文明逃过了其他危机，那么我应该不必害怕机器的最终统治。我们不应该完全抹杀，真正充足的休息与可能是充满疲惫的极为短暂的休息之间存在的差异；或者存在于强制性劳动与自觉工作之间的差异。

此外，我们不得不描绘一下英国社会的反应，在最近几年中，大多数英国人都表现出了一定的可塑性。我并不认为相信下面的事是不切实际的：我们高效的国家广播设施，以及短波长传输将为我们提供的越来越多的机会，在教师们通过个人影响帮助青少年学会利用它们之后，就可以很好地实现对青少年的系统教育。这并不是一种技术性的教育，而是追求闲暇的教育。最初可能只是少数人能聆听系统的教育课程；但最终将在这部分受益非常大的社会群体中成为习惯。

附带言之，请允许我再简短地谈一谈“计划”。眼下这个词非常热门，主要是与当前的企业界有关。但是还可以有针对更为根本性的发展的计划；针对今后社会改造的调整计划。在类似这样的计划中，训练有素的科学头脑必将发挥其作用。科学对于未来的洞见可能是极为有限的，但是就物质文明及其可能造成的影响而言，科学（我把与这个词有关的所有知识分支都包含在内了）至少比其他认识形式具备更好的可供预言使用的数据。

很久以前，有人写下了这样的话，“智慧与知识将成为你所处时代的稳定因素。”尽管政治家们可能会具有足够的智慧以解决他们注定要去处理的紧迫问题，但还应有一个可供他们利用的综合而明确的知识库。尤其是引领政府机构去与科学接触的方法，尽管近来已大幅改进，但还不够完善。无论如何，政治家都必然会去考虑当前而不是未来。最近我重读了培根的《新大西岛》，并且一直在思考他所说的所罗门宫。我们知道，所罗门宫的运作规程是错误的，因为哲学家是在陷入一位大法官的状态时完成它的；但是就一位哲学家能想象出一个由最出色的智者组成的致力于为未来发展收集知识的机构而言，他的想法是了不起的。当文明陷入危机而社会处于转型阶段时，是否可以有一座招收国家中最出色的智者而组成的宫殿，使其具有与

civilisation is in danger and society in transition, might there not be a House recruited from the best intellects in the country with functions similar (*mutatis mutandis*) to those of Bacon's fancy? A House devoid of politics, concerned rather with synthesising existing knowledge, with a sustained appraisement of the progress of knowledge, and continuously concerned with its bearing upon social readjustments. It is not to be pictured as composed of scientific authorities alone. It would be rather an intellectual exchange where thought would go ahead of immediate problems. I believe that the functions of such a House, in such days as ours, might well be real. Here I must leave them to your fancy, well aware that in the minds of many I may by this bare suggestion lose all reputation as a realist!

I will now hasten to my final words. Most of us have had a tendency in the past to fear the gift of leisure to the majority. To believe that it may be a great social benefit requires some mental readjustment, and a belief in the educability of the average man or woman. But if the political aspirations of the nations should grow sane, and the artificial economic problems of the world be solved, the combined and assured gifts of health, plenty, and leisure may prove to be the final justification of applied science. In a community advantaged by these, each individual will be free to develop his own innate powers, and, becoming more of an individual, will be less moved by those herd instincts which are always the major danger to the world.

It may be felt that, throughout this address, I have dwelt exclusively on the material benefits of science to the neglect of its cultural value. I would like to correct this in a single closing sentence. I believe that for those who cultivate it in a right and humble spirit, science is one of the humanities; no less.

(**132**, 381-394; 1933)

培根所设想的宫殿相似（在细节上需要作必要的改动）的功能呢？一座没有政治的宫殿，更愿意致力于对现有知识的综合，致力于对知识进步的持续性评估，以及始终坚持考虑它对于社会改良的意义。不该把它设想为只由科学权威所构成。它更可能是一个交流智慧的场所，在这里思想会超前于当前的问题。我相信，这样一座宫殿的功能在我们这样的时代中很可能会是真实的。现在我必须把它们留在你们的想象中，我很清楚，在很多人的头脑中，我可能由于这个直言不讳的提议而丧失了作为一个现实主义者的全部名誉！

现在我会尽快进入结尾部分。过去，我们中的很多人都有一种害怕把闲暇留给大多数人的倾向。要使人们相信闲暇可以是一种巨大的社会福利，就需要在思想上进行矫正，并且要抱有普通人可以被教化的信念。但是，如果国家的政治目标逐渐趋于理智，而且人为的世界经济问题得到了解决，那么确保同时得到健康、富足和休息就可以最终证明应用科学是正确的。在一个受益于上述因素的社会中，每个个体都将能够自由地表现自身特有的能力，而且由于变得更加个性化，所以更难于被群聚本能所驱动，后者常常是对世界的主要威胁。

可能有人认为，在整个这次演讲中，我只局限于介绍了科学的物质利益，而忽视了它的文化价值。我愿意用一句结束语来更正这一点。我相信，对于那些以健全和谦逊的精神耕耘的人来说，科学是一种人性；一如既往。

（王耀杨 翻译；刘京国 审稿）

# The Activity of Nerve Cells*

E. D. Adrian

## Editor's Note

**In his presidential address to the British Association, Edgar Adrian here summarizes what is known about the activity and organisation of nerve cells. The specialized, energy-dependent cells convey electrical messages along thread-like extensions, like the "spread of a flame along a fuse". But the problem is how these cells interact to form the nervous system. Groups of neurons can, he says, orchestrate simple behaviours, but complex activities, such as learning and memory, defy reduction to single cells or distinct brain regions. And foreshadowing the beliefs of many modern neuroscientists, Adrian adds that the "ceaseless electrical pulsations" of nerve cells will help researchers unravel the workings of the nervous system.**

SINCE the biologist seeks to understand life, he cannot be accused of lack of courage. But he can find out a great deal without approaching too near the central problem. He can find out how the living cell develops and how it behaves; he can follow many of the physical and chemical changes which take place in it, and could follow more if cells were not so inconveniently small. The immediate problems of the physiologist may be still further removed from the problem of life. They may deal, for example, with the mechanics of the vascular system or with the physical chemistry of blood pigments. But most physiologists aim at explaining the working of the body in terms of its constituent cells, and feel that this is a reasonable aim, even though we must take the cell for granted. Is it a reasonable aim when we are dealing with the working of the nervous system?

The nervous system is responsible for the behaviour of the organism as a whole: in fact, it makes the organism. A frog is killed when its brain and spinal cord are destroyed: its heart still beats and its muscles can still be made to contract, all the cells of its body but those of the brain and cord are as fully alive as they were before; but the frog is dead, and has become a bundle of living tissues with nothing to weld them into a living animal. This integrative action of the nervous system, to use Sherrington's classical phrase, we may be able to explain in terms of the reactions of the constituent nerve cells. We can at least discuss the point as physiologists. But the human organism includes a mind as well as a body. It may be best to follow Pawlow and to see how far we can go without bringing in the mind, but if the reactions of our nerve cells are to explain thought as well as action, we must face the prospect of becoming psychologists and metaphysicians as well. Fortunately, we need not yet go to such extremes.

---

* Presidential address to Section I (Physiology) of the British Association, delivered at Leicester on September 8.

# 神经细胞的活性*

埃德加·阿德里安

## 编者按

这篇文章来自时任英国科学促进会主席的埃德加·阿德里安对该学会所作的演讲，在这里他对神经细胞的组织结构及其活动进行了总结。这些分化的、依赖能量的细胞沿其丝状延伸结构传递电信号，就像“火苗沿着导火线的传播”一样。问题是，这些细胞是如何通过相互作用来组成神经系统的呢？阿德里安提出，神经元间的协同可以完成简单的行为，但是像学习和记忆这样的复杂活动是无法还原到单个细胞或者各个脑区的活动上的。另外，阿德里安还指出，神经细胞中“持续不断的电脉冲”将帮助研究者们破解神经系统的工作机制，这与现代神经学家们的观点不谋而合。

既然生物学家们在努力破解生命的秘密，我们就不能指责他们缺乏勇气。就算他们没能触及问题的最核心部分，也可以发现大量的事实。他们能发现活细胞是如何发育以及发挥功能的；他们也能追踪在细胞内发生的许多物理和化学变化；而且如果细胞不那么小的话，他们还可以研究得更深入。或许生理学家们目前研究的问题仍然与生命的本质问题相去甚远。例如，他们会去研究血管系统的机制或者血色素的物化性质。但是大部分生理学家的目标是用组成机体的细胞来解释机体的工作机制，并且认为这是一个合理的目标，尽管我们必须这么认为。而当我们研究神经系统的功能时，这个目标还合理吗？

神经系统从整体上控制着机体的行为：事实上是它构筑了有机体。当青蛙的脑和脊髓被破坏时，它就会死亡：虽然青蛙的心脏还在跳动，肌肉仍能收缩，除脑和脊髓之外的所有其他细胞都和以前一样充满活力；但青蛙死了，只剩下一大堆活组织而不能构成一个活的生物。按照谢林顿的经典说法，我们也许可以通过组成神经系统的神经细胞的反应活动来解释其整体功能。我们至少能从生理学家的角度讨论这个问题。但人类除了具有躯体之外还具有精神。或许最好的方法是沿着巴甫洛夫的脚步看看如果不考虑精神层面我们能够发现多少东西，如果用神经细胞的活动既解释思想又解释行为，那么我们就不得不面临同时成为心理学家和精神疗法家的可能。幸运的是，我们现在还不需要走这样的极端。

* 本文来自英国科学促进会主席于9月8日在莱斯特对I分会（生理学分会）发表的演讲。

The nervous system, the brain, spinal cord and peripheral nerves, is made up of a large number of living cells which grow, maintain themselves by the metabolism of food-stuffs, and carry out all the complex reactions of living protoplasm. In this there are enough problems for anyone; but we are concerned not with the general properties of living cells but with those special properties which enable the cells of the nervous system to perform their functions. Their function is to make the organism respond rapidly and effectively to changes in its environment, and to achieve this they have developed a specialised structure, and a complex arrangement in the body. They send out long threads of protoplasm which serve for the rapid transmission of signals, and they are linked to one another by elaborate branching connexions in the brain and the spinal cord.

## Development of the Nervous System

The mapping of this network of paths was begun many years ago, and was the first step in the analysis. No progress could have been made without it, and its results are of vital importance to neurology. We are now witnessing a fresh period of interest in the geography of the central nervous system, but the problem is not how the nerve cells and their fibres are arranged, but why they are arranged as they are. R. G. Harrison, in his recent Croonian lecture before the Royal Society, recalled the time when he first cultivated living nerve cells outside the body. That experiment, made twenty-three years ago, marks the new epoch better than any other, for, besides introducing the method of tissue culture, it settled a long and bitter controversy as to the origin of nerve fibres. Nowadays the most elaborate transplantation experiments are carried out by the embryologists on amphibian larvae. Animals are produced with supernumerary limbs, eyes, noses, and even spinal cords. The growing nervous system is faced with these unusual bodily arrangements, and by studying the changes induced in it we can form some idea of the factors which determine its normal structure.

A review published this summer by Detweiler gives a vivid impression of the plasticity of the developing nervous system in the hands of the experimenter. As a rule it accepts the extra limb or sense organ, links it by nerve fibres to the rest of the organism and may develop more nerve cells to deal with it. The forces which mould the nervous system seem to come partly from within the central mass of nerve cells and partly from the body outside. These forces may be chemical or electrical gradients, and often the nerve fibres seem to grow in particular directions because they cling mechanically to structures already laid down, for example, to the main arteries of the limbs. It is unlikely that a simple formula will be found for such a complex arrangement, but the fact remains that the arrangement can be profoundly modified at the will of the experimenter. Its detail seems to depend not so much on the innate properties of particular cells as on the environment provided by the rest of the organism.

## Reactions of the Neurons

This new embryological work supports the older in showing that the nervous system is

神经系统，即脑、脊髓和外周神经，是由大量活细胞组成的，这些活细胞利用食物代谢进行生长发育并维持活性，还要完成生物体的所有复杂行为。这里有太多的问题需要解决；然而我们关心的不是活细胞所具有的一般特性，而是那些使神经细胞发挥自身功能的特殊性质。神经细胞的功能是使生物体迅速而有效地对环境的改变作出反应，为了实现这个功能，它们形成了自己的特殊结构并在有机体内部形成了复杂的组织方式。它们发出长长的细胞质突起，用于快速传递信号，在脑和脊髓中它们通过精细的分支相互连接在一起。

## 神经系统的发育

许多年前人们就开始描绘这个复杂的网络，这是分析过程的第一步。如果没有这方面知识就无法开展下一步的工作，而且这项工作的研究成果对于神经病学也具有至关重要的意义。目前我们对中枢神经系统布局的研究进入了一个有趣的新阶段，不过问题不在于神经细胞及它们的纤维是如何分布的，而在于为什么它们会这样分布。最近，哈里森在英国皇家学会主办的克鲁尼安讲座上回顾了他第一次在体外培养活神经细胞的经历。这项在 23 年以前进行的实验在开创新纪元方面超越了其他实验，因为除了引进组织培养法外，它还平息了人们对神经纤维起源问题的长期激战。如今，胚胎学家们可以在两栖动物幼体中进行最精细的移植实验。人们可以制造出具有多余肢体、眼睛、鼻子甚至脊髓的动物。发育中的神经系统要面对这些不正常的身体构造，而通过研究其中发生的改变我们就能认识到一些决定其正常结构的因素。

在今年夏天发表的一篇综述中，德特韦勒生动地描述了发育中的神经系统在实验者手中的可塑性。在通常情况下，它会接受多余的肢体或感觉器官，通过神经纤维将其与身体其他部分联系起来，并发育出更多的神经细胞来支配它。塑造神经系统的力量似乎有一部分来自于神经细胞的核心，而另一部分来自于机体的外部。这些力可能来自于化学或电位梯度，而且在通常情况下神经纤维似乎会向特定的方向生长，因为它们会机械地附着在已经长好的结构上，比如四肢的大动脉上。要在这么复杂的构建中找到简单的规律是不太可能的，但事实上这些构建是可以按照实验者的意愿发生很大变化的。有机体其余部分构筑的环境对构建变化的影响似乎要大于某些细胞的固有特性对它的影响。

## 神经元的反应

这项新的胚胎学研究结果证明了原有的理论，即认为神经系统是由“神经元”——

made up of "neurons", cells with thread-like extensions, and that they are the only active elements in it. These elements are all cast in the same mould, but are shaped differently by the forces of development. To this we can now add the fact that all neurons seem to do their work in much the same way. The activity which they show is in some respects remarkably simple. It is essentially rhythmic: a series of rapid alternations between the resting and the active state, due probably to rapid breakdown and repair of the surface. This at least is a fair description of the way in which the nerve fibres carry out their function of conducting messages, and we can detect the same kind of pulsating activity in the nerve cells of the brain.

The evidence comes from the analysis of minute electric changes, for cell activity sets up electrical eddies in the surrounding fluid, and these can be measured with a minimum of interference. The clearest results are given by the peripheral nerve fibres which connect the central nervous system to the sense organs and the muscles. The nerve fibres are conveniently arranged in bundles to form the nerve trunks: each fibre is an independent conducting path and there may be a thousand such paths in a fair-sized nerve, but it is not a difficult matter to study what takes place in the single fibre when it conducts a message.

We may begin with an external stimulus acting on a sense organ, a structure which includes the sensitive ending of a nerve fibre as an essential part. The ending is excited by the stimulus, the delicate equilibrium of its surface is upset and the disturbance tends to spread along the fibre. The spreading is an active process: it takes place because the fibre has a store of energy ready to be liberated at a moment's notice, and because the changes which attend its liberation at one point upset the balance at the next point and cause the same activity there. The spread of a flame along a fuse is a well-worn analogy. But the nerve fibre is so constituted that a disturbance at any point is almost immediately cut short. The change spreads along it as a momentary wave—a brief impulse followed inevitably by a brief interval of rest and recovery. If the sense organ remains excited, a second impulse passes up the fibre, and then another and another so long as the stimulus is effective.

The impulses in a given nerve fibre are all alike in magnitude, rate of travel, etc., but the frequency at which they recur depends on the intensity of the stimulus, rising sometimes so high as 300 a second in each fibre, or falling so low as 10. All the nervous messages take this form.

The conducting threads or nerve fibres are exceedingly insensitive to changes in their environment: their endings in the sense organs are exceedingly sensitive. The sole function of the ending is to act as the trigger mechanism for firing off the impulses, and the sole function of the nerve fibre is to carry the message without distortion. Both are specialised parts of the neurone with specialised reactions, but it is important to note that these reactions are not peculiar to the nervous system. Muscle fibres, developed from the mesoderm and specialised for contraction, conduct impulses which seem to differ merely in their time relations from those in nerve fibres, and they can also be made to behave like the sensory endings by treatment with various salt solutions. In sodium chloride, for

有丝状突起的细胞组成的，而且它们是系统内唯一的活性成分。所有神经元都是按同一种模式生成的，但在发育时长成了不同的形状。关于这一点我们现在又有了一个新的发现，即发现所有神经元都以大致相同的方式工作。在某种程度上可以说它们进行的活动非常简单。这个过程是重复出现的：处于静息状态和活动状态之间的一系列快速转换很可能是由膜表面的快速降解和修复导致的。这种解释至少能合理地说明神经纤维在实现信息传递功能时所采取的方式，而且我们在脑神经细胞中也检测到了同样的节律性活动。

证据来自于对微小电位变化的分析，因为细胞活动会使周围液体形成电涡流，而这些涡流可以在最小的干扰下被测定。最清晰的结果是从把中枢神经系统连接到感觉器官和肌肉上的外周神经纤维中得到的。神经纤维集合成束形成神经干：每条纤维都是独立的传导通路，虽然在一条中等大小的神经干中可能有一千条这样的通路，但要研究单个纤维在传递信息时的情况并不是一件难事。

我们也许可以从作用于感觉器官的外部刺激入手，神经纤维的感觉末梢在感觉器官中是一个非常重要的部分。该末梢受到刺激后兴奋，其膜表面的微妙平衡被打破，而且这种扰动会沿着纤维传播下去。这种传播是一个主动的过程：它之所以能够发生是因为神经纤维提前储备好了能量以便在瞬间释放，而且因为在一个点上由能量释放引发的变化打破了下一个点的平衡并在那里产生了相同的变化。我们常用火苗沿导火线的传播来进行类比。然而神经纤维的结构如此完善以至于在任意点的扰动都可以马上被打断。变化以瞬时波的形式沿神经纤维传播——在一个短暂的冲动后必然紧接着短暂的休息恢复期。如果感觉器官仍处在兴奋状态，第二个冲动就又会沿着纤维传过来，只要存在有效的刺激，冲动就会不断地传过来。

特定神经纤维中的冲动在幅度和传播速度等方面都是相似的，但冲动产生的频率取决于刺激的强度，有时在每个纤维中可以达到300/秒，有时低至10/秒。所有由神经传播的信息都采用这种模式。

导电线或神经纤维对于周围环境的变化是非常不敏感的：但它们在感觉器官中的末梢却很敏感。末梢的唯一功能就是作为冲动的触发器，而神经纤维的唯一功能是准确无误地传递信息。两者都是神经元的特殊部分，具备特殊的反应，但值得一提的是这些反应并非神经系统所独有。从中胚层发育而来专门用来收缩的肌纤维也能传递冲动，与神经纤维传递的冲动仅存在时间关系上的差别，在各种盐溶液的作用下它们也能像感觉末梢那样工作。比如，在氯化钠溶液中，当肌肉受到牵拉时就会产生一系列的冲动，这些冲动就好像发生在一个唯一功能是充当“牵张感受器”

example, a series of impulses will be set up in a muscle fibre when it is stretched, as they would be in one of the sense organs the sole duty of which is to act as "stretch receptors". The muscle fibre makes a poor copy of the nervous mechanism, for it reacts jerkily and is often damaged in the process, but the ground-plan of the mechanism is the same.

Thus in the activities concerned in the rapid conduction and in the setting up of rhythmic trains of impulses, it does not appear that the cells of the nervous system have properties not shared in some degree by other tissues.

So far we have only considered what happens in nerve fibres. We can tap the messages which pass along the wires between the front line and headquarters, but this does not tell us how they are elaborated there. A great deal has been found out already by the analysis of reflexes—that is, by sending in a known combination of signals and finding what signals come out to the muscles; indeed, the great part of Sherrington's work on the spinal reflexes and Pawlow's on the brain has been carried out in this way. The results are so well known, however, that I shall deal here with a recent line of attack of an entirely different kind.

This method relies on the fact that nervous activity, in the central grey matter as in the peripheral nerves, is accompanied by electric changes. They seem to be a reliable index of the underlying activity, and by recording them we come a step nearer to the main problem. The chief difficulty is to interpret the records. In the cerebral cortex, for example, very large electric oscillations are constantly occurring, except in the deepest anaesthesia, but they vary from moment to moment and from place to place, and it is only in the visual cortex that they are under a fair degree of experimental control. Here they can be produced by shining a light in the eye (Fischer, Kornmüller and Tönnies) or stimulating the optic nerve (Bartley and Bishop), and the prospects of analysis are more hopeful.

At the moment, however, the most significant feature of these records from the brain lies in the appearance of the waves. Whenever a group of nerve cells is in action, in the cerebral cortex, the brain stem or the retina, and whether the nerve cells in question belong to a vertebrate, or an insect, the waves are alike in general form. Instead of the abrupt spikes which appear in a record from a nerve fibre when a train of impulses passes down it, we have more gradual potential changes which form a series of waves of smooth contour. In the simpler structures where most of the neurons are acting in unison, the waves may have a regular rhythm (5–90 or more a second), which rises and falls when the stimulus changes in intensity. It is often possible to make out both the abrupt nerve fibre impulses and the slower nerve cell waves, and to show that they occur together. In the cerebral cortex of an anaesthetised animal there is much more variety and less orderly repetition; the waves usually occur at irregular intervals; they vary in size and duration, and some of them may last for half a second or even longer.

的感觉器官之中。肌纤维并不是神经纤维的良好复制品，因为它只能间断性地作出反应而且冲动经常在传导过程中被损毁，但两者的基本作用机制是相同的。

因此在有关快速传递和冲动规律性形成的行为中，神经系统的细胞所具有的性质看上去与其他组织没有什么不同。

到目前为止我们只考虑了神经纤维中的情况。尽管我们能够从连接前线与指挥部之间的这段线路中截取传递的信息，但我们并不知道它们是怎样被制造出来的。人们在对反射的分析中已经取得了很大的进展——即通过发送一组已知信号并监测哪些信号会传递到肌肉中；实际上，谢林顿在脊髓反射方面的大部分工作和巴甫洛夫对脑的研究都是用这种方法进行的。不过他们取得的成果已经众所周知，我在这里要讲的是一种完全不同的新方法。

这种新方法基于一个事实，即无论是中枢灰质还是外周神经的活动都伴随着电位的改变。它们似乎是反映神经活动的可靠指标，通过记录它们，我们就又向解决主要问题迈进了一步。主要的困难在于对记录结果的解释。比如在大脑皮层，非常大的电振荡一直存在，除非处于最深度的麻醉之下，不过电振荡会随着时间和空间的不同不断发生变化，视觉皮层是唯一一个能让它们在一定程度下受到实验控制的地方。用光线照射眼睛（费希尔、科恩米勒和滕尼斯）或刺激视神经（巴特利和毕肖普）可以产生电振荡，这种分析方式是很有希望取得成功的。

但是现在，对于从大脑中获得的记录来说，波形是它们最重要的特征。只要一组神经细胞处于活动状态，我们就会得到大体类似的波，无论是在大脑皮层、脑干或者视网膜，也无论这些神经细胞是来自脊椎动物还是来自昆虫。与当一组冲动经过神经纤维时记录下来的尖峰不同，我们看到的多数是电位的逐渐变化，因而形成了一系列平滑的波。在大多数神经元同时起作用的简单结构中，波也许会有一个统一的节律（每秒 5~90 或者更多），周期性随刺激强度的变化有升有降。我们通常能辨认出突发的神经纤维冲动和平缓的神经细胞波，并且可以说明它们是同时发生的。在被麻醉动物的大脑皮层中，多为变化大且重复性不高的波；这些波出现的间隔通常是不规则的；它们的大小和持续时间不尽相同，有些可持续半秒或更长时间。

Nerve cell waves may be the wrong name, for they are probable due to the branching dendrites and not to the cell body of the neurone; but there can be no doubt that they represent a characteristic activity of the structures which make up the grey matter. They show that the same kind of rhythmic breakdown and repair of the surface takes place in this part of the neurone as in the nerve fibre, with the important difference that the changes develop and subside much less abruptly. The surface is not specialised for rapid conduction; the forces which restore the resting equilibrium are less powerful and there is more tendency to spontaneous breakdown and to long periods of uninterrupted activity. We know that the activity of the grey matter is far more readily influenced by chemical changes than is that of the nerve fibre with its elaborate fatty sheath and wrappings of connective tissue, and it seems probable that both chemical and electric changes may be concerned in the spread of activity from one neurone to another. How this spread takes place is still uncertain, and it is admittedly the most important problem we have to face.

In spite of this, we can claim to have some of the main outlines of neurone activity. Our nervous system is built up of cells with a specialised structure and reactions, but the reactions are of a type to be found in many other cells. The rhythmic beat of the heart is probably due to surface reactions not far different from those in the group of nerve cells which produce the rhythmic movements of breathing; and the factors, nervous and chemical, which regulate the heart beat are probably much the same as the factors which control the discharge of the neurone. We have a store of energy, replenished constantly by cell metabolism and liberated periodically by surface breakdown. The electrical gradients at the active point cause a spread of the breakdown to other regions, but sooner or later restoring forces come into play, the membranes are healed and the cycle is ready to be repeated. It is a long step from the mechanical precision of an impulse discharge in a nerve fibre to the irregularities of a record from the cerebral cortex, but there are many intermediate cases which will bridge the gap.

## The Nervous System as a Whole

So far as the units are concerned, the prospect is encouraging. The difficulties begin when we come to the work of the nervous system as a whole. Many of its reactions are mechanical enough and can be explained in terms of the activity of groups of neurons, but there is much that resists this kind of treatment. It is perhaps encouraging that the difficulties are greatest when the reactions depend on the cerebral cortex, when they involve learning and memory, or, if you prefer it, habit formation and conditioning. They have been clearly stated by Lashley, and most of them can be reduced in the end to a simple formula, the failure of anatomical models of the nervous system. The revolt from the anatomical model has been growing for many years, though it may be doubted whether its sponsors ever believed in it as much as their critics suppose. It gave us diagrams of nerve centres and pathways which were valuable enough when they referred to known anatomical structure, but not when they referred, as they often did, to hypothetical centres and to pathways canalised by use. These too may exist, but they are not the whole explanation of cortical activity.

神经细胞波也许是一种错误的叫法，因为它们可能源自树突分枝而非神经元细胞体本身；但毫无疑问这些波代表了灰质结构的本质性活动。它们说明：神经元的这部分也和神经纤维一样发生着周期性相同的膜表面裂解和修复，但最大的不同在于变化的发生和消失更为平稳。这些膜表面并非仅能进行快速传导；膜表面保持静息平衡的力量不够强大，因而有自发裂解和进行长期不间断活动的趋势。我们知道化学变化对灰质活性的影响要远远大于有致密脂肪鞘和结缔组织包层的神经纤维，当兴奋从一个神经元传向另一个神经元的时候，化学性质和电位都有可能发生变化。我们现在仍不知道这种传播是如何进行的，大家都承认这是我们不得不去面对的最重要的问题。

尽管如此，我们可以认为自己已经掌握了神经元活性的主要概况。我们的神经系统由具有特殊结构和反应的细胞组成，不过在许多其他细胞中也能发现这样的反应。引起心脏律动的膜表面反应可能与产生规律呼吸运动的神经细胞群体的膜表面反应没有明显的不同；调节心脏律动的神经及化学因子很可能也与控制神经元放电的因子近似相同。我们所储存的能量，一方面由细胞代谢不断地补充，另一方面从膜表面的裂解中周期性地得到释放。激活部位的电梯度促使裂解传播到其他部位，但储存的能量迟早要发挥作用，在膜得到修复后就又可以进行下一轮的循环了。从神经纤维释放冲动的精确性到在大脑皮层中记录下来的不规则性之间还有很大一段距离，不过大量有关中间过程的研究将架起联结两者的桥梁。

## 神经系统整体观

就各个组成部分的情况而言，前景是乐观的。然而当我们把神经系统作为一个整体进行研究时就出现了困难。神经系统的许多反应高度机制化，可以用神经元群的活动来解释，但有很多因素与这种处理方法相抵触。也许值得庆幸的是，当反应依赖于大脑皮层，当涉及学习和记忆，或者，在你愿意的情况下形成习惯和条件反射时难度最大。拉什利已经对此进行了明确的阐述，大部分结果最终都归结成了一个简单的结论，神经系统的解剖模型是失败的。反对解剖模型的意见已经存在了许多年，尽管人们怀疑发起者们过去对它的支持是否和现在对它的批评一样坚定。模型为我们提供了神经中枢和通路的概况，但是仅当其所指的是已知的解剖结构时才有足够的价值，如果像过去那样指的是假设的中枢和改造的通路，那价值就不明显了。它们也可能是存在的，但不能完全解释皮质的活动。

Clinical neurology is partly to blame for the emphasis laid on exact localisation. The neurologist must locate brain tumours by analysing the disturbances they produce; consequently he welcomes the slightest evidence of localisation of function in the cortex, and finds the anatomical model valuable for correlating his observations. Undoubtedly there are well-defined nervous pathways, clear differences in cell structure and localised activity in different parts of the brain. As a modern addition to the evidence we have Foerster's recent work on the electrical stimulation of the human cortex, and his finding that stimulation of the temporal lobe may cause sounds and words to arise in consciousness, whilst stimulation of the occipital lobe gives lights or images. Bard has given another remarkable example of strict cortical localisation by his observations on certain postural reactions in the cat. These depend on a limited area in the frontal region, are not affected by damage to other parts of the brain, but are permanently lost if the frontal area is destroyed. The danger nowadays is that we may pay too little attention to such facts; but it is true, nevertheless, that the localisation is a matter of areas rather than of single neurons. This is shown by examination of habit formation, and by the remarkable way in which the nervous system adapts itself to injury.

It has often been pointed out that we learn to recognise shapes—the letters of the alphabet, for example—however they are presented to us. The pattern of black and white made on our retina by the letter A need not fall on a particular set of retinal endings connected with particular cortical neurons. We have learnt to recognise a relation of lines and angles, a pattern of activity in the cortex rather than an activity of specific points. This kind of reaction is not due to our superior intelligence. Lashley finds it in the rat, and psychologists of the *Gestalt* school have pointed out examples from all manner of animals. There is the same neglect of specific neurons in the formation of motor habits, for if we have once learnt to write the letter A with our right hand, we can make a fair attempt to write it with any group of muscles which can control a pencil.

The adaptations to injury present a different aspect of the same story. An insect which has lost a leg will at once change its style of walking to make up for the loss. This may involve a complete alteration of the normal method, limbs which were advanced alternately being now advanced simultaneously. The activities of the nervous system are directed to a definite end, the forward movement of the animal—it uses whatever means are at its disposal and is not limited to particular pathways.

When the central nervous system is injured, there is more evidence of localised function, but the localisation is no hard-and-fast affair. A rat uses its occipital cortex in the formation of certain visual habits. When this part of the cortex is destroyed the habit is lost, but it can be re-learnt just as rapidly as before with what remains of the brain. A monkey's arm is paralysed if the corresponding motor area of the cortex is destroyed, but the paralysis soon passes away although there is no regeneration of the motor cortex. What is more remarkable is that the recovered functions are not associated with the development of a new visual region or motor region in the brain. Though they were originally localised, there is no longer any one part of the cortex which is essential.

临床神经病学因为将重点放在准确的定位上而备受指责。神经病学家们只有通过分析症状才能定位脑肿瘤；因此他们乐意接受在皮层中进行最细小的功能定位，并且发现解剖模型与观察结果可以相互关联。毫无疑问，大脑中存在清晰的神经通路、明显不同的细胞结构以及不同部位的局部活动。弗尔斯特最近关于人类皮层电刺激的研究为我们增加了最新的证据，他发现刺激颞叶可以使意识中出现声音和语言，刺激枕叶可以出现光或图像。巴德在观察了猫的某些姿势反射之后，给出了另一个值得关注的皮层精确定位的例子。它们依赖于额叶区的有限范围，不受脑其他部位损伤的影响，如果额叶受到损伤，这一功能就会永久丧失。现在的危机在于我们很少关注这些事实；不过定位肯定是在一个区域内而不是在单个的神经元上。对习惯化的考查以及神经系统适应损伤的奇特方式都证实了这一点。

人们经常说我们要学习识别形状，如字母表里的字母，其实它们就在我们面前。字母 A 在我们视网膜上形成的黑白图案不需要落到与特定皮层神经元相联系的特定视网膜神经末梢上。我们已经学会识别线与角之间的关系，这是大脑皮层中的一种活动形式，而不是某些特殊点的活动。这类反应与人类超群的智力无关。拉什利发现大鼠也具有这一识别能力，**格式塔**学派的心理学家在各种各样的动物身上都找到了类似的例子。在运动习性的形成过程中也同样会出现忽略某些特殊神经元的情况，因为一旦我们学会了用右手书写字母 A，我们就可以通过一定的努力让其他能够控制铅笔的肌肉群也能书写字母 A。

对损伤的适应反映了这一问题的另一个方面。一只失去一条腿的昆虫很快就会通过改变走路的姿势弥补缺腿的不足。这样做可能会完全改变原来的方式，以前交替移动的腿现在要同时移动。要达到的特定目标支配着神经系统的活动使动物往前移动，采用什么方式可以自行决定而不受具体模式的限制。

在中枢神经系统受到损伤时，我们可以得到更多有关定位功能的证据，但定位并不是一成不变的。大鼠用枕叶皮层来形成某种视觉习惯。当这部分皮层受到损坏时，这种习惯也会丢失，但它能够利用剩余的大脑皮层和从前一样快地再次学会。如果运动皮层区受到损坏，猴子的上肢就会瘫痪，但瘫痪的上肢会很快恢复功能，尽管运动皮层不能再生。更神奇的是这些功能的恢复并不是因为在大脑中形成了新的视觉区或者运动区。虽然这些功能原先有定位，但任何一部分皮层都不是绝对必要的。

In reactions where there is no evidence of localisation (for example, the learning of maze habits in the rat), Lashley finds that the important factor is the total mass of the cortex and not the presence of particular regions. The effect of an injury depends on its extent and not on its situation. It depends, too, on the amount of grey matter (nerve cells and dendrites) destroyed, and not on the cutting of connexions between the different parts of the cortex. Thus the ability of the brain to form new associations, and generally to control the behaviour of the animal, depends primarily on the total area covered by the nerve cells of the cortex and their interlacing dendrites. For certain reactions it depends to some extent on the arrangement of pathways, but this arrangement is not essential. There is more localisation of function in the large brain of man than in the very small brain of the rat, for different cortical regions may be completely equivalent when they are separated by 5 mm., but not when they are separated by 100 mm. But apart from this difference in scale, it is likely that the human cortex has the same mass effect and plasticity of function.

How do the individual neurons combine to produce a system which can recognise a triangle or direct the movements of the organism with such disregard of detailed structure? If particular neurons or pathways are not tuned to triangularity, how can the whole mass be tuned to it, and why should the tuning be more certain when the mass is greater? Our data may be at fault and the mass effect an illusion, but there is certainly enough evidence for it to be taken seriously. Though there is no solution at the moment, I cannot believe that one will not be found—a solution which need not go outside the conceptions of physiology. It should be possible, for example, to find out how many neurons must be combined to give a system which reacts in this way and what kind of structure they must form. The nervous systems of insects may provide the clue, for these may contain a few thousand nerve cells in place of the ten thousand million in the human brain. It is possible also to study the reactions of isolated parts of the central nervous system, to see how far their behaviour can be explained in terms of the units which compose them. The retina is an interesting example of this kind, for it contains an elaborate structure of nerve cells and dendrite connexions, and has some of the reactions which we might expect from a mosaic of sensory endings, and some which depend on interaction between the different neurons.

Even now, however, we can form some idea of the way in which the grey matter can act as a whole. The electric oscillations in the cortex and in the grey matter generally are often due to a large number of units pulsating in unison. Sometimes there are several competing rhythms, and sometimes the collective action breaks down altogether, to reappear from time to time when some part of the system is stimulated to greater activity. When these collective rhythms appear, the neurons are already acting as though they formed one unit. There is no need to regard the dendrites as forming a continuous network—electric forces may well bridge the gaps between them—but they may form a system in which activity can be transmitted more or less freely in all directions. The patterns of activity in a system of this kind would be like the ripples on the surface of a pond, with the difference that some of the ripples may occur spontaneously, whilst others are due to incoming signals. Interference figures and nodes of vibration may then be all-important. They would at least

在没有定位证据的反应中（比如大鼠迷宫行为的学习），拉什利发现关键因素在于皮层的整体而不是特定区域的存在。一个损伤造成的影响取决于它的范围而不是位置。损伤造成的影响还取决于被损坏的灰质（神经细胞和树突）的数量，而与皮层不同区域之间的连接是否被破坏无关。因此大脑形成新联系以及整体控制动物行为的能力主要取决于皮层神经细胞和它们交错排列的树突所占的整体区域。对于某些反应来说，它在一定程度上取决于通路的排列，但这种排列并不是不可缺少的。人的大脑要远远大于大鼠的大脑，因而具有更多的功能定位，因为当分隔为 5 毫米时，不同的皮层区域可能是完全相同的，但是当分隔为 100 毫米时就不相同了。不过除了这种在脑大小上的差别，人类的皮层很可能也具有同样的整体效应和功能可塑性。

如果不考虑具体的结构，这些单独的神经元是如何组合在一起形成一个系统来识别三角形和指挥生物体的运动的呢？如果单个的神经元或者通路不能识别三角形，那么整体又是怎么识别的，而且为何当这个整体越大时其识别能力就越强呢？我们的数据可能是错误的，这种整体效应只是一个错觉，但确实有足够的证据使我们必须认真对待这个问题。尽管现在还没有解决的方法，但我不相信将来人们找不到一个答案，一个不会超出生理学范畴的答案。比如应该可以找到要想形成一个以这种方式发生反应的系统需要多少个神经元，以及它们需要形成什么样的结构。昆虫的神经系统或许能为我们提供线索，因为昆虫可能只含有几千个神经细胞，而人脑中有 100 亿个。也可以通过研究中枢神经系统各独立部分的功能来考察它们的行为在多大程度上可以用组成它们的单元来解释。视网膜是一个有趣的例子，因为它含有由神经细胞和树突联系组成的复杂结构，而且它的一部分行为可以用感觉末梢的嵌合体来解释，而另一部分行为则依赖于不同神经元之间的相互作用。

然而，即使是现在，我们也能了解到灰质作为一个整体的工作方式。皮层和灰质中发生的电振荡通常是由于大量组成单元一起振动的结果。有时候会出现几个竞争的振荡节律，有时候集体行动完全停止，当系统中某个部分被刺激到具有更大的兴奋性时，集体行动会再现。当集体节奏出现的时候，这些神经元表现得像是形成了一个整体。没有必要认为树突形成了一个连续的网络，因为电场力完全可以打通它们之间的间隙，但树突会形成一个能使兴奋在各个方向上自由传播的系统。这种系统中的兴奋形式就像池塘表面的涟漪，不同之处在于有些涟漪可能是自发产生的，而另一些是由于接受了传入的信息而产生的。因此，干涉图和振动节点都非常重要。至少它们提供了在不需要进行特定点激发的情况下识别成三角形或成正方形等的关

give a basis for the recognition of relations such as those of triangularity or squareness without the need for an excitation of specific points, and they might be formed with less distortion in a large pond than in a small one.

This does not take us vary far: in fact, the major problems of the central nervous system are left in greater obscurity than ever. But no one can observe these ceaseless electrical pulsations without realising that they provide a fresh set of data, and may give a fresh outlook on the working of the brain. The facts are still too uncertain to be worth treating in greater detail. But they accumulate rapidly, and several lines of evidence seem to lead in the same direction. For the present, it is enough to state our problem, that of the organisation of neurons into the nervous system. It is still a physiological problem, and I hope that a solution will be found on physiological lines. If it cannot be found, it will be extremely interesting to see where the breakdown occurs; and if it can, it will be even more interesting to see what light it throws on the relation of the nervous system to the mind.

(**132**, 465-468; 1933)

系的基础，而且在大池塘中可能比在小池塘中失真度更低。

我们并没有因此取得很大的进步：事实上，中枢神经系统的主要问题比以前更令人困惑。但是每一个看到这些持续不断的电振荡的人都会认为它们提供了新的数据，而且可能会为大脑的研究开辟新途径。这些事实仍然不是很可靠，不值得我们投入更多的精力。但是这方面的证据越来越多，而且好几条证据都指向了同一个目标。现在我们完全可以提出关于神经元在神经系统中的构成问题。这仍旧是一个生理学问题，我希望能在生理学范畴内找到答案。如果找不到，我们也非常想了解问题出在哪里；如果能找到，我们更愿意知道它是怎样解释神经系统和思维之间的联系的。

（毛晨晖 翻译；刘力 审稿）

# Recent Developments in Television*

A. Church

## Editor's Note

**Companies in Europe and America were racing to develop the technology for television. As Archibald Church notes in this review, the scepticism widely expressed in 1926 after John Baird first demonstrated blurred and flickering television images was now being replaced by feverish excitement. In 1932, the Derby horse race had been televised and projected to a live audience in London, and the British Broadcasting Corporation had installed transmission equipment from Baird Television Ltd. Now engineers were developing improved displays based on cathode rays projected on fluorescent screens, and live broadcast was approaching feasibility. A finer screen resolution was needed, however and it was becoming necessary to allocate place in the broadcast spectrum for television signals.**

ALL development of the art of television is recent. It is less than ten years since John Baird first obtained televised images of simple stationary objects such as a Maltese cross. He first demonstrated "real" television, the instantaneous reception of optical images of moving subjects, images of which had been transmitted by means of a variable electric current, on January 27, 1926. Most of the scientific workers and publicists present at that demonstration, while impressed by the achievement, were frankly sceptical of television ever achieving any position as a medium of entertainment or of its being put to other commercial uses. The received images were recognisable, but blurred and flickering, and to many scientific workers, a proof of the impossibility of advance in television by a mechanical system of transmission and reception. Other scientific observers, though less antipathetic to the mechanical system, were unconvinced that television broadcasting would ever be practicable owing to the wide range of frequencies which would have to be made available if images with detail comparing with that obtainable on a cinema screen were to be received. This was the more vital criticism of television, as it applied not only to the mechanical means by which Baird obtained his first results but also to any other means, for example, the utilisation of cathode rays, which might afterwards be enlisted in the service of television.

Only minor modifications had been made of the original apparatus used when Baird gave his first demonstration to members of the British Association at Leeds in 1927. In 1926 the subject to be televised was bathed in light from a battery of powerful electric lamps. Between the photoelectric cells and the illuminated subject was a scanning device, a disc in which thirty holes were punched at regular intervals on a spiral and making five revolutions per second. The subject was thus scanned by a rotating optical element strip by strip, each strip being presented in sequence to a light sensitive element,

---

* Paper read before Section A (Mathematical and Physical Sciences) of the British Association at Leicester on September 13.

# 电视技术的最新进展*

阿奇博尔德·丘奇

## 编者按

欧洲和美洲的公司在电视技术的研制方面正在展开竞争。正如阿奇博尔德·丘奇在这篇评论文章中所说的：当约翰·贝尔德在1926年首次向公众演示那些模糊和闪烁的电视图像时，人们普遍对此持怀疑态度，但现在这项技术正如火如荼地发展着。1932年，有人把德比马赛拍摄下来并实时传送给伦敦的观众；而且英国广播公司也已经安装了贝尔德电视有限公司的转播设备。现在工程师们正在想办法把阴极射线投射到荧光屏上以改善图像的质量，并使现场直播成为可能。这需要有较高的屏幕分辨率，而且还需要在广播频带中为电视信号安插一定的位置。

电视技术的所有发展都是最近涌现出来的。从约翰·贝尔德第一次获得简单静态物体，例如马尔他十字形的电视图像到现在还不到10年时间。在1926年1月27日，贝尔德第一次演示了"真正"的电视，这个装置可以即时接收到运动物体的光学图像，图像的传输是通过电流的变化实现的。很多科学工作者和媒体人士都出席了这次演示会，虽然他们被这项成就深深震撼，但仍坦言对电视是否能成为娱乐业的媒介之一或是否能被应用于其他商业用途持怀疑态度。尽管人们可以分辨出接收到的图像，但比较模糊而且忽隐忽现，所以许多科学工作者认为，电视的发展不可能通过机械式的传送和接收系统来实现。尽管其他的科学观察者对机械系统的反对不那么强烈，但也不相信可以这样来实现电视的转播，因为电视图像要是能与电影院屏幕上播放的图像一样清晰，就需要有很宽的频率范围。这个提法对电视的发展更为致命，因为它不仅否定了贝尔德在获得初步成功时所应用的机械手段，也否定了将来有可能应用于电视技术的其他手段，如阴极射线。

在贝尔德1927年首次在利兹向英国科学促进会成员展示电视的时候，这套设备仅仅做了很小的改动。在1926年时，人们用一组功率很高的电灯照射要被电视转播的物体。在光电管和被照射的物体之间有一个扫描设备，扫描设备是一个圆盘，在圆盘的周边沿螺线每隔一定间隔排列着30个小孔，圆盘每秒转5圈。一个旋转的光学元件一条一条地扫描要被电视转播的物体，每一条信息都会按顺序传递到一个光敏元件——光电管上。光电管中电流强度的变化会改变位于接收端的氖灯的亮

* 这篇论文曾在英国科学促进会A分会（数学和物理学分会）于9月13日在莱斯特举行的会议上被宣读过。

the photoelectric cells. The varying strength of electric current transmitted by the photoelectric cells modified the light in a neon lamp at the receiving end, and this varying single light source was scanned in turn by a "Nipkow" disc synchronised with the disc at the transmitting end. The reconstituted image, two inches square, was seen by looking at the neon lamp through the scanning disc. Synchronism was obtained by the use of synchronous motors.

For the Leeds demonstration "noctovision" was used, the person televised being shielded from the direct glare of the lamps by a sheet of ebonite. In the meantime, however, Baird had made a further notable advance by his invention of the light spot method of scanning. To quote the text of his patent: "The scene or object to be transmitted is traversed by a spot of light, a light sensitive cell being so placed that light reflected back from the spot of light traversing the object falls on the cell." It is, in effect, an inversion of the flood-lighting method, and possesses the advantage that greatly increased signal strengths are obtained with considerable diminution in the intensity of the illumination to which the subject of transmission is exposed.

Abroad, the method was almost immediately applied by the Bell Telephone Company in the United States in carrying out a television transmission over a circuit between New York and Washington. The same year, 1927, Belin and Holweck achieved a measure of success in transmitting outlines and shadowgraphs using a cathode ray oscillograph (Fig. 1). The success of Baird had given an impetus to research in television in several countries as the patent records of England, the United States, Germany and France will testify.

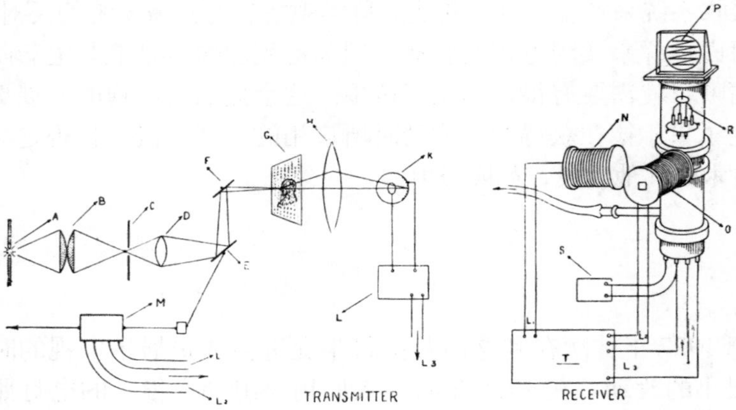


Fig. 1. Schematic diagram of Belin and Holweck's television apparatus.

On February 9, 1928, Baird achieved an ambition to be the first to televise across the Atlantic. The signals were picked up in the presence of Reuter's representative by an amateur operator at Hartsdale, a few miles from New York, the experimental receiver

度，且这个不断变化的单光源被一个与发送端扫描圆盘同步的“尼普科夫”盘（译者注：以德国发明家保罗·尼普科夫命名，尼普科夫发明螺盘旋转扫描器，用光电管把图像的序列光点转变为电脉冲，实现了最原始的电视传输和显示。）依次扫描。重新组合而成的图像面积为 2 平方英寸，我们可以通过扫描圆盘观察氖灯看到这个图像。同步的产生是由同步电机实现的。

在利兹演示的时候，贝尔德使用了“红外线电视”，即为了避免被转播的人被灯光眩射，在人与灯之间隔了一层硬质橡胶。另一个显著的改进是贝尔德发明的光点扫描法。他在自己的专利中是这样写的：“用一束光扫过要传输的场景或物体，把光敏元件放置在这束照射到物体上又被反射回来的光能够经过的位置上。”这实际上是泛光照明法的一种倒置，它的优点是：可以大大增加所得信号的强度，因而可以适当减少照射到被电视转播的物体上的光亮度。

在国外，美国的贝尔电话公司很快就开始应用这种方法通过一个电路在纽约和华盛顿之间实现了电视传输。同一年，也就是 1927 年，贝林和霍尔威克使用阴极射线示波器（图 1）成功地传送了轮廓线和影像图。在贝氏成功的激励下，好几个国家都开始开展电视方面的研究，英、美、德、法的大量专利记录可以证明这一点。

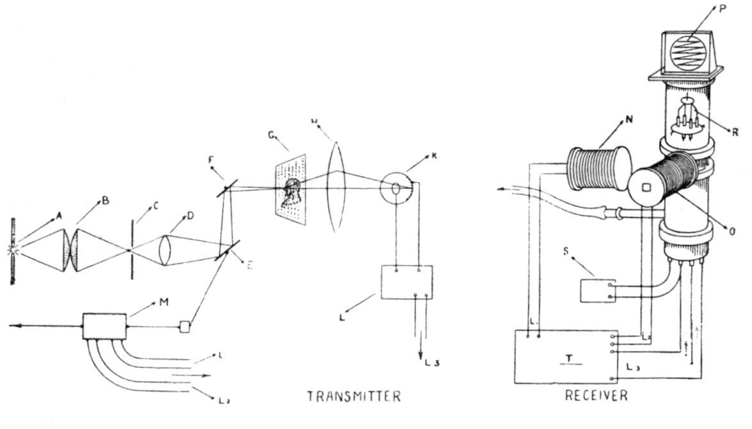


图 1. 贝林和霍尔威克所用电视设备的示意图

1928 年 2 月 9 日，贝尔德第一个实现了在大西洋两岸传送电视信号的目标。在距离纽约几英里远的哈茨戴尔镇，一个业余操作员当着路透社代理人的面接收了电视信号，他用实验接收设备在一个毛玻璃屏上显示出了大小约 3 平方英寸的图像。

showing an image about three inches square on a ground glass screen. This Baird followed almost immediately by a transmission from London to the s. s. *Berengaria* in mid-ocean. According to the chief staff engineer of the vessel, the "image varied from time to time in clarity, but movements could be clearly seen, and the image, when clear, was unmistakable". In these transmissions the wave-length used was 45 metres. The following year, using light spot transmission and cathode glow lamp with disc reconstruction, Baird demonstrated in engineering form at the British Association meeting in Cape Town, and the British Broadcasting Corporation agreed to provide facilities for a series of experimental television broadcasts by the Baird system on the London B.B.C. transmitter. At this time, the transmission of wording for instantaneous news broadcasts, telegram transmission in character, languages and other purposes was further developed by Baird and transmissions of this kind were featured in the experimental broadcasts.

In July 1930, the Baird Company gave its first public demonstration in a theatre, living artists and cinema films being transmitted from its studios in Long Acre, London, W.C.2, and reproduced on a multi-cellular lamp screen on the stage of the London Coliseum. The same year the youthful Baron von Ardenne in Germany commenced his researches on television, utilising the technique acquired in his development of cathode ray oscillograph tubes for the transmission and reception of television images, and within a year earned the distinction of being the first to demonstrate publicly cathode ray reception comparable with that produced by mechanical means. At first, von Ardenne received images transmitted by mechanical means, but later, by using a variable velocity constant intensity cathode stream instead of one of varying intensity and constant velocity, he was able to employ his cathode ray tubes for transmission and reception.

Meanwhile, researches into the possibilities of cathode ray television were engaging the attention of a large number of scientific workers in the laboratories of the Radio Corporation of America and its associated enterprises, independently by the Philco and other American companies, and by the Fernseh A. G. of Berlin, in which the Baird Company are equal partners with Bosch, Zeiss-Ikon, and Loewe. The last-named holds important von Ardenne patent rights. In the Fernseh A. G. laboratories, research in cathode ray television was directed towards the development and utilisation of "hard" tubes, that is, tubes at pressures below $10^{-5}$ mm., as contrasted with the "soft" tubes in use by the Loewe Company, the advantage claimed for the hard tube being its long life, an important consideration.

Proponents of mechanical methods, however, were by no means discouraged by the results obtained by the use of cathode ray tubes. The Baird Company, by using a mirror-drum instead of a Nipkow disc at the transmitting end, and at the receiving end using either a directly-modulated arc or a multiple Kerr cell in conjunction with a mirror-drum, was able to project fairly bright images on a screen about 6 ft. × 2 ft. in size, and demonstrated its results at the British Association centenary meeting in London, in the exhibition devoted to Mechanical Aids to Learning. This demonstration followed one in January 1931 in the Baird Laboratories at Long Acre of three-zone television, three 30-line mirror-drums

贝尔德很快又将伦敦的电视信号传送到航行在大洋中央的伯伦加莉亚号船上。该船的首席工程师说："图像的清晰度不太稳定，但可以很清楚地看到运动变化，图片在清晰的时候是准确无误的。"转播使用的波长为 45 米。第二年，使用光点传输法和带有可实现图像重建的圆盘的阴极辉光灯，贝尔德在英国科学促进会于开普敦召开的会议上按照工程学的模式进行了演示，英国广播公司（BBC）同意为在伦敦 BBC 的发射机上使用贝氏系统进行一系列的实验性电视转播提供设备。同时，贝尔德还研制出实时播送新闻广播节目的语音以及用电报传输字符、语言和其他内容的方式，类似这样的传输构成了实验性转播中的主要特征。

1930 年 7 月，贝尔德公司在一家剧院进行了首场公开演示，艺术家的现场表演和电影胶片从位于伦敦 W.C.2 区朗埃克的演播室中被传送出去，并重现在伦敦剧院舞台上的一个多管灯屏幕上。同一年，年轻的冯阿登爵士在德国开始了他对电视的研究，他采用自己研制的、专用于传送和接收电视图像的阴极射线示波管，在不到一年的时间里，他就因第一个向公众展示能与机械式接收系统性能相媲美的阴极射线接收器而声名卓著。起初，冯阿登接收的是通过机械手段传送的图像，但是后来他利用一个速度可变、强度不变的阴极电子流来代替速度不变、强度变化的电流，这样就使他的阴极射线管既能传送图像又能接收图像了。

与此同时，对阴极射线电视的研究吸引了许多在美国无线电公司及其联营企业，主要是飞歌公司和其他美国公司，以及在德国柏林电视机股份公司工作的科学工作者们的注意，在柏林电视机股份公司中，贝尔德公司与博世公司、蔡司伊康公司以及洛伊公司的股权地位相当。洛伊公司是冯阿登专利的主要拥有者。柏林电视机股份公司的实验室在研制阴极射线电视时采用的是"硬"管，即压力低于 $10^{-5}$ mm的管子，与之相反洛伊公司使用的是"软"管，"硬"管所具有的优势是寿命长，而寿命是人们主要考虑的因素。

然而，机械方法的支持者丝毫没有因阴极射线管所取得的成功而感到沮丧。贝尔德公司在发送端用镜面鼓代替尼普科夫圆盘，在接收端或者用一个直接被调制的弧光灯或者用克尔盒与一个镜面鼓联用，这样就能把很亮的图像投射到一个大小约 6 英尺 ×2 英尺的屏幕上，并且贝尔德公司在英国科学促进会于伦敦召开的成立百周年纪念大会上的以"机械手段辅助学习"为主题的展览中演示了他们的成果。1931 年 1 月，在贝尔德位于朗埃克的三段式电视实验室中，他们又演示了一次他们

being used to obtain an extended image. Later in the same month the Gramophone Company gave a similar performance in London at the Exhibition of the Physical and Optical Society, at which cinema films were transmitted by the multi-channel process and reproduced by means of a Kerr cell and mirror drum apparatus on a translucent screen. In the same year the Derby was televised by the Baird process.

In 1932 five major events in the progress of television took place. Fernseh A. G., the company organised to develop the Baird processes in Germany, built and installed a complete transmission equipment for the Ente Italiano per le Audizione Radiofoniche in Rome; the Derby was televised and projected at the time of its occurrence upon the screen of a London cinema by the Baird Company; the British Broadcasting Corporation installed television transmission equipment designed by Baird Television Ltd., for regular transmissions from its London studio (Fig. 2); and the Baird Company designed and marketed a much improved home television receiver, the Nipkow disc and neon tube of the old type being replaced by a mirror-drum and Kerr cell combination for projecting the received image on a translucent screen: and Dr. Alexanderson, of the American General Electric Company, successfully transmitted and received television images over a light-beam, with apparatus and by methods similar to those demonstrated by the Marconi Company at Leicester at the recent meeting of the British Association.

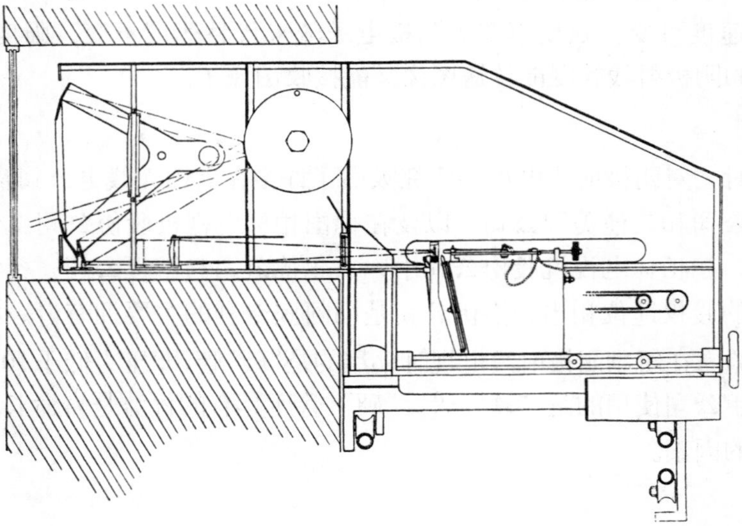

Fig. 2. A sectional scale drawing of the television transmitter as installed at Studio B. B., at Broadcasting House, London.

This year has been one of feverish activity on the part of all companies interested in the commercial exploitation of television, and of numerous independent research workers in various countries. Many interesting and ingenious modifications have been made in the cathode ray oscillographs. The Fernseh A. G. has made tubes with fluorescent ends with diameters up to 2 feet. Von Ardenne has devised a method of projecting the cathode ray

的成果,用 3 个 30 线的镜面鼓得到了持续时间较长的图像。在同一月的稍晚些时候,留声机有限公司在物理和光学学会于伦敦举办的展览上进行了类似的演示，他们用多通道方式传送电影胶片上的信息，并通过克尔盒和镜面鼓把重新生成的图像投射到一个半透明的屏幕上。同一年，贝氏方法被用于转播德比马赛。

1932 年发生了 5 件对电视业发展影响重大的事情。德国人为了应用贝尔德的技术组建了柏林电视机股份公司，公司为广播电台设于罗马的意大利办事处安装了一整套电视转播设备；贝尔德公司通过电视转播把德比赛马会的现场实时地传送到了伦敦电影院的大屏幕上；英国广播公司也安装了由贝尔德电视有限公司设计的电视转播设备，以用于其伦敦演播室的定期转播（图 2）；贝尔德公司还设计了一种更先进的家用电视接收设备并投放到市场中，在这种新设备中，原来用于把接收图像投射到半透明屏幕上的尼普科夫圆盘和老式氖管被镜面鼓和克尔盒的组合体所取代；美国通用电气公司的亚历山德森博士成功地利用光束发送和接收到了电视图像，他所用的设备和方法与马可尼公司在英国科学促进会最近于莱斯特召开的会议上所作的演示类似。

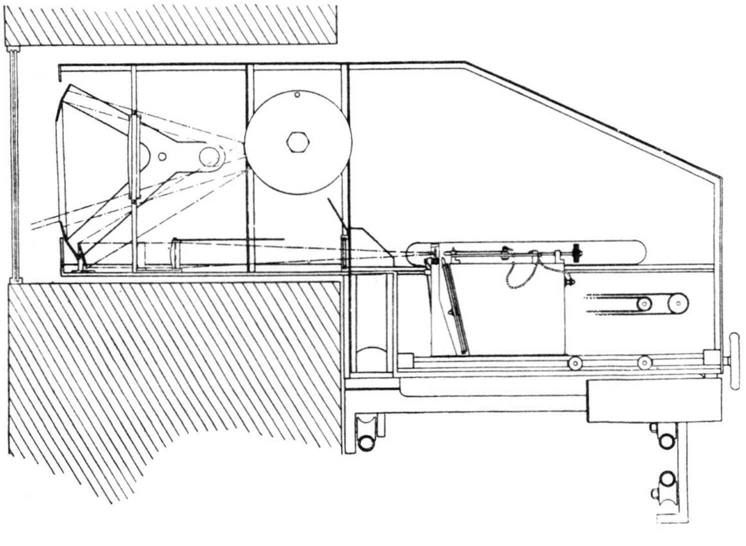

图 2. 安装在英国广播公司伦敦广播大楼内演播室中的电视发射机的截面图

今年，所有对电视商业开发感兴趣的公司和来自不同国家的大批独立研究者都表现出了很高的研究热情。大家对阴极射线示波器进行了大量有趣和富有创造力的改进。柏林电视机股份公司制造出了末端发荧光的管子，其直径可达 2 英尺。冯阿登设计了一种可以把从管内一个板上发射出来的阴极射线束投射到外部屏幕上的方

beam from a plate within the tube on to an external screen. Von Mihaly has developed a mechanical system by which the modulated light of the receiver is swept by a small rotating mirror at the axis of a stationary drum across a number of mirrors fixed on its inside surface, for which he claims superiority over the revolving mirror-drum. The Fernseh A. G. laboratories have constructed beautifully accurate mirror-screws with 90 and 120 reflecting surfaces of stainless steel. Dr. Vladimir Zworykin, the American research engineer, has made sensational claims for what he terms his iconoscope, which has been described as consisting of two devices—a photoelectric mosaic on which a scene is focused by a lens system, and a cathode ray gun which fires at this mosaic screen a stream of electron projectiles. The signal plate on which the scene to be televised is focused may be about 4 in.×5 in. in size and on this surface are millions of small photocells, each consisting of a minute silver globule sensitised by caesium. These globules are deposited on an insulating plate, such as a thin sheet of mica, the back of which is made conductive by a metal coating. Within the same glass bulb as the mosaic screen is the electron gun, which throws a beam of electrons at the screen and is made to sweep across the screen horizontally and vertically by deflecting coils as in an ordinary cathode ray tube. Whenever an electron hits a photocell, it neutralises part of the charge on the associated condenser. This discharge current is picked up, amplified and transmitted to the receiving cathode ray beam which is moving across a fluorescent screen in synchronism with the scanning beam. The varying discharge currents modulate this receiving beam and hence the screen at the receiver. It is reported that a similar device has been invented by Dr. Francis Henroteau, chief of the Dominion Observatory, Ottawa, who calls his invention the "super-eye". If the claims can be backed up by practical demonstrations, a new and important advance will be made in television.

Again and again in the last two years, it has been urged that finer resolution than that obtainable with the 30-line standard, 2.4 : 1 ratio, picture is necessary before television will become popular. This may or may not be so, but the true nature of the present position should now be realised. In the first place, it is easily demonstrable (and it has in fact already been put forward) that, with a 10 kc./sec. band-width, the intelligence-time transmission characteristic of a channel (at a reasonable picture-speed such as 12.5 per second to minimise flicker) is most economically filled at about this number of lines and ratio.

At the moment, pictures incomparably better than those possible with 30 lines, using mechanical reconstituting devices, are obtainable with cathode ray receiving apparatus which has become available this year. Such pictures were first demonstrated publicly in Great Britain by the Baird Company at this year's meeting at Leicester of the British Association and by Loewe, Fernseh A. G. and others at the Berlin Radio Exhibition, comprise 120–240 scanning strips, and require side band widths of from 150 kc./sec. to 1,000 kc./sec. for their proper transmission. In view of the Geneva convention, under which absolutely no provision was made for the proper expansion and development of television in the broadcast band of wave-lengths, an entirely new radio technique will have to be developed. Local areas, served by ultra short wave radio transmitters, seem an ideal

法。冯米哈伊开发了一套机械系统，在该系统中接收器中的调制光被一个旋转的小镜子扫过，小镜子位于一个静止圆筒的轴线上，正对着固定在圆筒内表面上的许多镜子，他宣称这套系统优于旋转的镜面鼓。柏林电视机股份公司的实验室还造出了非常精确的镜面螺旋，在螺旋轴上装有 90 和 120 个不锈钢的反射面。美国研发工程师维拉蒂米尔·斯福罗金惊人地宣布他设计出一种他所谓的光电摄像管，该管由两部分组成，一个是透镜系统把场景聚焦在其上的嵌镶光电阴极；另一个是向嵌镶光电阴极发射电子束的阴极射线枪。要转播的场景被聚焦到大小约 4 英寸 ×5 英寸的信号板上，信号板表面有数以百万计的小光电管，每个光电管都包含一个被铯敏化的，易于感光的小银球。这些小球被置于一块绝缘板上，譬如薄的云母片上，在其背面涂有一层金属因而可以导电。电子枪与嵌镶光电阴极被放在同一个玻璃泡内，在与普通阴极射线管相同的偏转线圈的作用下，电子枪发射的电子束水平和垂直地扫过嵌镶光电阴极。一旦一个电子打在了光电管上，它就会中和对应聚光器上的部分电荷。这种放电电流被采集、放大并发送到接收端的阴极射线束上，这些阴极射线束随着扫描束同时移动到另一侧的荧光屏上。不断变化的放电电流使接收端的阴极射线束被调制，因而也调制了接收端的屏幕。据报道，渥太华自治领天文台的台长弗朗西斯·亨罗托博士也发明了一种类似的设备，他把自己的发明称作“超级眼”。如果这些设计都能付诸实践，那么在电视领域就将出现具有重大意义的革新。

人们在过去的两年中一直认为：为了使电视得到普及，就必须研制出图像清晰度高于已有的 30 线标准、画面比例为 2.4 : 1 的电视。事实可能是这样，也可能不是这样,但我们应该清楚现在的真实情况。首先,很容易证明（实际上已经有人提出过）当带宽为 10 千赫时，一个频道的信息 – 时间传输特性（为了使闪烁最小化，应达到一个合理的图像速率，如每秒 12.5 次）采取这样的线数和比率最为经济。

目前，利用今年研制出的阴极射线接收设备所得到的图像的质量明显优于机械式接收设备重组而成的 30 线图像。贝尔德公司在英国科学促进会今年在莱斯特召开的会议上首次公开展示了这种质量的图像，洛伊公司、柏林电视机股份公司等其他公司在柏林无线电展览上也展示了同样的产品，包含 120~240 个扫描带，正常传输所需的边带带宽为 150 千赫到 1,000 千赫。因为日内瓦公约中没有任何一个条款在广播波段中为电视业的合理扩张和发展预留出一定的波长区，所以人们不得不想办法开发全新的无线电技术。在局部地区使用超短波无线电发射机似乎是一个理想的解决办法。然而，在实践中应用这种方法时遇到了很多困难，其中之一是许多地方

solution. In practice, however, many difficulties arise, not the least of which is the shielding effect in populous areas of buildings, steel structures, trees, rises in ground contour, etc. Research in this direction is progressing; in fact, experimental short-wave transmissions of high quality pictures (that is, of 120-line definition or more) have already commenced in the London area, the Crystal Palace towers being utilised for this purpose. But it may be a year or two before an established service throughout the country is achieved. In the meantime, further problems arise in connexion with distortion in amplifiers against which the weapons provided by Oliver Heaviside, to whose classic researches on the underlying electrical principles of distortion in communication engineering too little credit is given, are powerless. In extending the band-pass of an amplifier, the "temperature effect" dealt with by L. B. Turner in his inaugural address to the Institution of Electrical Engineers becomes an important factor in determining the interference level of a system; all the more so because an increase in the number of scanning strips in a picture involves the diminution, usually according to some power-function, of light available to affect the light sensitive cells. Further carefully directed research in this direction has become imperative for the transmission of actual scenes, as opposed to film broadcasts. For the projection of television pictures to large audiences in cinema theatres and elsewhere, Fernseh A. G. has recently demonstrated an "intermediate-film" method (Fig. 3). In this the televised image is received on a cinema film which is then developed and passed through an ordinary cinema projector, the time interval between the reception and projection being about 6 seconds if an ordinary reel of film is used, about 20 seconds if an endless loop of film is used, the "base" being first emulsified and dried, then exposed to the receiving scanning device, developed, projected and de-emulsified. This method shows great promise but much further work remains to be done on it.

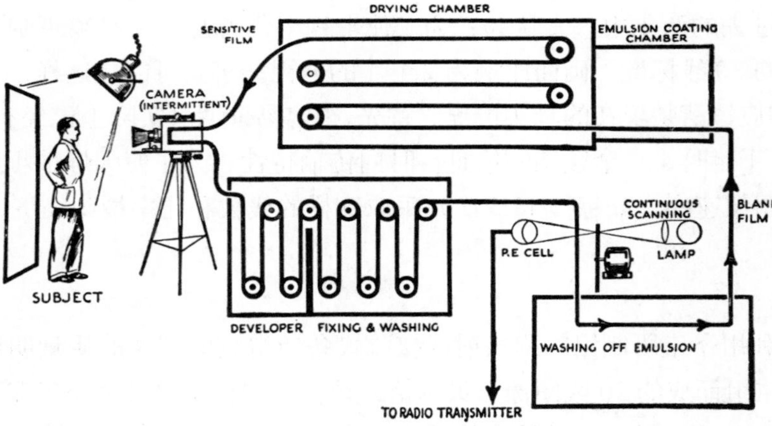


Fig. 3. Simplified diagram of the apparatus employed by Fernseh A. G. for the transmission of television by the intermediate film method.

(**132**, 502-505; 1933)

因建筑物、钢结构、树木和地平面以上的高地等导致了屏蔽效应。目前人们正在进行这方面的研究；实际上在伦敦，人们已经开始试验用短波传输高质量的图像（即清晰度达到120线或更高的图像），为此目的用上了水晶宫的双塔。但要在全国范围内建立这样的服务恐怕还需要一两年。与此同时又出现了许多与放大器失真有关的问题，虽然奥利弗·赫维赛德对通信工程中的基础电学失真原理进行了可靠的研究，但他的研究成果在实践中的可信度太低，因而对解决这个问题无能为力。如果扩大一个放大器的带通，那么特纳在电气工程师学会的就职演说中提到的“温度效应”就会成为决定系统受干扰程度的一个重要因素；更因为在一幅图中扫描带数量的增加会使照射到光敏元件上的光以幂函数的形式迅速下降。与胶片播放不同，我们需要对实际场景的转播定向进行更加细致的研究。为了给电影院或其他场所的广大观众放映电视图像，柏林电视机股份公司最近展示了“中间胶片”的使用方法（图3）。在这个过程中，电视图像被传送到一个电影胶片上，然后被冲洗并通过一个普通的电影放映机播放出来，如果使用的是普通胶卷，则接收和放映过程大约需要6秒，如果使用循环胶卷，则所需的时间约为20秒，“片基”首先被乳化和干燥，接着进入接收端的扫描设备，然后冲洗、放映和去乳化。尽管这种方法具有广阔的前景，但仍有很多更进一步的工作需要做。

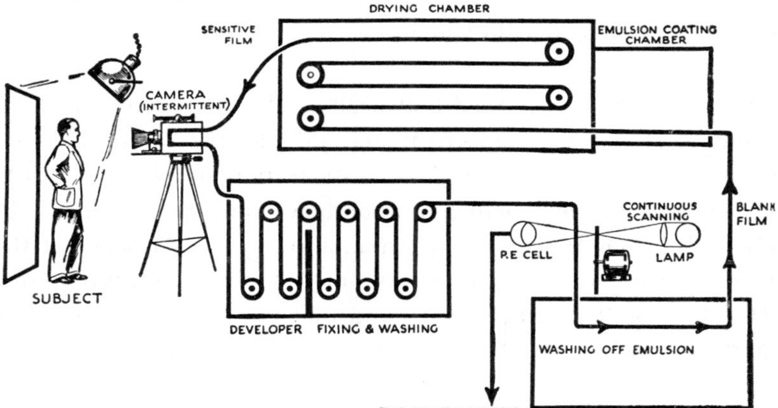


图3. 柏林电视机股份公司利用中间胶片法传送电视节目所用装置的示意图

（刘霞 翻译；赵见高 审稿）

# Heavy Hydrogen and Heavy Water

## Editor's Note

**Raymond Birge and D. H. Menzel had suggested in 1931 that the hydrogen in water and other materials might contain a small fraction of the isotope $^2H$, having atomic mass roughly twice that of the lighter isotope $^1H$. This review reports new techniques for separating "heavy water" containing the $^2H$ isotope, which has a different freezing and boiling point, from normal water. The nature of $^2H$ remained unclear: perhaps a bound state of two protons and one electron, or of two neutrons and a positron? Or perhaps the proton itself was composed of a neutron and positron? Few, it seems, considered the possibility, ultimately borne out by experiment, that the $^2H$ nucleus was made of one neutron and one proton.**

THE mass of the hydrogen atom, 1.00778±0.00015, found by Aston with the mass-spectrograph, appeared to be in very satisfactory agreement with the chemical atomic weight, which is one of the most accurately determined (A. Scott; Morley; Burt and Edgar). The discovery of the isotopes of oxygen, however, made it clear that the values found by the mass-spectrograph were referred to the oxygen isotope $O^{16}=16.000$, whilst the chemical values were referred to the isotopic mixture O=16.000. The factor for the conversion of mass-spectrograph values to chemical values now generally accepted is based on the spectroscopic abundance ratio $O^{16} : O^{18}$ determined by Mecke and Child[1], and Aston's value on the chemical standard then becomes 1.00756, which is certainly too low for the mass of the ordinary hydrogen atom.

Birge and Menzel[2] thereupon suggested that ordinary hydrogen contains a small amount of a heavier isotope, $H^2$, of mass approximately double that of the lighter isotope, $H^1$, and that only the latter was noticed in Aston's measurements. In order to reconcile the latter with the chemical atomic weights, an abundance ratio $H^1/H^2$ of 4,500 in ordinary hydrogen is required. It may be said at once that, although the presence of the isotope $H^2$ has been firmly established, it is present in very much smaller amount than this calculation suggests, say $H^1/H^2$ = 30,000±20 percent[3], and that the discrepancy between the mass-spectrograph and chemical values of the atomic weight still remains.

The presence of $H^2$ in ordinary hydrogen was proved by Urey, Brickwedde and Murphy[4], who examined the optical spectrum of samples from the residues of the evaporation of liquid hydrogen and found faint lines at the calculated positions for $H^2$. The broad $H^2_\alpha$ doublet was resolved and the separation agreed with theory. The relative abundance ratio $H^1/H^2$ was calculated as 4,000, which would explain very nicely the discrepancy just noted, but this result has since been shown to be incorrect. The isotope effect was also found in the Lyman series of hydrogen produced by a discharge in the vapour of "heavy" water[5].

# 重氢和重水

## 编者按

雷蒙德·伯奇和门泽尔在1931年提出：在水或其他物质所含的氢中，可能有一小部分是氢的同位素 $^2H$，其原子量约为较轻的同位素 $^1H$ 的2倍。这篇评论文章报导了用于分离含同位素 $^2H$ 的“重水”的新技术，重水和普通水具有不同的凝固点和沸点。人们当时还不清楚 $^2H$ 的本质：也许是处于束缚态的两个质子和一个电子，或是两个中子加一个正电子？或者质子本身就是由一个中子和一个正电子组成的？后来的实验最终证明：$^2H$ 原子核是由一个中子和一个质子构成的，但在当时几乎没有人是这么认为的。

阿斯顿用质谱方法得到的氢原子质量是 1.00778±0.00015，看起来与目前测定的最精确的原子量之一（斯科特；莫利；伯特和埃德加）——化学原子量吻合得相当好。但是，氧同位素的发现使我们明白，质谱方法所得到的结果指的是氧同位素 $O^{16}$ = 16.000，而化学结果则指的是同位素混合物 O = 16.000。现在普遍认可的将质谱结果转换成化学结果的换算因子是基于梅克和蔡尔德 [1] 测定的 $O^{16}$ : $O^{18}$ 的谱学丰度比，这样阿斯顿的结果按照化学标准就变成了 1.00756，这对于普通氢原子的质量而言无疑是太小了。

伯奇和门泽尔 [2] 由此提出，普通的氢中含有少量的较重同位素 $H^2$，其质量约为较轻同位素 $H^1$ 的二倍，而阿斯顿在测量时只注意到了后者。为了将阿斯顿的结果与化学原子量相调和，就要求普通氢中 $H^1/H^2$ 的丰度比为 4,500。于是立刻就可以说，尽管已经可靠地确定了同位素 $H^2$ 的存在，但是它的含量却远远低于计算值，比如 $H^1/H^2$ 为 30,000±20% [3]，并且，质谱方法与化学方法得到的原子量值仍然存在不一致。

尤里、布里克韦德和墨菲 [4] 证实了普通氢中有 $H^2$ 存在，他们检测了液氢挥发残余物样品的光谱，在计算出的 $H^2$ 位置上发现了微弱的谱线。对宽的 $H^2_\alpha$ 双线进行解析，双线分离与理论相吻合。相对丰度比 $H^1/H^2$ 的计算值是 4,000，它可以很好地解释刚才提到的不一致，而这个结果此前一直被认为是错误的。在“重”水蒸气放电所产生的氢莱曼线系中，也发现了同位素效应 [5]。

The presence of $H^2$ was then demonstrated by means of the mass-spectrograph by Bainbridge[6], who found the atomic mass 2.01351±0.00006 relative to He and 2.01351 ±0.00018 relative to $O^{16}$, the equivalent packing fraction being 0.675 percent. Mass-spectrograph evidence for $H^2$ was also found by Kallmann and Lazareff[7]. Grace[8] calculated theoretically the atomic weight $H^2$=2.0113±0.0012.

The nucleus of $H^2$, at first regarded as an association of two protons and one electron ($p_2e$), might clearly play an important part in the composition of nuclear structure[9]. The discovery of the neutron and the positron (positive electron) has given alternative possible structures for the nucleus of $H^2$ (which has been called the deuteron or deuton); for example, it may consist of two neutrons, conceived as primary uncharged particles of mass 1, and one positron. The proton, on this scheme, loses its supposed fundamental character as a constituent of atomic nuclei, and becomes an association of a neutron and a positron[10].

A partial separation of the isotopes $H^1$ and $H^2$ was achieved by E. W. Washburn and Urey[11], who examined the water from commercial electrolytic cells which had been operating two to three years. An examination of the optical spectrum of the hydrogen from this water showed an increase in the abundance of $H^2$. The oxygen from this water was combined with nitrogen and the nitric oxide spectrum examined. This showed that there was a decrease in the $O^{18}$ isotope concentration of about 8 percent. The ratio $H^1/H^2$ in natural terrestrial hydrogen might depend on the particular sample examined, since there might have been some separation in the method used in preparing the hydrogen. It has also been found that $H^2$ tends to "clean up" in a discharge tube[12], so that estimates of relative abundance based on optical emission spectra may well be erroneous. A marked increase in specific gravity, freezing point and boiling point, and a decrease in refractive index of water which had undergone prolonged electrolysis, were found[13].

Lewis and Macdonald started with twenty litres of water from an old electrolytic cell, which was half-normal in alkali, and electrolysed it between nickel electrodes with 250 amp. until the volume was reduced by ninety percent. One tenth was neutralised with carbon dioxide and the rest distilled. The two portions were recombined. The process was repeated until the volume had been reduced to half a cubic centimetre, the electrolysis being conducted below 35°, and preferably near 0°, in order to minimise loss by evaporation, and the current being reduced as the volume of liquid diminished. A difference in cathodic polarisation of 0.04 volt between $H^1$ and $H^2$ is reported. There was no accumulation of the heavy isotope of oxygen, $O^{18}$. As a final result, water of specific gravity 1.073, estimated to contain 65.7 percent of the hydrogen as $H^2$, was obtained. The relative losses of $H^1$ and $H^2$ were five to one, and a further reduction to one quarter of the final volume on electrolysis, it was supposed, would give water containing 99 percent of its hydrogen as $H^2$. The estimate of the concentration of $H^2$ in ordinary water as 1 in 6,500 given in this paper is too high.

Newell and Ficklen[14] examined the specific gravity of water from chromium plating baths

接着，班布里奇[6]利用质谱方法证明了 $H^2$ 的存在，他得到的原子量相对于氦为 2.01351±0.00006 而相对于 $O^{16}$ 为 2.01351±0.00018，当量敛集率为 0.675%。卡尔曼和拉扎雷夫[7]也用质谱得到了 $H^2$ 存在的证据。格雷斯[8]通过理论计算得到 $H^2$ 的原子量＝ 2.0113±0.0012。

最初被看作是由两个质子和一个电子结合而成（$p_2e$）的 $H^2$ 核，显然有可能在核结构的构成中充当着重要的角色[9]。中子和正电子（带正电荷的电子）的发现为 $H^2$ 核（即我们所说的氘核）提供了另外几个可能的结构；例如，它可以包含两个中子和一个正电子，其中，中子被认为是一种不带电荷的基本粒子，它的质量为 1。按照这一方案，质子不再具有作为原子核构成成分的基本特性，而成为中子与正电子的结合体[10]。

沃什伯恩和尤里[11]实现了同位素 $H^1$ 与 $H^2$ 的部分分离，他们考查了已使用两到三年的商业用电解池中的水。对水中的氢进行光谱检验，结果显示其中 $H^2$ 的丰度有所增加。令这种水中的氧与氮结合，对氮氧化物进行光谱检验。结果显示，$O^{18}$ 同位素的浓度下降了大约 8%。在地球上的天然氢中，比值 $H^1/H^2$ 可能会依赖于所检验的特定样品，因为用来制备氢的方法可能已经实现了某种程度上的分离。而且，还发现 $H^2$ 在放电管中有“清除”的趋势[12]，这使得根据发射光谱方法得到的相对丰度估计值很有可能是错误的。他们发现水在经过长期电解之后，其比重、凝固点和沸点显著升高，而折射率下降[13]。

刘易斯和麦克唐纳使用 20 升取自旧电解池的水（其中碱只有半当量浓度）开始进行实验，在 250 安培条件下用镍电极进行电解，直到液体体积减少了 90%为止。取十分之一液体用二氧化碳中和，将剩余液体进行蒸馏。然后将两部分重新混合。重复进行上述过程，直到体积减少到半个立方厘米，电解过程保持在 35º 以下进行，最好是在 0º 附近，以使挥发造成的损失减到最小，并随着液体体积的减小而降低电流。据报道，$H^1$ 和 $H^2$ 的阴极极化之间有 0.04 V 的差值。没有出现氧的重同位素 $O^{18}$ 的聚积。最后得到了比重为 1.073 的水，估计其中 65.7%的氢是 $H^2$。$H^1$ 和 $H^2$ 的相对损失为 5∶1，据推测，如果进一步电解，使液体体积减少到终体积的四分之一，那么在得到的水中就会有 99%的氢是 $H^2$。这篇论文中估计普通水中 $H^2$ 的浓度是 1/6,500，这个数值太高了。

纽厄尔和菲克伦[14]检测了已使用三年之久的镀铬浴中的水的比重：来自九个镀

which had been operating for periods up to three years: specimens from nine baths had specific gravities varying from 1.00002 to 1.00064.

When water is distilled through a fractionating column, a large separation of the isotopes of hydrogen and oxygen can be effected, especially if the distillation is carried out under reduced pressure[15]. A 20-ft. column was used and in two modes of operation: (i) the ordinary isotopic composition was maintained at the foot of the still, when a stationary state was reached after two days, the water at the head showing a diminished density of 60 parts in a million; and (ii) the ordinary isotopic composition was maintained at the head of the column and samples were taken daily from the foot, when the density rose by 70–80 parts per million above that of ordinary water. Although the heavy water has an appreciably lower vapour pressure than common water, the differences are rather illusory in connexion with separation by distillation, since there is an exchange of $H^1$ and $H^2$ atoms among the water molecules, and an appropriate calculation shows that it is not the vapour pressure itself but its square root which is proportional to the atomic fraction. Distillation under reduced pressure should be more effective. A large still in operation for two months has shown a steady increase in density of the water at the bottom of the still[16].

The method used by G. N. Lewis and Macdonald[17] in separating the hydrogen and oxygen of a given sample of water, and thus determining how much of the increase in density is due to $H^2$ and how much to $O^{18}$, depends on passing the steam over heated iron. This is cumbrous, and Lewis[18] has devised a method depending upon the exchange of isotopes in aqueous solution, as in the reaction with ammonia on water:

$$H^1H^2O + NH^1H^1H^1 = H^1H^1O + NH^1H^1H^2.$$

Ammonia in water may be regarded as forming ammonium hydroxide, $NH_4OH$, and again dehydrating, the two changes proceeding with great velocity, and as the fourth hydrogen of the ammonium group is exactly like the others, each hydrogen has an equal chance of being lost on dehydration. A rapid interchange of such hydrogen isotope as is present will give a nearly random distribution between $NH_3$ and $H_2O$. One mol of water at 0° absorbs nearly one mol of $NH_3$, and since ammonia has three hydrogen atoms, more than half the $H^2$ in the system will escape when the ammonia is pumped off. A sample from the still with an excess density over ordinary water of 0.000182 was saturated with ammonia at 0° and the ammonia pumped off at room temperature. After six repetitions of the process, the water had an excess density of 0.000085, so that at least 0.000097 of the original density excess was due to $H^2$. Another experiment consisted in using sulphur dioxide instead of ammonia:

$$H_2O^{18} + SO^{16}O^{16} = H_2O^{16} + SO^{16}O^{18},$$

When the density excess was reduced to 0.000109, so that 0.000073 at least of the original excess was due to $O^{18}$. In this crude experiment, 0.000170 of the 0.000182 is accounted for.

铬槽中的样品，其比重从 1.00002 到 1.00064 不等。

将水通过分馏柱进行蒸馏，可以实现氢和氧同位素的大量分离，特别是在减压条件下进行蒸馏时[15]。该实验要用到一根 20 英尺长的分馏柱，并有两种操作方法：(i) 保持分馏柱底部的正常同位素组成，两天后达到定态时，顶部的水密度减少了百万分之 60；(ii) 在柱顶部保持正常同位素组成，并且，当密度增加到比普通水大百万分之 70~80 时，每天从柱底部取走样品。尽管重水的蒸气压明显低于普通水，但是这个差异对于用蒸馏方法进行的分离过程来说还是很不可靠的，因为水分子之间存在着 $H^1$ 与 $H^2$ 原子的交换，并且，通过适当的计算可以得出，与原子分数成比例的不是蒸气压本身，而是其平方根。减压条件下的蒸馏应该更加有效。在使用大分馏柱蒸馏两个月的过程中，柱底部水的密度会稳步增长[16]。

刘易斯和麦克唐纳[17]用来分离给定水样中的氢和氧，并由此确定 $H^2$ 和 $O^{18}$ 对水的密度增加各自有多大贡献的方法，依赖于将水蒸气通过灼热的铁。这种方法很是麻烦，于是刘易斯[18]设计出了一种依赖于同位素在水溶液中发生交换的方法，例如在水和氨的反应中：

$$H^1H^2O + NH^1H^1H^1 = H^1H^1O + NH^1H^1H^2$$

可以认为水中的氨先形成氢氧化铵，$NH_4OH$，再脱水，两个变化都是高速进行的，因为铵根中的第四个氢与其他三个是完全等同的，所以每个氢都有相同的机会在脱水过程中被丢掉。氢同位素之间的快速交换会使 $H^1$ 和 $H^2$ 在氨和水中趋于随机分布。0º 下，1 mol 水吸收约 1 mol 氨，由于氨中有三个氢原子，所以超过一半的 $H^2$ 将随着氨被泵出而脱离系统。从分馏柱中取出一份密度比普通水高 0.000182 的样品，在 0º 下用氨饱和，再于室温下将氨泵出。将此过程重复六次之后，水的密度过量值为 0.000085，可见在最初的密度过量值中至少有 0.000097 是由 $H^2$ 造成的。另外一个实验是用二氧化硫来代替氨：

$$H_2O^{18} + SO^{16}O^{16} = H_2O^{16} + SO^{16}O^{18},$$

当密度过量值减少到 0.000109 时，可以得到在最初的密度过量值中至少有 0.000073 是由 $O^{18}$ 造成的。利用这个粗略的实验可以解释 0.000182 中的 0.000170。

In precision work the isotopic composition of the ammonia will have to be found, particularly if it has been prepared from electrolytic hydrogen, and precautions must be taken against any large loss of water by evaporation.

It is interesting to note that Holmboe[19] has reported that electrolytic hydrogen is more active in ammonia synthesis than other equally pure hydrogen obtained by reduction of steam by iron: the velocity of reaction was 10–40 percent greater with electrolytic hydrogen.

An alternative method of separation of $H^2$ from electrolytic hydrogen is suggested by experiments by Bleakney, Gould and Taylor[20], who report that an enrichment in $H^1H^2$ occurs when the gas is progressively removed from charcoal on which it has been adsorbed, in agreement with some theoretical results of Eyring.

Practically pure "heavy water", $H^2_2O$, was obtained by Lewis and Macdonald[21], whose experiments on its physical properties were carried out with 0.12 c.c. of liquid in which the proportion of $H^1$ isotope was probably not greater than 0.01 percent. The freezing point was found to be +3.8° and the boiling point 101.42°. The vapour pressure curve was established and the following values for the ratio $p_2/p_1$, where $p_1$ is the vapour pressure of ordinary water and $p_2$ that of heavy water, were found:

| $t$℃ | 20 | 30 | 40 | 50 | 60 | 70 | 80 | 90 | 100 | 110 |
|---|---|---|---|---|---|---|---|---|---|---|
| $p_2/p_1$ | 0.87 | 0.88 | 0.89 | 0.90 | 0.913 | 0.923 | 0.933 | 0.942 | 0.949 | 0.956 |

The usual calculation shows that the latent heat of evaporation is greater than that of ordinary water by 259±3 or 4 gm. cal. per mol. The density at 25° was found to be 1.1056 and the temperature of maximum density +11.6°. The values of *vol./(vol.* at 4°) were as follows:

| $t$℃ | 5 | 10 | 15 | 20 | 25 | 30 | 35 | 40 |
|---|---|---|---|---|---|---|---|---|
| $V^t_4$ | 0.99987 | 0.99948 | 0.99958 | 1.00016 | 1.0011 | 1.00243 | 1.00415 | 1.00605 |

In the various respects in which water is said to be an abnormal liquid, heavy water ($H^2_2O$) seems to be more abnormal, but the difference between the two becomes smaller with rising temperature.

Several miscellaneous investigations on $H^2$ and $H^2_2O$ have recently been reported. The nuclear spin[22] of $H^2$ is (by exclusion) probably 2/2, or twice that of $H^1$; the emission spectrum of hydrogen with 25 percent $H^1H^1$ , 50 percent $H^1H^2$ and 25 percent $H^2H^2$, and the electronic band spectrum due to neutral $OH^2$, have been examined[22, 23].

The mobility of the ions in $H^2_2O$ was examined[24] by determining the conductivities of hydrogen and potassium chlorides in ordinary water and in nearly pure $H^2_2O$. A special

要进行精确的研究就必须知道氨的同位素组成，尤其是在用电解氢方法制备它时，并且必须采取预防措施避免由蒸发造成的大量水分损失。

有意思的是，霍尔姆博[19]曾报道，在氨的合成中，电解氢比用铁还原水蒸气得到的同样纯度的氢更活泼：采用电解氢时的反应速率要快10%~40%。

布利克尼、古尔德和泰勒[20]通过实验提出了另外一种从电解氢中分离 $H^2$ 的方法，他们报道说气体在逐渐离开吸附它的木炭时会发生 $H^1H^2$ 富集的现象，这与艾林得到的某些理论结果是一致的。

刘易斯和麦克唐纳[21]得到了几乎完全纯的"重水" $H^2_2O$，他们用0.12立方厘米重水液体样品进行物理性质方面的实验，其中 $H^1$ 同位素的含量可能不超过0.01%。实验测得其凝固点为+3.8º，沸点为101.42º。他们建立了蒸气压曲线，得到了如下的 $p_2/p_1$ 值，其中 $p_1$ 是普通水的蒸气压，$p_2$ 是重水的蒸气压：

| $t$℃ | 20 | 30 | 40 | 50 | 60 | 70 | 80 | 90 | 100 | 110 |
|---|---|---|---|---|---|---|---|---|---|---|
| $p_2/p_1$ | 0.87 | 0.88 | 0.89 | 0.90 | 0.913 | 0.923 | 0.933 | 0.942 | 0.949 | 0.956 |

通过常规计算可以得到，重水的蒸发潜热比普通水的大259±3或259±4 g · cal/mol。25º时，重水密度为1.1056，温度为+11.6º时密度最大。下面列出了不同温度下重水的体积与4º下重水体积的比值：

| $t$℃ | 5 | 10 | 15 | 20 | 25 | 30 | 35 | 40 |
|---|---|---|---|---|---|---|---|---|
| $V_4^t$ | 0.99987 | 0.99948 | 0.99958 | 1.00016 | 1.0011 | 1.00243 | 1.00415 | 1.00605 |

在水作为一种反常液体的各个方面中，重水( $H^2_2O$)都表现得更为反常，但是二者之间的差异随着温度升高而逐渐减小。

最近报道了几项关于 $H^2$ 和 $H^2_2O$ 的五花八门的研究成果。$H^2$ 的核自旋[22]（由于不相容）可能是2/2，或者说是 $H^1$ 核自旋的二倍；由25% $H^1H^1$、50% $H^1H^2$ 和25% $H^2H^2$ 组成的氢的发射光谱，以及由中性 $OH^2$ 产生的电子带状光谱也已得到了检测[22,23]。

通过测定普通水和几乎纯的 $H^2_2O$ 中氢和氯化钾的电导率就得到了离子在 $H^2_2O$ 中的迁移率[24]。实验中所用的是一个专用的吸量管式电解池，内装0.25立方厘米

pipette cell containing 0.25 c.c. of liquid, with bare platinum wire electrodes, was used. The amount of $H^2_2O$ in the electrolytic liquid was determined from the density, and the resistances were extrapolated from 97 percent $H^2_2O$ to 100 percent. The ratios of the equivalent conductances in ordinary water and $H^2_2O$ were thus obtained. Results at five temperatures from 5° to 18° were found. It is assumed that the ratio of equivalent conductance to equivalent conductance at infinite dilution is the same for each electrolyte in the two solvents and that the ratio of the mobilities of the $K^+$ and $Cl^-$ ions is the same in both solvents. The mobilities at 18° for $H^{2+}$, $K^+$ and $Cl^-$ in pure $H^2_2O$ are then calculated as 213.7, 54.5 and 55.3, if the corresponding mobilities of $H^{1+}$ , $K^+$ and $Cl^-$ are 315.2, 64.2 and 65.2. It thus appears that the ionic mobilities in heavy water are distinctly smaller than in ordinary water. The values of the conductance ratios are believed to be accurate to half percent.

Lewis, even before he had succeeded in concentrating $H^2$, had predicted that $H^2H^2O$ would not support life and would be lethal to higher organisms. He then found experimentally[25] that minute seeds of tobacco (*Nicotina tabacum* var. *purpurea*) responded to this test. Twelve seeds were placed in pairs in six similar glass tubes and to each of three tubes 0.02 c.c. of ordinary distilled water and to each of the other three tubes 0.02 c.c. of pure $H^2_2O$ were added. The six tubes were hermetically sealed and placed in a thermostat at 25°. The three pairs of seeds in ordinary water began to sprout in two days, and at the end of a fortnight had formed well developed seedlings. The seeds in $H^2_2O$ showed macroscopically no development: they have been put in ordinary water but the result is not yet reported. Six entirely similar tubes, each containing two seeds, were filled alternately with ordinary distilled water and with water in which half the hydrogen was $H^2$. At the end of four days, all six seeds in ordinary water gave well-developed seedlings, whilst those in the heavier water all showed about the same degree of sprouting as occurs in ordinary water in two days.

The toxic effect of ordinary distilled water is familiar[26]. A peculiar effect of thermal treatment of water on its capacity for promoting the development of cells of *Spirogyra*, reported by Lloyd and Barnes[26], was attributed to the different proportions of polymerised water molecules in freshly condensed steam and freshly melted ice. Ice[27] has been regarded as $(H_2O)_n$, perhaps $(H_2O)_3$, liquid water as largely $(H_2O)_2$ with some $(H_2O)_3$ and $H_2O$, and dry steam as $H_2O$. At 20°, it has been calculated, there is 31.1 percent of liquid ice in liquid water, and freshly melted ice should contain much more $(H_2O)_3$ than freshly condensed steam, since the changes of polymerisation are not rapid. In freshly melted ice, rich in trihydrol, the cells of *Spirogyra* developed normally, whilst freshly condensed steam, rich in dihydrol and monohydrol, killed the cells. Barnes and Jahn[28] have since reported that *Euglena* develops much more rapidly in water from freshly melted ice than in condensed steam.

Evidence regarding the effect of thermal treatment on the physical properties of water is, however, conflicting. Wills and Boeker[29] say that the diamagnetic susceptibility is altered by such treatment, whilst Menzies[30] found no alteration of vapour pressure,

液体，并备以裸露的铂丝电极。电解液中$H^2_2O$的量是通过密度来确定的，电阻是由97%的$H^2_2O$外推到100%得到的。由此得到了普通水与$H^2_2O$中当量电导的比值，已得到了在5°到18°之间五个温度下的结果。人们假定，对于这两种溶剂中的每种电解液来说，当量电导与无限稀释条件下的当量电导之比都是一样的，并且在两种溶剂中$K^+$和$Cl^-$迁移率的比值也是一样的。若$H^{1+}$、$K^+$和$Cl^-$的相应迁移率为315.2、64.2和65.2，则可以计算出18°时$H^{2+}$、$K^+$和$Cl^-$在纯$H^2_2O$中的迁移率分别为213.7、54.5和55.3。由此看来，重水中的离子迁移率明显小于普通水中的。一般认为，电导率之比的数值可以精确到0.5个百分比。

刘易斯甚至在还没有成功地浓缩$H^2$之前，就已经预言，$H^2H^2O$不能支持生命而且对于高级生物体来说会是致命的。后来他通过实验发现[25]，烟草（紫色变种）的小粒种子对这个实验有响应。将十二粒种子成对放在六个类似的玻璃管中，在其中三个管子中加入0.02立方厘米普通蒸馏水，在另外三个管子中加入0.02立方厘米纯$H^2_2O$。将六个管子密封并置于25°的恒温器中。普通水中的三对种子在两天内就开始萌芽，并且在两周结束时长成了发育良好的幼苗。$H^2_2O$中的种子没有显示出肉眼可见的发育：这些种子现在已经被置于普通水中，但目前还没有报道结果。在六个完全类似的管子中各放入两粒种子，然后交替加入普通蒸馏水和其中一半的氢为$H^2$的水。到四天结束时，普通水中的六粒种子全部都长出了发育良好的幼苗，而在较重水中的六粒种子都只呈现出普通水中的种子在大约两天时的发育程度。

我们对于普通蒸馏水的毒性作用是熟悉的[26]。据劳埃德和巴恩斯报道[26]，通过对水进行热处理可以对其促进水绵细胞发育的能力产生特殊的影响，这一奇怪作用的原因是新制冷凝蒸气和新制熔融冰中聚合态水分子有不同比例。曾经认为冰[27]是$(H_2O)_n$，可能是$(H_2O)_3$，液态水主要是$(H_2O)_2$以及一些$(H_2O)_3$和$H_2O$，干蒸气则是$H_2O$。已经计算出，在20°时，液态水中有31.1%的液态冰形式，而新制熔融冰中所含的$(H_2O)_3$应多于新制冷凝蒸气，因为多聚状态的改变不是很快。在富含三聚水的新制熔融冰中，水绵细胞可以正常地发育，而富含二聚水和单聚水的新制冷凝蒸气则会杀死细胞。巴恩斯和贾恩曾报道[28]，裸藻在新制熔融冰中的生长速度要远远高于在冷凝蒸气中的生长速度。

不过，证明热处理对水的物理性质是否有影响的证据是相互冲突的。威尔斯和伯克尔[29]认为，热处理会改变抗磁磁化率；而孟席斯[30]发现这种处理未能使蒸气

and La Mer and Miller[31] no change of refractive index, by such treatment. The latest speculations on the constitution of liquid water[32] postulate a tetrahedral co-ordination of water molecules (five $H_2O$ molecules in a group) in ice and two other forms in addition in liquid water.

Until 1894, chemists had no suspicion that the atmosphere contained any constituents other than those recognised by Lavoisier a century previously, and it has required the lapse of a century and a half to establish the existence in water, which like air is one of the commonest materials available to chemists, of anything more than two supposed "elements", hydrogen and oxygen, each of which is now known to consist of a mixture of at least two different kinds of atoms. The chemical properties of the heavy hydrogen isotope are very probably different from those of ordinary hydrogen. A new organic chemistry, in which each of the compounds containing carbon (of which there are also at least two isotopes, $C^{12}$ and $C^{13}$) and hydrogen is duplicated by the synthesis of a "heavy" partner—at present a mere nightmare—will in lapse of time no doubt become an accomplished fact. The use of heavy waters in medical treatment still awaits investigation.

(**132**, 536-538; 1933)

---

References:

1 *Phys. Rev.*, **36**, 330 (1930); compare Naudé, *Z. Phys.*, **68**, 362 (1931).

2 *Phys. Rev.*, **37**, 1669 (1931).

3 Bleakney, *Phys. Rev.*, **41**, 32 (1932).

4 *Phys. Rev.*, **40**, 1 (1932).

5 Ballardow and White, *Phys. Rev.*, **43**, 941 (1933).

6 *Phys. Rev.*, **41**, 115 (1932).

7 *Naturwissenschaften*, **20**, 206, 472 (1932); possible $H^3$. Compare also Conrad, *Z. Phys.*, **75**, 504 (1932), neutral $H^3$ particles in canal rays; Lewis and Spedding, *Phys. Rev.*, **43**, 964 (1933), find no spectroscopic evidence of $H^3$, to 1 part in $10^6$, in very nearly pure $H^2_2$; relative fine structures of $H^1$ and $H^2$ are given.

8 *J. Amer. Chem. Soc.*, **54**, 2562 (1932).

9 Harkins, *J. Amer. Chem. Soc.*, **54**, 1254 (1932).

10 Sexl, *Nature*, **132**, 174 (1933).

11 *Proc. Nat. Acad. Sci.*, **18**, 496 (1932).

12 Lewis, G. N., and Spedding, *Phys. Rev.*, **43**, 964 (1933).

13 Washburn, Smith and Fransden, *J. Chem. Phys.*, **1**, 288 (1933); Lewis, G. N., and Macdonald, *J. Chem. Phys.*, **1**, 341 (1933).

14 *J. Amer. Chem. Soc.*, **55**, 2167 (1933).

15 Lewis, G. N., and Cornish, *J. Amer. Chem. Soc.*, **55**, 2616 (1933).

16 Lewis, G. N., *J. Amer. Chem. Soc.*, **55**, 3502 (1933).

17 *J. Chem. Phys.*, **1**, 341 (1933).

18 *J. Amer. Chem. Soc.*, **55**, 3502 (1933).

19 Pincass, *Die industrielle Herstellung von Wasserstoff*, 53 (1933).

20 *Phys. Rev.*, **43**, 497 (1933).

21 *J. Amer. Chem. Soc.*, **55**, 3057 (1933); *Nature*, **132**, 248 (1933).

22 Lewis and Ashley, *Phys. Rev.*, **43**, 837 (1933). Ashley, *Phys. Rev.*, **43**, 770 (1933).

23 Chamberlain and Cutter, *Phys. Rev.*, **43**, 772 (1933).

24 Lewis and Doody, *J. Amer. Chem. Soc.*, **55**, 3504 (1933).

压发生变化；拉默和米勒[31]则发现这种处理也没有改变折射率。关于液态水结构的最新推测[32]认为，除了冰中存在的水分子的四面体配位结构（每一族中有五个水分子）以外，还另有其他两种形式存在于液态水中。

到 1894 年的时候，化学家们就已经不再怀疑大气中除了有拉瓦锡在一个世纪之前所辨识出的那些组分之外，还可能包含任何其他的组分。而对于水这种像空气一样对于化学家来说极易获取的最为常见的物质，化学家却要经过一个半世纪才认识到其中存在着除两种假定“元素”——氢和氧以外的东西，现在我们知道，氢和氧都是由至少两种不同的原子混合而成的。重氢同位素的化学性质极有可能与普通氢的不同。每种含碳（它也有至少两种同位素，$C^{12}$ 和 $C^{13}$）和氢的化合物都将通过合成其“重”伙伴而得到复制，这种新型的有机化学，尽管从现在看来只不过是一场噩梦，但随着时间的流逝必将成为既成的事实。重水在医疗中的应用还有待于研究。

（王耀杨 翻译；李芝芬 审稿）

25 *J. Amer. Chem. Soc.*, **55**, 3503 (1933).

26 Lloyd and Barnes, *Proc. Nat. Acad. Sci.*, **18**, 426 (1932). *Nature*, **129**, 691 (1932).

27 Barnes, *Proc. Roy. Soc.*, A, **125**, 670 (1929).

28 *Proc. Nat. Acad. Sci.*, **19**, 638 (1933).

29 *Phys. Rev.*, **42**, 687 (1932).

30 *Proc. Nat. Acad. Sci.*, **18**, 567 (1932).

31 *Phys. Rev.*, **43**, 207 (1933).

32 Fowler and Bernal, *J. Chem. Phys.* (August 1933). *T. Faraday Soc.*, **29**, 1049 (1933).

# Internal Temperature of Stars

G. Gamow and L. Landau

## Editor's Note

**In the early 1930s astronomers were still at a loss to understand the high internal temperatures of stars, since they had yet to comprehend fully the process of nuclear fusion. George Gamow was a Russian physicist who emigrated to the United States in the late 1930s and there first articulated the "Big Bang" theory of how the universe began. Here he and his compatriot Lev Landau, one of the leading scientists of the Soviet era, try to constrain internal stellar temperatures by observing that lithium should be consumed by nuclear reaction with hydrogen before it can reach the star's surface, if the temperature inside exceeds several millions of degrees.**

IT may be of interest to notice that the investigation of the process of thermal transformation of light elements in stars[1] enables us to check the upper limit for the temperature of internal regions. In fact, so far as lithium is present, for example, on the star surface, it is natural to accept that it is in equilibrium with the lithium content in the internal regions of the star near the stellar nucleus, where the production of different elements takes place. On its way from the stellar nucleus through the hot regions of the star, lithium atoms will be partly destroyed by thermal collisions with hydrogen atoms ($Li^7 + H^1 \rightarrow 2He^4$) and will not reach the surface at all if the temperature of the internal regions is too high.

For the rate of the reaction in question we have:

$$\omega \sim \int \pi\left(\frac{h}{mv}\right)^2 \cdot e^{-2\pi Ze^2/hv} \cdot v \cdot N \cdot 4\pi v^2 \left(\frac{m}{2\pi kT}\right)^{3/2} \cdot e^{-mv^2/2kT}\, dv \qquad (1)$$

where $Z$ is the atomic number of the element, $v$ and $N$ the velocity and density of protons, and $T$ the absolute temperature.

Calculating the integral we obtain:

$$\omega \sim Nh^{5/3} \frac{(4\pi Ze^2)^{1/3}}{m^{4/3}(kT)^{2/3}}\, e^{-3/2(m/kT)^{1/3}(2\pi Ze^2/h)^{2/3}} \qquad (1^1)$$

On the other hand, in the time $1/\omega$ a lithium atom will travel through the distance

$$l \sim \sqrt{D/\omega} \qquad (2)$$

where the diffusion coefficient $D$ is given by the expression:

$$D \sim (kT)^{1/2} / N^1 \sigma M^{1/2} m^{1/2} \qquad (2^1)$$

# 恒星的内部温度

乔治·伽莫夫，列夫·朗道

## 编者按

20 世纪 30 年代早期的天文学家们仍然不能理解恒星内部的温度为什么会那么高，因为他们那时还没有完全了解核聚变反应。乔治·伽莫夫本是一位俄罗斯的物理学家，他于 30 年代后期移居美国，并在美国首先明确地阐明了关于宇宙起源的“大爆炸”理论。在这篇文章中，伽莫夫和他的同胞，苏联时代最有名的科学家之一列夫·朗道一起提出：如果恒星的内部温度超过了几百万度，那么锂就应该因不断与氢发生核反应而在到达恒星表面前被完全消耗掉，所以恒星的温度不可能有那么高。

我们注意到一个很有意思的事情：对恒星内部轻元素热转变过程的研究 [1] 使我们能够验证恒星内部区域的温度上限。事实上，如果以恒星表面处的锂为例，我们会很自然地认为它的含量应该与星核附近的锂含量平衡，我们知道星核处是生成各种不同元素的地方。锂原子在从星核处穿越恒星热区的过程中会因同氢原子发生热碰撞（$Li^7+H^1 \rightarrow 2He^4$）而被部分摧毁，如果内部区域温度太高的话，锂原子将无法到达恒星表面。

上述过程的反应速率为：

$$\omega \sim \int \pi\left(\frac{h}{mv}\right)^2 \cdot e^{-2\pi Ze^2/hv} \cdot v \cdot N \cdot 4\pi v^2\left(\frac{m}{2\pi kT}\right)^{3/2} \cdot e^{-mv^2/2kT}\, dv \tag{1}$$

这里 $Z$ 是元素的原子数，$v$ 是速度，$N$ 是质子密度，$T$ 是绝对温度。

将上式积分后我们得到：

$$\omega \sim Nh^{5/3}\,\frac{(4\pi Ze^2)^{1/3}}{m^{4/3}(kT)^{2/3}}\, e^{-3/2(m/kT)^{1/3}(2\pi Ze^2/h)^{2/3}} \tag{1$^1$}$$

另一方面，在 $1/\omega$ 的时间里，一个锂原子将穿过的距离是：

$$l \sim \sqrt{D/\omega} \tag{2}$$

其中的扩散系数 $D$ 可以表示为：

$$D \sim (kT)^{1/2}/N^1\sigma M^{1/2}m^{1/2} \tag{2$^1$}$$

Here $N^1$ is the total number of atoms in a cubic centimeter, $\sigma$ the cross-section of collision, and $M$ the atomic weight of the atoms in question.

Using ($1^1$) and ($2^1$), we obtain from (2):

$$l \sim \frac{m^{5/12}(kT)^{7/12}}{\sqrt{NN^1}\,\sigma^{1/2}h^{5/6}M^{1/4}(4\pi Ze^2)^{1/6}}\, e^{3/4(m/kT)^{1/3}(2\pi Ze^2/h)^{2/3}} \tag{3}$$

Accepting $N \sim N^1 \sim 10^{24}$ and $\sigma \sim 10^{-18}$ cm.$^2$, we obtain for lithium ($Z = 3$) the following numbers:

| $T$ (C°) | $10^6$ | $5\times10^6$ | $10^7$ | $5\times10^7$ | $10^8$ |
|---|---|---|---|---|---|
| $l$ (cm.) | $10^{13}$ | $10^6$ | $10^4$ | 10 | 1 |

From this table the conclusion is reached that either lithium is present on the star surface only occasionally or that no regions with temperatures of more than several millions of degrees can exist in the interior of a star.

(**132**, 567; 1933)

G. Gamow and L. Landau: Ksoochia Basa, Khibini, Aug. 10.

Reference:
1 Atkinson and Houtermans, *Z. Phys.*, 54, 656 (1929).

这里 $N^1$ 为 1 立方厘米体积内的总原子数，$\sigma$ 是碰撞的横截面积，$M$ 是与该过程相关的原子的原子量。

把 ($1^1$) 和 ($2^1$) 代入 (2)，我们得到：

$$l \sim \frac{m^{5/12}(kT)^{7/12}}{\sqrt{NN^1}\,\sigma^{1/2}h^{5/6}M^{1/4}(4\pi Ze^2)^{1/6}}\,e^{3/4(m/kT)^{1/3}(2\pi Ze^2/h)^{2/3}} \qquad (3)$$

考虑到 $N \sim N^1 \sim 10^{24}$ 和 $\sigma \sim 10^{-18}$ cm$^2$，对于锂 ($Z = 3$) 我们可以得到下面的数字：

| $T$(℃) | $10^6$ | $5\times10^6$ | $10^7$ | $5\times10^7$ | $10^8$ |
|---|---|---|---|---|---|
| $l$(cm) | $10^{13}$ | $10^6$ | $10^4$ | 10 | 1 |

根据这个表我们可以得出以下结论：要么锂元素在恒星表面的存在量很少，要么在一个恒星内部不可能存在温度超过几百万度的高温区。

（魏韧 翻译；蒋世仰 审稿）

# X-Ray Analysis of Fibres

W. T. Astbury

## Editor's Note

**The author here is William Astbury, whose work on the X-ray diffraction of fibrous biomolecules anticipated the structural insights of Linus Pauling, Maurice Wilkins, Francis Crick and James Watson. His work on keratin, the main protein component of hair, led him to postulate specific secondary structures in proteins: characteristic conformations adopted by the molecular chains of amino acids. In this summary of a meeting at the British Association, Astbury applauds the collaboration of botanists and physicists in addressing the structures of biological fibres—a collaboration that is still not unproblematic today. Astbury's description of proteins as "infinitely variable and adjustable molecular patterns", with structural as well as enzymatic roles, foreshadows the puzzle of how these patterns are encoded in the molecules' chemical composition.**

"PRESENT methods can still go far, but I am convinced that progress ... is about to gain a great impetus from the application of those new methods of research which chemistry is inheriting from physics: X-ray analysis ..."* So spake in general terms the president of the British Association in his address on the evening of September 6: on the following morning, Sections A (Mathematical and Physical Sciences) and K (Botany) foregathered to demonstrate the point in somewhat more detail. That physicists should hobnob with botanists—and not simply for the purpose of drinking tea—and on the following Monday† even be invited into the stronghold of vitalistically-minded zoologists is a very definite cause for congratulation, in spite of the dark mutterings of some that it is all very well to talk about the structure of molecules and adopt such an attitude of pitiable optimism in the face of "life" and all the tremendous tale of the activities of living organisms!

In opening the joint discussion of Sections A and K, Mr. W. T. Astbury outlined some developments in the X-ray interpretation of the properties of hair, feathers and other protein structures. Recent progress in our knowledge of the molecular structure of natural fibres arises largely out of the recognition by X-ray means that the solid state of fibres is a crystalline state, generally imperfect, it is true, yet nevertheless sufficiently organised to give valuable information about the form and properties of the giant molecules which orthodox chemistry suggests as their basis. The crystallites are sub-microscopic, but it can be seen at once from X-ray photographs that they are always *effectively* long and thin and lie with their long axes either roughly parallel to the fibre axis, as in silk and hair, or

---

* "Some Chemical Aspects of Life" (see *Nature*, Sept. 9, p. 389).

† Discussion on the structure of protoplasm, Section D, Sept. 11.

# 纤维的X射线分析

威廉·阿斯特伯里

## 编者按

本文作者威廉·阿斯特伯里在含纤维生物分子的X射线衍射方面的研究先于莱纳斯·鲍林、莫里斯·威尔金斯、弗朗西斯·克里克和詹姆斯·沃森对结构的分析。他通过对毛发中主要的蛋白质成分——角蛋白的研究推出蛋白质所特有的次级结构：氨基酸分子链的特殊构造。在这篇对英国科学促进会的一次会议的纪要中，阿斯特伯里高度评价了植物学家和物理学家在探索生物纤维结构时的良好合作，这样的合作在今天也未必那么容易实现。阿斯特伯里认为蛋白质"分子的结构变化多端并且可以改变"，可以构成一种组织，也可以是一种酶，这意味着人们在对这些结构按分子化学构成进行编码时会感到很困惑。

"目前的方法还可以更进一步，但是我确信这一进展……将会从新研究方法的应用中获得巨大的推动力，即在化学中借用物理学的方法：X射线分析……"* 英国科学促进会主席于9月6日晚间所做的演讲中就是这样概括的；第二天早上，A分会（数学和物理学）和K分会（植物学）在一起更详细地论证了这一观点。物理学家与植物学家在一起畅谈不仅仅是为了喝茶，在下一个周一时†他们甚至要被邀请到持活力论思想的动物学家的大本营中，这件事值得大加庆祝，尽管仍然有一些暗地里的非议，认为不该这样谈论分子的结构和在面对"生命"与所有关于活体之活动性的奇妙现象时采取如此卑微的乐观态度！

在A分会与K分会的联席讨论开始时，阿斯特伯里先生概述了X射线在解释毛发、羽毛和其他蛋白质结构的性质方面的一些进展。我们最近在认识天然纤维分子结构上取得的进展很大程度上来自于借助X射线法得到的认识，即固态纤维处于结晶状态，一般是有瑕疵的，然而虽然如此，这对于给出有关巨型分子的形式和性质方面的有价值信息已经足够了，而巨型分子被认为是传统化学的基础。微晶是亚微观的，不过通过X射线照片就立刻可以看到，它们**实际上**是细长的，具有长轴，并且其长轴或者大致与纤维轴平行，就像在丝和毛发中那样，或者呈螺旋形环绕于

*《生命的某些化学面貌》（见《自然》，9月9日，第389页）

† 关于原生质结构的讨论，D节，9月11日。

arranged spirally round it, as in ramie and cotton.

In the light of a mass of experimental evidence of one sort and another—and it must be emphasised that the study of the fine structure of biological subjects has advanced and will continue to advance only through a close alliance between all the various methods of attack—the conclusion seems irresistible that these crystallites, or organised aggregates, which make up the body of the fibre substance and which we must now identify with Nägeli's micelles, are simply bundles of long chain-molecules, bundles of varying size and degree of perfection of organisation, and probably without any particularly sharp demarcation one from another. In the case of fibres of cellulose and natural silk, when the X-ray data are submitted to detailed analysis and compared with the results of tensile experiments and the findings of organic chemistry, this concept leads further to the decision that the chain-molecules are stereo-chemically fully extended; but we immediately encounter difficulties when we try to apply these ideas to the study of protein structures other than silk, such as hair, collagen, muscle, etc. The main obstacle, however, is removed by the discovery and interpretation of the X-ray photograph of *stretched* hair, a photograph which shows that the molecule or complex of hair keratin, when pulled, undergoes a reversible intra-molecular transformation into an elongated stereo-isomer in which the polypeptide chains are analogous in form to those of silk fibroin, that is to say, are fully extended and correspond to the normal polypeptide chains of the chemist. It follows, therefore, that the chains in unstretched hair are in equilibrium in a folded state, so that the mechanism of its extraordinary long-range elasticity is inherent in the keratin molecule itself: by the application of tension in the presence of water the keratin molecule can be stretched to roughly twice its equilibrium length, to which it returns exactly when the tension is removed.

More recent work on this problem indicates now that the "unit" of the keratin complex is actually a polypeptide sheet or "grid" in which the main-chains are linked side-to-side by a long series of roughly co-planar cross-linkages formed by the side-chains of the various amino-acid residues incorporated in the structure. The folds in the main-chains of unstretched hair referred to above lie apparently in planes transverse to the side-chains, as one would perhaps rather expect: each grid simply flattens out when pulled in the direction of the main-chains, thereby giving rise to a complex system of stresses and strains which must be the basis of the observed long-range elasticity. From this point of view the elastic properties of keratin are in no way different in principle from those of the simpler molecules; the latter, too, are susceptible of distortion within the limits imposed by inter-bond angles, electrostatic attractions, rotation about bonds, and so on, but in keratin the possibilities are so enormously enhanced by the length and mobility of both main-chains and side-chains that at first sight we appear to be dealing with a new phenomenon.

The most beautiful example of this line of reasoning is afforded by feather keratin, which gives an X-ray photograph at the moment unique in crystal analysis. Besides revealing quantitatively and for the first time the truly heroic proportions of a protein molecule, this photograph shows also that the molecule or complex of feather keratin can be stretched

纤维轴周围，就像在苎麻和棉中那样。

根据大量这类或那类的实验证据——而且必须要强调的是，只有通过与各种攻坚方法紧密结合，对生物材料精细结构的研究才取得了今天的进步并且还将继续进步——结论看来是确凿无疑的，我们现在必须将这些构成纤维状物质实体的微晶或有组织的团聚体看作是内格里胶束，它们只是大小和组织化完美程度各不相同的长链分子束，而且彼此之间可能不具有任何鲜明的分界线。对于纤维素和天然丝中的纤维来说，在对 X 射线数据进行细致分析并与张力实验的结果和有机化学的结论进行比较时，由这一观念可以进一步得出链状分子在立体化学上是完全伸展的论断；但是当我们试图用这些思想研究除丝以外的蛋白质结构，如毛发、胶原蛋白和肌肉等时，便立即遭遇到了困难。不过主要的障碍已经排除了，因为发现和解释了**伸长**毛发的 X 射线照片，该照片显示，毛发角蛋白的分子或复合物在拉紧时发生了可逆的分子内转化，变成伸长的立体异构体，其中的多肽链具有与丝蛋白类似的形式，也就是说是完全展开的，相当于化学家所说的普通多肽链。由此可以知道，未拉伸毛发中的链处于折叠状态的平衡之中，因此具有非常高的弹性就成为角蛋白分子的固有特性：在有水存在时施加拉力，可以将角蛋白分子拉伸到约为其平衡长度的两倍，去掉拉力后分子又精确地回复到平衡长度。

目前对这一问题的最新研究结果表明，角蛋白复合物的“单元”实际上是多肽层或“栅格”，其中主链通过一长列基本上共平面的交联并排地连在一起，这些交联结构是由包含在结构中的各种氨基酸残基的侧链形成的。上面谈到的未伸展毛发中主链的折叠明显位于横截侧链的平面内，人们也许会更期待这样的结果：每一栅格在受到主链方向上的拉伸时只是变平，从而形成了一个复杂的应力应变系统，这必然就是已观测到的高弹性的基础。从这个角度来看，角蛋白的弹性性质与较简单的分子没有任何原则上的分别；后者也会在一定限度内易受由于键间夹角、静电吸引和相对于键的旋转等所造成的变形的影响，但在角蛋白中，由于主链和侧链的长度和运动性极大地增加了变形的可能性，以至于乍看起来我们就像是在面对一种新现象。

羽毛角蛋白是这一系列推理的最好实例，它的 X 射线照片在晶体学分析中是独一无二的。除去定量地以及首次真正全面地揭示蛋白质分子结构之外，这张照片还表明，羽毛角蛋白分子或复合物可以连续且可逆地伸长多达其平衡长度的 7%！看

continuously and reversibly up to as much as 7 percent of its equilibrium length! It seems clear, too, that we are again operating with a net- or grid-like system, a molecular device which we may feel sure is common in biological structures, and of which the elastic properties are of fundamental importance for our knowledge of the mechanism of both growth and movement.

The paper presented by Dr. J. B. Speakman on the co-ordination of chemistry and X-ray analysis in fibre research followed admirably on the above account, emphasising as it did once more the extreme fruitfulness of a union of branches which, alone in fields of such bewildering complexity, might well prove barren. There is a pronounced difference in the lateral swelling of wool or hair in weak and strong acids, the former being far more effective. Considerations based on the Donnan equilibrium indicate why this should be so, and the argument is given stereo-chemical form, so to speak, by the corresponding X-ray photographs, which show how, in hydrochloric acid, for example, the main outlines of the keratin complex are scarcely disturbed, though in quite a dilute solution of chloracetic acid the diffraction pattern is obliterated completely, only to return in all perfection when the acid is removed by washing and drying. It was pointed out by Speakman how this observation offers a possible means of estimating the size of the grid-like units of keratin suggested by X-ray analysis; for we should be able, from a study of heats of reaction and swelling, to measure the total inter-grid cohesion in the extended form ($\beta$-keratin) as compared with that in the single-chain protein of silk, to which X-rays have shown the main chains of $\beta$-keratin to be analogous (see above). Experiments to this end are in progress.

The study of the effects of de-aminating animal hairs provides a still more instructive example of the value of X-ray and chemical collaboration. Stretched hair, as is well known, can be "set" in the elongated form by exposure to steam, and X-rays show that this is due to a re-distribution of cross-linkages in the keratin grid, whereby a new equilibrium configuration is taken up with the main-chains in the extended state. The reversibility of the intra-molecular transformation is thus destroyed by prolonged steaming, and the photograph of $\beta$-keratin persists. The remarkable thing now is that it is found that de-aminated hair has lost this power of "permanent set", and to an extent depending on the degree of de-amination. The change can be followed throughout by means of X-rays, which show at once whether the $\beta$-photograph is "set" after a given amount of de-amination and steaming of the fibre in the stretched state.

The experiments are a most valuable contribution to our knowledge of the chemistry of keratin, and therefore of all proteins, for we may now feel confident not only that the process of "setting" wool and hair involves the $-NH_2$ groups of the basic side-chains, but also that the contractile power of keratin is by no means destroyed—rather is its range extended—on their removal. In view of the theory of K. H. Meyer that the contractile power of muscle arises from attractions between basic and acidic side-chains of one and the same main-chain, it is clear that this discovery may have far-reaching implications.

来同样明显的是，我们还是在处理一个网状或栅格状体系，我们可以确信这是一种在生物结构中常见的分子构成，而且其弹性性质对于我们认识生长和运动的机制具有非常重要的意义。

斯皮克曼博士提交的那篇关于在纤维研究中协同使用化学分析法和 X 射线分析法的论文很好地说明了上述观点，文中不止一次地强调，在这些令人困惑的复杂领域中独自做努力很可能一无所获，但把各个分支结合起来就会硕果累累。毛或发在弱酸和强酸中的侧向膨胀存在着明显差异，前者要更为显著。根据唐南平衡可以解释为什么会如此，其论述是以立体化学形式给出的，可以说，相应的 X 射线照片说明，例如在盐酸中，角蛋白复合物的主体轮廓几乎没有被打乱，而在相当稀释的氯乙酸中衍射图案则完全消失，直到通过清洗及干燥将酸去除后才得以完全复原。斯皮克曼指出，这一观察结果说明利用 X 射线分析法也许可以估计角蛋白栅格状单元的尺寸；因为我们应该可以根据对反应热和膨胀热的研究来测定伸展形式（$\beta$- 角蛋白）中栅格间的总内聚力，从而与丝中某种单链蛋白的内聚力进行比较，X 射线图显示 $\beta$-角蛋白与该单链蛋白具有类似的主链结构（参见上文）。以此为目的的实验正在进行中。

对于动物毛发脱氨基效应的研究为我们提供了一个更有利于说明同时使用 X 射线法和化学分析法的价值的实例。大家都知道，拉伸的毛发会因暴露于水蒸气中而被“变”为伸长形式，X 射线显示这是角蛋白栅格中的交联结构进行重新分布的结果，此时处于伸展状态的主链转变为一种新的平衡构型。于是分子内转化的可逆性会因长时间的蒸汽处理而被破坏，而 $\beta$- 角蛋白的照片保持不变。现在值得关注的事情是已发现脱氨基的毛发失去了这种“永久应变”的能力，并且在一定程度上取决于脱氨基的程度。利用 X 射线法可以全程跟踪这种变化，它能马上显示出在对处于拉伸状态的纤维进行某种程度的脱氨基和蒸汽处理之后，$\beta$- 照片是否“变”了。

上述实验对于我们认识角蛋白的化学性质乃至所有蛋白质的化学性质都是很有价值的；因为我们现在不仅可以确信毛和发的“变化”过程涉及碱性侧链的 $-NH_2$ 基团，而且了解到角蛋白在移动时其收缩能力完全没有遭到破坏，其范围反而增大了。根据迈耶的理论，肌肉具有收缩能力是因为同一主链中酸性和碱性侧链之间的吸引，很明显这一发现可能具有深远的含义。

The botanists were offered an elegant piece of structure analysis by Dr. R. D. Preston who, continuing the work of Astbury, Marwick and Bernal which brought to light that the cell-wall of the alga, *Valonia ventricosa*, is constructed of two sets of cellulose chains crossing according to some regular plan at an angle near a right angle, described the present state of an X-ray exploration of the whole of the wall of a single complete cell. Since a normal photograph taken at any point of the wall gives the two cellulose directions at that point, the method adopted is to follow up one of the directions exactly as one follows lines of force with a small compass needle, the results being afterwards plotted both on the cell-wall itself and on a large-scale model made from a bladder.

The investigation is necessarily a prolonged one with the modest apparatus available, but already the findings are of a highly intriguing character. They show to date that the molecular structure of this cellulose *balloon* is built up in spiral fashion, exactly as are the cellulose *fibres* ramie, cotton, etc. The completion of the investigation will no doubt be eagerly awaited, for there is a widespread interest in the structure and metabolism of *Valonia*. The single cells of this alga are the first to be explored in detail by X-ray methods, and the discovery that it shares with the fibres a spiral architecture must be of deep significance for the problem of the mechanism of growth.

The mechanism of growth was also indirectly the subject of a fascinating contribution by Mr. J. Thewlis, who showed how X-rays have revealed the arrangement of the apatite crystals which constitute the enamel of teeth. Tooth enamel, like so many other biological structures, is of a fibrous nature, the hexagonal axis of the apatite crystals being the fibre axis. In human enamel there are two sets of fibres, one with the fibre axis inclined at about 20° to the normal to the tooth surface and on the same side as the tip, the other at about 10° and on the opposite side to the tip. In dog's enamel the fibre axis is at right angles to the surface of the tooth. Variations in the perfection of fibre orientation are observed, and three kinds of enamel can be distinguished. In human teeth it is found that one kind is associated with clinically immune teeth, and the other two with clinically susceptible teeth. Here again the verdict of X-ray analysis must ultimately prove of fundamental importance in the study of living things, and it is to be hoped that this most promising field of investigation will soon be extended so as to take in the effects of the action of vitamins.

The biological implications of recent advances in the X-ray analysis of protein fibres were again dealt with by Mr. W. T. Astbury at the discussion on the structure of protoplasm. No doubt some of the zoologists present were not a little shocked at such heresy, but nevertheless the message of X-rays seems clear enough. The proteins are infinitely variable and adjustable molecular patterns, exquisitely sensitive to changes in physical and chemical environment, and capable of functioning not only as enzymes but also as the material embodiment of the genes. Surely they are no other than the very patterns of life!

(**132**, 593-595; 1933)

普雷斯顿博士为植物学家们提供了一篇有关结构分析的精彩文章，他延续了阿斯特伯里、马威克和伯纳尔的工作——即发现单球法囊藻的细胞壁是由两组纤维素链按某种规则的方式以接近于直角的角度交叉构成的，描述了目前用 X 射线研究单个完整细胞的细胞壁整体的状况。由于从细胞壁任何一点所得到的普通照片都给出该点处的两个纤维素方向，可以采用一种方法准确跟踪其中的一个方向，就像用小磁针追寻磁力线的方向一样，之后将结果同时画在细胞壁上和用球囊制成的大尺度模型上。

这项研究必定是一项可以利用现成的简单设备来进行的长期工作，不过已有的发现已经引起了人们的广泛关注。目前的发现表明这个纤维素**气囊**的分子结构是依螺旋形构建的，恰如苎麻、棉等纤维素**纤维**一样。由于人们对法囊藻的代谢和结构都很感兴趣，所以大家在急切地等待着研究的完成。这种水藻的单个细胞是第一个用 X 射线方法进行精细研究的实例，研究结果表明它与纤维都具有螺旋形构造，这一发现对于生长机制问题必然会有深远的影响。

生长机制还是泽尔利斯先生在一篇众所关注的文章中间接提到的主题，他展示了如何用 X 射线法说明构成牙釉质的磷灰石晶体的排布方式。像许多其他生物结构一样，牙釉质具有纤维的性质，磷灰石晶体中六方晶系的轴就是纤维轴。人类的牙釉质中有两组纤维，其中之一的纤维轴与牙表面的法线方向大约呈 20º 角并与顶部位于同侧，另一组则大约呈 10º 角且与顶部位于异侧。在狗的牙釉质中纤维轴与牙表面成直角。通过观测纤维取向的精确度就可以区分出三类牙釉质。在人类牙齿中发现，其中一类与临床免疫牙有关，另外两类则与临床敏感牙有关。这个例子再次证明 X 射线分析最终一定会在生命体研究中发挥重要的作用，而且可以期待这一最具发展前景的研究领域将很快地拓展到对维生素作用效果的研究中去。

阿斯特伯里先生在讨论原生质结构时再次谈到了最近在用 X 射线分析蛋白质纤维上取得的进展对于生物学的意义。无疑，在场的一些动物学家会因这种异端言论而受到不小的触动，但 X 射线给出的信息毕竟已足够清晰。蛋白质分子的结构变化多端并且可以改变，对于物理和化学环境的变化极为敏感，不仅能够作为酶还能作为基因的物质化身发挥作用。确切地说，它们就是生命的具体形式！

（王耀杨 翻译；吕扬 审稿）

# Production of High Magnetic Fields at Low Temperatures

K. Mendelssohn

## Editor's Note

**Kurt Mendelssohn here reports an important experimental advance in the generation of powerful magnetic fields at low temperatures. Using superconducting alloys able to bear field strengths up to 22,000 gauss at a temperature of just 2 K, he and colleagues had experimented with a transformer-like arrangement of magnetically coupled coils. A magnetic field of 1,000 gauss created in a conducting primary coil was made to induce current in a secondary superconducting coil. With a dense coil solenoid as part of the second coil, the device could produce a field of 22,000 gauss in a small volume. This achievement, Mendelssohn points out, might be used to create extremely low temperatures by the method of adiabatic demagnetization.**

THE use of a supra-conductor (therefore completely free from Joule heating) has been more than once suggested for the production of magnetic fields at low temperatures. The magnetic field obtainable by this means is limited by the magnetic threshold value at which supra-conductivity ceases. Still, considerable fields can be obtained by the use of alloys (investigated in Leiden[1]) the threshold value of which is 22,000 gauss at 2° K., a strength which is sufficient for many experiments.

The chief remaining difficulty lies in the heat conductivity of the leads to the supra-conducting coil. This problem of heat conduction through the leads can be eliminated by transferring the necessary energy for the magnetic field by induction. The suggested arrangement is similar in principle to a transformer, the primary circuit of which is normally conducting and the secondary circuit of which is supra-conducting. The primary circuit consists of a D. C. source and the primary of the transformer; the supra-conducting secondary circuit consists of a secondary with a few turns of large radius and a solenoid with many narrow turns for producing the high field. On closing the primary circuit the magnetic energy transferred to the secondary is shared with the solenoid. With this arrangement, one produces, to some extent, condensation of the lines of force. Calculation shows that for given geometrical dimensions there is an optimum ratio for the number of turns in the secondary coil to that in the solenoid. In this way, within the limits of the usual dimensions of an apparatus, it is easily possible with a primary field of about 1,000 gauss to obtain a field of 22,000 gauss in the space of a few cubic centimetres.

The method should be specially suitable whenever it is desired to produce fairly high magnetic fields at low temperatures in not too large a volume, as, for example, in the production of extremely low temperatures by the adiabatic demagnetisation of paramagnetic substances[2]. According to the experiments of Kürti and Simon[3], Giauque and MacDougall[4] and de Haas and his co-workers[5], it should be possible, with the above

# 低温下强磁场的产生

库尔特·门德尔松

## 编者按

在这篇文章中，库尔特·门德尔松报告了自己在制造低温强磁场的实验技术上取得的重大突破。在温度仅为 2 K 的情况下，利用可以承受高达 22,000 高斯强磁场的超导合金，他和同事们用一种类似于变压器的线圈排布方式的磁耦合线圈进行实验。他们首先在导电的初级线圈上施加 1,000 高斯的磁场以便在次级超导线圈上产生感应电流。次级线圈的一部分是缠得很密的螺线管，这台装置可以在一较小的空间内产生 22,000 高斯的磁场。门德尔松指出：这项技术的成功也许可以用于通过绝热退磁法产生极低温。

已经不止一次有人提出可以利用超导体（完全没有焦耳热）在低温下产生磁场。但用这种方式获得的磁场要受到超导电性消失所对应的磁场阈值的限制。尽管如此，利用温度为 2 K 时阈值可达 22,000 高斯的合金（在莱顿的研究结果 [1]）仍可以产生强度可观的磁场，这个强度对许多实验来说是足够了。

剩下的主要困难在于超导体线圈的引线存在热传导。我们可以通过磁场感应传递必要的能量来消除导线中的热传导问题。已提出的实验装置在原理上与变压器相类似，其主回路是正常传导的回路，而次级回路是超导回路。主回路包括直流源和变压器的初级回路；而次级超导回路则包含一个由几匝粗线圈绕成的次级回路和一个用来产生强磁场的由许多匝线圈密绕成的螺线管。当主回路接通时，传递到次级回路的磁能中的一部分分到螺线管上了。我们利用这台装置在一定程度上使磁力线变密了。计算表明，对于给定的几何尺寸，存在次级线圈匝数与螺线管匝数的一个最佳比值。这样，在通常的装置尺寸的极限内，我们很容易由 1,000 高斯的初级场在几个立方厘米的空间内获得高达 22,000 高斯的磁场。

这个方法应该特别适用于要求在低温下的一块不太大的体积内产生超强磁场的情况，例如利用顺磁物质的绝热退磁产生极低温的情况 [2]。根据库尔蒂和西蒙 [3]、吉奥克和麦克杜格尔 [4] 以及德哈斯及其同事们 [5] 的实验，用上述装置从 1 K 的初始温度得到 0.1 K 以下的温度应该是可以办到的。由于消除了沿着电流导线的热传导，

arrangement, to obtain temperatures below 0.1° K. from a starting point of 1° K. Since heat conductivity along the current leads is eliminated, and since heat capacities at helium temperatures are so minute, a few cubic centimetres of liquid helium should suffice to cool the whole arrangement.

Experiments with an apparatus embodying the above methods are being made in this laboratory.

(**132**, 602; 1933)

K. Mendelssohn: Clarendon Laboratory, Oxford. Sept. 28.

References:
1 de Haas, W. J., and Voogd, J., *Comm. Leiden*, No. 214b (1931).
2 Debye, P., *Ann. Phys.* (4) **81**, 1154 (1926); Giauque,W. F., *J. Amer. Chem. Soc.*, **49**, 1864 (1927).
3 Kürti, N., and Simon, F., *Naturwiss.*, **21**, 178 (1933).
4 Giauque, W. F., and MacDougall, D. P., *Phys. Rev.*, **44**, 235 (1933).
5 de Haas, W. J., *Nature*, **132**, 372 (Sept. 9, 1933).

而且在液氦温区热容量也很小，所以几立方厘米的液氦就足以冷却整台装置了。

我们正在实验室中利用根据上述方法设计的仪器进行实验。

（沈乃澂 翻译；赵见高 审稿）

# Natural Colouring Matters and Their Analogues*

R. Robinson

## Editor's Note

**Robert Robinson, a professor at the University of Oxford, was the outstanding British chemist in the inter-war years. He was chiefly responsible for determining the structure of the colouring matter of flowers (with his wife Gertrude Robinson). During his chemistry course to undergraduates at Oxford, it was his custom to nominate a day in the early spring when he would identify the anthocyanins in any flowers members of his audience could gather: this was a challenge to young women in the group to present him with extravagant bunches of flowers.**

THE chemist has been attracted to the investigation of natural and artificial colouring matters for a variety of reasons, including not only colour-pleasure, the incentive of the knowledge that chlorophyll and haemoglobin perform some of the most important functions in vital processes, and the industrial importance of dyestuffs and pigments, but also on account of the fact that visible colour more than any other property facilitates the experimental study of organic substances whether by analysis or synthesis. It furnishes a standard of homogeneity or a measure of concentration, it is an invaluable guide in the search for methods of separation and purification, and it at once indicates, by its appearance or disappearance, the occurrence of a chemical reaction. Small wonder that the successful outcome of the investigation of many colourless substances has awaited the discovery of some characteristic colour-reaction; a noteworthy example being vitamin A.

A catalogue of outstanding achievements in this field invites destructive criticism. I do not fear this, however, in recalling the researches of Laurent, Kekulé, Baeyer and Heumann on indigo; of Sir William Perkin, Hofmann, Otto and Emil Fischer, Meldola and many others on the basic dyes; of Griess and his host of followers on the azo-compounds; of Arthur Perkin and of Kostanecki on the flavones and flavonols; of Willstätter on the respiratory pigments and the anthocyanins; and, not least, of Hans Fischer on the synthesis of the prosthetic group of the blood pigment.

No attempt can be made to cover this vast field, but the mere mention of these topics serves to prove the immense theoretical and practical value of a study of organic colouring matters. The work proceeds, and a long chapter of great chemical and biological interest on the natural carotinoid pigments is even now being written by Karrer, Kuhn and others.

---

* From the presidential address before Section B (Chemistry) of the British Association, delivered at Leicester on September 7.

# 天然染色物质及其类似物*

罗伯特·鲁宾逊

## 编者按

牛津大学教授罗伯特·鲁宾逊是两次世界大战之间英国杰出的化学家。他的主要研究成果是对花中显色物质结构的测定（与他的夫人格特鲁德·鲁宾逊合作）。他在牛津大学给学生们上化学课时，习惯于用听课学生所能采集到的花中的花青苷的名字来命名早春中的某一天：这对于在人群中想给他献上一大束鲜花的年轻妇女来说是很有挑战性的。

有很多理由吸引化学家从事天然和人造染色物质的研究，不仅由于色彩能引起愉悦感，可以更深入地认识叶绿素和血红蛋白在生命过程中履行的某些重要功能，以及染料与颜料对于工业的重要性，还由于可见的颜色比任何其他性质都更适合用于有机物质的实验研究，无论是分析还是合成。可见的颜色可以提供同质性的标准或者说是浓度的量度，在寻求分离和提纯方法中起着难以估量的指导作用，并且，颜色的出现和消失可以立刻指示化学反应的发生。难怪很多无色物质的研究最终得以成功都有待于某种特征性显色反应的发现；维生素 A 就是一个显著的例子。

列出这一领域中的杰出成就会招致严厉的批评。然而，在回顾以下这些人的研究工作时，我不怕受到批评，其中包括劳伦特、凯库勒、拜耳和霍伊曼对于靛蓝染料的研究；威廉·珀金爵士、霍夫曼、奥托和埃米尔·费歇尔、麦尔多拉以及其他很多学者对于碱性染料的研究；格里斯及他的众多追随者对于偶氮化合物的研究；阿瑟·珀金与科斯塔尼基对于黄酮和黄酮醇的研究；维尔施泰特对于呼吸色素和花青苷的研究；同等重要的还有汉斯·费歇尔在合成血色素辅基方面的研究。

要想设法覆盖这么广阔的研究领域是不可能的，但是，仅仅提及上述研究主题，就足以证明研究有机染色物质在理论和实践上的重大价值。研究仍在继续，甚至到了今天，卡勒、库恩以及其他学者还在谱写着新的壮丽篇章——他们揭示了天然类胡萝卜素的巨大化学和生物学价值。

---

* 本文引自作者作为主席在 9 月 7 日于莱斯特举行的英国科学促进会 B 分会（化学）会上所作的发言。

## Occurrence of Anthocyanins and their Derivatives

The brilliant and pioneering researches of Richard Willstätter and his co-workers since 1914 have established the main features of the chemistry of the anthocyanins, which were recognised as saccharides, occasionally acylated, of the anthocyanidins. They exhibit amphoteric character, forming salts with both acids and bases. Thus the violet pigment cyanin, which can be isolated from blue cornflowers, red roses, deep red dahlias and other flowers, forms a blue sodium salt and a red hydrochloride. The hydrolysis of the latter by means of hot aqueous hydrochloric acid into cyanidin chloride and glucose is represented by the equation:

$$\underset{\text{cyanin chloride}}{C_{27}H_{31}O_{16}Cl} + 2H_2O = \underset{\text{cyanidin chloride}}{C_{15}H_{11}O_6Cl} + \underset{\text{glucose}}{2C_6H_{12}O_6}$$

The constitution of cyanidin chloride has been established by analysis and numerous syntheses; the first of these (Willstätter and Mallison) utilised the reduction of quercetin by means of magnesium in aqueous methyl alcoholic hydrochloric acid solution.

In this process a widely distributed anthoxanthin yields a widely distributed anthocyanidin, and the temptation to assume that similar reactions occur in the plant laboratory is very great. There is, however, very little justification for this view, and the experimental support brought forward in its favour will not survive careful scrutiny. The alleged crystalline anthocyans prepared by the reduction of natural flavones or plant extracts containing them are nothing but the said flavones with a small proportion of adsorbed colouring matter of anthocyanidin type. It seems much more probable that the flavones and anthocyanins are independently synthesised, although perhaps from a common starting point. The existence of genetic factors which control the occurrence of anthoxanthins independent of that of anthocyanins is strong evidence in favour of this view.

The anthocyanidins which have been isolated are pelargonidin, cyanidin, peonidin, delphinidin, petunidin, malvidin and hirsutidin, represented as chlorides. All have been synthesised by unambiguous methods and the synthetic specimens have been carefully compared and identified with the natural products. Pelargonidin, cyanidin and delphinidin are the fundamental types, peonidin being a methyl ether of cyanidin and petunidin, malvidin and hirsutidin being, respectively, the mono-, di- and trimethyl ethers of delphinidin.

The greater number of the anthocyanins fall into a comparatively restricted number of categories, including: (*a*) the 3-monoglycosides and 3-monogalactosides, (*b*) the 3-rhamnoglycosides and other 3-pentoseglycosides, (*c*) the 3-biosides, (*d*) the 3:5-diglycosides, and (*e*) the acylated anthocyanins. It is unnecessary to recount the steps taken in reaching these conclusions, but they have been finally justified by synthesis in many instances.

## 花青苷及其衍生物的发现

自 1914 年以来，理查德·维尔施泰特与其合作者对花青苷进行了杰出的开创性研究，已经勾勒出花青苷化学性质的主要特征。花青苷被认为是花青素的糖化物，有时是酰基化的。它们显示出两性特征，与酸和碱都可以形成盐。因此，可以从蓝色矢车菊、红玫瑰、深红色大丽花和其他一些花中分离得到的紫色颜料矢车菊色素苷能够形成一种蓝色的钠盐和一种红色的盐酸盐。后者在热的盐酸溶液中水解成氯化矢车菊色素和葡萄糖，用化学方程式表示如下：

$$C_{27}H_{31}O_{16}Cl + 2H_2O = C_{15}H_{11}O_6Cl + 2C_6H_{12}O_6$$

氯化矢车菊色素苷　　　氯化矢车菊色素　葡萄糖

通过分析和大量的合成已经确定了氯化矢车菊色素的结构；最早的方法由维尔施泰特和马利松创立，是在甲醇－盐酸水溶液中用镁还原槲皮苷。

在这一过程中，广泛分布的花黄素生成了广泛分布的花青素，这极大地诱惑人们去设想类似的反应可以发生在植物实验室中。不过，几乎没有什么证据可以支持上述观点，对其有利的实验证据经不住仔细的推敲。所谓通过还原天然黄酮或含黄酮的植物提取物而制备出的结晶花青素只不过是吸附了少量花青素类染色物质的上述黄酮。看来黄酮和花青苷各自独立合成的可能性更大，尽管合成可能始于同一起点。控制花黄素和花青苷出现的遗传因子相互独立就是对这种观点的有力支持。

已分离出来的花青素有：花葵素、矢车菊色素、芍药花色素、飞燕草色素、矮牵牛色素、锦葵色素和报春色素，都具有氯化物的形式。人们已经通过明确的方法合成了上述所有色素，并且对合成物和天然产物进行了仔细的比较和鉴别。花葵素、矢车菊色素和飞燕草色素为基本类型，芍药花色素是矢车菊色素的甲基醚，矮牵牛色素、锦葵色素和报春色素则分别是飞燕草色素的单甲基、二甲基和三甲基醚。

大多数花青苷可以分为相对有限的几个类别，包括：(*a*) 3– 单葡萄糖苷和 3– 单半乳糖苷，(*b*) 3– 鼠李糖葡萄糖苷和其他 3– 戊糖葡萄糖苷，(*c*) 3– 二糖苷，(*d*) 3, 5– 二葡萄糖苷，以及 (*e*) 酰基化的花青苷。不必详述得到这些结论所经历的每一个步骤，因为它们已经最终被众多的合成实例所证实。

In group (*a*) we find callistephin, the monoglycoside of pelargonidin occurring as one of the pigments of the aster and as the main pigment of scarlet carnations and many other flowers; the related galactoside, fragarin, is the colouring matter of the strawberry.

In the cyanidin series the corresponding pair is chrysanthemin and idaein, the former of wide distribution and the latter occurring in the skins of cranberries and in the leaves of the copper beech.

Peonidin 3-monoglycoside, termed oxycoccicyanin, is found in the skins of the larger American cranberries and oenin or malvidin 3-monoglycoside is the colouring matter of the skins of purple-black grapes, as well as of certain cyclamen and primulae. The delphinidin representative undoubtedly occurs in bilberries in admixture with other pigments, and it has not yet been fully examined; the petunidin and hirsutidin representatives have not been isolated from natural sources, although there is reason to believe that the former occurs in the berries of the Darwin barberry and the latter has been synthesised.

In groups (*b*) and (*c*) we find large classes of anthocyanins of which only a few representatives have been closely studied. These include keracyanin (cyanidin 3-rhamnoglycoside), probably identical with antirrhinin (isolated by Miss R. Scott-Moncrieff), and mecocyanin, a pigment of red poppies which is now recognised by synthesis as cyanidin 3-gentiobioside. There is very little doubt that pelargonidin 3-rhamnoglycoside colours the scarlet gloxinia and that pelargonidin 3-biosides are of widespread occurrence, for example, in the ordinary orange-red nasturtium and in the flowers of the scarlet runner bean.

The anthocyanins of groups (*a*), (*b*) and (*c*), when derived from the same anthocyanidin, exhibit similar behaviour as indicators. Thus chrysanthemin, keracyanin and mecocyanin all give a violet solution in aqueous soda and this becomes blue on the addition of caustic alkali. On partial hydrolysis, mecocyanin and antirrhinin actually yield chrysanthemin.

The anthocyanins of class (*d*) are the most widely distributed and best-known members of this series of natural pigments; they include pelargonin, the colouring matter of the scarlet pelargonium and possibly the first anthocyanin to be obtained in a crystalline condition (Molisch's experiment), also cyanin, the isolation of which from the blue cornflower by Willstätter and Everest in 1914 was the first of an impressive series of investigations.

Peonin from the deep red peony and malvin from the wild mallow or from certain primulas, are the peonidin and malvidin representatives in this group, which is completed by petunin and hirsutin. Quite recently the delphinidin member has been isolated from *Salvia patens*.

在 (*a*) 组中我们发现翠菊苷，即花葵素的单葡萄糖苷，是翠菊中的一种色素，也是鲜红色康乃馨和其他很多种花中的主要色素；与之相关的半乳糖苷，即草莓苷，是草莓中的染色物质。

在矢车菊色素系列中有一对对应色素，就是紫菀苷和山越橘苷。前者分布广泛，后者存在于越橘的果皮和紫叶山毛榉的叶子中。

芍药花色素的 3– 单葡萄糖苷，被称为洋越橘苷，是在更大的美洲越橘的果皮中发现的；而葡萄色素，或者说锦葵色素 –3– 单葡萄糖苷，是紫黑色葡萄的果皮以及仙客来和报春花中的染色物质。飞燕草色素的代表物无疑出现在欧洲越橘中，并且与其他多种色素混合在一起，至今尚未对其进行全面的考察；矮牵牛色素与报春色素的代表物还没有从其天然来源中分离出来，尽管有理由相信前者存在于达尔文小檗的浆果之中，而后者已经被合成出来。

在 (*b*) 组和 (*c*) 组中，我们发现了很多种花青苷，但只有少数几种被人们认真研究过。其中包括凯拉花青（即 3– 鼠李糖葡萄糖矢车菊色素苷），可能与之一样的有金鱼草苷（由斯科特 – 蒙克里夫小姐分离得到）和袂康花色苷。袂康花色苷是红罂粟中的一种色素，已通过合成辨识为 3– 龙胆二糖矢车菊色素苷。几乎没有人怀疑鲜红色大岩桐的颜色来自于 3– 鼠李糖葡萄糖花葵苷，而 3– 二糖花葵苷则是广泛存在的，比如存在于普通的橘红色旱金莲花和鲜红色的红花菜豆之中。

如果 (*a*)、(*b*) 和 (*c*) 组中的花青苷是由同一种花青素衍生而成的，那么在它们作为指示剂时就会显示出类似的性质。所以在苏打水溶液中加入紫菀苷、凯拉花青和袂康花色苷时溶液都会变为紫色，加入苛性碱之后又变成蓝色。通过不完全水解，袂康花色苷和金鱼草苷也会产生紫菀苷。

(*d*) 组中的花青苷分布最为广泛，是这一天然色素系列中最广为人知的成员，包括花葵苷和矢车菊色素苷。花葵苷是鲜红色天竺葵中的染色物质，可能还是第一个由实验得到的结晶态花青苷（莫利希试验）；矢车菊色素苷是 1914 年维尔施泰特和埃弗里斯特从蓝色矢车菊中分离出来的，由此引出了一系列令人难忘的研究工作。

从深红色芍药中得到的芍药色素苷和取自野生锦葵或某些报春花中的锦葵色素苷，是这一组中芍药花色素和锦葵色素的代表物，该组中还有矮牵牛色素苷和报春色素苷。最近，从鼠尾草中分离出了飞燕草色素中的成员。

The anthocyanins of group (*d*) differ from those of groups (*a*), (*b*) and (*c*) in their alkali colour reactions and in their marked instability to aqueous sodium hydroxide. Thus cyanin, which compares with mecocyanin in group (*c*), gives a pure blue solution in aqueous soda and the dilute solution becomes very quickly yellow on the addition of sodium hydroxide.

Pelargonin, cyanin, peonin, malvin and hirsutin have all been synthesised.

The anthocyanins can be characterised and qualitatively distinguished by their distribution between immiscible solvents, and in the case of disaccharides the use of *n*-butyl alcohol is convenient.

Acylated anthocyanins occur in all the anthocyanidin series; thus, on hydrolysis, delphinin, the pigment of species of delphinium, furnishes *p*-hydroxybenzoic acid as well as glucose and delphinidin.

Many other delphinidin derivatives are acylated by means of *p*-hydroxycinnamic acid, probably attached to the sugar hydroxyls, and pelargonin and cyanin also occur in acylated forms. These so-called complex anthocyanins are characterised by high distribution numbers; they are usually acylated 3:5-dimonosides, but in the delphinidin series, gentianin and violanin appear to be *p*-hydroxycinnamates of delphinidin monoglycoside and rhamnoglycoside respectively (Karrer). There is also some evidence of another type of depside anthocyanin in which the acyl group is directly attached to the anthocyanidin molecule and the glycoside group is borne by the hydroxyl of the acid residue.

## Anthocyanins as Indicators and the Colours of Flowers

(With Mrs. G. M. Robinson)

The amphoteric character of the anthocyanins accounts for the exhibition of a wide variety of colours in a range of solutions of graded hydrogen ion concentration, and this method, using buffered solutions, can be employed for the characterisation of anthocyanidins and anthocyanins. Under the specified conditions the results are fully reproducible and the hydrogen ion concentration values have been controlled by electrical methods as well as by the use of indicators. Thus, if the *p*H of an acid cyanin solution is increased until the violet tone matches that of an alkaline cyanin solution, the *p*H of which is decreased in order to reach the same condition, then the *p*H of the violet solution will be found to be 7.0–9.0, depending on the shade of violet produced. Cyanin is red in solutions of *p*H 3.0 or less, violet at *p*H 8.5 and blue at *p*H 11.0. The red, violet and blue forms are the oxonium salt, the colour-base and the salt of the colour-base.

Now cyanin was isolated by Willstätter and his colleagues from the blue cornflower and from the red rose, and it seemed quite a simple step to assume that the cell-sap in the (*d*) 组花青苷与 (*a*)、(*b*) 和 (*c*) 组花青苷的不同之处表现在它们在碱性条件下的显色反应和在氢氧化钠水溶液中显著的不稳定性。比如矢车菊色素苷，与 (*c*) 组中的袂康花色苷相比，它在苏打水溶液中会形成纯蓝色的溶液，而其稀溶液在加入氢氧化钠后快速变成黄色。

花葵苷、矢车菊色素苷、芍药色素苷、锦葵色素苷和报春色素苷都已被合成出来。

通过各种花青苷在互不相溶的溶剂中的分配情况，可以对它们加以分辨和定性鉴别，对于二糖来说，使用正丁醇就很方便。

花青素系列中的全体成员都是花青苷的酰基化物；例如，来自飞燕草中的色素——飞燕草色素苷在水解时会产生对羟基苯甲酸、葡萄糖和飞燕草色素。

很多其他的飞燕草色素衍生物也是通过对羟基肉桂酸酰基化得到的，酰基基团可能连接在糖羟基上，而且花葵苷和矢车菊色素苷也能以酰基化形式出现。这些所谓的复合花青苷以高分配系数为特征，它们通常是 3,5– 二单糖苷酰基化物。但是在飞燕草色素系列中，龙胆晶苷和堇菜苷似乎分别是单葡萄糖飞燕草苷和鼠李葡萄糖飞燕草苷的对羟基肉桂酸酯（卡勒）。还有某些证据表明存在另一种缩酚酸类型的花青苷，其中酰基基团直接连在花青素分子上，而葡萄糖苷基则连接在酸残基的羟基之上。

## 作为指示剂的花青苷和花的颜色

（与鲁宾逊夫人合作）

花青苷具有两性的性质可以解释它在一系列氢离子浓度逐次变化的溶液中呈现出多种颜色的原因，这种涉及缓冲溶液的方法可以用来鉴别花青素和花青苷。在指定条件下，结果是完全可以再现的，因为氢离子的浓度值可以用电学法或指示剂来控制。因此，如果某酸性矢车菊色素苷溶液的 pH 值不断升高直到其溶液显现的紫色与为达到同样条件 pH 值不断下降的碱性矢车菊色素苷溶液的颜色相符合，这时测得紫色溶液的 pH 值为 7.0~9.0，具体数值取决于所产生的紫色的深浅。矢车菊色素苷在 pH 值为 3.0 或更低的溶液中为红色，在 pH 值 8.5 时为紫色，在 pH 值 11.0 时为蓝色。红色、紫色和蓝色三种形式分别对应的是鎓盐、生色基和生色基的盐。

既然矢车菊色素苷是维尔施泰特及其同事从蓝色矢车菊和红色玫瑰中分离出来的，那么似乎很容易得出如下假定，即矢车菊的细胞液为碱性，玫瑰的细胞液为酸性，

cornflower was alkaline and that in the rose acid, particularly in view of the fact that the absorption spectra of the coloured aqueous extracts correspond with these conditions.

It has indeed been generally assumed that the indicator colour of the anthocyanin will give a measure of the hydrogen ion concentration of the cell-sap, but unfortunately this method cannot be relied upon for several reasons. In the first place there is a glaring anomaly in the fact that direct measurement by electrical methods (glass electrode as arranged by Mrs. Kerridge) shows that the cell-saps are all well on the acid side of the neutral point. Thus the conventional view for red flowers may well be correct, but some special circumstances must be invoked in the case of blue flowers.

Turning at once to the blue cornflower (the cultivated annual kind), a blue filtered extract made with distilled water was found to be sufficiently acid to turn blue litmus red. Using 3 gm. of petals in 14 c.c. of distilled water (*p*H 6.3 owing to dissolved carbon dioxide), the *p*H was 4.9. (These quantities were used throughout the experiments and the use of larger relative quantities of the petals did not alter the hydrogen ion concentration appreciably.) Addition of a buffered solution of *p*H 4.4 did not affect the colour, but the colour changed to violet when the B.D.H. Universal Buffer, *p*H 9.0, was added. It was at once apparent that the only simple explanation is that the cyanin anion is present in a complex form, giving a stable aggregate with a negative charge; in some way the strength of cyanin colour-base as an acid must be vastly increased.

Some form of colloidal solution was considered most likely to fulfil the necessary conditions, and Dr. Conmar Robinson, of the Chemistry Department, University College, London, kindly examined a filtered, distilled water extract of blue cornflowers and reported as follows:

"The solution contains ultramicrons easily visible in the slit ultramicroscope, but small enough to be in fairly rapid Brownian movement. Microcataphoresis showed them to be negatively charged. Without more quantitative work it is impossible to say if these particles can represent the bulk of the material present, but this seems probable if the solution is very dilute; the possibility of observing a colloidal impurity is always a trap. The visibility of the ultramicrons suggests a lyophobic colloid. It is, however, not precipitated even by 2*N* NaCl, which indicates that a protective colloid is also present."

Our next step was to attempt the production of blue cyanin sols stable in neutral or weakly acid solution, and some measure of success was achieved, although the solutions are by no means so stable as those from the blue cornflower.

If a little crystalline cyanin chloride is added to boiling tap-water (*p*H 8.0) then the usual violet solution results (see above), the colour being what we consider "normal". If, however, the cyanin is triturated in the cold for a minute with the water and gradually heated to boiling with shaking, then a beautiful blue solution results. The fact that the same materials can be used to produce two entirely different results shows that it can only

尤其是在考虑到有色水提物的吸收光谱与上述情况相吻合的情况下。

人们确实曾普遍认为花青苷指示剂的颜色可以度量细胞液中的氢离子浓度，然而遗憾的是，由于多种原因，这种方法并不可靠。最主要的原因是存在如下的明显异常，即利用电学法直接测量（凯里奇夫人使用的是玻璃电极）细胞液的 pH 值时，毫无例外地显示酸性。因此，认为花朵颜色为红色的传统观点很可能是恰如其分的，而在花朵颜色为蓝色时就必须借助于某些特殊情况来加以解释。

下面来谈谈蓝色的矢车菊（一种一年生栽培类型的植物）。用蒸馏水处理矢车菊得到一种蓝色的过滤提取物，它具有足以令蓝色石蕊变红的酸性。将 3 克花瓣和 14 毫升蒸馏水（溶解的二氧化碳使蒸馏水的 pH 值为 6.3）混合后，pH 值为 4.9。（整个实验中都会用到这一数量关系，增加花瓣的相对用量不会明显改变氢离子的浓度。）加入 pH 值为 4.4 的缓冲溶液不会改变溶液的颜色，但是当加入 pH 值为 9.0 的 B.D.H. 通用缓冲液（译者注：B.D.H. 为英国著名的化学品公司）时，颜色变为紫色。很明显，唯一的简单解释就是矢车菊色素苷的阴离子是以复合体形式存在的，在负电荷条件下形成稳定的聚集体；在某种情况下，矢车菊色素苷生色基作为酸的强度必定会大幅度增加。

人们认为胶体溶液的某些形式最有可能满足上面实验结果所需的条件。伦敦大学学院化学系的康马·鲁宾逊博士对蓝色矢车菊经过滤的蒸馏水提取物进行了细致的检测，并给出了下面的报道：

“溶液中含有在缝隙超显微镜下很容易观察到的超微粒子，但它们的尺寸很小足以发生相当快速的布朗运动。微阳离子电泳显示它们是带负电荷的。在没有进行更多定量研究的前提下，还不能说这些微粒就是溶液中溶质的团块，不过，在极稀溶液中，这种说法似乎有可能成立，但观察到的是胶体中的杂质的可能性也是始终存在的。超微粒子的可视性暗示着它们是疏液胶体。可是，即使是用 2*N* 的 NaCl 也不能使其沉淀，这说明还存在着一种保护胶体。”

我们下一步的目标是努力制备出在中性或弱酸性溶液中稳定的蓝色矢车菊色素苷溶胶，目前已经取得了某种程度上的成功，只是溶液没有蓝色矢车菊的溶液那么稳定。

如果向沸腾的自来水（pH 8.0）中加入少量结晶态的氯化矢车菊色素苷，那么就会出现常见的紫色溶液（见上面的描述），我们认为这种颜色是“正常的”。但是，如果将其在低温下加水研磨一分钟，再逐渐加热到沸腾并不断摇动，就会产生漂亮的蓝色溶液。同种物质可以用来产生两种完全不同的结果，这说明只有矢车菊色素

be the state of aggregation of the cyanin which can have stabilised the anionic charge and hence produced a blue colour under the conditions that normally produce a violet solution. If very small quantities of cyanin chloride are employed, this phenomenon can be reproduced using distilled water. Willstätter and Everest found that their cornflower extracts contained xylan and other polysaccharides, and we have attempted to produce blue acid cyanin solutions in the presence of various polysaccharides. The addition of dispersed xylan and various kinds of starch, also agar-agar, makes the preparation of blue solutions of *p*H about 7.5 a very simple matter, but we have not yet found a way of imitating the cornflower solution in respect to its stability at *p*H 5.0.

Probably these colloid associations are much more readily formed at values of *p*H between 5.5 and 6.5, and on the whole the blue flowers have less acid cell-saps than the red flowers. The petals of the rose, in contrast with the cornflower, constitute an exception (*p*H 5.6).

It must be emphasised that variations of *p*H are quite insufficient in themselves to account for the colour changes and it is evident that the most important single factor for flower colour, given the nature of the anthocyanin, is the question of the condition of the pigment in solution, and it would appear that *all blue flowers are coloured by colloidal solutions of their respective pigments.*

Methods for the determination of the hydrogen ion concentration of the cell-sap of flowers depending on the use of the flower colours as indicators may be sound, but only if it can be guaranteed that the colloidal condition of the pigment solution is not altered by the extraction with the buffered solutions which are employed. In any event, the results bear no relation to the colours observed *in vitro* using isolated anthocyanins, and they cannot be transferred from flower to flower: the colour series depends almost as much on the other conditions in the cell-sap as on the hydrogen ion concentration and on the nature of the anthocyanin. Another aspect of *p*H of the cell-saps is that the higher values appear to be associated with the formation of delphinidin derivatives. The remarkable distribution in the tropaeolum—Empress of India—is as follows: leaf, delphinidin diglycoside (*p*H 5.6); calyx, cyanidin 3-bioside (*p*H 5.0); flower, pelargonidin 3-bioside (*p*H 4.5). On the other hand, three scabious with anthocyanins based respectively on pelargonidin, cyanidin and delphinidin had all the same petal *p*H, 5.0.

We have already discussed elsewhere the influence of certain substances termed co-pigments on the colour of anthocyanin solutions; these effects are to be detected in strongly acid solution and the presence or absence of these substances is undoubtedly a factor to be taken into consideration. The extent to which the co-pigment effect is bound up with colloid phenomenon is a matter for future experiment and discussion, but it is convenient to maintain the term co-pigment for the present.

Dr. E. A. H. Roberts has observed the shift of the absorption bands of chrysanthemin and oenin chlorides on the addition of papaverine (strongly blueing effect) and narcotine (weak

苷的聚集状态才能稳定负离子电荷因而能在通常产生紫色溶液的条件下呈现出蓝色。如果使用很少量的氯化矢车菊色素苷，则使用蒸馏水也能重现这种现象。维尔施泰特与埃弗里斯特发现他们的矢车菊提取物含有木聚糖和其他多糖，我们已经尝试在存在各种多糖的条件下制备蓝色的酸性矢车菊色素苷溶液。加入分散的木聚糖、各种类型的淀粉以及琼脂使得制备 pH 值大约为 7.5 的蓝色溶液成为一件非常简单的事情，但是我们还没有找到一种方法能达到矢车菊色素苷在 pH 值为 5.0 时所具有的稳定性。

可能 pH 值在 5.5 和 6.5 之间时，形成上述缔合胶体要容易得多。总的来说，蓝花所含的酸性细胞液要少于红花。玫瑰花瓣与矢车菊形成对比，构成了一个特例（pH 5.6）。

必须要强调的是，pH 值的变化本身远不足以解释颜色的变化，虽然决定花色的最重要的单一因素，即赋予花青苷本质特征的因素，是溶液中色素的存在条件，可能**所有蓝色花朵的颜色都来自于各自所含色素的胶体溶液**。

测定花朵细胞液中氢离子浓度的方法取决于所用指示剂的花的颜色，这种说法可能是合理的，但必须有这样一个前提，即要保证色素溶液的胶体状态不会因提取时所用的缓冲溶液而改变。无论如何，这些结果与在体外观测被分离出来的花青苷所看到的颜色没有关系，并且一朵花的结果不适用于另一朵花：颜色系列依赖于细胞液中其他条件的程度几乎与依赖于氢离子浓度以及花青苷的本性的程度相同。关于细胞液 pH 值的另一个问题是，较高的 pH 值可能与飞燕草色素衍生物的形成有关。它们在旱金莲印度女皇中的显著分布情况如下：叶，二葡萄糖飞燕草色素苷（pH 5.6）；花萼，3– 二糖矢车菊色素苷（pH 5.0）；花，3– 二糖花葵苷（pH 4.5）。另一方面，所含花青苷的种类分别基于花葵素、矢车菊色素和飞燕草色素的三种山萝卜属植物，其花瓣却具有相同的 pH 值——5.0。

我们曾在其他地方讨论过被称为辅色素的物质对于花青苷溶液颜色的影响；这些效应可以在强酸性溶液中检测到，而辅色素的存在与否无疑是一个需要考虑的因素。辅色素对胶体现象到底有多大影响是以后的实验和讨论要解决的事，但为了方便起见，还是暂时保留辅色素这个术语为好。

罗伯茨博士曾观测到紫菀苷和葡萄色素氯化物在加入罂粟碱（强烈的致蓝色效应）和那可汀（微弱的影响）后的吸收谱带位移现象，并且将此现象与使用戊醇时

effect), and correlated this with a corresponding change (lowering) of the distribution number of the anthocyanin using amyl alcohol.

It seems clear that papaverine salts and oenin salts combine in solution. The relation between the distribution number of oenin chloride and the concentration of the pigment seems to require the assumption that the molecules of the anthocyanin are associated (2 mols.) in aqueous solution and free in amyl alcohol. Chrysanthemin and idaein behave similarly, also malvidin 3-galactoside. This phenomenon appears to be related to that of co-pigmentation.

The naturally occurring co-pigments include the anthoxanthins (flavone and flavonol saccharides, etc.) and tannins and some efficient substances not yet identified.

The justification for assuming the operation of this factor can best be indicated by an example. Certain herbaceous phlox contain pelargonin, but have a much bluer-red colour than other flowers coloured by this anthocyanin. But the same observation applies to the extract in 1 percent hydrochloric acid, and moreover the presence of much anthoxanthin is noted. Hence, all the circumstances point to co-pigmentation of the pelargonin salt in the flower petal.

Finally, we do not know whether or not traces of iron and other inorganic substances may affect flower colour. In this connexion the case of the blue hydrangea is always quoted, and we have observed that when the stalks of red hydrangea flowers are immersed in very dilute aqueous ferric chloride, the flowers slowly become blue. The ashes of many flowers contain 1–2 percent $Fe_2O_3$, and the anthocyanin test for iron is one of the most delicate known.

(**132**, 625-628; 1933)

花青苷分配系数的相应变化（降低）联系起来。

显然罂粟碱盐酸盐和葡萄色素氯化物在溶液中能够结合。建立葡萄色素氯化物的分配系数与色素浓度之间的关系似乎需要假设花青苷分子在水溶液中是 2 个分子结合成的复合体，而在戊醇中则是游离的。紫菀苷、山越橘苷和锦葵色素 –3– 半乳糖苷也有类似的性质。看来这种现象与辅色素的作用有关。

天然存在的辅色素包括花黄素（黄酮和黄酮醇的糖化物等等）和鞣酸，以及一些尚未鉴别出来的有效物质。

用一个例子可以最有效地证实辅色素产生作用的假定是成立的。某些草本夹竹桃属植物中含有花葵苷，但是与其他由于含有这种花青苷而显色的花相比，其红色中掺杂着更多的蓝色。但在对其 1%盐酸提取物进行同样的观测后还会发现这些草本夹竹桃属植物中存在大量的花黄素。可见，所有事实都表明在花瓣中存在花葵苷的盐的辅色素效应。

最后，我们仍然不知道痕量的铁或者其他无机物是否可以影响花的颜色。关于这一点，大家经常会举蓝色绣球花的例子，我们曾观测到，当把红色绣球花的花梗浸入到极稀的氯化铁水溶液中时，花朵会慢慢变蓝。很多种花的燃烧灰烬中都含有 1% ~2%的 $Fe_2O_3$，并且用花青苷来检验铁是最灵敏的已知方法之一。

（王耀杨 翻译；汪长征 审稿）

# Atomic Transmutation and the Temperatures of Stars

A. S. Eddington

## Editor's Note

**Here English astronomer Arthur Eddington challenges a recent claim in *Nature*, by Soviet physicists George Gamow and Lev Landau, that the internal temperature of stars can be gauged by whether or not lithium can be detected at their surfaces. Gamow and Landau argued that if the temperature exceeds several million degrees, lithium would be destroyed by reaction with hydrogen before it could reach the surface. Not so, says Eddington, because the lithium would be carried not by slow diffusion but by more rapid circulation currents induced by the star's rotation. That would make its presence consistent with the temperatures (up to 10–20 million degrees) that astronomers had estimated.**

THE letter of Gamow and Landau[1] suggests that an upper limit to the internal temperature of a star can be obtained by considering the disintegration of lithium. Investigations of this kind will probably be of great importance in the future development of astrophysics, but the actual proposal of Gamow and Landau rests on an assumption which is scarcely likely to be true. They postulate that any lithium found at the surface must have been carried there by diffusion from the central region, where it is presumed to have been created. Diffusion in a star is an exceedingly slow process, the time of relaxation being of the order $10^{13}$ years[2]. It would make small progress during the maximum age of the giant stars. But there is a process of mixing which is likely to operate much faster, namely, the circulating currents in meridian planes indirectly caused by the rotation of the star. The order of magnitude is indicated in an example treated by the writer in which the speed of the vertical current was found to be 60 metres a year[3]. The example was chosen with the view of giving an upper limit to the amount of this circulation; but, allowing for slower currents in an average star, the lithium will be brought to the surface far more quickly in this way than by diffusion.

It is difficult to see how any consistent theory of distribution could be given if diffusion alone were operating. If there is time for lithium produced at the centre to reach the surface, there is time for the heavy elements to have disappeared from the surface by downward diffusion; or if it is supposed that they, like lithium, were created at the centre, there is no mechanism by which they could ever reach the surface. In the steady distribution towards which diffusion is slowly tending, there should not be a single atom of lead in the outer half of the volume of the star.

The existence of these circulating currents will raise the upper limits given by Gamow and Landau. Since the disintegration is sensitive to changes of temperature, the increase may

# 原子嬗变和恒星温度

阿瑟·爱丁顿

## 编者按

*在这篇文章中，英国天文学家阿瑟·爱丁顿对苏联物理学家乔治·伽莫夫和列夫·朗道最近发表在《自然》杂志中的观点提出质疑，他们认为在恒星表面是否能检测到锂元素可以作为判断其内部温度高低的标准。伽莫夫和朗道声称：如果温度超过了几百万度，锂在到达恒星表面之前就会因与氢发生反应而被完全破坏。爱丁顿说，并非如此，因为锂不是被缓慢的扩散过程而是被更快的由恒星自转产生的环流所带动的。这样锂在恒星表面的存在与天文学家推算出的恒星内部温度（高达 10~20 百万度）之间就不再矛盾了。*

伽莫夫和朗道在快讯 [1] 中提出：恒星内部温度的上限可以通过对锂元素衰变的考虑得到。这一研究对天体物理学未来的发展很可能是至关重要的，但伽莫夫和朗道就这一问题的提议是建立在一个几乎不可能成立的假设基础上的。他们假设在恒星表面发现的所有锂元素都是在中心区域产生并通过扩散而来的，而实际上锂有可能是在恒星表面产生。恒星内部的扩散过程非常缓慢，其弛豫时间的数量级可达 $10^{13}$ 年 [2]。仅在年龄最大的巨星中会出现少许快一点的扩散，但是还可能有一个过程会使混合过程速度加快，那就是间接由恒星自转引起的在子午面上的环流。作者通过对一个实例的分析得出垂直流的速度约为 60 米 / 年 [3]。选择这个例子的目的在于由它可以得出环流效应的上限；但就算在大多数恒星中环流速度会慢一些，锂元素以这种方式到达表面仍要远快于通过扩散的方式。

如果只有扩散这一个过程在起作用，我们就很难给出一个自洽的分布理论。如果在恒星中心产生的锂有足够的时间扩散到恒星表面，那么所有的重元素就会通过向下的扩散过程从表面消失；如果假设重元素像锂一样产生于恒星的中心，那么我们将无法说明它们是如何到达恒星表面的。如果认为扩散是一个缓慢进行的稳态分布过程，则在恒星的靠外的一半体积内一个铅原子也不可能找到。

环流效应的存在将会提高伽莫夫和朗道给出的恒星内部温度的上限。由于衰变过程对温度变化非常敏感，所以增加值不会太大；但这也许足以使我们安然接受通

not be very large; but it may well be sufficient to remove any difficulty in accepting the temperatures of the order $10^7$–$2\times10^7$ found by astronomical methods, whilst negativing any suggestion of considerably higher temperatures.

(**132**, 639; 1933)

A. S. Eddington: Observatory, Cambridge, Oct. 9.

References:

1 *Nature*, **132**, 567 (Oct. 7, 1933).

2 *Internal Constitution of the Stars*, §§195—196.

3 *Monthly Notices R.A.S.*, **90**, 54 (1929).

过天文方法得到的恒星内部温度的数量级 $10^7$~$2\times10^7$，同时也否定了认为恒星内部温度显著高于这个值的提议。

（魏韧 翻译；邓祖淦 审稿）

# Free Radicals

S. S.

## Editor's Note

**This review of the understanding of free radicals in chemistry, based on a discussion meeting in Cambridge, shows how sophisticated mechanistic organic chemistry had become by the 1930s. Free radicals are chemical entities (atoms or molecules) that have "unpaired" electrons, occupying an electron orbital by themselves. They are generally highly reactive, and sometimes feature as transient intermediates in chemical reactions. The discussion shows how quantum theory of chemical bonding was already becoming useful to understand them. Prominent at the meeting was the young German chemist Karl Zielger, whose understanding of free radicals later enabled him to develop catalysts for making polymers with controlled molecular structures—work that won him the 1963 Nobel Prize with Giulio Natta.**

THE General Discussion on "Free Radicals" held by the Faraday Society at Cambridge on September 28–30 was noteworthy for the large attendance of distinguished foreign visitors as well as for the number and range of the papers presented. It is impossible to do justice to all the contributions in a short review; what follows must be regarded as a personal impression of the more salient features of the discussion.

The definition of a free radical presents some difficulty. Probably the best "working specification" is that of Wieland, quoted by Prof. T. M. Lowry in his opening paper. "Free radicals are complexes of abnormal valency which possess additive properties, but do not carry an electric charge and are not ions." This definition, like most of the others which have been attempted, is open to criticism; in particular, charged free radicals, for example, $CH_2^+$, which contain an odd number of electrons, are familiar in positive ray work and were discussed later in the meeting.

In the opening paper, Prof. Lowry laid stress on the significance of free radicals for theories of valency and of the mechanism of organic reactions. In terms of the electronic theory, the splitting of a covalent link may be thought of as taking place unsymmetrically, giving two ions of opposite sign, or the link may be broken symmetrically so that each fragment of the molecule retains one of the electrons of the link and is a free radical. In the early days of the electronic theory of valency, it was thought that stable molecules might contain covalent linkages with any degree of polarity from a neutral bond like that between the carbon atoms in ethane to the polar bond in NaCl. There is now a considerable body of physical evidence which indicates that the two types of linkage are fairly sharply marked off from one another. It is true that dipole moment determinations show that a single covalency can exhibit some degree of polarity, but this is always far

# 自由基

S.S.

## 编者按

这篇根据剑桥大学的一次讨论会写成的评论文章介绍了人们对化学中自由基的理解，从这篇文章中可以看出有机化学机理研究在20世纪30年代已经发展到了相当高的水平。自由基是带有“不成对”电子，本身占据一个电子轨道的化学基团（原子或分子）。它们通常具有很强的化学反应活性，有时在化学反应中可以作为瞬态中间产物。这次讨论表明关于化学键的量子理论已经逐渐成为理解自由基的有效手段。在讨论会上表现最突出的是德国年轻的化学家卡尔·齐格勒，后来他利用自己对自由基的理解开发出许多可以控制聚合物分子结构的催化剂——该项工作使他和朱利奥·纳塔一起赢得了1963年的诺贝尔奖。

剑桥大学法拉第学会于9月28日~30日举行了关于“自由基”的研讨会，出席此次会议的国外著名访问学者的人数之多，大会所递交的论文数量之大、范围之广都是非常引人瞩目的。我不可能在一个简短的综述里一一阐述所有的论文，所以应把下文看作是我个人对讨论中较为突出部分的印象。

给自由基下定义存在一定的困难。最好的“规范性定义”可能是劳里教授在开篇论文中所引用的威兰的定义。“自由基是具有异常化合价和附加性质的复合物，但是它不带电荷，也不是离子。”和大多数其他曾经提出过的定义一样，这一定义也很容易受到批评，尤其是在考虑带电荷的自由基时，而这种带电荷的自由基是阳极射线研究中比较常见的物质，如拥有奇数个电子的$CH_2^+$，会议的后期讨论了这种自由基。

劳里教授在开篇论文中强调了自由基对于化合价理论和有机反应机理的理论的重要性。根据电子理论，共价键可能会发生不对称的断裂，这样就形成了两个电荷符号相反的离子；也可能出现共价键的断裂是对称的情况，这样断开的每一个分子都保留着共价键中的其中一个电子，从而形成一个自由基。在早期的价键电子理论中，人们认为稳定的分子中都含有具有一定极性的共价键，其极性的大小介于乙烷中两个碳原子间共价键的极性到氯化钠中极性键的极性之间。目前有很多物理学证据表明这两种键具有非常显著的区别。对偶极矩的测定显示，单个共价键可以表现出一定程度的极性，但极性的大小远远小于电子从一个原子转移到另一个原子所形成的偶极矩的大小，在晶体结构和拉曼光谱方面积累的数据也说明离子键和共价键

short of the moment to be expected for the transference of an electron from one atom to another. The accumulating data on crystal structure and Raman spectra also give an experimental distinction between ionic and covalent linkages.

It follows that two main types of mechanism must be considered for organic reactions. Lapworth has shown that the formation of cyanhydrins is essentially an ionic reaction, and Lowry formulates it thus

$$>C = O \rightleftharpoons >\overset{+}{C}-\overset{-}{O} + \overset{-}{C}N \rightarrow >C-\overset{-}{O}$$
$$\underset{CN}{|}$$

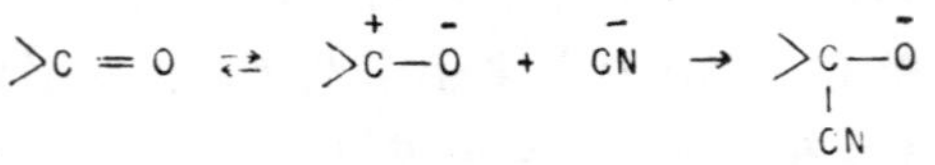

with an intermediate polarisation of the double bond. On the other hand, the thermal decomposition of hydrocarbons and many photochemical changes cannot be formulated as ionic reactions. Thus Norrish has found that the photochemical decomposition of methyl ethyl ketone follows the course:

$$\begin{matrix} CH_3 \\ C_2H_5 \end{matrix}\!\!>\!C = O \rightarrow \begin{matrix} CH_3 \\ C_2H_5 \end{matrix} C = O \rightarrow \begin{matrix} CH_3 \\ C_2H_5 \end{matrix} + CO \rightarrow \left.\begin{matrix} C_2H_6 \\ C_3H_8 \\ C_4H_{10} \end{matrix}\right\} + CO$$

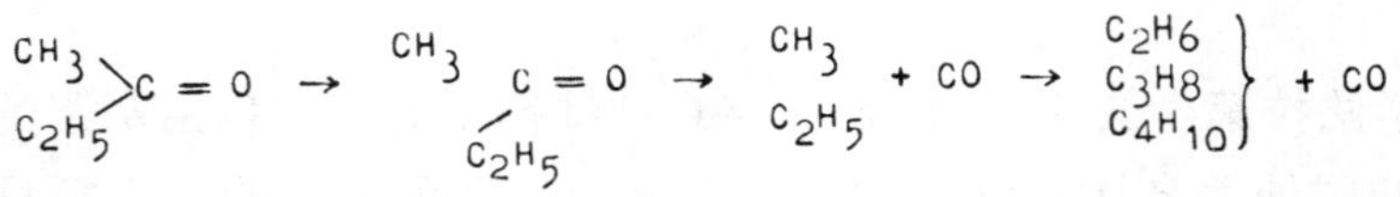

The ultimate products are carbon monoxide and an equivalent mixture of nearly equal parts of ethane, propane and butane. It is evident that these products are most readily accounted for by the intermediate formation of the free radicals methyl and ethyl.

It is convenient here to mention a remarkable result obtained by Norrish for higher ketones. With methyl butyl ketone the products of photochemical decomposition are acetone and propylene.

$$\begin{matrix} CH_3 \\ CH_3 \cdot CH_2 \cdot CH_2 \cdot CH_2 \end{matrix}\!\!>\!CO \rightarrow CH_3 \cdot CH = CH_2 + \begin{matrix} CH_3 \\ CH_3 \end{matrix}\!\!>\!CO$$

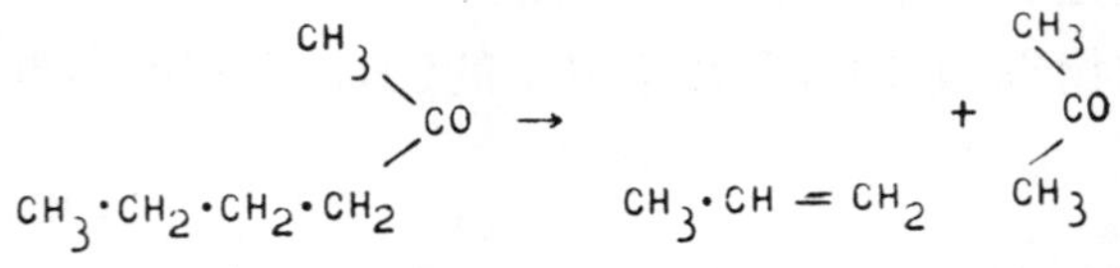

Since the radiation used is that absorbed by the carbonyl group, this reaction presents an interesting problem in molecular mechanics. It can be shown that nearly all the energy absorbed by the carbonyl group reappears as the energy of disruption of a bond in another part of the molecule.

Most of the free radicals met with in organic chemistry have one unsatisfied valency and therefore contain an odd number of electrons. These odd molecules should exhibit the paramagnetism due to an unbalanced electronic spin; this has been verified experimentally for inorganic free radicals, such as $NO_2$, $ClO_2$, etc., and more recently by Sugden for the typical organic free radicals, the ketyls ($R_2C-O-K$). These substances have a high degree of stability and can be kept for an indefinite time; on the other hand, Paneth estimates the

在实验中存在差异。

　　因此，考虑有机反应时必须考虑两种主要的反应机制。拉普沃思曾指出氰醇的形成过程实质上是一个离子反应，因而，劳里用一个双键的瞬态极化阐述了这一过程。

$$>C = O \rightleftharpoons >\overset{+}{C}-\overset{-}{O} + \overset{-}{C}N \rightarrow >\overset{-}{C}-\overset{-}{O} \\ \underset{CN}{|}$$

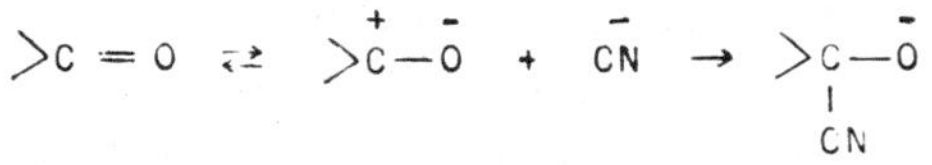

另一方面，烃的热分解和许多光化学变化都不能以离子反应的形式表达。诺里什发现甲乙酮的光化学分解过程可以表示如下：

$$\overset{CH_3}{\underset{C_2H_5}{}}>C = O \rightarrow \overset{CH_3}{} \quad C = O \rightarrow \overset{CH_3}{\underset{C_2H_5}{}} + CO \rightarrow \left. \overset{C_2H_6}{\underset{C_4H_{10}}{C_3H_8}} \right\} + CO$$

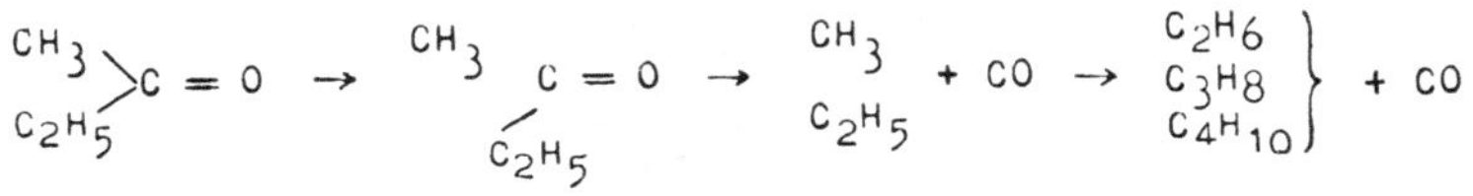

最终产物是一氧化碳和等量的乙烷、丙烷和丁烷的混合物，混合物中三种成分的含量几乎相等。显然，这些产物很容易用甲基自由基中间体和乙基自由基中间体的形成来进行解释。

　　说到这里我们很自然地会提到诺里什在对高碳数酮的研究中所得到的重要结论。甲丁酮的光化学分解产物是丙酮和丙烯。

$$\underset{CH_3 \cdot CH_2 \cdot CH_2 \cdot CH_2}{\overset{CH_3}{CO}} \rightarrow CH_3 \cdot CH = CH_2 + \underset{CH_3}{\overset{CH_3}{CO}}$$

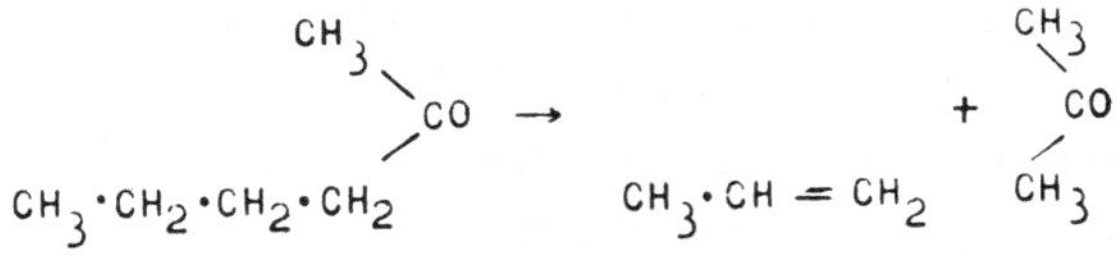

由于用来催化上述光化学反应的辐射是被羰基所吸收的，因而这一反应体现出了分子力学中的一个有趣问题。可以看出，羰基所吸收的能量几乎都用于分子另一部分的化学键断裂。

　　有机化学中的大多数自由基都有一个未饱和的化合价，因而它们都含有奇数个电子。由于含有未配对的电子自旋，这些含奇数个电子的分子应该表现出顺磁性，$NO_2$、$ClO_2$ 等无机自由基的顺磁性已经被实验所证实，最近，萨格登也证实了典型的有机自由基羰游基（$R_2C-O-K$）的顺磁性。这些自由基具有很高的稳定性，可以存在无限长的时间；而另一方面，帕内特估计甲基自由基的平均寿命为千分之几秒。

average life of a methyl radical as a few thousandths of a second. Free radicals thus fall into two groups, the stable type with a long life, and the evanescent type with a very short average life.

Many organic radicals of the first type have been prepared since Gomberg, in 1900, discovered triphenylmethyl. A valuable review of this series of compounds was given by Prof. Ziegler. The factors which favour the dissociation of the hexa-aryl ethane molecule appear to be the unsaturation and the volume of the substituents, and of these, volume appears to be more important. Thus pentaphenyl ethyl and pentaphenyl cyclopentadienyl appear to exist entirely as the free radical. For the latter substance an interesting symmetrical electronic formula (I) has been suggested by Löwenbein in which a ring is formed by five three electron links. The introduction of substituents containing triple bonds appears to have little effect in promoting the dissociation of the ethane linkage.

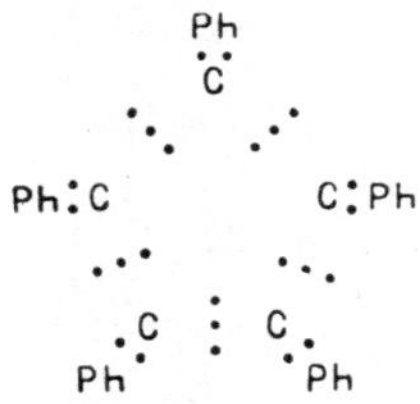


I

The number of radicals of the triphenyl methyl type now known is very large and progress is to be expected rather in the accurate physico-chemical study of known complexes than in the preparation of new substances. Ziegler and his co-workers have already developed accurate methods for determining the energy changes which accompany the dissociation of hexa-aryl ethanes; these have so far only been applied to hexaphenyl ethane. The rate of dissociation has been followed by three reactions (with $I_2$, NO, and $O_2$) and is found to be constant in a number of different solvents. The temperature coefficient of reaction velocity gives a heat of activation of 19 Cal. This is much less than the heat of splitting of the usual C–C bond, namely, c. 70 Cal. Ziegler has also worked out an accurate optical method of determining the degree of dissociation of hexaphenyl ethane in various solvents. The temperature coefficient of the dissociation constant gives a heat of dissociation of about 11 Cal.

These measurements are of interest in connexion with a quantum mechanical theory of triphenyl methyls contributed by Prof. E. Hückel. In Hückel's theory of benzene the stability and planar configuration of the ring are ascribed to resonances between six electrons, one from each carbon atom, which are designated *ph* electrons. In hexaphenyl ethane the aromatic nuclei must, on stereochemical grounds, be arranged at or near tetrahedral angles around the central carbon atoms, and with this arrangement it is not possible to have interaction between the *ph* electrons of one aromatic nucleus and another. In triphenyl methyl, however, the three phenyl groups can approach a planar configuration with links to the central carbon atom at 120°. A marked interaction between the electrons of the three nuclei can then occur which stabilises the free radical. This

因此，自由基分为两类，一类是具有较长寿命的稳定型，另一类是具有很短平均寿命的短暂型。

自从 1900 年冈伯格发现三苯甲基以来，人们已经制备了许多稳定型的有机自由基。齐格勒教授曾写过一篇关于这一系列化合物的有价值的综述。促使六芳基乙烷离解的因素似乎是不饱和性和取代基的体积，其中取代基的体积似乎是主要因素。因此，五苯乙基和五苯环戊二烯基似乎完全以自由基的形式存在。对于后者，勒文贝恩提出了一个有趣的对称电子式 (I)，在这个电子式中，五个三电子键形成了一个环。而含有三键的取代基的引入似乎并没有对乙烷键的离解起到任何促进作用。

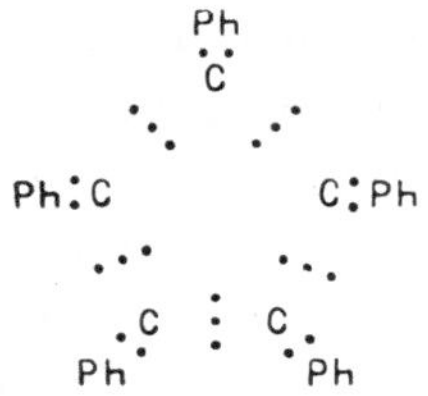

I

现在我们知道，三苯甲基类自由基的数量很多，而且与新物质的制备相比，我们更期待在已知复合物的精确物理化学研究上取得新进展。齐格勒和他的同事们已经研制出了精确测定六芳基乙烷离解过程中相应能量变化的方法，不过，至今为止这些方法只适用于六苯基乙烷。他们发现，通过六苯基乙烷的三个反应（与 $I_2$、NO、和 $O_2$ 的反应）可以测得它的离解速率，而且在多种不同的溶剂中其离解速率都是不变的。由反应速度的温度系数给出 19 大卡的活化热，这远远小于通常 C–C 键断裂所需的约 70 大卡的热量。齐格勒还设计出一种精确的光学方法来测定六苯基乙烷在各种不同溶剂中的离解度。解离常数的温度系数给出约 11 大卡的离解热。

这些测定与休克尔教授提出的三苯甲基的量子力学理论有着有趣的联系。在休克尔教授关于苯的理论中，苯环的稳定性和平面结构是由六个电子间的共振所决定的，每个碳原子提供一个电子，这些电子被称为 $p_h$ 电子。在立体化学中，六苯基乙烷中的芳香基必须以四面体角或接近四面体角的方式排列在中心碳原子的周围，这样各个芳香基中的 $p_h$ 电子就不可能发生相互作用。然而在三苯甲基中，三个苯基可近似形成一个平面结构，与中心碳原子形成 120º 的夹角。这样三个苯基中的电子之间就会发生明显的相互作用，从而使自由基更加稳定。必须从 C–C 键断裂所需的能量中减去稳定能，才能得到六苯基乙烷分子的活化热。休克尔把这种稳定能称为“静

energy of stabilisation must be subtracted from the heat of rupture of the C–C bond to give the heat of activation of the hexaphenyl ethane molecule. Hückel terms the energy of stabilisation the "static bond strain", and computes its value approximately for typical substituted ethanes. With six aromatic substituents the static bond strain is 55 Cal., in fair agreement with Ziegler's experimental results. The strain decreases rapidly with the number of aromatic substituents; for one phenyl group in the molecule it is only 12 Cal.

Another discussion of free radicals in terms of quantum mechanics was contributed by Prof. J. E. Lennard-Jones, who applied the method of molecular orbitals to investigate the structure of the $CH_3$, $CH_2$, and CH radicals. Particular interest attaches to the structure of $CH_2$, which has a singlet normal state and not, as might have been expected, a triplet state. The production of $CH_2$ from $CH_3$ involves not only the removal of a hydrogen atom but also an "energy of reorganisation" of the electrons in the $CH_2$ residue so that the net spin becomes zero. A rather cruder way of expressing this result (since it refers to a particular atom and not to the molecule as a whole) is to state that whilst $CH_3$ contains quadrivalent carbon, $CH_2$ contains bivalent carbon. This energy must play an important part in many chemical and photochemical changes. Thus carbon monoxide is known from spectroscopic evidence to be $^1\Sigma$ with bivalent carbon, whilst the carbonyl group in ketones may be regarded as containing quadrivalent carbon. Hence the photochemical change studied by Norrish in which carbon monoxide is formed from the lower ketones must involve an energy of reorganisation.

A number of papers were contributed on the chemical reactions of radicals of short life. The simplest of all free radicals is, of course, atomic hydrogen, which can be produced in high concentrations by a discharge through hydrogen at pressures of less than 1 mm. This radical has the comparatively long life of about one second, and some recent work on its chemical properties and those of atomic oxygen was described by Hartek. At low temperatures (liquid air or hydrogen) some very striking results have been obtained. With oxygen, atomic hydrogen gave high yields of hydrogen peroxide, with mercury a solid product containing 70 percent of HgH, and with ethylene ethane was formed. In the last reaction, the apparatus was capable of producing 500 c.c. of ethane, measured at atmospheric pressure, in 15 minutes.

The use of free methyl and ethyl to synthesise organometallic compounds was described by Paneth. Amongst the compounds isolated was the long sought for antimony analogue of cacodyl, $(CH_3)_2Sb.Sb(CH_3)_2$. This substance is spontaneously inflammable in air and melts at 17.5°C. In the liquid state and in solution it is nearly colourless, but on solidification becomes bright red. Horn, Polanyi and Style described experiments showing that methyl and ethyl are formed by the action of sodium on alkyl halides at 200°–300°C. The radicals were detected in two ways: (*a*) by using them to initiate the chain reaction between hydrogen and chlorine; and (*b*) by interaction with iodine to give alkyl iodides which were frozen out and determined by the usual analytical methods. The interesting radical methylene, $CH_2$, was obtained by Belchez as the primary product of the thermal decomposition of methane on a platinum surface at 1,100°C. and 0.1 mm. pressure. The

态键应力”，并近似计算了有典型取代基的乙烷的静态键应力值。当有六个芳香取代基时，静态键应力为 55 大卡，这与齐格勒的实验结果完全一致。这种键应力随芳香取代基数目的减少而迅速减小，当分子中只有一个苯基取代基时，静态键应力仅为 12 大卡。

伦纳德 - 琼斯教授提出了另一种根据量子力学来讨论自由基的想法，他利用分子轨道法来研究 $CH_3$、$CH_2$ 和 CH 自由基的结构。$CH_2$ 的结构是正常单态而不是预期的三重态，这引起了人们特别的关注。由 $CH_3$ 生成 $CH_2$ 不仅需要去掉一个氢原子，余下的 $CH_2$ 中的电子还需要一个“重组能”，这样净自旋才能为零。用一种更粗略的方式来表达（因为结果更适用于一个特定的原子，而不是整个分子）就是在 $CH_3$ 中含有四价碳，而 $CH_2$ 中的碳为二价。这种能量在许多化学变化和光化学变化中都起着非常重要的作用。光谱学的证据证明一氧化碳为 $^1\Sigma$，具有二价碳原子，而酮类中的羰基会被认为含有四价碳原子。因此，在诺里什研究的光化学变化中，由低碳数酮形成一氧化碳的反应一定需要有重组能。

许多投稿的文章都是关于短寿命的自由基的化学反应的。在所有的自由基中最简单的自然是氢原子。当压强小于 1 毫米汞柱时，氢气在放电条件下可以产生高浓度的氢原子。这种自由基有着相对较长的寿命，大约是 1 秒。哈特克描述了最近的一些对氢原子和氧原子自由基的化学性质的研究。他在低温下（液态空气或氢气）得到了一些非常惊人的结果。氢原子与氧反应可以生成大量的过氧化氢，与汞反应可以生成含有 70% 氢化汞的固体产物，与乙烯反应可以生成乙烷。当压强为 1 个大气压时，后一个反应在 15 分钟内可以生成 500 毫升的乙烷。

潘内特描述了用游离的甲基和乙基来合成金属有机化合物的方法。经过长期的寻找，在分离出的化合物中得到了类似于二甲砷基的锑化物 $(CH_3)_2Sb.Sb(CH_3)_2$。这种物质在空气中易自燃，熔点为 17.5℃。液态时和溶液中它几乎是无色的，但固态时它变为亮红色。霍姆、波拉尼和斯泰尔描述的实验说明钠与卤代烃在 200℃ ~300℃的温度下发生反应可以生成甲基和乙基。生成的自由基可以通过两种方法来检测：(*a*) 用它们来引发氢与氯之间的链反应；(*b*) 通过与碘发生作用生成碘代烃，碘代烃在被冻结后再用普通的分析方法进行测定。贝尔兹在 1,100℃的高温和 0.1 毫米汞柱的低压条件下在铂表面进行了甲烷的热分解反应，得到的主要产物就是众所关注的亚甲基自由基 $CH_2$。这种自由基是通过与碘镜的反应来识别的，反应生

radical was identified by reaction with an iodine mirror and the subsequent formation of the additive compound $CH_2I_2Hg_2$ of melting point 230 °C.

Finally, a number of papers were devoted to the study of free radicals in electric discharges by spectroscopic or positive ray methods. Of these there is only space to mention the important report by Mecke on "Free Radicals and Spectroscopy". Spectroscopic methods not only detect the presence of free radicals but also for diatomic radicals give exact information about their dimensions and the strength of the interatomic linkage. It is true that polyatomic radicals and molecules give spectra of such complexity that a full analysis is difficult, but Mecke pointed out that there is a good deal of evidence for regarding simple radicals as the bricks from which larger molecules are built up. Their dimensions show little change when they form part of a larger molecule, and similar linkages have similar binding energies in diatomic radicals and in larger collections of atoms. Thus the accurate spectroscopic data for diatomic radicals and molecules can be applied with little modification to the discussion of the dimensions and strength of linkages in more complex systems.

(**132**, 665-667; 1933)

成了熔点为230℃的加成化合物$CH_2I_2Hg_2$。

最后，有许多论文都专门讨论了用光谱法或阳极射线法对放电过程中的自由基进行的研究。在这些论文中，只有一处提到了梅克的那篇关于“自由基和光谱”的重要报告。光谱法不仅能检测到自由基的存在，而且能够提供关于双原子自由基的原子间键的长度和强度的准确信息。确实，多原子自由基和多原子分子的光谱相当复杂，难以进行全面的分析。但是梅克指出，有很多证据证明可以把简单自由基看作是构成大分子的砖石。当它们形成大分子的一部分时，它们的尺寸几乎没有改变，而且在双原子自由基和多原子自由基中相似的键具有相似的键能。因此，双原子自由基和分子的准确光谱数据可以几乎不加修改地应用到对更复杂体系的键的长度和强度的讨论中。

（李世媛 翻译；汪长征 审稿）

# The Origin of Tektites

V. S. Dubey

## Editor's Note

**Leonard James Spencer's theory that the bead-shaped glassy silica minerals called tektites are frozen droplets of molten rock ejected over very long distances in meteorite impacts on Earth is supported here by V. S. Dubey in Benares, who reports measurements of radioactivity from eight tektite samples worldwide. He finds that seven of them have very similar levels of the radioactive element radium, which supports the idea that they all came from the same source. Furthermore, this radium content matches that of terrestrial granites, but not that of iron meteorites, which suggests that the tektites were caused by melting of terrestrial rock in the impact, rather than being fragments of the impacting body itself.**

IN his contributions to *Nature* on the "Origin of Tektites" Dr. L. J. Spencer[1] has put forward the view "that tektites are not meteoric, though they are connected with the fall of large meteoric masses, but that they have resulted from the fusion of terrestrial rocks, especially in sandy deserts, by the heat so developed".

The radioactivity of eight specimens of tektites and of some pieces of glass of different kinds was determined with the view of deciding whether they were meteoric or terrestrial in origin. I am obliged to Dr. H. Michel of the Natural History Museum of Vienna, and to the Trustees of the British Museum, for these specimens. The problem was suggested by Prof. H. Mache, of the Technical High School of Vienna, and the work was carried out in his laboratory. The results of determinations are given in the accompanying table.

| | | $Ra\times10^{-12}$ per gm. | $Th\times10^{-5}$ per gm. |
|---|---|---|---|
| 1. | Moldavite .. .. .. | 1.07 | 1.08 |
| 2. | Moldavite (Habří, Bohemia) | 1.02 | 1.60 |
| 3. | Moldavite (Probsch) .. .. | 0.78 | 1.60 |
| 4. | Moldavite (Radomolice, Bohemia) | 0.99 | 1.86 |
| 5. | Billitonite .. .. .. .. | 0.96 | 0.96 |
| 6. | Australite (Lake Eyre district) | 0.96 | 0.50 |
| 7. | Australite (Victoria) .. .. | 0.85 | 1.84 |
| 8. | Darwin glass (Tasmania) .. .. | 0.50 | 1.13 |
| 9. | Glass (Old beads) .. .. | 0.48 | |

These results show that the radium content of all the tektites except Darwin glass falls between $0.9\times10^{-12}$ and $1.00\times10^{-12}$. A difference of $0.1\times10^{-12}$ is found even in different parts of the same rock and has no significance.

This constancy in the radioactive contents of tektites coming from such distant parts of

# 玻陨石的成因

杜贝

## 编者按

伦纳德·詹姆斯·斯潘塞认为：现在被大家称为玻陨石的珠状硅质玻璃矿石就是在陨石撞击地球的瞬间由飞溅到很远的熔融岩石液滴凝固而成的。印度贝拿勒斯的杜贝用事实证明了斯潘塞的这个观点，他从世界各地选取了8个玻陨石样品，然后对它们的放射性组分含量进行测量，他在本文中报告了测量的结果。他发现在8个玻陨石样品中有7个样品的放射性元素镭含量处于同一水平，这说明它们有相同的起源。此外他还发现：玻陨石样品中的镭含量与地球上的花岗岩接近，而与从天而降的铁陨石不同，这说明玻陨石是由陆地上的岩石被撞击后熔融形成的，并非撞击物本身的碎片。

斯潘塞博士在《自然》杂志上发表了一篇题为《玻陨石的成因》的文章[1]，他在文中指出“尽管这些玻陨石与大量流星体的坠落有关，但它们并不是陨石的一部分，它们是由地球上，特别是沙漠中的岩石在陨石撞击地球产生的高温下熔融生成的。”

为了判断玻陨石到底是由陆地岩石还是由陨石形成的，我们对8个玻陨石样品和一些种类不同的玻璃片进行了放射性测定。感谢维也纳自然历史博物馆的米歇尔博士和大英博物馆的受托管理人为我们提供了样品。这一问题由维也纳技术中学的马谢教授提出，测定工作也是在他的实验室里完成的。测定结果见下表。

| | | 镭含量 $\times 10^{-12}$/克 | 钍含量 $\times 10^{-5}$/克 |
|---|---|---|---|
| 1. | 绿玻陨石 | 1.07 | 1.08 |
| 2. | 绿玻陨石（哈伯，波希米亚） | 1.02 | 1.60 |
| 3. | 绿玻陨石（普罗施） | 0.78 | 1.60 |
| 4. | 绿玻陨石（拉多莫里斯，波希米亚） | 0.99 | 1.86 |
| 5. | 勿里洞玻陨石 | 0.96 | 0.96 |
| 6. | 澳大利亚玻陨石（艾尔湖地区） | 0.96 | 0.50 |
| 7. | 澳大利亚玻陨石（维多利亚） | 0.85 | 1.84 |
| 8. | 达尔文玻陨石（塔斯马尼亚） | 0.50 | 1.13 |
| 9. | 玻璃（古老的玻璃珠） | 0.48 | |

上述结果表明，除达尔文玻璃外，所有其他玻陨石的镭含量均在 $0.9\times10^{-12}$ ~ $1.00\times10^{-12}$ 之间。而即使是同一块岩石不同部分之间的镭含量差别也能达到 $0.1\times10^{-12}$，所以这种差别是无关紧要的。

来自世界上相隔很远的地区——欧洲、亚洲和澳洲的玻陨石均具有相同的放射

the world as Europe, Asia and Australia clearly suggests some kind of genetic relationship. It is difficult to imagine that glass formed in three different continents from different raw materials should have the same radium content.

The radioactive contents of several kinds of glass, including glass beads of prehistoric age, was determined, but the values found were low and very different, the highest being $0.48\times10^{-12}$ per gm. There is no possibility of these tektites deriving their radioactive contents from iron meteorites in any way, as these meteorites are very poor in radium, the amount being of the order of $10^{-14}$.

The radioactivity of Darwin glass differs from all other tektites considerably and agrees more with glass than with tektites. In this connexion the similarity of silica glass from Wabar and Henbury to the Darwin glass as observed by Dr. Spencer is noteworthy.

The value $1.00\times10^{-12}$ per gm. found for the tektites seems fairly in accord with several such determinations made for granites, which represent the salic part of the earth's crust[2], and show a similar chemical composition. This strongly suggests that these tektites are derived from some mass which agrees in chemical composition as well as in radioactivity with the granitic layer of the earth.

It will be interesting to determine the radioactive content of the tektites recently discovered in French Indo-China and described by Prof. Lacroix, and of those discovered in the Philippine Islands[1]. The determination of the radioactivity of the glasses discovered at Rub' al Khali in Arabia, and at Henbury in Central Australia, will throw further light on the origin of tektites.

(**132**, 678; 1933)

V. S. Dubey: Department of Geology, Benares Hindu University.

---

References:

1 Spencer, L. J., "Origin of Tektites", *Nature*, **131**, 117 (Jan. 28, 1933); 876 (June 17,1933).

2 Piggot, C. S., *Amer. J. Sci.*, 5, **21**, 35 (January 1931).

性含量，这显然说明它们在起源上具有一定的相关性。很难想象，在三个不同的大陆中由不同原岩形成的玻陨石会具有相同的镭含量。

我们测定了几种玻璃状物质中的放射性含量，包括史前时代的玻璃珠，然而测得的值都比较低，相互之间的差别也很大，最大值高达每克 $0.48 \times 10^{-12}$。这些玻陨石中的放射性组分绝对不可能来自于铁陨石，因为铁陨石的镭含量很低，量级在 $10^{-14}$ 左右。

达尔文玻璃的放射性与所有其他玻陨石的差别非常大，倒是与玻璃更为相似。关于这一点，斯宾塞博士发现瓦巴地区和亨伯里地区的硅质玻璃与达尔文玻璃的相似性值得注意。

玻陨石中的镭含量为每克 $1.00 \times 10^{-12}$，似乎与地壳中的硅铝质部分——花岗岩的几组测定结果非常符合[2]，化学成分也类似。这充分说明这些玻陨石来源于一些在化学成分和放射性上都与地球上的花岗岩层相匹配的岩体。

倘若能够对拉克鲁瓦教授曾经提到的新近在法属印度支那地区发现的玻陨石以及在菲律宾群岛发现的玻陨石[1]进行放射性含量的测定，那将会很有意义；如果能对在阿拉伯半岛鲁卜哈利以及澳大利亚中部亨伯里发现的硅质玻璃的放射性含量进行测定，则会更进一步地揭示玻陨石的成因。

（齐红艳 翻译；张忠杰 审稿）

# The Origin of Tektites

J. B. Scrivenor

## Editor's Note

**Not everyone accepted without reservation Spencer's hypothesis, announced earlier in *Nature*, that tektite minerals were formed from rock melted in meteorite impacts. J. B. Scrivenor here raises the objection that this mechanism ought sometimes to produce only partly fused rock, which has not been observed. But he acknowledges that the idea fits with the findings of tiny beads of iron and nickel—the most common metals in meteorites—in some tektites. Scrivenor accepts that Spencer's theory is therefore probably still the best on offer.**

WITH reference to Dr. L. J. Spencer's letter in Nature of October 7, p. 571, on the origin of tektites, the strongest argument against his suggestion that they were formed by the fusion of terrestrial material in meteorite craters is that no tektite has yet been described, so far as I am aware, containing partially fused rock or sand. A further possible objection that no tektite hitherto described contains so many vesicles as glass from meteorite craters is discounted by Prof. A. Lacroix's description of 95 kgm. of tektites from the island of Hainan and the neighbouring mainland, among which glass that originally enclosed vesicles of more than a decimeter in diameter is of frequent occurrence ("Les Tectites de l'Indochine", Paris, 1932, appendix following p. 235). On the other hand, Dr. Spencer's suggestion finds support in the presence of metallic spheres, resembling those of the Wabar glass, in Darwin glass and in tektites from Indo-China, as described in his letter; and also in the presence of nickel in three Malayan tektites, proved by analyses by Mr. J. C. Shenton. As Dr. Spencer remarks, the evidence for tektites being meteoric is entirely negative; and although his suggestion cannot yet be accepted unreservedly, it appeals to me as the best yet proposed for the origin of these bodies.

(**132**, 678; 1933)

J. B. Scrivenor: 68 Chaucer Road, Bedford, Oct. 9.

# 玻陨石的成因

斯克里夫纳

编者按

并不是所有的人都毫无保留地接受斯潘塞在《自然》杂志上发表的假说，即认为玻陨石是由地球上的岩石在被陨石撞击后熔融形成的。斯克里夫纳在本文中就提出了不同的意见，他认为：斯潘塞的机制有时应该能形成部分熔融的岩石，但至今也没有人看到过部分熔融的岩石。不过，他承认斯潘塞的观点与在玻陨石中发现的小铁珠和小镍珠相吻合，而铁和镍是陨石中最常见的金属。因此斯克里夫纳仍然把斯潘塞的理论看作是目前对玻陨石成因的最佳解释。

斯潘塞博士在10月7日出版的《自然》杂志的第571页上发表了一篇有关玻陨石成因的文章，他认为玻陨石是由陨石坑内的地球物质熔融形成的，反驳这一观点的最强有力的论据是：据我所知，在迄今为止发现的玻陨石中，没有任何一种包含了部分熔融的岩石或者砂砾。另一个可能反驳上述观点的证据是：拉克鲁瓦教授在描述海南岛及邻近大陆的重达95千克的玻陨石时忽视了这样一个问题，即迄今为止所提到的任何一种玻陨石都不含有与陨石坑中的玻璃数量相当的气泡，而在这些陨石坑中经常可以见到含有直径大于1分米气泡的玻璃（《印度支那的玻陨石》，巴黎，1932年，第235页后附录）。另一方面，金属球的存在支持了斯潘塞博士的观点，正如他在信中所指出的，在达尔文玻璃和印度支那玻陨石中存在的金属球类似于瓦巴玻璃中的金属球；而申顿先生经过分析证明三块马来玻陨石中含有镍，这一发现也支持了斯潘塞博士的观点。正如斯潘塞博士所述，没有任何证据能够证明玻陨石是陨石的碎片；现在虽然还不能毫无保留地接受斯潘塞博士的观点，但在我看来，他的观点是目前人们对玻陨石成因的最佳解释。

（齐红艳 翻译；张忠杰 审稿）

# New Results in Cosmic Ray Measurements*

E. Regener

## Editor's Note

**Erich Regener reports in more detail on his observations of the ionisation caused by cosmic rays in the upper atmosphere. Using electrometers born aloft in balloons, he and colleagues made a number of measurements at very high altitudes, where the air pressure fell below 50 mm Hg. In three trials, their devices gave consistent results; a fourth did not, but Regener noted that other researchers had observed a magnetic storm on this day which may have disturbed the measurements. In total, the data suggested that the cosmic radiation consisted of three distinct components of different penetrating power.**

IN recent years I have endeavoured to explore the decay of the intensity of cosmic radiation over as wide a range as possible after its entrance into the earth's atmosphere. I believe that such an investigation is indispensable before a theory of the nature of cosmic radiation can be put forward. In *Nature*[1] and in the *Physikalische Zeitschrift*[2] I have already given some preliminary account of our measurements of the intensity of the cosmic radiation in the upper atmosphere. I propose to give here some further results, obtained in recent ascents with registering balloons, but first a few improvements of the apparatus which we have introduced must be described.

The balloon electrometer includes an electrometer system (a thin Wollaston wire, a quartz sling giving the directing power), the photographic objective, projecting the electrometer wire on the photographic plate. The wire is illuminated every four minutes from the side, so that it appears bright on a dark background on the photographic plate. There is also an aneroid barometer for the measurement of the air pressure and a bimetallic lamella for measuring the temperature. The movement of the aneroid, when the pressure decreases, limits by a pointer the image of the electrometer wire on the photographic plate. Since the measurement of the pressure is the most delicate part, especially when the pressure is low, we have added to the ordinary aneroid a second one, which only starts indicating when the pressure falls below one hundred millimetres. By observing the balloons in the air with two theodolites from a base of three to four kilometres, we have been able to prove that the measurements of the pressure with these two aneroids are fairly exact. The agreement with the height deduced from the pressure measurements was very good.

We have also employed another form of balloon electrometer. Our balloon electrometers hitherto constructed each had the ionisation chamber filled with air at a pressure of three or four to five atmospheres. The new electrometer has an *open* ionisation chamber, that is to say, a chamber communicating with the air outside through a tube containing

* Paper before Section A (Mathematical and Physical Sciences) of the British Association, delivered at Leicester on September 8.

# 宇宙射线测量中的新结果*

埃里克·雷格纳

## 编者按

埃里克·雷格纳详细地报告了他在研究高层大气中宇宙射线的电离作用时得到的观察结果。他和他的同事利用气球载静电计在气压低于50毫米汞柱的高海拔区做了多次实验。他们的装置在前三次实验中给出了一致的结果；但第四次的实验结果与前三次有偏离，不过雷格纳指出其他研究人员在第四次实验的那天观测到了磁暴，这也许是导致实验结果出现偏离的原因。所有这些数据都说明了宇宙辐射是由三种穿透力明显不同的成分组成的。

在最近几年里，我一直致力于探索宇宙辐射进入地球大气层后在尽可能广的范围内的强度衰减。我确信这项研究在我们提出一个有关宇宙辐射性质的理论之前是必不可少的。我已经在《自然》[1]杂志和《物理杂志》[2]上对我们测量高层大气中宇宙辐射强度的方法作了初步的说明。在这里我想给出一些更进一步的结论，是我们最近用探空气球的上升实验得到的，但首先我必须描述一下我们对这些仪器所做的改进。

探空气球静电计包括一个静电计系统（一根细的沃拉斯顿铂丝，一个提供下坠动力的石英吊坠）和一个将静电计的铂丝投影到摄影底片上的照相物镜。来自边缘的光每隔4分钟把铂丝照亮一次，所以铂丝在摄影底片的暗背景中出现一条亮线。还有一个用于测量气压的无液气压计和一个用于测量温度的双金属片。当压力下降时，无液气压计的运动通过一个指针来限制静电计的铂丝在摄影底片上的图像。因为气压测量是最精细的部分，尤其是当压力很低时，因此除这个普通的无液气压计外我们又添加了第二个无液气压计，新添的气压计只有在气压低于100毫米汞柱时才开始有显示。通过在3~4千米高的基地上用2个经纬仪观察空中的气球，我们已经能够验证用这两个气球上的无液气压计测量出来的压力是非常精确的，从压力测量中推导出来的高度与实际高度非常吻合。

我们也使用过另一种形式的气球静电计。至今为止，我们使用的每一只气球静电计都配有电离室，室内充有3或4到5个大气压的空气。而新的静电计有一个**开放**的电离室，也就是说，电离室是通过一根装有五氧化二磷的管子同外部大气相通的。

---

* 这篇论文曾在英国科学促进会A分会（数学和物理学分会）于9月8日在莱斯特举行的会议上被宣读过。

phosphorus pentoxide. The pressure in this chamber decreases as the balloon rises in the free atmosphere, and the ionisation chamber in this case must be larger in order to obtain adequate sensitivity. But such an arrangement is very convenient for measuring the absolute value of the ionisation due to the radiation, because it is much easier to obtain the saturation current at a low pressure. In the ordinary ionisation chamber, which is filled with gas at high pressure, it is well known that it is very difficult to obtain the saturation current.

Fig. 1 shows the results of the four best registrations of the cosmic radiation with the closed balloon electrometer. The minimum values of the air pressure on these four ascents are respectively:

August 12, 1932: 22 mm. mercury, 5.4 atmospheres pressure in the ionisation chamber.

January 3, 1933: 34 mm. mercury, 4.45 atmospheres.

March 9, 1933: 17.6 mm. mercury (this is the lowest pressure hitherto reached), 3.28 atmospheres.

March 29, 1933: 32 mm. mercury, 5.33 atmospheres.

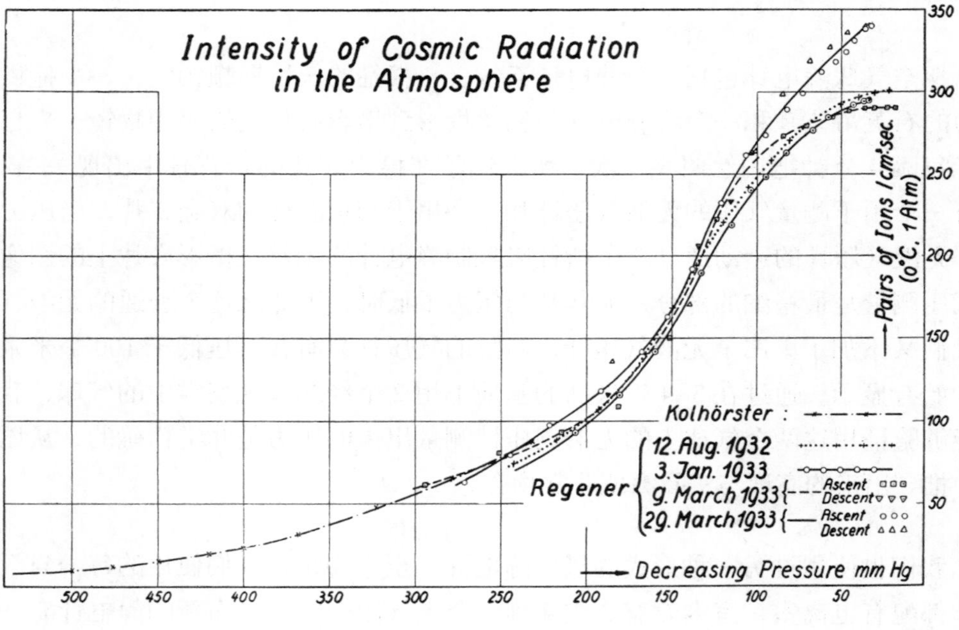


Fig. 1.

It is noteworthy that the first three ascents agree very well among themselves. Also the

因此，当气球在自由大气中上升时，电离室内的气压也会随着下降，而且此时的电离室必须做得更大一些，以获得足够的灵敏度。开放电离室的设计非常便于测量由辐射产生的电离的绝对值，因为在低压下更容易达到电流的饱和。大家都知道在充有高压气体的普通电离室中，电流很难达到饱和。

图 1 中显示的是我们用密闭气球静电计测量宇宙辐射的四次最佳实验结果。在这四次升空过程中达到的气压的最小值分别为：

1932 年 8 月 12 日，22 毫米汞柱，电离室内为 5.4 个大气压。

1933 年 1 月 3 日，34 毫米汞柱，室内 4.45 个大气压。

1933 年 3 月 9 日，17.6 毫米汞柱（这是迄今为止达到的最低气压值），室内 3.28 个大气压。

1933 年 3 月 29 日，32 毫米汞柱，5.33 个大气压。

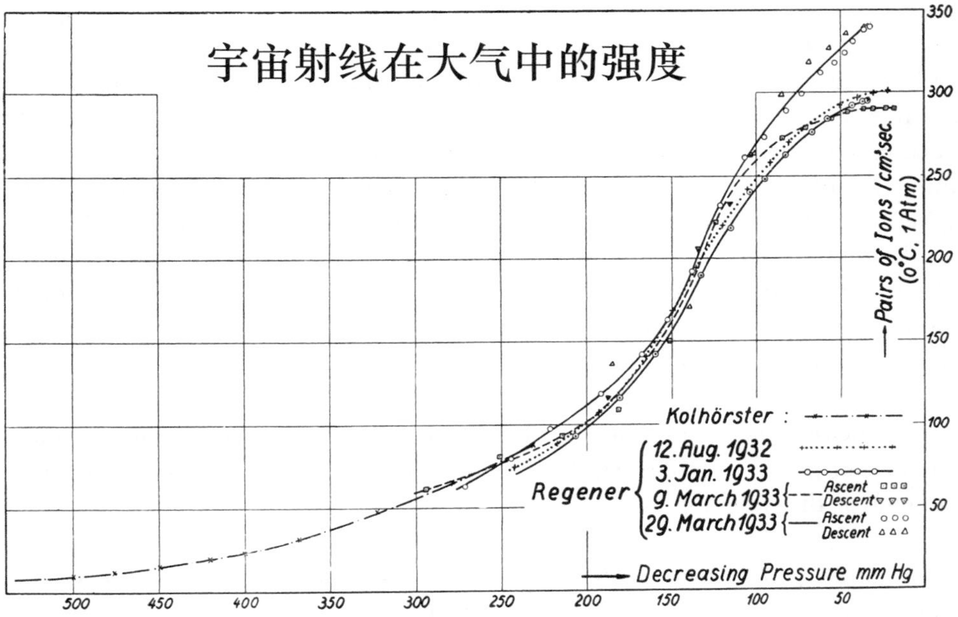


图 1

值得注意的是，前 3 次升空的结果相互之间很一致，第 4 次升空在气压为

fourth ascent agrees with the others very well at the medium heights at a pressure of 150 mm. mercury (that is, at a height of about twelve kilometres). But in the upper atmosphere, that is, at pressures of less than 100 mm., at heights greater than fifteen kilometres, and even more so at heights of twenty kilometres, the intensity begins to be much greater than on the other ascents, so that the maximum value is nearly fifteen percent greater than on the other ascents. This is probably *not* due to the inaccuracy of the measurements. It can be seen that the middle parts of the fourth curve agree very well with the others. Moreover the fourth registration, of March 29, 1933, is the best of all with the closed electrometers. It was also possible to obtain observations during the descent of the balloon (Fig. 1). These observations showed that the ordinary and the secondary aneroids worked very well.

The temperature during the hour in which the balloon was in the stratosphere varies comparatively little, from 6.5° to 11 °C. That is due to the "Cellophane" case, surrounding the electrometer like the glass of a forcing house and protecting it against the cold in the stratosphere.

We believe that the difference of the fourth curve from the others is real, and we have tried to find an explanation. We searched for the cause in the circumstances accompanying the four ascents. On the fourth ascent there was a new moon and we thought that perhaps radioactivity of the moon was the cause of the greater intensity on this day; for on the other ascents the moon was not in the sky. Incidentally, it should be noted that at a pressure of twenty or thirty millimetres of mercury, already one-third of the $\gamma$-radiation of ordinary radioactive bodies could penetrate into the atmosphere. But a little calculation shows that the radioactivity of the moon would have to be improbably great to do this, so this explanation cannot be true. Then we inquired into the magnetic disturbances on the four days. Both Prof. A. Nippoldt at Potsdam and Dr. A. Corlin in northern Sweden informed me that on March 29 there was a magnetic disturbance of medium strength, but the other days were magnetically calm. It would be remarkable if there were a connexion between the magnetic intensity and the intensity of the cosmic rays in the highest parts of the atmosphere, and only in the highest parts; that is to say, that there are additional rays (soft rays) there, perhaps coming from a sunspot. But up to now we have observed this but once. Further observations are necessary in order to ascertain whether this is real.

From the measurements of the decay of the intensity of the cosmic radiation in Lake Constance, my collaborator, Dr. W. Kramer[3], has deduced that there are many components of the radiation.

From Sir James Jeans's hypothesis, one can calculate that the hardest two components correspond to the annihilation of a helium atom and of a proton. But there are many assumptions in this calculation. It is often objected that the fact ascertained in our ionisation curve in the atmosphere, that the ionisation curve approaches a maximum value at the top of the atmosphere, is *not* in favour of the hypothesis, that the primary radiation is electromagnetic. Electromagnetic radiation coming from outside into the atmosphere

150毫米汞柱左右的中高度区（即在高度约为12千米时）所得的结果与前3次也很一致。但是到了上层大气中，即在气压低于100毫米汞柱，高度大于15千米甚至达到20千米时，其强度开始超过其他三次实验，最大值比其他几次实验高出近15%。这很可能不是由测量的不准确造成的。我们可以看到，第四个曲线的中部同其他曲线的中部非常吻合。而且，在1933年3月29日进行的第四次实验中我们采用了密闭的气压计，效果应该是最好的。在气球下降过程中，我们也可以记录观测数据（见图1）。这些观测结果表明，普通无液气压计和第二个无液气压计的工作状态都非常好。

当气球在平流层飞行时，温度变化相对比较小——从6.5℃到11℃。那是因为“玻璃房”效应，静电计的周围被像温室的玻璃一样包裹着，使它能够抵御平流层的寒冷。

我们相信，第四次实验得到的曲线与前三次结果之间的差别是真实的，而且我们曾试过做出解释。我们在四次实验所处的环境中寻找原因。在第四次实验时，出现了一轮新月，我们认为，月面的放射性或许是造成那天强度更大的原因，因为在其他几次实验中，天上没有出现月亮。顺便说一下，我们应该知道，当气压低到20或30毫米汞柱时，一般的放射性物体发射的$\gamma$射线就已经有三分之一能够透过大气了。但在经过了简单的计算之后，我们发现月亮的辐射不可能造成这么大的影响，所以这个解释是不正确的。接着，我们又查询了这四天里磁场扰动的情况。德国波茨坦的尼波德教授和瑞典北部的科林博士告诉我，在3月29日出现过一次中等强度的磁扰，而在另外三天内没有发生磁扰。如果在大气层顶部的磁场强度和宇宙射线强度之间存在着关联，而且这种关联只发生在大气层顶部，这一现象是非常值得关注的；这意味着，那里还有其他射线（软射线）存在，它们也许来自于太阳黑子。但是因为这样的现象我们至今只观察到过一次，要证实这种关联是否存在有必要进行进一步的观测。

根据在康斯坦次湖进行的宇宙辐射强度衰变的测量结果，我的同事克雷默[3]博士曾经作出推断，即宇宙辐射是由多种成分组成的。

根据詹姆斯·金斯爵士的假设，我们能够计算出宇宙射线中最硬的两种成分与氦原子和质子的湮灭有关，但在计算过程中用到了许多假设。我们在整个大气层中得到的电离曲线证明，电离曲线在大气层顶部时会达到最大值；对于这一事实不支持初级宇宙射线为电磁辐射的假设，常常遭到众人的置疑。来自外太空的电磁辐射在进入地球大气层后会产生次级辐射，我们会在较低的大气层中，比如20

of the earth will produce secondary radiation, and we shall find a maximum value of the intensity in the lower atmosphere, perhaps at twenty kilometres, and the intensity will diminish towards the top of the atmosphere.

It is easy to show, however, that the observed form of the ionisation curve agrees with the assumption that the radiation is electromagnetic. The observed curve is altered by the fact that the rays come from all directions. The rays coming from the side, that is, the rays which are already saturated with secondary radiation, because of the long distance they have travelled, are of greater account. My collaborator, Mr. B. Gross[4], has shown that it is possible to calculate from the curve observed for rays incident in all directions the corresponding curve of uni-directional rays. If the function for the rays from all directions be $I_x$, and $\psi x$ be the corresponding function for the intensity of rays coming from one direction only, then $\psi x = I_x - I_x \frac{dI_x}{dx}$. The curve for rays entering the atmosphere vertically shows that their intensity diminishes towards the top of the atmosphere. Thus it agrees with the suggestion that at least a part of the radiation is electromagnetic. There is also a second maximum produced by the second component of the soft part of the radiation.

I would like to add a few words about the analysis of the radiation into its components. My collaborator, Dr. E. Lenz[5], has worked out a useful method for finding whether the radiation is monochromatic or contains more than one component. This method is independent of any assumption regarding the nature of the rays. Suppose that the intensity is a monotonic function of the absorption of monochromatic radiation. When the intensity $I$ is multiplied by the thickness $d$ of the absorbing layer, this gives a curve with a maximum at a certain value of $d$. If the radiation consists of two components of different penetrating power, then there are two maxima in the curve (let us say in the *deformed* curve), deduced from the original curve by multiplying the intensity by the thickness of the layer. When our experimental results are plotted in this way, the curve shows that the radiation in the atmosphere consists of two or three components of different penetrating power.

It is also possible in an experimental way to decide whether the decomposition of the radiation in components is real. When the intensity of radiation in the free atmosphere is observed with an open ionisation chamber, we do the same as we have just done in a mathematical way. The ordinary curve of the intensity of the radiation is a curve obtained with an ionisation chamber containing air at a pressure of one atmosphere. When we work with an open ionisation chamber, we find a value of the current in the chamber which is smaller in the same ratio as the pressure in the air, and thus in the chamber also, is smaller than the normal pressure. Thus we obtain directly a deformed ionisation curve, because the pressure is in proportion to the mass of the layer which is penetrated by the rays.

The two measurements made with such an ionisation chamber do not quite satisfy us yet. The first chamber employed was too small (volume only 22 litres) and therefore the sensitivity was inadequate. The second chamber had a volume of 105 litres and therefore the sensitivity was sufficient. A photographic record obtained on August 30 gave

千米处，发现射线强度达到最大值，而后在逐渐接近大气层顶部的过程中强度会有所下降。

然而，我们很容易证明，通过实验得到的电离曲线与宇宙射线是电磁辐射的假设并不矛盾。射线来自于各个方向的事实改变了观测到的曲线。来自于侧面的射线，也就是那些在穿越了很长距离之后次级辐射已经达到饱和的射线，是非常重要的。我的同事格罗斯[4]先生曾经指出，根据观察到的来自各个方向的辐射曲线可以计算出与单一方向对应的辐射曲线。假设来自各个方向的射线的函数是 $I_x$，只来自于一个方向的射线强度函数是 $\psi x$，则 $\psi x = I_x - I_x \frac{dI_x}{dx}$。我们从垂直射入大气层的辐射曲线中可以看到，它们的强度在到达大气层顶部时会下降。因此，这与至少有一部分射线是电磁辐射的观点相符。射线中软射线部分的次级成分还会产生第二个极大值。

对于分析射线的各种成分，我还想再多说几句。我的同事伦兹博士[5]已经找到了一种区分射线到底是单组分还是多组分的方法，该方法独立于任何有关宇宙射线性质的假说。假定强度是对单色辐射进行吸收的单调函数，则用强度 $I$ 乘以吸收层的厚度 $d$ 得到的曲线会在厚度 $d$ 为某一特定值时达到一个最大值。如果射线包含两个穿透力不同的成分，则在原始曲线的强度值上乘以吸收层的厚度之后，曲线上就会出现两个最大值（让我们把这条曲线称作**变形后的**曲线）。当我们把自己的实验结果用这种方式处理时，从得到的曲线上可以看出，大气中的辐射包含两个或三个穿透力不同的成分。

我们也可以用实验方法来确认对辐射成分的分解是否是正确的。当我们用一个开放的电离室测量自由大气中的射线强度时，我们还用刚刚用过的数学方法来处理。普通的辐射强度曲线是用包含一个大气压空气的电离室得到的。当我们用一个开放电离室做试验时，我们会发现电离室中的电流值小于在同样比例的空气压力下——同时也是电离室中的压力下的电流值，也小于常压下的电流值。这样我们就直接得到了一个变形的电离曲线，因为压力与射线透过的物质层的质量成正比。

我们用这样的电离室做了两次实验，结果都不十分令人满意。第一次实验使用的电离室太小（体积仅为 22 升），因而灵敏度不够高；第二次实验所用的电离室体积为 105 升，这样灵敏度就足够高了。8 月 30 日得到的照相纪录给出了很好的结果，

good results, but unfortunately the temperature of the instrument went down very low, below −20 °C., and therefore the corrections needed were a little greater than usual. The apparatus had become too heavy (3.7 kgm.) for our balloons and we did not employ sufficient safeguards against the cold. But on working out the registrations, the curve (Fig. 2) is already better than those with the closed chamber, and agrees very well with the deformed curve calculated above. The second maximum is also noticeable as in the deformed curve, but this maximum is not very distinct and we shall try to ensure more favourable conditions so that as few corrections as possible are necessary. This part of the curve, I believe, is most important for the analysis and the explanation of the curve.

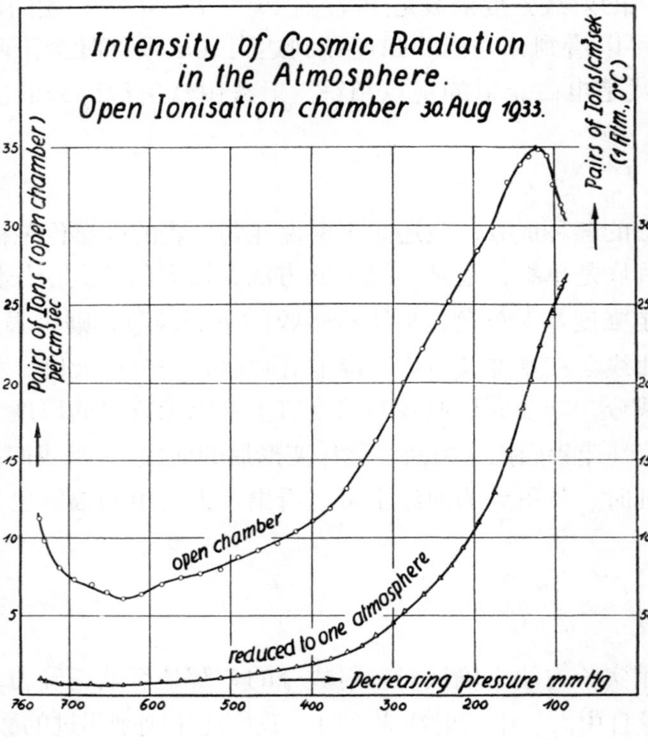


Fig. 2.

In general, the method of employing the open ionisation chamber is very convenient if one wishes to obtain the whole curve from sea-level to the top of the atmosphere, because the observed values with the open chamber vary only from 1 to 5, while the ionisation in the closed chamber varies from 1 to 150. Thus, in Fig. 2, the normal intensity curve is more accurate in the lower parts than with the closed chamber. The values for the normal curve are obtained from the values with the open chamber by multiplying them by $p_0/p$.

I offer my thanks to Mr. B. Auer for helping me in the measurements and to the

但不幸的是，这个装置的温度降到了 –20℃以下，因而所需的校正值略大于正常值。对于我们的气球来说，这个装置已经很重了（3.7 千克），所以我们没有安装抵御冷气的防护设施。但根据测量结果绘制的曲线（图 2）仍然会好于密闭电离室得到的结果，并且与用上述方法计算出来的变形曲线吻合得很好。在变形的曲线中也可以看到第二个最大值，但是，这个最大值并不是很明显，我们将设法确保更有利的实验条件，尽可能地避免各种修正。我认为曲线的这个部分对于我们分析和解释这条曲线至关重要。

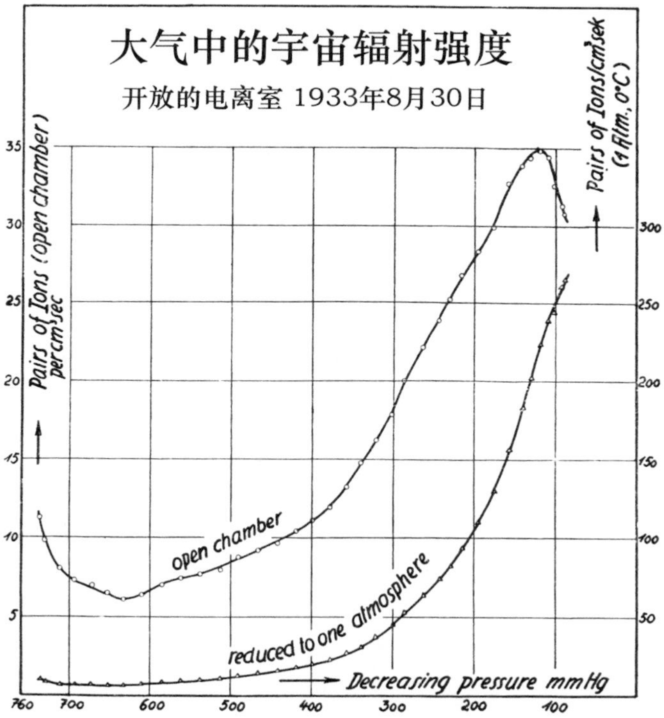


图 2.

一般而言，如果我们想得到一条从海平面到大气层顶部的完整曲线，用开放电离室进行测量是很方便的，因为开放电离室的观测值只在 1 到 5 之间变化，而封闭电离室的测量值则会从 1 一直变化到 150。因此，在图 2 中，开放电离室的标准强度曲线在较低部分会比密闭电离室的更精确，密闭电离室标准曲线上的值是由开放电离室的值乘以 $p_0/p$ 得到的。

我要感谢奥尔先生在测量中给我的帮助，以及“德国科学临时学会”对这项研

Notgemeinschaft der Deutschen Wissenschaft for supporting my investigations.

(**132**, 696-698; 1933)

E. Regener: Technical High School, Stuttgart.

---

References:

1 Regener, E., *Nature*, **130**, 364 (1932).
2 Regener, E., *Phys. Z.*, **34**, 306 (1933).
3 Kramer, W., *Z. Phys.*, **85**, 411 (1933).
4 Gross, B., *Z. Phys.*, **83**, 214 (1933).
5 Lenz, E., *Z. Phys.*, **83**, 194 (1933).

究工作的支持。

（刘霞 翻译；马宇蒨 审稿）

# Interaction of Hard $\gamma$-Rays with Atomic Nuclei

## Editor's Note

**Two Chinese physicists from the National Tsing Hua University here describe experiments in which hard gamma rays kick electrons out of lead or aluminium. They suggested that the data imply some kind of nuclear disintegration triggered by the gamma rays. However, as Ernest Rutherford notes in a short addendum to the paper, the authors had sent him a letter along with their paper clearly indicating that they had not yet heard about recent results demonstrating the creation of electron-positron pairs from energetic gamma rays in the strong field in the vicinity of the atomic nucleus. This process of pair creation, he suggests, might well provide a more natural explanation for the experimental results.**

IT is known that when a pencil of hard $\gamma$-rays of thorium-C″ passes through lead, in addition to the absorption by electrons of the shell, there exists a type of nuclear absorption, accompanied by the emission of characteristic radiations of frequencies different from the primary[1]. The intensity of such radiations has been estimated, and it has been found that the total energy of the characteristic radiations emitted is much smaller than the total energy of the primary radiation absorbed by the nuclei[2]. This would be expected, if we assume that a nuclear disintegration occurs in such a process, so that a part of the absorbed energy is spent. From this point of view, we have tried to detect electrons which might be ejected from the lead nuclei by the primary $\gamma$-quanta.

In our experiment, the $\gamma$-ray source was a radiumthorium preparation equivalent to 10 mgm. of radium. Two Geiger–Müller counters, one having an aluminium wall and the other a lead wall, were used. The counters had equal inner dimensions and approximately equal mass per square cm. of the wall (that is, 0.92 mm. thick for the aluminium counter and 0.22 mm. thick for the lead counter). Let $N_{Al}$ and $N_{Pb}$ be the number of electrons produced in equal time intervals by a given beam of $\gamma$-rays in the aluminium and lead counters respectively. The ratio $N_{Pb}/N_{Al}$ as a function of the wave-length $\lambda$ of the incident $\gamma$-radiation will at first decrease with decreasing $\lambda$, due to the diminishing photoelectric absorption of lead. As the wave-length further decreases, the ratio $N_{Pb}/N_{Al}$ might, however, rise again, if the heavy lead nuclei begin to be disintegrated by $\gamma$-quanta of wave-length less than a certain value and the electrons ejected from the lead nuclei in the disintegration process add themselves to $N_{Pb}$.

By using a beam of $\gamma$-rays of thorium-C″ filtered through 2 cm. of lead and scattered by iron at different angles, we measured the ratios $N_{Pb}/N_{Al}$ for $\gamma$-rays of different wave-lengths. The experimental result is shown in the accompanying table, where $N_{Pb}/N_{Al}$ is multiplied by a constant $k$ such that the value $kN_{Pb}/N_{Al}$ is unity for the scattered radiation at 23°.

# 硬$\gamma$射线和原子核的反应

## 编者按

两位来自国立清华大学的中国物理学家在文中介绍了他们用硬$\gamma$射线将铅和铝中的电子轰击出来的实验。他们认为实验数据说明$\gamma$射线引发了某种形式的核衰变。然而，欧内斯特·卢瑟福在这篇论文后面的简短评论中指出：从作者随论文邮寄给他的一封信中可以明显看出，他们还不知道最近的一项研究成果，即在原子核附近的强场中，高能$\gamma$射线会产生电子–正电子对。卢瑟福认为用产生正负电子对来解释两位中国物理学家的实验结果也许会显得更合理一些。

众所周知，当一束由钍 C″ 放射出的硬$\gamma$射线穿过铅时，除了出现铅的外层电子对$\gamma$射线的吸收以外，还会出现铅原子核对$\gamma$射线的吸收，并伴随着发出和初级辐射具有不同频率的特征辐射[1]。这种特征辐射的强度已经被估算过了，即放射出的特征辐射的总能量远远小于被原子核吸收的初级辐射的总能量[2]。我们可以预见，如果假设原子核在这一过程中发生了衰变，那么原子核吸收的一部分能量就会在此过程中被消耗掉。从这种观点出发，我们测量了由初级$\gamma$粒子从铅原子核中打出来的电子。

我们在实验中采用的$\gamma$射线源是镭–钍合成的放射源，相当于 10 毫克的镭放射源。所使用的两个盖革–缪勒计数器，一个是铝壁，另一个是铅壁。两个计数器具有相同的内壁尺寸，并且每平方厘米壁的质量也大约相等（即 0.92 毫米厚的铝计数器和 0.22 毫米厚的铅计数器）。用 $N_{\mathrm{Al}}$ 和 $N_{\mathrm{Pb}}$ 分别表示在相同的时间间隔内，由给定的$\gamma$射线在铝计数器和铅计数器中产生的电子数目。比值 $N_{\mathrm{Pb}}/N_{\mathrm{Al}}$ 是入射$\gamma$射线波长$\lambda$的函数，在开始阶段由于铅的光电吸收不断减弱，所以将会随着$\lambda$的减小而减小。然而，当波长$\lambda$进一步减小时，比值 $N_{\mathrm{Pb}}/N_{\mathrm{Al}}$ 可能反而会变大。这是因为波长小于某个特定值的$\gamma$粒子可能会引起重铅核的衰变，在铅核衰变过程中放射出来的电子会增加 $N_{\mathrm{Pb}}$ 的值。

将一束由钍 C″ 放射出的$\gamma$射线用 2 厘米厚的铅板过滤，再经过铁散射到不同的方向，我们测量了对应不同波长$\gamma$射线的 $N_{\mathrm{Pb}}/N_{\mathrm{Al}}$ 比值。下表中给出了相关的实验结果，其中 $N_{\mathrm{Pb}}/N_{\mathrm{Al}}$ 要乘以一个常数 $k$，这样，我们把在辐射射线散射角度为 23° 时的 $kN_{\mathrm{Pb}}/N_{\mathrm{Al}}$ 值作为单位 1。

| | λ(x.u.) | $kN_{Pb}/N_{Al}$ |
|---|---|---|
| Primary radiation | 4.7 | 1.16±0.04 |
| Scattered radiation at 23° | 6.6 | 1.00 |
| Scattered radiation at 46° | 12.1 | 1.23±0.08 |

In the table, the ratio $N_{Pb}/N_{Al}$ for $\lambda$ = 6.6 x.u. is seen to be smaller than that for $\lambda$ = 12.1 x.u., and for $\lambda$ = 4.7 x.u. it again rises as was expected if electrons were ejected from the lead nuclei by the hard radiation. The difference of the two ratios for $\lambda$ = 4.7 x.u. and 6.6 x.u. is about 16 percent. Now, the increase of the ratio $N_{Pb}/N_{Al}$ for $\lambda$ = 4.7 x.u. might also result from a difference in the scattering effect of the lead nuclei and aluminium nuclei towards the Compton recoil electrons produced in the counter walls by the incident $\gamma$-rays. If this were the case, the difference of the ratios for $\gamma$ = 6.6 x.u. and 4.7 x.u. should be more pronounced by using counters of thicker walls, since the effect of scattering increases with thickness of the wall. But the same result, namely, a difference of about 16 percent between the two ratios, was obtained when the experiment was repeated with a lead counter with walls 0.3 mm. thick and an aluminium one with walls 1.2 mm. thick. Therefore the above result seems to support the view that the lead nuclei are disintegrated by the hard $\gamma$-rays.

The details of the experiment will be published elsewhere.

C. Y. Chao and T. T. Kung

* * *

It is obvious from a letter to me which accompanied the above communication that Prof. Chao and Mr. Kung have not yet heard of the recent work concerning the positive electron, and in particular of the creation of a pair of electrons, a negative and a positive, by the conversion of a $\gamma$-ray of high energy in the strong electric field of a nucleus. The experiments they describe provide valuable additional evidence of this phenomenon, and would doubtless have been interpreted by them in this way rather than as a nuclear disintegration. It is interesting to note that the magnitude of the effect is about the same as is found in other experiments.

Rutherford

(**132**, 709; 1933)

C. Y. Chao and T. T. Kung: Department of Physics, National Tsing Hua University, Peiping, China, Sept. 4.

References:

1 Chao, *Phys. Rev.*, **33**, 1519 (1930); Gray and Tarrant, *Proc. Roy. Soc.*, A, **136**, 662 (1932).

2 Gray and Tarrant, *Proc. Roy. Soc.*, A, **136**, 662 (1932). Chao, *Science Reports of National Tsing Hua University*, lst series, **1**, 159 (1932).

| | λ（$10^{-11}$ 厘米） | $kN_{Pb}/N_{Al}$ |
|---|---|---|
| 初级辐射 | 4.7 | $1.16 \pm 0.04$ |
| 辐射散射角为 23° | 6.6 | 1.00 |
| 辐射散射角为 46° | 12.1 | $1.23 \pm 0.08$ |

在上面的表格中，$\lambda=6.6\times10^{-11}$ 厘米时的 $N_{Pb}/N_{Al}$ 值小于 $\lambda=12.1\times10^{-11}$ 厘米时的相应值，而当 $\lambda=4.7\times10^{-11}$ 厘米时，如我们所预料的那样，硬 $\gamma$ 射线引发铅核放射出电子，从而使 $N_{Pb}/N_{Al}$ 值增大。这个比值在 $\lambda=4.7\times10^{-11}$ 厘米时与 $\lambda=6.6\times10^{-11}$ 厘米时相差大约 16%。也许有人认为，当 $\lambda=4.7\times10^{-11}$ 厘米时比值 $N_{Pb}/N_{Al}$ 的增加还有可能是由于铅核和铝核对入射 $\gamma$ 射线在计数器管壁上产生的康普顿反冲电子的散射效应的差别导致的。如果真是这样的话，那么 $\lambda=6.6\times10^{-11}$ 厘米和 $4.7\times10^{-11}$ 厘米时的 $N_{Al}/N_{Pb}$ 值之差在使用管壁较厚的计数器时应该更加显著，因为散射效应会随着管壁的增厚而增强。但是，当我们使用壁厚为 0.3 毫米的铝计数器和壁厚为 1.2 毫米的铝计数器重复上面的实验时，我们得到了相同的结果，也就是两个 $N_{Pb}/N_{Al}$ 比值之间仍相差约 16%。这样看来，以上结果支持了硬 $\gamma$ 射线引发铅核发生衰变的观点。

实验的具体细节将发表在其他地方。

赵忠尧，龚祖同

*　　*　　*

从与以上这篇通讯一块寄给我的信中可以明显看出，赵教授和龚先生还不知道最近关于正电子的研究工作，特别是关于在一个原子核的强电场中，高能 $\gamma$ 射线可以转化产生一对电子，即一个正电子和一个负电子的情况。他们描述的实验又一次为这一现象提供了非常有价值的证据，毫无疑问，该实验现象应该被他们解释为高能 $\gamma$ 射线产生了正负电子对，而不是原子核的衰变。值得注意的是，这一效应的强度与在其他实验中观测到的强度大致相同。

卢瑟福

（王静 翻译；尚仁成 审稿）

# A Suggested Explanation of β-Ray Activity

M. N. Saha and D. S. Kothari

## Editor's Note

**Radioactive beta decay had proven most baffling. Unlike alpha particles, beta particles were emitted not with a well-defined energy, but with a broad range of energies, and physicists had established that these energies were created in the nuclear process itself, not as the electron interacted with shell electrons. Here Indian physicists Meghnad Saha and Daulat Singh Kothari suggest that the mystery might be settled by the recently discovered process in which a gamma photon can create an electron and its antimatter partner, a positron. The electron so created might have any kinetic energy, depending on the photon's energy. This attempted explanation seemed promising, though physicists still knew nothing of the weak nuclear force or of neutrinos, which a proper explanation would require.**

THE $\beta$-ray activity of radioactive bodies has until now proved to be a very baffling problem. The points at issue are summarised in Gamow's "Constitution of Atomic Nuclei", etc. (pp. 52–54), and in "Radiations from Radioactive Bodies" by Rutherford, Chadwick and Ellis (p. 385). They are also discussed at some length by Bohr in his Faraday lecture (1930).

Briefly speaking, the chief points under discussion are the following: the disintegration electrons ($\beta$-rays) from a radioactive body are not emitted with a single velocity as in the case of $\alpha$-rays, but show a distribution of velocities over wide ranges, though the breaking-up of the atom is a unitary process, as is proved by the fact that the life-period is definite and there is one electron for each disintegrating atom. It has further been proved that the continuous distribution of velocities is a nuclear process, and not due to action of the surrounding shell of electrons.

It appears that the $\beta$-ray disintegration admits of a very simple explanation on the basis of the recent experiments by Anderson and Neddermeyer, and Curie and Joliot on the production of positrons by the impact of hard $\gamma$-rays with the nuclei of elements. These experiments have been interpreted by Blackett and Occhialini as indicating the conversion of a $\gamma$-ray quantum into an electron and a positron near the nucleus. Curie and Joliot have brought further evidence in favour of this view by showing that $\gamma$-rays of thorium C″ (energy $2.6\times10^{6}$ electron volts) are converted inside all matter into an electron (mass $9\times10^{-28}$ gm., energy $m_0c^2 = 0.51\times10^{6}$ eV) and a positron (having the same mass and energy as the electron), the excess energy being distributed as the kinetic energy of the two particles, and the energy of the residual quantum. They have denoted this phenomenon by the term "materialisation of light quanta". They have further shown that a proton is a complex structure, being a compound of the neutron and a positron. As pointed out by Blackett and Occhialini, this explains the anomalous absorption of $\gamma$-ray quanta observed

# β射线放射性的一种可能的解释

梅格纳德·萨哈，道拉特·科塔里

## 编者按

*放射性 $\beta$ 衰变是最令人困惑不解的。与 $\alpha$ 粒子不同，$\beta$ 粒子的能量不是固定的，而是存在一个很宽的范围，物理学家们已经证实这些能量是核过程本身产生的，并非电子与壳层电子相互作用的结果。两位印度物理学家梅格纳德·萨哈和道拉特·辛格·科塔里在本文中提出：由于最近发现 $\gamma$ 光子可以产生一个电子和它的反粒子——正电子，这个谜有可能会随之得到破解。在这个过程中产生的电子也许会具有一定的动能，这取决于光子的能量。这种尝试性的解释看似前景光明，但那时的物理学家对弱核力和中微子仍一无所知，而只有了解了弱核力和中微子，才能得到这个问题的正确解释。*

放射性物质的 $\beta$ 射线放射性一直以来都是一个非常令人困惑不解的问题。在伽莫夫的《原子核的结构》（第 52~54 页）及卢瑟福、查德威克和埃利斯的《放射性物质的辐射》（第 385 页）等著作中都总结了一些有争议的论点。玻尔在法拉第讲座（1930 年）中也对这些观点进行了详细的讨论。

简言之，争论的主要方面是：原子有确定的衰变寿命以及每个发生衰变的原子发射一个电子这些事实已经证明原子的衰变是一个单一的过程，但是由放射性物质放射出的衰变电子（$\beta$ 射线）并没有像 $\alpha$ 射线那样具有单一的速度，而是出现了速度分布在一个很大范围内的情况。人们还进一步证明了速度的连续分布与核过程有关，而与核外电子壳层的作用无关。

最近，安德森、尼德迈耶以及居里、约里奥进行了硬 $\gamma$ 射线轰击原子核产生正电子的实验，在此基础之上看似可以给出关于 $\beta$ 衰变的一个非常简单的解释。布莱克特和奥基亚利尼对这些实验的解释是：一个 $\gamma$ 粒子在原子核附近转化成了一个负电子和一个正电子。居里和约里奥为这个观点提供了进一步的证据，他们的实验表明钍 C″ 的 $\gamma$ 射线（能量为 $2.6\times10^6$ 电子伏特）在所有的材料中都会转化为一个负电子（质量为 $9\times10^{-28}$ 克，能量为 $m_0c^2=0.51\times10^6$ 电子伏特）和一个正电子（质量和能量与负电子相同），多余的能量除了分配给正负两个电子作为动能外，还将分配给剩余的量子，他们把这种现象称为“光量子的物质化”。他们进一步指出，质子具有复杂的内部结构，包括一个中子和一个正电子。布莱克特和奥基亚利尼指出，格雷和塔兰特观察到的反常 $\gamma$ 射线吸收也能用此进行解释，但根特纳发现，能量在 1.1 百万电

by Gray and Tarrant, which Gentner has found to commence with the $\gamma$-ray possessing the limiting energy 1.1 million electron volts.

The discovery, which is confirmed by so many workers, promises to be of great importance, as it establishes for the first time, on experimental grounds, the splitting up of a quantum into two charged particles of opposite sign. Many astrophysicists have postulated the probability of the annihilation of the proton and the electron with their mass energies converted into quanta, but the actual process, as revealed by these experiments, seems to be very different. For the quantum breaks up into charged particles possessing opposite charges, but having equal mass, and the positron being absorbed by the neutron forms the proton which is thus seen to be complex. The phenomenon is therefore not a "materialisation of the quantum" as Curie and Joliot suggest, for the neutron appears to be the fundamental mass-particle, but it consists in a splitting of the quantum into two fundamental opposite charges. We may call it "electro-division of the quantum".

Let us see how we can explain $\beta$-ray activity. If the "electro-division of a quantum" can be brought about by a nucleus when the quantum hits it from the outside, it is much more probable that the $\gamma$-rays produced within the nucleus itself should be completely split up into an electron and a positron. The electron will come out as a $\beta$-ray, but a positron will not be able to come out if the conversion takes place within the potential barrier. It will attach itself mainly to some one of the numerous neutrons which are present in the nucleus, and thus form a proton. The positive charge of the nucleus will therefore be increased by unity.

It is not difficult to explain the continuous distribution of $\beta$-ray energy. The $\gamma$-ray may suffer this "internal electro-division" anywhere within the nucleus, and hence the velocities imparted to the resulting electrons may vary within wide limits. The exact mathematical calculation can be carried out only when more data are forthcoming. The positron combining with the neutron will give rise to the softer $\gamma$-rays which are always present in a $\beta$-ray disintegration.

According to the above view, the $\beta$-ray emission is only a secondary process, the primary phenomenon which starts this chain of events being the generation of a primary $\gamma$-ray. We can now ask ourselves: How is this $\gamma$-ray generated? It must be due to the passage of an $\alpha$-particle or proton from one barrier to another. Gamow, and also Condon and Gurney have postulated the existence of only one barrier in a radioactive nucleus for explaining the emission of $\alpha$-rays, with definite velocity, but several lines of argument indicate that there may be more than one barrier present in the nucleus. When an $\alpha$-particle crosses from one barrier to the other, the $\gamma$-ray responsible for the whole chain of events leading to the $\beta$-ray disintegration is emitted. The life-period is therefore determined by the time of leakage of an $\alpha$-particle or proton from one barrier to another, and this explains why the life-periods of $\beta$-ray bodies are of the same order as those of $\alpha$-ray bodies, and have a definite value.

(**132**, 747; 1933)

M. N. Saha and D. S. Kothari: Department of Physics, Allahabad University, Oct. 20.

子伏特以上的 $\gamma$ 射线才能发生这种反常吸收过程。

这个发现已经被很多研究人员所确认，当然也必定有着非常重大的意义，因为这是第一次在实验基础上确立：一个量子可以劈裂成两个带有相反电荷的粒子。很多天体物理学家都认为一个质子和一个电子有可能会发生湮灭并且将其质能转化为量子，但是实际的过程，正如在实验中所看到的那样，是很难发生的。因为一个量子会分裂成一对带相反电荷但质量相等的粒子，并且其中的正电子会被中子吸收形成质子，由此可以认为质子具有复杂的结构。因此，这个现象并不是居里和约里奥所说的“量子的物质化”过程，因为中子看似一个有质量的基本粒子，但是它却存在于量子分裂成两个电量相反的电荷的过程中。我们可以把这个过程称为“量子的电分离”。

那么，让我们来看看 $\beta$ 射线的放射性该如何解释。如果外部量子轰击原子核时会引发“量子的电分离”，那么在该原子核内部产生的 $\gamma$ 射线更有可能会完全分裂成一个负电子和一个正电子。电子将以 $\beta$ 射线的形式发射出来，但是如果这个分裂过程发生在势垒当中，那么正电子就不能被发射出来。正电子将和存在于原子核中的大量中子当中的一个相结合，形成一个质子。这样，原子核的正电量将因此增加一个单位。

而 $\beta$ 射线能量的连续分布也不难解释。$\gamma$ 射线可以在原子核中的任意位置发生“内部电分离”，这样，$\gamma$ 射线转化产生的电子的速度就会在很宽的范围内变化。只有得到更多的实验数据，我们才能进行严格的数学计算。和中子结合的正电子将产生软 $\gamma$ 射线，这种软 $\gamma$ 射线经常出现在 $\beta$ 衰变反应中。

根据上面的观点，$\beta$ 射线的发射只是一个二级过程，初级 $\gamma$ 射线的产生才是引发这个反应链的最初原因。现在我们可以问问自己：这种 $\gamma$ 射线是如何产生的呢？一定是因为一个 $\alpha$ 粒子或者一个质子从一个势垒穿越到另一个势垒而产生的。伽莫夫以及康登和格尼曾经以放射性原子核中只存在一个势垒出发解释了具有确定速度的 $\alpha$ 射线的放射，但是一些争论表明，原子核中可能会有不止一个势垒。在一个 $\alpha$ 粒子穿越一个势垒来到另一个势垒的过程中产生了引发 $\beta$ 衰变链的 $\gamma$ 射线。所以 $\beta$ 射线放射性的周期取决于 $\alpha$ 粒子或质子从一个势垒到另一个势垒所用的时间，这就解释了为什么 $\beta$ 射线的寿命周期和 $\alpha$ 射线的寿命周期有相同的量级并且有确定量值。

（王静 翻译；尚仁成 审稿）

# The General Nature of the Gene Concept*

R. R. Gate

## Editor's Note

**The discovery that DNA is the molecule of heredity was so profound that it is hard to imagine how people previously understood genes as concepts. When R. Ruggles Gates wrote this article, James Watson and Francis Crick's discovery was twenty years in the future, and the concept of the gene was nebulous in the extreme. Scientists were agreed that genes resided in chromosomes, but the nature of the genes themselves was completely unknown. Were they living things, or inorganic? Did they reproduce by duplication or fission? Were they indivisible, like elementary particles? How big were they? Were they all the same size, or all different? Could you hope to see genes arranged on a chromosome? In 1933, no answers were possible.**

THE conception of the gene has resulted from two lines of biological evidence: (1) The amazing stability of the germ plasm, as expressed in the facts of heredity; (2) its occasional instability, as shown by the occurrence of mutations. That external forces, such as X-rays, impinging upon the germinal material should produce changes, is not surprising but inevitable. That the resulting effects are inherited, however, shows that the organism is incapable of regulating against changes in this particular part of its cell structure.

It appears that these phenomena of stability and inherited change can only be understood by recognising that some substances or structures in the chromosomes must maintain in general their spatial relationships and chemical nature, not only from one generation of organisms to another, but also with only minor changes through thousands, and in some cases even millions, of years. However protoplasm grows, these substances must be self-reproducing, with a permanence equal to that of the species itself, for when they change the species changes.

While emphasising these conclusions, which seem inevitable from the modern genetical work, I do not wish to minimise the importance of the cytoplasm. It has been shown, for example, by the investigations of embryologists (for example, Conklin, Lillie) that the visibly differentiated substances in various animal eggs can be displaced and rearranged by centrifuging, without affecting the development, yet if the fundamental hyaline ground substance of the egg-cell is disturbed, distortions of development will be produced. This and the facts of egg polarity argue strongly for a more or less determinate spatial arrangement of the cytoplasmic materials, at least in many animal egg-cells. It has also been shown by reciprocal crossing of plant species that some species are differentiated

* From a paper read on September 12 at a joint discussion of Sections D (Zoology), I (Physiology) and K (Botany) at the Leicester meeting of the British Association on "The Nature of the Gene".

# 有关基因概念的一般本质*

拉各尔斯·盖茨

## 编者按

能发现 DNA 是遗传分子真是一个了不起的成就，很难想象在此之前人们是怎样理解基因这个概念的。在拉各尔斯·盖茨写这篇文章的时候，詹姆斯·沃森和弗朗西斯·克里克的发现还是 20 年以后的事，所以基因的概念是非常模糊的。科学家们一致认为基因是存在于染色体中的，但对基因的本质却一无所知。它们是生命体，还是无机物？它们是通过复制或分裂方式增殖的吗？它们像基本粒子一样无法分割吗？它们有多大？它们具有同样的大小，还是各不相同？人们能看到基因在一条染色体中的排列吗？在 1933 年的时候，没有人能回答这些问题。

基因的概念基于以下两条生物学证据：(1) 种质具有惊人的稳定性，表现为遗传；(2) 它也有偶发的不稳定性，表现为突变。接触像 X 射线这样的外部因素会使遗传物质发生变化，这并不奇怪也无法避免。然而，这种变化导致的结果却是可遗传的，这表明，生物体没有能力对其细胞结构中这一特殊部分的变化进行调节。

遗传的稳定性和可遗传的变异这两种现象似乎只能这样来解释：染色体中的一些物质或者结构不仅会在生物体从一代传给下一代的时候大体保持原有的空间关系和化学性质，而且在跨越千年，甚至有时候可达几百万年的过程中，都只发生微小的变化。不管原生质如何生长，遗传物质都必须以保持自身物种永远不变的方式自我复制，因为当遗传物质发生变化时物种也就发生了变化。

上述结论似乎是现代遗传学研究必然得到的结果，然而在强调这些结论的同时，我并不想忽略细胞质的重要性。有例子显示，胚胎学家们（例如：康克林和利利）通过研究发现，在各种动物的卵中那些明显分化的物质可以用离心的方法移除和重排，并且不影响卵的发育。而如果将卵细胞中基本透明的基质搅乱，畸形的发育就会出现。这个现象和卵极性的事实有力地说明了细胞质中的物质具有或多或少的定向空间分布，至少在许多动物的卵细胞中是这样的。此外植物物种的正反交也表明，一些物种的区别仅仅在于它们的核内组分不同，而另一些物种还因细胞质的不同而

* 9 月 12 日英国科学促进会在莱斯特召开了关于“基因本质”的会议，本文是在 D 分会（动物学）、I 分会（生理学）和 K 分会（植物学）共同讨论时宣读的一篇论文。

only as regards their nuclear content, while in others the cytoplasm differs as well.

The spatial arrangement of the genic materials within the chromosomes is therefore not different in principle from that shown to exist in the cytoplasm of certain animal eggs. The main difference is that the chromosome is a thread-shaped structure and is believed to be differentiated only along its length, that is, its differentiation is regarded as one-dimensional rather than three-dimensional.

In what sense do genes exist? The gene is probably the last in the long series of representative particles beginning with Darwin's "gemmules" and the "pangens" of de Vries, which were formulated to account for the phenomena of heredity. With advancing knowledge, such conceptions have tended to lose their formal character as ultimate particles reproducing by fission, and to become more physiological and more closely related to the known structure and activities of the cell. They lost their morphological nature when the conception of the unit character was given up many years ago. Bridges's conception of genic balance is essentially physiological. As Sir Frederick Gowland Hopkins has said of all organic units, "The characteristic of a living unit ... is that it is heterogeneous .... The special attribute of such systems from a chemical point of view is that these reactions are organised". What is the nature of the organisation which leads us to the conception of the gene?

In 1915, I first pointed out that a gene represents a *difference*—a fact so obvious that its importance is in danger of being overlooked. Johannsen, who invented the term "gene", afterwards (1923) expressed the same point of view. Our actual knowledge of genes, apart from speculation, is derived entirely from their differential effects in development and from the phenomena of linkage and crossing-over. The visible difference in the developed organism is the product of an initial germinal difference which must have arisen at some time through a mutation. The great majority of biologists will agree in locating the genic materials in the chromosomes. In the endeavour to get a more intimate picture of the nature of the gene, we must therefore explore the structure of the chromosome. It is also necessary to remember that, like everything else in the organic world, the genes, as well as the chromosomes, must have had an evolutionary history.

There have been two main theories of chromosome structure. According to one theory, the core of the chromosome contains a continuous thread or chromonema, which takes on a spiral form in various stages of mitosis. Cytologists have brought strong evidence for the existence of chromonemata in plant cells. The investigations, particularly of Sharp and Kaufmann in the United States and of Hedayetullah (1931) and Perry (1932) in my laboratory, have given a clear and definite picture of the chromosome during the cycle of mitosis. These accounts agree in finding the chromosome to be a double structure throughout the mitotic cycle, containing two chromonemata which are spirally twisted about each other in anaphase, telophase and prophase, each chromonema splitting before the chromosome halves separate in metaphase. There is also much wider evidence for the existence of a chromonema as a continuous thread embedded in the matrix of the

不同。

因此，染色体中基因物质的空间分布与某些动物卵细胞质中基因物质的空间分布没有原则上的区别。主要的区别在于染色体是一种线状结构，而且只能沿着其长度方向进行分化，也就是说，染色体的分化是一维而非三维的。

基因的存在有何种意义呢？基因很可能是从达尔文的“芽球”与德弗里斯的“泛子”开始的一系列代表性微粒的延续，而这些微粒概念的提出都是用来解释遗传现象的。随着人们认知水平的不断提高，这些概念也开始逐渐失去它们作为分裂复制的终极微粒的正式特征，变得越来越生理学化，越来越接近细胞的已知结构和活性。当很多年前单位性状的概念被抛弃的时候，这些概念就已经失去了形态特征。而布里奇斯的基因平衡观点本质上是属于生理学范畴的。正如弗雷德里克·高兰·霍普金斯爵士对所有有机单元的描述那样：“一个生命单位的特征……是其异质性……从化学角度来看，生命单位的这一特征表现为化学反应的有序性。”这种把我们引向基因概念的有序性到底具有什么样的本质呢？

在 1915 年，我首先提出一个基因代表一种**差异**——这一事实如此明显以至于它的重要性有被忽略的危险。不久以后（1923 年），“基因”这个名词的发明者约翰森也表达了同样的观点。我们对基因的真正认知，除去推测以外，完全来自于它们在发育过程中的分化效应和连锁与交换的现象。在成熟生物体上看见的差异均来自于原始胚种的差异，这种差异是在某个时期通过突变产生的。绝大多数生物学家都相信基因物质位于染色体中。因此为了更进一步地了解基因的本质，我们就必须探究染色体的结构。有必要提醒的是，像有机世界里的所有其他事物一样，基因以及染色体也一定会有进化的历史。

现在主要有两种有关染色体结构的理论。其中一种理论认为染色体的核心包含有连续的细丝或染色丝，在细胞有丝分裂的不同阶段呈现螺旋状。细胞学家们已经在植物细胞中发现了证明染色丝存在的有力证据。特别是美国的夏普和考夫曼，以及本实验室的海德亚图拉（1931 年）和佩里（1932 年）已经通过研究清楚明白地揭示出了染色体在细胞有丝分裂周期中的变化情况。这印证了在细胞有丝分裂周期中的染色体是一种含有两条染色体丝的双链结构：在有丝分裂后期、有丝分裂末期和有丝分裂前期两条染色丝螺旋卷曲在一起，在有丝分裂中期染色体平分之前，两条染色丝分离。还有更多的证据证明染色丝是存在的，它作为一种连续的细丝存在于

chromosome. The genes must then be contained in this thread, and they must undergo duplication into two series before these are separated by the longitudinal fission of the chromonemata. The duplication of the chromonemata must then be the fundamental process on which the phenomena of heredity depend.

Another theory of chromosome structure which has been much in vogue in recent years and has found perhaps its strongest support in animal cells is that of the chromomeres. According to this view, the chromosomes in prophase and telophase are made up of granules or chromomeres strung together on a fine connecting thread. Various attempts have naturally been made to identify these discrete chromomeres with the genes. They are perhaps most clearly demonstrated in such work as that of Wenrich on grasshoppers. The chromomeres in cytological preparations, however, differ greatly in size, and their number appears to be smaller than present estimates of the number of genes. Bridges has spoken of them as the houses in which the genes live. If this is the case, it would appear that whole families or even villages of genes must live in one house. Belling (1928) endeavoured to count the number of chromomeres in certain plant nuclei and has arrived at 1,400–2,500.

In a posthumous paper recently published, as well as in earlier papers, Dr. Belling strongly supports the chromomere theory, from observations of smear preparations of pollen mother cells in various lilies. Not only does he deny that the chromosomes are split in telophase, but he also holds the novel view that the prophase split in the chromomeres is not accompanied by division of the thread connecting them. Instead, he thinks connecting threads are formed *de novo* between the new daughter chromomeres, thus linking them up into a new chromosome. The chief merit of such a view appears to be that it would obviate many of the serious difficulties which still exist with regard to all current theories of chiasmatypy and crossing-over. The fact that such diverse views can be held by competent cytologists, shows the extreme difficulty of crucial observation in this field.

Recent observations now in progress in my laboratory indicate that chromomeres may not exist, at least in plant cells. We are finding that, in some cases at any rate, the appearance of a string of beads or a moniliform thread, when critically analysed, is due to the presence of two spirally intertwined chromonemata, the nodes and internodes of which give the superficial appearance of a single chain of chromomeres. It is therefore desirable that a re-investigation, particularly of animal chromosomes, be undertaken, to make certain whether chromomeres actually exist or whether they will bear the general interpretation here suggested. In the meantime, it appears that the core of many plant chromosomes is a continuous structure, not broken up into visibly discrete bodies. As the imagination of many genetical investigators has been caught by the idea of discreteness both in the gene and within the visible chromosome, it is well to emphasise this point.

The absolute discreteness of the genes within the chromonemata does not appear to be an essential part of the gene theory. It is well known that many of the Protozoa have

染色体基质中。那么基因一定包含在这条细丝中，并且一定是在染色丝纵向分裂将其分离之前复制为两份的。染色丝的复制一定就是遗传现象发生的基础。

另一个关于染色体结构的理论是染色粒理论，这个理论近年来非常流行，对其最强有力的支持多半来自动物细胞。按照这个理论，染色体在有丝分裂的前期和末期是由串在一条细丝上的颗粒或者染色粒组成的。自然会有各种各样的方法来证明这些不连续的染色粒带有基因。温里克在蝗虫上做的实验也许就是对上述理论的最清晰的证明。然而，用细胞学方法制备的染色粒在大小上差别很大，它们的数量也低于目前估计的基因数量。布里奇斯曾把染色粒比喻成房子，而基因就生活在里面。如果真是这样的话，那整个基因家族甚至整个基因村落就不得不生活在一间房子里了。贝林（1928 年）曾努力计算过某种植物细胞核中的染色粒数量，得到的结果是 1,400~2,500 个。

在最近发表的一篇贝林博士生前写的文章以及一些早期的论文中，贝林博士强烈支持染色粒理论，他的根据来自于对各种百合花粉母细胞涂片的观察结果。他不但否定了染色体在有丝分裂的末期分离，而且还提出了新的观点，即认为在有丝分裂的前期，连接染色粒的细丝并不随着染色粒的分离而分离。相反，他认为这些粘连的细丝在新生的子染色粒间重新形成，进而把它们组合成一条新的染色体。这种观点的主要优点在于它能消除存在于所有有关染色体交叉和交换的现存理论中的许多严重困扰。事实上，一些有水平的细胞学家们也可以持有不同的观点，这表明在该领域里得到关键的观察结果是极其困难的。

本试验室在近期的观察中得到的最新资料表明，染色粒也许并不存在，至少在植物细胞中是这样的。我们发现至少在某些时候，经过精密的分析，一串珠子或一条念珠形的线其实是由两条染色丝螺旋缠绕形成的，这些染色体丝上的节点和节间段在表现上类似于一条染色粒的单链。因此人们需要对此进行重新研究，尤其是对动物的染色体，以弄清楚染色粒是否确实存在，以及它们是否符合本文提到的普遍解释。同时，许多植物染色体的核心都具有连续的结构，并不会被破坏成可见的不连续部分。因为许多遗传学研究人员的想象力都已经被基因和可见染色体内部具有不连续性的观念所束缚，所以最好强调一下这一点。

染色丝中基因的绝对不连续性并不是基因理论的关键部分。众所周知，许多原生动物都拥有为数众多的染色体，这些染色体发生纵向分裂并展现出更高等生物中

numerous chromosomes which undergo longitudinal fission and exhibit the usual features of the chromosomes in higher organisms. Are we to suppose that these chromosomes are as highly differentiated along their lengths as the evidence of crossing-over leads us to believe they must be in higher plants and animals? I find it impossible to accept such a view, which would be virtually a denial of evolution except in the embryological sense. The alternative is to assume that, when the mitotic mechanism first evolved in the Protista, the chromosomes were perhaps differentiated from each other but each was uniform along its length. From this point of view the mitotic mechanism would be a striking example corresponding with Berg's idea of nomogenesis.

The development of the mitotic figure may be regarded as one of the main evolutionary achievements of unicellular organisms. We may reasonably suppose that it appeared there in its simplest form and that the chromosomes in these groups of organisms remained more or less longitudinally homogeneous. We may then think of the evolution of higher plants and animals as having taken place through internal differentiation of the chromosomes, combined with adhesion of the products of cell division into multicellular aggregates. Thus would gradually arise the condition which has been postulated for higher organisms as a result of experiments in crossing-over, that is, a set of chromosomes not homogeneous but longitudinally differentiated. According to this view, all the developments of evolution in multicellular groups were foreshadowed or at least made possible by the mitotic mechanism achieved by the Protista. Just as the simplest cell aggregates consist of undifferentiated cells, so their individual chromosomes are internally homogeneous, each containing a different type of genic material.

The current view of genes, as developed particularly in connexion with *Drosophila*, tacitly assumes that all genes are of the same kind. If the views here expressed have any validity, then it seems more reasonable to suppose that a portion of an original chromosome, not necessarily of minimum size, underwent a mutation. Later, a portion of this would undergo a different change, and so on until a series of genes or chemically different segments of various sizes would result. This would lead ultimately to some genes of minimum dimensions, although others might be larger, and segments of the original unchanged chromosome might remain. It would appear probable, however, that in this process the majority of genes would ere now have reached the minimum size. (I find that East in 1929 also emphasised the view that genes are probably of various sizes.)

Some workers have of course taken an entirely different view of the origin and history of genes, regarding them as the primordial bodies or organic units from and by which protoplasm has since been constructed. Numerous comparisons have been drawn between genes on one hand and bacteriophage and virus particles on the other, based on their supposed similarity in size and action. While such comparisons are suggestive, the view of the genes as differentiated at a later stage of evolution within the originally homogeneous chromosomes seems on the whole more probable, and on this view there is no need to regard them as indivisible, discrete bodies of uniform size and nature.

染色体所具有的一般特征。我们是否可以假设这些原生动物的染色体沿着其长度方向进行高度分化，而杂交实验的证据让我们有理由相信这么高的分化程度只能存在于更高等的动物和植物中？我发现接受这样的观点是不可能的，因为它除了在胚胎学上的意义以外，实际上是对进化论的一种否定。或者可以这样假设：当有丝分裂机制首次在原生动物中形成时，染色体也许就是可以互相区分的，但是每条染色体都沿其长度方向保持一致。从这样的观点来看，有丝分裂机制竟是印证贝尔格的循规进化学说的一个生动实例。

有丝分裂象的发展可以看作是单细胞生物进化的主要成就之一。我们可以合理地假设单细胞生物的有丝分裂具有最简单的形式，而且这些生物体的染色体或多或少地保持了纵向的相同性。然后我们可以认为更高级动物和植物的进化是通过染色体的内部分化实现的，并伴随着细胞分裂成多细胞簇的产物附着。由此就会逐渐出现通过杂交实验产生更高等生物的必要条件，即一组染色体不再相同而是在纵向上产生了分化。按照这种观点，多细胞簇中的所有进化发展都已被预示或者至少因原生动物所具有的有丝分裂机制而成为可能。同样地，最简单的细胞簇是由未分化的细胞构成，因此它们的每条染色体在本质上都是相同的，但包含着类别不同的遗传物质。

随着基因研究尤其是与果蝇有关的研究的发展，人们现在对基因的看法是默认所有的基因都属于同一类型。如果上述观点成立的话，那么假定在最初的染色体中有一部分（不必是最少的部分）发生了突变似乎显得更合理。接着，这部分染色体会经历不同的变化直至产生一系列基因，或具有各种不同大小、不同化学性质的片段。这也许最终会导致出现一些具有最小尺寸的基因，尽管其他一些基因的尺寸可能比较大，而最初未发生变化的染色体片断也许会保留下来。然而在这样的一个过程中大多数基因在此之前可能就已经达到最小尺寸了。（我发现在 1929 年伊斯特也强调过这样的观点：基因可能具有不同的大小。）

当然也有一些人对基因的起源和历史有着完全不同的观点，认为基因一直是构建原生质的原始模块或者有机单位。人们在基因与噬菌体之间以及基因与病毒颗粒之间进行了大量的对比分析，这些对比分析都基于认为它们在尺寸和行为上具有相似性。虽然上述对比对我们很有启发，但认为基因是在本来相同的染色体进化后期发生分化的观点似乎更有可能成立，而且根据这个观点也没有必要把它们看作是一种具有相同尺寸和本质、不可分割也不连续的模块。

Various estimates of gene size have been made in *Drosophila*. One of the latest, by Gowen and Gay (1933), arrives at a minimum size of $10^{-18}$ cm.$^3$, the number of loci in the nucleus being estimated at more than 14,000. This maximum size would only allow space for about fifteen protein molecules. There is at present a large margin of error in such estimates. From measurements of spermheads and chromosome lengths, these authors draw the interesting conclusion that the chromosomes are all arranged end-to-end in the *Drosophila* spermhead.

The view of gene origin within the chromosomes as sketched above appears to be supported by the fact that the genes are now known not to be uniformly distributed in the chromosomes. The *Y*-chromosome has long been recognised as nearly empty of genes, but later work of Dobzhansky (1933) and others shows that one third or more of the length of the *X*-chromosome at the right or proximal end near the spindle fibre attachment is also inert. In this region only one mutation, "bobbed bristles", is known to occur, and crossing-over apparently does not take place. Possibly these inert or "empty" segments may represent an earlier unmutated condition of the chromosomes. The bulk of the chromosome is probably composed of thymonucleic acid, but it does not necessarily follow that the genes embedded in the chromonema axis are derivatives of that substance.

Although Belling believed that each chromomere contains a visible gene, yet the bulk of evidence leads to the conclusion that the genes are ultramicroscopic, and Bridges (1932) has recently expressed the view that they are unimolecular. It has been more usual to picture them as definitely organised bodies containing a score or a few hundred molecules and reproducing either organically by fission or chemically by duplication. The idea that each gene is a single molecule, while avoiding the possibility of its divisibility, appears to add difficulties of another kind. It is difficult to see why a tenuous chain of single unlike molecules should persist in the core of the chromosome, as it would be necessary to assume. Chemical forces alone could scarcely be expected to hold such a chain together, even if we rely upon the properties of the carbon atom. On the other hand, whatever physical forces give the chromosome its unity as a structure, might also be concerned (1) in organising each group of like or unlike molecules into a gene, and (2) in maintaining their axial arrangement in the chromosome. Could one molecule exert its catalytic effect while maintaining its position undisturbed in the chromonema? And could it duplicate itself when the row of genes divided? The mere asking of such questions shows that we do not know whether genes should be regarded as organic or inorganic groupings, and it indicates also that the time-honoured phenomena of growth and reproduction formerly associated with such bodies are in some danger of being lost, although it must equally be said that they have not yet been eliminated.

The "scute" series of genes in *Drosophila* has become increasingly difficult to interpret on the prevalent conception of the gene as a body which can never be fractionated but can only undergo change (mutation) as a whole. On the other hand, the theory of step allelomorphism as developed by Dubinin (1932) and others is entirely in harmony with

各种估测基因大小的研究在果蝇上展开。其中最近的一个数据是由高恩和盖伊（1933 年）估测的，他们认为基因的最小尺寸可达 $10^{-18}$ $cm^3$，而细胞核中基因位点的数目估计在 14,000 个以上。基因的最大尺寸只能容纳大约 15 个蛋白质分子。目前这类估测都存在很大的误差。这些作者根据对精子头部和染色体长度的测量结束，得出了一个有趣的结论：果蝇精子头部的染色体全部都是端 – 端排布的。

以上简单描述了基因来源于染色体的观点。现在已经知道基因并不是均匀地分布在染色体中，这一现象似乎是对上述观点的有利佐证。*Y* 染色体一直被认为是几乎没有基因存在的。而多布赞斯基（1933 年）和其他人后来的研究工作表明 *X* 染色体的右侧或者靠近纺锤丝附着点的近端有三分之一或者更长的部分也是惰性的。在这个区域只有一种突变会发生，那就是“截刚毛突变”，而交叉互换不会发生。也许这种惰性或者“没有基因的”片段代表着一种染色体早期未发生突变的情况。大部分染色体很可能都是由胸腺核酸组成的，但镶嵌在染色丝轴上的基因并不一定是该物质的衍生物。

尽管贝林认为每个染色粒都含有一个可见的基因，但是大量的事实说明基因是普通显微镜无法看到的，最近布里奇斯（1932 年）提出了基因是单分子物质的观点。而人们通常把基因看作是有确定结构的实体，由二十个或几百个分子组成，通过有机性的分裂或者化学上的复制实现自身的繁殖。把基因看作是一个单分子虽然排除了它的可分割性，但似乎又增加了另一个麻烦，很难想象一条由各不相似的分子组成的脆弱的链竟可以稳定地保持在染色体的核心上，因而我们必须这样假设。仅靠化学力几乎不可能将这样的链结合在一起，即使我们信赖碳原子的特性。另一方面，如果使得染色体具有统一结构的是物理作用力，那么也许要考虑：(1) 如何将每一个相似分子或各不相似的分子的组分组织起来变成基因；(2) 如何保持这些组分在染色体中沿轴向排列。当一个分子在染色丝中保持自己的位置不受干扰时它能发挥它的催化效应么？当一行基因被分开时它会进行自我复制么？提出这样的问题只能说明我们还不知道基因应该被归为有机类还是无机类。这些疑问还暗示，由来已久的生长和繁殖现象从前与基因相关，现在有可能会失去这种联系，尽管同样会有人认为这种联系目前还没有被消除掉。

当前流行的观念认为基因是一个不能被分开，而只能作为一个整体发生改变（突变）的实体，用这样的观念解释果蝇的“鳞甲”基因系列变得越来越困难。另一方面，由杜比宁（1932 年）等人发展的阶梯型对偶基因学说与我在上文中提到的基因进化观

the view of gene evolution which I have outlined above. On the assumption that genes are indivisible in all circumstances, it has been necessary to make them smaller and smaller, until the limit is now reached in the single molecule. But surely, if the atom itself can be disrupted by suitable forces, it is not unreasonable to suppose that something of a similar kind may happen to a group of molecules constituting a gene.

The genetic study of variegations in plants has also led to the view that the genes involved are compound structures, the somatic segregation of which results in the variegated condition. The studies of Emerson on the varieties of maize with variegated pericarp, of Baur on *Antirrhinum*, Eyster on maize and *Verbena*, Demerec on *Delphinium* and *Drosophila* are notable in this connexion. Eyster (1928) adopts the hypothesis that the genes causing variegation are compound structures composed of a constant number of "genomeres" which may or may not be of the same chemical or physical nature. Demerec (1931), however, explains the variegation in *Delphinium* as a result of highly mutable genes. It remains to be seen whether the divisibility of the gene in somatic tissues or the high mutability of such genes will supply the explanation.

We prefer to think of genes as differentiations of many kinds and sizes which have arisen in the core of the chromosome during its evolution, making it a nest of catalytic substances, most of them having specific effects mainly on the development of particular organs. By different processes of translocation in the nucleus, genes tend to become shifted from their original positions. The result is that genes affecting quite different organs come to occupy adjacent positions in the chromosomes. It seems quite likely that, from a historical point of view, mutation has been a much more orderly process than might be supposed from the present disorderly arrangement of the genes in *Drosophila*. The fact that the genes have been scrambled in this way seems to show that mere position within the chromosome is of little or no significance.

(**132**, 768-770; 1933)

点完全吻合。假定基因在任何环境下都是不可分割的，人们必然会不断地缩小它的尺度，到现在已经达到了单个分子的极限。但是当然了，如果原子本身可以被合适的力分解开来，那么假定类似的事情会在一群构成基因的分子中发生就没有什么不合理了。

对植物颜色变化的遗传学研究也证明了所涉及的基因具有复合结构，对其进行体细胞分离会导致杂色的情况。在此类研究中令人关注的有：用杂色果皮研究玉米多样性的埃默森、研究金鱼草的鲍亚、研究玉米和马鞭草的艾斯特以及研究飞燕草和果蝇的德梅雷茨。艾斯特（1928 年）采用的假说认为引起杂色的基因是一些由恒定数量“基因粒”构成的复合结构，这些基因粒的化学性质或物理性质可能相同，也可能不相同。而德梅雷茨（1931 年）认为飞燕草的杂色是由非常容易突变的基因引起的。体组织中基因的不可分割性或者这类基因的高度易突变性是否能解释这一现象还有待进一步的观察。

我们倾向于把基因看作是具有各种类型和尺寸的分化产物，这些分化产物出现在进化过程中的染色体的核心中，并使之成为催化物质的中心，这些催化物质中的大部分对于特定器官的发育具有特异性作用。通过在细胞核内发生的各种转运过程，基因易于从原来的位置移开。其结果是，控制完全不同的器官的基因在染色体上占据了相邻的位置。从历史的角度来看，突变过程很可能远比人们假定果蝇基因中目前的无序排列要有序得多。基因以这样的方式混杂排列在一起的事实似乎告诉我们，仅仅考虑基因在染色体上的位置是没有意义的。

（刘振明 翻译；刘京国 审稿）

# Latitude Effect of Cosmic Radiation

J. A. Prins

## Editor's Note

**Earlier experiments by Jacob Clay, Arthur Compton and others had suggested that the flux of cosmic rays has a minimum close to the equator. Here J. A. Prins reports results measured using an ionisation chamber carried by the S.S. *Springfontein* during a voyage from Holland to South Africa, which also showed a clear minimum near the equator. Unfortunately, he says, his apparatus had broken down, and he could not gather data from southern latitudes, which might have helped clarify an apparent difference noted by other researchers between the flux in the two hemispheres. But the results did suggest that most cosmic rays were charged particles, which would be influenced by the Earth's magnetic field and find penetration easiest near the poles.**

IT was found for the first time by Clay[1] on voyages between Holland and Java that the intensity of cosmic radiation has a minimum in the neighbourhood of the magnetic equator. The extensive survey directed by Compton[2] confirmed the existence of this "latitude effect" and showed it to be more pronounced at higher altitude. More accurate results at sea-level are due to an investigation of Clay and Berlage[3]. As this again refers to the line from Holland to Java, I thought it would be worth while to perform analogous measurements on a trip from Holland to South Africa. During this investigation Hoerlin[4] published results he obtained on the line Peru—Strait of Magellan—Hamburg. These results and those of the other authors as given by Clay are represented in Fig. 1 by continuous curves, my own results by open circles. Clearly the latter lie somewhat closer to Clay's curve than to Hoerlin's.

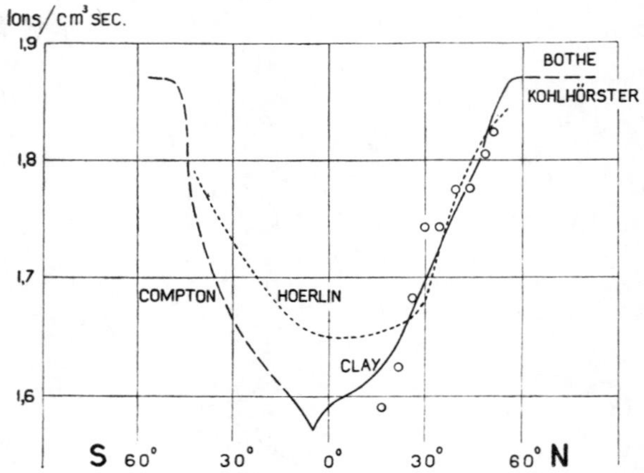


Fig. 1. Latitude effect of cosmic radiation. Circles indicate results of author. Vertical scale indicates number of pairs of ions in normal air.

# 宇宙射线的纬度效应

约翰·普林斯

## 编者按

雅各布·克莱、阿瑟·康普顿和其他人的早期实验曾经说明宇宙射线的通量在靠近赤道处有一个最小值。本文中，普林斯报告了他在从荷兰开往南非的斯普林方廷号远洋轮上利用装载于船上的电离室测量得到的结果，该结果同样说明在赤道附近会出现一个最小值。他说，不幸的是他的仪器坏了，所以没有能够收集到南纬的数据，这使他失去了一个证明其他研究人员所指出的宇宙射线在南北半球的通量存在明显不同的机会。但他的结果确实表明了大多数的宇宙射线都是带电粒子，它们会受到地球磁场的影响，而且在两极附近最易穿透。

克莱[1]在往返于荷兰和爪哇之间的旅行中首次发现宇宙射线的强度在地磁赤道附近存在一个最小值。康普顿[2]通过广泛的调查证实了“纬度效应”的存在，并发现在高纬度地区这种效应会更明显。克莱和贝尔拉赫[3]在海平面上进行测量得到了更为精确的结果。考虑到他们的调查也是在从荷兰至爪哇的航线上进行的，我认为有必要在从荷兰到南非的航线上进行类似的测量，以便于比较。就在我做这个实验的同时，霍尔林[4]发表了他在秘鲁—麦哲伦海峡—汉堡一线测量得到的结果。这些结果连同克莱给出的其他人的结果都画在图1中，用连续曲线代表；我的结果用空心圆圈表示。把我的结果分别与克莱和霍尔林的结果相比较后发现：我的结果与克莱的结果更接近。

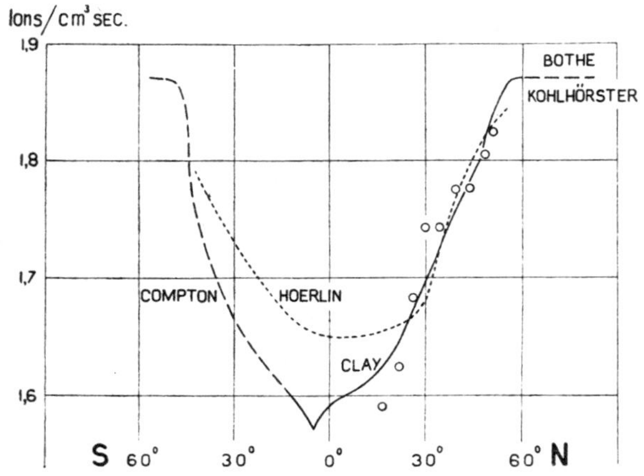


图1. 宇宙射线的纬度效应。圆圈代表作者的结果，纵坐标表示在标准大气中产生的离子对数量。

Unfortunately, my apparatus broke down in the tropics, so I have not been able to get evidence on the remarkable difference between the southern and northern hemispheres as indicated by Hoerlin's results. Though we may feel satisfied that an equatorial minimum of the same order of magnitude is found by all investigators (indicating that the cosmic radiation consists largely of a cosmic rain of charged particles) it would seem that an accurate repetition of this kind of measurement to obtain the exact shape of the curve is not superfluous.

Regarding my observations, the following particulars may be given. The ionisation chamber had a volume of 3 litres and contained argon at a pressure of 30 atm. It was shielded by 8 cm. of iron and was placed in a hut on board the S.S. *Springfontein* of the Holland Africa line, the deck over it being of negligible thickness. The wall of the ionisation chamber was brought to 120 v. and the ionisation current collected on an insulated rod connected to a Lindemann electrometer and to a small capacity (4 cm.). To start an observation, the earthing key of the rod was opened and a stop-watch set running at the same moment. The electrometer was kept at zero by gradually applying a potential to the capacity so as to compensate the charge due to the ionisation current. After some time (about 6 min.) the potential (about 3 v.) was read on a voltmeter. From this the number of ions produced in the chamber per $cm.^3$ per sec. may be deduced, assuming saturation. This number is called the "intensity" of cosmic radiation. A small correction for barometric pressure was applied to it (2.4 percent for 1 cm. mercury). In the graph in Fig. 1 these values (like those of Hoerlin) have been multiplied by such a factor (1/33.2) as to make the value at 50° coincide with the value given by Clay for normal air.

I wish to thank the Groninger Universiteitsfonds for a grant of money, Prof. Coster for allowing the apparatus to be made in the workshop of his laboratory, Prof. Clay for some kind advice and finally the directors of the Holland Africa line and the crew of the S.S. *Springfontein* for their kind collaboration.

(**132**, 781; 1933)

J. A. Prins: Natuurkundig Laboratorium der Rijks-Universiteit, Groningen, Oct. 19.

---

References:
1 Clay, J., *Proc. Amsterdam*, **30**, 1115 (1927); **31**, 1091 (1928).
2 Compton, A. H., *Phys. Rev.*, **43**, 387 (1933).
3 Clay, J., and Berlage, H. P., *Naturwiss.*, **20**, 687 (1932); Clay, J., *Naturwiss.*, **21**, 43 (1933).
4 Hoerlin, H., *Nature*, **132**, 61 (July 8, 1933).

不幸的是，进入热带地区以后我的仪器失效了，因此，我无法验证在霍尔林的结果中所指出的南北半球间的明显差异。虽然我们对所有调查者都发现在赤道附近宇宙射线存在同量级的最小值感到满意（这表明宇宙射线主要是由一系列宇宙中的带电粒子组成的），但精确地重复进行此类测量以得到该曲线的准确形状仍然是有必要的。

以下是我的观测过程。电离室的容积为 3 升，里面充有 30 个标准大气压的氩气。在用 8 cm 厚的铁板屏蔽后，电离室被放在往返于荷兰—非洲航线的斯普林方廷号远洋轮上的一个小屋里，铁板屏蔽上方的甲板厚度相对而言可忽略不计。电离室的壁上加有 120 伏的电压，在一根与一个林德曼静电计和一个小电容（4 cm）相连的绝缘棒上收集电离电流。在开始观测之前，先打开绝缘棒的接地开关，同时开始用跑表计时。为了保持静电计的示数为零，需要不断增加电容上的电压以补偿由于电离电流引起的电荷变化。过一段时间（大约 6 分钟）再读出电压表上的电位值（约为 3 伏）。假定这时已经达到了饱和状态，则由此可以推算出电离室中每秒每立方厘米产生的离子数，这个数被称为宇宙射线的“强度”。我对气压表的压力进行了小的修正（1 cm 汞柱修正了 2.4%）。为了使纬度为 50º 时的值与克莱在标准大气中得到的值一致，图 1 曲线上的这些值（和霍尔林的结果类似）都已经乘上了这样的一个因子（1/33.2）。

我要感谢格罗宁根大学基金会给予的资助，感谢科斯特教授让我在他的实验室中制作仪器，感谢克莱教授为我提供了一些好的建议，最后我还要感谢荷兰—非洲航线的负责人以及斯普林方廷号上全体船员的积极配合。

（刘霞 翻译；马宇蒨 审稿）

# Atomic Transmutation and Stellar Temperatures

T. E. Sterne

## Editor's Note

**George Gamow and Lev Landau in the Soviet Union had recently argued that the astronomical observations suggesting stars have internal temperatures of tens of millions of degrees should be inconsistent with the presence of lithium on their surfaces, since this should be burnt up in the interior in nuclear reactions with hydrogen. Arthur Eddington then wrote to *Nature* to dispute the idea. Here Theodore Eugene Sterne of Harvard College Observatory weighs in, saying that Eddington's objection invokes conditions under which stars would be unstable, but that lithium might actually be formed as well as destroyed en route to the stellar surface, if temperatures were even higher than Eddington supposed.**

GAMOW and Landau[1] suggest either that lithium of mass 7 can be present only occasionally on a star's surface, or that no regions with temperatures of more than several millions of degrees can exist in the interior of a star; their argument is that at higher temperatures lithium could not find its way by diffusion from "the internal regions of the star, where the production of different elements takes place" to the surface, before being disintegrated. Eddington[2] has replied by noticing that the presence of ascending currents may decrease the time required for the ascent of the lithium, so as to remove the difficulty in accepting the central temperatures of the order of $2\times10^7$ found for his models, "whilst negativing any suggestion of considerably higher temperatures".

Most will agree with Eddington that temperatures of only some few millions of degrees are too low for the liberation of sufficient energy; his central temperatures are about the lowest which will yield the correct rates of liberation. But it appears from our present knowledge of disintegrations that an Eddington star would be violently over-stable, unless there were some other important source of energy than transmutations. Stellar matter at his central temperatures would behave not merely like gunpowder, but like gunpowder at just so high a temperature as to be deteriorating steadily, with any decrease in temperature stopping its liberation of energy, and any increase causing it to explode! Eddington shows[3] that one of his stars will be over-stable if the rate $\varepsilon$ of liberation of energy increases more rapidly than about $T^3$, unless there is a delay of the order of months or years between an increase in $T$ and the resulting change in $\varepsilon$. The most important contribution to the total energy liberated by transmutations comes from the disappearance of hydrogen because of its large packing fraction, and the rate at which the speed of disappearance of hydrogen increases with the energy of the collisions can be calculated by Gamow's theory[4] of the nucleus. Except for a constant factor, the calculated speeds appear to be in satisfactory agreement with the observed speeds[5]; the factor does not particularly concern us because we are interested in the exponent, $s$ say, of $T$ for that temperature at which $\varepsilon$

# 原子嬗变和恒星温度

西奥多·尤金·斯特恩

## 编者按

苏联的乔治·伽莫夫和列夫·朗道最近提出：从天文观测推断恒星的内部温度高达几千万度，这与恒星表面存在锂元素的事实相矛盾，因为锂在恒星内部会与氢发生核反应从而被消耗掉。阿瑟·爱丁顿在《自然》杂志上撰文反对这个观点。在这里，哈佛大学天文台的西奥多·尤金·斯特恩也加入了讨论，他说爱丁顿的反对意见是以恒星处于不稳态为条件的，不过当温度高于爱丁顿所设想的温度时，也许可以认为锂在向恒星表面扩散的途中，损耗和生成的过程在同步进行着。

伽莫夫和朗道[1]认为，或者质量数为 7 的锂元素只能偶尔在恒星表面存在，或者恒星内部根本不存在温度超过几百万度的区域。他们的理由是当温度更高时，锂在衰变之前恐怕无法从“合成各种元素的恒星内部”扩散到恒星表面。爱丁顿[2]回复道：由恒星自转引起的上升流或许会减少锂元素在上升过程中所用的时间，所以可以排除接受他模型中认为恒星中心温度为 $2\times10^7$ 量级的困难，“同时也否定了认为恒星内部温度显著高于这个值的提议”。

大多数人都认同爱丁顿的观点，即认为几百万度的温度对于恒星释放充足的能量来说是太低了；爱丁顿模型的中心区温度大约是能保证恒星以适当速率释放能量的最低温度。但根据我们目前对衰变过程的认识，在除嬗变外没有其他重要能量来源的情况下，爱丁顿模型中的恒星将是极端超稳定的。恒星物质在他假定的中心温度下表现得不仅像火药，而且还是在这样的高温下会不断质变的火药，如果温度稍有下降，它就会停止能量的释放，而如果温度略有提高它将发生爆炸！爱丁顿证实[3]，如果能量释放速度 $\varepsilon$ 比 $T^3$ 增加得更快，那么他的恒星中的一个将会是超稳定的，除非在 $T$ 的增加和由此引起的 $\varepsilon$ 的改变之间有数月或数年的延迟。在嬗变过程释放的总能量中有很大一部分来自于氢元素的消耗，因为氢元素所占的比例较大，氢元素消失的速率随碰撞能量的增加而增大，这一速率可以根据伽莫夫的核理论[4]计算出来。计算出来的速率在乘上一个常数因子后似乎同观测到的结果吻合得很好[5]；这个因子和我们的关系不大，因为我们感兴趣的是 $T$ 的指数因子 $s$，在某一特定温度下我们要考虑 $s$ 取什么样的值才能使 $\varepsilon$ 的数量级与 $L/M$ 相符。在温度为 $T$ 时，

is of the right order of magnitude to agree with $L/M$. One can calculate s, considering the statistical distribution over all energies of collision at a temperature $T$, and it is found[6] that $s$ lies between 9 and 30. There is no delay, and an Eddington star with $\varepsilon$ varying like $T^{15}$ would be violently over-stable. These figures refer to the disintegration of lithium; $s$ is increased, and matters are made considerably worse, if elements other than lithium are being disintegrated. The possibility that there may be another important source of sub-atomic energy, "annihilation", cannot be disproved, but there is not the least experimental evidence for the occurrence of any kind of annihilation that could supply useful energy to a star. The creation and disappearance of positive electrons would serve merely to increase the specific heat of the material, while at Eddington's temperatures even this increase would probably be trivial.

It is difficult to see how more than traces of elements like lithium could be formed at temperatures no higher than Eddington's, but if the temperatures are considerably higher than his, then the lithium can be made[7] as well as disintegrated, and by the aid of ascending currents some of it could perhaps appear on the surface. Since it would not be subjected to disintegration *alone* throughout the trip to the surface, for a time the abundance might even increase. If elements are being made as well as being disintegrated, the difficulty of over-stability is avoided, for there is no longer an $\varepsilon$ which increases rapidly with $T$, but merely an $\varepsilon$ which depends upon the rate of loss of energy by radiation into space.

There is still another way out of the difficulty raised by Gamow and Landau, and that is that lithium may have been present from the beginning in the star's atmosphere, while diffusion and currents may not yet have carried all of it into the far interior where transmutations occur. This is consistent with Eddington's calculations[8], for the vertical current of 60 metres a year which he found was an upper limit which applied to the neighbourhood of the surface only; at a place where $\varepsilon$ and the mean value of $\varepsilon$ interior to this are nearly equal (as presumably they are in regions where transmutations occur frequently) the vertical velocity by Eddington's calculations is considerably less. In this case the internal temperatures could well be as high as Eddington's, or higher. The considerations of over-stability suggest the higher temperatures.

(**132**, 893; 1933)

T. E. Sterne: Harvard College Observatory, Cambridge, Mass., Nov. 6.

References:
1 *Nature*, **132**, 567 (Oct. 7, 1933).
2 *Nature*, **132**, 639 (Oct. 21, 1933).
3 *Internal Constitution of the Stars*, § 136.
4 *Z. Phys.*, **52**, 510 (1928).
5 Lawrence, *et al.*, *Phys. Rev.*, **42**, 150 (1932); Henderson, *Phys. Rev.*, **43**, 98 (1933).
6 A paper of the author's on this and allied topics is published in the *Mon. Not. R.A.S.*, **93**, No. 9 (Oct. 1933).
7 A paper of the author's on the equilibrium of transmutations is in the *Mon. Not. R.A.S.*, **93**, No. 9 (Oct. 1933).
8 *Mon. Not. R.A.S.*, **90**, 54 (1929).

我们可以通过所有碰撞能量的统计分布计算出 $s$ 值，结果发现这个指数因子的范围在 9 到 30 之间[6]。如果没有延迟，$\varepsilon$ 按照 $T^{15}$ 变化的爱丁顿恒星将会是极端超稳定的。这些数字来源于锂元素的衰变；如果除锂之外还有其他元素发生衰变，$s$ 会增加，于是问题将变得更糟。我们不能排除可能存在另外一种重要的亚原子源，"湮灭"，但是现在还没有丝毫实验上的证据可以证明某种形式的湮灭能为恒星提供可用的能量。正电子的产生和湮灭只会提高物质的比热，而在爱丁顿所说的温度下即使是这样的增长也是微不足道的。

很难想象在不高于爱丁顿温度的情况下，恒星还能生成少量像锂这样的元素，但如果温度显著地高于爱丁顿的温度，则锂可能在产生[7]的同时也在分解，而且在上升流的作用下，其中一部分锂也许能到达恒星表面。由于锂在朝恒星表面运动的过程中不会**只**在分解，在一段时间内锂的丰度可能还会增加。如果元素在产生的同时也在衰变，那么超稳定性的问题就可以迎刃而解了，因为 $\varepsilon$ 不再随 $T$ 的升高而迅速增长，它只取决于向太空辐射造成的能量损失率。

还有一种方法可以解决伽莫夫和朗道提出的难题，锂可能从一开始就存在于恒星的大气中，而扩散和气流也许并没有把所有的锂元素都带到恒星很深的内部，也就是嬗变过程发生的地方。这同爱丁顿的计算结果是一致的[8]，他所说的 60 米 / 年的垂直流只不过是一个上限，仅仅适用于恒星的表面附近；在 $\varepsilon$ 和 $\varepsilon$ 的内部平均值大致相等的地方（这个区域也被认为是嬗变过程频繁发生的区域），由爱丁顿计算出的垂直速度大大低于 60 米 / 年[8]。如果事实果真如此，则恒星的内部温度可以等于或高于爱丁顿的温度。而超稳定性的存在需要有更高的温度。

（魏韧 翻译；邓祖淦 审稿）

# Oxygen Affinity of Muscle Haemoglobin

R. Hill

## Editor's Note

**That the red colouring matter in muscle and blood is similar but not identical is borne out by this paper, with its evidence that the absorption of light differs between the two tissues. It had been suggested already that "muscle haemoglobin" has only half the molecular weight of blood haemoglobin; this paper shows also that the two have different affinities for binding oxygen (which is their biological function). In fact it turns out that "muscle haemoglobin", now called myoglobin, has only a quarter the mass of blood haemoglobin, something revealed in crystallographic work at Cambridge in 1958, which earned John Kendrew the 1962 Nobel Prize in chemistry.**

THE fact that the haemoglobin within red muscle is a substance different from the haemoglobin in the circulation, has now been definitely established. The pigment has been isolated and prepared in a crystalline condition by Theorell[1], and measurements by Svedberg showed a molecular weight of half that of the blood pigment.

It is therefore interesting to consider properties indicating the function of this pigment in red muscle. It can be shown by a simple experiment that muscle haemoglobin has a higher affinity for oxygen than the haemoglobin of blood. Muscle haemoglobin shows its sharpest absorption band ($\alpha$) at 5,800 A., that of ordinary blood being at about 5,770 A. A mixture of the two pigments in dilute solution is subjected to different tensions of oxygen under physiological conditions of temperature and *p*H. At higher oxygen pressures the $\alpha$ band occupies an intermediate position characteristic of the mixture; as the oxygen tension is lowered, the $\alpha$ band approaches 5,800 A. There must therefore be a considerable difference in affinity for oxygen between the two pigments under physiological conditions.

By means of a rapid spectroscopic method of measuring dissociation curves, the oxygen affinity of muscle haemoglobin has been compared with that of the haemoglobin of blood in a borate buffer at *p*H 9.3 and 17 ℃. The method consists in introducing different amounts of a dilute ($10^{-4}$ m.) haemoglobin solution into an evacuated vessel. The fluid is previously saturated with air, and the total amount of oxygen introduced into the vessel can be calculated. The percentage of oxyhaemoglobin is estimated using the principle of Krogh's method, by comparison with optical mixtures of oxyhaemoglobin and haemoglobin. The tension of oxygen in the vessel can then be calculated. For mammalian haemoglobin in borate buffer at *p*H 9 and 18 ℃., the unoccupied volume of the vessel is of the same order as that of the fluid, and equilibrium can be quickly established. Such a rapid method is essential when dealing with haemoglobin under conditions in which

# 肌肉中血红蛋白的氧亲和力

罗伯特·希尔

## 编者按

肌肉中的和血液中的红色物质虽然相似但不相同这一点主要被本文提供的数据——这两种组织在光吸收上存在差异——所证实。曾有人提出，“肌肉中血红蛋白”的分子量只是血液中血红蛋白分子量的一半，本文对它们的分析结果还表明，两者对氧有不同的亲和力（这一点与它们的生物学功能相关）。实际上后来证实：现在被称为肌红蛋白的“肌肉中血红蛋白”其实只有血红蛋白质量的四分之一。该结果由1958年剑桥大学的结晶学研究成果所证实，约翰·肯德鲁因此赢得了1962年的诺贝尔化学奖。

红色肌肉中的血红蛋白是一种与血液循环体系中的血红蛋白不同的物质，这一事实已经得到了确认。红色肌肉中的色素分子已经被特奥雷尔分离并制备成晶体形式[1]，斯韦德贝里的测定结果表明，红色肌肉中的色素分子的分子量是血液中色素分子的一半。

因此，认识那些反映红色肌肉中色素分子功能的性质自然是人们的兴趣所在。通过一个简单的实验就能揭示，肌肉中的血红蛋白比血液中的血红蛋白具有更高的氧气亲和力。肌肉中血红蛋白的最强光吸收带（$\alpha$）出现在5,800 Å，而通常血液的最强光吸收带则出现在5,770 Å附近。在与生理环境相同的温度和pH值条件下，两种色素分子的低浓度混合液被施以不同的氧分压。结果是，在氧分压较高的情况下，$\alpha$吸收带出现在一个比较靠中间的位置，这正是两种色素混合物的特征；随着氧分压的降低，$\alpha$吸收带的位置则逼近5,800 Å。由此可以得出的结论是，在生理条件下这两种色素分子对氧的亲和力必然存在相当大的差异。

通过利用一种测量氧解离曲线的快速光谱学方法，我们在pH值为9.3、温度为17 ℃的硼酸盐缓冲液中比较了肌肉中血红蛋白与血液中血红蛋白的氧亲和力。具体方法是：向一个被抽成真空的容器中加入不同量的血红蛋白稀溶液（$10^{-4}$摩尔）。这些溶液在加入之前是被空气饱和的，因此，加入到真空容器中的氧的总量是可以被计算出来的。根据克罗格方法的原理，通过与氧合血红蛋白和无氧血红蛋白的光学混合物进行比较，我们可以估算出氧合血红蛋白所占的百分比，继而我们可以计算出容器中的氧分压。对于溶解在pH值为9.0、温度为18 ℃的硼酸盐缓冲液中的哺乳动物血红蛋白而言，其溶液和容器中溶液上空的体积处于同一量级，因此氧气在二者之间的平衡能很快就被建立。当涉及血红蛋白有可能转变成高铁血红蛋白的条件时——这对肌肉

it is likely to change to methaemoglobin, this being apparently the case with muscle haemoglobin.

Fig. 1 shows two dissociation curves; one being that of the haemoglobin of ox blood, the other that of the muscle haemoglobin extracted from the perfused ox heart at *p*H 9.3 and 17 ℃.

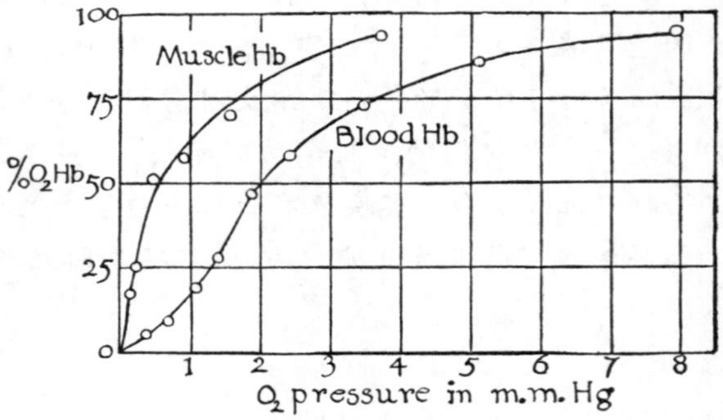


Fig. 1.

That the distinctive properties of muscle haemoglobin are due to its protein, globin, can be shown. If the globin is separated and combined with pure haemin from blood, the $\alpha$ band of the resulting oxyhaemoglobin, like the original muscle haemoglobin, still appears in the position 5,800 A. The combination of muscle globin with mesoporphyrin has a very sharp absorption spectrum identical in quality with that produced from globin of blood; the sharp band in the red region is, however, 15 A. displaced toward the red end of the spectrum. Thus the specificity of the globin is shown both in the case of the oxyhaemoglobin and after its reaction with porphyrin.

It seems clear that the presence of muscle haemoglobin within the muscle cells will be of definite advantage in oxygen transport. The actual amount of haemoglobin in the heart muscle is of the same order as the amount of haemoglobin in the capillaries. The dissociation curve is decidedly less inflected than that of the blood pigment. (This is in accord with the measurement of the molecular weight given in Theorell's paper.) In the middle range of the dissociation curve there is a large difference in the relative saturations at equilibrium, which will allow the muscle pigment to take up the oxygen from the blood. The respiration of the cells, containing in the case of red muscle a large amount of the oxidase-cytochrome system, can continue at very low pressures of oxygen. The muscle haemoglobin, with its relatively high affinity for oxygen, can be the intermediate carrier of molecular oxygen from the blood to the oxidase-cytochrome system in the cells.

(**132**, 897-898; 1933)

R. Hill: School of Biochemistry, Cambridge, Nov. 3.

---

Reference:

1 Theorell, A. H. T., *Biochem. Z.*, 1, 252 (1932).

中的血红蛋白而言是显然会发生的——这样一种快速检测方法就成为非常必要的了。

图 1 展示了两条解离曲线，其中一条（右边的）代表的是牛血液中的血红蛋白，另一条（左边的）代表的是从在 pH 值为 9.3、温度为 17 ℃时灌注的牛心脏的肌肉中提取的血红蛋白。

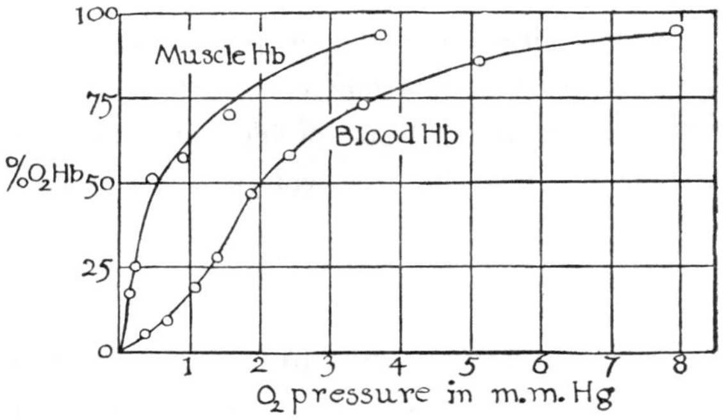


图 1.

肌肉中血红蛋白表现出来的不同特性是源自其组成中的蛋白质（球蛋白）部分，这一点是可以被证明的。如果把其中的球蛋白部分分离出来，并与来自血液中的氯高铁血红素结合的话，所产生的氧合血红蛋白的 $\alpha$ 吸收带仍会出现在 5,800 Å，这与原来的肌肉中血红蛋白是一样的。肌肉中血红蛋白的球蛋白部分与中卟啉分子的结合会产生一个非常尖的吸收谱，其情形等同于血液中的球蛋白。但是，在红光区的那个很尖的吸收带向光谱的红色末端偏移了 15 Å。以上结果表明，球蛋白的特异性无论是在其形成氧合血红蛋白时还是在其与卟啉辅因子结合后都会彰显出来。

似乎颇为清楚的是，肌细胞中血红蛋白的存在对于氧气的运输肯定是有利的。心肌中血红蛋白的实际含量与毛细血管中血红蛋白的含量处于相同的量级，其氧解离曲线的弯曲程度明显低于血液中所含色素的解离曲线。（这与特奥雷尔所发表论文中给出的分子量测定结果相吻合）。在这两种蛋白质的解离曲线的中间部分，处于平衡时的相对氧饱和度存在很大差异，这就使得肌肉中的血红蛋白能够从血液中摄取氧气。细胞的呼吸作用——就红色肌肉而言涉及大量的氧化酶 – 细胞色素蛋白质——能够在氧分压很低时仍然继续发生。具有较高氧亲和力的肌肉中血红蛋白可以作为中间载体把分子氧从血液转运到细胞中的氧化酶 – 细胞色素系统中去。

（姜薇 翻译；吕增益 审稿）

# The Positive Electron

P. M. S. Blackett

## Editor's Note

**The discovery of the positive electron, although consistent with Dirac's theory of electrons, created problems for nuclear physicists eager for a plain account of how positive electrons are generated—most often by the interaction of energetic $\gamma$-rays with heavy particles or even atomic nuclei. Blackett's approach to the problem in this article is very much that of an experimentalist: how best to explain the fragmentary experimental data so far accumulated about positrons.**

THE discovery of the positive electron arose from the study of cosmic radiation by the cloud method[1]. Amongst the tracks of the particles of very great energy, associated with cosmic radiation, were found some which differed from the tracks of negative electrons only by being curved by a magnetic field in the opposite direction. Terrestrial sources of positive electrons of lower energy are now also available, since it has been found that they are produced when hard gamma rays are absorbed by matter, and also in certain cases of nuclear transformation. The production of positive electrons in the laboratory is therefore an easy matter.

The charge and mass of a positive electron can be calculated from the ionisation it produces. For example, Anderson[2] has estimated that the difference between the ionisation due to fast positive and negative electrons with the same curvature in a magnetic field, is not as much as 20 percent. Since for *very fast* particles the ionisation depends on the square of the charge but scarcely at all on the mass, the charge on a positive electron cannot differ by as much as 10 percent from that on a negative electron. On the other hand, for *slow* particles with given charge, the ionisation varies as the mass, so the same equality of ionisation indicates that the masses must be within 20 percent. To obtain further information as to the properties of positive electrons, it is convenient to study in detail the simplest case known of their production; namely, that in which a beam of homogeneous gamma rays is absorbed by heavy elements.

The well-filtered gamma radiation from thorium-C″ is nearly homogeneous and has an energy of $2.62\times10^6$ volts. It has been found by Anderson and Neddermeyer[3], by Curie and Joliot[4] and by Meitner and Philipp[5] that when such rays fall on a heavy element, positive electrons are ejected.

Positive electrons are also produced when the radiation from beryllium, bombarded by alpha rays, is absorbed[6]. Though this radiation is complex, consisting of neutrons together with gamma rays of rather more than $5.0\times10^6$ volts energy, Curie and Joliot[6] have shown

# 正电子

帕特里克·布莱克特

编者按

正电子的发现虽然和狄拉克的电子理论相一致，但却给渴望清楚地解释正电子是如何产生的核物理学家们带来了一系列核物理上亟待解决的问题——通常情况下，正电子是在高能 $\gamma$ 射线和重粒子甚至是和原子核的相互作用下产生的。布莱克特在这篇文章中对这个问题的处理非常符合一个实验科学家的身份：如何以最佳方式去解释当时断断续续积累起来的关于正电子的实验数据。

用云室法对宇宙射线的研究引发了正电子的发现[1]。在和宇宙辐射有关的高能粒子的轨迹中，发现了一些与负电子轨迹完全一致，只是在磁场作用下偏转方向与其相反的轨迹。现在在地球上，我们也能获得低能的正电子，因为已经有研究发现，在物质吸收硬 $\gamma$ 射线以及在一些核反应发生时都可以产生正电子。因而，在实验室中获得正电子已经是一件很简单的事情了。

可以根据电离情况计算出正电子的电量和质量。比如，安德森[2]估计由于快正负电子在磁场中产生相同的偏转轨迹，因而它们之间的电离情况的差别不会大于 20%。因为对**非常快**的粒子来说，电离情况依赖于粒子电量的平方，但是与粒子的质量几乎无关，而正负电子电量之间的差别不可能有 10% 那么大。另外，对于电量一定的**慢**粒子，电离情况随粒子质量的变化而变化，所以，相同的电离情况意味着正负电子之间的质量差别应该小于 20%。为了得到与正电子性质有关的进一步的信息，我们可以详细地研究产生正电子的最简单的情况，也就是说，研究重元素吸收单色 $\gamma$ 射线的情况。

由钍 C″ 放射出的 $\gamma$ 射线经过严格的过滤后将基本达到单色的状态，并带有 $2.62\times10^6$ 伏特的能量。安德森和尼德迈耶[3]，居里和约里奥[4]，迈特纳和菲利普[5]都发现，当这样的射线照射重元素时，就会产生正电子。

铍受到 $\alpha$ 粒子轰击后的辐射产物被重元素吸收时也可以产生正电子[6]。虽然这种辐射产物很复杂，包括中子和能量大于 $5.0\times10^6$ 伏特的 $\gamma$ 射线，但是居里和约里奥[6]已经通过吸收实验表明，正电子的确主要是由重元素吸收 $\gamma$ 射线而产生的。

by absorption experiments that the positive electrons are certainly mainly due to the latter.

The following table, which is derived from the work of Curie and Joliot, Grinberg[7], and some unpublished results of Chadwick, Blackett and Occhialini, gives the numbers of positive electrons ejected in a forward direction from different elements by various radiations, the numbers being expressed as a fraction of the observed number of negative electrons. These percentages give only a rough indication of the frequency of production of positive electrons, since the actual angular distributions are not known, and since the effect of the particular experimental arrangement may be considerable.

Number of Positive Electrons produced when Gamma Rays are Absorbed.

| Source | Energy of gamma ray | Absorber | | |
|---|---|---|---|---|
| | | U | Pb | Al |
| Ra | 1.0 to $2.2\times10^6$ volts | | 3% | |
| ThC″ | $2.62\times10^6$ volts | | 10% | very small |
| Po+Be | 5 to $6\times10^6$ volts | more than 40% | 40% | 5% |

The ejected negative electrons comprise two groups, consisting of the photo-electrons with the whole energy of the quanta, that is with $2.62\times10^6$ volts, and the Compton electrons which have a maximum energy of $2.39\times10^6$ volts in a forward direction. The table shows that the number of positive electrons increases rapidly with the energy of the quanta and with the atomic number of the absorber.

If from these figures the effective area of a heavy atom for the production of a positive electron by a quantum of $5\times10^6$ volts is calculated, values are found which are rather larger than the area of cross-section of the nucleus. This fact makes it improbable that the production of the positive electrons is mainly a nuclear phenomenon.

This view is strengthened by consideration of the energies of the particles. The maximum energy of the positive electrons produced by a given radiation appears to be about the same for all absorbers. If the particles had a nuclear origin, a variation with the type of nucleus would be expected.

For the $5.0\times10^6$ and the $2.62\times10^6$ volt radiations, the maximum energies of the positive electrons are found to be about 4 and $1.6\times10^6$ volts respectively, that is, in each case about a million volts less than the energy of the quantum.

If the positive electrons are indeed produced outside the nucleus, many important conclusions follow:

综合居里、约里奥、格林伯格[7]的工作，以及查德威克、布莱克特、奥基亚利尼未发表的结果可以得到下表的数据。此表给出了不同元素在不同放射反应中前向发射的正电子数量与观测到的负电子数量的比值。因为我们并不知道正电子角分布的实际情况，而且可能还应该考虑某个特定的实验装置对实验结果的影响，因此，这些比值只是对正电子产生频率的粗略表示。

吸收 $\gamma$ 射线所产生的正电子数量

| 射线源 | $\gamma$ 射线能量 | 吸收物质 | | |
|---|---|---|---|---|
| | | 铀 | 铅 | 铝 |
| 镭 | $1.0\times10^6$~$2.2\times10^6$ 伏特 | | 3% | |
| 钍 C″ | $2.62\times10^6$ 伏特 | | 10% | 极小 |
| 钋和铍 | $5\times10^6$~$6\times10^6$ 伏特 | 大于 40% | 40% | 5% |

发射出的负电子包含两种成分，一种是带有量子全部能量的光电子，能量为 $2.62\times10^6$ 伏特；另一种是前向发射时最高能量为 $2.39\times10^6$ 伏特的康普顿电子。如表格所示，正电子的数量随着量子能量和吸收物质原子序数的增加而迅速增加。

如果从上面的数据出发，计算出重原子在吸收一个能量为 $5\times10^6$ 伏特的量子后产生正电子的有效面积，则得到的结果远远大于相应原子核的横截面积。这个结果表明，正电子的产生不可能主要是与原子核有关的现象。

对粒子能量的考虑会使以上的观点更令人信服。对于各种不同的吸收物质，在给定的辐射下产生的正电子的最高能量似乎都是大致相同的。如果产生的粒子是由 $\gamma$ 射线与原子核发生反应所致，那么，不同类型的原子核所产生的粒子的能量应该是不一样的。

吸收了辐射能量为 $5.0\times10^6$ 伏特和 $2.62\times10^6$ 伏特的正电子，其最大能量分别约为 $4\times10^6$ 伏特和 $1.6\times10^6$ 伏特，也就是说，在各种情况下，正电子的能量都要比量子能量大约少 100 万伏特。

如果正电子确实是在原子核外产生的，那么就有以下几个重要结论：

(*a*) Since there is certainly no room, in atomic theory, for the permanent existence of positive electrons well outside a nucleus, then a positive electron that comes from there must be born there, and if born there, an equal negative electron must be born simultaneously in order to conserve electric charge. This is confirmed by the experimental observation that pairs of tracks do occur, which almost certainly are to be interpreted as due to the simultaneous ejection of a positive and a negative electron.

To produce such a pair of electrons with opposite charges requires an expenditure of energy $(m_1+m_2)c^2$. If both particles have the electronic mass, this energy amounts to $1.01\times10^6$ volts, so that in the case of the $2.62\times10^6$ volt radiation, no pair of positive and negative electrons can have more energy than $1.61\times10^6$ volts energy. Anderson has found this to be the case. Again, the maximum energy of a single positive electron producing an unpaired track should also be $1.61\times10^6$ volts. An experimental determination of this maximum energy is being made by Chadwick, Blackett and Occhialini, and their preliminary results* give the value of $1.58\pm0.07\times10^6$ volts, in excellent agreement with the theory.

(*b*) The positive electron must have a spin of $\frac{1}{2}$ and so obey the Fermi-Dirac statistics. For since energy is observed to be conserved during the birth process, it is to be expected that linear and angular momentum are also conserved. So if a quantum gives rise to a pair of particles, one of which has a spin of $\frac{1}{2}\frac{h}{2\pi}$, the other must have the same spin, since a quantum can only excite changes for which the angular momentum changes by 0 or 1. The argument is still valid even if possible changes in the nuclear spin are taken into account, for these must also be integral.

(*c*) A necessary consequence of the occurrence of the process whereby a quantum interacts with an atom to produce a pair of electrons of opposite sign, is the occurrence of the reverse process, in which a positive electron and a negative electron interact with each other and the field of an atom to produce a single quantum of radiation. Since the conditions for this occurrence cannot be rare, a positive electron cannot be expected to exist for more than a short time in matter at ordinary densities.

These conclusions as to the existence and the properties of positive electrons have been derived from the experimental data by the use of simple physical principles. That Dirac's theory of the electron predicts the existence of particles with just these properties, gives strong reason to believe in the essential correctness of his theory.

Dirac succeeded in formulating the wave equation for an electron moving in a potential

---

* The mass of the positive electron can be calculated from the equation

$$E_{max.} = hv - (m_1 + m_2)c^2$$

Using the values $hv = 2.62\times10^6$ volts, $E_{max.} = 1.58\pm0.07\times10^6$ volts.

We find $$m_2 = (1.04 \pm 0.14)m_1.$$

This calculation affords probably the most accurate estimate of the mass of a positive electron yet available.

(*a*) 根据原子理论，既然肯定没有正电子在原子核外长期存在的余地，那么来自那里的正电子必然是在那里产生的，而如果那里产生了正电子，考虑到电荷守恒，那里也必将同时产生一个带有相同电量的负电子。实验上确实观测到了成对的粒子轨迹，这显然可以解释成同时发射出正负电子对，实验有力地证明了以上的结论。

要产生这样一对正负电子需要消耗的能量为 $(m_1+m_2)c^2$。如果两个粒子的质量都与电子相同，那么这个能量就是 $1.01\times10^6$ 伏特，这样，在辐射能量为 $2.62\times10^6$ 伏特时，产生的正负电子对的能量就不可能超过 $1.61\times10^6$ 伏特。安德森证实了上述的情况。此外，没有形成成对轨迹的单个正电子的最大能量应该也是 $1.61\times10^6$ 伏特。查德威克、布莱克特和奥基亚利尼用实验测定了这个能量的最大值，他们得到的初步结果 * 是（$1.58\pm0.07$）$\times10^6$ 伏特，和理论值非常吻合。

(*b*) 正电子应该具有 $\frac{1}{2}$ 的自旋，并遵循费米－狄拉克统计。由于观察到能量在正负电子产生阶段是守恒的，那么可以预见，在该阶段动量和角动量也是守恒的。因为一个量子只能激发角动量改变 0 或 1 的变化，所以如果一个量子产生一对粒子，其中一个带有自旋 $\frac{1}{2}\frac{h}{2\pi}$，另一个一定具有相同的自旋。即使把可能出现的把原子核自旋的变化也考虑进来，这个论点仍然成立，因为这些自旋的变化应该也是按整数变化的。

(*c*) 一个量子和一个原子相互作用产生一对电性相反的电子，这个过程的必然结果是会出现一个逆过程，在这个逆过程中，一个正电子和一个负电子相互作用并与一个原子场作用以产生一个量子的辐射。由于发生这种情况的条件并不罕见，因而可以预期，在一般密度的物质中，正电子是不可能长期存在的。

根据实验数据并运用简单的物理原理，我们得到了关于正电子的存在状态及其性质的结论。狄拉克的电子理论预言了具有这些性质的粒子的存在，因而有充分的理由相信他的理论是基本正确的。

狄拉克成功地构建了电子在势场中运动的波动方程，并保证了方程的相对论不

* 正电子的质量可以通过以下方程

$$E_{\max}=h\nu-(m_1+m_2)c^2$$

并代入 $h\nu=2.62\times10^6$伏特，$E_{\max}=1.58\pm0.07\times10^6$伏特得到。

我们发现 $$m_2=(1.04\pm0.14)m_1$$

这个结果给出了迄今为止人们对正电子质量的最为精确的估计值。

field in such a way as to make it relativistically invariant. The solution of this new wave equation not only led, in the case of the hydrogen atom, to a complete explanation of the fine structure of the spectral lines, but also to a rational explanation of the spin and magnetic moment of the electron itself.

However, in addition to the solutions corresponding to the normal electronic levels found experimentally, were others which seemed to correspond to no observed facts. These solutions seemed to predict the existence of states in which the electrons possessed a negative kinetic energy, and therefore did not correspond to particles in any usual sense. These states could not be ignored, because transitions must theoretically occur between them and the normal states corresponding to positive kinetic energy. Dirac suggested that the difficulty might be avoided if it were supposed that all the negative energy states are normally occupied, and further, that the totality of electrons in such states produce no external field.

On this view, only an unoccupied state or "hole" would correspond to an observed particle. It followed from the theory that such unoccupied states should behave in an external field like particles with the same mass and spin as a negative electron but with a positive charge. The experimental discovery of the positive electron has therefore removed a very serious theoretical difficulty, and by so doing, has greatly extended the field of phenomena over which Dirac's theory may be applied.

Owing to analytical difficulties, the work of applying Dirac's theory to special cases has not progressed far, but Oppenheimer and Plesset[8] have calculated approximately the probability of the production of pairs of electrons of opposite charge when hard gamma rays are absorbed by matter. So far as these theoretical results go, they are in rough agreement with the experimental conclusions, both as regards the order of magnitude of the effect and its dependence on the energy of the quantum and the atomic number of the absorber.

The calculations give for the extra absorption by lead and tin of the $2.62\times10^6$ volt radiation, due to the production of positive electrons, the values of 25 percent and 15 percent of the absorption by the normal scattering and photoelectric processes. These figures are roughly those observed experimentally by Tarrant and Gray. So one may conclude that a large part of the anomalous absorption may be attributed to the production of positive electrons.

One would expect that the absorbed energy would be re-radiated in two ways. An ejected positive electron may disappear by the reverse process to that which produced it, that is, by reacting with a negative electron and a nucleus, to give a single quantum of a million volts energy (see (*c*) above). Or it can disappear, according to Dirac's theory, by another type of process, in which a positive electron reacts with a *free* or *lightly bound* negative electron so

变性。对于氢原子而言，这个新波动方程的解不仅完全解释了谱线的精细结构，还给出了电子本身存在自旋和磁矩的合理解释。

然而，除了与实验中观测到的正常电子能级相对应的解以外，还有一些解不与任何可观测到的现象相对应。这些解似乎预见到了电子具有负动能的状态，因而无法对应于任何一般意义上的粒子。这些电子态不能被忽略，因为理论上存在这些电子态和对应于正动能的正常态之间的量子跃迁。狄拉克提出，如果假设正常情况下所有的负能态都被占满，并且这些态上的所有电子都不产生外场，那么这个理论上的困难就被排除了。

从这个观点来看，只有未被占据的负能电子态或“空穴”才能对应于实验上可观测到的粒子。根据理论进一步得出，这些未被占据的负能电子态在外场中表现得就像一些与负电子具有相同质量和自旋，但带有相反电荷的粒子。实验上发现了正电子进而解决了一个重大的理论难题，而在这个理论难题得到解决之后，狄拉克理论可以解释的现象也随之得到了极大的扩展。

由于分析上的困难，将狄拉克理论应用于某些特殊现象的工作并没有深入开展，但是奥本海默和普莱赛特[8]已经大致地计算了物质吸收硬 $\gamma$ 射线时产生带相反电荷的电子对的几率。这些理论上的结果，无论在反应发生的量级上，还是在反应对量子能量和吸收物质原子序数的依赖情况上，都与实验结果大致吻合。

由理论计算得出：由于正电子的产生，铅和锡作为吸收物质额外多吸收了 $2.62 \times 10^6$ 伏特的辐射能量，这个能量是正常散射情况下所吸收能量的 25%，或是光电反应过程中所吸收能量的 15%。这些数据与塔兰特和格雷观测到的实验结果基本一致。因此我们可以得到这样的结论：大部分的反常吸收都有可能归因于正电子的产生。

我们可以预期，吸收的能量可以以两种方式再次辐射。一是发射出来的一个正电子可能会在与使其产生相逆的过程中消失，也就是说，和一个负电子以及原子核发生相互作用，产生一个能量为 100 万伏特量级的量子（见上面的结论 (*c*)）。二是按照狄拉克的理论，正电子也可以以另一种方式消失，即正电子和一个**自由的**或处于**弱束缚状态的**负电子发生相互作用后，两者都消失并放射出两个能量为 50 万伏特

that both disappear with the emission of two quanta of half a million volts energy.* It is remarkable that the re-emitted radiation is estimated by Gray and Tarrant to be composed mainly of just these two energies, of one half and one million volts. However, Fermi and Uhlenbeck[9] have found that the theoretical intensity of the hard component is far smaller than that observed.

This absorption of hard gamma rays by atoms, resulting in the production of pairs of oppositely charged electrons, may be thought of as a photoelectric absorption by the "virtual" electrons, that is, by electrons with negative kinetic energy, near the nucleus. According to Beck[10], these virtual electrons may be considered to have a binding energy of the order of 2 $mc^2$. Beck also shows that the number of these virtual electrons which are effective for the absorption are proportional to the square of the atomic number and that they amount to about one for each lead atom. The theory also indicates that the birth process takes place within a distance of $h/2\pi mc = 3.85\times10^{-11}$ cm. of the nucleus, that is, well inside the *K* ring.

Curie and Joliot[11] have found that positive electrons are produced when *aluminium* and *boron* are bombarded by alpha particles, and that these positive electrons have a higher energy than the accompanying negative electrons. *Silver*, *lithium* and *paraffin*, however, give no positive electrons. Curie and Joliot suggest that the positive electrons originate in the disintegrating nucleus, but it seems possible that they may be produced mainly outside the nucleus by the internal conversion of a gamma ray emitted by the nucleus. To explain the effect in this way, the probability of internal conversion must be nearly unity.† The greater energy of the positives may be explained by the fact that a positive electron gains kinetic energy and a negative electron loses it, on escaping from the field of a nucleus. This resulting difference in kinetic energy will be the larger the nearer to the nucleus that the pair is born, and so should be larger in the case of such an internal conversion process, which depends on a spherical wave, than in the usual case of external absorption, which depends on a plane wave.

Though it was in association with cosmic radiation that positive electrons were first detected, the exact part they play in these complicated phenomena is not yet clear. But certain facts are established[12]. (*i*) Of the fast particles which produce the cosmic ray ionisation at sea-level, about half are positive and half negative electrons. Their energies range from a few million to nearly $10^{10}$ volts. (*ii*) The same ratio is found in the "showers". The showers appear therefore to represent the birth of multiple pairs of positive and negative electrons, as a result of one or more collision processes induced

* Dirac's calculation of this annihilation probability gives a positive electron a life of less than $10^{-9}$ sec. in water, the life being inversely proportional to the density. If this predicted process is verified experimentally, it will be possible to assume the reverse process, the creation of a pair of electrons of opposite sign by the collision of two quanta of high energy. This latter process would then be the first case known of the "interference" of quanta; it is conceivable that this process has considerable cosmological importance.

† Oppenheimer and Plesset (*loc. cit.*) predict theoretically far smaller values.

的量子。* 值得注意的是，由塔兰特和格雷估计的再次辐射的能量主要就是由这两部分所组成，即 50 万伏特和 100 万伏特。但是，费米和乌伦贝克 [9] 发现，理论上硬成分的辐射能量的强度要远远小于实验上的观测值。

我们可以把原子吸收硬 $\gamma$ 射线从而产生带有相反电荷的电子对的过程看作是一个通过“虚”电子来实现的光电吸收过程，这个“虚”电子即原子核附近具有负动能的电子。根据贝克 [10] 的理论研究，我们可以认为这些虚电子具有 $2mc^2$ 量级的结合能。贝克还表示，吸收过程中的有效虚电子数和原子序数的平方成正比，并且每个铅原子中大约有一个虚电子。理论结果还显示，电子对的产生过程发生在与原子核的距离小于 $h/2\pi mc = 3.85 \times 10^{-11}$ cm 的范围内，这个范围恰好在 $K$ 壳层之内。

居里和约里奥 [11] 发现，当**铝**和**硼**被 $\alpha$ 粒子轰击时产生正电子，而这些正电子的能量高于伴随其产生的负电子的能量。然而**银**、**锂**、**石蜡**在 $\alpha$ 粒子轰击下没有产生正电子。居里和约里奥认为，正电子是在原子核的裂变过程中产生的，但是似乎是由原子核发射出的 $\gamma$ 射线内转换而成，而这个过程有可能主要发生在原子核之外。为了用这种方式解释正电子的产生，$\gamma$ 射线的内转化几率必须接近单位 1。† 正电子比负电子能量高可以解释为：为了从原子核势场中逃逸，正电子要获得能量，而负电子要损失能量。电子对产生的位置越靠近原子核则最终的动能差异也将越大，因而对于上述的内转换过程这个能量的差异也会大于通常的外部吸收过程，因为前者依赖于球面波，而后者依赖于平面波。

虽然正电子的最初发现和宇宙辐射有关，但目前还不清楚正电子在这个复杂现象中到底扮演什么样的角色。不过有以下几点是可以肯定的 [12]：(*i*) 在海平面上发生宇宙射线电离的快粒子中，正负电子大约各占一半。它们的能量从几百万伏特到将近 $10^{10}$ 伏特不等。(*ii*) 在“簇射”中也得到了相同的正负电子比。因此簇射似乎意味着由初级辐射引发的一次或多次碰撞过程导致了许多对正负电子的产生。狄拉克理

* 狄拉克计算了这种湮灭的几率，结果表明一个正电子在水中的寿命要小于 $10^{-9}$ 秒，并且其寿命与密度成反比。如果这个预测的过程得到了实验上的证明，那么就可以假定逆过程是有可能存在的，即通过两个高能量子的碰撞产生一对符号相反的电子。后一个过程后来成为第一例已知的量子“干涉”；可想而知这个过程所具有的重大宇宙学意义。

† 奥本海默和普莱塞特（在上述引文中）预测的理论值要小得多。

by the primary radiation. Dirac's theory shows that the production of single pairs is of primary importance in the absorption of both gamma rays and particles of high energy[13], but has, as yet, given no hint of the cause of the multiple pairs forming the showers. (*iii*) It has been shown that the majority of the particles incident on the earth's atmosphere are positively charged[14].

Since protons are rarely observed at sea-level, it is probable that the positively charged incident particles are not protons but positive electrons. If this is so, the main part of the flux of cosmic radiation in inter-galactic space must be in the form of positive electrons; and since the total mass of this radiation has been estimated as possibly as large as 1/1,000 part of the mass of all the stars and nebulae[15], it appears that the positive electron, though rare, because ephemeral, on earth, is an important constituent of the universe as a whole.

(**132**, 917-919; 1933)

---

References:

1 Anderson, *Science*, **76**, 238 (1932). Blackett and Occhialini, *Proc. Roy. Soc.*, A. **139**, 699 (1933).

2 Anderson, *Phys. Rev.*, **43**, 491 (1933). *Phys. Rev.*, **44**, 406 (1933).

3 Anderson and Neddermeyer, *Phys, Rev.*, **43**, 1034 (1933).

4 Curie and Joliot, *C. R. Acad. Sci.*, **196**, 1581 (1933).

5 Meitner and Philipp, *Naturwissenschaften*, **24**, 468 (1933).

6 Chadwick, Blackett and Occhialini, *Nature*, **131**, 473 (1933). Meitner and Philipp, *Naturwissenschaften*, **15**, 286 (1933). Curie and Joliot, *C.R. Acad. Sci.*, **196**, 405 (1933).

7 Grinberg, *C. R. Acad. Sci.*, **197**, 318 (1933).

8 Oppenheimer and Plesset, *Phys. Rev.*, **44**, 53 (1933).

9 Fermi and Uhlenbeck, *Phys. Rev.*, **44**, 510 (1933).

10 Beck, *Zeit. Phys.*, **83**, 498 (1933).

11 Curie and Joliot, *C. R. Acad. Sci.*, **196**, 1885 (1933).

12 Anderson, *Phys, Rev.*, **41**, 405 (1932); Kunze, *Zeit. Phys.*, **80**, 559 (1933); Blackett and Occhialini, *loc. cit.*

13 Furry and Carlson, *Phys. Rev.*, **44**, 237 (1933).

14 Johnson, *Phys. Rev.*, **43**, 1059 (1933).

15 Lemaitre, *Nature*, **128**, 704 (1931).

论指出，在吸收 $\gamma$ 射线和高能粒子的过程中产生了单个电子对，这具有重大的意义[13]，但是到现在为止，这些还不能为形成簇射的多个电子对的产生机制提供线索。(*iii*) 事实表明，绝大多数入射到地球大气层中的粒子都带有正电荷[14]。

由于在海平面上极少能探测到质子，那么带正电荷的入射粒子就很有可能是正电子而不是质子。如果事实的确如此，那么跨星系空间的宇宙射线流将主要由正电子构成；既然已经估算出这些辐射粒子的总质量大约是所有恒星和星云质量的1/1,000[15]，那么可以认为，虽然正电子因为寿命短暂而在地球上很少见，但它仍然是整个宇宙的重要组成部分。

（王静 翻译；李军刚 审稿）

# Heavy Hydrogen*

E. Rutherford

## Editor's Note

**Discoveries thought at first to be of purely scientific interest often find important applications. Such is likely to be the case, Ernest Rutherford notes here, with the discovery of the isotopic constitution of the elements, in particular of hydrogen. It had become possible to isolate water containing almost pure heavy hydrogen, opening up new avenues of research including the study of how the heavier isotopes affect basic processes such as diffusion and the activity of living organisms. As a projectile for studying nuclear processes, the heavy hydrogen nucleus had already been used to induce elemental transmutation. Rutherford favours the name "diplogen" for heavy hydrogen and "diplon" for its nucleus, over the American proposal of "deuton". The isotope is now called deuterium.**

IN the history of physical science, it is a commonplace that a new discovery which at first appears to be of purely scientific interest, ultimately, within a period of twenty years or more, is found to have useful practical applications. This is well illustrated by the discovery of the rare gases in the atmosphere, neon and argon, which are now used in quantity for industrial purposes. The fundamental discovery in 1919 of the isotopic constitution of the majority of our elements, so largely due to Aston, at first sight appeared to be of purely scientific significance, but it may ultimately have wide practical consequences in many directions.

It is scarcely necessary to discuss in detail the history of the discovery and separation of heavy hydrogen, in which scientific workers in the United States have taken such a leading part. The proof that oxygen was not a simple element but contained two isotopes in small quantity of masses 17 and 18, indicated that there was a small discrepancy of about two parts in 10,000 between the measurements of the relative masses of hydrogen and oxygen found by Aston and those found by direct physical and chemical methods. Birge and Mendel suggested that this discrepancy might be due to the presence of an isotope of mass 2 present in ordinary hydrogen. This gave the necessary impetus to Urey, Brickwedder and Murphy to test whether the presence of $H^2$ could be detected by direct optical methods. The experiments were successful in showing a small trace of $H^2$, estimated initially at about 1 in 4,000 of the $H^1$ isotope. The wave-length of the $\alpha$ line of $H^2$ was found to be 1.79 A. greater than for $H^1$—a result agreeing closely with the theoretical value to be expected for an isotope of hydrogen of mass 2. The mass of the new isotope was directly measured by Bainbridge, using a modified type of mass-spectrograph, and found to be 2.0136, slightly less than the weight of the ordinary hydrogen molecule, 2.0156, in terms of O=16.

---

* Address delivered in opening a discussion on "Heavy Hydrogen" at the Royal Society on December 14.

# 重氢*

欧内斯特·卢瑟福

## 编者按

尽管许多发现一开始只具有纯学术价值，但随后常常会发现它们还具有重要的应用价值。欧内斯特·卢瑟福在这篇文章中指出发现同位素成分很可能就是这样的一个例子，尤其是氢元素。氢的同位素被发现之后，人们纯化几乎只含重氢的水就成了可能，这开启了许多新的研究领域，例如，较重的同位素如何影响扩散及生物体的行为等基本过程。另外，作为研究核反应的轰击粒子，重氢核早先就已经被用于诱导元素发生嬗变。美国科学家建议用“deuton”表示重氢，而卢瑟福更喜欢用“diplogen”表示重氢，用“diplon”表示重氢核。氢的这种同位素现在被称为“氘(deuterium)”。

在物理学的发展史中，经常会遇到这样的事，一项最初只具有纯学术价值的新发现在经过了 20 年或者更长的时间以后最终被人们发现还具有实际上的应用价值。大气中稀有气体氖和氩的发现就是很好的例子，如今这两种气体已经大量用于工业用途。1919 年人们发现大多数元素都有同位素，这个主要应归功于阿斯顿的重要发现，乍看起来似乎只具有纯学术上的意义，但是将来它可能会在很多方面都具有广泛的实际应用价值。

发现和分离重氢的过程我无需赘述，在该过程中美国科学工作者发挥了先驱的作用。氧并非单纯的元素，它还有两个质量数为 17 和 18 的低丰度同位素，这使阿斯顿测量氢、氧相对质量的方法与直接用物理、化学方法测量所得的结果存在大约万分之二的误差。伯奇和门德尔认为产生这种误差的原因可能与普通氢中存在质量数为 2 的同位素有关。这个想法促使尤里、布里克韦德和墨菲联想到是否可以直接用光学方法检测到 $H^2$ 的存在。他们在实验中成功地找到了极少量的 $H^2$，最初估计 $H^2$ 的含量约为 $H^1$ 同位素的 1/4,000。$H^2\alpha$ 线的波长比 $H^1$ 的相应波长长 1.79 Å——如果认为氢具有质量数为 2 的同位素，根据理论计算出的结果与此非常一致。班布里奇采用一种改良的质谱仪直接测得这种新同位素的质量为 2.0136（在 O=16 的前提下），略低于普通氢分子的重量 2.0156。

* 本文是 12 月 14 日英国皇家学会在讨论“重氢”时的开题演讲。

We have no definite evidence of the exact constitution of $H^2$, whether it should be regarded as a simple entity or built up of two or more constituents. It was at first natural to suppose that the $H^2$ nucleus might be made up of two protons and a negative electron, but the subsequent discovery of the neutron indicated that it might rather be a close combination of a neutron and a proton. Taking Chadwick's value of the mass of the neutron as 1.0067, the sum of the masses of the proton and neutron is 2.0145, while the mass of the $H^2$ nucleus is slightly less, 2.0136, indicating that the binding energy of the neutron-proton combination is less than one million volts. If this be the case, it is to be expected that the $H^2$ nucleus should be broken up by collision with a swift $\alpha$-particle. In conjunction with Mr. Kempton, I have made experiments to test this, but have been unable to detect with certainty the presence of any neutrons when heavy water was bombarded by $\alpha$-particles from polonium. The number of neutrons, if any, was certainly less than 1 percent of the number of neutrons released from a sheet of beryllium under the same conditions. If the disruption of $H^2$ with an emission of a neutron occurs, it must happen very rarely compared with the number of violent collisions between the $\alpha$-particles and the $H^2$ nucleus.

It is interesting to note here a suggestion made by Lawrence. He found in his experiments on the bombardment of matter by high-speed $H^2$ ions that a group of protons of nearly the same speed was released from a number of elements. In explanation, he suggested that the $H^2$ nucleus broke up into a neutron and proton either in the bombarded nucleus or in the strong field in its neighbourhood. For the conservation of energy to hold, it is necessary to suppose that the mass of the neutron is much lower than that found by Chadwick, namely, 1.0006 instead of 1.0067. On this view, the $H^2$ nucleus contains a store of energy corresponding to about five million volts, and this is occasionally released in nuclear collisions. Further experiments are required to test the validity of this idea.

It was of interest to me also to examine whether the fields of force near the $H^1$ and $H^2$ nuclei are the same. This was tested by comparing the distribution with the velocity of the recoil $H^1$ and $H^2$ atoms when $\alpha$-particles pass through ordinary and heavy hydrogen respectively. While the recoil $H^2$ particles travel, as is to be expected, slightly farther than the $H^1$ particles, to a first approximation the number and distribution of the recoil atoms were about the same in the two cases. Since in a close collision the $\alpha$-particles and the $H^2$ nucleus approach within $10^{-12}$ cm. of each other, these results indicate that the scattering fields are sensibly the same for $H^1$ and $H^2$ nuclei, even up to these very small distances.

Some success in concentrating $H^2$ was initially obtained by fractionating liquid hydrogen. Washburn and Urey noted that there was a greater concentration of $H^2$ in old electrolytic cells and found the $H^2$ was rapidly enriched in the residues after electrolysis. This general method was first used on a large scale by Lewis and Macdonald of the University of California in order to obtain a concentrated preparation of heavy water. By this method they have obtained quantities of heavy water of the order of several hundred cubic centimetres practically in a pure state. It has been concluded that one atom of $H^2$ is normally present with 6,500 atoms of ordinary hydrogen. Lewis and his collaborators find

我们没有明确的证据证明 $H^2$ 的具体构成，无法确定应把它看作是一个简单的实体还是由两种或多种成分构成的。起初人们很自然地想到 $H^2$ 核可能是由两个质子和一个负电子组成的，但在发现了中子之后人们更倾向于把它看作是一个中子和一个质子的紧密结合体。如果认为中子的质量等于查德威克的测量值 1.0067，那么质子与中子的质量和就是 2.0145，而 $H^2$ 核的质量为 2.0136，略小于质子和中子的质量和，这意味着中子 – 质子的结合能小于 100 万伏特。如果真是如此，$H^2$ 核就会在高速 $\alpha$ 粒子的撞击下破碎。和肯普顿先生一起合作，我曾用实验试图验证这一点，但在用来自钋的 $\alpha$ 粒子轰击重水时，我不确定自己是否检测到了中子。即使真有中子被释放出来，数量也肯定少于在相同条件下从铍层中放出的中子数目的 1%。如果 $H^2$ 核在分裂时果真能够发射出一个中子，其发生的几率与 $\alpha$ 粒子和 $H^2$ 核之间发生剧烈撞击的数目相比也是非常非常小的。

值得注意的是劳伦斯曾提出过一个想法。他在实验中发现，在用高速 $H^2$ 离子轰击实物时，很多元素都能释放出速度基本相同的一组质子。他的解释是，$H^2$ 核在被轰击的核中或周围存在强场的情况下分裂成了一个中子和一个质子。要使能量保持恒定，就必须假定中子的质量低于查德威克发现的值，即，是 1.0006 而不是 1.0067。按此观点，$H^2$ 核中包含着约 500 万伏特的能量，这些能量有时会在核碰撞时被释放出来。上述观点的正确性需要更多的实验来验证。

我对考查 $H^1$ 核与 $H^2$ 核周围的力场是否相同也很感兴趣。检测的方法是：首先让 $\alpha$ 粒子分别通过普通氢和重氢，然后对比反弹的 $H^1$ 原子和 $H^2$ 原子的速度分布。虽然正如我们所料，反弹的 $H^2$ 粒子的射程比 $H^1$ 粒子稍微远一点，但作为一级近似在两种情况下反弹原子的数目和分布是大致相同的。由于在 $\alpha$ 粒子和 $H^2$ 核发生近距离碰撞时两者之间的距离不到 $10^{-12}$ cm，上述结果表明 $H^1$ 核和 $H^2$ 核的散射场明显相同，即使在这样小的距离内也是如此。

人们最初是通过分馏液氢成功得到高浓度的 $H^2$ 的。沃什伯恩和尤里注意到在用旧了的电解电池中 $H^2$ 的浓度更高，他们还发现 $H^2$ 在电解后的残余物中能很快地富集。加利福尼亚大学的刘易斯和麦克唐纳最先大规模地采用这种方法来制备高浓度的重水制剂。他们利用这种方法已经得到了几百立方厘米的纯态重水。一般认为，在每 6,500 个普通氢原子中会出现一个 $H^2$ 原子。刘易斯和他的合作者们发现，这种新型水的密度比普通水约高出 11%，其凝固点为 3.8℃，沸点为 101.42℃。它在 11.6℃时

that the density of this new water is about 11 percent higher than that of ordinary water, while its freezing point is 3.8 ℃. and its boiling point 101.42 ℃. The maximum density is found to occur at 11.6 ℃. instead of at 4 ℃. as in normal water.

It is of interest also to refer to another means of concentration carried out by utilising pure diffusion methods. Prof. Hertz informs me that he has been able to obtain the new isotopes in small quantity in a pure state by applying to ordinary hydrogen the elaborate diffusion method worked out by him. He states that he has obtained heavy hydrogen so pure that he has been unable to detect in its spectrum the $\alpha$-line of ordinary hydrogen. Dr. P. Harteck, working in the Cavendish Laboratory, has been responsible for a preparation of about 25 c.c. of the new heavy water for use in experiments on the transformation of matter.

It is obvious that this new discovery opens up a wide and important field of work. On account of its greater mass, it is to be expected that the rate of diffusion and the rate of chemical reaction will differ when $H^2$ is substituted for $H^1$, while the compounds formed with the new isotope are to be expected in some cases to exhibit rather different properties from the normal hydrogen compounds. Similarly, this new discovery opens up interesting questions on the effect of heavy water in altering the normal physical and chemical processes in animal and plant life. A certain amount of information is already available in this interesting field of inquiry.

There is one question of much interest to me to which I should like to refer, namely, the use of $H^2$ nuclei as swift projectiles for studying the transformation of the elements. It was a happy coincidence that when Prof. Lewis had prepared concentrated samples of $H^2$, Prof. Lawrence of the same University had in working order his ingenious apparatus for obtaining high-speed ions corresponding to more than a million volts in energy. Lawrence found that the high-speed $H^2$ ions were much more effective in many cases than protons of equal energy in causing transformations of new kinds in a number of elements. For example, when lithium is bombarded with $H^2$ ions, $\alpha$-particles are ejected with a speed considerably greater than the swiftest $\alpha$-particle from radioactive substances. It is now clear that an $H^2$ particle occasionally enters the nucleus of lithium of mass 6, and the resulting nucleus then breaks up into two $\alpha$-particles, escaping in nearly opposite directions. The correctness of this view is well shown by the Wilson chamber photographs of the tracks of the $\alpha$-particles obtained by Dee and Walton.

The action of $H^2$ on the lithium isotope of mass 7 is even more complicated, for Oliphant and I have observed that $\alpha$-particles are liberated over a wide range of velocities. In this case, it seems that the capture of $H^2$ by the lithium nucleus of mass 7 results in the break up of the system into two $\alpha$-particles and a neutron. We estimate that the maximum energy of the ejected neutron may be as great as fifteen million volts. We have confirmed this conclusion by finding that neutrons can be detected in numbers corresponding to this mode of transformation using $H^2$ particles of energy about 200,000 volts. Lauritsen found that a copious supply of neutrons could be obtained by bombarding beryllium with $H^2$

密度最大，而普通水在 4℃时密度最大。

另一件有意思的事情是利用纯粹的扩散法也可以进行浓缩。赫兹教授告诉我，他已经能够利用自己精心设计的扩散方式从普通氢中提取到了少量纯度较高的新同位素。他声称自己用这种方式得到的重氢纯度非常高，甚至在它的光谱中已无法检测到普通氢的 $\alpha$ 线。在卡文迪什实验室工作的哈特克博士曾负责制备约 25 立方厘米的新型重水制剂用于物质转化的实验。

很明显，这一新发现开辟了一个广阔而有重大意义的研究领域。由于 $H^2$ 质量较大，所以当用它替换 $H^1$ 后，扩散速率和化学反应速率都会有所变化，而且可以预期，在某些情况下由这种新同位素形成的化合物将呈现出与普通氢化合物颇为不同的性质。同样，这一新发现也给人们提出了一个有趣的课题，即重水对于改变动植物体内正常的物理和化学过程有何影响。在这个引人注目的研究领域中已经有了一些资料。

有一个我非常感兴趣也愿意在此提出的问题，就是采用 $H^2$ 核作为快速轰击粒子来研究元素的嬗变。凑巧的是：在刘易斯教授制备出高浓度的 $H^2$ 样品之时，同一所大学的劳伦斯教授也顺利地利用精心设计的仪器产生了能量超过 100 万伏特的高速离子。劳伦斯发现在多数情况下，高速运动的 $H^2$ 离子比具有相同能量的质子更容易使一些元素发生新型衰变。例如，当锂被 $H^2$ 离子轰击时，其发射的 $\alpha$ 粒子的速度明显高于放射性物质发出的最快的 $\alpha$ 粒子的速度。现在已经清楚地知道：在这个过程中，一个 $H^2$ 粒子偶然进入了质量数为 6 的锂核，合成的原子核随即分裂成了两个 $\alpha$ 粒子，并分别沿大致相反的方向逃逸。迪伊和瓦耳顿利用威尔逊云室拍摄了 $\alpha$ 粒子的轨迹，由此证明这种说法是完全正确的。

用 $H^2$ 作用于质量数为 7 的锂同位素将会得到更为复杂的结果，奥利芬特和我观察到其释放出的 $\alpha$ 粒子有很宽的速度范围。这种情况似乎说明质量数为 7 的锂核在俘获了 $H^2$ 之后分裂成两个 $\alpha$ 粒子和一个中子。我们估计被发射出来的中子所具有的最大能量可以达到 1,500 万伏特。我们已经通过以下方式证实了这一结论，即当用能量约为 200,000 伏特的 $H^2$ 粒子时，我们检测到了大量按照这种转化模式嬗变的中子。劳里森发现用 $H^2$ 粒子轰击铍可以得到数量众多的中子，而劳伦斯虽然也用极

particles, while Lawrence obtained large numbers from lithium with very fast $H^2$ particles, but he inclines to believe that most of the neutrons observed in his experiments arise from the break up of the $H^2$ nucleus into a neutron and a proton.

As already mentioned, Lawrence has observed that $H^2$ bombardment gives rise to one or more groups of fast protons from a number of elements. These observations have been confirmed by Cockcroft and Walton for several light elements such as lithium, carbon and iron, using $H^2$ particles of energy about 500,000 volts, but they have failed to observe proton groups from copper and gold. In general, it appears that the $H^2$ particle is remarkably effective in causing the transformation of many elements, resulting in a number of cases in the liberation of $\alpha$-particles as well as protons and neutrons. There can be no doubt that this new projectile, as well as the proton, will prove of great service in studying the processes which take place in the transformation of the elements, and this will give further important information on the structure of nuclei.

It is obvious that this new isotope, which can be obtained in reasonable quantity in a pure state so easily, will prove of such great importance to science that it is desirable to give it a definite name. Urey has proposed the name "deuterium" for the new isotope. It is important also that an appropriate title should be given to the $H^2$ nucleus, not only as a projectile for atomic transmutations, but as a possible constituent of atomic nuclei. Lewis has suggested the name "deuton" or "deuteron" for this nucleus. While we all realise that the first discoverer has a strong claim in suggesting an appropriate name for a new substance, the question of a suitable nomenclature is in this case of such general importance to scientific men that it deserves very careful consideration.

While the name "deuton" is in some ways suitable, it has for me the objection that it is liable in the spoken word to be confused with neutron, and this difficulty is accentuated by the recent discovery that neutrons are liberated in many cases from elements bombarded by deutons. In consultation with some of my physical and chemical colleagues, some time before these names were announced, the name "diplogen" (*διπλοῖς*, double) for heavy hydrogen, and "diplon" for the nucleus seemed to meet with some favour. Whatever view may eventually be taken on this question, it is important that the new isotope should have a definite symbol allotted to it, and the symbol "D" seems appropriate.

(**132**, 955-956; 1933)

快的 $H^2$ 粒子从锂中得到了很多中子，但他倾向于相信在他实验中观测到的大部分中子应由 $H^2$ 核分裂成一个中子和一个质子而产生。

如上所述，劳伦斯曾观测到：在被 $H^2$ 轰击时，许多元素都会发射出一组或多组快质子。考克饶夫和瓦耳顿用能量约为 500,000 伏特的 $H^2$ 粒子轰击锂、碳和铁等轻元素的实验证实了劳伦斯的研究结果，但他们用铜和金做实验时却没能观测到质子组。总的来说，$H^2$ 粒子对元素发生嬗变具有很明显的促进作用，它能使多种元素释放出 $\alpha$ 粒子以及质子和中子。毫无疑问，这种新的轰击粒子和质子在元素嬗变过程的研究中将发挥极大的作用，而且它也将给出关于核结构的更多重要信息。

很明显，制备适量具有一定纯度的这种新同位素是很容易做到的，它将被证明具有很大的科学价值，所以应该给它起一个确定的名字。尤里曾提出用“deuterium”来命名这个新同位素。给 $H^2$ 核取一个合适的名字也很重要，因为它不仅是一种引起原子嬗变的轰击粒子，而且还有可能是构成原子核的一个成分。刘易斯曾把这种核称为“deuton”或“deuteron”。虽然我们都知道，第一个发现的人最有资格为新物质确定一个适当的名字，但合理命名 $H^2$ 的问题对于科学界人士而言具有如此普遍的重要意义以至于值得非常慎重地去考虑这件事。

尽管从某种意义上看“deuton”这个名字还算恰当，但我不赞成用这个名字，因为它在口语中与中子很容易混淆，再加上人们最近发现被氘核轰击的元素通常会释放出中子，从而使将二者的明确区分显得尤为重要。在提出下面这些名字之前，我征求过几个物理界和化学界同事的意见，大家似乎倾向于称重氢为“diplogen”（双），而把对应的原子核称为“diplon”。不管大家最终定下来的是哪一个名字，都应该给这个新同位素分配一个确定的元素符号，我看符号“D”就挺合适。

（王耀杨 翻译；李芝芬 审稿）

# Possible Chemical Nature of Tobacco Mosaic Virus

E. Barton-Wright and A. M. McBain

## Editor's Note

**Are viruses alive or not? That question is still debated today, although it is perhaps best answered by recognising that viruses—genetic material in a protein coat, which hijacks the replication machinery of host cells—reveal these categories to be too vague at the molecular scale. Here plant virologists Eustace Barton-Wright and Alan McBain in Scotland help to initiate the debate with experiments that, in retrospect, offer a central part of the puzzle. They separate the tobacco mosaic virus into its protein and nucleic-acid (RNA) components, and find the latter is the key to infection. But lacking knowledge of RNA, and with biochemistry fixated on proteins, they cannot interpret the results other than to guess that viruses may be enzymatic.**

IN a series of observations, Vinson and Petre[1] claim that the virus disease of tobacco mosaic behaves as a chemical compound. We have repeated this work in detail and confirmed it in every particular, and we are also of the opinion that the virus in this case behaves as a chemical compound and not as a living organism.

In our own investigations, we have employed Johnson's so-called No. 1 mosaic and we are indebted to Dr. Bewley, of the Cheshunt Research Station, for our source of the disease. The disease was transferred to *Nicotiana Macrophylla* by juice inoculation.

We have particularly examined the mixed phosphate eleuate described by Vinson and Petre. This was found to be highly infectious (plants inoculated, 10; plants diseased, 10). The eleuate was found to contain protein (xanthoproteic and biuret test). On gently warming, the protein was precipitated. It could also be precipitated by saturated, but not by half-saturated, ammonium sulphate solution. Contrary to the statement of Vinson and Petre, we found that when the eleuate was brought to *p*H 5 and acetone added (two volumes of acetone to one of eleuate) a heavy white precipitate fell. The acetone precipitate was found to contain protein and proved to be infectious (plants inoculated, 5; plants diseased, 5).

It was observed that the acetone precipitate could be separated into two fractions, a white crystalline solid and a gelatinous portion which proved to be protein. The question arose as to whether the virus was present in the protein fraction or in the white crystalline solid, or whether both were needed to bring about infection. Infection with protein alone induced disease (plants inoculated, 5; plants diseased, 5). We were quite unable to free the protein from virus.

# 烟草花叶病毒的可能化学本质

尤斯塔斯·巴顿 – 赖特，艾伦·麦克贝恩

编者按

病毒是不是活的呢？这是一个今天还在被争议着的问题，目前最好的回答可能是：我们需要认识到，以遗传物质被包裹在一层蛋白质外套中并劫持宿主细胞复制机器为特征的病毒说明，这样的生物分类法在分子尺度就显得过于模糊了。在本文中，苏格兰植物病毒学家尤斯塔斯·巴顿 - 赖特和艾伦·麦克贝恩通过他们的实验帮助启动了一场争辩。回过头去看，他们的实验结果为揭开此谜提供了关键内容。他们将烟草花叶病毒分离成了蛋白质和核酸（RNA）两种组分，并发现后者是导致感染发生的关键所在。但是，由于当时人们缺乏对 RNA（核糖核酸）的知识，生物化学的重点被聚焦在蛋白质身上，所以他们对上述结果的唯一解释只是猜测病毒可能属于一种酶类物质。

在一系列的观察中，文森和彼得[1]声称导致烟草花叶疾病的表现表明这种病毒为一种化合物。我们详细地重复了这项研究工作，完全证实了他们所有的观察结果，我们得出了同样的观点：在这里病毒表现为一种化合物，而非活的有机生命。

在我们自己的研究中，采用的是约翰逊的所谓的 1 号花叶。我们要特别感谢柴斯罕特研究站的比利博士为我们提供的病原。这种疾病被通过汁液接种的方式转移到烟草中。

我们特别检测了文森和彼得所描述的混合磷酸洗出液。这种洗出液被发现具有很强的感染性（接种植株：10 ；染病植株：10)。我们发现洗出液中含有蛋白质（黄色蛋白质反应和双缩脲检测）。当温和加热时，蛋白质发生了沉淀。饱和的（非半饱和的）硫酸铵溶液也可以使蛋白质发生沉淀。与文森和彼得所报道的观察不同的是：我们发现，如果将洗出液的 pH 值调节到 5 并加入丙酮时（每单位体积的洗出液中加入 2 单位体积的丙酮），就会出现大量的白色沉淀。我们发现这些丙酮沉淀物中含有蛋白质，而且已证明它们具有感染性（接种植株：5 ；染病植株：5)。

我们观察到，丙酮沉淀物可以被分离为两个组分，其中之一是白色结晶固体，另一部分的胶状物质被证明是蛋白质。接下来的问题是：病毒究竟是存在于蛋白质组分中，还是存在于白色结晶固体中，还是说导致感染时二种组分都是必需的。仅用蛋白质组分感染植物，也导致了染病（接种植株：5 ；染病植株：5)。当试图将蛋白质组分与病毒分开时，我们面临了相当的难度。

The white crystalline solid was purified by repeated precipitation with acetone, washed with ether and dried in a vacuum desiccator. It proved to be mainly composed of phosphate, but considerable organic matter was also present as it charred on heating. It was found to contain *no* nitrogen and proved infectious (first inoculation: plants inoculated, 5, plants diseased, 5; second inoculation: plants inoculated, 8, plants diseased, 8). The protein fraction apparently plays no part in infection. The following experiments confirm the fact that protein plays no part in bringing about the disease. The addition of 1 percent solution of safranin to the phosphate eleuate produced a slow precipitate. This was separated on the centrifuge, suspended in water and the safranin removed with normal amyl alcohol. The aqueous solution was found to be infectious and contained no protein, phosphate or nitrogen.

As a control, sap from healthy plants was treated in exactly the same way as that from diseased plants. The behaviour of the mixed phosphate eleuate with acetone was quite different. Instead of the heavy white precipitate described above, a faint opalescence appeared which did not settle for many hours.

That plant viruses are not living organisms has been previously suggested. It has been stated that they are possibly enzymic in nature. Vinson and Petre are of the opinion that tobacco mosaic virus is of the nature of a simple protein. The isolation by us of a white crystalline compound which contains no nitrogen and yet is highly infectious appears to us to preclude the possibility of tobacco mosaic virus being of the nature of a living organism. In its precipitation with safranin it shows affinities with the proteolytic enzymes, but until we have made further investigation of the substance we can make no definite statement as to whether or not it is enzymic in nature.

(**132**, 1003-1004; 1933)

E. Barton-Wright, Alan M. McBain: Scottish Society for Research in Plant Breeding, Corstorphine, Edinburgh, 12.

---

Reference:

1 *Contrib. Boyce Thompson Instit.*, **1**, 479 (1929). **3**, 131 (1931). See also Vinson, *Phytopath.*, **23**, 35 (1933).

白色结晶固体被通过反复的丙酮沉淀而纯化，然后用乙醚清洗，并用真空干燥器进行了干燥。分析结果表明，这些白色结晶固体的主要成分为磷酸盐，但也含有相当量的有机物，因为加热时它会变焦。我们发现这些纯化的样品中**不含有**氮，但却被证实具有感染性（第一次接种：接种植株，5，染病植株，5；第二次接种：接种植株，8，染病植株，8）。其中的蛋白质组分显然在感染过程中不发挥什么作用。下面的实验结果也证实，蛋白质在导致疾病过程中并不发挥任何作用。在磷酸洗出液中加入 1% 的番红染料液会产生缓慢的沉淀。这样的沉淀被用离心机分离出来，重新悬浮于水，其中的番红染料再用标准的戊醇去除。所得到的水溶液被发现具有感染性，而且不含有蛋白质、磷酸盐或氮。

作为对照，来自健康植株的体液也用与以上处理染病植株体液精确一样的方法进行处理。用丙酮处理健康植株获得的混合磷酸洗出液表现出相当不同的行为。与前面描述的大量白色沉淀不同，这里出现的是清淡的乳白色沉淀，而且它们在过了很多个小时之后都不沉降下去。

植物病毒并非活的生物这一点先前已经被他人提出来过。有观点认为，它们可能本质上属于酶类物质。文森和彼得的看法是，烟草花叶病毒从本质上而言是一种简单的蛋白质。我们分离到了一种白色晶体化合物，它不含氮，但却具有很强的感染性。我们觉得，这些证据使我们能够排除烟草花叶病毒本质上属于一种活的生命体的可能性。在番红沉淀物中，表现出了与蛋白质水解酶的亲和性，但在对这些物质进行进一步研究之前，我们不能确切地陈述烟草花叶病毒从本质上是否真的属于酶类物质。

（韩玲俐 翻译；昌增益 审稿）

# Appendix: Index by Subject
# 附录：学科分类目录

## Physics
## 物理学

## Chemistry
## 化学

# Biology
# 生物学

## Astronomy
## 天文学

## Geoscience
## 地球科学

## Engineering & Technology
## 工程技术